M000102048

ORGANIC SYNTHESES WITH CARBON-14

ORGANIC SYNTHESES WITH CARBON-14

RICHARD R. MUCCINO
Chemical Research Department
Hoffmann-La Roche Inc.
Nutley, New Jersey

A Wiley-Interscience Publication

JOHN WILEY & SONS
New York / Chichester / Brisbane / Toronto / Singapore

Copyright © 1983 by John Wiley & Sons, Inc.

All rights reserved. Published simultaneously in Canada.

Reproduction or translation of any part of this book beyond that permitted by Section 107 or 108 of the 1976 United States Copyright Act without the permission of the copyright owner is unlawful. Requests for permission or further information should be addressed to the Permissions Department, John Wiley & Sons, Inc.

Library of Congress Cataloging in Publication Data:

Muccino, Richard R. (Richard Robert)
Organic syntheses with carbon-14.

"A Wiley-Interscience publication."
Includes indexes.
1. Chemistry, Organic—Synthesis. 2. Carbon—Isotopes. I. Title. II. Title: Organic syntheses with carbon-fourteen.
QD262.M77 547'.2 82-2817
ISBN 0-471-05165-9 AACR2

Printed in the United States of America

10 9 8 7 6 5 4 3 2 1

PREFACE

The publications which have appeared since the writing of *Isotopic Carbon* (1949) by Calvin, Heidelberger, Reid, Tolbert, and Yankwich and *Organic Syntheses with Isotopes* (1958) by Murray and Williams signal fulfillment of the conviction of the authors of the former book that "isotopic carbon as a tracer will very soon find its place as a routine tool in many kinds of scientific laboratories." Procedures for the syntheses of the common carbon-14-labeled intermediates are well established, and the present trend is toward the publication of relatively complex labeled syntheses. The scattering of this labeling information over journals covering a broad range of disciplines makes its retrieval from the original literature very time-consuming. Consequently, there seemed to be a need for a comprehensive survey of the literature dealing with ^{14}C-labeling procedures which would illustrate the key entry points of a ^{14}C label into various classes of compounds, such as steroids, penicillins, or benzodiazepines, as well as the techniques used to introduce a ^{14}C label into various positions of simpler intermediates.

Because of the enormous number of references to ^{14}C-labeled compounds, the synthetic methods are presented using structural transformations, which was the plan successfully used by Djerassi in *Steroid Reactions* and by subsequent authors. Because of the widespread use of ^{14}C compounds in chemistry, biology, medicine, and other areas, this book has the same problems of classification as its predecessors. Each chapter is organized according to functional groups, in which the entries are arranged according to parent structures in increasing order of complexity. Difficulties in classification are encountered when a number of labeled intermediates are involved in the synthesis of a target molecule thus requiring an extended labeling route to be broken down into its key components for easier classification. Other problems are encountered when the labeled functional group is a minor element in, for example, a complex heterocycle, and so to offset the sometimes arbitrary classifications, the reader is urged to rely upon the subject and formula indexes as the ultimate sources for locating specific compounds. Since nonlabeled steps are not included in the transformations and radioactive syntheses are designed to conserve the number of radioactive steps, the preparation of some compounds may appear trivial when in fact a major effort may have been made in the preparation of the nonradioactive starting material. Reactions giving low yields are not omitted, since yield is often a secondary consideration if there is no other approach to preparing the labeled derivative or inserting the label in the desired position.

Literature coverage is from 1968 through 1979 in *Chemical Abstracts* via a computer search, from 1970 through 1979 in *Chemicus Index,* and from 1965 through 1979 in *The Journal of Labelled Compounds and Radiopharmaceuticals.* Certain other references extend back to 1966 to complement Schütte's *Radioactive Isotope in der organischen Chemie und Biochemie* as much as possible.

This book should be most helpful to the biochemist who has no great expertise in synthesis and wishes to find the details of established procedures for preparing labeled compounds, to the organic chemist who routinely prepares labeled compounds but needs a comprehensive survey of the area to be able to compare and perhaps extend established procedures to synthesize related compounds, and to "that rapidly becoming extinct breed of organic chemist, the literature browser, who will encounter stimuli to ponder a multitude of unsolved problems," as identified by Djerassi in *Steroid Reactions.* While there are synthesis scale and isotope enrichment differences between labeling with ^{14}C and ^{13}C, there are certainly enough similarities so that this survey should also prove valuable to those working with the stable isotope.

I wish to acknowledge the many resources at Hoffmann–La Roche without which the writing of this book would have been impossible, as well as the management of the Chemical Research Department for their indulgence during this period. In particular, I am grateful to Dr. Peter Sorter of the Scientific Literature Department for the literature computer searches performed, to Ms. Phyllis Deline of the Scientific Library for retrieving copies of over two thousand references, to Mr. Adam Irski of the Research Records Department for completely revising all the nomenclature and rendering it into the format of *Chemical Abstracts* (9th Collective period 1972–1976); and to Ms. Marilyn Satchwell for transcribing handwritten structures into the first draft. For critically reading one or more of the chapters, I wish to thank Drs. N. Cohen, K. Fahrenholtz, A. Felix, E. Heimer, U. Hengartner, G. Holland, D. Keith, I. Kompis, E. P. Oliveto, C. W. Perry, M. Poonian, P. Rosen, M. Schlageter, S. Tam and A. Walser. For reading the entire manuscript and offering many helpful suggestions, I wish to thank Drs. R. Nystrom, L. Pichat and N. Flück and Mr. D. Malarek.

RICHARD R. MUCCINO

Nutley, New Jersey
February 1983

CONTENTS

1

Carboxylic Acids

Unsubstituted Acids

1-1 Aliphatic Acids

$$R\text{-}COONa(K) \xrightarrow[200\text{-}400^\circ C]{4\text{-}5\ atm\ {}^*CO_2} R\text{-}{}^*COOH$$

Optimal conditions for $^*CO_2$ exchange in aliphatic carboxylic acids were determined for 24 compounds; chemical yields 80-98%, radiochemical yields 35-88%.

A. Szabolcs, J. Szammer, and L. Noszko, Tetrahedron, 30, 3647 (1974).

$$HO\text{-}CH_2CH_2Cl \xrightarrow[2.\ \ H_2SO_4(82\%)]{1.\ \ K^*CN,\ EtOH\ (71\%)} CH_2{=}CH^*COOH$$

Acrylic acid [2-Propenoic-1-^{14}C acid]

F. Asinger, A. Saus, B. Fell, and J. Pfeifer, J. Prakt. Chem., 314, 80 (1972).

$$CH_2{=}CHMgBr \xrightarrow[THF]{{}^*CO_2} CH_2{=}CH\text{-}{}^*COOH \quad (80\%)$$

Acrylic acid [2-Propenoic-1-^{14}C acid]

L. Pichat, M. Herbert, and F. Aubert, J. Label. Compounds, 1, 66 (1965).

$HC{\equiv}CMgBr \xrightarrow{*CO_2} HC{\equiv}C\text{-}*COOH$ (20%)

2-Propynoic-
1-^{14}C acid

C. George, E. W. Gill, and J. A. Hudson, J. Chem. Soc. (C), 74 (1970).

$CH_3\text{-}CH(CH_3)Br \xrightarrow[2.\ *CO_2]{1.\ Mg,\ Et_2O} CH_3\text{-}CH(CH_3)*COOH$ (56%)

2-Methylpropanoic-
1-^{14}C acid

F. P. Schmook and O. E. Polansky, Monatsch. Chem., 100, 1640 (1969).

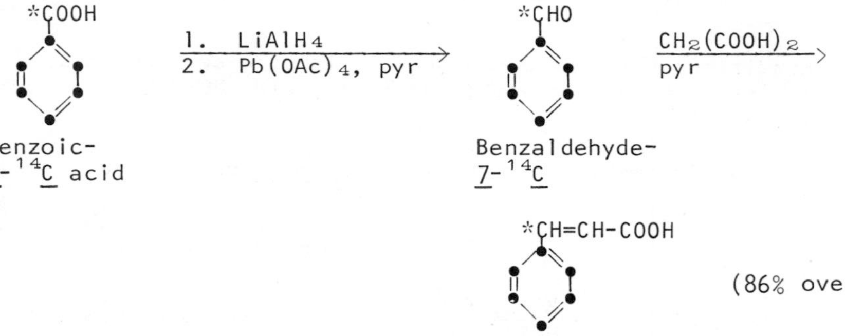

Benzoic-
7-^{14}C acid

1. $LiAlH_4$
2. $Pb(OAc)_4$, pyr

Benzaldehyde-
7-^{14}C

$CH_2(COOH)_2$
pyr

(86% overall)

Cinnamic acid
[3-Phenyl-2-propenoic-
β-^{14}C acid]

M. Herbert, G. Rochas, and L. Pichat, J. Label. Compounds, 4, 240 (1968).

$*CH_3*CH_2*CH(*CH_3)*CH(NH_2)*COOH \xrightarrow[2.\ KMnO_4]{1.\ ninhydrin,\ H_2O}$

L-Isoleucine-U-^{14}C

$*CH_3*CH_2*CH(*CH_3)*COOH$ (38%)

(S)-2-Methylbutanoic-
U-^{14}C acid

When the intermediate (S)-2-methylbutanol-U-^{14}C was treated with pyridine at 90°C and then oxidized, (RS)-2-methylbutanoic-U-^{14}C acid was obtained in 35% yield.

N. M. Bale. R. Cahill, N. M. Davies, M. B. Mitchell, E. H. Smith, and D. H. G. Crout, J. Chem. Soc., Perkin Trans. I, 101 (1978).

$BrCH_2{}^*COOC_2H_5$ —(1. $(C_6H_5)_3P$; 2. NaOH; 3. CH_3COCH_3)→ $CH_3-C(CH_3)=CH^*COOC_2H_5$ —NaOH→ $CH_3-C(CH_3)=CH^*COOH$

Bromoacetic-1-^{14}C acid ethyl ester

3-Methyl-2-butenoic-1-^{14}C acid ethyl ester

3-Methyl-2-butenoic-1-^{14}C acid

A. O. Colonna and E. G. Gros, J. Label. Compounds, 7, 84 (1971).

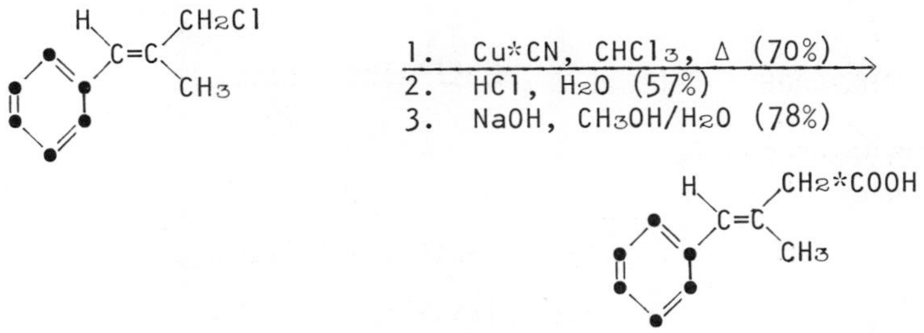

(E)-3-Methyl-4-phenyl-3-butenoic-1-^{14}C acid

U. Valcavi, J. Label. Compounds, 10, 143 (1974).

$Br^*CH_2COOC_2H_5$ —(1. $P(OC_2H_5)$ (89-90%); 2. NaH, DME; 3. $CH_3COCH_2CH_2CH_3$ (58-59%); 4. 20% aq.NaOH (78-95%))→

Bromoacetic-2-^{14}C acid ethyl ester

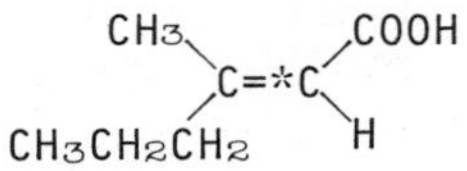

(E)-3-Methyl-2-hexenoic-2-^{14}C acid

(85/15 ratio of E/Z was obtained from which pure E was separated.)

Similarly:

$CH_3CH_2CH_2C(=O)\text{-}{*}CH_3$ —[1. $(C_2H_5O)_2P(=O)CHNaCOOC_2H_5$; 2. NaOH]→

2-Pentanone-1-^{14}C

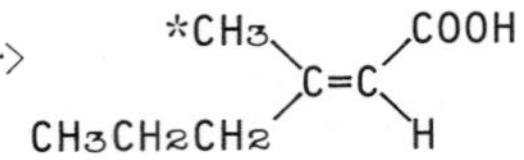

(E)-3-(Methyl-^{14}C)-2-hexenoic acid

J. L. Rabinowitz and M. Zanger, J. Label. Compounds, 8, 657 (1972).

$CH_3(CH_2)_{12}CHO$ + $BrCH_2{*}COOC_2H_5$ —[Reformatsky reaction]→

Bromoacetic-1-^{14}C acid ethyl ester

$CH_3(CH_2)_{12}CHOHCH_2{*}COOH$ (32%) —[boric anhydride, Δ]→

(R,S)-3-Hydroxyhexadecanoic-1-^{14}C acid

$CH_3(CH_2)_{12}CH{=}CH{*}COOH$ (38%)

(E)-2-Hexadecenoic-1-^{14}C acid

J. A. Jones and M. Blecher, J. Lipid Res., 7, 422 (1966).

$CH_3\text{-}(CH_2)_5\text{-}C{\equiv}C\text{-}CH_2Br$ →

1. $MgBrC{\equiv}C(CH_2)_5CH_2Cl$
2. H_2, Lindlar catalyst
3. $Na{*}CN$, DMSO, Δ
4. HCl/MeOH (78%)
5. $LiAlH_4$, Et_2O

$CH_3(CH_2)_5CH{=}CHCH_2CH{=}CH(CH_2)_5CH_2{*}CH_2OH$

8,11-Octadecadien-1-ol-1-^{14}C

1. CH_3-SO_2Cl
2. $(CH_3)_2CHCH_2ONa$, i-BuOH, $CH_2(COOEt)_2$, Δ
3. KOH, EtOH/H O
4. Quinoline, Cu, Δ

→

$CH_3(CH_2)_5(CH{=}CHCH_2)_2(CH_2)_5{*}CH_2CH_2COOH$ (53% overall from Na*CN)

Eicosa-10,13-dienoic-3-^{14}C acid

Cl-$(CH_2)_8$-$C{\equiv}CH$

1. $CH_3(CH_2)_5$-$C{\equiv}C$-CH_2Br
2. H_2, Lindlar catalyst
3. Na*CN
4. hydrolysis

→

$CH_3(CH_2)_5(CH{=}CHCH_2)_2(CH_2)_7{*}COOH$

Eicosa-10,13-dienoic-1-^{14}C acid

$BrCH_2C{\equiv}CCH_2C{\equiv}C(CH_2)_5CH_3$

1. $Cl(CH_2)_5C{\equiv}CH$
2. steps as above

→

$CH_3(CH_2)_5(CH{=}CHCH_2)_2CH{=}CH(CH_2)_5{*}COOH$

Eicosa-7,10,13-trienoic-1-^{14}C acid

$HC{\equiv}C(CH_2)_8COOH$

1. $CH_3(CH_2)_4C{\equiv}C$-CH_2Br
2. H_2, Lindlar catalyst
3. CH_3OH
4. $LiAlH_4$
5. CH_3-SO_2Cl
6. Na*CN
7. hydrolysis

→

$CH_3(CH_2)_4CH{=}CH$-CH_2-$CH{=}CH(CH_2)_8CH_2{*}COOH$

Eicosa-11,14-dienoic-1-^{14}C acid

$BrCH_2C{\equiv}CCH_2C{\equiv}C(CH_2)_4CH_3$

1. $Cl(CH_2)_6C{\equiv}CH$
2. H_2, Lindlar catalyst
3. Na*CN
4. hydrolysis

→

$CH_3(CH_2)_4CH{=}CHCH_2CH{=}CHCH_2CH{=}CH(CH_2)_6{*}COOH$

Eicosa-8,11,14-trienoic-1-^{14}C acid

J. Budny and H. Sprecher, Biochem. Biophys. Acta, 239, 190 (1971); H. Sprecher and C.-J. Lee, Biochem. Biophys. Acta, 388, 113 (1975).

1-2 Alicyclic Acids

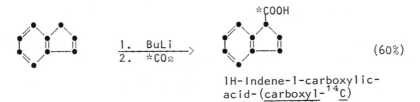

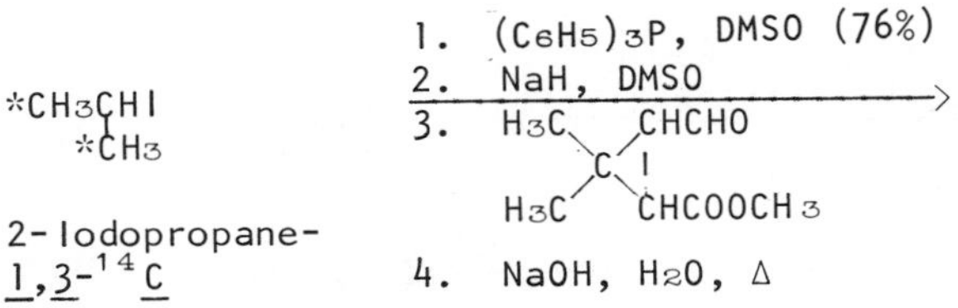
*CH3CHI
*CH3
1. (C6H5)3P, DMSO (76%)
2. NaH, DMSO
3. H3C CHCHO
C
H3C CHCOOCH3
4. NaOH, H2O, Δ

2-Iodopropane-1,3-^{14}C

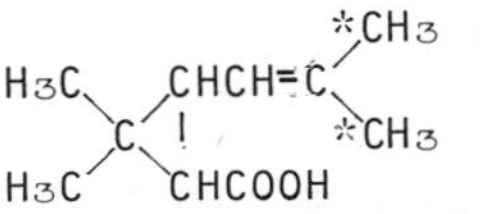
*CH3
H3C CHCH=C
C
*CH3
H3C CHCOOH

(20-24% from isopropyl iodide)

(+)-trans-Chrysanthemic acid
[(1R-trans)-2,2-Dimethyl-3-(2-methyl-^{14}C-1-propenyl-3 ^{14}C cyclopropane carboxylic acid]

L. Crombie, C. F. Doherty, and G. Pattenden, J. Chem. Soc. (C), 1076 (1970); J. Chem. Soc. (C), 2739 (1971).

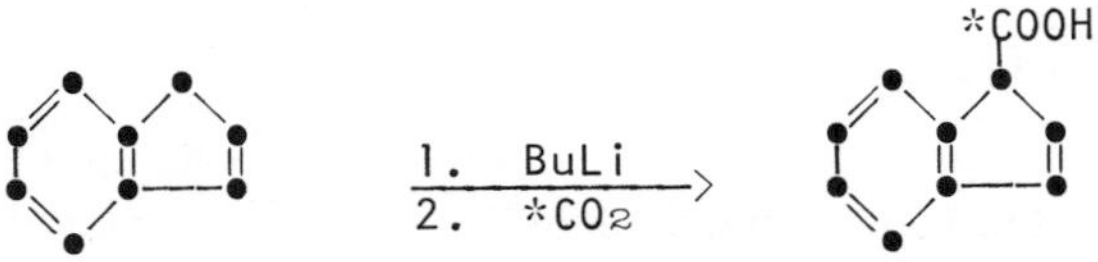
*COOH
1. BuLi
2. *CO2

(60%)

1H-Indene-1-carboxylic-acid-(carboxyl-^{14}C)

A. G. Sakhabutdinov, V. G. Lipovich, and I. V. Kalechits, Zh. Org. Khim., 11, 1728 (1975).

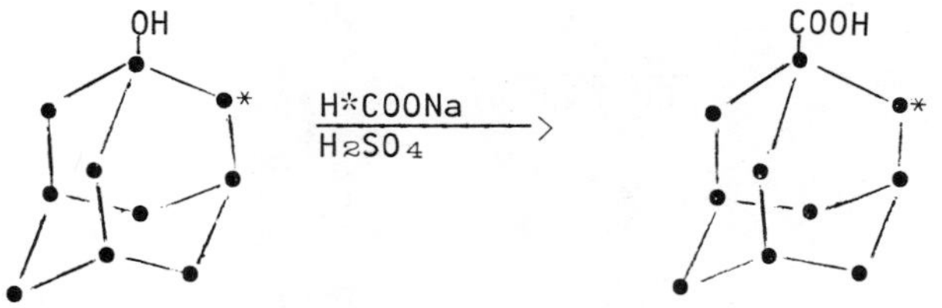
OH
H*COONa
H2SO4
COOH

(82%)

Adamantane-carboxylic acid
[Tricyclo[3.3.1.$3^{3,7}$] decane carboxylic-1-^{14}C acid]

A. J. Villani and F. R. Pfeiffer, J. Pharm. Sci., 65, 1243 (1976).

1-3 Aromatic Acids

CH_3*COOH —— 1. $PO(OEt)_3$ (90%); 2. $BrMg(CH_2)_5MgBr$, ether (97%) ——>

Acetic-1-^{14}C acid

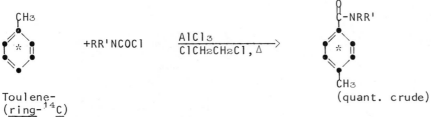

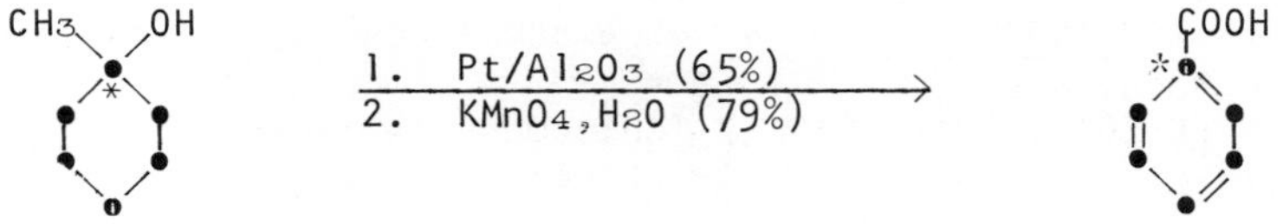
CH3
OH
1. Pt/Al2O3 (65%)
2. KMnO4,H2O (79%)
COOH

1-Methylcyclohexanol-1-^{14}C

Benzoic-1-^{14}C acid

S. Oae, N. Furukawa, M. Kise, and M. Kawanishi, Bull. Chem. Soc. Jap., 39, 1212 (1966).

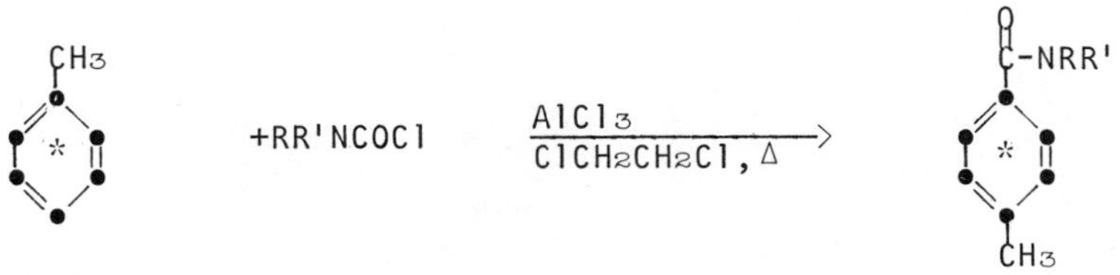
CH3
+RR'NCOCl
AlCl3
ClCH2CH2Cl, Δ
O
C-NRR'
CH3

Toulene-(ring-^{14}C)

(quant. crude)

R=CH_3, R'=C_6H_5, or R=R'=C_6H_5

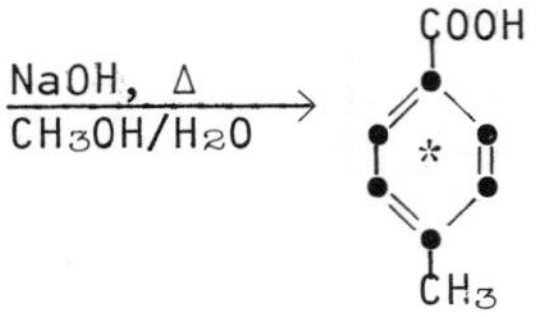
NaOH, Δ
CH_3OH/H_2O
COOH
*
CH_3

(61%)

p-Toluic acid
[4-Methylbenzoic-(ring-U-^{14}C)acid]

Y.-T. Lin, R. J. Dummell, M. A. Leaffer, and M. Tanabe, J. Label. Compound. Radiopharm., 12, 631 (1976).

Substituted Acids

1-4 Ethereal Acids

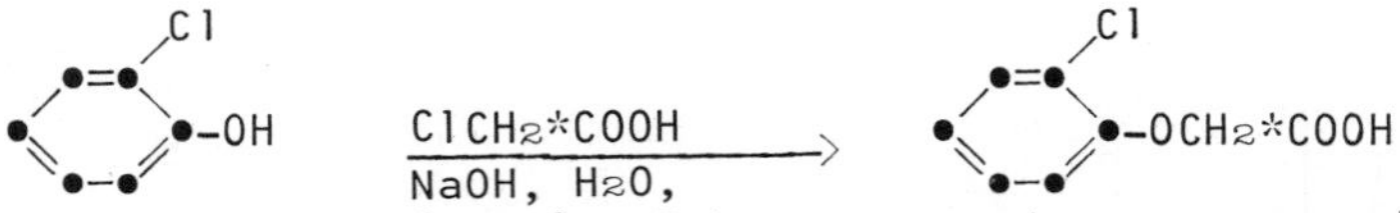
Cl
-OH
$ClCH_2{*}COOH$
NaOH, H_2O,
60-70°C, 7 hr
Cl
$-OCH_2{*}COOH$

(38%)

2-(Chlorophenoxy)acetic-1-^{14}C acid

F. J. Marshall, R. E. McMahon, and W. B. Lacefield, J. Label. Compounds, 8, 461 (1972).

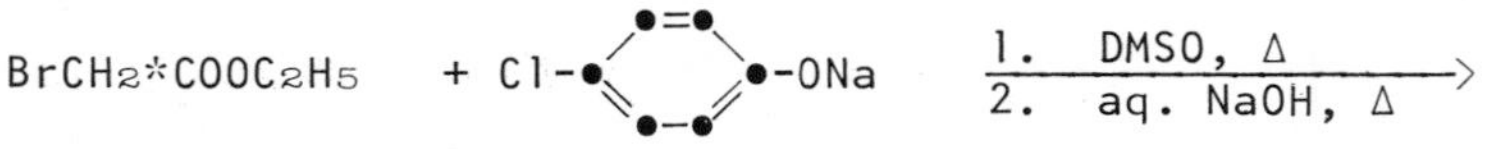
$BrCH_2{*}COOC_2H_5$
+ Cl-
-ONa
1. DMSO, Δ
2. aq. NaOH, Δ

Bromoacetic-1-^{14}C acid ethyl ester

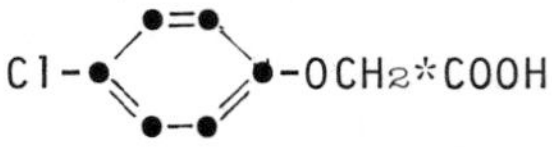
Cl-
$-OCH_2{*}COOH$

(68%)

4-(Chlorophenoxy)acetic-1-^{14}C acid

4-Fluorophenoxyacetic-1-^{14}C acid (54%) and 4-nitro-3-methylphenoxyacetic-1-^{14}C acid ethyl ester (99%) were also prepared by this method.

M. Look, J. Label. Compound. Radiopharm., 15, 545 (1978).

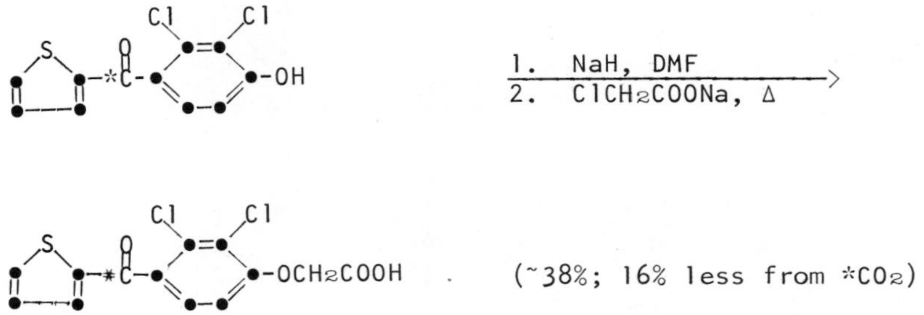
Cl
Cl
S
O
-*C-
-OH
1. NaH, DMF
2. ClCH₂COONa, Δ
Cl
Cl
S
O
-*C-
-OCH₂COOH
(~38%; 16% less from *CO₂)

Tienilic acid
[2,3-Dichloro-4-(2-thienyl(carbonyl-^{14}C))-phenoxylacetic acid]

M. Herbert and L. Pichat, J. Label. Compound. Radiopharm., 12, 437 (1976).

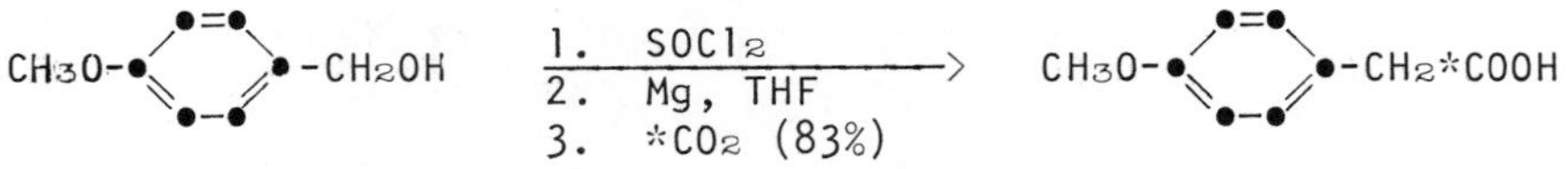
CH₃O-
-CH₂OH
1. SOCl₂
2. Mg, THF
3. *CO₂ (83%)
CH₃O-
-CH₂*COOH

4-Methoxybenzeneacetic-1-^{14}C acid

R. C. Thomas, J. Label. Compounds, 11, 355 (1975).

C₄H₉O-
(CH₃*CO)₂O
ZnCl₂

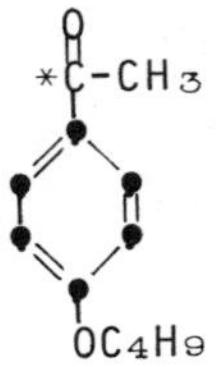

(56%)

1. Morpholine, S, Δ, 12 hr
2. NaOH, EtOH Δ, 12 hr

1-(4-Butoxyphenyl)ethanone-1-^{14}C

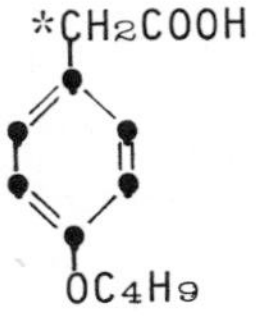

1. EtOH, H_2SO_4 (57%)
2. $NH_2OH.HCl$, CH_3ONa, CH_3OH, Δ, 1 hr (40%)

4-Butoxybenzeneacetic-α-^{14}C acid

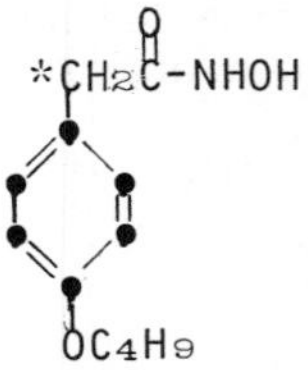

4-Butoxy-N-hydroxybenzeneacetamide-α-^{14}C

C. Gillet, J. Thiriaux, N. P. Buu-Hoi, G. Lambelin, R. Roncucci, and M. J. Simon, J. Label. Compounds, 2, 143 (1966).

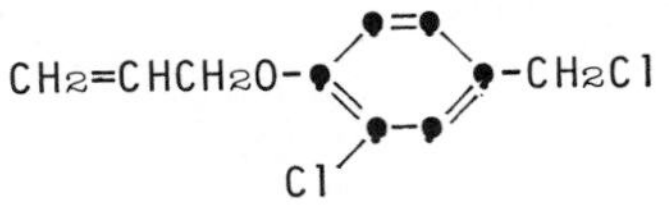

1. K*CN, DMSO, 50°C
2. KOH, H_2O/EtOH, 90°C

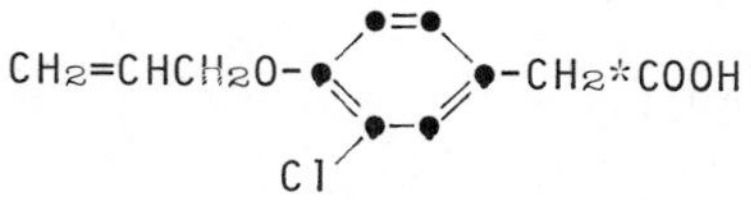

(75%)

3-Chloro-4-(3-propenyloxy)-
benzeneacetic-1-^{14}C acid

C. L. Gillet, M. F. Gautier, R. R. Roncucci, M.-J. E. Simon, and G. E. Lambelin, J. Label. Compounds, 9, 167 (1973).

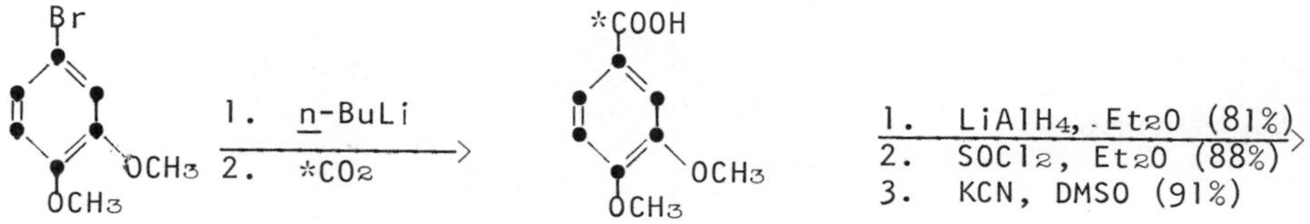

Veratric acid
[3,4-Dimethoxybenzoic-
7-^{14}C acid]

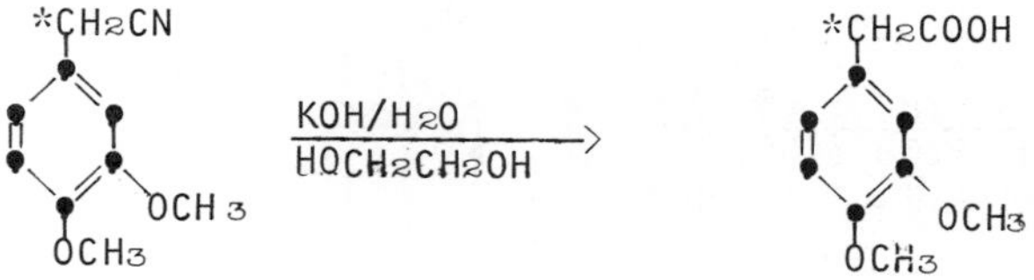

95%

3,4-Dimethoxybenzene-
acetonitrile-α-^{14}C

Homoveratric acid
[3,4-Dimethoxybenzene-
acetic-α-^{14}C acid]

S. D. Ithakissios, G. Tsatsas, J. Nikokavouras, and A. Tsolis, J. Label. Compounds, 10, 369 (1974).

Ethyl atropate
[α-(Methylene-^{14}C)-
benzeneacetic acid]

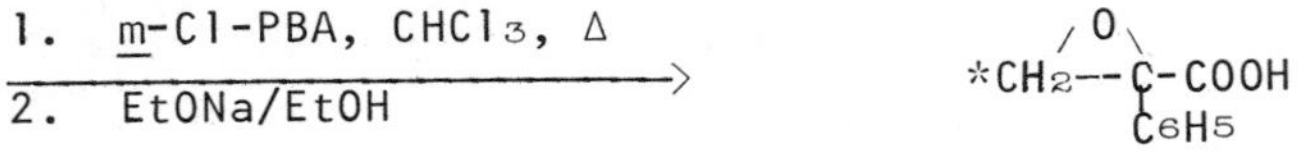
1. m-Cl-PBA, CHCl3, Δ
2. EtONa/EtOH
O
*CH2--C-COOH
C6H5

2-Phenyl-2-oxiranecarboxylic-3-^{14}C acid

J. A. Fee, G. D. Hegeman, and G. L. Kenyon, Biochemistry, 13, 2533 (1974).

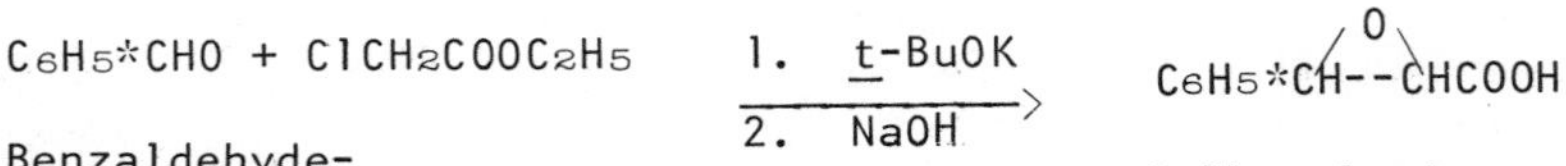
C6H5*CHO + ClCH2COOC2H5
1. t-BuOK
2. NaOH
O
C6H5*CH--CHCOOH

Benzaldehyde-7-^{14}C

3-Phenyloxiranecarboxylic-3-^{14}C acid

J. Domagala and J. Wemple, Tetrahedron Lett., 1179 (1973).

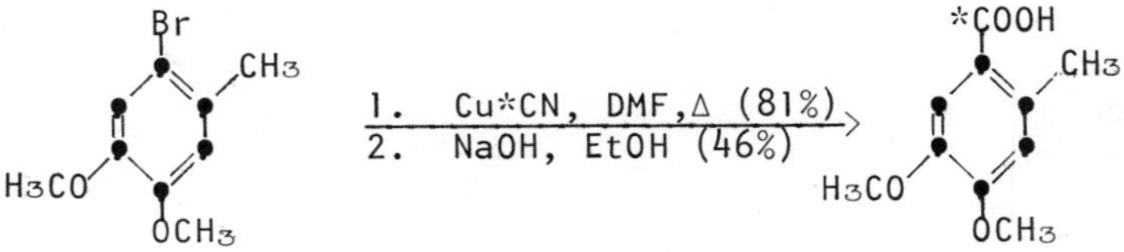
Br
CH3
H3CO
OCH3
1. Cu*CN, DMF,Δ (81%)
2. NaOH, EtOH (46%)
*COOH
CH3
H3CO
OCH3

4,5-Dimethoxy-2-methylbenzoic-7-^{14}C acid

B. Olesch and H. Böhm, Arch. Pharm., 305, 222 (1972).

$ICH_2{*}COOH$ + RSH —(aq. NaOH)→ R-S-$CH_2{*}COOH$

Iodoacetic-1-^{14}C acid

R=C_2H_5; (Ethylthio)acetic-1-^{14}C acid (93%)
R=n-C_3H_7; (Propylthio)acetic-1-^{14}C acid (75%)
R=i-C_3H_7; (1-Methylethylthio)-acetic-1-^{14}C acid (91%)
R=C_6H_5; (Phenylthio)acetic-1-^{14}C acid (97%)
R=$CH_2C_6H_5$; (Phenylmethylthio)-acetic-1-^{14}C acid (96%)

Y. C. Lee, M. G. J. Hayes, and D. B. McCormick, Biochem. Pharmacol., 19, 2825 (1970).

1-5 Halo Acids

$ClCH_2{*}COOH$ —(1. CH_2N_2; 2. KF, CH_3CONH_2, Δ, 3. Zn, NaOH)→ $FCH_2{*}COONa$ (60% overall)

Chloroacetic-1-^{14}C acid → Fluoroacetic-1-^{14}C acid

P. F. V. Ward and N. S. Haskisson, Biochim. Biophys. Acta, 115, 515 (1966).

CH_3CCl_3 —(1. n-BuLi, THF, -104°C; 2. $*CO_2$)→ $CH_3-C(Cl)_2-{*}COOH$ (55%)

Dalapon
[2,2-Dichloropropanoic-1-^{14}C acid]

$Cl_3{*}CCOOH$ —(1. CH_2N_2(quant.); 2. $SiHCl_3$, CH_2Cl_2, $(n\text{-}Bu)_3N$, Δ)→ $Cl_2{*}CHCOOCH_3$

Trichloroacetic-2-^{14}C acid

—(1. NaH, DMF/THF; 2. CH_3I } (72%); 3. 90% HCOOH, Et_2O (95%))→ $CH_3{*}C(Cl)_2COOH$ (39% overall)

Dalapon
[2,2-Dichloropropanoic-2-^{14}C acid]

F. S. Tanaka and R. G. Wien, J. Label. Compound. Radiopharm., 12, 41 (1976).

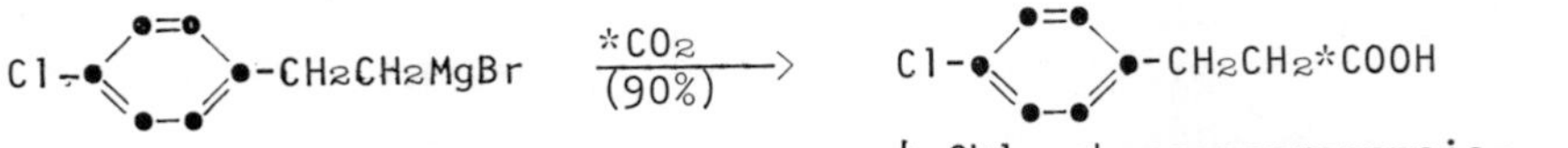

Cl-
-CH2CH2MgBr
*CO2
(90%)
Cl-
-CH2CH2*COOH

4-Chlorobenzenepropanoic-1-^{14}C acid

1. $LiAlH_4$, THF (95%)
2. $SOCl_2$, C_6H_6, pyr (90%)
3. NaCN, DMSO, Δ (95%)
4. NaOH, KOH, H_2O, glycol (98%)

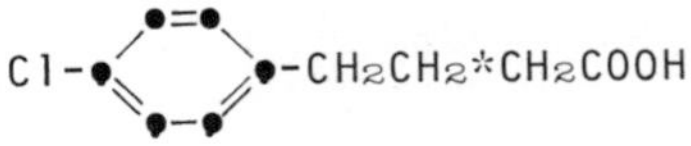

Cl-
-CH2CH2*CH2COOH

4-Chlorobenzenebutanoic-α-^{14}C acid

W. Den Hollander, P. J. Van der Jagt, and B. Van Zanten, J. Label. Compounds, 8, 3 (1972).

(p-$IC_6H_4)_2CH{*}CH_3$ $\xrightarrow[\text{AcOH}]{H_2CrO_4}$

1,1-Di-(4-iodophenyl) ethane-2-^{14}C

(31%; 20% from $*CH_3I$)

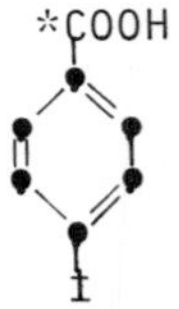

*COOH
I

4-Iodobenzoic-7-^{14}C acid

At room temperature, 25% of the oxidation product is formed via a 1,2-migration of the p-iodophenyl group to give a molar activity of p-iodobenzoic acid half that of the starting material; the remainder of the oxidation product is formed via an oxidative degradation yielding inactive p-iodobenzoic acid. At reflux temperature, only 17% of the product is formed via oxidative rearrangement.

H. H. Szmont, J. Colón, and J. Castrillón, J. Org. Chem., 36, 573 (1971).

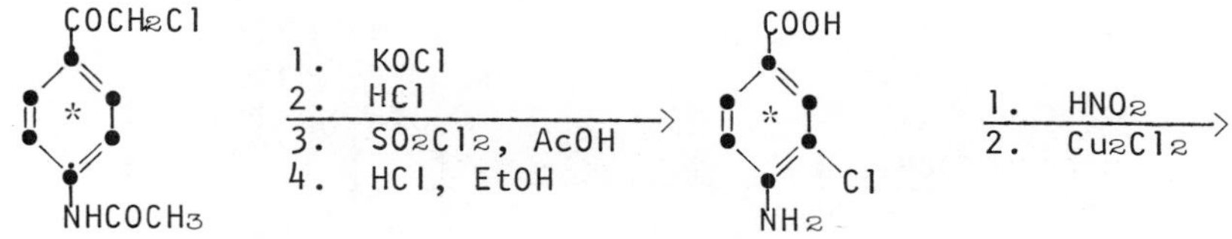
COCH2Cl
NHCOCH3
1. KOCl
2. HCl
3. SO2Cl2, AcOH
4. HCl, EtOH
COOH
Cl
NH2
1. HNO2
2. Cu2Cl2

N-[(4-chloroacetyl)-phenyl] acetamide-(ring-^{14}C)

4-Amino-3-chlorobenzoic (ring-^{14}C) acid

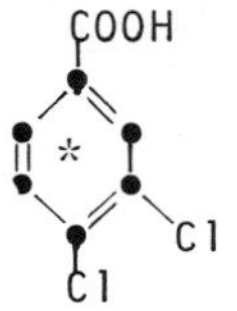
COOH
Cl
Cl

3,4-Dichlorobenzoic-(ring-^{14}C) acid

The 4-chlorobenzoic-(ring-^{14}C) acid derivative was prepared in a similar manner.

F. S. Tanaka, J. Agr. Food Chem., 18, 213 (1970).

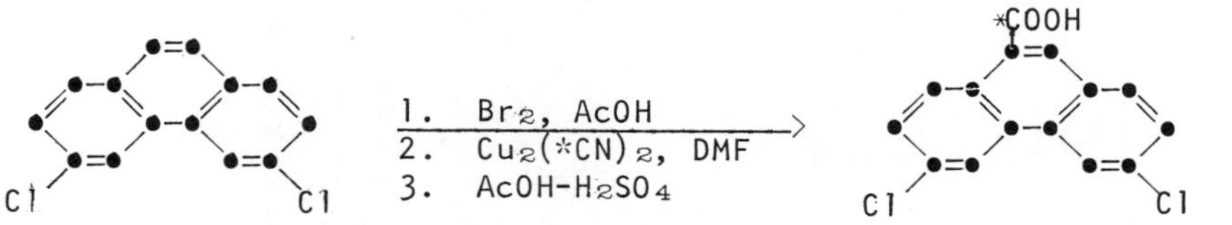
Cl
Cl
1. Br2, AcOH
2. Cu2(*CN)2, DMF
3. AcOH-H2SO4
*COOH
Cl
Cl

3,6-Dichlorophen-anthrene

3,6-Dichlorophen-anthrene-9-carboxylic acid-(carboxyl-^{14}C)

P.-L. Chien and C. C. Cheng, Mikrochim. Acta, 401 (1973).

1-6 Nitro Acids

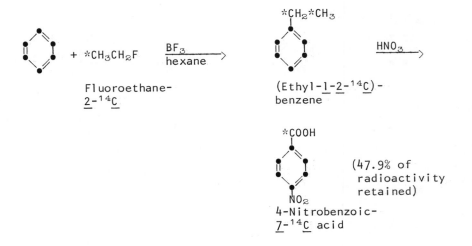

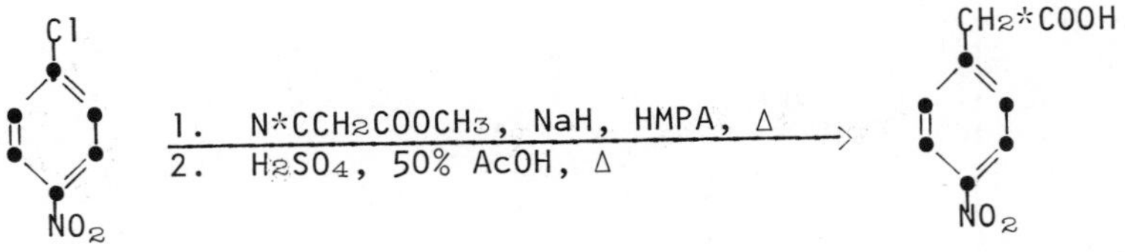
Cl
1. N*CCH2COOCH3, NaH, HMPA, Δ
2. H2SO4, 50% AcOH, Δ
NO2
CH2*COOH
NO2

4-Nitrobenzene-acetic-1-^{14}C acid

J. I. DeGraw and J. S. Engstrom, J. Label. Compounds, 11, 233 (1975).

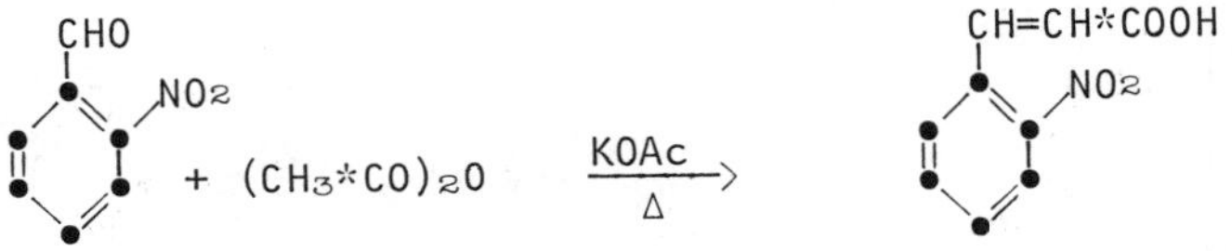
CHO
NO2
+ (CH3*CO)2O
KOAc
Δ
CH=CH*COOH
NO2

(70% Crude)

[E]-o-Nitrocinnamic acid
[[E]-3-(2-Nitrophenyl)-2-propenoic-1-^{14}C acid]

R. F. C. Brown and R. J. Smith, Aust. J. Chem., 25, 607 (1972).

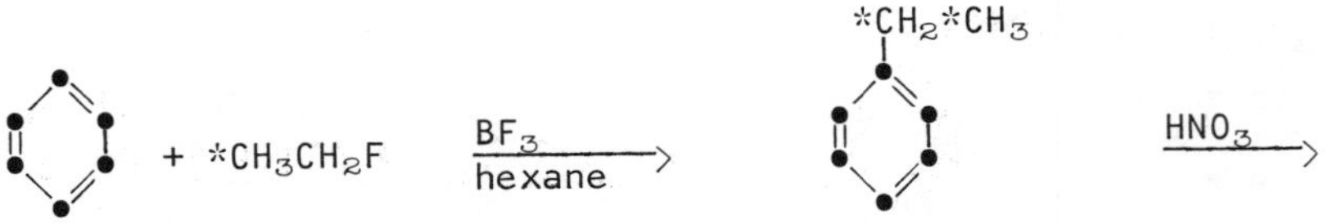
+ *CH3CH2F
BF3
hexane
*CH2*CH3
HNO3

Fluoroethane-2-^{14}C

(Ethyl-1-2-^{14}C)-benzene

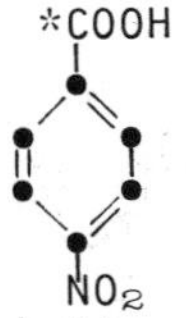
*COOH
NO2

(47.9% of radioactivity retained)

4-Nitrobenzoic-7-^{14}C acid

The ^{14}C label in ethylbenzene is essentially completely scrambled, indicating a mechanism involving an ethyl carbonium ion (electrophile) intermediate which equilibrates the label via an internal hydride shift. The same alkylation reaction was carried out in nitromethane, and the resulting 4-nitrobenzoic acid product retained only 3.5% of the radioactivity. The ^{14}C label is therefore retained in the methyl group, indicating a mechanism involving a nonionized complex intermediate which is positionally selective.

A. Natsubori and R. Nakane, J. Org. Chem., 35, 3372 (1970).

1-7 Aldehydic Acids

H*C≡*CH + HCHO —(Cu_2C_2; 120°C, pressure)→ $HOCH_2$-*C≡*C-CH_2OH (45%)

Acetylene-^{14}C → 2-Butyne-1,4-diol-2,3-^{14}C

—(Cl_2; 100°C)→ OHC-*C(Cl)=*C(Cl)-COOH

Mucochloric acid
[(Z)-2,3-Dichloro-4-oxo-2-butenoic-2,3-^{14}C acid]

T. F. Burger, J. Label. Compounds, 4, 262 (1968).

1-8 Keto Acids

$ClCH_2$*CN —(1. $ZnCl_2$, HCl, 1,2,4-Triethoxybenzene; 2. NaH, $CH_2(COOC_2H_5)_2$ (57%); 3. aq. HCl (66%))→

Chloroacetonitrile-1-^{14}C

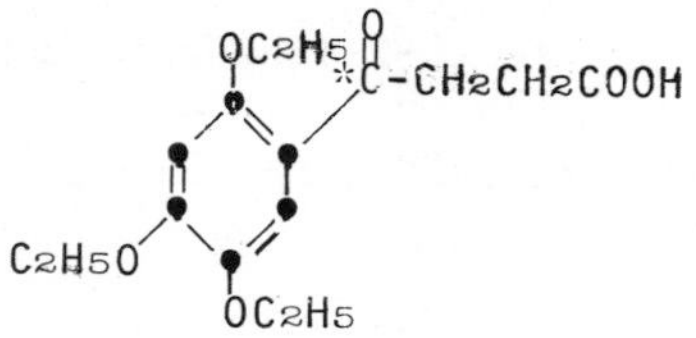

OC_2H_5
*C-CH_2CH_2COOH
C_2H_5O
OC_2H_5

(11% overall)

2,4,5-Triethoxy-γ-oxobenzenebutanoic-γ-^{14}C acid

N. Hayashi, T. Toga, and T. Murata, J. Label. Compounds, 10, 609 (1974).

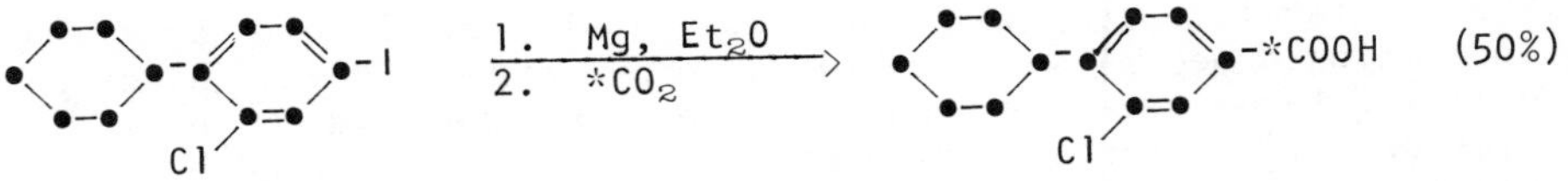
Cl
1. Mg, Et_2O
2. $*CO_2$
-*COOH
(50%)
Cl

3-Chloro-4-cyclohexyl-
benzoic-<u>7</u>-^{14}<u>C</u> acid

1. $SOCl_2$
2. $LiC(COOSi(CH_3)_3)_2CH_2COOSi(CH_3)_3$
3. H_2O

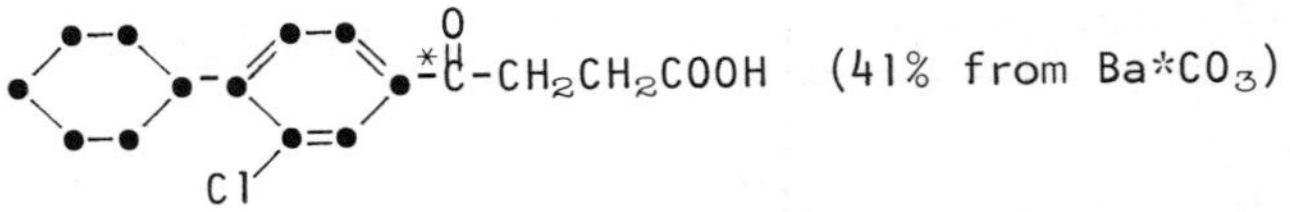
O
*C-CH_2CH_2COOH
(41% from $Ba*CO_3$)
Cl

3-Chloro-4-cyclohexyl-γ-
oxobenzenebutanoic-<u>γ</u>-^{14}<u>C</u> acid

L. Pichat, J. P. Beaucourt, M. Herbert, F. Krausz, and J. C. Breliere, <u>J. Label. Compound. Radiopharm.</u>, <u>12</u>, 483 (1976).

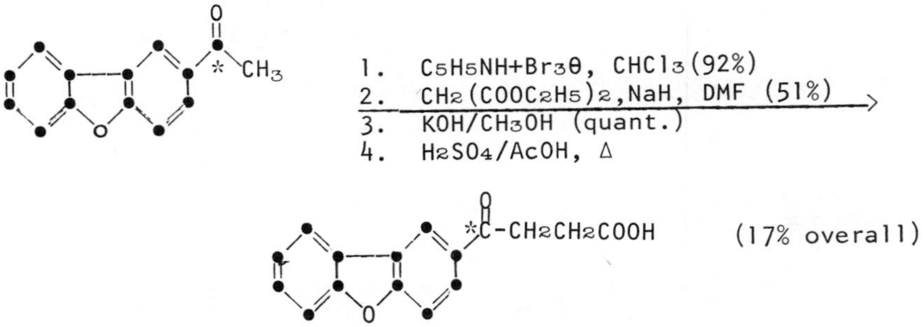
O
*
CH_3
O
1. $C_5H_5NH^+Br_3^\ominus$, $CHCl_3$ (92%)
2. $CH_2(COOC_2H_5)_2$, NaH, DMF (51%)
3. KOH/CH_3OH (quant.)
4. H_2SO_4/AcOH, Δ
O
*C-CH_2CH_2COOH
(17% overall)
O

Furobufen
[γ-Oxo-2-dibenzofuranbutanoic-<u>γ</u>-^{14}<u>C</u> acid]

E. S. Ferdinandi, <u>J. Label. Compound. Radiopharm.</u>, <u>12</u>, 357 (1976).

$C_6H_5{*}COCl$ $\xrightarrow[\text{2. } H_2O]{\text{1. } LiC(COOSi(CH_3)_3)_2CH(CH_3)COOSi(CH_3)_3\text{, glyme}}$

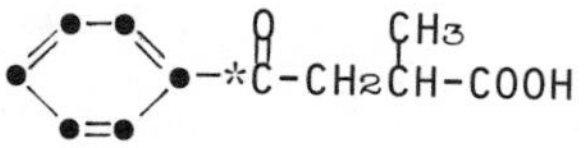

(66%)

α-Methyl-γ-oxobenzene-butanoic-γ-^{14}C acid

L. Pichat, J. P. Beaucourt, F. Krausz, and C. Moulineau, J. Label. Compound. Radiopharm., 12, 347 (1976).

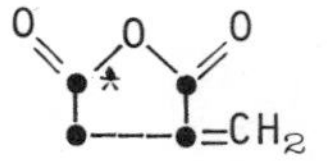

Itaconic anhydride

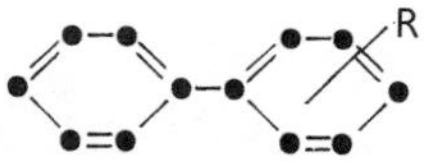

$\xrightarrow{AlCl_3,\ CH_2Cl_2}$

[Dihydro-3-methylene-2,5-furandione-5-^{14}C]

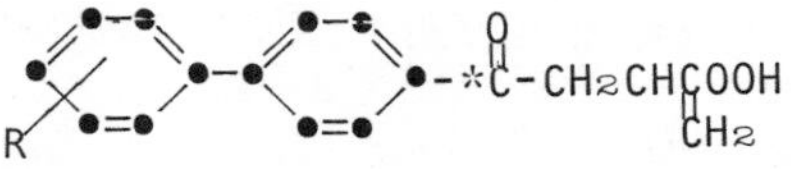

R = H; α-Methylene-γ-oxo(1,1'-biphenyl)-4-butanoic-γ-^{14}C acid (33%)

R = o-Cl; 2'-Chloro-α-methylene-γ-oxo(1,1'-biphenyl)-4-butanoic-γ-^{14}C acid (55%)

R = p-Cl; 4'-Chloro-α-methylene-γ-oxo(1,1'-biphenyl)-4-butanoic-γ-^{14}C acid (42%)

The unsymmetrical anhydride is believed to give exclusively the 4-^{14}C labeled product.

H. Cousse, B. Bonnaud, L. Pichat, and F. Aubert, J. Label. Compound Radiopharm., 12, 491 (1976).

$CH_2{=}CHCH_2CH_2{*}COCH_3$ $\xrightarrow[\text{2. } 30\%\ H_2O_2,\ AcOH,\ \Delta]{\text{1. } O_3,\ CH_2Cl_2,\ -78°C}$

5-Hexen-2-one-2-^{14}C

CH_3-*C(=O)-CH_2CH_2-COOH (91%; 63% from CO_2)

Levulinic acid
[4-Oxopentanoic-_4_-^{14}_C_ acid]

R. L. Ellsworth, G. J. Gatto, M. T. Meriwether, and H. E. Mertel, _J. Label. Compound. Radiopharm._, _15_, 613 (1978).

CH_3*$COCH_2COOC_2H_5$ —(1. $BrCH_2COOC_2H_5$, Na, toluene, Δ; 2. 7% HCl, Δ)→

Ethyl acetoacetate
[3-Oxobutanoic-_3_-^{14}_C_ acid ethyl ester]
(75% from sodium acetate-_1_-^{14}_C_)

CH_3*C(=O)-CH_2CH_2COOH (57%)

Levulinic acid
[4-Oxopentanoic-_4_-^{14}_C_ acid

I. Nakatsuka, M. Hazue, Y. Makari, K. Kawahara, M. Endo, and A. Yoshitake, _J. Label. Compound. Radiopharm._, _12_, 395 (1976).

CH_3-CH(OH)-CH_2C≡CH —(1. 2 equiv. _n_-BuLi, Et_2O/hexane; 2. 2 equiv. *CO_2)→

CH_3CH(OH)-CH_2C≡C-*COOH (44%; 22% from *CO_2)

5-Hydroxy-2-hexynoic-_1_-^{14}_C_ acid

—(1. H_2, Lindlar catalyst, THF; 2. CrO_3, H_2SO_4, acetone, 0°C)→

CH_3C(=O)-CH_2CH=CH*COOH + CH_3C(=O)-CH=CHCH_2*COOH

(E)-5-Oxo-2-hexenoic-_1_-^{14}_C_ acid (E)-5-Oxo-3-hexenoic-_1_-^{14}_C_ acid

The C-2 alkene product predominated in the equilibrium mixture, no <u>cis</u> isomer was observed; the unlabeled reation gave a 16% yield.

C. M. Harris and T. M. Harris, <u>J. Org. Chem.</u>, <u>36</u>, 2181 (1971).

$CH_3(CH_2)_{12}COCl$ + $CH_3COCH_2{*}COOC_2H_5$ —(1. condensation; 2. decarboxylation)→

$CH_3(CH_2)_{12}C(=O)\text{-}CH_2{*}COOH$ (35%)

3-Oxyhexedecanoic-<u>1</u>-^{14}<u>C</u> acid

J. A. Jones and M. Blecher, <u>J. Lipid Res.</u>, <u>7</u>, 422 (1966).

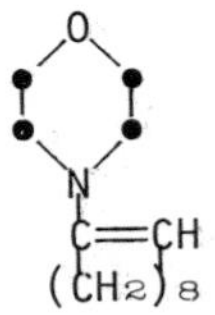

+ $CH_3(CH_2)_8{*}COCl$ —(1. $(C_2H_5)_3N$, $CHCl_3$; 2. HCl)→

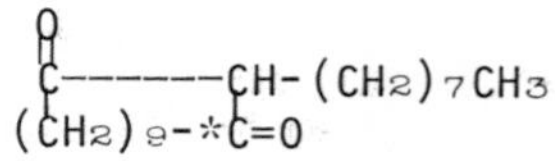

(27%) —(aq. NaOH; EtOH, Δ)→

2-Octylcyclododecane-1,
3-dione-<u>1</u>,<u>3</u>-^{14}<u>C</u>

$CH_3(CH_2)_8{*}C(=O)(CH_2)_9{*}COOH$ (96%)

11-Oxoeicosanoic-<u>1</u>,<u>11</u>-^{14}<u>C</u> acid

13-Oxodocosanoic-<u>1</u>,<u>13</u>-^{14}<u>C</u> acid was similarly prepared.

J. S. V. Hunter and R. J. Light, <u>Biochemistry</u>, <u>9</u>, 4283 (1970).

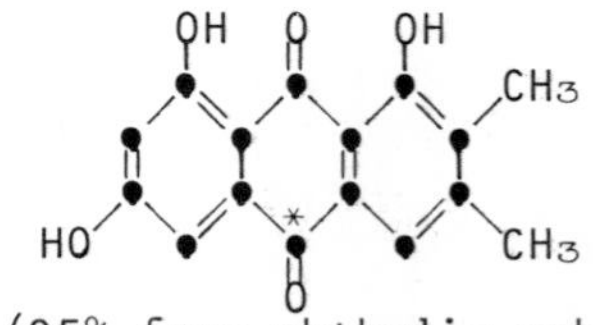

(25% from phthalic anhydride)

1. NBS, azo-bisisobutyronitrile
2. NaOAc, Ac_2O
3. AgO, NaOH

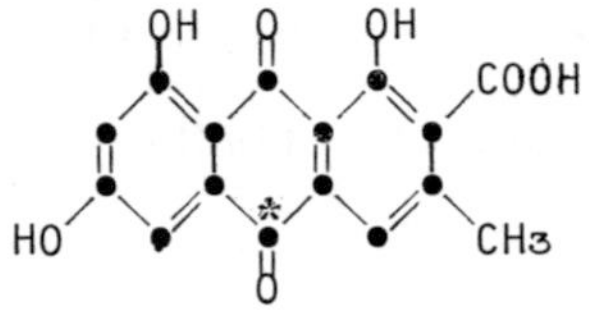

(10% for three steps) +

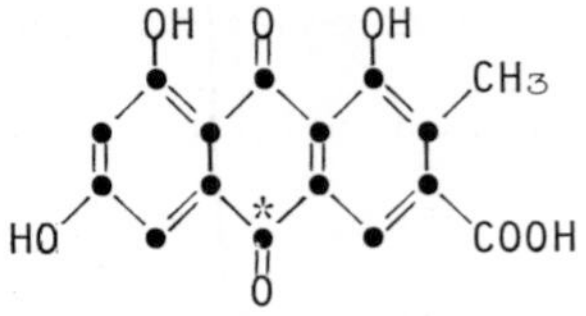

Endocrocin
[9,10-Dihydro-1,6,8-trihydroxy-3-methyl-9,10-dioxo-2-anthracenecarboxylic-10-^{14}C acid]

Isomer

B. Franck, V. Ohnsorge, and H. Flasch, Tetrahedron Lett., 3773, (1970).

1-9 Hydroxy Acids

$C_6H_5CH(OH)(SO_3H)$ $\xrightarrow[\text{2. } H_2SO_4]{\text{1. } K{*}CNH_2O}$ $C_6H_5CH(OH){*}COOH$ (~70%)

dl-Mandelic acid
[α-Hydroxybenzeneacetic-1-^{14}C acid]

G. Blaschke, Chem. Ber., 107, 232 (1974).

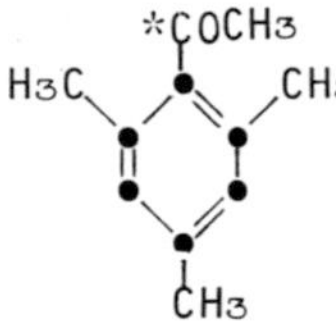

$\xrightarrow[\text{EtONa}]{(C_2H_5O)_2CO}$

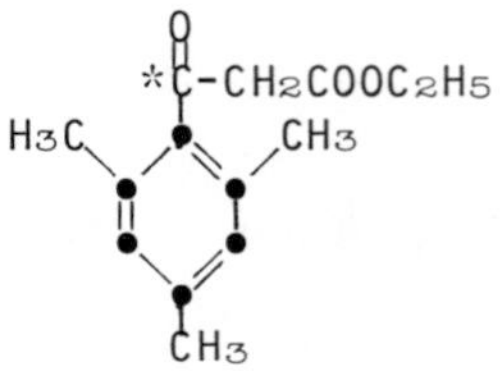

(32%)

1-(2,4,6-Trimethylphenyl)-ethanone-1-^{14}C

2,4,6-Trimethyl-β-oxobenzenepropanoic-β ^{14}C acid ethyl ester

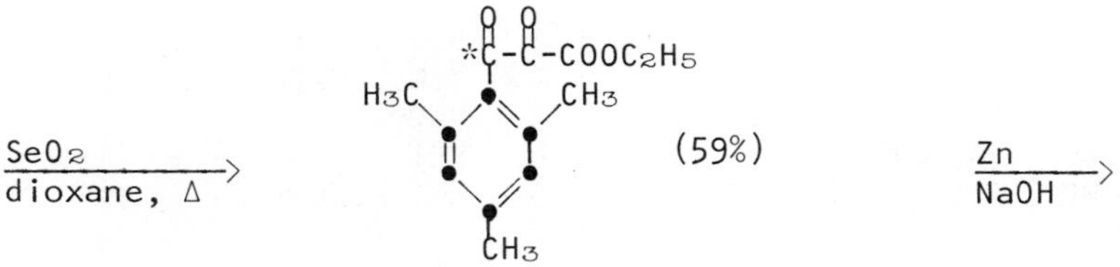
SeO2
dioxane, Δ
*C-C-COOC2H5
H3C
CH3
CH3
(59%)
Zn
NaOH

2,4,6-Trimethyl-α,β-dioxobenzenepropanoic-β-^{14}C acid ethyl ester

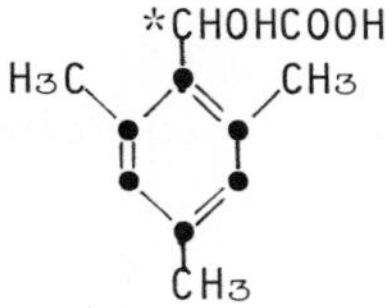
*CHOHCOOH
H3C
CH3
CH3

(90%) A mechanism is discussed.

α-Hydroxy-2,4,6-trimethylbenzeneacetic-α-^{14}C acid

H. Rodé-Gowal, H. L. Dao, and H. Dahn, Helv. Chim. Acta, 57, 2209 (1974).

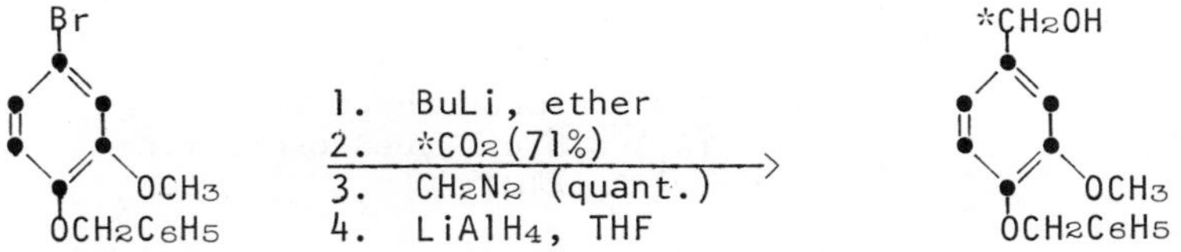
Br
OCH3
OCH2C6H5
1. BuLi, ether
2. *CO2 (71%)
3. CH2N2 (quant.)
4. LiAlH4, THF
*CH2OH
OCH3
OCH2C6H5

(55% from $^{*}CO_2$)

3-Methoxy-4-(phenylmethoxy)-benzenemethanol-^{14}C

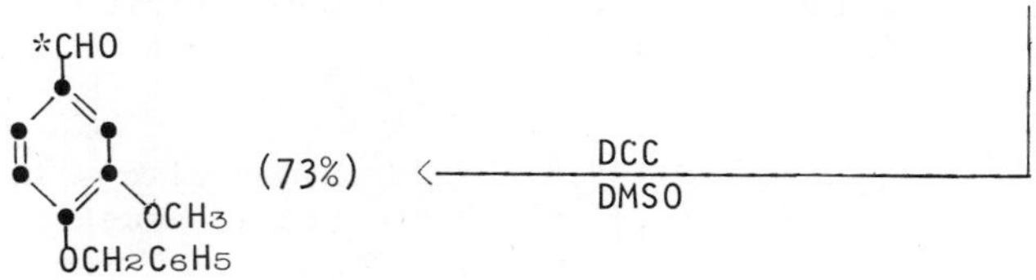
*CHO
OCH3
OCH2C6H5
(73%)
DCC
DMSO

3-Methoxy-4-(phenylmethoxy)-benzaldehyde-^{14}C

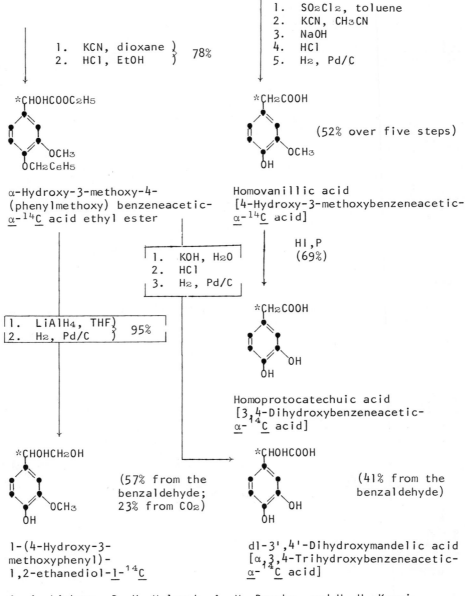

1. KCN, dioxane
2. HCl, EtOH
78%

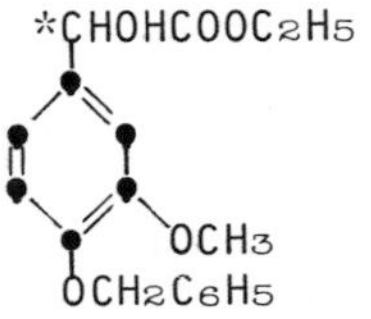

α-Hydroxy-3-methoxy-4-(phenylmethoxy) benzeneacetic-α-^{14}C acid ethyl ester

1. SO_2Cl_2, toluene
2. KCN, CH_3CN
3. NaOH
4. HCl
5. H_2, Pd/C

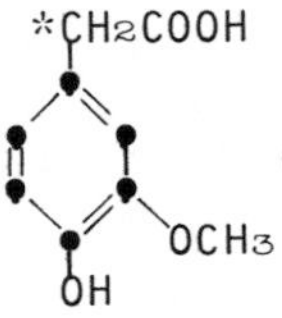

(52% over five steps)

Homovanillic acid [4-Hydroxy-3-methoxybenzeneacetic-α-^{14}C acid]

HI, P (69%)

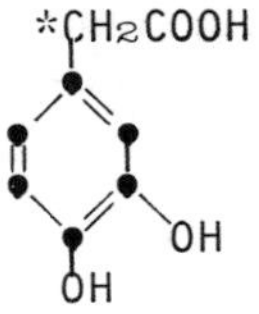

Homoprotocatechuic acid [3,4-Dihydroxybenzeneacetic-α-^{14}C acid]

1. $LiAlH_4$, THF
2. H_2, Pd/C
95%

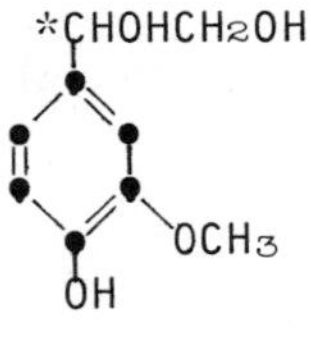

(57% from the benzaldehyde; 23% from CO_2)

1-(4-Hydroxy-3-methoxyphenyl)-1,2-ethanediol-1-^{14}C

1. KOH, H_2O
2. HCl
3. H_2, Pd/C

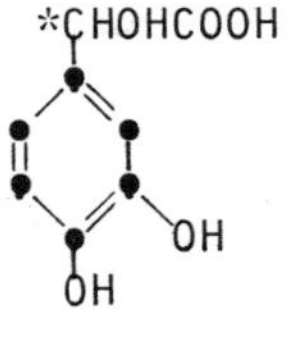

(41% from the benzaldehyde)

dl-3',4'-Dihydroxymandelic acid [α,3,4-Trihydroxybenzeneacetic-α-^{14}C acid]

A. A. Liebman, D. H. Malarek, A. M. Dorsky, and H. H. Kaegi, J. Label. Compounds, 7, 449 (1971).

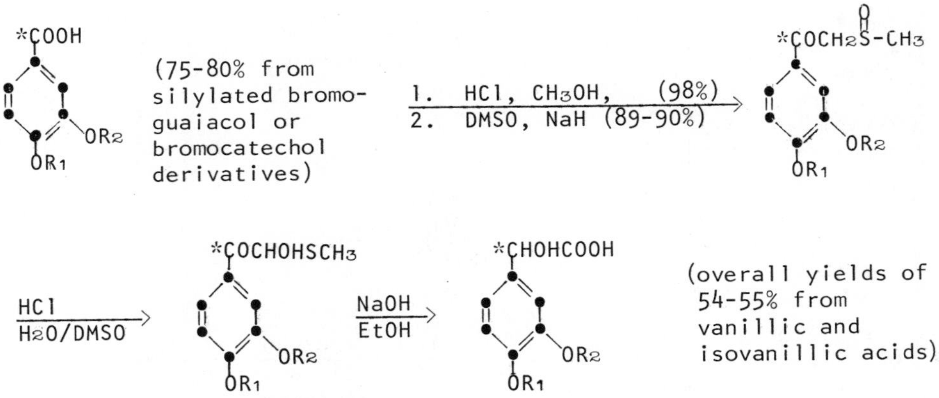
*COOH
OR2
OR1
(75-80% from silylated bromo-guaiacol or bromocatechol derivatives)
1. HCl, CH3OH, (98%)
2. DMSO, NaH (89-90%)
*COCH2S-CH3
O
HCl
H2O/DMSO
*COCHOHSCH3
NaOH
EtOH
*CHOHCOOH
(overall yields of 54-55% from vanillic and isovanillic acids)

R_1=H, R_2=CH_3; α,4-Dihydroxy-3-methoxybenzeneacetic-α-^{14}C acid
R_1=CH_3, R_2=H; α,3-Dihydroxy-4-methoxybenzeneacetic-α-^{14}C acid

Also:

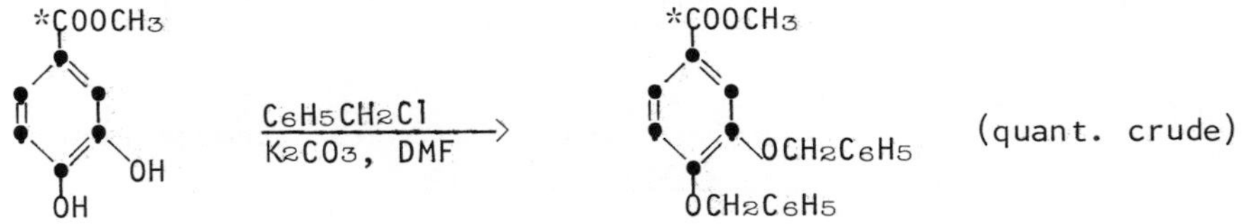
*COOCH3
OH
OH
C6H5CH2Cl
K2CO3, DMF
*COOCH3
OCH2C6H5
OCH2C6H5
(quant. crude)

3,4-Dihydroxy-benzoic-1-^{14}C acid methyl ester

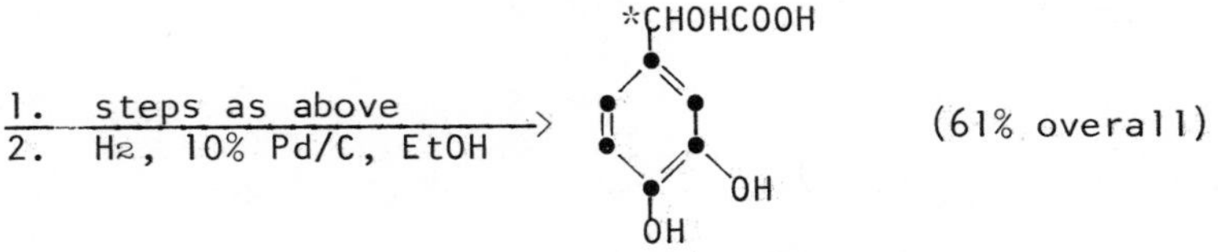
1. steps as above
2. H2, 10% Pd/C, EtOH
*CHOHCOOH
OH
OH
(61% overall)

α,3,4-Trihydroxybenzene-acetic-α-^{14}C acid

L. Pichat and J. Tostain, J. Label. Compound. Radiopharm., 13, 587, (1977).

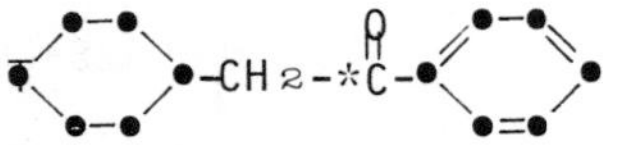
-CH2-*C-
O

1. Br_2, AcOH (91%)
2. KOH,Δ, EtOH/H_2O (71%)

2-Cyclohexyl-1-phenylethanone-1-^{14}C

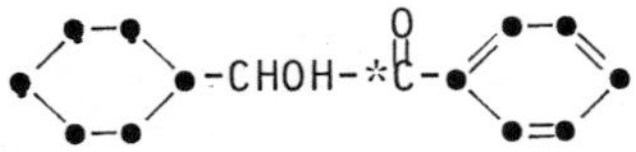
-CHOH-*C-
O

$CuSO_4.5H_2O$
pyr/H_2O

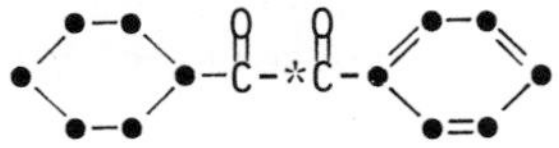
-C-*C-
O O

(80%)

KOH, EtOH/H_2O
(benzilic-acid-type rearrangement)

1-Phenyl-2-cyclohexyl-ethanedione-1-^{14}C

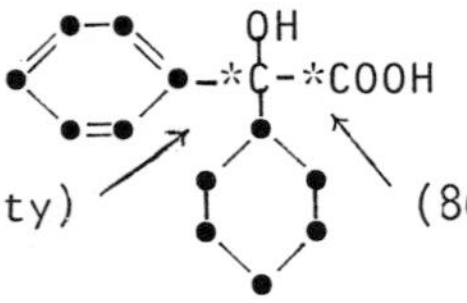
OH
-*C-*COOH

(45% yield)

(20% activity) (80% activity)

α-Hydroxy-α-cyclohexylbenzeneacetic-(α, carboxyl-^{14}C) acid

The position of label was determined by decarboxylation; the phenyl to cyclohexyl migration ratio was 4:1.

A. Novelli, M. J. Vernengo, M. C. G. Barrio, and J. R. Barrio, An. Assoc. Quim. Argent., 60, 119 (1972).

CH_2=CH-*COOH

1. Br_2
2. CH_2N_2
3. KOAc, AcOH

HO-CH_2CHOH*COOH (43% from Ba*CO_3)

Acrylic acid [2-Propenoic-1-^{14}C acid]

Glyceric acid [2,3-Dihydroxypropanoic-1-^{14}C acid]

L. Pichat, M. Herbert, and F. Aubert, J. Label. Compounds, 1, 66 (1965).

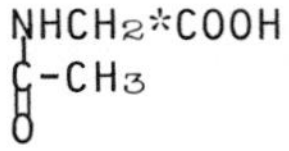

(83-85% from glycine-1-^{14}C) $\xrightarrow[NaOAc,\ Ac_2O]{C_6H_5CHO,\ \Delta}$

N-Acetylglycine-1-^{14}C

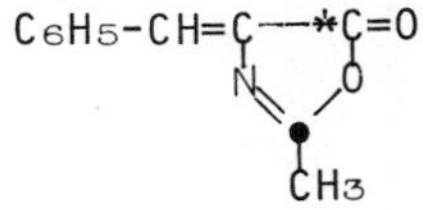

(52%) $\xrightarrow[2.\ IN\ H_2SO_4,\Delta\ (72\%)]{1.\ CH_3COCH_3,\ H_2O,\Delta\ (70\%)}$

Azlactone
[(2-Methyl-4-(phenylmethylene)-5(4H)-oxazolone-5-^{14}C]

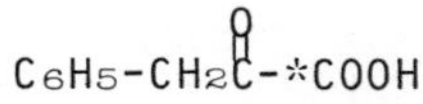

(72%) $\xrightarrow[HCl]{Zn}$ C_6H_5-CH_2CHOH*COOH

Phenylpyruvic acid-^{14}C

3-Phenyllactic acid
[3-Phenyl-2-hydroxy-propanoic-1-^{14}C acid]

H.-W. Liebisch, G. C. Bhasvar, and H. R. Schütte, Z. Chem., 12, 220 (1972).

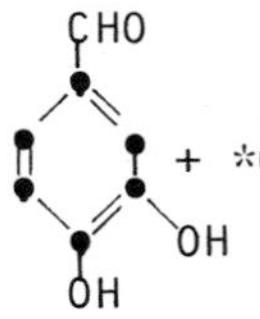

+ *CH_2(COOH) $\xrightarrow[aniline]{pyr}$

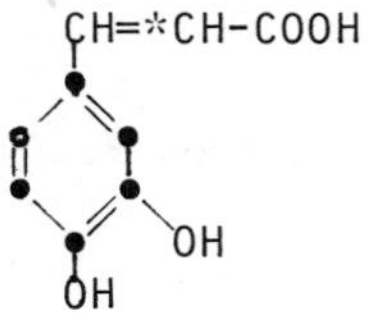

(42%)

3-[3,4-Dihydroxyphenyl]-2-propenoic-α-^{14}C acid

J. F. DeBardeleben and L. C. Teng, J. Label. Compounds, 6, 34 (1970); for the similar preparation of 3-(4-acetoxy-3-methoxyphenyl)-2-propenoic-α-^{14}C acid, see H. H. Balba and G. G. Still, J. Label. Compound. Radiopharm., 15, 309 (1978).

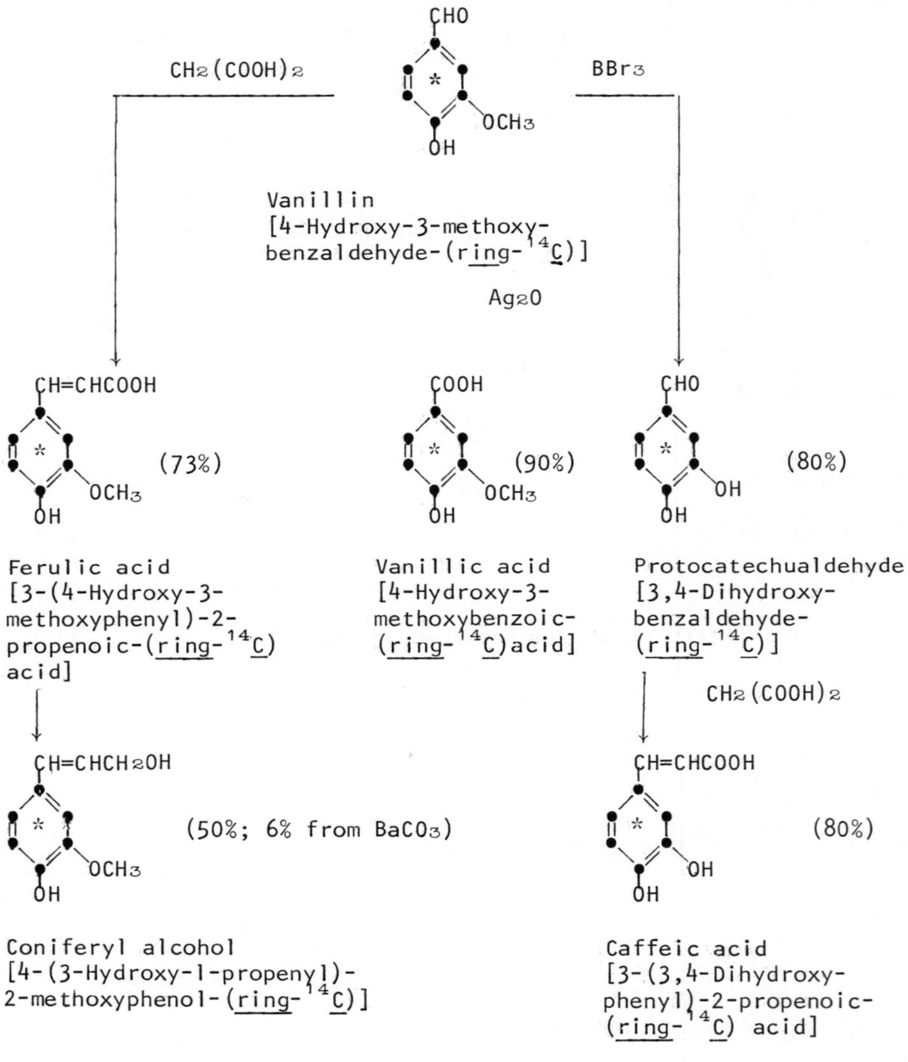
CHO
OCH3
OH
$CH_2(COOH)_2$
BBr_3
Vanillin
[4-Hydroxy-3-methoxybenzaldehyde-(ring-^{14}C)]
Ag_2O
CH=CHCOOH
OCH3
OH
(73%)
COOH
OCH3
OH
(90%)
CHO
OH
OH
(80%)
Ferulic acid
[3-(4-Hydroxy-3-methoxyphenyl)-2-propenoic-(ring-^{14}C) acid]
Vanillic acid
[4-Hydroxy-3-methoxybenzoic-(ring-^{14}C)acid]
Protocatechualdehyde
[3,4-Dihydroxybenzaldehyde-(ring-^{14}C)]
$CH_2(COOH)_2$
CH=CHCH2OH
OCH3
OH
(50%; 6% from $BaCO_3$)
CH=CHCOOH
OH
OH
(80%)
Coniferyl alcohol
[4-(3-Hydroxy-1-propenyl)-2-methoxyphenol-(ring-^{14}C)]
Caffeic acid
[3-(3,4-Dihydroxyphenyl)-2-propenoic-(ring-^{14}C) acid]

Similarly

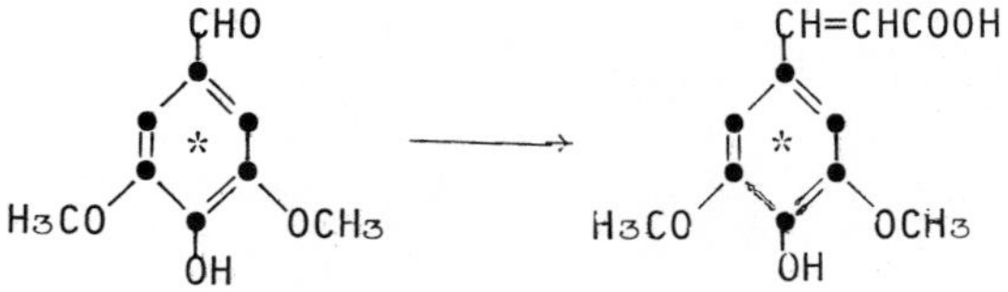

(80%)

Syringaldehyde
[4-Hydroxy-3,5-dimethoxybenzaldehyde-(ring-^{14}C)]

Sinapic acid
[3-(4-Hydroxy-3,5-dimethoxyphenyl)-2-propenoic-(ring-^{14}C) acid]

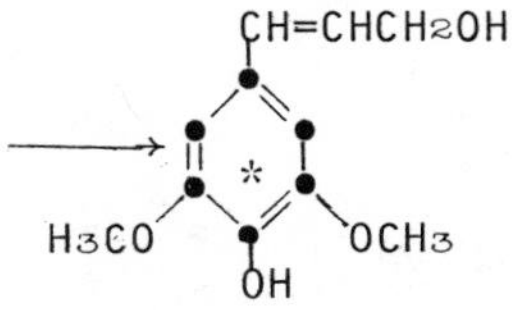

(42%; 2% from Ba*CO_3)

Sinapin alcohol
[4-(3-Hydroxy-1-propenyl)-2,6-dimethoxyphenol-(ring)-^{14}C)]

K. Haider, J. Label. Compounds, 2, 174 (1966).

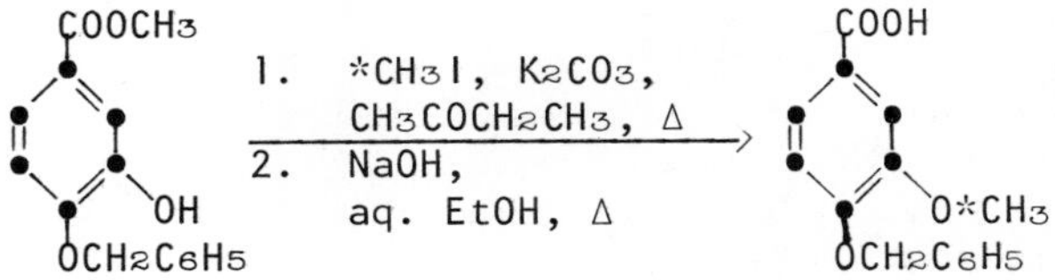

(85% based on *CH_3I consumed)

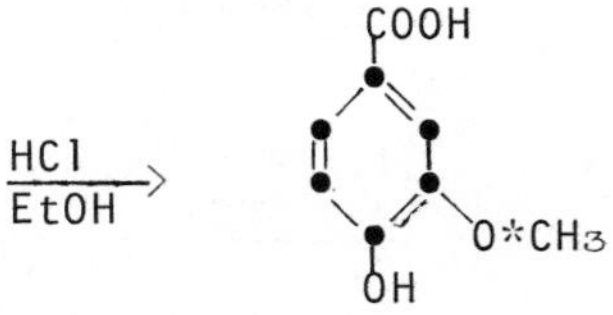

(80%)

Vanillic acid
[4-Hydroxy-3-methoxy-^{14}C)-benzoic acid]

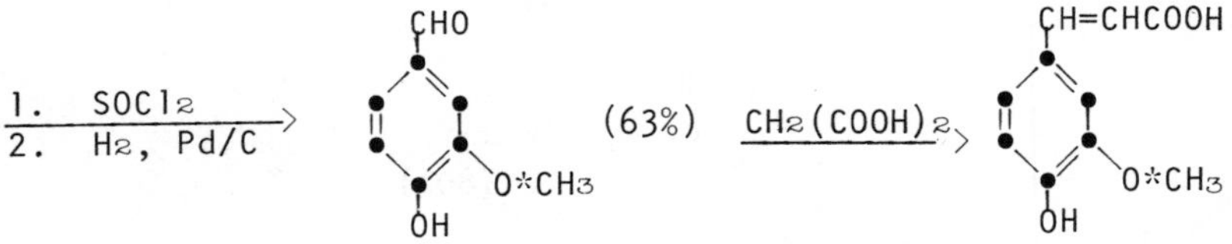
CHO
1. SOCl2
2. H2, Pd/C
O*CH3
OH
(63%)
CH2(COOH)2
CH=CHCOOH
O*CH3
OH

Vanillin
[4-Hydroxy-3-(methoxy-^{14}C)-benzaldehyde]

Ferulic acid
[3-(4-Hydroxy-3-(methoxy-^{14}C)phenyl-2-propenoic acid]

Similarly:

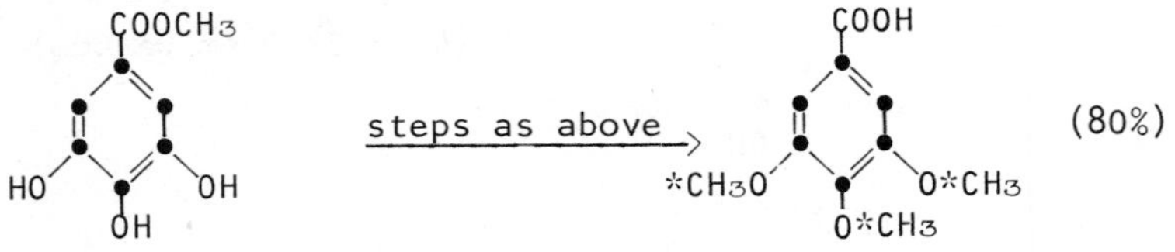
COOCH3
HO
OH
OH
steps as above
COOH
*CH3O
O*CH3
O*CH3
(80%)

Gallic acid

(3,4,5-Trimethoxy-^{14}C)benzoic acid

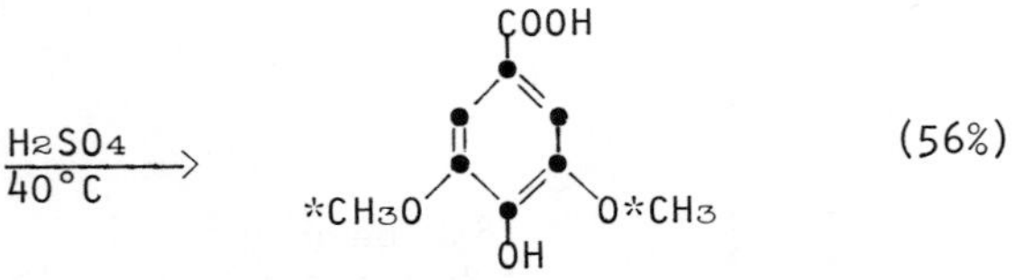
H2SO4
40°C
COOH
*CH3O
O*CH3
OH
(56%)

Syringic acid
[4-Hydroxy-3,5-(dimethoxy-^{14}C)benzoic acid]

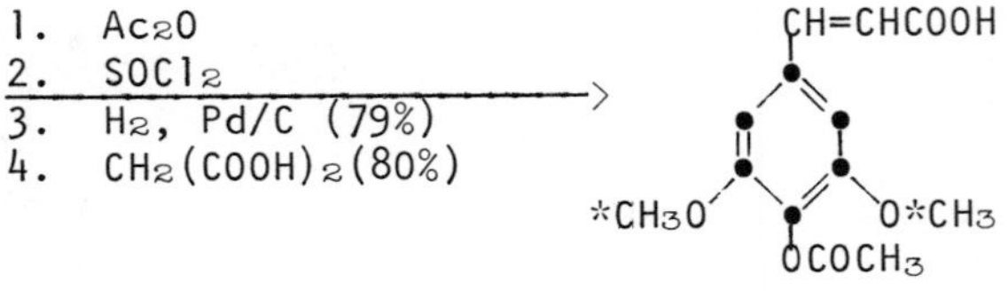
1. Ac2O
2. SOCl2
3. H2, Pd/C (79%)
4. CH2(COOH)2 (80%)
CH=CHCOOH
*CH3O
O*CH3
OCOCH3

Acetyl sinapic acid
[3-(4-Acetyloxy-3,4-(dimethoxy-^{14}C)phenyl)-2-propenoic acid]

K. Haider and S. Lim, J. Label. Compounds, 1, 294 (1965).

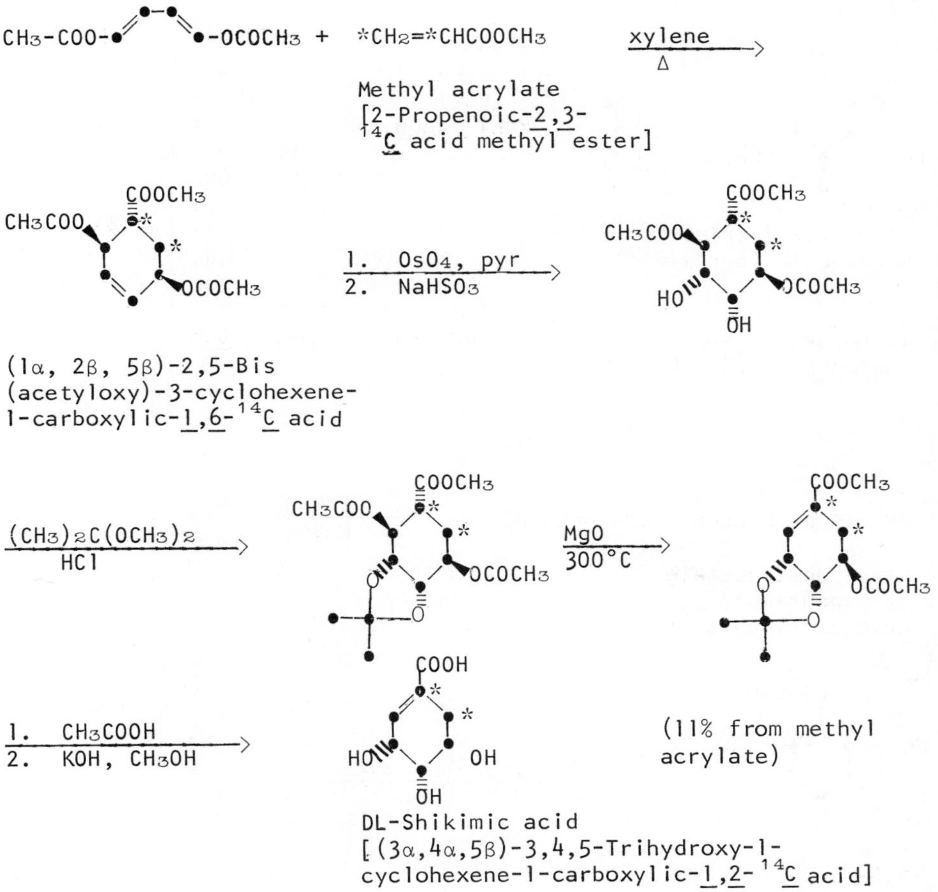
CH₃-COO- -OCOCH₃ + *CH₂=*CHCOOCH₃
xylene
Δ
Methyl acrylate
[2-Propenoic-2,3-¹⁴C acid methyl ester]
COOCH₃
CH₃COO
OCOCH₃
1. OsO₄, pyr
2. NaHSO₃
HO
OH
(1α, 2β, 5β)-2,5-Bis
(acetyloxy)-3-cyclohexene-
1-carboxylic-1,6-¹⁴C acid
(CH₃)₂C(OCH₃)₂
HCl
MgO
300°C
1. CH₃COOH
2. KOH, CH₃OH
COOH
(11% from methyl
acrylate)
DL-Shikimic acid
[(3α,4α,5β)-3,4,5-Trihydroxy-1-
cyclohexene-1-carboxylic-1,2-¹⁴C acid]

B. Chabannes, L. Pichat, M. Herbert, and H. Pacheco, J. Label. Compounds, 1, 102 (1965).

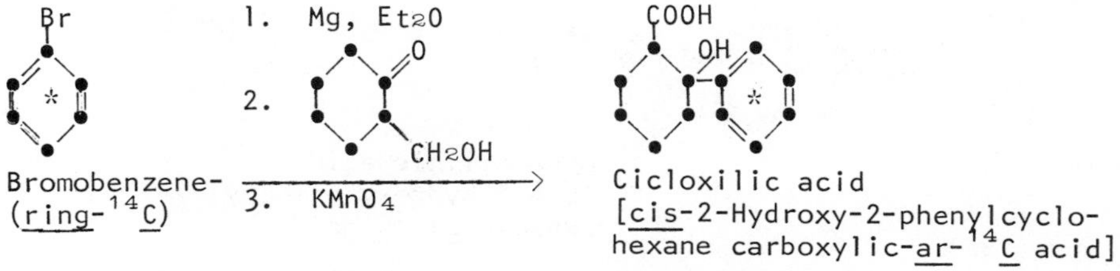
Br
1. Mg, Et₂O
2.
CH₂OH
3. KMnO₄
COOH
OH
Bromobenzene-
(ring-¹⁴C)
Cicloxilic acid
[cis-2-Hydroxy-2-phenylcyclo-
hexane carboxylic-ar-¹⁴C acid]

G. Bramanti, M. Sacanni, P. Schiantarelli, and W. Murmann, Arzneim.-Forsch.-(Drug Res.), 28, (11), 1242 (1978).

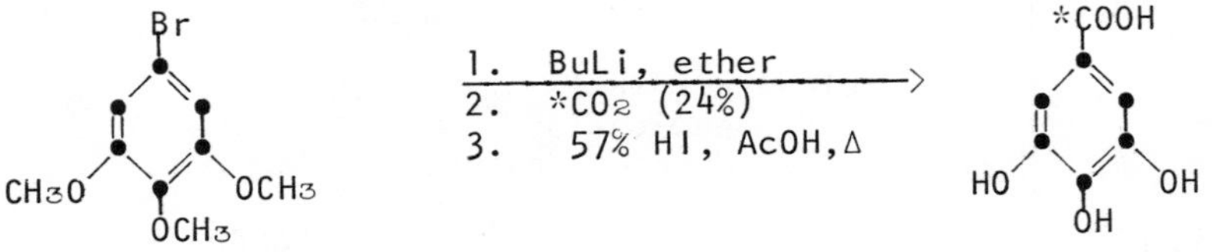
Br
1. BuLi, ether
2. *CO2 (24%)
3. 57% HI, AcOH,Δ
CH3O
OCH3
OCH3
*COOH
HO
OH
OH

(6% from $BaCO_3$)

(from 1,2,3-trimethoxybenzene in four steps)

Gallic acid
[3,4,5-Trihydroxybenzoic-7-^{14}C acid]

I. Kozak, L. Kronrad, and M. Prochazka, J. Label. Compound. Radiopharm, 15, 401 (1978).

$CH_3{*}COCH_2COOC_2H_5$ + $CH_3CH{=}CHCOOC_2H_5$ $\xrightarrow[\text{2. } H_2SO_4]{\text{1. EtONa, EtOH}}$

Ethyl acetoacetate
[3-Oxobutanoic-3-^{14}C acid ethyl ester]

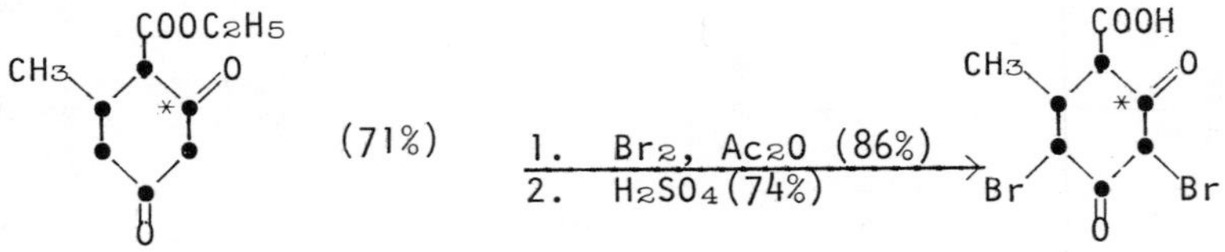
COOC2H5
CH3
O
O
(71%)
1. Br2, Ac2O (86%)
2. H2SO4 (74%)
COOH
CH3
O
Br
Br
O

2,4-Dioxo-6-methylcyclohexanecarboxylic-2-^{14}C acid ethyl ester

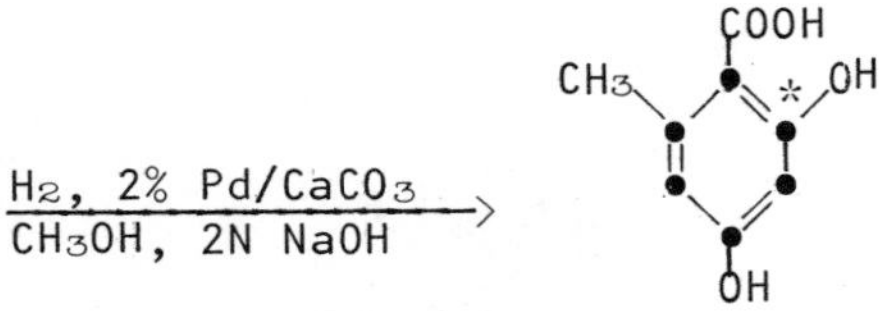
H2, 2% Pd/CaCO3
CH3OH, 2N NaOH
COOH
CH3
OH
OH

(82% yield; 37% overall)

o-Orsellinic acid
[2,4-Dihydroxy-6-methylbenzoic-2-^{14}C acid]

A. Univerricht, P. Pfützner, B. Stecher, and H. R. Schütte, Z. Chem., 12, 289 (1972).

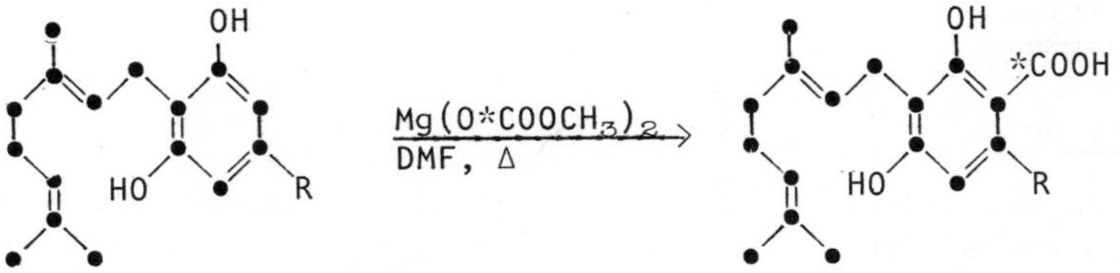
OH
HO
R
Mg(O*COOCH3)2
DMF, Δ
OH
*COOH
HO
R

R=C_3H_7; Cannabigerovarinic acid [(E)-3-(3,7-Dimethyl-2,6-octadienyl)-2,4-dihydroxy-6-propylbenzoic acid-(carboxyl-^{14}C)]

R=CH_3; Cannabergerorcinic acid [(E)-3-(3,7-Dimethyl-2,6-octadienyl)-2,4-dihydroxy-6-methylbenzoic acid-(carboxyl-^{14}C)]

Similarly prepared:

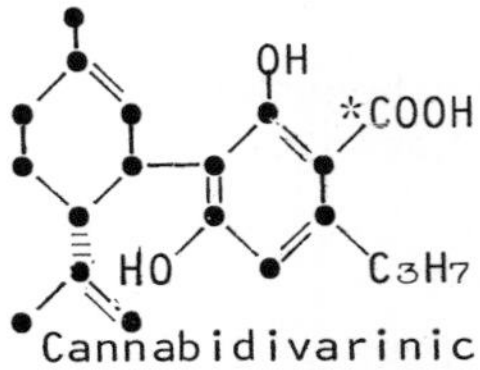
OH
*COOH
HO
C3H7

Cannabidivarinic acid [2,4-Dihydroxy-3-(3-methyl-6-(1-methylethenyl)-2-cyclohexen-1-yl)-6-propylbenzoic-7-^{14}C acid]

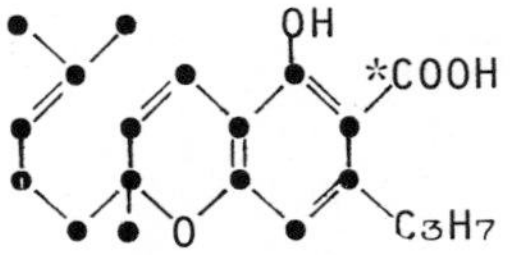
OH
*COOH
O
C3H7

dl-Cannabichromevarinic acid [5-Hydroxy-2-methyl-2-(4-methyl-3-pentenyl)-7-propyl-2H-1-benzopyran-6-carboxylic-^{14}C acid]

Y. Shoyama, H. Hirano, and I. Nishioka, J. Label. Compound. Radiopharm., 14, 835 (1978).

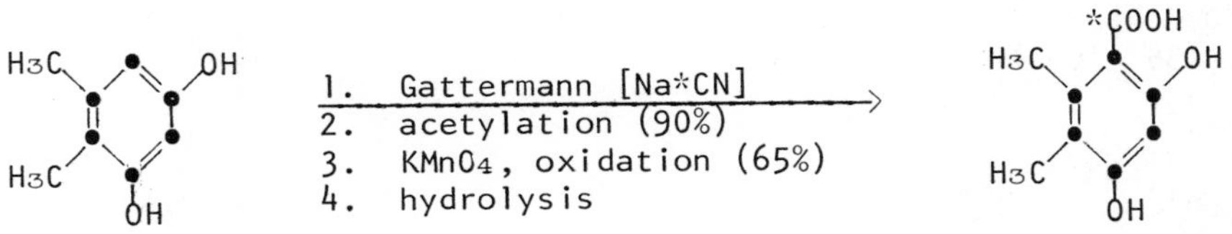
H3C
OH
H3C
OH
1. Gattermann [Na*CN]
2. acetylation (90%)
3. KMnO4, oxidation (65%)
4. hydrolysis
*COOH
H3C
OH
H3C
OH

2,4-Dihydroxy-5,6-dimethylbenzoic-7-^{14}C acid

J. Better and S. Gatenbeck, Acta Chem. Scand. B, 31, 391 (1977).

1-10 Amino Acids

(A) α-Amino Acids

Additional Abbreviations: IUPAC-IUB Commission recommendations are used in most cases; AcOH, acetic acid; Boc, *tert*-butyloxycarbonyl; Bzl, benzyl; DCC, dicyclohexylcarbodiimide; DME, dimethoxyethane; DMF, dimethylformamide; *t*Bu, *tert*-butyl; TEPP, tetraethylpyrophosphite; TFA, trifluoroacetic acid; Z, benzylcarbonyl.

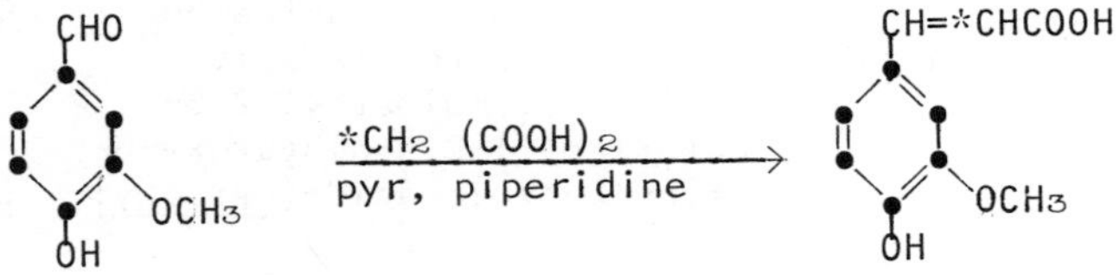
CHO
OCH3
OH
*CH2 (COOH)2
pyr, piperidine
CH=*CHCOOH
OCH3
OH

(46% 1st crop;
75% total yield)

Ferulic acid
[3-(4-Hydroxy-3-methoxyphenyl)-2-propenoic-2-^{14}C acid]

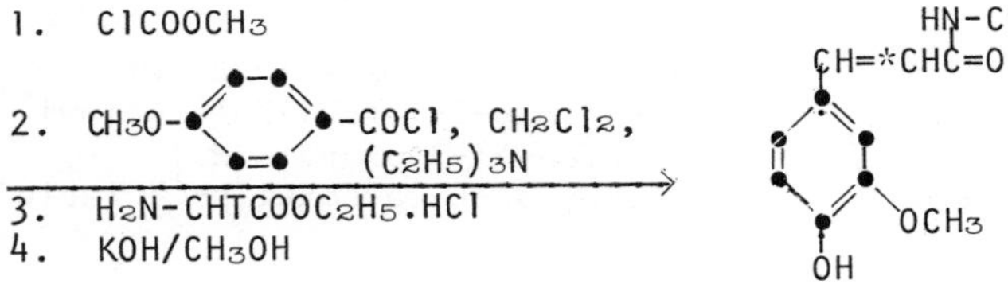
1. ClCOOCH3
2. CH3O- -COCl, CH2Cl2,
(C2H5)3N
3. H2N-CHTCOOC2H5.HCl
4. KOH/CH3OH
HN-CHTCOOH
CH=*CHC=O
OCH3
OH

(43% 1st crop;
75% total yield)

N-Feruloyl-glycine
[N-[3-(4-Hydroxy-3-methoxyphenyl)-oxo-2-propenyl-2-^{14}C)]glycine-2-t]

H. DePooter, I. Pe', and C. F. Van Sumere, *J. Label. Compounds*, **10**, 135 (1974).

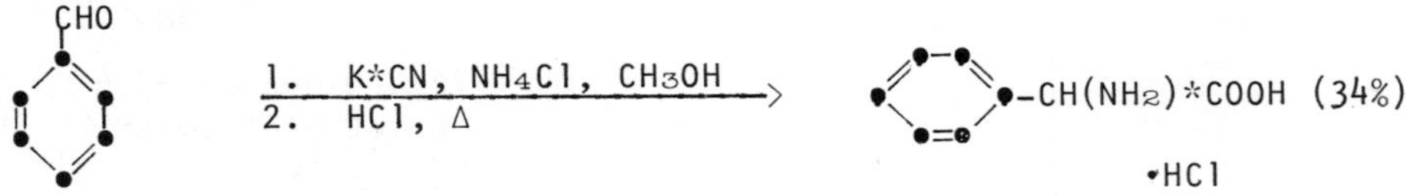
CHO
1. K*CN, NH4Cl, CH3OH
2. HCl, Δ
-CH(NH2)*COOH (34%)
•HCl

DL-2-Phenylglycine
[α-Aminobenzeneacetic-1-^{14}C acid hydrochloride]

The racemic mixture was resolved into the L-isomer (22%) and D-isomer (19%) via the chloroacetyl chloride derivative using hog kidney acylase.

R. Billings and H. R. Sullivan, J. Label. Compounds, 3, 17 (1967)

$HOCH_2CH(NHCOCF_3)CO_2Bzl$ $\xrightarrow[\text{4-dimethylaminopyridine}]{ZNH^*CH_2^*CO_2C(CH_3)_3}$

$ZNH^*CH_2^*CO_2CH_2CH(NHCOCF_3)CO_2Bzl$ $\longrightarrow$
1. H_2, Pd/C, CH_3OH
2. $LiNO_2$, $ClCH_2COOH$
3. acylase I

$N_2{}^*CH-{}^*C(=O)-OCH_2CH(NH_2)COOH$ (49% from glycine-U-^{14}C)

L-Serine (diazoacetate-1-2-^{14}C) ester

T. J. Curphey and D. S. Daniel J. Org. Chem., 43 4666 (1978).

$HO^*CH_2{}^*CH(NH\text{-}Z)^*COOBzl$ + CH_2CH_2OH ($NH\text{-}Z$) $\longrightarrow$
1. quinoline, $CHCl_3$, phenylphosphorodichloridate
2. Z-ethanolamine, pyr

N-[(Phenylmethoxy)-carbonyl]-L-serine-1,2,3,-^{14}C phenylmethyl ester (55% yield from L-Serine-1,2,3-^{14}C)

N-Z-ethanolamine

$NH_2CH_2CH_2O-P(=O)(OH)-O^*CH_2{}^*CH(NH_2)^*COOH$ (13%; 7% from L-serine-U-^{14}C)

L-Serine-1,2,3-^{14}C 2-aminoethyl-hydrogen phosphate ester

L-serine-U-^{14}C-L-serine-U-^{14}C phosphate was prepared in 4% yield.

Similarly prepared:

L-Serine ethanolamine-1,2-^{14}C phosphate
(14% from ethanolamine-1,2-^{14}C)

L-Serine-t ethanolamine-1,2-^{14}C phosphate
[15% from Z compounds)

L-Threonine-U-^{14}C ethanolamine phosphate
(5.7% from L-threonine-U-^{14}C)

L-Threonine-U-^{14}C-L-threonine-U-^{14}C phosphate (isolated in 4% yield)

L-Threonine ethanolamine-1,2-^{14}C phosphate
(11.7% from ethanolamine-1,2-^{14}C)

G. Porcellati, J. Label. Compounds, 3, 316 (1967).

$HSCH_2CHNH_2COOH \cdot HCl$ + $ClCH_2{}^*COOH$ $\xrightarrow[\text{pH 8-9}]{\text{NaOH}}$

L-Cysteine hydrochloride

$HOO{}^*CCH_2SCH_2CH(NH_2)COOH$ (100%)

Carbocysteine
[S-(Carboxy-^{14}C-methyl)-L-cysteine]

P. Hermann, K. Stalla, J. Schwimmer, I. Willhardt, and I. Kutschera, J. Prakt. Chem., 311, 1018 (1969).

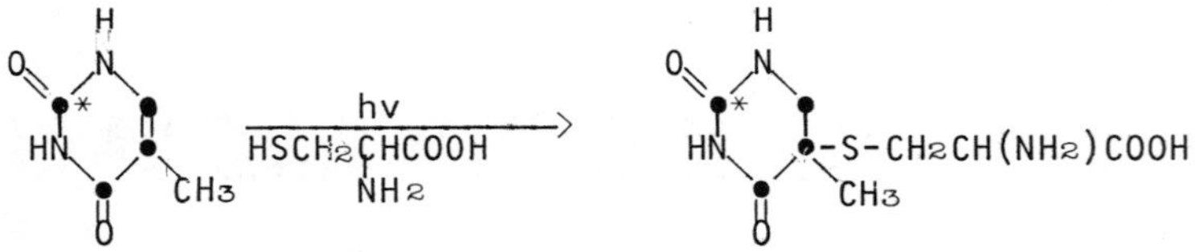

Thymine
[5-Methyl-2,4(1H,3H)-pyrimidinedione-2-^{14}C)

S-(Hexahydro-5-methyl-2,4-dioxo-5-pyrimidyl-2-^{14}C)-L-cysteine

K. C. Smith, Biochem. Biophys. Res. Commun., 39, 1011 (1970).

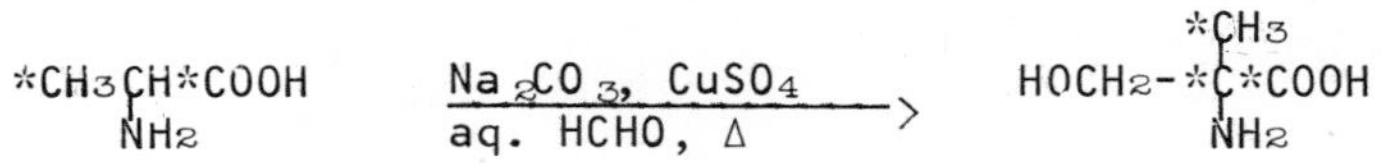
*CH3CH*COOH
NH2
Na2CO3, CuSO4
aq. HCHO, Δ
*CH3
HOCH2-*C*COOH
NH2

L-Alanine-U-^{14}C

DL-α-(Methyl-^{14}C)-serine-1,2-^{14}C

U. Nelson and S. Agurell, Acta Chem. Scand., 23, 3393 (1969).

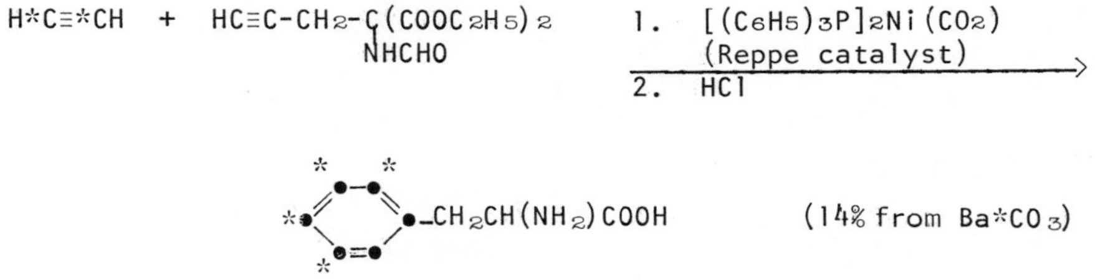
H*C≡*CH + HC≡C-CH2-C(COOC2H5)2
NHCHO
1. [(C6H5)3P]2Ni(CO2)
(Reppe catalyst)
2. HCl
-CH2CH(NH2)COOH
(14% from Ba*CO3)

DL-Phenylalanine-2',3',4',5'-^{14}C

Use of the Ziegler catalyst gave an overall yield of 6% from Ba*CO_3.

L. Pichat, P. N. Liem, and J. P. Guermont, Bull. Soc. Chim. Fr., 4224 (1972).

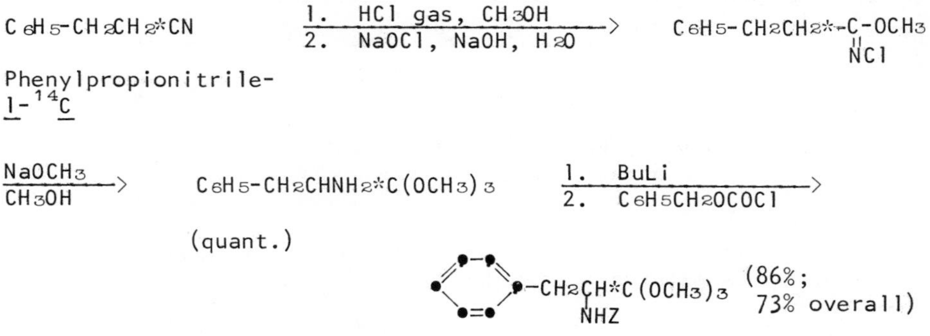
C6H5-CH2CH2*CN
1. HCl gas, CH3OH
2. NaOCl, NaOH, H2O
C6H5-CH2CH2*-C-OCH3
NCl
Phenylpropionitrile-1-14C
NaOCH3
CH3OH
C6H5-CH2CHNH2*C(OCH3)3
1. BuLi
2. C6H5CH2OCOCl
(quant.)
-CH2CH*C(OCH3)3
NHZ
(86%; 73% overall)

N-Z-Phenylalanine-1-^{14}C methylorthoester
[(2,2,2-Trimethoxy-1-(phenylmethyl)ethyl-2-^{14}C)-carbamic acid phenylmethyl ester]

C. R. Partington and M. P. Mertes, J. Label. Compound. Radiopharm., 14, 223 (1978).

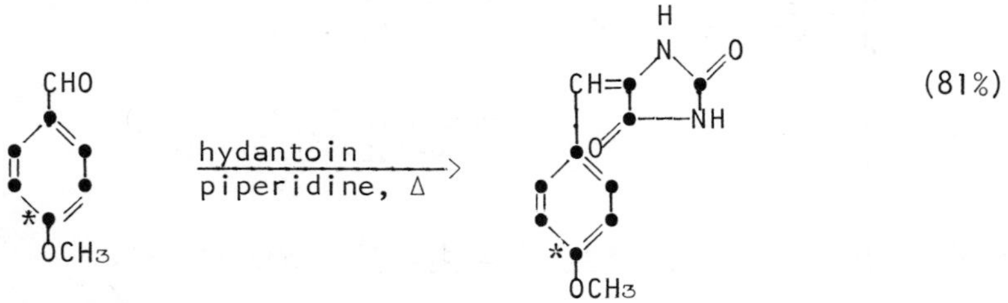
CHO
*
OCH3
hydantoin
piperidine, Δ
H
N
O
CH=
NH
O
*
OCH3
(81%)

Anisaldehyde
[4-Methoxybenzaldehyde-4-^{14}C]

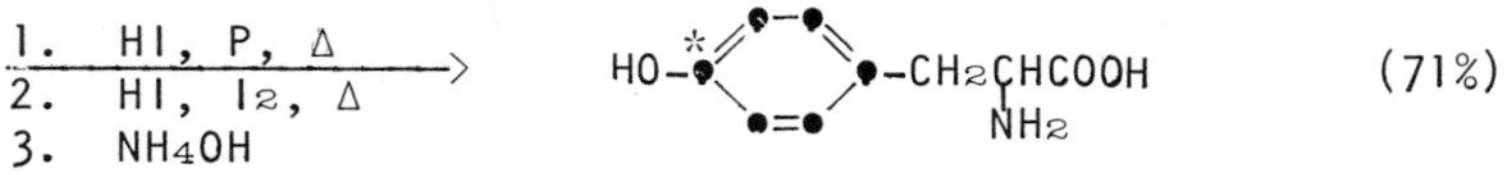
1. HI, P, Δ
2. HI, I2, Δ
3. NH4OH
HO-
*
-CH2CHCOOH
NH2
(71%)

dl-Tyrosine
[β-(p-Hydroxyphenyl-4-^{14}C)-alanine]

J. H. Kim, C. R. Creger, and J. R. Couch, J. Label. Compounds, 5, 35 (1969).

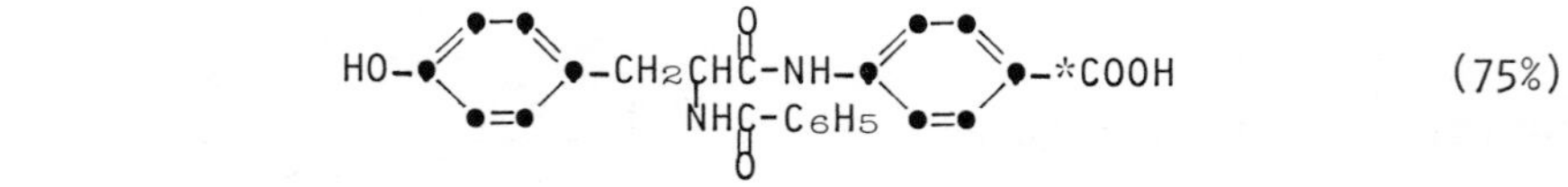
HO-
-CH2CHCOOH
NHCOC6H5
1.
N-CH3, ClCOOC2H5, THF
2. NH2-
-*COOH, p-TSA, THF
HO-
-CH2CHC-NH-
O
NHC-C6H5
O
-*COOH
(75%)

(S)-4-[[2-(Benzoylamino)-3-(4-hydroxyphenyl)-1-oxopropyl]amino]benzoic-7-^{14}C acid

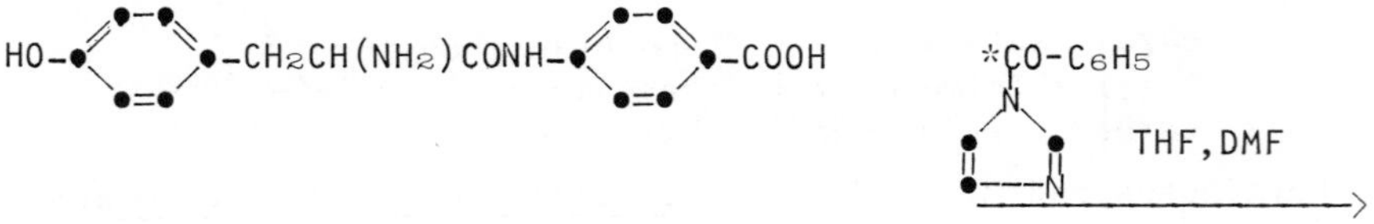
HO-
-CH2CH(NH2)CONH-
-COOH
*CO-C6H5
N
N
THF,DMF

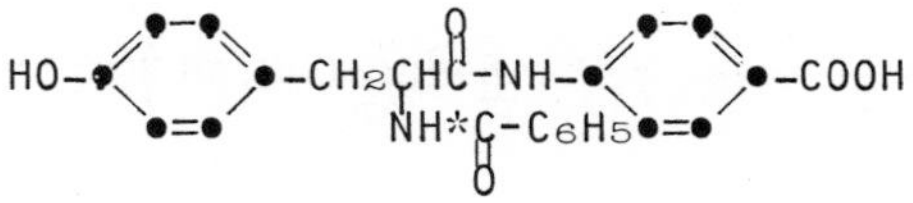

(23% from C_6H_5COOH)

(S)-4-[[2-(Benzoylamino-carbonyl-^{14}C)-3-(4-hydroxyphenyl)-1-oxopropyl]amino]benzoic acid

H. Yoshino, Y. Tsuchiya, T. Sato, K. Kinoshita, and M. Uchiyama, J. Label. Compound. Radiopharm., 15, 1 (1978).

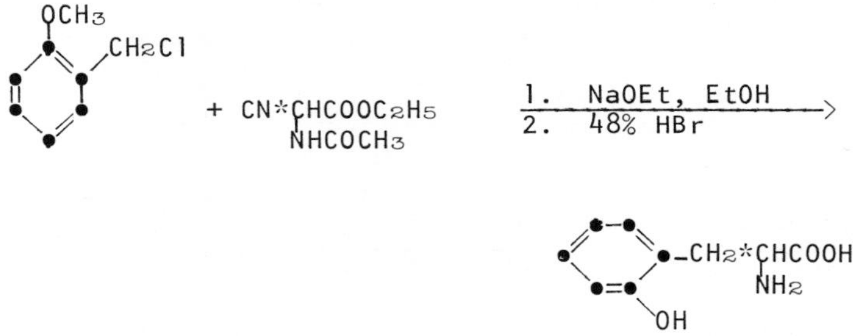
1. NaOEt, EtOH
2. 48% HBr

DL-o-Tyrosine
[DL-2-Hydroxyphenylalanine-α-^{14}C]

The racemic mixture was resolved giving a 30% yield of the L-isomer and a 26% yield of the D-isomer as the ethyl ester.

C. Petitclerc, A. D'Iorio, and N. L. Benoiton, J. Label. Compounds, 5, 265 (1969).

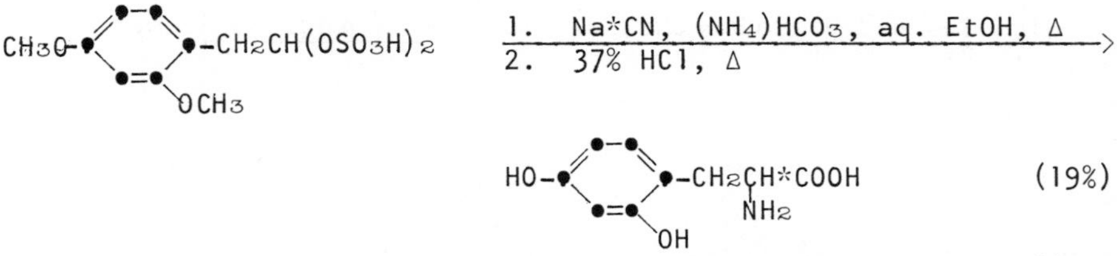
1. Na*CN, (NH4)HCO3, aq. EtOH, Δ
2. 37% HCl, Δ
(19%)

2,4-Dihydroxy-DL-phenylalanine-[14]C

R. T. Calvert, M. S. Spring, and J. R. Stoker, J. Pharm. Pharmac., 24, 972 (1972).

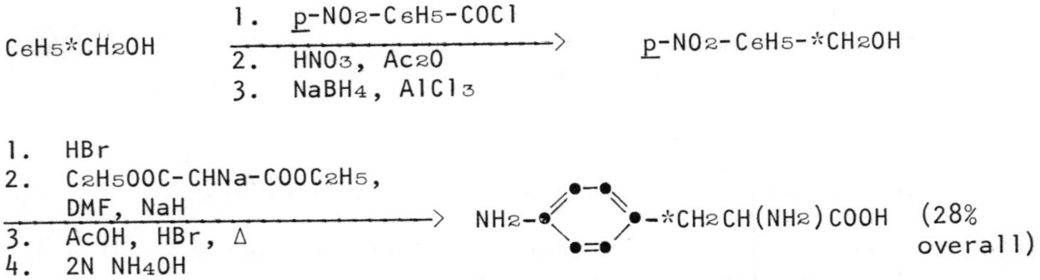
C6H5*CH2OH
1. p-NO2-C6H5-COCl
2. HNO3, Ac2O
3. NaBH4, AlCl3
p-NO2-C6H5-*CH2OH
1. HBr
2. C2H5OOC-CHNa-COOC2H5, DMF, NaH
3. AcOH, HBr, Δ
4. 2N NH4OH
5. H2, Pd/C
NH2-
-*CH2CH(NH2)COOH
(28% overall)

4-Amino-DL-phenylalanine-β-^{14}C

R. Cardillo, C. Fuganti, 'D, Ghiringhelli, D. Giangrasso, P. Grasselli, and A. Santopietro-Amisano, Tetrahedron, 30, 459 (1974).

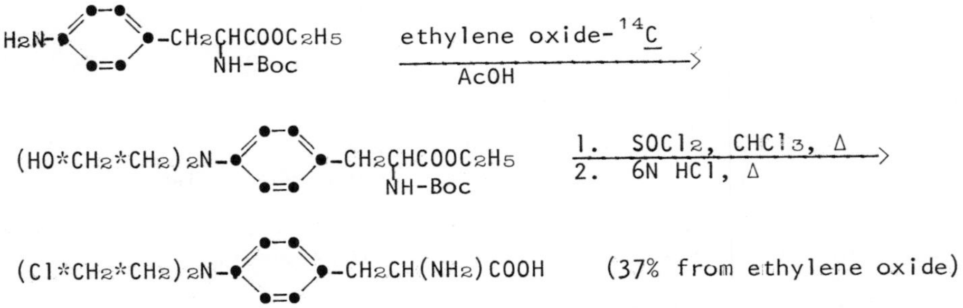
H2N-
-CH2CHCOOC2H5
NH-Boc
ethylene oxide-14C
AcOH
(HO*CH2*CH2)2N-
-CH2CHCOOC2H5
NH-Boc
1. SOCl2, CHCl3, Δ
2. 6N HCl, Δ
(Cl*CH2*CH2)2N-
-CH2CH(NH2)COOH
(37% from ethylene oxide)

Melphalan
[4-[Bis(2-Chloroethyl-1,2-^{14}C)amino]-L-phenylalanine]

C. Nicholas and D. Godeneche, J. Label. Compound. Radiopharm. 14, 205 (1978).

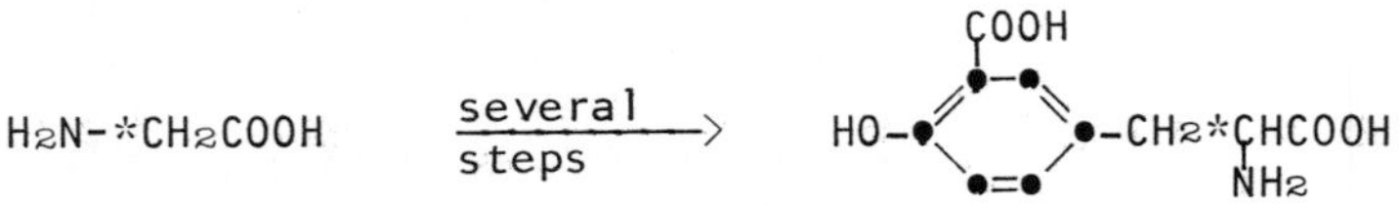
H2N-*CH2COOH
several steps
COOH
HO-
-CH2*CHCOOH
NH2

3-Carboxy-L-tyrosine-α-^{14}C

P. O. Larsen and E. Wieczorkowska, J. Label. Compounds, 10, 287 (1974); Acta Chem. Scand., B31, 109 (1977).

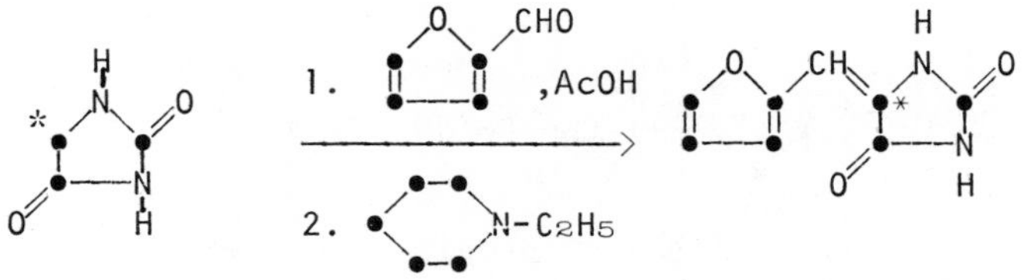

(56% from glycine)

Hydantoin [2,3-Imidazolidinedione-5-^{14}C]

5-(2-Furanylmethylene)-2,4-imidazolidinedione-5-^{14}C

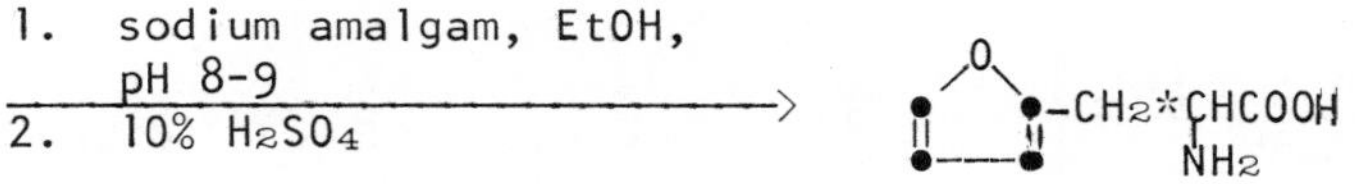

(47% from glycine)

DL-3-(2'-Furyl)-alanine [α-Amino-2-furanpropanoic-α-^{14}C acid]

V. Tolman. J. Hanus, and K. Veres, J. Label. Compounds, 4, 243 (1968).

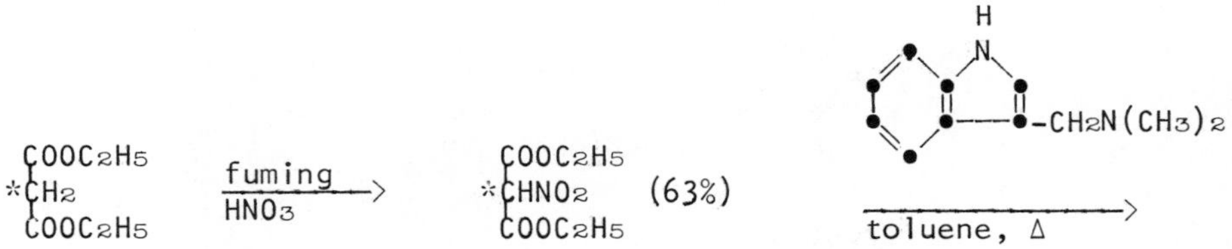

Propanedioic-2-^{14}C diethyl ester

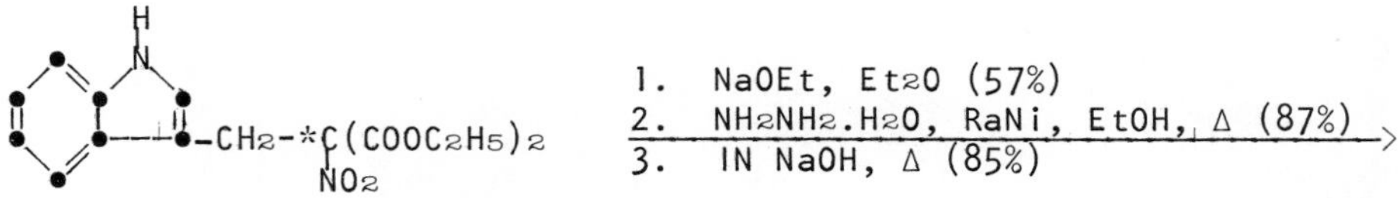

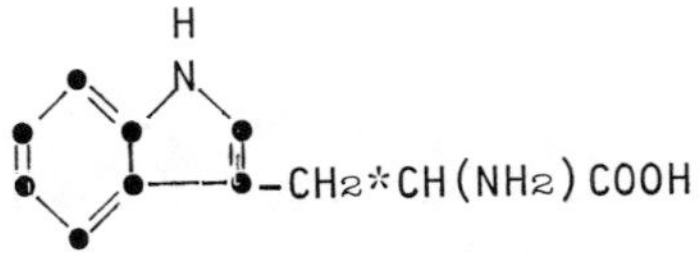
H
N
-CH2*CH(NH2)COOH

Tryptophan
[α-Aminoindole-3-propionic-α-^{14}C acid]

H. Lehmann, D. Gros, and H. R. Schütte, Z. Chem., 11, 426 (1971).

*HCHO —(indole, 40% $NH(CH_3)_2$ / AcOH)→

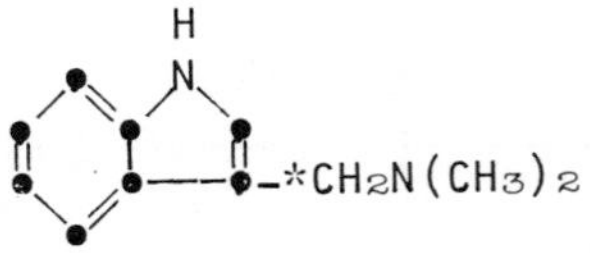
H
N
-*CH2N(CH3)2

(88%)

Formaldehyde-^{14}C

Gramine
[N,N-Dimethyl-1H-indole-3-(methanamine-^{14}C)]

1. $C_2H_5OOC-CH(NHCHO)COOC_2H_5$ (90%)
2. NaOH
3. AcOH
(63%)

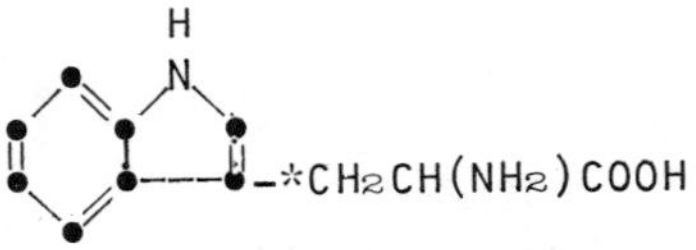
H
N
-*CH2CH(NH2)COOH

(2nd crop brought overall yield from from $BaCO_3$ to 44%)

Tryptophan
[α-Aminoindole-3-propionic acid-β-^{14}C]

E. Schreier, Helv. Chim. Acta, 59, 585 (1976).

$CH_3CH^*COOCH_2CH_3$
$PO(OCH_2CH_3)_2$

+

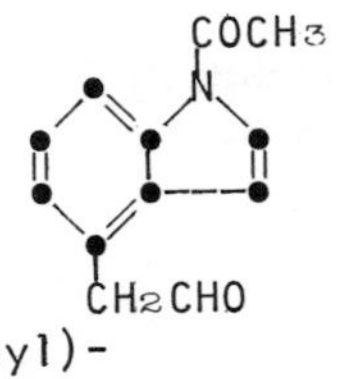
COCH3
N
CH2CHO

1. NaH, DME
2. IN CH_3ONa

2-(Diethoxyphosphinyl)-propanoic-1-^{14}C acid ethyl ester

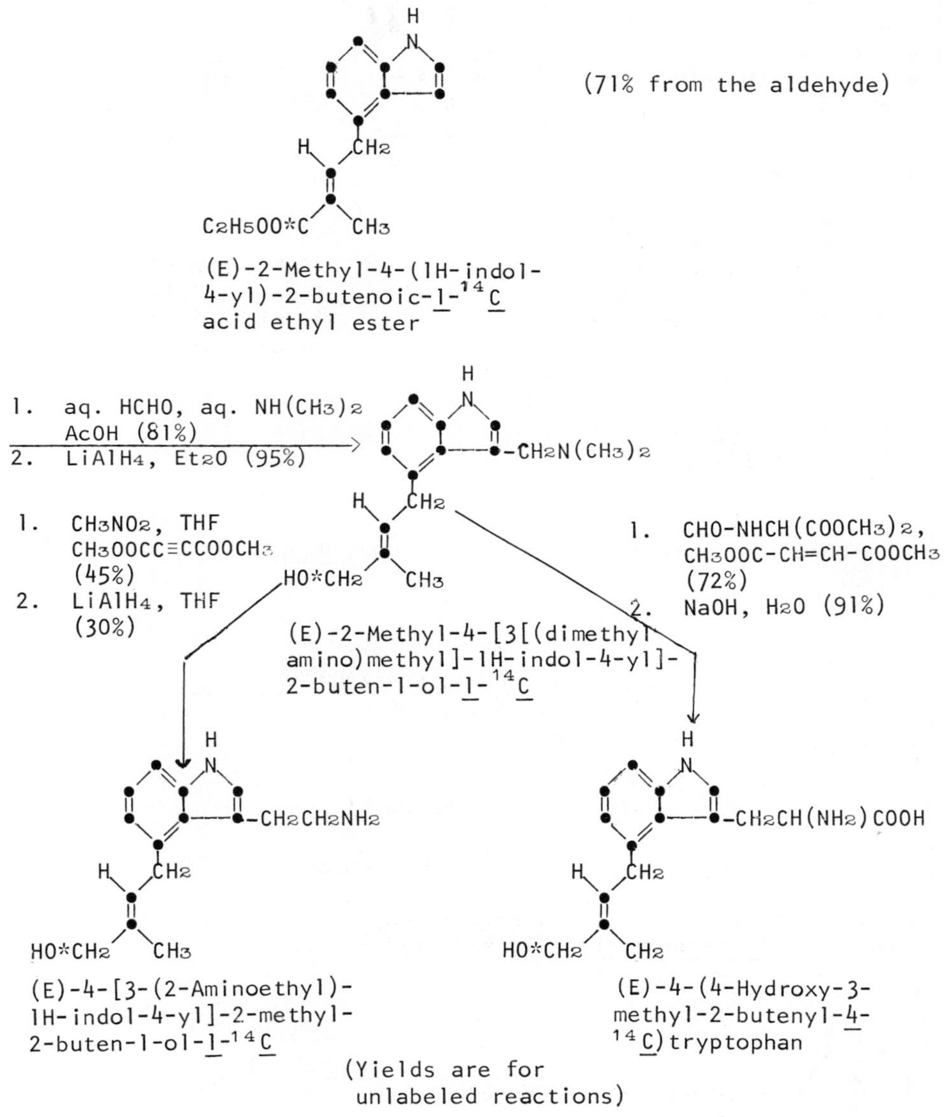
(71% from the aldehyde)
(E)-2-Methyl-4-(1H-indol-4-yl)-2-butenoic-1-14C acid ethyl ester
1. aq. HCHO, aq. NH(CH3)2 AcOH (81%)
2. LiAlH4, Et2O (95%)
(E)-2-Methyl-4-[3[(dimethylamino)methyl]-1H-indol-4-yl]-2-buten-1-ol-1-14C
1. CH3NO2, THF CH3OOCC≡CCOOCH3 (45%)
2. LiAlH4, THF (30%)
1. CHO-NHCH(COOCH3)2, CH3OOC-CH=CH-COOCH3 (72%)
2. NaOH, H2O (91%)
(E)-4-[3-(2-Aminoethyl)-1H-indol-4-yl]-2-methyl-2-buten-1-ol-1-14C
(E)-4-(4-Hydroxy-3-methyl-2-butenyl-4-14C)tryptophan
(Yields are for unlabeled reactions)

H. Plieninger, C. Wagner, and H. Immel, Ann. Chem., 743, 95 (1971).

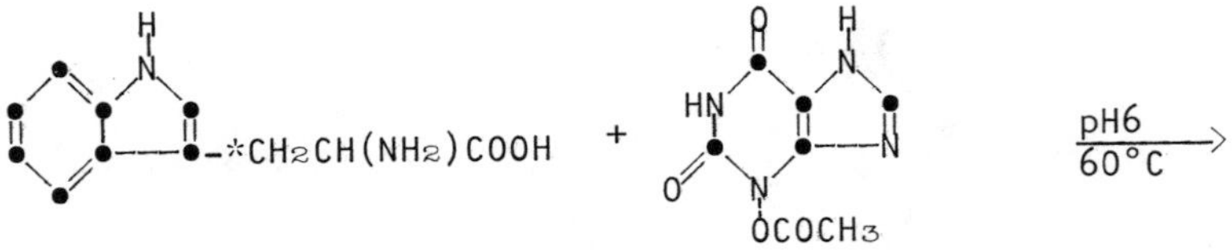

*CH2CH(NH2)COOH
+
HN
O
N
OCOCH3
pH6
60°C

Tryptophan-β-^{14}C

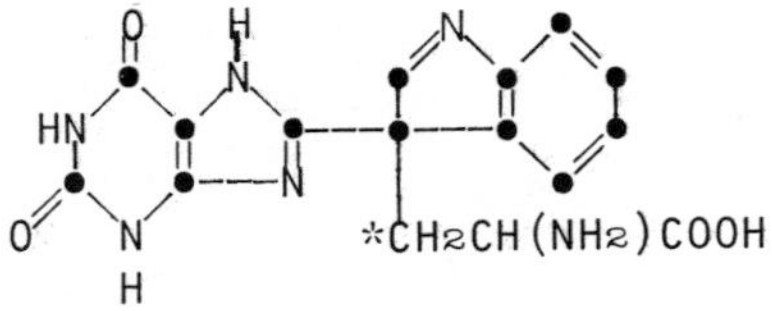

HN
O
N
H
*CH2CH(NH2)COOH

(30% yield of both isomers, epimeric at indole C-3, separable by chromatomgraphy)

α-Amino-3-(2,3,6,7-tetrahydro-2,6-dioxo-1H-purin-8-yl)-3H-indole-3-propanoic-β-^{14}C acid

G. Stöhrer, G. Salemnick, and G. B. Brown, Biochemistry, 12, 5084 (1973).

$CH_3S(CH_2)_2CH(NH_2)$*COOH —— 1. CH_3I, HOAc/90% HCOOH; 2. AgOH, H_2O ——>

DL-Methionine-1-^{14}C

HOC$H_2CH_2CH(NH_2)$*COOH (41%)

DL-Homoserine-1-^{14}C

E. Leete, G. E. Davis, C. R. Hutchinson, K. W. Woo, and M. R. Chedekell, Phytochemistry, 13, 427 (1974).

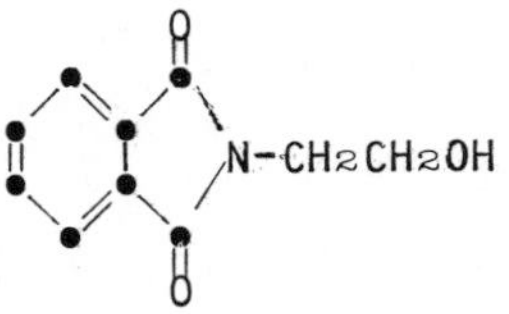

N-CH2CH2OH

+ Br*CH_2COOCH_3 —— 1. NaH, C_6H_6, Δ (65%); 2. LiI, collidine, Δ (46%) ——>

Bromoacetic-2-^{14}C acid methyl ester

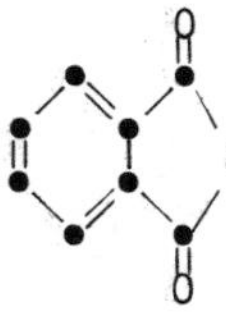

N-$CH_2CH_2O^*CH_2COOH$ $\xrightarrow[THF]{B_2H_6}$

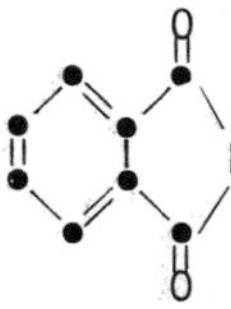

N-$CH_2CH_2O^*CH_2CH_2OH$ (96%)

1. $SOCl_2$, pyr, C_6H_6 (91%)
2. sodium ethylphthalimidomalonate, KI, DMF, Δ (36%)
3. 6N HCl, Δ (66%)

$HCl \cdot H_2NCH_2CH_2O^*CH_2CH_2CH(NH_2)COOH$

DL-2-Amino-4-(2-aminoethoxy)-butanoic-4-^{14}C acid hydrochloride

Using ethyl phthalimidomalonate-2-^{14}C, DL-2-amino-4-(2-aminoethoxy) butanoic-2-^{14}C acid was also prepared.

Y.-Y. Liu, E. Thom, and A. A. Liebman, Can. J. Chem., 56, 2853 (1978).

$CH_3SCH_2{}^*CH_2Cl$ $\xrightarrow[Na,\ EtOH]{C_2H_5OOC-CH(NHCOCH_3)-COOC_2H_5}$ $CH_3SCH_2-{}^*CH_2-C(COOC_2H_5)(NHCOCH_3)-COOC_2H_5$

1. NaOH
2. HCl
3. Δ

$CH_3SCH_2-{}^*CH_2CH(NHCOCH_3)COOC_2H_5$

2-(Acetylamino)-4-(methylthio)butanoic-3-^{14}C acid ethyl ester

1. α-chymotrypsine (resolution)
2. HCl

$CH_3SCH_2{}^*CH_2CH(NH_2)COOH$

D-Methionine-3-^{14}C (11% overall)

\+

L-Methionine-3-^{14}C (13% overall)

L. Pichat and J. P. Beaucourt, J. Label. Compounds, 10, 103 (1974).

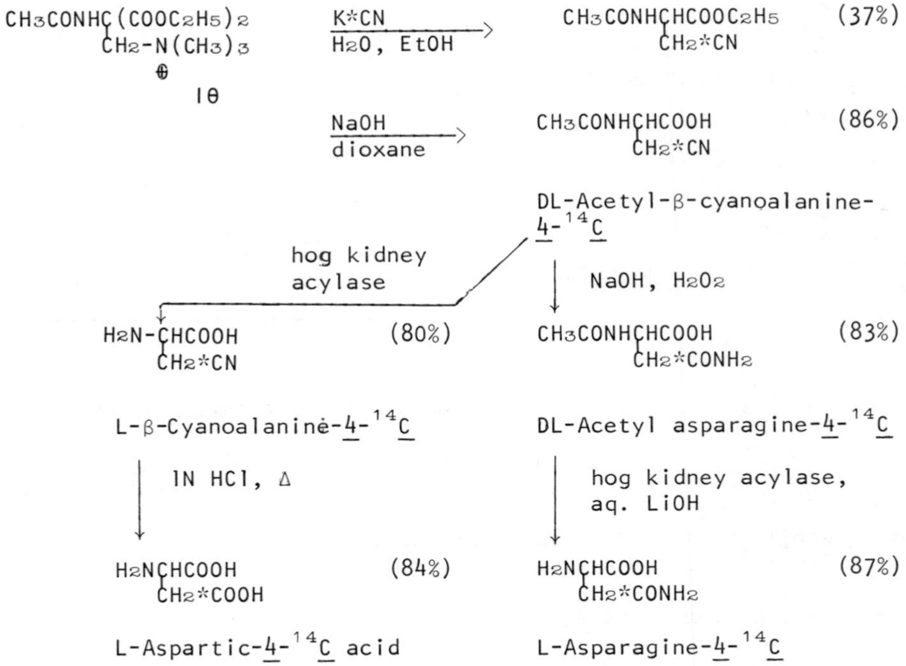
CH3CONHC(COOC2H5)2
CH2-N(CH3)3
K*CN
H2O, EtOH
CH3CONHCHCOOC2H5
CH2*CN
(37%)
NaOH
dioxane
CH3CONHCHCOOH
CH2*CN
(86%)
DL-Acetyl-β-cyanoalanine-4-14C
hog kidney
acylase
NaOH, H2O2
H2N-CHCOOH
CH2*CN
(80%)
CH3CONHCHCOOH
CH2*CONH2
(83%)
L-β-Cyanoalanine-4-14C
DL-Acetyl asparagine-4-14C
1N HCl, Δ
hog kidney acylase,
aq. LiOH
H2NCHCOOH
CH2*COOH
(84%)
H2NCHCOOH
CH2*CONH2
(87%)
L-Aspartic-4-14C acid
L-Asparagine-4-14C

Y.-H. Giza and C. Ressler, J. Label. Compounds, 5, 142 (1969).

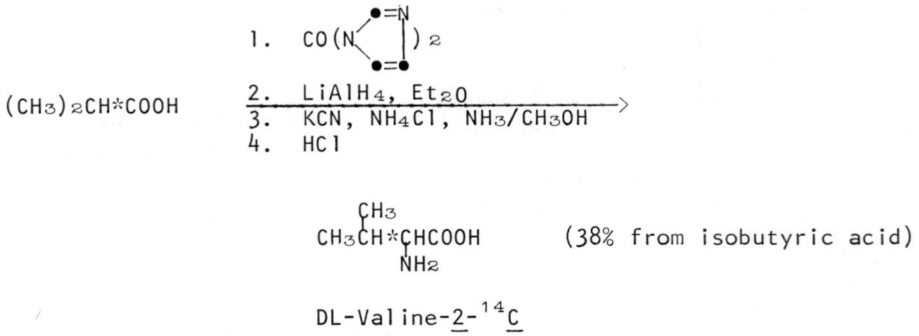
(CH3)2CH*COOH
1. CO(N)2
2. LiAlH4, Et2O
3. KCN, NH4Cl, NH3/CH3OH
4. HCl
CH3
CH3CH*CHCOOH
NH2
(38% from isobutyric acid)
DL-Valine-2-14C

L. Pichat, P. Nhuliem, and J.-P. Guermont, Bull. Soc. Chim. Fr., 837 (1971).

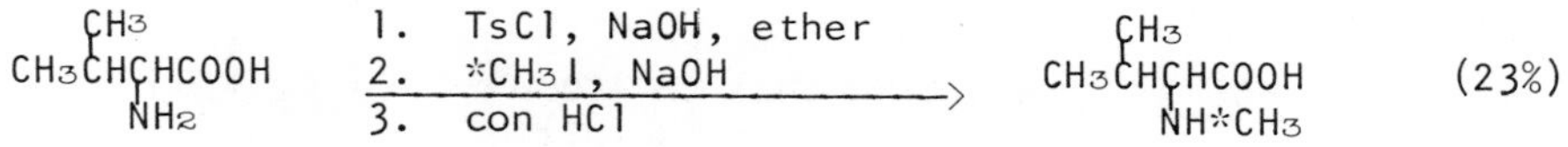

Valine

N-(Methyl-^{14}C)valine

H. Elias and W. S. Change, J. Label. Compounds, 2, 413 (1966).

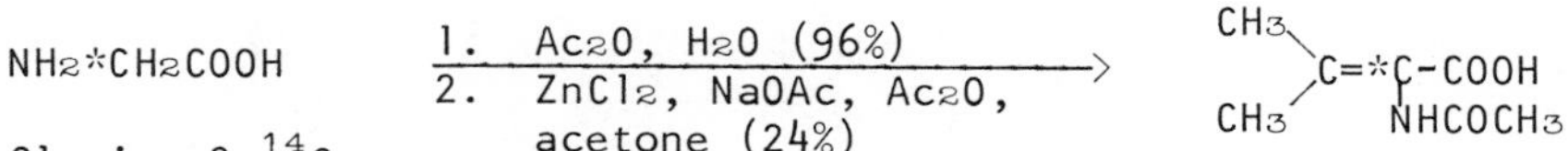

Glycine-2-^{14}C

2-(Acetylamino)-3-methyl-2-propenoic-2-^{14}C acid

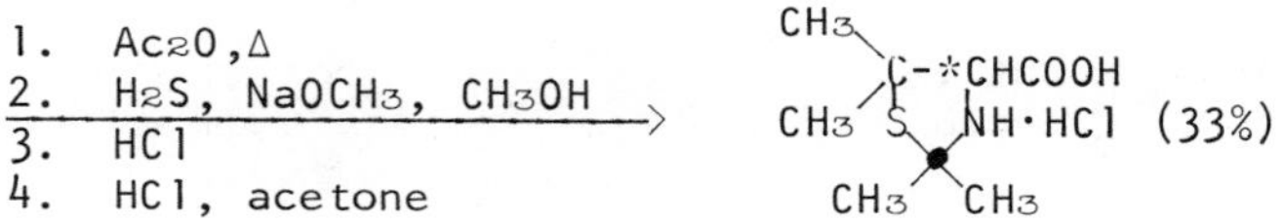

DL-Isopropylidenpenicillamine-2-^{14}C hydrochloride

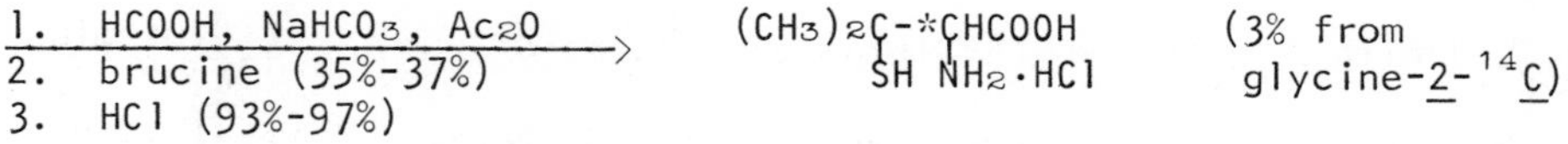

L-Penicillamine [3-Mercapto-L-valine-2-^{14}C hydrochloride]

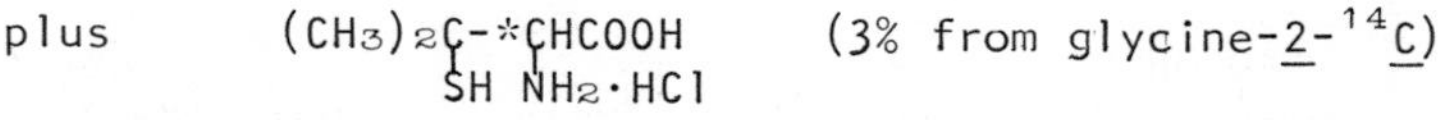

D-Penicillamine [3-Mercapto-D-valine-2-^{14}C hydrochloride]

D. Donnert and F. Planas-Bohne, Arzneim.-Forsch.-(Drug Res.), 22, 1423 (1972).

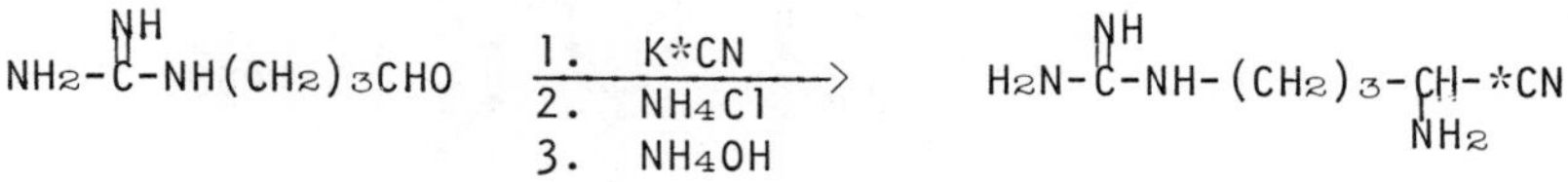

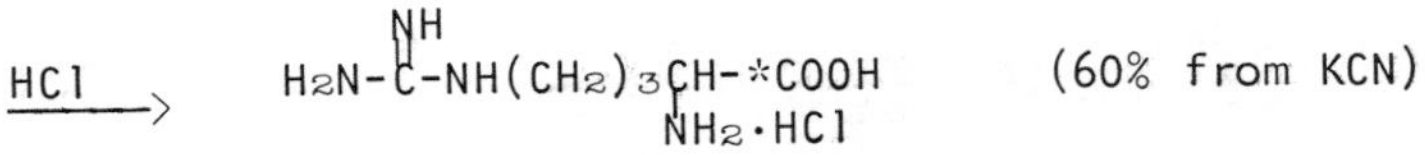

DL-Arginine-1-^{14}C hydrochloride

L. Pichat, J. P. Guermont, and P. N. Liem, J. Label. Compounds, 4, 251 (1968).

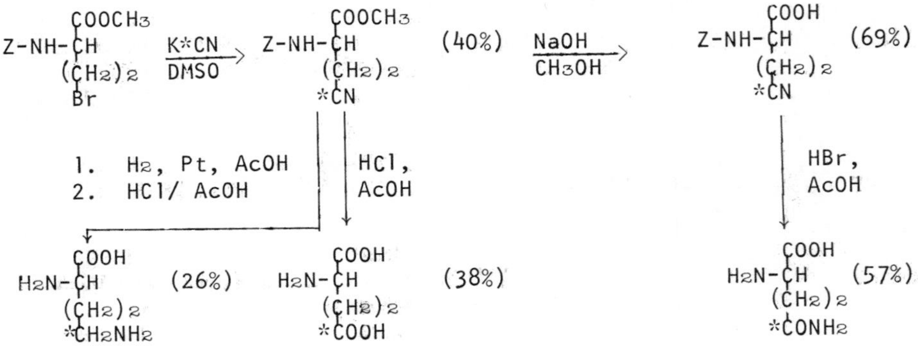

L-Ornithine-5-^{14}C L-Glutamic-5-^{14}C acid L-Glutamine-5-^{14}C

M. Havránek, H. Kopecká-Schadtová, and K. Vereš, J. Label. Compounds, 6, 345 (1970).

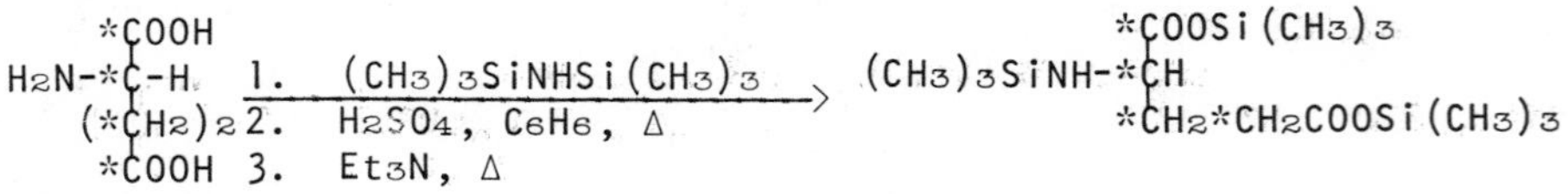

L-Glutamic acid-U-^{14}C

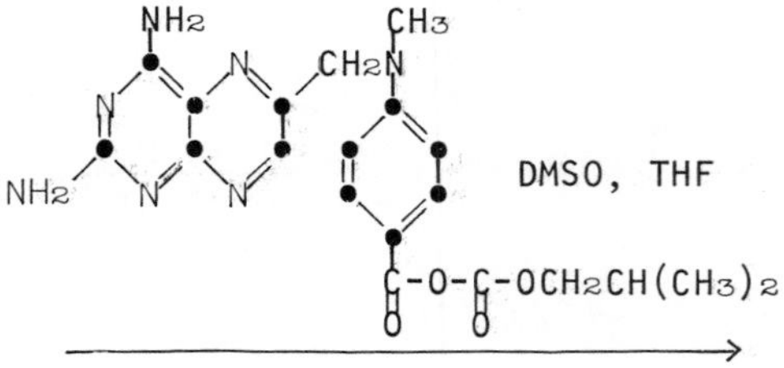

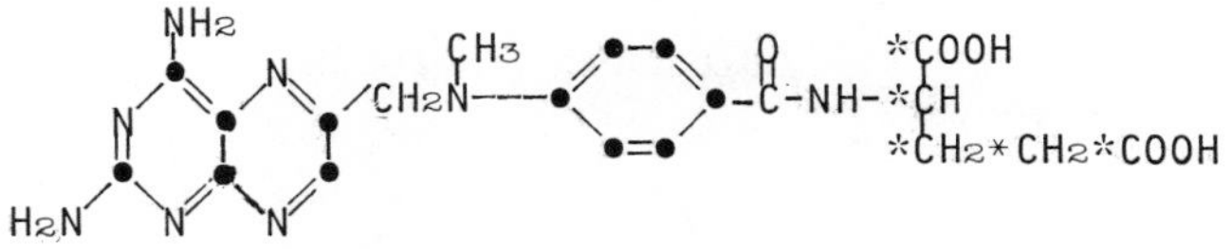

(∿50%)

Methotrexate
[N-(4-[(2,4-Diamino-6-pteridnyl)methyl]methylamino)-benzoyl-(L-glutamic-U-^{14}C acid

M. G. Nair and C. M. Baugh, J. Label. Compound. Radiopharm., 13, 147 (1977).

$(CH_3)_2CHCH_2{*}CHO$ $\xrightarrow[\text{2. HCl}]{\text{1. KCN, } NH_4Cl\text{, } NH_3/CH_3OH}$

3-Methylbutanol-1-^{14}C

$(CH_3)_2CHCH_2{*}CH(NH_2)COOH$ (45% from Ba*CO$_3$)

DL-Leucine-2-^{14}C

L. Pichat, P. Nhuliem, and J.-P. Guermont, Bull. Soc. Chim. Fr., 837 (1971).

$(C_2H_5OOC)_2{*}CHNHCOCH_3$ $\xrightarrow[\text{2. conc. HCl, } \Delta]{\text{1. } (CH_3)_3COK\text{, DMSO; } CH_3CH_2CHBrCH_3\text{, } \Delta}$ $CH_3CH_2CH(CH_3){*}CH(NH_2)COOH$

Diethyl acetamidomalonate
[(Acetylamino)-propanedioic-2-^{14}C acid diethyl ester]

DL-Isoleucine-2-^{14}C
(5% yield containing 60% DL-isoleucine and 40% DL-alloisoleucine)

$(C_2H_5OOC)_2CH_2$ $\xrightarrow{\text{1. NaOEt, } CH_3CH_2CHBrCH_3\text{, } \Delta\text{; 2. KOH, } H_2O\text{; 3. } NaN_3\text{, } H_2SO_4}$ (18% yield containing 53% DL-isoleucine-2-^{14}C and 47% DL-alloisoleucine-2-^{14}C)

$(C_2H_5OOC)_2C{=}CHCH_3$ $\xrightarrow{\text{1. } {*}CH_3CH_2MgI\text{; 2. KOH, } H_2O\text{; 3. } NaN_3\text{, } H_2SO_4}$ ${*}CH_3CH_2CH(CH_3)CH(NH_2)COOH$ (2.3% yield)

Isoleucine-5-^{14}C

$COOC_2H_5$
$C{=}CHCH_2CH_3$
$COOC_2H_5$

1. $^*CH_3MgBr$
2. steps as above

→ $CH_3CH_2CH(^*CH_3)CH(NH_2)COOH$

Isoleucine-6-^{14}C

D. H. G. Crout, N. M. Davies, E. H. Smith, and D. Whitehouse, J. Chem. Soc., Perkin I, 671 (1972).

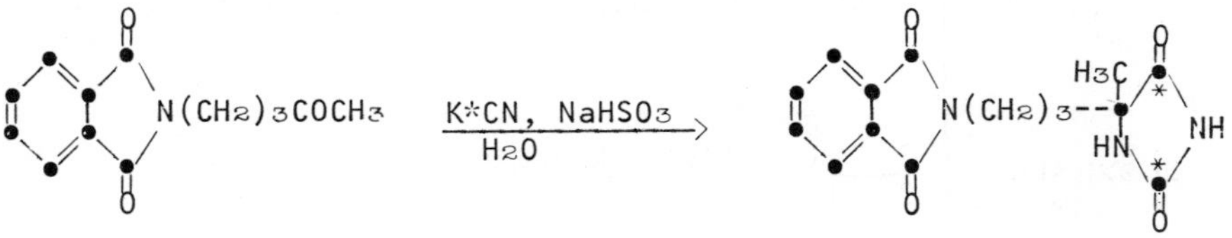
N(CH2)3COCH3
K*CN, NaHSO3
H2O
N(CH2)3
H3C
NH
HN

1. $Ba(OH)_2$, Δ
2. HCl, Δ
3. Amberlite IR-120-CP

→ $NH_2-(CH_2)_3C(CH_3)(NH_2)^*COOH \cdot 2HCl$ (91%)

α-Methyl-(+)-ornithine-1-^{14}C dihydrochloride

M. M. Adel-Monem, N. E. Newton, B. C. Ho, and C. E. Weeks, J. Med. Chem., 18, 600 (1975).

L-Amino acid —(L-amino acid oxidase / 1M-tris-HCl, pH 7.7)→ α-Oxo acid

(Yields ~80% from L-amino acids, ~40% from DL-amino acids.)

Amino acids used:

L-Leucine-U-^{14}C
L-Isoleucine-U-^{14}C
L-Valine-U-^{14}C
L-Leucine-1-^{14}C
DL-Valine-1-^{14}C
L-Isoleucine-1-^{14}C

H. W. Rüdiger, U. Langenbeck, and H. W. Goedde, Biochem. J., 126, 445 (1972).

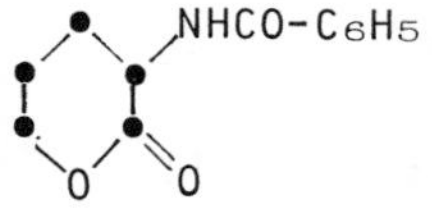

$\xrightarrow[\text{DMF, 153°C}]{\text{Na*CN}}$ NC*-$CH_2CH_2CH_2$CHCOONa (61% from NaCN)
with NHCOC$_6$H$_5$ on the CH

$\xrightarrow[\text{2. HCl}]{\text{1. } H_2\text{, } PtO_2\text{, } CH_3COOH/HCl}$ H_2N*$CH_2CH_2CH_2CH_2$CHCOOH
with NH_2 on the CH

DL-Lysine-<u>6</u>-[14]<u>C</u>

L. Pichat, J. Tostain, and C. Baret, <u>Bull. Soc. Chim. Fr.</u>, 1837 (1970).

H_2N-$(CH_2)_4$*CH(NH_2)COOH

DL-Lysine-<u>2</u>-[14]<u>C</u>

1. <u>p</u>-TsCl, acetone, NaHCO (56%)
2. C_6H_5COCl, Et_2O, NaOH/H_2O (61%)
3. $(CH_3O)_2SO_2$, NaOH/H_2O (54%)
4. 40% HBr, Δ (26%)

CH_3NH-$(CH_2)_4$*CH(NH_2)COOH

DL-ω-N-Methyllysine-<u>2</u>-[14]<u>C</u>

P. Korzan and T. J. Gilbertson, <u>Phytochemistry</u>, <u>13</u>, 435 (1974).

$COOCH_3$
*CHNHCHO
$COOCH_3$

1. Na, EtOH
2. $CH_3SCH_2CH_2CH_2CH_2Cl$, Δ
3. HCl, Δ

CH_3-S$CH_2CH_2CH_2CH_2$*CH(NH_2)COOH (35%)

DL-2-Amino-6-(methylthio)caproic acid [(R,S)-2-amino-6-(methylthio) hexanoic-<u>2</u>-[14]<u>C</u> acid]

C. Lee and G. S. Serif, <u>Biochemistry</u>, <u>9</u>, 2068 (1970).

CHO
$(CH_2)_3$
CHO

1. K*CN, 2N HCl
2. NH_4HCO_3, 25% NH_3, 95°

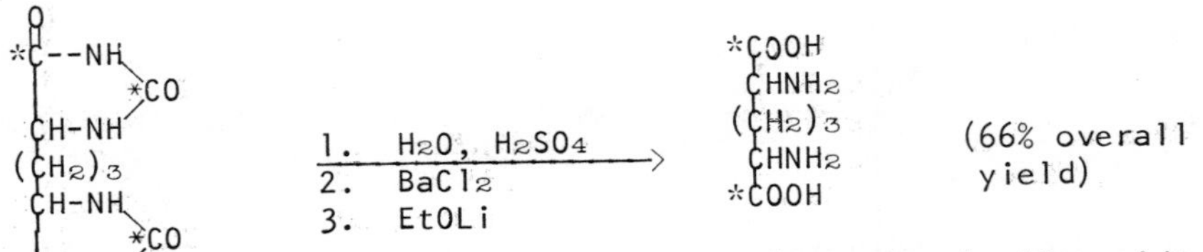
1. H2O, H2SO4
2. BaCl2
3. EtOLi
(66% overall yield)

2,6-Diaminopimelic acid [2,6-Diaminoheptanedioic-1,7-^{14}C acid]

A. Arendt and A. Kolodziejczyk, J. Label. Compounds, 9, 457 (1973).

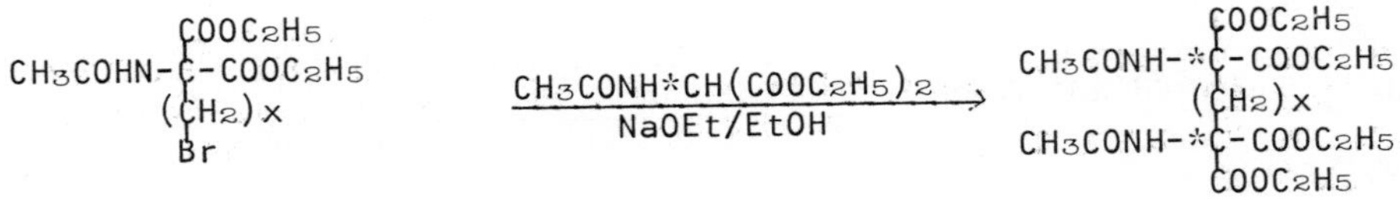
CH3CONH*CH(COOC2H5)2
NaOEt/EtOH

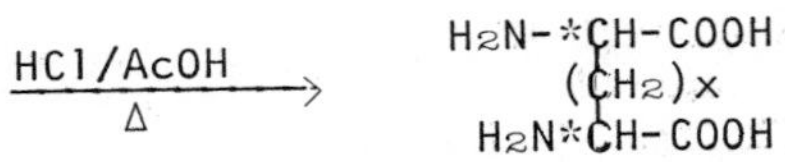
HCl/AcOH
Δ

X=4, DL-2,7-Diamino suberic-2,7-^{14}C acid (52%)
X=5, DL-2,8-Diamino azelaic-2,8-^{14}C acid (64%)
X=6, DL-2,9-Diamino sebacic-2,9-^{14}C acid (78%)

also [X=3] DL-2,6-Diamino-pimelic-2,6-^{14}C acid (50%)

J. Hanuš and K. Vereš, J. Label. Compounds, 6, 143 (1970).

(B) β-Amino Acids

$BrCH_2COOH$ —(1. K*CN[AgCN], aq.NaOH (90%); 2. H_2, 10% Pd/C, 1N HCl (81%))→ $H_2N{*}CH_2CH_2COOH$

3-Aminopropanoic-3-^{14}C acid

C. W. Perry, W. Burger, G. J. Bader, and A. A. Liebman, J. Label. Compounds, 11, 583 (1975).

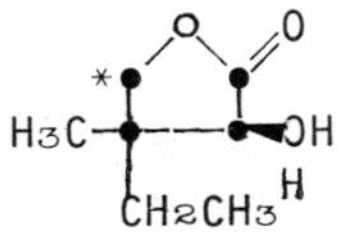

[2R; 3R,S]

$\xrightarrow[CH_3OH]{H_2N-CH_2CH_2COOK}$

$HO^*CH_2C(CH_3)(CH_2CH_3)-CHOHC(=O)-NHCH_2CH_2COOH$ (27% yield from [$^*CH_2O$]n; epimeric at C-4 of oxobutyl group)

β-Ethyl-norpantothenic acid
[N-(2-Hydroxy-3-(hydroxymethyl-^{14}C)-3-methyl-1-oxopentyl)-β-alanine]

E. Draeger and T. Wieland, Ann. Chem., 760, 104 (1972).

$CH_3CHBrCOOC_2H_5$ $\xrightarrow[EtOH,\Delta]{K^*CN}$ $CH_3CH^*(CN)COOC_2H_5$

2-(Cyano-^{14}C)-propanoic acid ethyl ester

$\xrightarrow[2.\ conc.\ HCl,\ \Delta]{1.\ H_2,\ PtO_2,\ AcOH}$ $H_2N^*CH_2CH(CH_3)COOH$ (28% from K*CN)

β-Aminoisobutyric acid (BAIBA)
[3-Amino-2-methylpropanoic-3-^{14}C acid]

J. H. Lukas and G. B. Gerber, J. Label. Compounds, 1, 229 (1965).

$CH_2{=}\ CHCH_2{}^*COONa$ $\xrightarrow[sealed\ tube]{NH_3,\ \Delta}$ $CH_3CH(NH_2)CH_2{}^*COOH$ (54%)

3-Butenoic-1-^{14}C acid sodium salt

DL-3-Aminobutanoic-1-^{14}C acid

E. L. Winnacker, M. M. Herbst, and H. A. Barker, Biochim. Biophys. Acta, 237, 280 (1970).

(C) γ-Amino Acids

$BrCH_2CH_2COOH \xrightarrow{K{*}CN} N{*}C\text{-}CH_2CH_2COOH \xrightarrow[Pt]{H_2}$

3-(Cyano-^{14}C)-propanoic acid

$H_2N\text{-}{*}CH_2CH_2CH_2COOH$ (71% yield from K*CN)

4-Aminobutanoic-4-^{14}C acid

H. R. Schütte and A. Unverricht, Z. Chem., 11, 107 (1971); see also A. J. Villani, W. L. Mendelson, and D. W. Blackburn, J. Label. Compounds, 9, 269 (1973).

$BrCH_2CH_2COOC_2H_5 \xrightarrow[EtOH,\Delta]{H{*}CN} N{*}C\text{-}CH_2CH_2COOC_2H_5$ (65%)

1. H_2, PtO_2, Ac_2O
2. 6N HCl, Δ (quant.)
3. 1,2-C_6H_4-$(CO)_2NCOOC_2H_5$

→

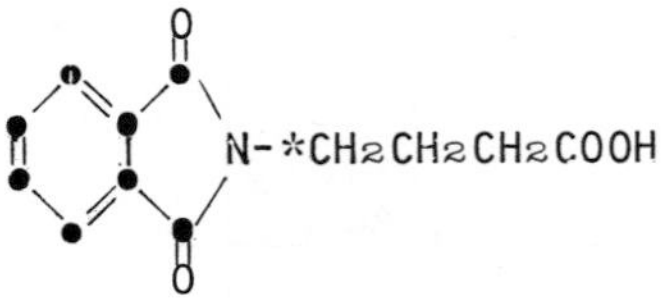
N-*CH2CH2CH2COOH

1. Br_2,PCl_3,Δ
2. $CaCO_3$,H_2O,Δ
3. 6N HCl,Δ

→ $H_2N{*}CH_2CH_2CHOHCOOH$ 23% overall

4-Amino-2-hydroxybutanoic-4-^{14}C acid

L. P. Bouthillier, J. J. Pushpathadam, and Y. Binette, Can. J. Biochem., 44, 171 (1966).

$CH_3(CH_2)_{14}{*}COOH$

Hexadecanoic-1-^{14}C acid

1. $SOCl_2$, light petroleum, Δ
2. (-) carnitine·HCl, CF_3COOH
3. HCl

→

$Cl^{\ominus}(CH_3)_3N^{\oplus}CH_2CHCH_2COOH$ with $O\text{-}{*}C(=O)\text{-}(CH_2)_{14}CH_3$ on the CH (50%)

Hexadecanoyl-L-(-)-carnitine chloride
[3-Carboxy-2-(1-oxohexadecyloxy-1-^{14}C)-N,N,N-trimethylpropanaminium chloride]

Similarly, trans-2-hexadecenoyl-1-^{14}C-L(-) carnitine chloride was prepared in 47% yield (using oxalyl chloride instead of thionyl chloride).

$CH_3-(CH_2)_{12}-COCH_2{}^*COOCH_3$

3-Oxohexadecanoic-1-^{14}C acid methyl ester

1. $(CH_2OH)_2$, P-TSA, toluene
2. alkaline hydrolysis
3. $SOCl_2$, Δ, light petroleum
4. (-) carnitine·HCl, CF_3COOH
5. $HClO_4$

→

$(CH_3)_3N^{\oplus}CH_2CHCH_2COOH$; $O-{}^*C(=O)-CH_2C(=O)(CH_2)_{12}CH_3$; $ClO_4^{\ominus}$

(19.2% from carnitine)

1. $NaBH_4$, pH 7.5
2. HCl

→ $Cl^{\ominus}(CH_3)_3N^{\oplus}CH_2CHCH_2COOH$; $O-{}^*C(=O)-CH_2CHOH(CH_2)_{12}CH_3$ (45%)

DL-3-Hydroxyhexadecanoyl-L-(-)-carnitine chloride [3-Carboxy-2-(3-hydroxy-1-oxyhexadecyloxy-1-^{14}C)-N,N,N-trimethylpropanaminium chloride]

A. Al-Arif and M. Blecher, Biochim. Biophys. Acta, 248, 416 (1971).

(D) δ-Amino Acids

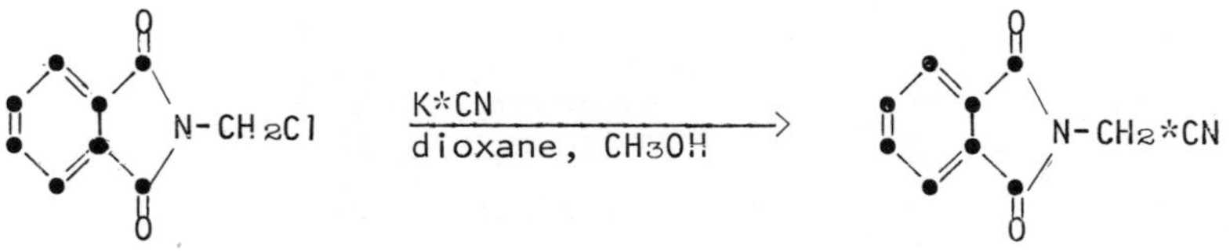
N-CH2Cl
K*CN
dioxane, CH3OH
N-CH2*CN

(95%)

Phthalimidoacetonitrile [1,3-Dihydro-1,3-dioxo-2H-isoindole-2-acetonitrile-1-^{14}C]

$\xrightarrow[\Delta]{HCl,\ AcOH}$

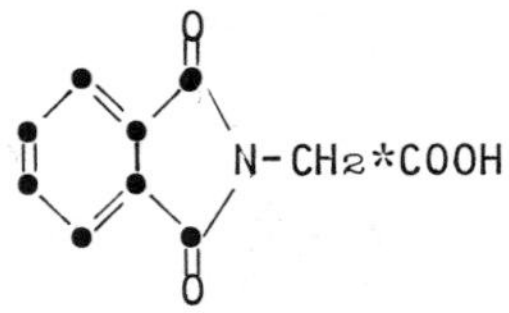
N-CH₂*COOH

(90%; 86% based on K*CN)

Phthaloylglycine-1-^{14}C

1. $SOCl_2$ (100%)
2. diazomethane (95%)
3. HBr, AcOH

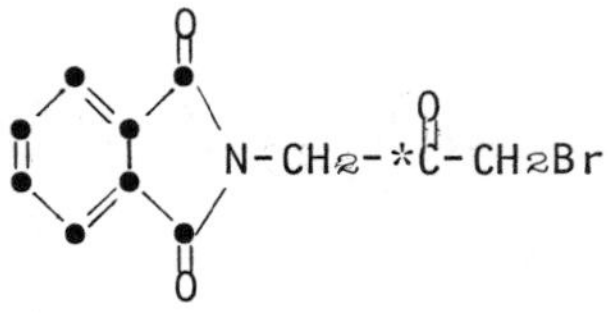
N-CH₂-*C-CH₂Br

(77% based on K*CN)

1. $NaCH(COO\text{-}t\text{-}Bu)_2$, DMF
2. HCl, AcOH, Δ

$H_2NCH_2{*}C(=O)\text{-}CH_2CH_2COOH \cdot HCl$ (56% based on K*CN)

δ-Aminolevulinic acid [5-Amino-4-oxopentanoic-4-^{14}C acid hydrochloride]

A. E. A. Mitta, A. M. Ferramola, H. A. Sancovich, and M. Grinstein, J. Label. Compounds, 3, 20 (1967).

(E) Other Amino Acids

$H_2N{*}CH_2COOH \xrightarrow[NaOH,\ H_2O]{ClCH_2COOH} N({*}CH_2COOH)_3$ (95-100%)

Glycine-2-^{14}C

Nitrilotriacetic acid [N,N-Bis(carboxymethyl)glycine-2,2',2''-^{14}C]

M. Bentov, A. Levi, and E. D. Bergmann, J. Label. Compounds, 3, 338 (1967).

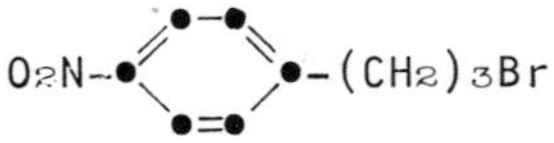
O₂N-
-(CH₂)₃Br

1. K*CN
2. H_2SO_4

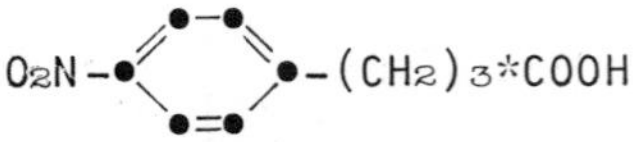
O₂N-
-(CH₂)₃*COOH

(75%)

4-Nitrobenzenebutanoic-1-^{14}C acid (50% from K*CN)

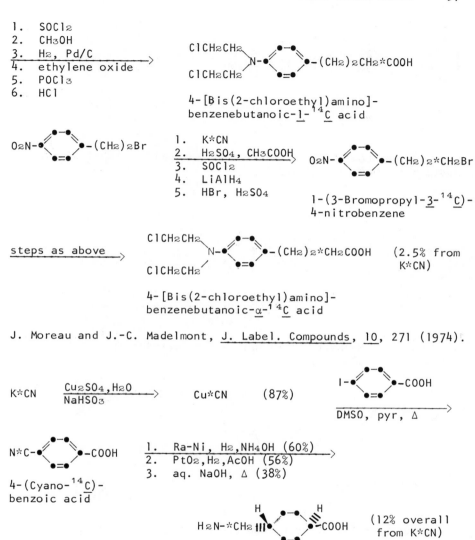

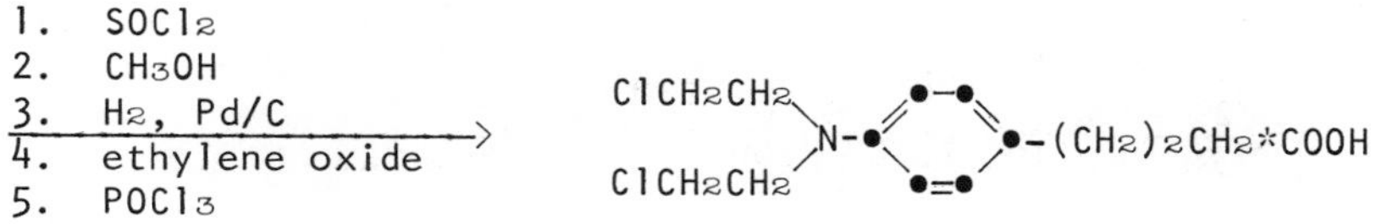
1. SOCl2
2. CH3OH
3. H2, Pd/C
4. ethylene oxide
5. POCl3
6. HCl
ClCH2CH2
ClCH2CH2
N-
-(CH2)2CH2*COOH

4-[Bis(2-chloroethyl)amino]-
benzenebutanoic-1-^{14}C acid

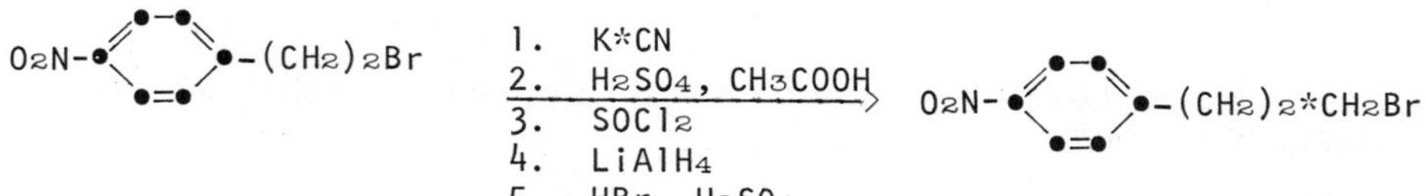
O2N-
-(CH2)2Br
1. K*CN
2. H2SO4, CH3COOH
3. SOCl2
4. LiAlH4
5. HBr, H2SO4
O2N-
-(CH2)2*CH2Br

1-(3-Bromopropyl-3-^{14}C)-
4-nitrobenzene

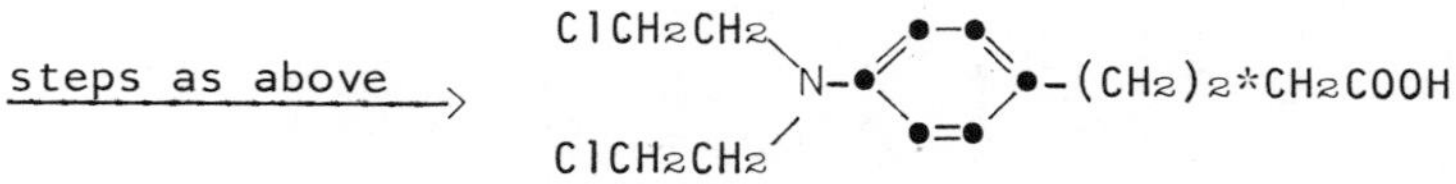
steps as above
ClCH2CH2
ClCH2CH2
N-
-(CH2)2*CH2COOH

(2.5% from K*CN)

4-[Bis(2-chloroethyl)amino]-
benzenebutanoic-α-^{14}C acid

J. Moreau and J.-C. Madelmont, J. Label. Compounds, 10, 271 (1974).

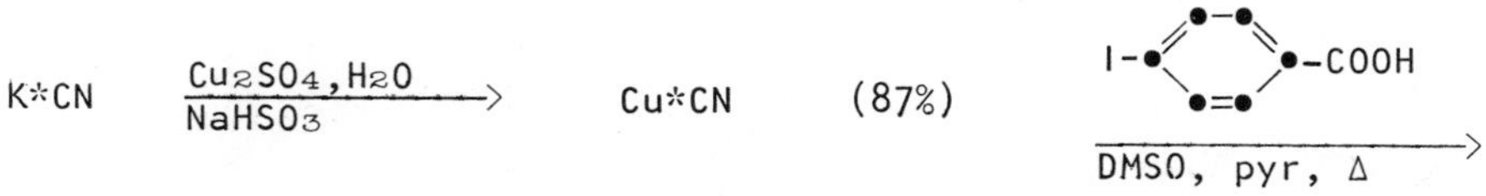
K*CN
Cu2SO4,H2O
NaHSO3
Cu*CN
(87%)
I-
-COOH
DMSO, pyr, Δ

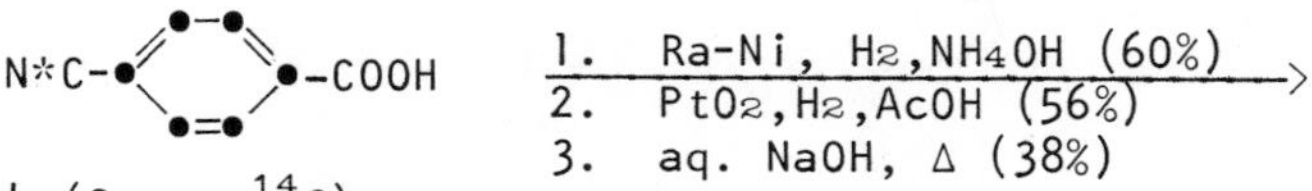
N*C-
-COOH
1. Ra-Ni, H2,NH4OH (60%)
2. PtO2,H2,AcOH (56%)
3. aq. NaOH, Δ (38%)

4-(Cyano-^{14}C)-
benzoic acid

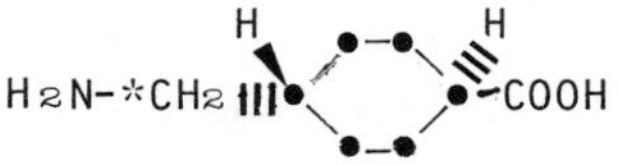
H
H
H2N-*CH2
COOH

(12% overall from K*CN)

Tranexamic acid
[trans-4-(Aminomethyl-^{14}C)-
cyclohexanecarboxylic acid]

J. Lundström, G. Westin-Sjödahl, and N. A. Jönsson, J. Label. Compound. Radiopharm., 12, 307 (1976).

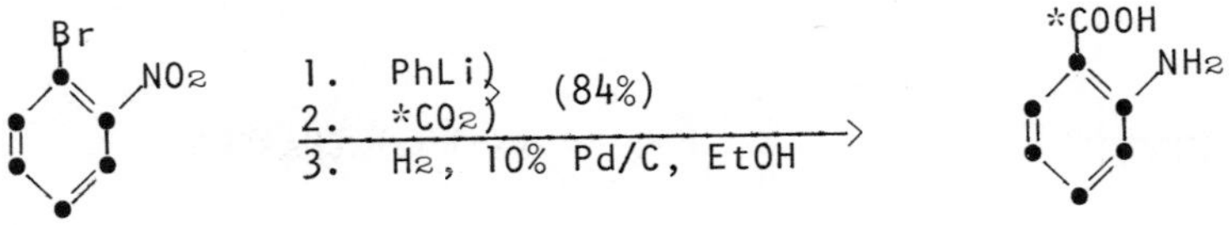
Br
NO2
1. PhLi
2. *CO2
(84%)
3. H2, 10% Pd/C, EtOH
*COOH
NH2

Anthranilic acid
[2-Aminobenzoic-7-^{14}C acid]

L. Weiss, M. Loy, S. S. Hecht, and D. Hoffman, J. Label. Compound. Radiopharm., 14, 119 (1978).

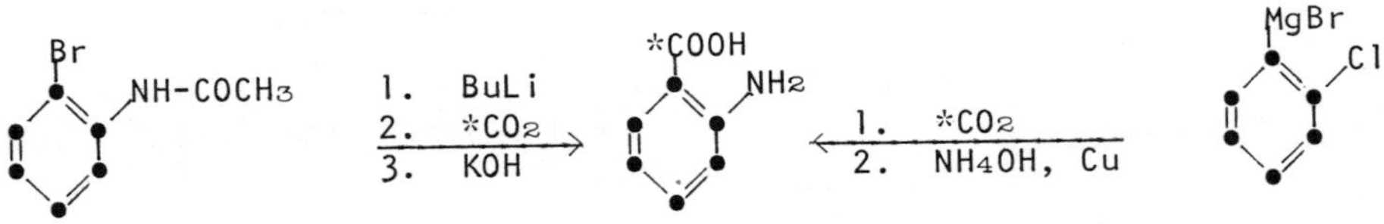
Br
NH-COCH3
1. BuLi
2. *CO2
3. KOH
*COOH
NH2
1. *CO2
2. NH4OH, Cu
MgBr
Cl

(10% overall yield to product)

Anthranilic acid
[2-Aminobenzoic-7-^{14}C acid]

(26% overall yield to product)

N. VanBac, M. Herbert, L. Pichat, and N. Dat-Xuong, J. Label. Compounds, 9, 545 (1973).

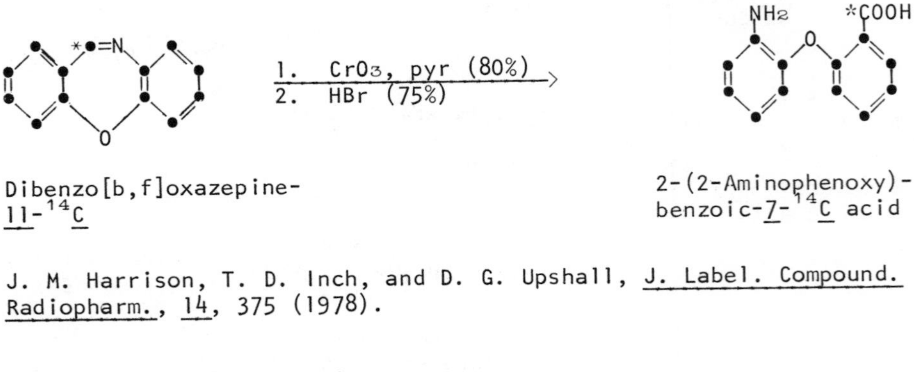
*=N
O
1. CrO3, pyr (80%)
2. HBr (75%)
NH2
O
*COOH

Dibenzo[b,f]oxazepine-11-^{14}C

2-(2-Aminophenoxy)-benzoic-7-^{14}C acid

J. M. Harrison, T. D. Inch, and D. G. Upshall, J. Label. Compound. Radiopharm., 14, 375 (1978).

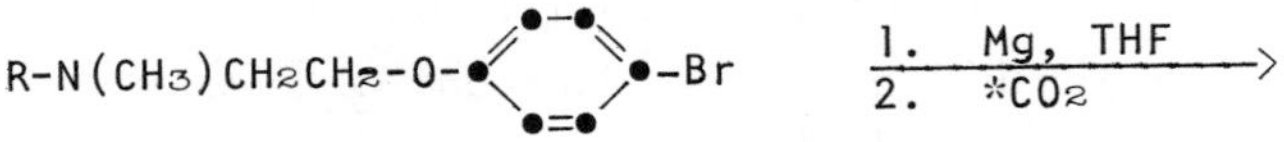
R-N(CH3)CH2CH2-O-
-Br
1. Mg, THF
2. *CO2

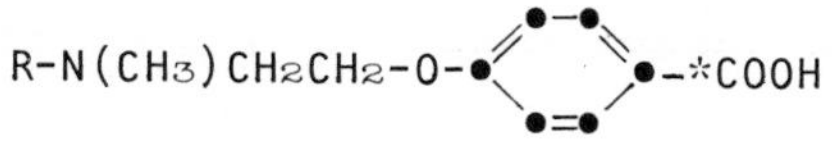
R-N(CH3)CH2CH2-O-
-*COOH

(82%)

R = CH_3; 4-[2-(Dimethylamino)ethoxy]-benzoic-7-^{14}C acid
R = $C_6H_5CH_2$; 4-[2-[Methyl(phenylmethyl)-amino]ethoxy]benzoic-7-^{14}C acid

R. L. Wineholt, J. D. Johnson, P. J. Heck, and H. H. Kaegi, J. Label. Compounds, 6, 53 (1970).

L-Phenylalanine-U-^{14}C methyl ester·HCl + Z-L-Proline-p-nitrophenyl ester → 1. Et_3N, CH_2Cl_2 (87%) 2. H_2, 10% Pd/$BaSO_4$, AcOH (16%)

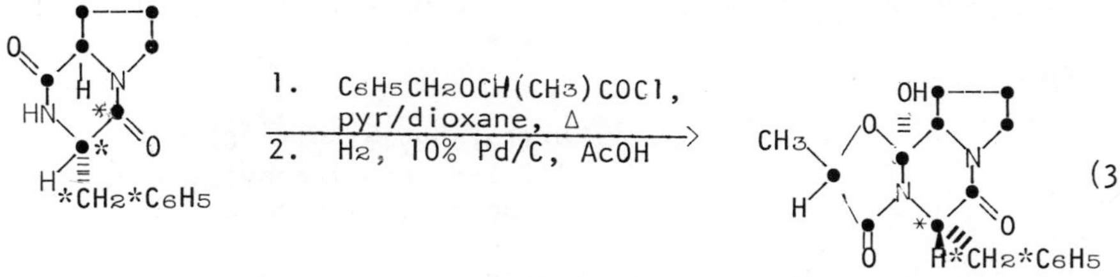
1. C6H5CH2OCH(CH3)COCl, pyr/dioxane, Δ
2. H2, 10% Pd/C, AcOH
*CH2*C6H5
CH3
OH
H*CH2*C6H5

(35%)

[5S-(5α,10bα)]-Tetrahydro-10b-hydroxy-2-methyl-5[(phenyl-U-^{14}C)methyl-^{14}C]-δH-oxazolo[3,2a]pyrrolo[2,1c]pyrazine-3,6(2H,5H)-dione-6-^{14}C

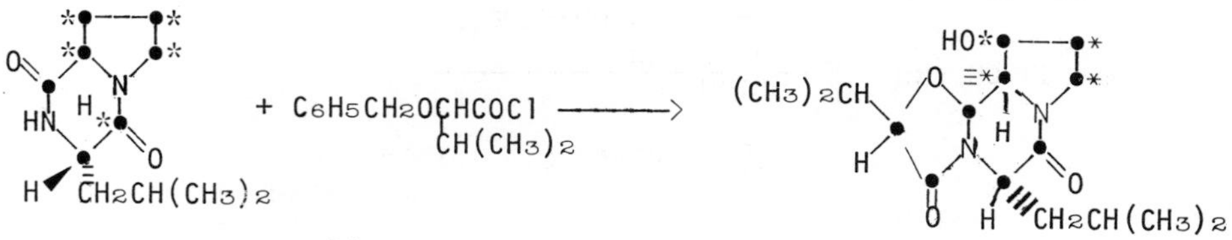
+ C6H5CH2OCHCOCl
CH(CH3)2
CH2CH(CH3)2
(CH3)2CH
HO*
CH2CH(CH3)2

(from L-proline-U-^{14}C)

[5S-5α,10bα)]-Tetrahydro-10b-hydroxy-2-(1-methylethyl)-5-(2-methylpropyl)-δH-oxazolo[3,2a]pyrrolo[2,1c]pyrazine-3,6(2H,5H)-dione-6,8,9,11-^{14}C

D. Gröger, U. Syring, and S. Johne, Pharmazie, 30, 440 (1975).

1-11 Miscellaneous Acids

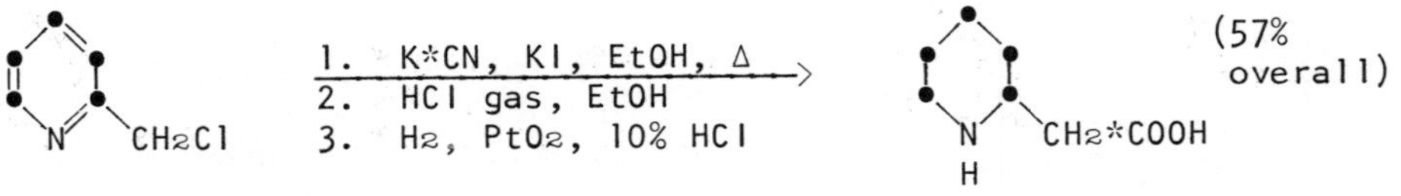
CH2Cl
1. K*CN, KI, EtOH, Δ
2. HCl gas, EtOH
3. H2, PtO2, 10% HCl
N
H
CH2*COOH
(57% overall)

Piperidine-2-acetic-$\underline{1}$-$^{14}\underline{C}$ acid

W. D. Marshall, T. T. Nguyen, D. B. MacLean, and I. D. Spenser, <u>Can. J. Chem.</u>, <u>53</u>, 41 (1975).

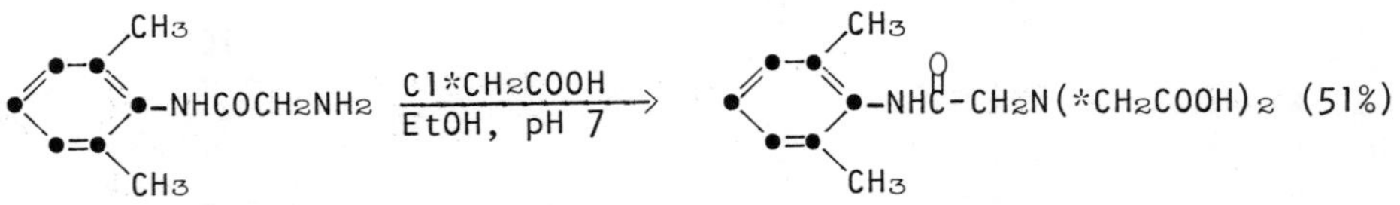
CH3
-NHCOCH2NH2
CH3
Cl*CH2COOH
EtOH, pH 7
CH3
-NHC-CH2N(*CH2COOH)2
CH3
(51%)

N-(Carboxymethyl-$^{14}\underline{C}$)-N-[2-[(2,6-dimethylphenyl]amino]-2-oxoethyl]glycine-$\underline{2}$-$^{14}\underline{C}$

P. S. Callery, W. C. Faith, M. D. Loberg, A. T. Fields, E. B. Harvey, and M. D. Cooper, <u>J. Med. Chem.</u>, <u>19</u>, 962 (1976).

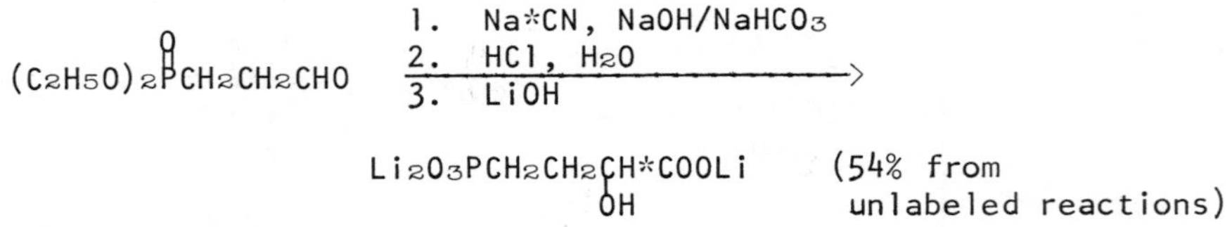
(C2H5O)2PCH2CH2CHO
1. Na*CN, NaOH/NaHCO3
2. HCl, H2O
3. LiOH
Li2O3PCH2CH2CH*COOLi
OH
(54% from unlabeled reactions)

Trilithium 3-(carboxy-$^{14}\underline{C}$)-3-hydroxypropyl-1-phosphonic acid

K.-C. Tang, B. E. Tropp, and R. Engel, <u>Tetrahedron</u>, <u>34</u>, 2873 (1978).

$Br{*}CH_2COOCH_3$ $\xrightarrow[\text{2. 30\% } H_2O_2]{\text{1. } CH_3SH,\ NaOCH_3/CH_3OH,\ \Delta}$ $CH_3SO_2{*}CH_2COOCH_3$

Bromoacetic-2-^{14}C acid methyl ester

$\xrightarrow[\text{2. } I(CH_2)_3CHOAc(CH_2)_4CH_3,\ NaH, DMF]{\text{1. } I(CH_2)_6COOCH_3,\ NaH,\ DMF}$ $CH_3SO_2\text{-}{*}C(COOCH_3)\text{-}(CH_2)_6COOH$ with $(CH_2)_3CH(OCOCH_3)(CH_2)_4CH_3$ on the starred carbon

$\xrightarrow[\text{2. } NaOH/CH_3OH]{\text{1. } (CH_3)_2SO,\ NaCl,\ H_2O}$

$CH_3(CH_2)_4CHOH(CH_2)_3{*}CH(SO_2CH_3)(CH_2)_6COOH$ (50% overall)

8-(Methylsulfonyl)-12-hydroxyheptadecanoic-8-^{14}C acid

R. L. Smith, J. B. Bicking, N. P. Gould, T.-J. Lee, C. M. Robb, F. A. Kuehl, Jr., L. R. Mandel, and E. J. Cragoe, Jr., J. Med. Chem., 20, 540 (1977).

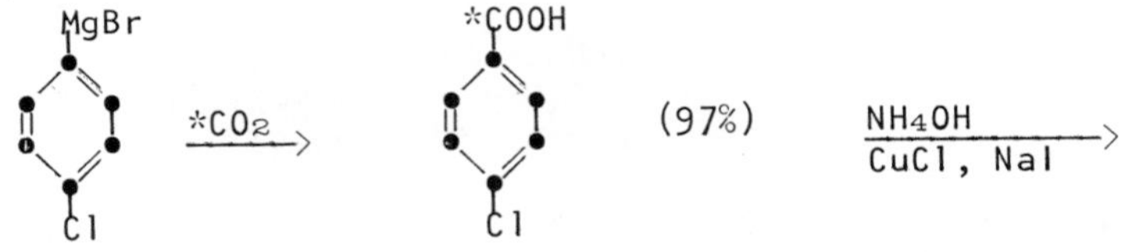
MgBr
Cl
*CO2
*COOH
Cl
(97%)
NH4OH
CuCl, NaI

4-Chlorobenzoic-7-^{14}C acid

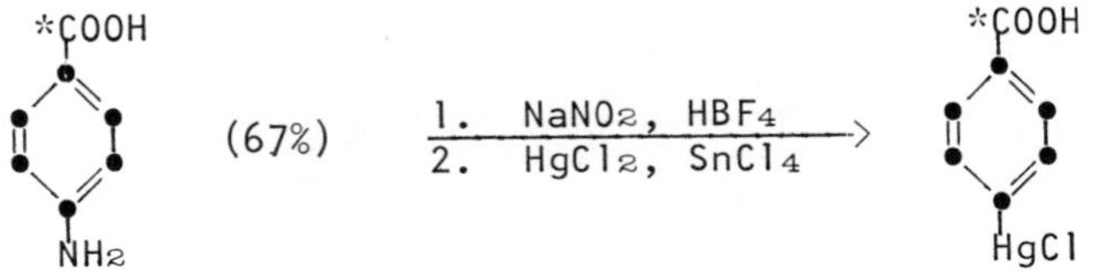
*COOH
NH2
(67%)
1. NaNO2, HBF4
2. HgCl2, SnCl4
*COOH
HgCl

(51% from p-aminobenzoic acid; 30-35% from $BaCO_3$)

4-Aminobenzoic-7-^{14}C acid

[(4-Carboxy-^{14}C)-phenyl]chloromercury

M. Herbert, L. Pichat, and C. Fabignon, J. Label. Compounds, 4, 256 (1968).

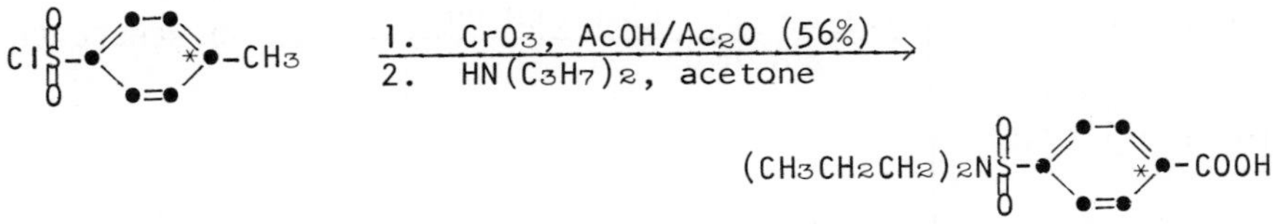
1. CrO3, AcOH/Ac2O (56%)
2. HN(C3H7)2, acetone

Probenecid
[4-[(Dipropylamino)sulfonyl]-benzoic-1-^{14}C acid]

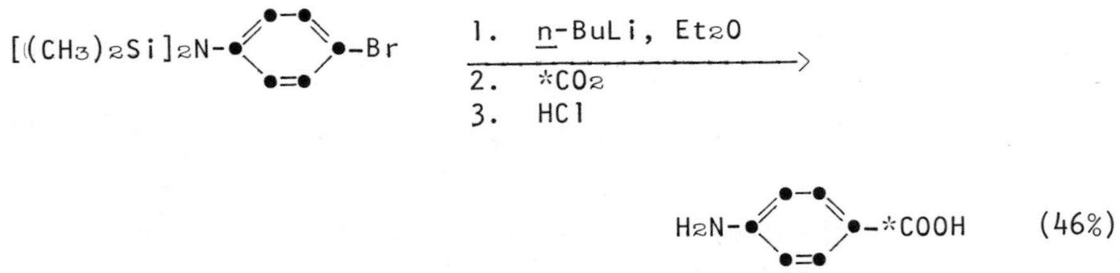
1. n-BuLi, Et2O
2. *CO2
3. HCl
(46%)

4-Aminobenzoic-7-^{14}C acid

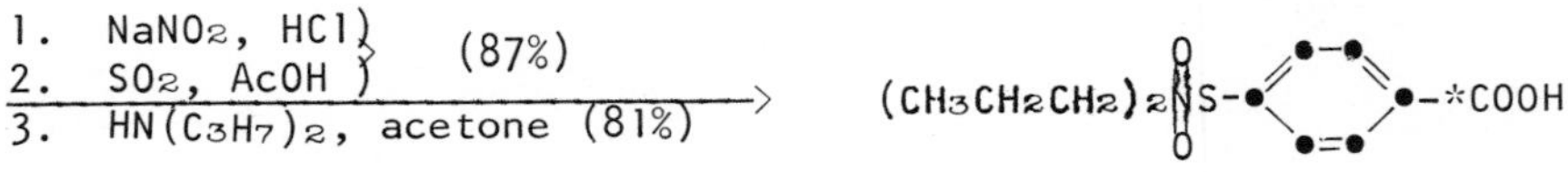
1. NaNO2, HCl
2. SO2, AcOH
(87%)
3. HN(C3H7)2, acetone (81%)

Probenecid
[4-[(Dipropylamino)sulfonyl]-benzoic-7-^{14}C acid]

R. L. Ellsworth, T. E. Maxim, and H. E. Mertel, J. Label. Compound. Radiopharm., 15, 111 (1978).

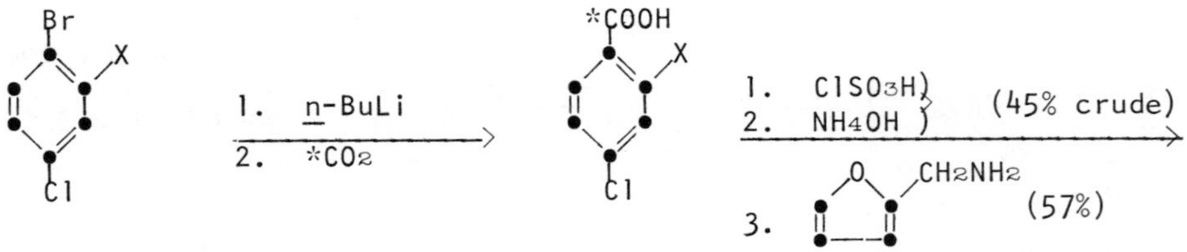
1. n-BuLi
2. *CO2
1. ClSO3H
2. NH4OH
(45% crude)
3.
(57%)

1, X=Cl, 2,4-Dichlorobenzoic-7-^{14}C acid (98%)

2, X=F, 4-Chloro-2-fluorobenzoic-7-^{14}C acid (quant.)

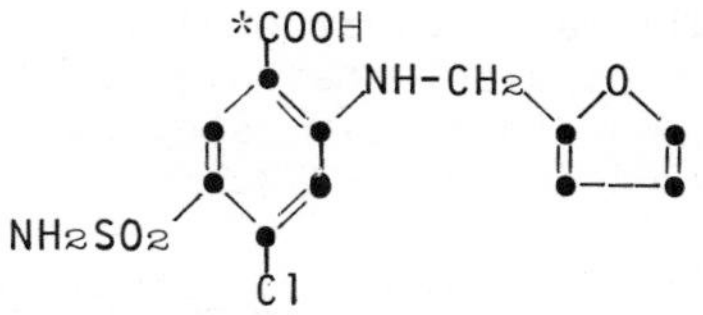

Furosemide
[5-(Aminosulfonyl)-4-chloro-2-[(2-furanylmethyl)amino]benzoic-_7_-^{14}_C_ acid]

C. W. Perry, G. J. Bader, A. A. Liebman, R. Barner, and J. Wuersch, _J. Org. Chem._, _43_, 4391 (1978); see also A. A. Liebman, A. M. Dorsky, and D. H. Malarek, _J. Label. Compounds_, _10_, 399 (1974).

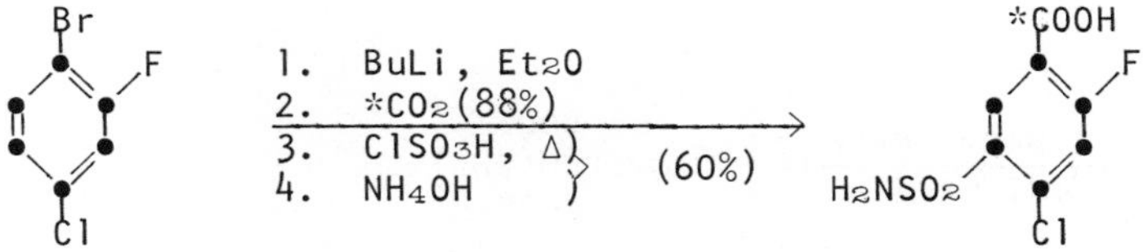
1. BuLi, Et_2O
2. $*CO_2$ (88%)
3. $ClSO_3H$, Δ
4. NH_4OH
(60%)

5-(Aminosulfonyl)-4-chloro-2-fluorobenzoic-_7_-^{14}_C_ acid

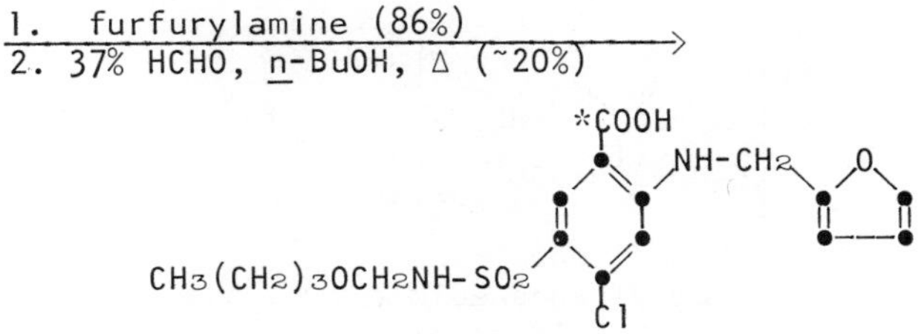
1. furfurylamine (86%)
2. 37% HCHO, _n_-BuOH, Δ (~20%)

(8% overall)

5-[[(Butoxymethyl)amino]sulfonyl]-4-chloro-2-[(2-furanylmethyl)amino]benzoic-_7_-^{14}_C_ acid

H. Parnes, _J. Label. Compound. Radiopharm._, _15_, 253 (1978).

1-12 Polycarboxylic Acids

$$R\text{-}CH_2COONa \xrightarrow[\Delta]{*CO_2} R\text{-}CH_2{*}COONa$$

A number of aliphatic dicarboxylic acid salts were exchanged with labeled carbon dioxide. Malonic acid, methyl malonic acid, ethylmalonic acid, succinic acid, etc. were prepared in yields from 0-85% with exchanges of 0-77%.

A. Szaboles and J. Szammer, J. Label. Compounds, 10, 113 (1974).

K*CN —(1. $BrCH_2COOH$, aq. NaOH; 2. 12N NaOH, Δ; 3. $CaCl_2$; 4. 20% HCl)→ $HOO^*C-CH_2{}^*COOH$ (88% overall)

Malonic acid
[Propanedioic-1,3-^{14}C acid]

D. Bánfi, J. Volfard, and Z. Mészáros, J. Label. Compounds, 11, 409 (1975).

$COOC_2H_5$ / $^*CH_2$ / $COOC_2H_5$ —(1. C_4H_9Br, NaOEt; 2. KOH, EtOH)→ COOK / $^*CH(CH_2)_3CH_3$ / $COOC_2H_5$

Propanedioic-2-^{14}C acid diethyl ester

Butylpropanedioic-2-^{14}C acid potassium salt ethyl ester

—(1. $SOCl_2$; 2. C_6H_5-NHNAc-C_6H_5; 3. NaOH)→

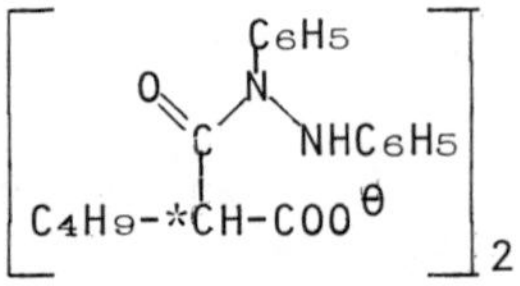

C6H5
O
N
C
NHC6H5
C4H9-*CH-COO⊖
2

Ca^{2+} (30% overall)

Bumadizon
(Butylpropanedioic-2-^{14}C acid mono(1,2-diphenylhydrazide) calcium salt]

G. Ludwig and I.-M. Ache, Arzneim.-Forsch.-(Drug Res.), 23, 1226 (1973).

$CH_2=CHCH_2CH_2MgBr$ —($^*CO_2$)→ $CH_2=CHCH_2CH_2{}^*COOH$ (93.5%)

4-Pentenoic-1-^{14}C acid

$\xrightarrow[K_2CO_3,\ NaIO_4]{KMnO_4}$ HOO*C-CH_2CH_2-*COOH (66% from $BaCO_3$)

Succinic acid
[Butanedioic acid-1,4-^{14}C]

M. Herbert, L. Pichat, and C. Fabignon, J. Label. Compounds, 4, 248 (1968).

$ClCH_2CHClCOOCH_3$ $\xrightarrow[2.\ K^*CN,\ CH_3OH,\ NaHCO_3\ (70\text{-}80\%)]{1.\ quinoline}$

N*C-CH=CH-$COOCH_3$ (E/Z mixture, 5:1)

3-(Cyano-^{14}C)-2-propenoic acid methyl ester

$\xrightarrow{HCl}$ 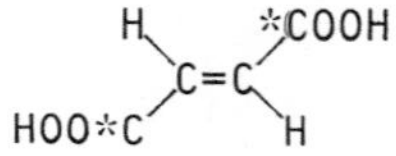
H
*COOH
C=C
HOO*C
H
(45% from K*CN) + HOO*C-CH_2CHOH-*COOH (9%)

Fumaric acid
[(E)-2-Butenedioic-1,4-^{14}C acid]

DL-Malic acid
[2-Hydroxybutanedioic-1,4-^{14}C acid]

H. Rutner and R. Rapun, J. Label. Compounds, 9, 65 (1973).

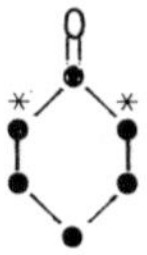
O
*
*

$\xrightarrow[2.\ C_2H_5COCH_3,\ CHCl_3,\ KOH\ (37\%)]{1.\ C_6H_5OH,EtSH,\ HCl,\ C_6H_6 (81\%)}$

Cyclohexanone-2,6-^{14}C

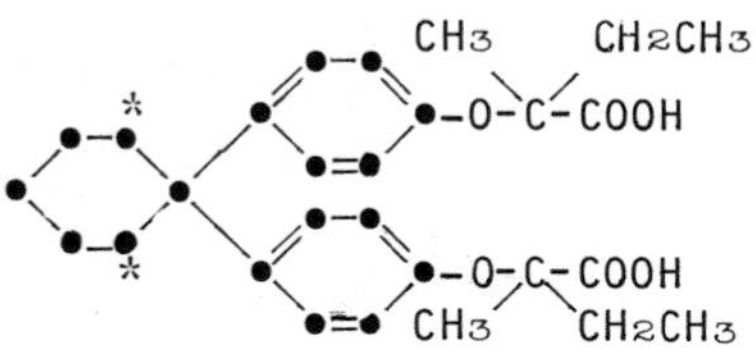
CH3
CH2CH3
*
-O-C-COOH
*
-O-C-COOH
CH3
CH2CH3
(12% from K*CN)

2,2'-[(Cyclohexylidene-2,6-^{14}C)bis(4,1-phenyleneoxy)]bis[2-methylbutanoic acid]

A. Yoshitake, Y. Makari, K. Kawahara, and T. Doi, J. Label. Compound. Radiopharm., 12, 247 (1976).

CH_2--C(OH)--CH_2 / *COOH COOH *COOH —(1. Δ; 2. H_2O, Δ)→ CH_2=C-COOH / CH_2-*COOH (14-15% chemical yield; 7% radiochemical yield)

Citric Acid
[2-Hydroxy-1,2,3-propanetricarboxylic acid (1,3-carboxyl-^{14}C)]

Itaconic Acid
[Methylenebutanedioic-4-^{14}C acid]

D. R. Campbell, J. Label. Compounds, 11, 365 (1975).

$CH_2ClC(=CH_2)$-$COOCH_3$ —(1. K*CN, H_2O; 2. conc. HCl)→ CH_2=C-COOH / CH_2-*COOH (44%)

Itaconic acid
[Methylenebutanedioic-4-^{14}C acid]

—(1. Br_2, AcOH; 2. $(CF_3CO)_2O$; 3. Et_3N, Et_2O)→

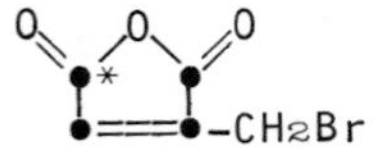

(27% crude from KCN)

—(1. H_2O; 2. conc. HCl) (42%)→ $BrCH_2$-C-COOH / CH-*COOH

Bromomesaconic acid
[(E)-2-(Bromomethyl)-2-butenedioic-4-^{14}C acid]

R. A. Laursen, W.-C Shen, and K. G. Zahka, J. Med. Chem., 14, 619 (1971); see also H. Coussee, B. Bonnaud, L. Pichat, and F. Aubert, J. Label. Compound. Radiopharm., 12, 491 (1976).

C_6H_5CH=C(CN)-$COOC_2H_5$ —(1. Na*CN, EtOH/H_2O, Et_3N; 2. HCl, 100°C; 3. NH_3, EtOH/Et_2O)→

C_6H_5-CH(*COOH)$CH_2COOH \cdot 2NH_3$

2-Phenylbutanedioic-1-^{14}C acid

B. Z. Askinazi, S. M. Chiznik, and N. Y. Kozarinskaya, Khim.-Farm. Zh., 12, 82 (1978).

$Br(CH_2)_5Br$ $\xrightarrow[\text{2. HCl}]{\text{1. K*CN}}$ $HOO{*}C-(CH_2)_5-{*}COOH$ (88%)

Pimelic acid
[Heptanedioic-1,7-^{14}C acid]

J. Brugidou, H. Christol, and Y. Langourieux, Bull. Soc. Chim. Fr., 4062 (1970).

$BrMg(CH_2)_5MgBr$ $\xrightarrow{{*}CO_2}$ $HOO{*}C(CH_2)_5{*}COOH$ (65%)

Pimelic acid
[Heptanedioic acid-1,7-^{14}C acid]

T. Masuike, N. Furukawa, and S. Oae, Bull. Chem. Soc. Jap., 44, 448 (1971).

$${*}COOCH_2C_6H_5 \\ CHNa \\ {*}COOCH_2C_6H_5$$

Malonic-1,3-^{14}C acid di(methylphenyl) ester sodium salt

$+\ BrCH_2(CH_2)_3COOC_2H_5 \xrightarrow{DMF}$

$${*}COOCH_2C_6H_5 \\ CH-(CH_2)_4COOC_2H_5 \\ {*}COOCH_2C_6H_5$$

(position of label was confirmed by decarboxylation to radioinactive 6-bromohexanoate)

$\xrightarrow[\text{2. distillation}]{\text{1. hydrogenolysis}}$ $HOO{*}C-(CH_2)_5COOC_2H_5$

Monoethyl pimelic acid
[Heptanedioic-1-^{14}C acid monoethyl ester]

J. I. Crowley and H. Rapoport, J. Amer. Chem. Soc., 92, 6363 (1970).

$BrCH_2{*}COOCH_3$

Bromoacetic-1-^{14}C acid methyl ester

1. $(C_6H_5)_3P$, C_6H_6 (90%)
2. NaOH, H_2O (83%)
3. CH_3I, EtOAc, Δ (80%)

$\longrightarrow (C_6H_5)_3\overset{+}{P}-CH(CH_3){*}COOCH_3\ \ I^{\ominus}$

1-(Methoxycarbonyl-^{14}C)ethyltriphenylphosphonium iodide

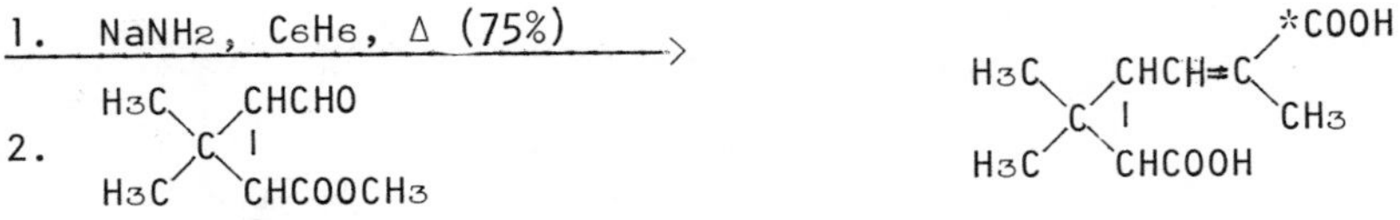
1. NaNH2, C6H6, Δ (75%)
H3C CHCHO
2. C
H3C CHCOOCH3
3. NaOH, CH3OH
*COOH
H3C CHCH=C
C CH3
H3C CHCOOH

(25% from methyl bromoacetate)

(+)-trans-Chrysanthemum dicarboxylic acid
[[1α,2β(E)]-3-[(2-Carboxy-^{14}C)-1-propenyl)]-2,2-dimethylcyclopropanecarboxylic acid]

L. Crombie, C. F. Doherty, and G. Pattenden, J. Chem. Soc. (C), 1076 (1970); J. Chem. Soc. (C), 2739 (1971).

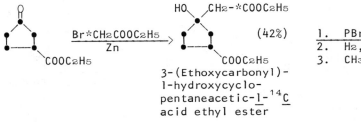

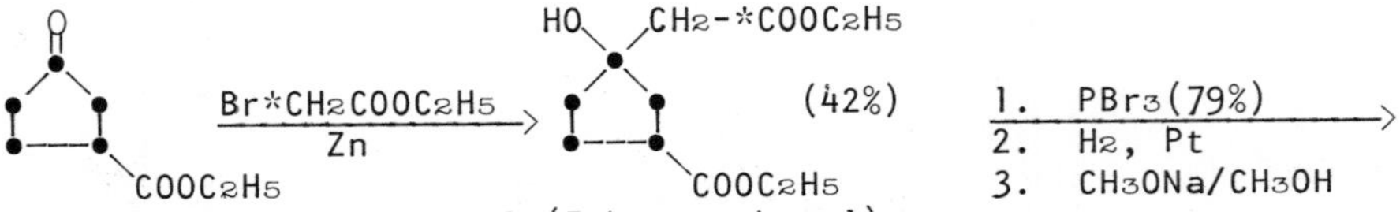
COOC2H5
Br*CH2COOC2H5
Zn
HO CH2-*COOC2H5
(42%)
COOC2H5
1. PBr3 (79%)
2. H2, Pt
3. CH3ONa/CH3OH

3-(Ethoxycarbonyl)-1-hydroxycyclopentaneacetic-1-^{14}C acid ethyl ester

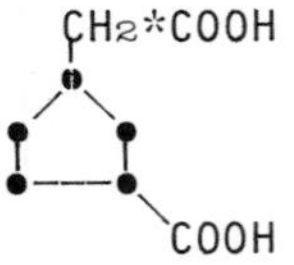
CH2*COOH
COOH

3-Carboxycyclopentaneacetic-1-^{14}C acid

Product is a mixture of cis and trans isomers. Pure cis was crystallized after equilibration of the mixture with hydrochloric acid. Thermal decarboxylation of the product gave inactive norcamphor.

C. Delrue, M. Heude, C. Bouchoule, and M. Blanchard, Bull. Soc. Chim. Fr., 1026 (1971).

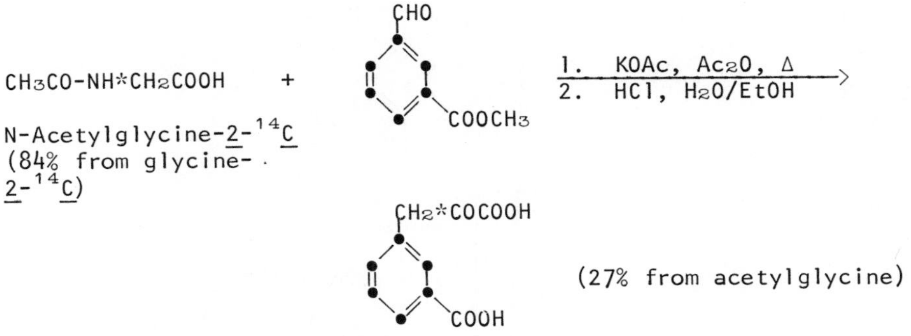
$CH_3CO-NH*CH_2COOH$ +
CHO
$COOCH_3$
1. KOAc, Ac_2O, Δ
2. HCl, H_2O/EtOH
$CH_2*COCOOH$
COOH
(27% from acetylglycine)

N-Acetylglycine-2-^{14}C (84% from glycine-2-^{14}C)

3-Carboxy-α-oxobenzenepropanoic-α-^{14}C acid

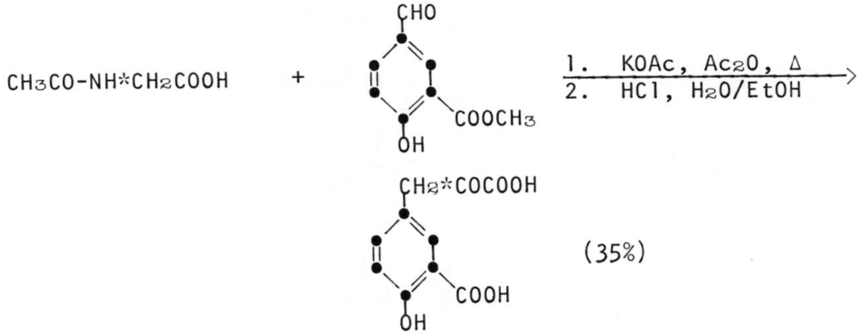
$CH_3CO-NH*CH_2COOH$ +
CHO
$COOCH_3$
OH
1. KOAc, Ac_2O, Δ
2. HCl, H_2O/EtOH
$CH_2*COCOOH$
COOH
OH
(35%)

3-Carboxy-4-hydroxy-α-oxobenzenepropanoic-α-^{14}C acid

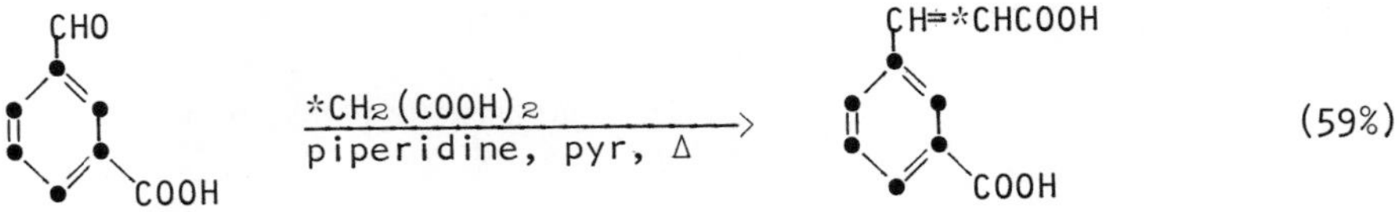
CHO
COOH
$*CH_2(COOH)_2$
piperidine, pyr, Δ
CH=*CHCOOH
COOH
(59%)

(E)-3-(2-Carboxyethenyl-2-^{14}C) benzoic acid

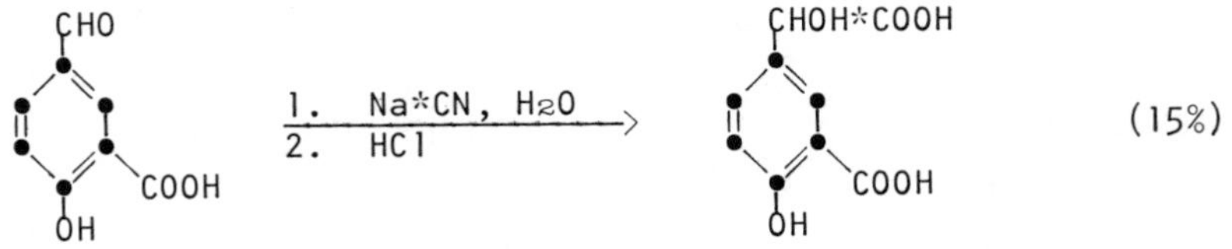
CHO
COOH
OH
1. Na*CN, H2O
2. HCl
CHOH*COOH
COOH
OH
(15%)

3-Carboxy-α,4-dihydroxy-benzeneacetic-1-^{14}C acid

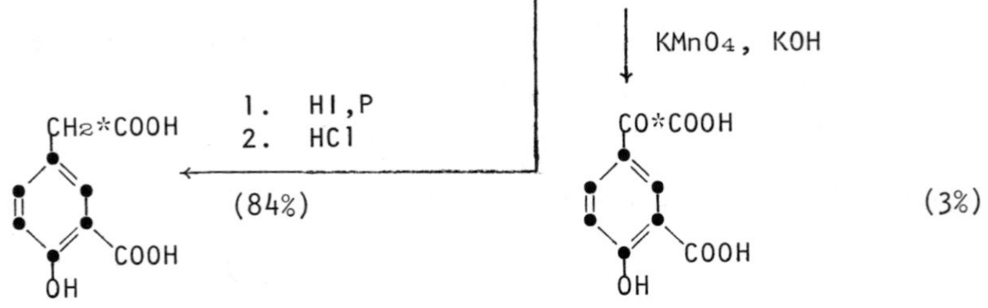
KMnO4, KOH
1. HI,P
2. HCl
(84%)
CH2*COOH
COOH
OH
CO*COOH
COOH
OH
(3%)

3-Carboxy-4-hydroxy-benzeneacetic-1-^{14}C acid

3-Carboxy-4-hydroxy-α-oxobenzeneacetic-1-^{14}C acid

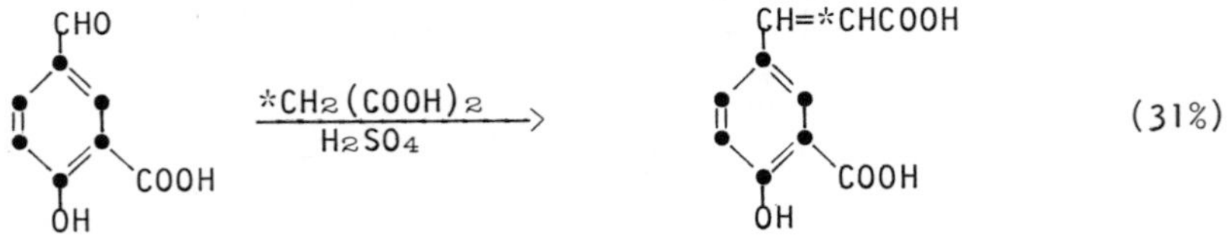
CHO
COOH
OH
*CH2(COOH)2
H2SO4
CH=*CHCOOH
COOH
OH
(31%)

(E)-5-(2-Carboxylethenyl-2-^{14}C)-2-hydroxybenzoic acid

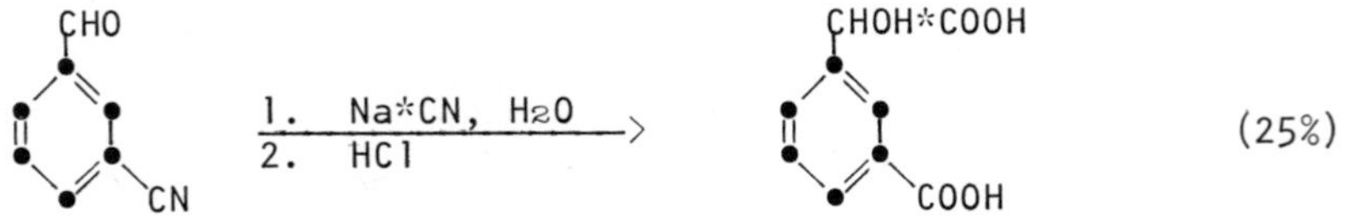
CHO
CN
1. Na*CN, H2O
2. HCl
CHOH*COOH
COOH
(25%)

3-Carboxy-α-hydroxybenzeneacetic-1-^{14}C acid

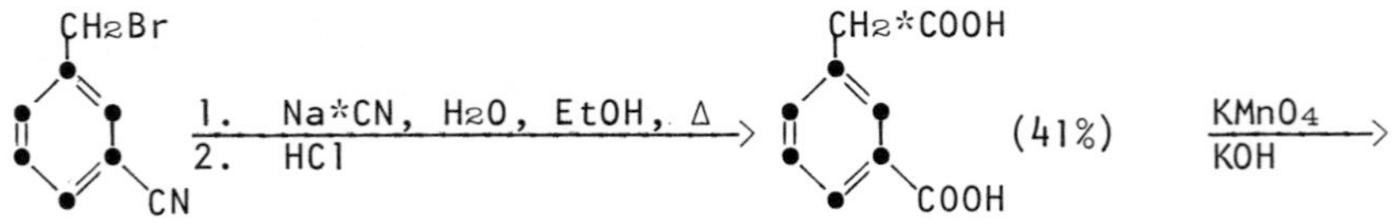
CH2Br
CN
1. Na*CN, H2O, EtOH, Δ
2. HCl
CH2*COOH
COOH
(41%)
KMnO4
KOH

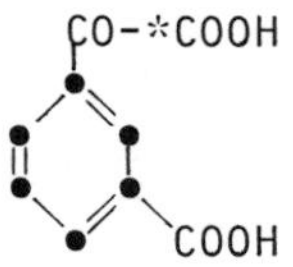

(36%)

3-Carboxy-α-oxobenzeneacetic-1-^{14}C acid

3-(3-Carboxy-4-hydroxyphenyl)-DL-alanine-2-^{14}C was similarly prepared.

P. O. Larsen and E. Wieczorkowska, J. Label. Compounds, 10, 287 (1974); Acta Chem. Scand., B31, 109 (1977).

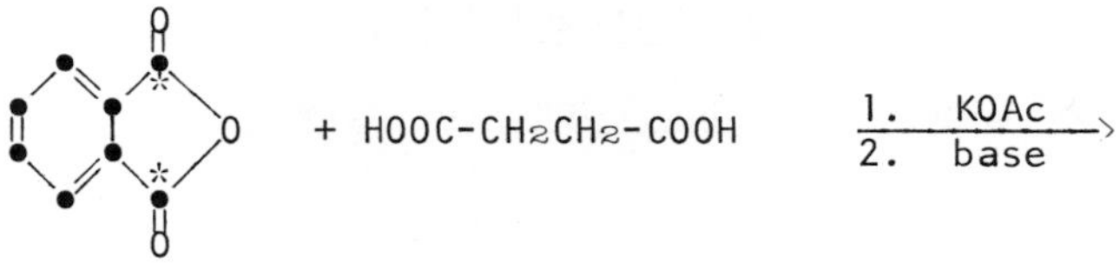
+ HOOC-CH2CH2-COOH
1. KOAc
2. base

1,3-Isobenzofurandione-1,3-^{14}C

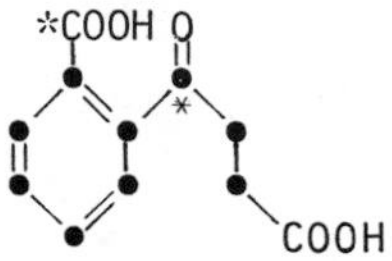

2-(Carboxy-^{14}C)-γ-oxobenzenebutanoic-γ-^{14}C acid

P. Dansette and R. Azerad, Biochem. Biophys. Res. Commun., 40, 1090 (1970).

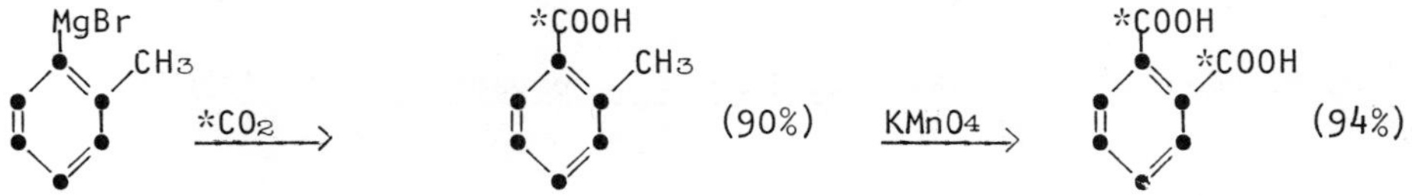
*CO2
(90%)
KMnO4
(94%)

2-Methylbenzoic-7-^{14}C acid

Phthalic acid [1,2-Benzenedicarboxylic acid (carboxyl-^{14}C)]

W. Maul, J. Label. Compounds, 5, 250 (1969).

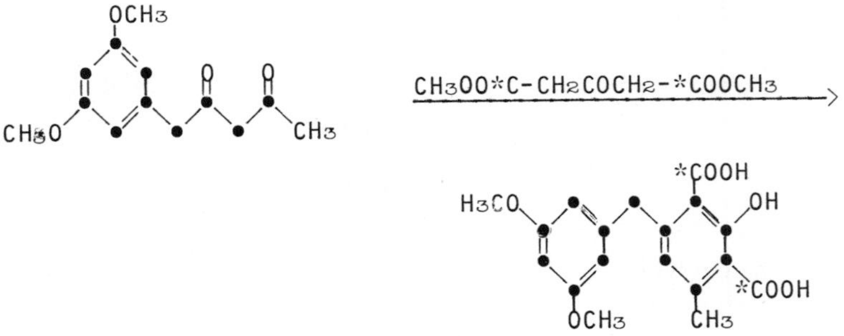
OCH3
CH3O
CH3
CH3OO*C-CH2COCH2-*COOCH3
*COOH
H3CO
OH
*COOH
OCH3
CH3

Mühlemann's dicarboxylic acid
[2-Hydroxy-4-(3,5-dimethoxyphenyl)-6-methylbenzene-1,3-dicarboxylic acid (carboxyl-^{14}C)]

W. Steglich and W. Reininger, J. Chem. Soc. (D), 178 (1970.

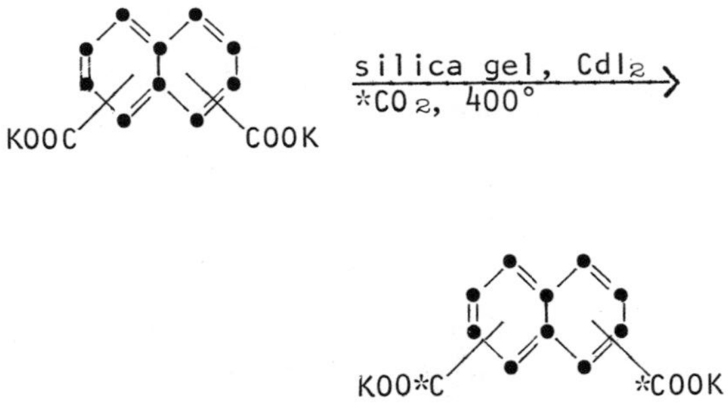
KOOC
COOK
silica gel, CdI2
*CO2, 400°
KOO*C
*COOK

(64-79% recovery; incorporations of 64-95% radioactivity)

Naphthalendicarboxylic acid
dipotassium salt-[carboxyl-^{14}C]

Transcarboxylation reactions were carried out on a number of naphthalene, pyridine, and furan systems.

J. Ratusky and R. Tykva, J. Label. Compounds, 5, 211 (1969).

2

Carboxylic Acid Derivatives

Esters

2-1 Unsubstituted Aliphatic Esters

$$R\text{-}CH_2Cl + {}^{*}CH_3{}^{*}COONa \xrightarrow[\text{xylene}]{(C_2H_5)_3N,\ AcOH} {}^{*}CH_3{}^{*}\overset{O}{\overset{\|}{C}}\text{-}OCH_2R$$

R = C_6H_5-; Acetic-1,2-^{14}C acid phenylmethyl ester (50%)

R = $C_6H_5CH_2$-; Acetic-1,2-^{14}C acid 2-phenylethyl ester (52%)

R = $CH_3(CH_2)_8CH_2$-; Acetic-1,2-^{14}C acid undecyl ester (32%)

R. A. Comes and R. W. Jenkins, Jr., J. Label. Compounds, 8, 575 (1972).

CH3*CO-
-R
m-Cl-PBA
CH3*COO-
-R

R=OCH_3, CH_3, H, Cl, CN

4-Substituted phenylethanones-1-^{14}C → Acetic-1-^{14}C acid 4-substituted phenyl esters

B. W. Palmer and A. Fry, J. Amer. Chem. Soc., 92, 2580 (1970).

C_6H_5-*$COCH_3$ $\xrightarrow[70\%\ HClO_4,\ CH_3OH]{Th(NO_3)_3}$ $C_6H_5CH_2$-*$COOCH_3$

1-Phenylethanone-1-^{14}C

Benzeneacetic-1-^{14}C acid methyl ester

An 84% yield was obtained for the unlabeled reaction; the position of the label was determined by degradation reactions and a mechanism involving phenyl migration was proposed.

A. McKillop, B. P. Swann, and E. C. Taylor, J. Amer. Chem. Soc., 93, 4919 (1971).

C_5H_{11}-*COOH $\xrightarrow[2.\ CrO_3,\ pyr\ (75\%)]{1.\ LiAlH_4,\ Et_2O\ (92\%)}$ C_5H_{11}-*CHO

Hexanoic-1-^{14}C acid (78% from $BaCO_3$)

Hexanal-1-^{14}C

$\xrightarrow[2.\ diazomethane\ (90\%)]{1.\ CH_2(COOH)_2,\ pyr,\ \Delta\ (66\%)}$ C_5H_{11}*CH=CHCOOCH_3

(E)-2-Octenoic-3-^{14}C acid methyl ester

J. P. Schmit, V. Van deVelde, and M. Piraux, J. Label. Compounds, 11, 51 (1975).

$CH_3(CH_2)_6$*$CH_2C \equiv CH$ $\xrightarrow[2.\ ClCH_2(CH_2)_4CH_2Cl]{1.\ Li}$

Dec-1-yne-3-^{14}C

$CH_3(CH_2)_6$*$CH_2C{\equiv}C(CH_2)_5CH_2Cl$ (65%) $\xrightarrow[2.\ saponification]{1.\ diazoacetic\ ester\ copper\text{-}bronze}$

1-Chlorohexadec-7-yne-9-^{14}C

$CH_3(CH_2)_6{}^*CH_2C=C(CH_2)_5CH_2Cl$ (bridged by CH–COOH) (63%) — 1. $SOCl_2$ 2. $ZnCl_2$ 3. $LiAlH_4$ →

$CH_3(CH_2)_6{}^*CH_2C=C(CH_2)_5CH_2Cl$ (bridged by CH_2) (50%) — 1. NaCN (99%) 2. hydrolysis (78%) 3. diazomethane →

$CH_3(CH_2)_6{}^*CH_2C=C(CH_2)_6COOCH_3$ (bridged by CH_2) (17% from dec-1-yne-3-^{14}C; 10% from octanoic-1-^{14}C acid)

Malvalic acid methyl ester
[2-(Octyl-1-^{14}C)-1-cyclopropene-1-heptanoic acid methyl ester]

Similarly:

$CH_3(CH_2)_7C=C(CH_2)_5CH_2Cl$ (bridged by CH_2) — 1. Na*CN 2. hydrolysis 3. diazomethane →

$CH_3(CH_2)_7C=C(CH_2)_6{}^*COOCH_3$ (bridged by CH_2) (77%)

2-Octyl-1-cyclopropene-1-heptanoic-1-^{14}C acid methyl ester

$CH_3(CH_2)_7C{\equiv}C(CH_2)_6COOCH_3$ — 1. ethyl diazoacetate-2-^{14}C 2. six steps →

$CH_3(CH_2)_7C=C(CH_2)_6COOCH_3$ (bridged by $^*CH_2$) (23%)

2-Octyl-1-(cyclopropene-3-^{14}C)-heptanoic acid methyl ester

W. J. Gensler, K. W. Pober, D. W. Solomon, R. Yanase, and M. B. Floyd, J. Chem. Soc., (D,) Chem. Commun., 287 (1970).

$^{*}CH_3[C{\equiv}C]_2H$ $\xrightarrow[DMF/CH_3OH,\ NH_2OH{\cdot}HCl,\ CuCl]{IC{\equiv}CCH_2CH{=}CH[CH_2]_7COOCH_3}$

Penta-1,3-diyne-5-^{14}C

$^{*}CH_3[C{\equiv}C]_3CH_2CH{=}CH[CH_2]_7COOCH_3$

(Z)-Octadec-9-ene-12,14,16-triynoic-18-^{14}C acid methyl ester

$OH^{*}C\text{-}[CH_2]_7COOCH_3$ $\xrightarrow[2.\ AgNO_3,\ I_2/CH_2Cl_2\ (48\%)]{1.\ (CH_3)_3SiC{\equiv}CCH_2CH\text{-}P(C_6H_5)_3\ (79\%)}$

$I\text{-}C{\equiv}CCH_2CH{=}^{*}CH[CH_2]_7COOCH_3$ $\xrightarrow[DMF,\ CH_3OH,\ NH_2OH{\cdot}HCl,\ CuCl]{CH_3[C{\equiv}C]_2H}$

(Z)-13-Iodotridec-9-en-12-ynoic-9-^{14}C acid methyl ester

$CH_3[C{\equiv}C]_3CH_2CH{=}^{*}CH[CH_2]_7COOCH_3$ (53%)

(Z)-Octadec-9-ene-12,14,16-triynoic-9-^{14}C acid methyl ester

$CH_3\text{-}C{\equiv}C\text{-}Si(CH_3)_3$ $\xrightarrow[2.\ ^{*}CH_3CH_2I]{1.\ (CH_3)_2N(CH_2)_2N(CH_3)_2,\ EtO,\ BuLi}$

$^{*}CH_3(CH_2)_2C{\equiv}C\text{-}Si(CH_3)_3$ $\xrightarrow[2.\ KCN,\ H_2O;\ 3.\ 13\text{-iodoester-}9\text{-}^{14}C]{1.\ AgNO_3,\ Et_2O/EtOH}$

$^{*}CH_3(CH_2)_2(C{\equiv}C)_2CH_2CH{=}CH(CH_2)_7COOCH_3$ (17%)

(Z)-Octadec-9-ene-12,14-diynoic-18-^{14}C acid methyl ester

$(C_6H_5)_3P{=}^{*}CHCOOCH_3 + OHC\text{-}[C{\equiv}C]_2CH_2CH{=}CH[CH_2]_7COOCH_3 \longrightarrow$

$CH_3OOC\text{-}^{*}CH{=}CH[C{\equiv}C]_2CH_2CH{=}CH[CH_2]_7COOCH_3$

(E,Z)-Octadeca-2,9-diene-4,6-diynedioic-2-^{14}C dimethyl ester

An 83% yield of a mixture of cis and trans isomers labeled at position 2 was obtained; the mixture was separable by chromatography.

$I-C\equiv CCH_2CH{=}{}^*CH[CH_2]_7COOCH_3$

(Z)-13-Iodotridec-9-en-12-ynoic-9-^{14}C acid methyl ester

→ ($HC\equiv C-CONH_2$) → $NH_2OC-[C\equiv C]_2CH_2CH{=}{}^*CH[CH_2]_7COOCH_3$ (13%)

(Z)-15-Aminocarbonylpentadec-9-ene-12,14-diynoic-9-^{14}C acid methyl ester

→ ($HC\equiv CCH(OC_2H_5)_2$) → $OHC-[C\equiv C]_2CH_2CH{=}{}^*CH[CH_2]_7COOCH_3$ (48%)

(Z)-15-Formylpentadec-9-ene-12,14-diynoic-9-^{14}C acid methyl ester

→ ($CH_3(CH_2)_2C\equiv CH$) → $CH_3(CH_2)_2-(C\equiv C)_2CH_2CH{=}{}^*CH(CH_2)_7COOCH_3$ (57%)

(Z)-Octadec-9-ene-12,14-diynoic-9-^{14}C acid methyl ester

→ ($CH_2{=}CHCH_2C\equiv CH$, as above) → $CH_2{=}CHCH_2(C\equiv C)_2CH_2CH{=}{}^*CH(CH_2)_7COOCH_3$ (17%)

(Z)-Octadec-9,17-diene-12,14-diynoic-9-^{14}C acid methyl ester

A. G. Fallis, M. T. W. Hearn, Sir Ewart R. H. Jones, V. Thaller, and J. L. Turner, J. Chem. Soc., Perkin Trans. 1, 743 (1973); M. Ahmed, Sir Ewart R. H. Jones, M. T. W. Hearn, and V. Thaller, J. Chem. Res., 1579 (1977).

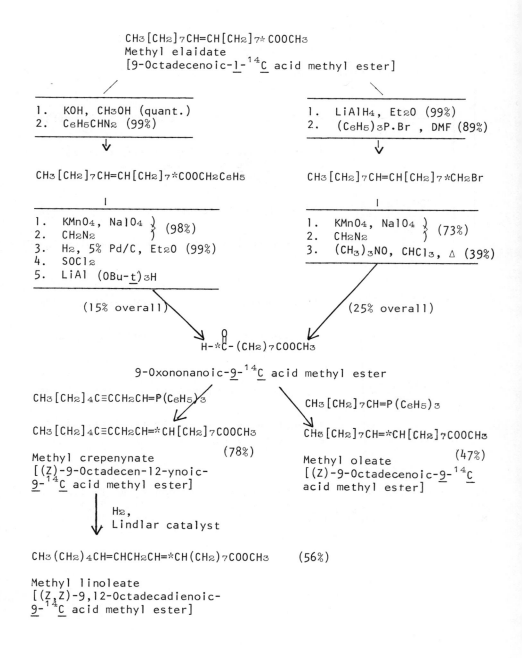

$CH_3[CH_2]_7CH{=}CH[CH_2]_7{*}COOCH_3$
Methyl elaidate
[9-Octadecenoic-1-^{14}C acid methyl ester]

Left route:

1. KOH, CH_3OH (quant.)
2. $C_6H_5CHN_2$ (99%)

↓

$CH_3[CH_2]_7CH{=}CH[CH_2]_7{*}COOCH_2C_6H_5$

1. $KMnO_4$, $NaIO_4$ } (98%)
2. CH_2N_2
3. H_2, 5% Pd/C, Et_2O (99%)
4. $SOCl_2$
5. LiAl $(OBu\text{-}t)_3H$

(15% overall) ↓

Right route:

1. $LiAlH_4$, Et_2O (99%)
2. $(C_6H_5)_3P.Br$, DMF (89%)

↓

$CH_3[CH_2]_7CH{=}CH[CH_2]_7{*}CH_2Br$

1. $KMnO_4$, $NaIO_4$ } (73%)
2. CH_2N_2
3. $(CH_3)_3NO$, $CHCl_3$, Δ (39%)

(25% overall) ↓

$H{-}{*}\overset{O}{\overset{\|}{C}}{-}(CH_2)_7COOCH_3$

9-Oxononanoic-9-^{14}C acid methyl ester

Left: $CH_3[CH_2]_4C{\equiv}CCH_2CH{=}P(C_6H_5)_3$ ↓

$CH_3[CH_2]_4C{\equiv}CCH_2CH{=}{*}CH[CH_2]_7COOCH_3$ (78%)

Methyl crepenynate
[(Z)-9-Octadecen-12-ynoic-9-^{14}C acid methyl ester]

↓ H_2, Lindlar catalyst

$CH_3(CH_2)_4CH{=}CHCH_2CH{=}{*}CH(CH_2)_7COOCH_3$ (56%)

Methyl linoleate
[(Z,Z)-9,12-Octadecadienoic-9-^{14}C acid methyl ester]

Right: $CH_3[CH_2]_7CH{=}P(C_6H_5)_3$ ↓

$CH_3[CH_2]_7CH{=}{*}CH[CH_2]_7COOCH_3$ (47%)

Methyl oleate
[(Z)-9-Octadecenoic-9-^{14}C acid methyl ester]

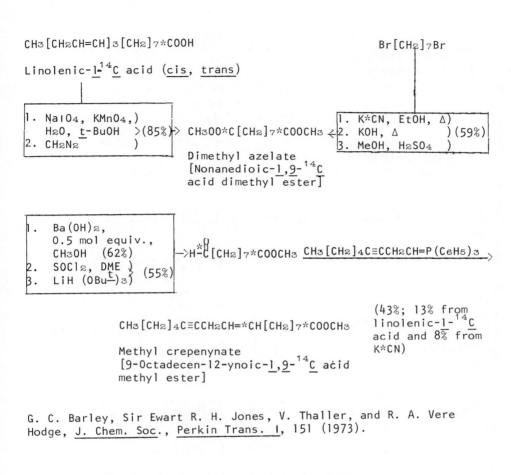

$CH_3[CH_2CH=CH]_3[CH_2]_7{}^*COOH$

Linolenic-1-^{14}C acid (*cis*, *trans*)

1. $NaIO_4$, $KMnO_4$, H_2O, *t*-BuOH
2. CH_2N_2

(85%) →

$CH_3OO{}^*C[CH_2]_7{}^*COOCH_3$

Dimethyl azelate
[Nonanedioic-1,9-^{14}C acid dimethyl ester]

← (59%)

1. K^*CN, EtOH, Δ
2. KOH, Δ
3. MeOH, H_2SO_4

$Br[CH_2]_7Br$

1. $Ba(OH)_2$, 0.5 mol equiv., CH_3OH (62%)
2. $SOCl_2$, DME
3. $LiH(OBu\text{-}t)_3$

(55%) →

$H{}^*C(O)[CH_2]_7{}^*COOCH_3$ $\xrightarrow{CH_3[CH_2]_4C{\equiv}CCH_2CH=P(C_6H_5)_3}$

$CH_3[CH_2]_4C{\equiv}CCH_2CH={}^*CH[CH_2]_7{}^*COOCH_3$

Methyl crepenynate
[9-Octadecen-12-ynoic-1,9-^{14}C acid methyl ester]

(43%; 13% from linolenic-1-^{14}C acid and 8% from K^*CN)

G. C. Barley, Sir Ewart R. H. Jones, V. Thaller, and R. A. Vere Hodge, *J. Chem. Soc.*, *Perkin Trans. I*, 151 (1973).

$^*CHN_2COOC_2H_5$

Ethyl diazoacetate-2-^{14}C

1. $CH_3(CH_2)_7C \equiv C(CH_2)_7COOCH_3$, Cu
2. KOH, *n*-propanol, Δ

→

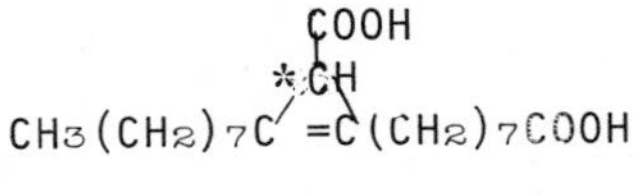
COOH
*CH
CH3(CH2)7C =C(CH2)7COOH

(22%; two steps)

1. 70% $HClO_4$, Ac_2O
2. $NaBH_4$, DMSO, pyr
3. diazomethane
→

$CH_3(CH_2)_7C(=C)(CH_2)_7COOCH_3$ with *CH_2 bridging the double bond (26%; three steps)

Methyl sterculate
[2-Octyl-(cyclopropene-3-^{14}C) octanoic acid methyl ester]

N. E. Pawlowski, J. E. Nixon, D. J. Lee, and R. O. Sinnhuber, *J. Label. Compounds*, 10, 45 (1974).

CH_3-$[CH_2]_7$-$[CH{=}CHCH_2]_2$-$[CH_2]_5Cl$ → 1. K*CN, DMSO (94%); 2. HCl, CH_3OH (14%)

$CH_3[CH_2]_7$-$[CH{=}CHCH_2]_2$-$[CH_2]_5$-*$COOCH_3$

8,11-Eicosadienoic-1-^{14}C acid methyl ester

J. C. Castuma, R. R. Brenner, C. P. Arciprete, and A. E. A. Mitta, *An. Asoc. Quim. Argent.*, 60, 55 (1972).

$CH_3[CH_2]_4[CH{=}CHCH_2]_2$-$[CH_2]_8Cl$ → 1. K*CN, DMSO; 2. HCl, CH_3OH

$CH_3[CH_2]_4$-$[CH{=}CHCH_2]_2$-$[CH_2]_8$-*$COOCH_3$

11,14-Eicosadienoic-1-^{14}C acid methyl ester

A. Catala, C. A. Arciprete, R. R. Brenner, and A. E. A. Mitta, *An. Asoc. Quim. Argent.*, 58, 47 (1970).

2-2 Substituted Aliphatic Esters

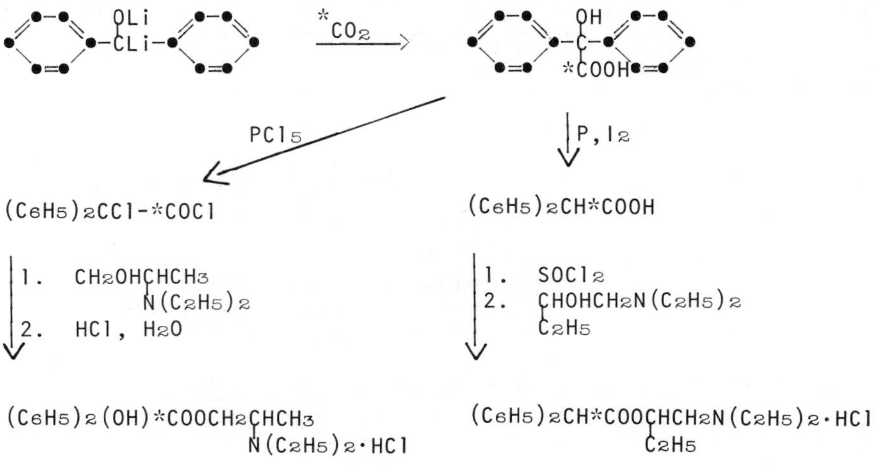
OLi
CLi
*CO2
OH
C
*COOH
PCl5
P, I2
(C6H5)2CCl-*COCl
(C6H5)2CH*COOH
1. CH2OHCHCH3
N(C2H5)2
2. HCl, H2O
1. SOCl2
2. CHOHCH2N(C2H5)2
C2H5
(C6H5)2(OH)*COOCH2CHCH3
N(C2H5)2·HCl
(C6H5)2CH*COOCHCH2N(C2H5)2·HCl
C2H5

Metamisyl
[α-Hydroxy-α-phenylbenzene-acetic-1-^{14}C acid 2-(diethyl-amino)-2-methylethyl ester hydrochloride]

Etherophene
[α-Phenylbenzeneacetic-1-^{14}C acid [1-ethyl-2-(diethyl amino)]ethyl ester hydrochloride]

A. D. Bulat, Y. Y. Usaevich, B. Z. Askinazi, and L. I. Vekshina, Khim.-Farm.Zh., 11, 86 (1977).

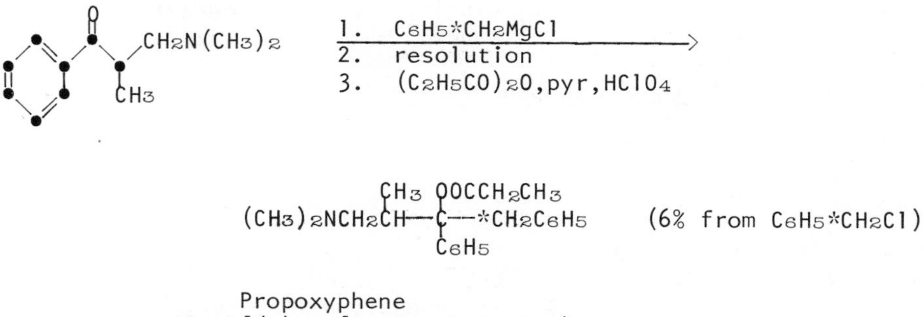
O
CH2N(CH3)2
CH3
1. C6H5*CH2MgCl
2. resolution
3. (C2H5CO)2O, pyr, HClO4
CH3 OOCCH2CH3
(CH3)2NCH2CH—C—*CH2C6H5
C6H5
(6% from C6H5*CH2Cl)

Propoxyphene
[(S)-α-[2-Dimethylamino)-1-methylethyl]-α-phenyl-benzeneethanol-β-^{14}C propanoate]

J. A. Kepler and G. F. Taylor, J. Label. Compounds, 6, 199 (1970).

$(CH_3)_2NCH_2{*}CH_2OH$

2-(Dimethylamino)ethanol-1-^{14}C

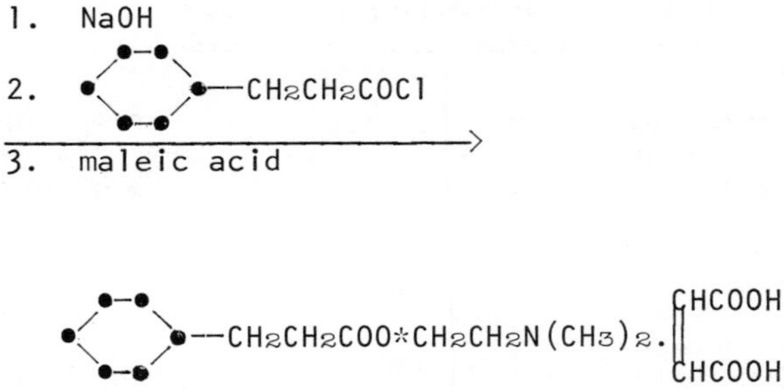

Cyprodenate
[Cyclohexanepropanoic acid
2-(dimethylamino)ethyl-1-^{14}C
ester (Z)-butenedioate]

Y. Dormand, J. C. Levron, and A. Benakis, Arzneim.-Forsch.-(Drug Res.), 25, 194 (1975).

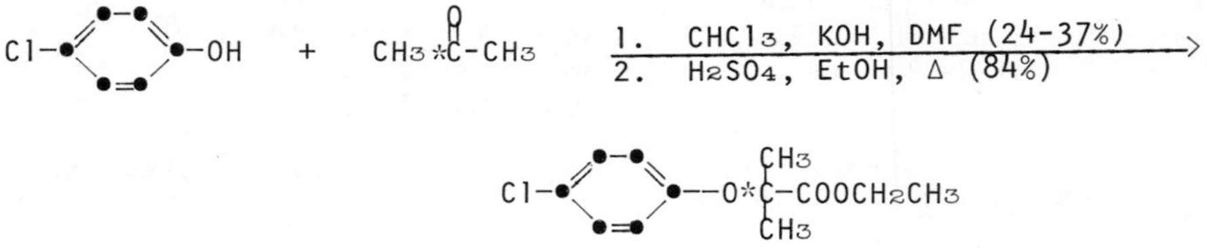

Ethyl clofibrate
[2-(4-Chlorophenoxy)-2-methylpropanoic-2-^{14}C acid ethyl ester]

E. Ferdinandi, J. Label. Compounds, 11, 287 (1975).

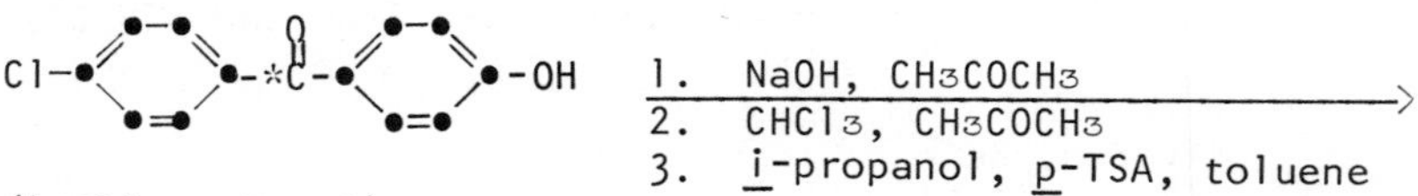

(4-Chlorophenyl)-(4-hydroxyphenyl)-methanone-^{14}C

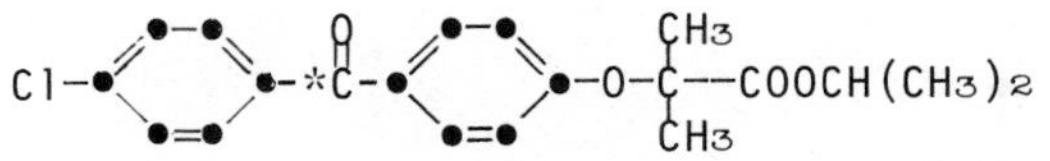

(6% from $Ba^{*}CO_3$)

Procetofene
[2-[4-(4-Chlorobenzoyl-7-^{14}C)phenoxy]-
2-methylpropanoic acid 1-methylethyl ester]

C. Luu Duc, Arzneim.-Forsch.-(Drug Res.), 26, 894 (1976).

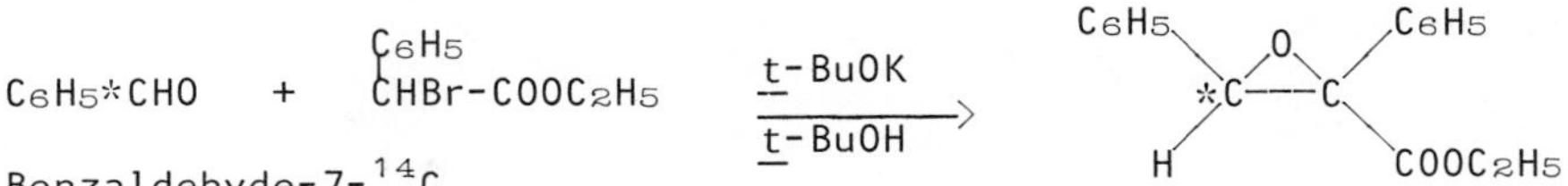

Benzaldehyde-7-^{14}C

2,3-Diphenyloxirane carboxylic-3-^{14}C acid

R. A. Gorski, D. J. Gagli, and J. Wemple, J. Amer. Chem. Soc., 98, 4588 (1976).

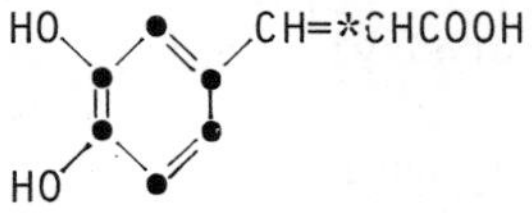

3-(3,4-Dihydroxyphenyl)-
2-propenoic-2-^{14}C acid.

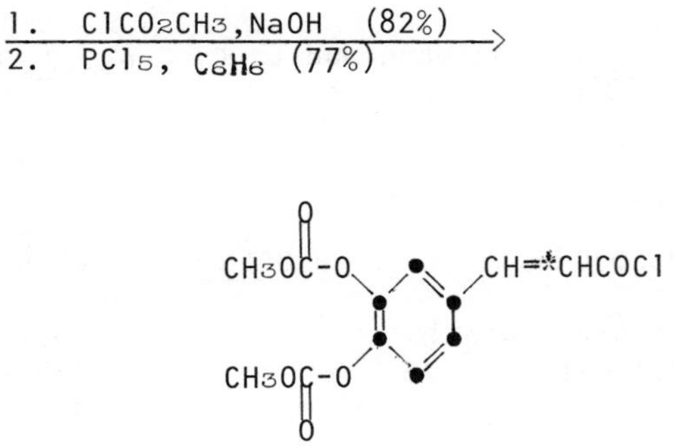

1.

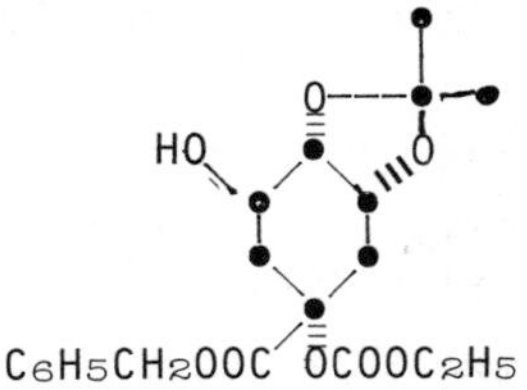
HO
O
O
$C_6H_5CH_2OOC$ $OCOOC_2H_5$

benzene, pyr.
(~25% from quinic acid) (58%) →

2. NaOH, CH_3OH
3. AcOH, Δ

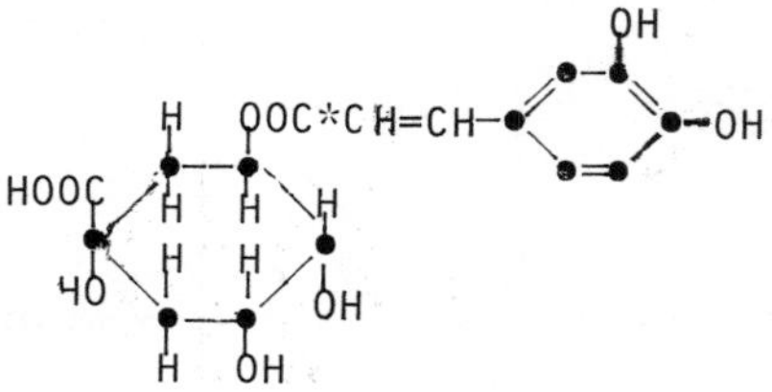
OH
OOC*CH=CH
OH
HOOC
H
HO
OH
OH

Chlorogenic acid
[[1S-(1α,3β,4α,5α)]-3-[[3-(3,4-Dihydroxyphenyl-1-oxo-2-propenyl-2-^{14}C]oxy]-1,4,5-trihydroxycyclohexanecarboxylic acid]

J. F. DeBardeleben and L. C. Teng, J. Label. Compounds, 6, 34 (1970).

$*CH_3COOC_2H_5$ —NaOEt→ $*CH_3C(=O)$ $*CH_2COOC_2H_5$ (46%)

Acetic-2-^{14}C acid ethyl ester

Ethyl acetoacetate [3-Oxobutanoic-2,4-^{14}C acid ethyl ester]

K. Figge and H. P. Voss, J. Label. Compounds, 9, 23 (1973).

CH_3*COCl

1. $CH_3CH_2OOC-CH(MgOEt)-COOC(CH_3)_3$, Et_2O
2. p-TSA, C_6H_6, Δ
→

Acetyl-1-^{14}C chloride

$CH_3{*}COCH_2COOC_2H_5$ (75% from sodium acetate-1-^{14}C)

Ethyl acetoacetate
[3-Oxobutanoic-3-^{14}C acid ethyl ester]

I. Nakatsuka, M. Hazue, Y. Makari, K. Kawahara, M. Endo, and A. Yoshitake, J. Label. Compound.Radiopharm., 12, 395 (1976).

$CH_3{*}COCH_3$ $\xrightarrow[NaOEt,\ C_6H_6]{(COOCH_2CH_3)_2}$ $CH_3{*}C(=O)\text{-}CH_2C(=O)\text{-}COOC_2H_5$ (76%)

2-Propanone-2-^{14}C

2,4-Dioxopentanoic-4-^{14}C acid ethyl ester

R. C. Thomas, J. Label. Compound.Radiopharm., 15, 461 (1978).

$CH_3{*}COOCH_2CH_3 + (CH_3CH_2O)_2CHCOOC_2H_5$ $\xrightarrow[toluene,\ \Delta]{NaH}$

Acetic-1-^{14}C acid ethyl ester

$(CH_3CH_2O)_2CH\text{-}C(ONa)\text{=}CH\text{-}{*}COOC_2H_5$

4,4-Diethoxy-3-hydroxy-2-butenoic-1-^{14}C acid ethyl ester sodium salt

V. Jezdić, N. Razumenić, M. Skakun, S. Albahari, and J. Odavić-Josić, J. Label. Compounds, 6, 88 (1970).

$CH_3\text{-}C(N(C_2H_5)_2)\text{=}CHCOOCH_3$ $\xrightarrow[2.\ H_2O,\ \Delta]{1.\ {*}CH_3I,\ \Delta,\ \text{sealed tube}}$ $CH_3\text{-}C(=O)\text{-}CH({*}CH_3)COOCH_3$ (87%)

2-(Methyl-^{14}C)-3-Oxobutanoic acid methyl ester

N. M. Bale, R. Cahill, N. M. Davies, M. B. Mitchell, E. H. Smith, and D. H. G. Crout, J. Chem. Soc., Perkin Trans. I, 101 (1978).

$C_6H_5{*}COCH_3$ $\xrightarrow[NaNH_2]{CH_2ClCOOC_2H_5}$ 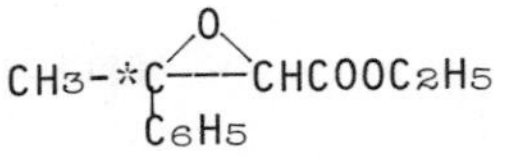 (62%)

1-Phenylethanone-1-^{14}C

3-Methyl-3-phenyloxiranecarboxylic-3-^{14}C acid ethyl ester

P. J. Stang, D. P. Fox, C. J. Collins, and C. R. Watson, Jr., J. Org. Chem., 43, 364 (1978).

$C_6H_5{*}COCH_3$ + $CH_3CHBrCOOC_2H_5$ $\xrightarrow[\text{condensation}]{\text{Darzens}}$

1-Phenyl-ethanone-1-^{14}C

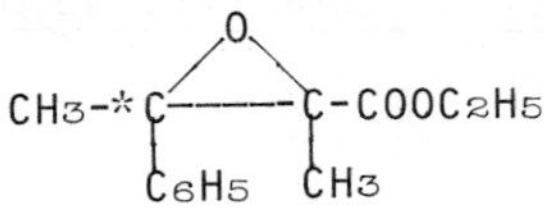 (65% E; 35% Z)

2,3-Dimethyl-3-phenyloxiranecarboxylic-3-^{14}C acid ethyl ester

The product was used to determine ethoxycarbonyl migration in the rearrangement of epoxides with $BF_3{\cdot}OEt_2$.

J. Kagan, D. A. Agdeppa, Jr., S. P. Singh, D. A. Mayers, C. Boyajian, C. Poorker, and B. E. Firth, J. Amer. Chem. Soc., 98, 4581 (1976).

$CH_3{*}COCH_3$ + $COOC_2H_5$–$COOC_2H_5$ $\xrightarrow{Na,\ EtOH}$ $CH_3{*}COCH_2COCOOC_2H_5$ (65%)

2-Propanone-2-^{14}C

2,4-Dioxopentanoic-4-^{14}C acid ethyl ester

H. Minato, T. Nagasaki, and Y. Katsuyama, J. Label. Compounds, 11, 275 (1975).

$CH_3CH_2CH_2{*}COOH$

Butyric-1-^{14}C acid

1. C_6H_5COCl (76%)
2. $CH_3COCHNaCOOC_2H_5$
3. HCl

$$CH_3CH_2CH_2{}^{*}\overset{O}{\overset{\|}{C}}CH_2COOC_2H_5$$

3-Oxo-Hexanoic-3-^{14}C acid ethyl ester

D. P. Thornhill and D. S. Sitar, J. Label. Compounds, 7, 145 (1971).

$$Br^{*}CH_2COOCH_3 \xrightarrow[2.\ NaH]{1.\ P(OCH_3)_3} (CH_3O)_3P{=}^{*}CHCOOCH_3$$

Bromoacetic-2-^{14}C acid methyl ester

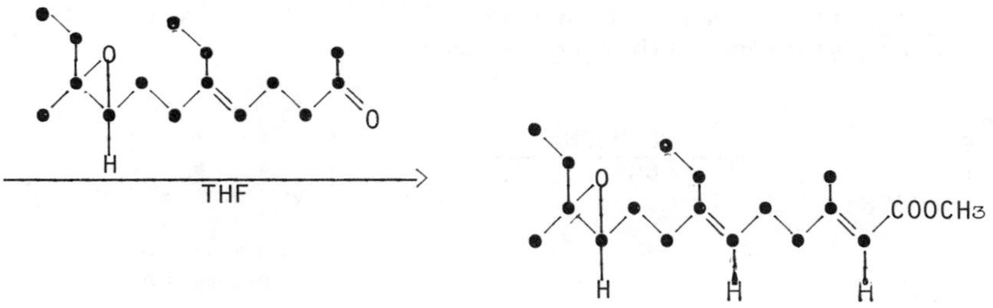
O
O
H
THF
O
COOCH3
H
H
H

Juvenile hormones
[2α(E,E,3α)-7-Ethyl-9-(3-ethyl-3-methyloxiranyl)-3-methyl-2,6-nonadienoic-2-^{14}C acid methyl ester]

Conditions are described for obtaining a 6% yield of the all trans or a 23% yield of the all cis isomer.

W. Hafferl, R. Zurflüh, and L. Dunham, J. Label. Compounds, 7, 331 (1971).

2-3 Alicyclic Esters

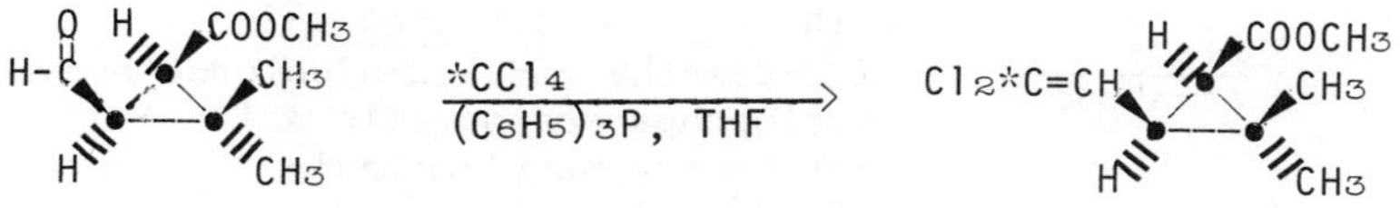
O
H-C
H
COOCH3
CH3
H
CH3
*CCl4
(C6H5)3P, THF
Cl2*C=CH
H
COOCH3
CH3
H
CH3

(62%)

[1R,cis]-isomer

1. KOH, CH_3OH, Δ (62%)
2. $SOCl_2$, CH_2Cl_2, Δ
3. 3-phenoxybenzyl alcohol, pyr/toluene (85%)

→

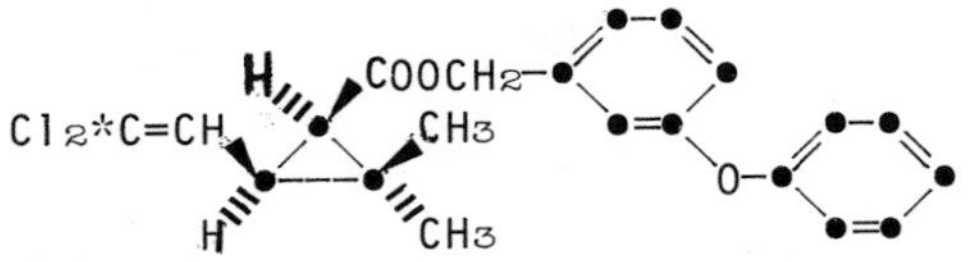

$Cl_2{*}C=CH$
$COOCH_2$
CH_3
CH_3
H
H
O

(33% overall)

Permethrin
[(1R-*cis*)-3-(2,2-Dichloroethenyl-*2*-^{14}*C*)-2,2-dimethylcyclopropanecarboxylic acid (3-phenoxyphenyl)methyl ester]

The [1R,*trans*] isomer was also prepared in 35% overall yield in a similar manner starting with *trans* aldehyde.

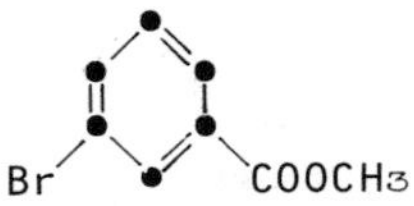

Br
$COOCH_3$

1. $*C_6H_5ONa$, Cu
2. SBMA

→

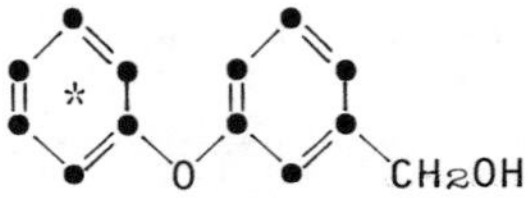

*
O
CH_2OH

3-(Phenoxy-*U*-^{14}*C*)-benzenemethanol

steps as above →

[1R-*cis*]- or [1R-*trans*]-3-2,2-Dimethyl-3-(2,2-dichloroethenyl)-cyclopropanecarboxylic acid [(3-phenoxy-*U*-^{14}*C*)phenyl]methyl ester (21-28% yields)

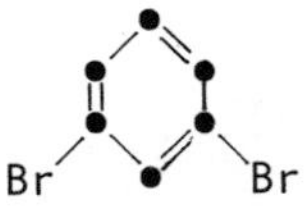

Br
Br

1. C_6H_5ONa, Cu
2. Mg, $*CO_2$
3. SBMA

→

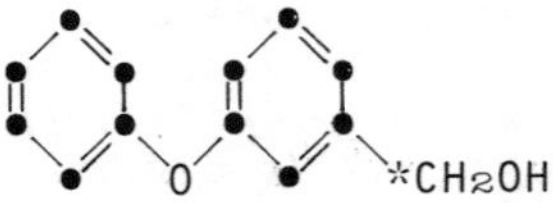

O
$*CH_2OH$

3-Phenoxybenzene methanol-*1*-^{14}*C*

steps as above →

[1R-*cis*]- or [1R-*trans*]-3-2,2-Dimethyl-3-(2,2-dichloroethenyl)-cyclopropanecarboxylic acid (3-phenoxyphenyl)methyl-^{14}*C* ester (58-86% yields)

SBMA = sodium bis(2-methoxyethoxy)aluminum hydride.

M. Elliot, N. J. Janes, D. A. Pulman, L. C. Gaughan, T. Unai, and J. E. Casida, J. Agr. Food Chem., 24, 270 (1976); I. Nakatsuka, F. Shono, and A. Yoshitake, J. Label. Compound. Radiopharm., 13, 561 (1977).

$*CO_2 \xrightarrow[THF]{LiAlH_4} H*CHO$ (50-70%) $\xrightarrow{C_6H_5\text{-}CNa(COOC_2H_5)_2}$

*CH2
C6H5-C - COOC2H5
(55%)
CH2=CHCH=CHN(CH3)2
benzene

Ethyl atropate
[α-(Methylene-^{14}C)benzene-acetic acid ethyl ester]

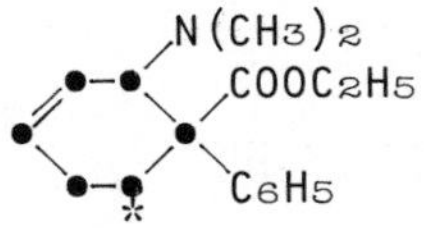
N(CH3)2
COOC2H5
C6H5

(13% from $BaCO_3$)

Tilidine
[trans-(+)-2-Dimethylamino)-1-phenyl-3-(cyclohexene-6-^{14}C)-1-carboxylic acid ethyl ester]

K. O. Vollmer and F. W. Koss, Arzneim.-Forsch.-(Drug Res.), 20, 990 (1970).

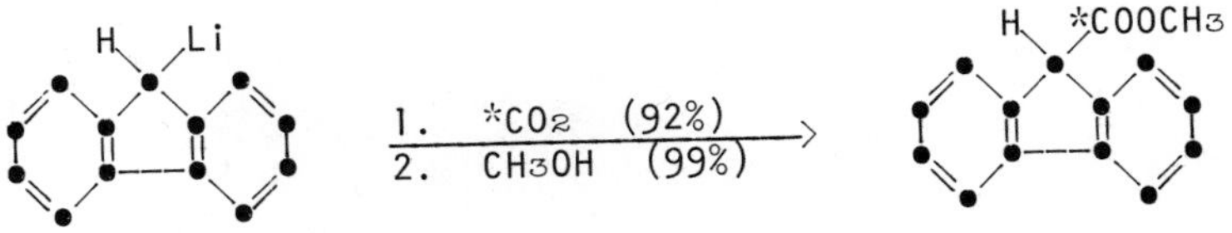
H
Li
1. *CO2 (92%)
2. CH3OH (99%)
H
*COOCH3

9H-Fluorene-9-carboxylic acid methyl ester-(carboxyl-^{14}C)

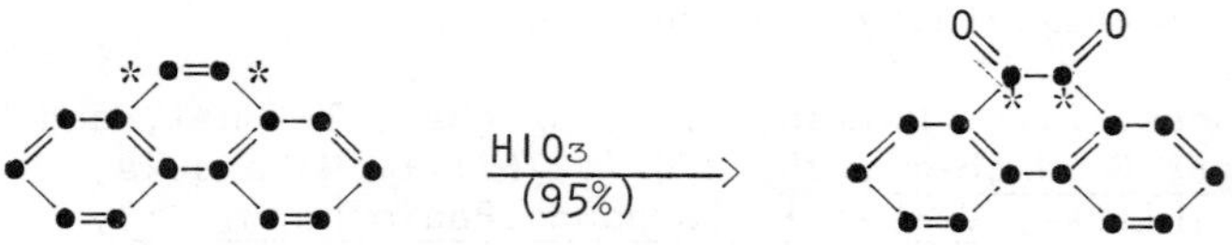
HIO3
(95%)

Phenanthrene-9,10-^{14}C

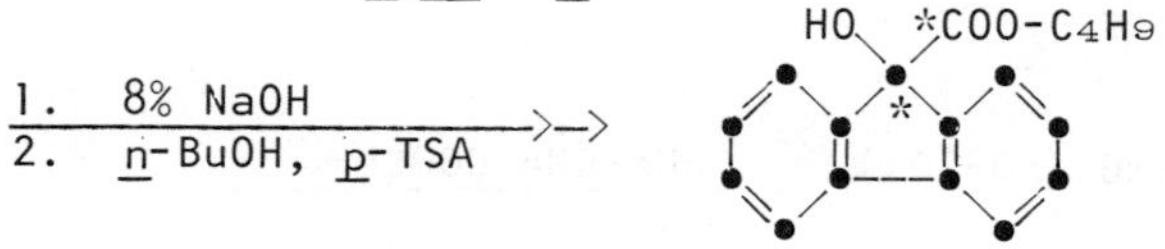
1. 8% NaOH
2. n-BuOH, p-TSA
HO *COO-C4H9

(69%; 26% from Ba*CO_3)

9-Hydroxy-9H-fluorene-9-carboxylic acid butyl ester-(9,carboxyl-^{14}C)

K. D. Göhler and H. R. Schütte, Z. Chem., 10, 190 (1970).

2-4 Aromatic Esters

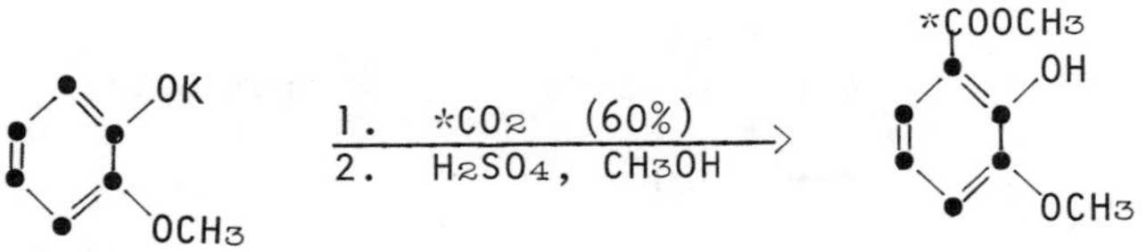
OK
OCH3
1. *CO2 (60%)
2. H2SO4, CH3OH
*COOCH3
OH
OCH3

2-Hydroxy-3-methoxybenzoic-7-^{14}C acid methyl ester

E. J. Merrill and A. D. Lewis, J. Label. Compound.Radiopharm., 13, 385 (1977).

C_5H_{11}*CH=CHCOOCH$_3$

Δ^2-trans-Octenoic-3-^{14}C acid methyl ester

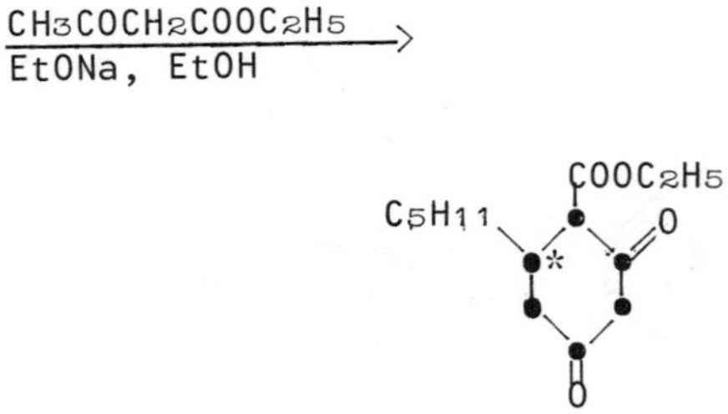
CH3COCH2COOC2H5
EtONa, EtOH
COOC2H5
C5H11
O
O

(72%)

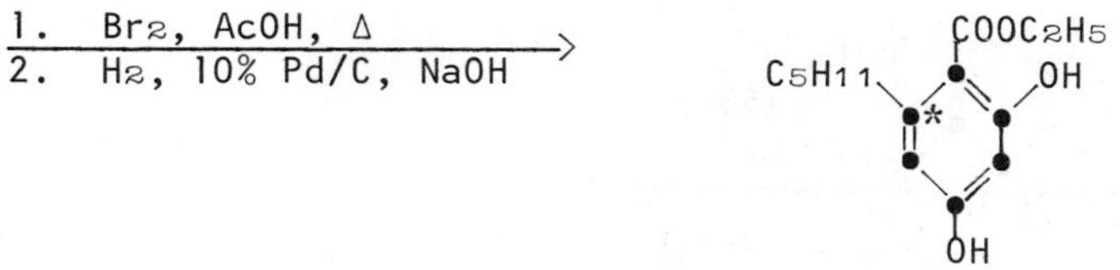
1. Br2, AcOH, Δ
2. H2, 10% Pd/C, NaOH
COOC2H5
C5H11
OH
OH

(39%)

Olivetolic acid ethyl ester
[2,4-Dihydroxy-6-pentyl-benzoic-6-^{14}C acid ethyl ester]

J. P. Schmit, V. Van deVelde, and M. Piraux, J. Label. Compounds, 11, 51 (1975).

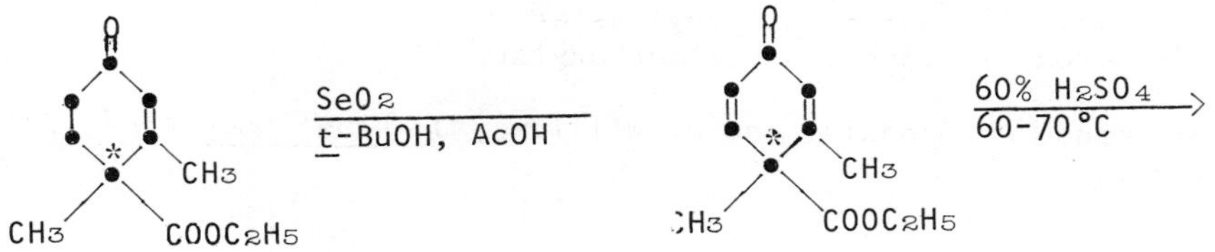
O
CH3
CH3
COOC2H5
SeO2
t-BuOH, AcOH
O
CH3
CH3
COOC2H5
60% H2SO4
60-70°C

(30%, 2% from *CH_3COOH)

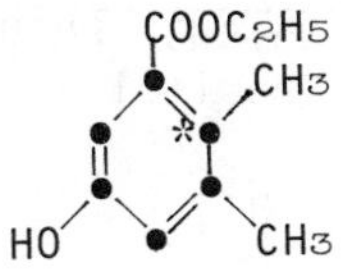
COOC2H5
CH3
HO
CH3

(50% yield)

2,3-Dimethyl-5-hydroxybenzoic-2-^{14}C acid ethyl ester

Degradation reactions determined that 99.8% of the label was in position 2 and 0.2% in position 1; a mechanism is proposed for the 1-^{14}C product.

T. Suehiro and S. Yamazaki, Bull. Chem. Soc. Jap., 48, 3655 (1975).

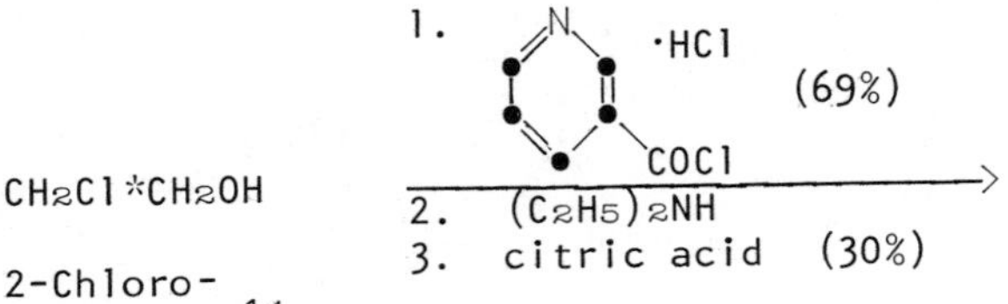
1.
·HCl
(69%)
COCl
$CH_2Cl{*}CH_2OH$
2. $(C_2H_5)_2NH$
3. citric acid (30%)

2-Chloro-
ethanol-1-^{14}C

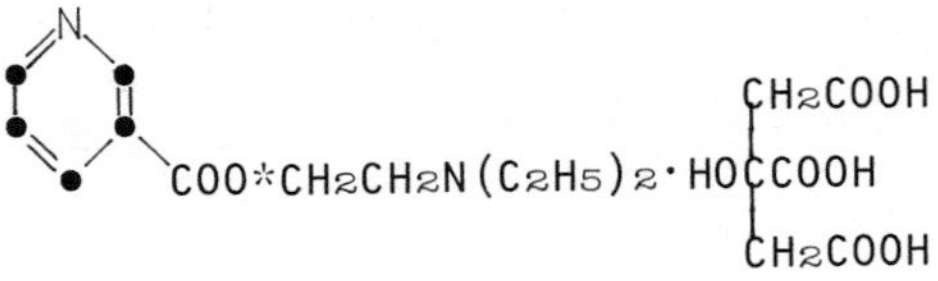
$COO{*}CH_2CH_2N(C_2H_5)_2 \cdot HOC(COOH)(CH_2COOH)_2$

(8% from sodium acetate)

3-Pyridinecarboxylic acid
2-(diethylamino-1-^{14}C) ethyl ester
2-hydroxy-1,2,3-propanetricarboxylate

J. Lintermans, A. Benakis, and J. Williams, J. Label Compounds, 7, 533 (1971).

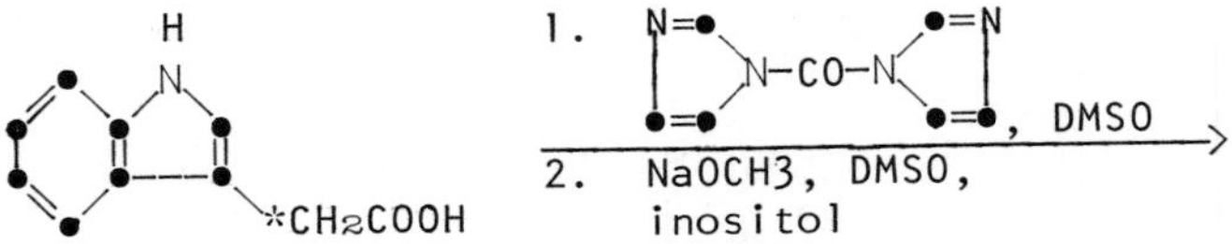
H
$*CH_2COOH$
1.
N-CO-N
, DMSO
2. $NaOCH_3$, DMSO,
inositol

1H-Indole-3-acetic-
α-^{14}C acid

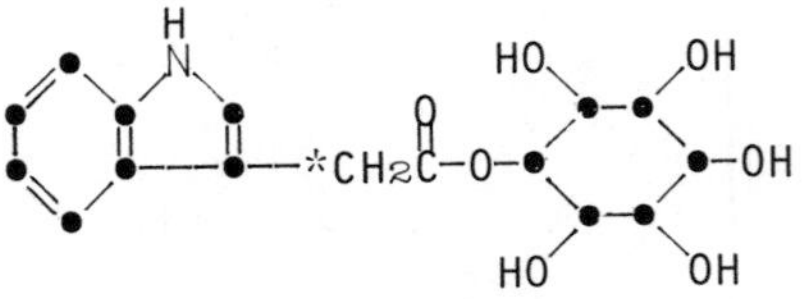
H
HO
OH
$*CH_2C-O-$
OH
HO
OH

(23%)

myo-Inositol-1-(1H-indole-3-acetate)-α-^{14}C

J. Nowacki, J. D. Cohen, and R. S. Bandurski, J. Label. Compound. Radiopharm., 15, 325 (1978).

2-5   Thio Esters

$$K*CN \xrightarrow[\text{DMF}]{CS_2} KS\overset{\displaystyle S}{\underset{\displaystyle \|}{C}}-*CN \xrightarrow{H_2O}$$

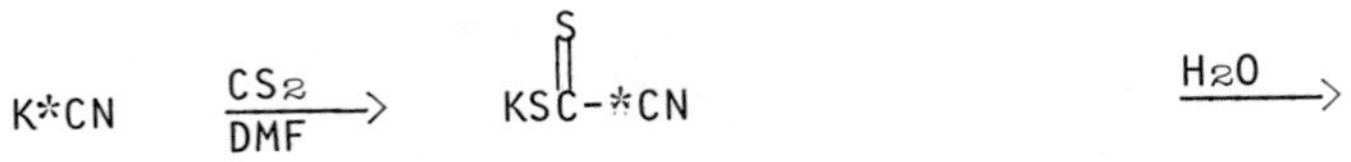

Carbono-(cyanido-^{14}C)-
dithioic acid
potassium salt

$$KS-\overset{*CN}{\underset{\displaystyle |}{C}} = \overset{*CN}{\underset{\displaystyle |}{C}}-SK$$

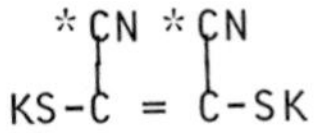

2,3-Dimercapto-2-
butene-(dinitrile-^{14}C)
dipotassium salt

J. Seda, M. Faud, and R. Tykva, J. Label. Compound. Radiopharm.,
14, 673 (1978).

$$C_6H_5-S*CH_2-\overset{\displaystyle O}{\underset{\displaystyle \|}{C}}-CH_2Cl \quad (95\%) \xrightarrow[\Delta]{CH_3COOH, \; CH_3COOK}$$

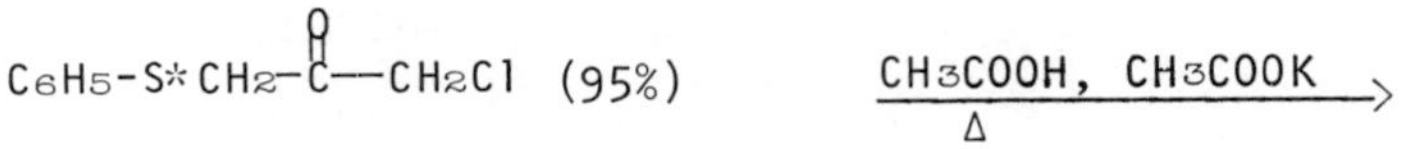

1-Chloro-3-phenylmercapto
propanone-3-^{14}C

$$CH_3\underset{\displaystyle \underset{OAc}{|}}{C}H*\overset{\displaystyle O}{\underset{\displaystyle \|}{C}}-SC_6H_5$$

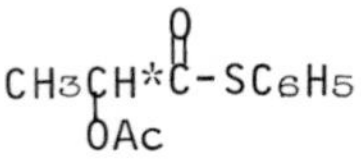

2-(Acetyloxy)propanethioic-1-^{14}C
acid S-phenyl ester

The position of the label was determined by degradation studies;
a mechanism was proposed.

V. Rosnati, F. Sannicolo, and G. Pagani, Gazz. Chim. Ital., 99,
152 (1969); V. Rosnati, F. Sannicolo, and G. Zecchi, Tetrahedron
Lett., 599 (1970).

$$C_6H_5-*\overset{\displaystyle O}{CH-CHCOONa} \xrightarrow[C_6H_5SH]{SOCl_2} C_6H_5-*\overset{\displaystyle O}{CH-CH}\overset{\displaystyle O}{\underset{\displaystyle \|}{C}}-SC_6H_5$$

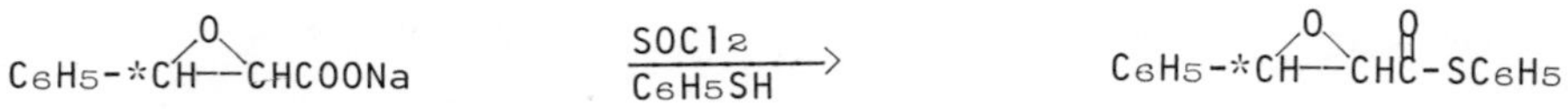

BF3·Et2O
HOCH=*C——C-SC6H5
C6H5 O

α-(Hydroxymethylene)benzene
ethanethioic-α-^{14}C acid

The thiol ester group migrates from position 2 to position 3 during the rearrangement; the position of the label was determined by degradation reactions.

J. Domagala and J. Wemple, Tetrahedron Lett., 1179 (1973).

C6H5
O
C6H5
*C
C
H
COOC2H5
1. HBr, C6H6
2. NaH, THF
3. NaOH
4. ClCOS-C6H5
THF

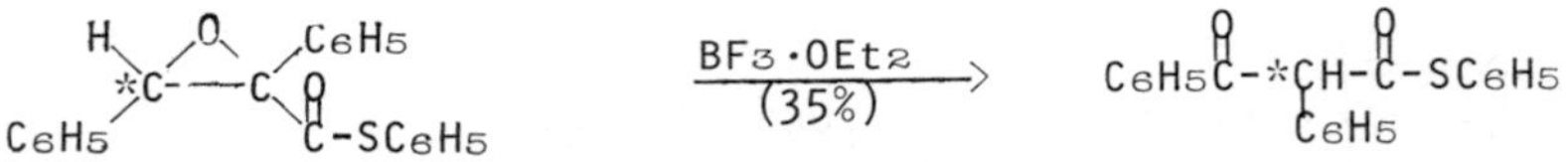
H
O
C6H5
*C
C
C6H5
C-SC6H5
BF3·OEt2
(35%)
C6H5C-*CH-C-SC6H5
C6H5

2,3-Diphenyloxirane-
carbothioic-3-[14]C
acid S-phenyl ester

β-Oxo-α-phenylbenzene-
propane thioic-α-[14]C
acid S-phenyl ester

Results imply that the thiol ester group predominantly migrates with little hydrogen migration (∿2%); other products were obtained also.

R. A. Gorski, D. J. Gagli, and J. Wemple, J. Amer. Chem. Soc., 98, 4588 (1976).

2-6 Polyesters

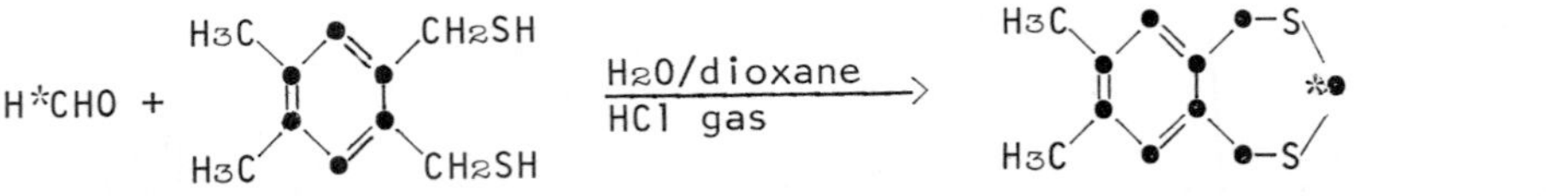
H*CHO +
H3C
CH2SH
H3C
CH2SH
H2O/dioxane
HCl gas
H3C
S
*
H3C
S

Formaldehyde-[14]C

1,5-Dihydro-7,8-dimethyl-
2,4-benzodithiepine-
3-[14]C

1. BuLi, Et_2O (70%)
2. $ClCOOC_2H_5$ (70%)
3. Raney-Ni, EtOH (80%) $\longrightarrow$ $*CH_2(COOC_2H_5)_2$ (35% from $BaCO_3$)

Ethyl malonate
[Propanedioic-2-^{14}C acid diethyl ester]

L. Pichat and J. P. Noel, J. Label. Compound. Radiopharm., 15, 753 (1978).

$*CH_3COOC_2H_5 + C_2H_5OOC\text{-}COOC_2H_5 \xrightarrow[Et_2O]{NaOEt/EtOH}$ $C_2H_5OOC\text{-}CO*CH_2COOC_2H_5$

Acetic-2-^{14}C acid ethyl ester

Ethyl oxaloacetate
[2-Oxobutanedioic-3-^{14}C acid diethyl ester]

D. C. H. Bigg, J. Label. Compound. Radiopharm., 12, 571 (1976).

$*CH_3C(=O)\text{-}*CH_2C(=O)\text{-}OC_2H_5$ + $HO\text{-}*CH_2CH_2SCH_2*CH_2OH$ $\longrightarrow$

3-Oxobutanoic-2,4-^{14}C acid ethyl ester

2,2'-Thiobisethanol-1,1'-^{14}C

$*CH_3C(=O)\text{-}*CH_2C(=O)\text{-}O*CH_2CH_2SCH_2*CH_2O\text{-}C(=O)*CH_2C(=O)\text{-}*CH_3$ (72%) $\xrightarrow{NH_3}$

3-Oxobutanoic-2,4-^{14}C acid thiodi-2,1-ethanediyl-1-^{14}C

$*CH_3\text{-}C(NH_2)=*CHC(=O)\text{-}O*CH_2CH_2SCH_2*CH_2O\text{-}C(=O)\text{-}*CH=C(NH_2)\text{-}*CH_3$

3-Amino-2-butenoic-2,4-^{14}C acid thiodi-2,1-ethanediyl-1-^{14}C ester

K. Figge and H. P. Voss, J. Label. Compounds, 9, 23 (1973).

$CH_3(CH_2)_{13}OTs$ → (1. K*CN, DMSO, Δ; 2. 1M KOH, EtOH; 3. $SOCl_2$; 4. glycerol, pyr/benzene) →

$CH_3(CH_2)_{13}{*}COO-CH_2$
$CH_3(CH_2)_{13}{*}COO-CH$
$CH_3(CH_2)_{13}{*}COO-CH_2$

Pentadecanoic-1-^{14}C acid 1,2,3-propanetriyl ester

W. W. Christie and M. L. Hunter, Biochim. Biophys. Acta, 316, 282 (1973).

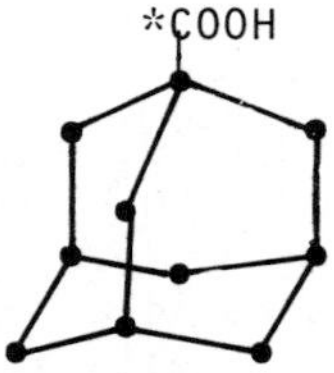
*COOH

1. $SOCl_2$ (quant.)
2. 1,2-isopropylidene-sn-glycerol, pyr, CH_2Cl_2
3. HCl, CH_3OH
4. oleoyl chloride, pyr, CH_2Cl_2

Adamantanecarboxylic acid [Tricyclo[3.3.1.1^{3,7}]dodecane-1-carboxylic acid -(carboxyl-^{14}C)]

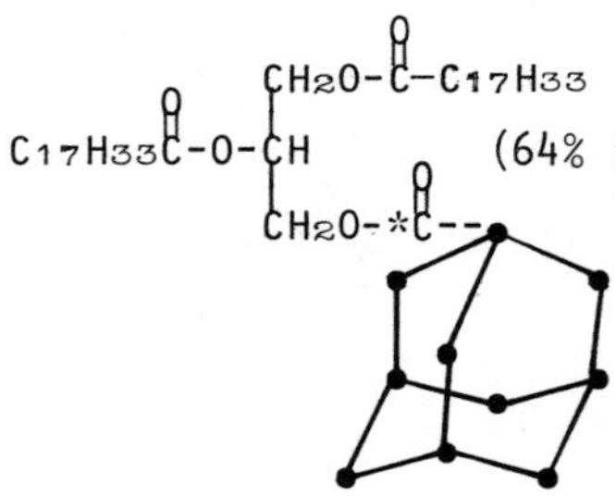
CH2O-C-C17H33
C17H33C-O-CH
CH2O-*C--

(64% from the acid)

2,3-Bis[(1-oxo-9-octadecenyloxy]propyl ester tricyclo[3.3.1.1^{3,7}]dodecane-1-carboxylic acid - (carboxyl-^{14}C)

A. J. Villani and F. R. Pfeiffer, J. Pharm. Sci., 65, 1243 (1976).

2-7 Lactones

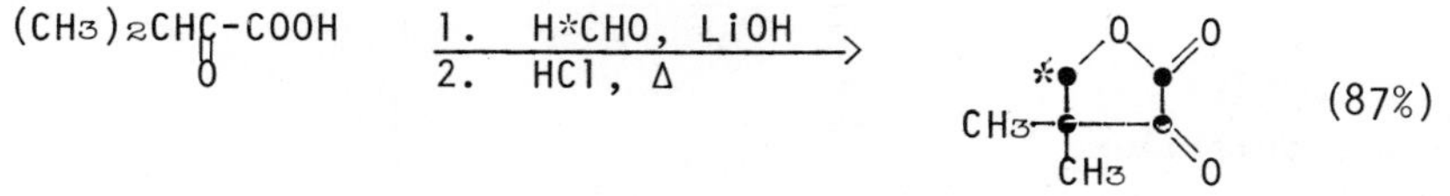
(CH3)2CHC-COOH
O
1. H*CHO, LiOH
2. HCl, Δ
O
O
*
CH3
CH3
O
(87%)

Keto-pantolactone
[Dihydro-4,4-dimethyl-2,3-furandione-5-^{14}C]

1. pH 7
2. NaBH4, pH 8
3. HCl, Δ
O
O
*
CH3
CH3
OH
(83%)

Pantolactone
[Dihydro-3-hydroxy-4,4-dimethyl-2(3H)-furanone-5-^{14}C]

H. L. King, Jr., R. E. Dyar, and D. R. Wilken, J.Biol. Chem., 249, 4689 (1974).

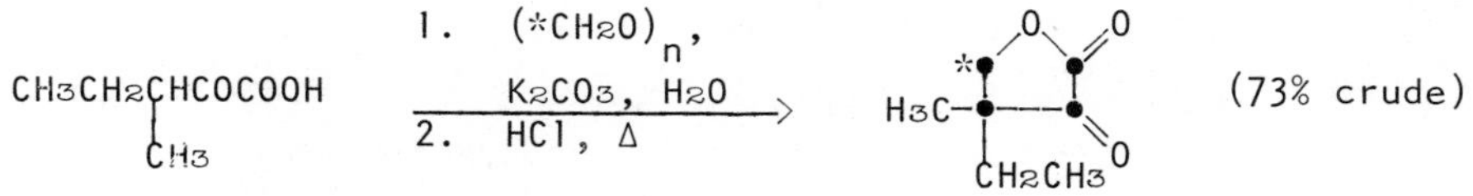
CH3CH2CHCOCOOH
CH3
1. (*CH2O)n,
K2CO3, H2O
2. HCl, Δ
O
O
*
H3C
CH2CH3
O
(73% crude)

4-Ethyldihydro-4-methyl-2,3-furandione-5-^{14}C

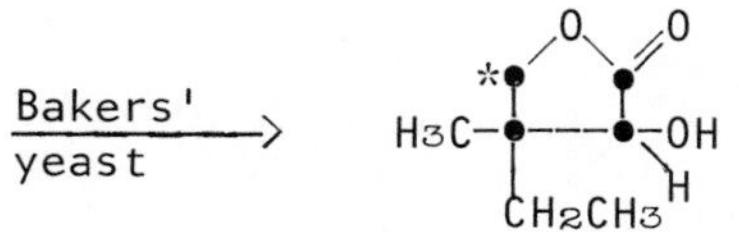
Bakers' yeast
O
O
*
H3C
OH
H
CH2CH3

4-Ethyldihydro-3-hydroxy-4-methyl-2(3H)-furanone-5-^{14}C

E. Draeger and T. Wieland, Ann. Chem., 760, 104 (1972).

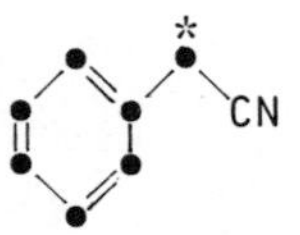

$\xrightarrow[\text{Na, EtOH}]{(COOC_2H_5)_2}$

Benzene acetonitrile-α-^{14}C

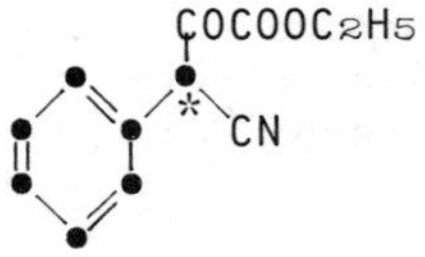

(86%) $\xrightarrow[\text{NaOEt, EtOH}]{C_6H_5CH_2CN}$

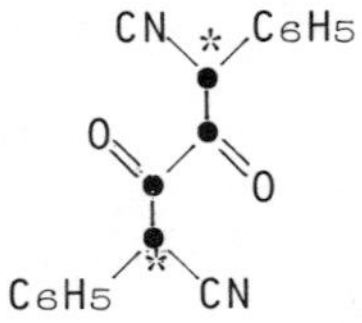

(67%)

1. HI, HOAc, Δ
2. Ac_2O, Δ

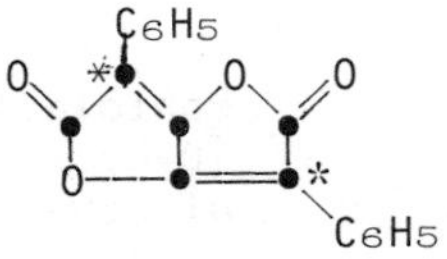

(35%) $\xrightarrow[\Delta]{\text{NaOH}}$

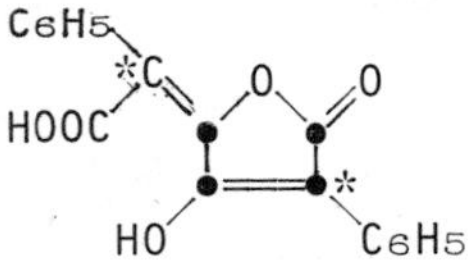

(71%; 14% from benzyl cyanide)

Pulvinic acid
[α-(3-Hydroxy-5-oxo-4-phenyl-2(5H)-furanylidene-4-^{14}C)
benzeneacetic-α-^{14}C]

Similarly:

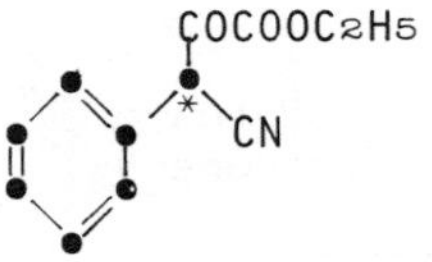

\+

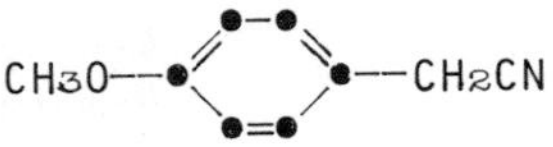

1. NaOEt, EtOH
2. steps as above →

β-Cyano-α-oxobenzene
propanoic-β-^{14}C acid
ethyl ester

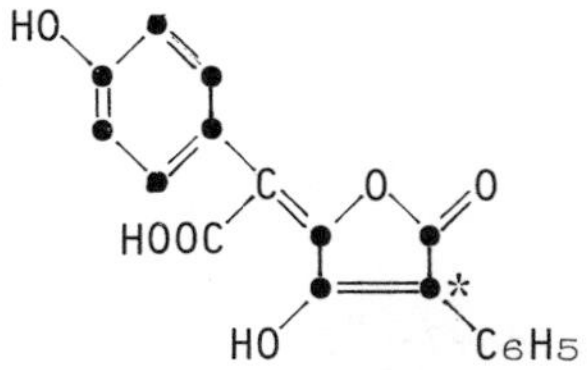

(~3% overall)

+

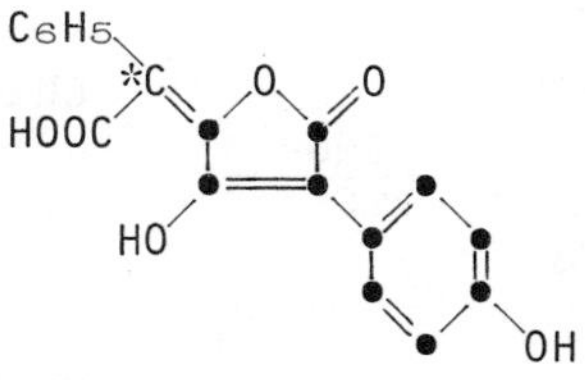

(~7% overall)

4'-Hydroxypulvinic acid
[4-Hydroxy-α-(3-hydroxy-5-oxo-4-phenyl-2(5H)-furanylidene-4-^{14}C) benzeneacetic acid]

4-Hydroxypulvinic acid
[α-[3-Hydroxy-4-(4-hydroxyphenyl)-5-oxo-2(5H)-furanylidene]benzene acetic-α-^{14}C acid

H. E. Noppel, K.-H. Schweer, and F. von Massow, J. Label. Compound. Radiopharm., 12, 79 (1976).

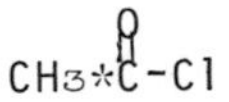

Acetyl-1-^{14}C chloride

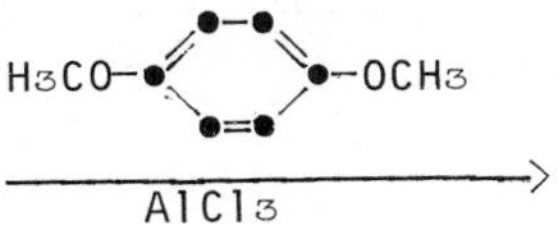

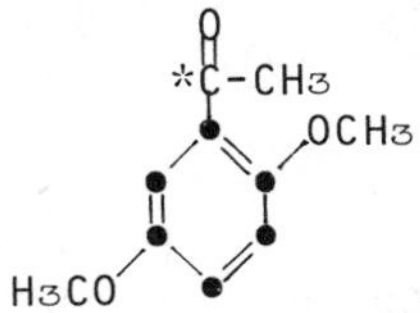

1-(2,5-Dimethoxyphenyl) ethanone-1-^{14}C

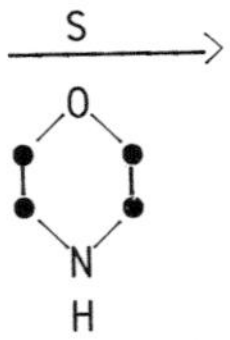

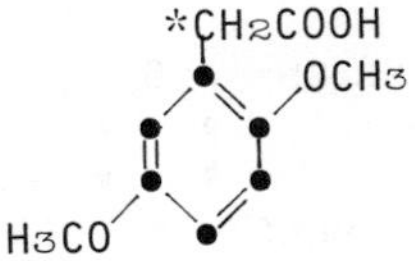

2,5-Dimethoxybenzeneacetic-α^{14}C acid

(48% HBr) →

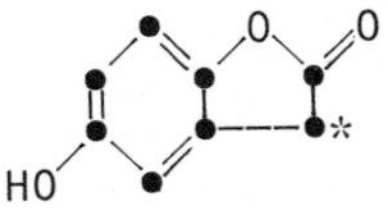

Homogentistic acid lactone
[5-Hydroxy-2(3H)-benzofuranone-3^{14}C]

S. Seltzer, J. Label. Compounds, 9, 643 (1973).

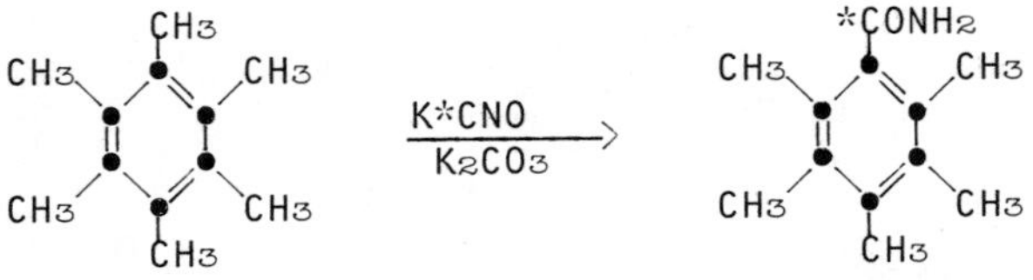
CH3
CH3
CH3
CH3
CH3
CH3
K*CNO
K2CO3
*CONH2
CH3
CH3
CH3
CH3
CH3

Pentamethylbenzamide-7-^{14}C

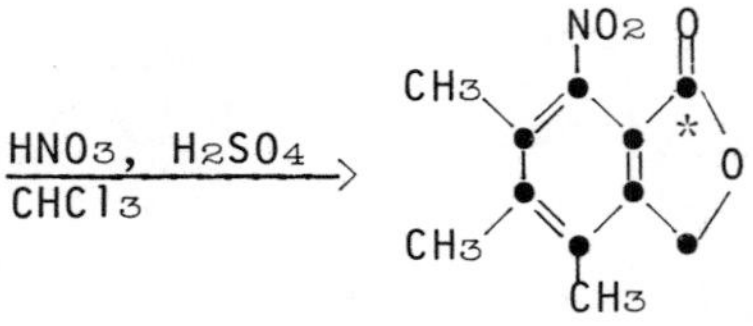
HNO3, H2SO4
CHCl3
NO2
O
CH3
*
O
CH3
CH3

(~28%)

A mechanism was proposed.

4,5,6-Trimethyl-7-nitro-1(3H)-isobenzofuranone-1-^{14}C

I. S. Isaev, L. A. Ostashevskaya, A. A. Morozov, L. M. Besschetnova, and V. A. Koptyug, Zh. Org. Khim., 7, 2321 (1971) [English Translation, pp. 2412-2417].

$C_2H_5OOC\text{-}^*CH_2COOC_2H_5$ → 1. KOH, C_6H_5; 2. CH_3I, DMA; 3. KOH, H_2O/DMSO → $HOOC\text{-}^*CH(CH_3)COOH$ (55%)

Diethylmalonate-2-^{14}C

Methyl malonic acid [2-Methylpropanedioic-2-^{14}C acid]

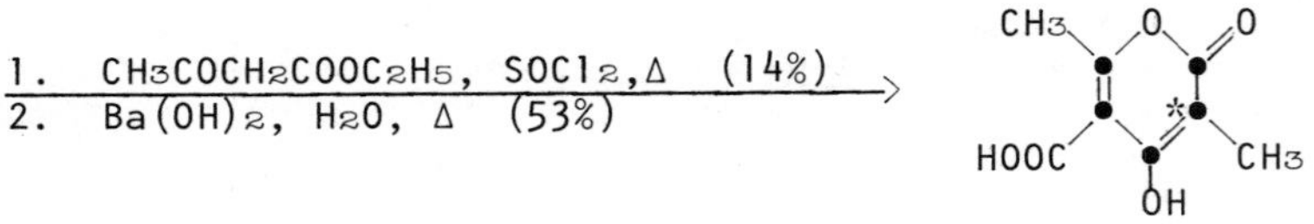
1. CH3COCH2COOC2H5, SOCl2,Δ (14%)
2. Ba(OH)2, H2O, Δ (53%)
CH3
O
O
*
HOOC
CH3
OH

4-Hydroxy-3,6-dimethyl-2-oxo-2H-pyran-5-carboxylic-3-^{14}C acid

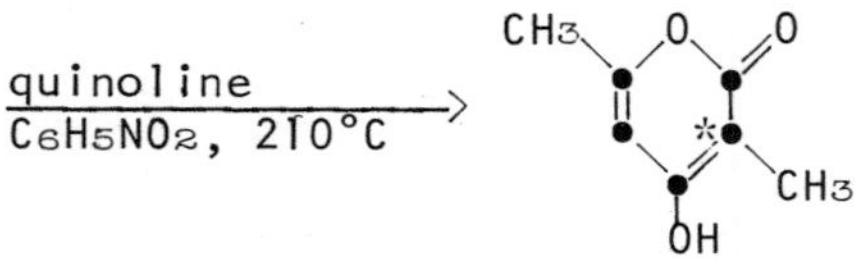
quinoline
C6H5NO2, 210°C
CH3
O
O
*
CH3
OH

(65%)

4-Hydroxy-3,6-dimethyl-2H-pyran-2-one-3-^{14}C

T. E. Acker, P. E. Brenneisen, and S. W. Tanenbaum, J. Amer. Chem. Soc., 88, 834 (1966).

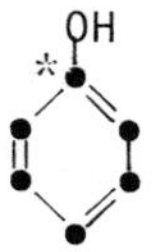

+ $COOH-CH(CH_2)_5CH_3-COOH$ $\xrightarrow{ZnCl_2,\ POCl_3}$

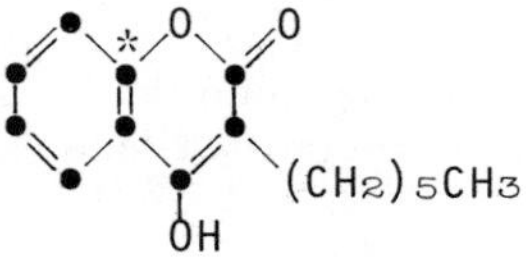

(48%)

Phenol-1-^{14}C

4-Hydroxy-3-hexyl-2H-1-benzopyran-2-one-8a-^{14}C

A. B. Susan, A. Avramescu, and M. Dinescu, J. Label. Compounds, 4, 317 (1968).

$^*CH_2(COOC_6H_5)_2$ $\xrightarrow{AlCl_3}$

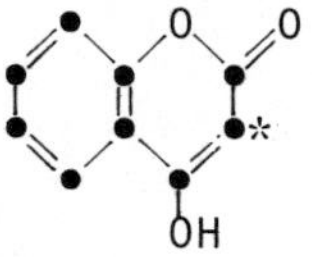

(60%)

Propanedioic-2-^{14}C acid diphenyl ester

4-Hydroxycoumarin
[4-Hydroxy-2H-1-benzopyran-2-one-3-^{14}C]

1. $CH_3COCH{=}CH{-}C_6H_4R$ quinoline, H_2O
2. Na_2CO

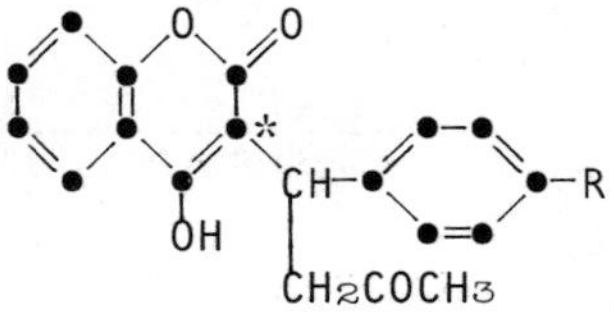

R=H, 3-[1-Phenyl-3-oxobutyl]-4-hydroxy-2H-1-benzopyran-2-one-3-^{14}C (39%)
R=p-NO_2, 3-[1-(4-Nitrophenyl)-3-oxobutyl]-4-hydroxy-2H-1-benzopyran-2-one-3-^{14}C (72%)
R=p-Cl, 3-[1-(4-Chlorophenyl)-3-oxobutyl]-4-hydroxy-2H-1-benzopyran-2-one-3-^{14}C [Coumachlor] (42%)

A. B. Susan, M. Dinescu, and L. Gavat, J. Label. Compounds, 4, 312, (1968).

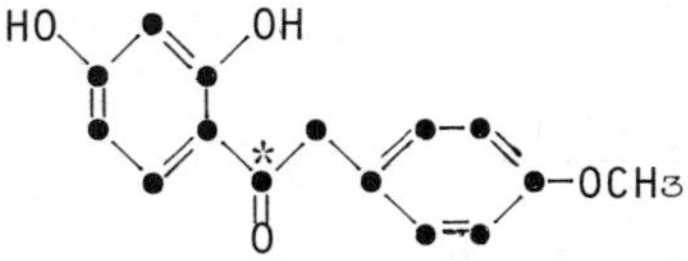

1-(2,4-Dihydroxyphenyl)-
2-(4-methoxyphenyl)ethanone-1-^{14}C

1. $ClCH_2COOC_2H_5$, K_2CO_3, acetone, Δ
2. KOH, CH_3OH, Δ
3. HI, Ac_2O, Δ

→

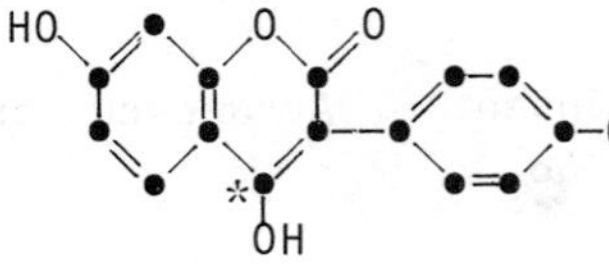

(9%)

3-(4-Hydroxyphenyl)-4,7-dihydroxy-2H-1-benzopyran-2-one-4-^{14}C

T. Inoue and M. Fujita, Chem. Pharm. Bull. (Tokyo), 25, 3226 (1977); P. M. Dewick, W. Barzand, and H. Grisebach, Phytochemistry, 9, 775 (1970); W. Barz, Ch. Adamek, and J. Berlin, Phytochemistry, 9, 1735 (1970).

$CH_3{*}COCH_2COOC_2H_5$

3-Oxobutanoic-3-^{14}C acid ethyl ester

1. SO_2Cl_2
2. resorcinol, $POCl_3$, Δ

→

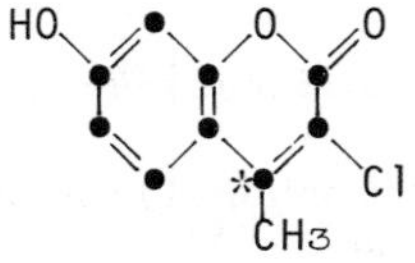

(53% overall)

3-Chloro-4-methyl-7-hydroxycoumarin-4-^{14}C

J. P. H. Müller, A. Attar, H.-J. Kurth, and D. Bieniek, J. Label. Compound. Radiopharm., 15, 261 (1978).

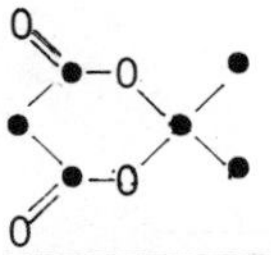

$(CH_3)_2CH{*}CHO$ → (piperidine, acetic acid, $CHCl_3$ (50%))

2-Methylpropanal-1-^{14}C

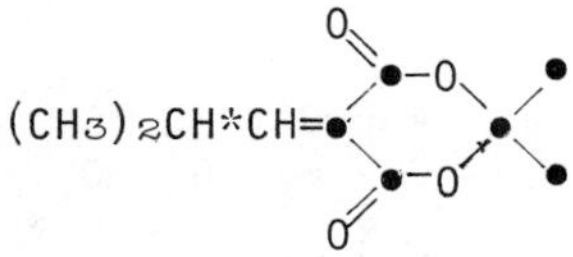

(50%; 5% from $Ba{*}CO_3$)

2,2-Dimethyl-5-(2-methylpropylidene-1-^{14}C)-1,3-dioxane-4,6-dione

→ ($C_6H_5CHN_2$, $CHCl_3$)

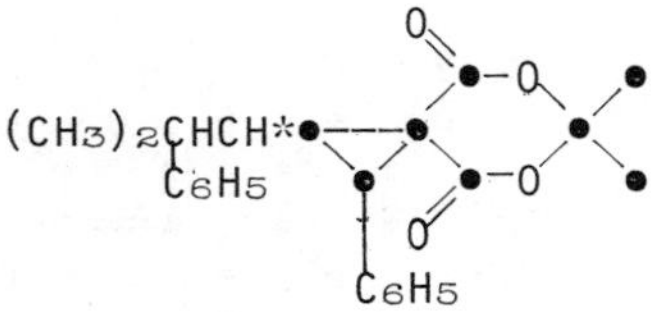

(28%)

2-(1'-Phenylisobutyl)-3-phenylcyclopropane-1,1-dicarboxylic-2-^{14}C acid isopropylidene acylal

Degradation of the product showed that the insertion reaction occurs without scrambling and that >99% of the label is in position 2.

F. P. Schmook and O. E. Polansky, Monatsh. Chem., 100, 1640 (1969).

2-8 Anhydrides

$CH_2{=}C(COOH)CH_2{-}{*}COOH$ (37% from $Na{*}CN$) → (CH_3COCl, Δ)

Itaconic acid
[Methylenebutanedioic-4-^{14}C acid]

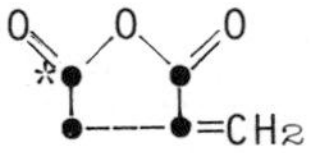

Itaconic anhydride
[Dihydro-3-methylene-2,5-furandione-5-^{14}C]

H. Cousse, B. Bonnaud, L. Pichat, and F. Aubert, J. Label. Compound. Radiopharm., 12, 491 (1976).

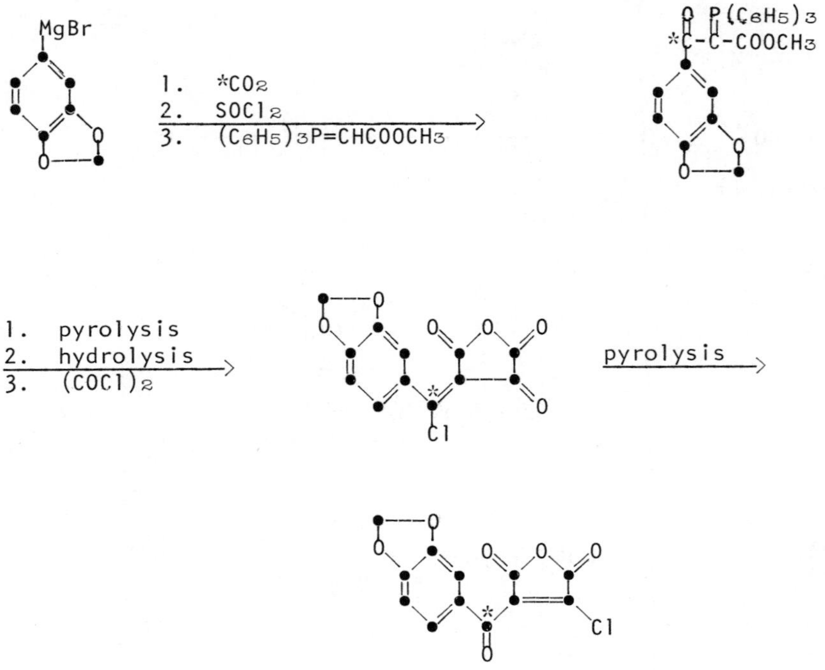
MgBr
1. *CO2
2. SOCl2
3. (C6H5)3P=CHCOOCH3
O P(C6H5)3
*C-C-COOCH3
1. pyrolysis
2. hydrolysis
3. (COCl)2
Cl
pyrolysis
Cl

3-[(1,3-Benzodioxol-(5-ylcarbonyl-^{14}C)]-4-chloro-2,5-furandione

The integrity of the carbon atom attached to the aromatic ring was confirmed by degradation reactions.

L. Crombie and D. P. Reynolds, J. Chem. Soc., Chem. Commun., 256 (1973); see also J. Chem. Soc., Perkin Trans. I, 146 (1977).

$(C_2H_5O)_2P(O)CH_2COOC_2H_5$ → (1. base; 2. $*CH_3I$) → $(C_2H_5O)_2P(O)CH(*CH_3)COOC_2H_5$

→ (1. NaH, DME; 2. $CH_3CH_2CH=CHCOCOOC_2H_5$) → $CH_3CH_2CH=CH-C(COOC_2H_5)=C(*CH_3)-COOC_2H_5$ → (NaOH / EtOH)

2-(1-Butenyl)-3-(methyl-^{14}C)-2-butenedioic acid diethyl ester

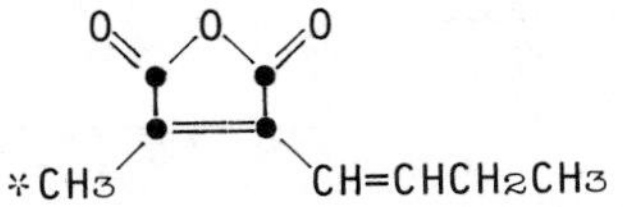
O
O
O
*CH3
CH=CHCH2CH3

3-(1-Butenyl)-4-(methyl-^{14}C)-2,5-furandione

R. K. Huff, C. E. Moppett, and J. K. Sutherland, J. Chem. Soc. Perkin Trans. I, 2584 (1972).

Cl
Cl
Cl
Cl
Cl
Cl
+
O
O
O
*
*
100°C, 14 hr
toluene

Maleic anhydride
[2,5-Furandione-3,4-^{14}C]

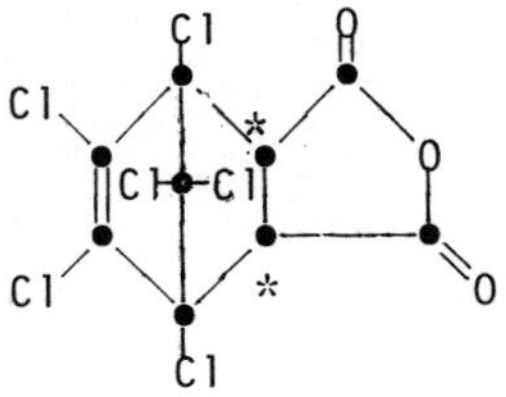
Cl
Cl
Cl
Cl-Cl
Cl
O
O
O
*
*

(3aα,4α,7α,7aα,)-4,5,6,7,8,8-Hexachloro-3a,4,7,7a-tetrahydro-4,7-methanoisobenzofuran-1,3-dione-3a,7a-^{14}C

K. L. Huhtanen and H. W. Dorough, J. Label. Compound.Radiopharm., 14, 321 (1978).

2-9 Acid Halides

$*CHCl{=}*CCl_2$ —(O_2, hν / C_6H_5COOH, Et_3N)→ $*CHCl_2*COCl$ (60%)

Trichloroethene-1,2-^{14}C → Dichloroacetyl-1,2-^{14}C chloride

W. B. Burton and T. F. Sullivan, *J. Agr. Food Chem.*, **20**, 1180, (1972).

C_2H_5MgI —(1. $*CO_2$; 2. PBr_3)→ $CH_3CHBr*COBr$

2-Bromopropanoyl-1-^{14}C bromide

B. Duhm, W. Maul, H. Medenwald, K. Patzchke, and L. A. Wegner, *Arzneim.-Forsch.-(Drug Res.)*, **24**, 632 (1974); see also W. Maul, *J. Label. Compound. Radiopharm.*, **12**, 181 (1976).

2-10 Amides

$H*COONa$ —($(CH_3)_2NH{\cdot}HCl$)→ $H*CON(CH_3)_2$ (33%)

N,N-Dimethylformamide-^{14}C

—(1. $(CH_3O)_2SO_2$; 2. CH_3ONa/CH_3OH)→ $H*C(OCH_3)_2N(CH_3)_2$ (70%)

1,1-Dimethoxy-N,N-Dimethylmethanamine-1-^{14}C

K. K. Chan, J. A. Staroscik, and W. Sadée, *J. Med. Chem.*, **20**, 598 (1977).

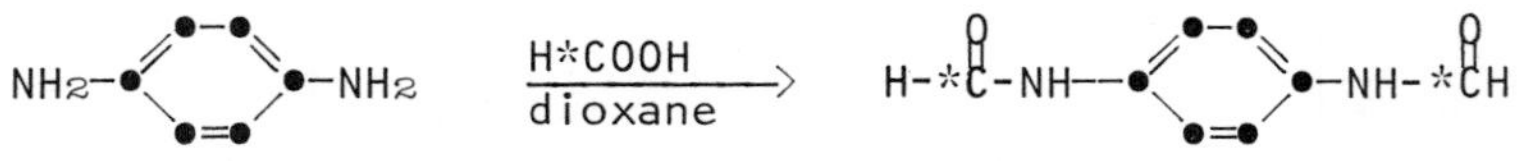

NH2
NH2
H*COOH
dioxane
H-*C-NH
NH-*CH

(74%)

N,N'-1,4-Phenylenebis-[formamide-^{14}C]

Similarly, N,N'-diformyl-^{14}C-N,N'-dimethyl-p-phenylenediamine was prepared in 94% yield.

M. Sekiya, S. Takayama, J. Suzuki, and K. Suzuki, Chem. Pharm. Bull., 20, 2669 (1972).

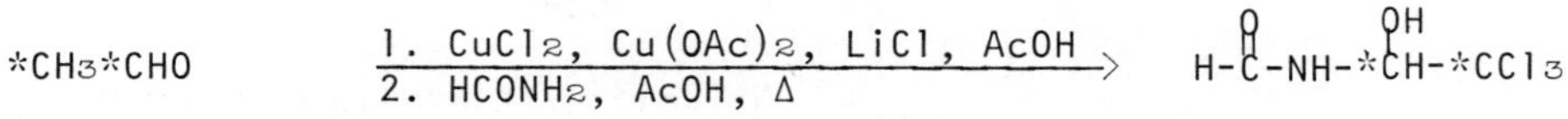
*CH3*CHO
1. CuCl2, Cu(OAc)2, LiCl, AcOH
2. HCONH2, AcOH, Δ
H-C-NH-*CH-*CCl3
O
OH

Acetaldehyde-1,2-^{14}C

N-(2,2,2-Trichloro-1-hydroxyethyl-1,2-^{14}C)-formamide

M. Stiasni and W. Ost, J. Label. Compounds, 9, 133, (1973).

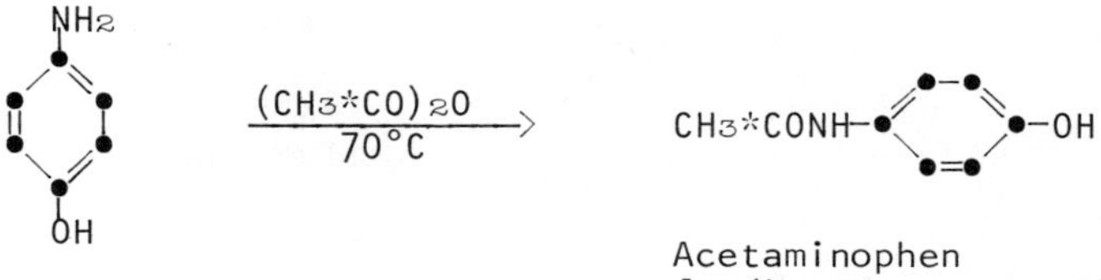
NH2
OH
(CH3*CO)2O
70°C
CH3*CONH
OH

(51%)

Acetaminophen
[N-(4-Hydroxyphenyl)acetamide-1-^{14}C]

S. Stavchansky and P. Wu, J. Label. Compound. Radiopharm., 14, 337 (1978).

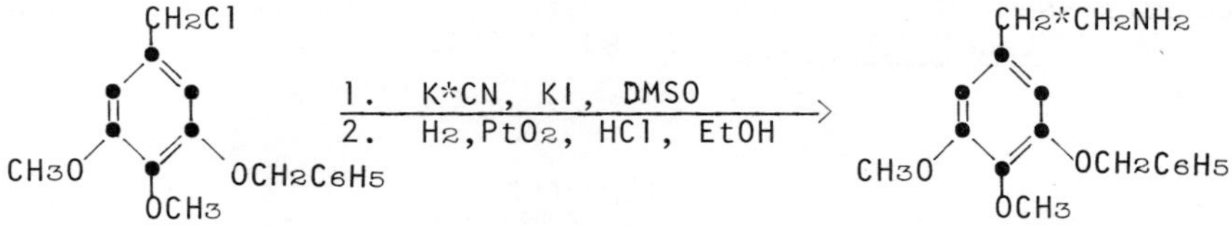
CH2Cl
CH3O
OCH2C6H5
OCH3
1. K*CN, KI, DMSO
2. H2,PtO2, HCl, EtOH
CH2*CH2NH2
CH3O
OCH2C6H5
OCH3

(40%)

4,5-Dimethoxy-3-(phenylmethoxy) benzene-ethanamine-α-^{14}C

1. $CH_3{}^*COONa$, H_2O (~70%)
2. H_2, PdO, EtOH (~51%)
→

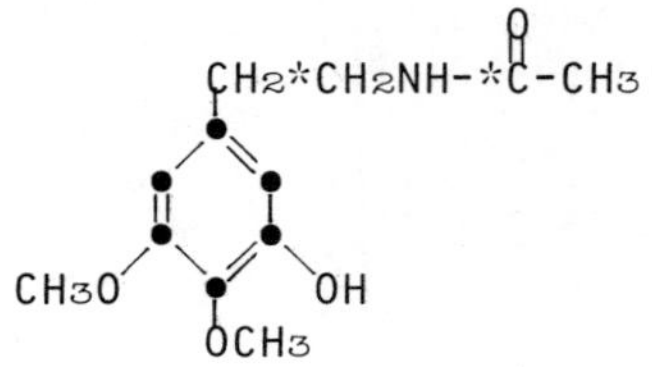
CH2*CH2NH-*C-CH3
O
CH3O
OH
OCH3

N-[2-(3-Hydroxy-4,5-dimethoxyphenyl)ethyl-1-^{14}C]acetamide-1-^{14}C

G. V. Kapadia, G. S. Rao, E. Leete, M. B. E. Fayez, Y. N. Vaishnav, and H. M. Fales, J. Amer. Chem. Soc., 92, 6943 (1970).

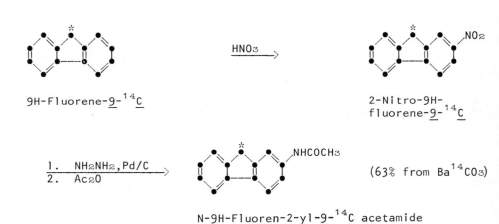

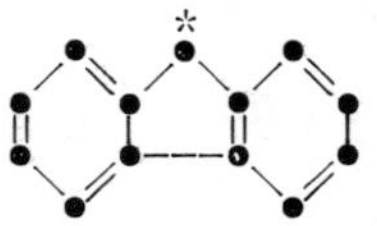

9H-Fluorene-9-^{14}C

HNO_3 →

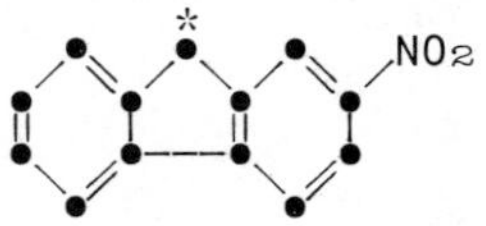
NO2

2-Nitro-9H-fluorene-9-^{14}C

1. NH_2NH_2, Pd/C
2. Ac_2O
→

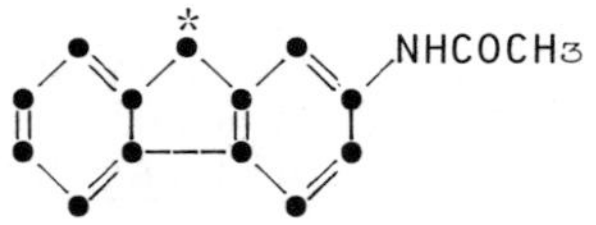
NHCOCH3

(63% from $Ba^{14}CO_3$)

N-9H-Fluoren-2-yl-9-^{14}C acetamide

Nguyen-Hoang-Nam, H. Hoellinger, M. Herbert, Nguyen-Dat-Xuong, and L. Pichat, J. Label. Compounds, 6, 99 (1970).

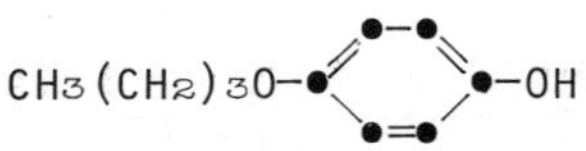
CH3(CH2)3O
OH

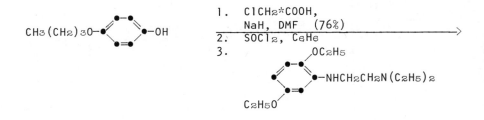

1. $ClCH_2{}^*COOH$, NaH, DMF (76%)
2. $SOCl_2$, C_6H_6
3.

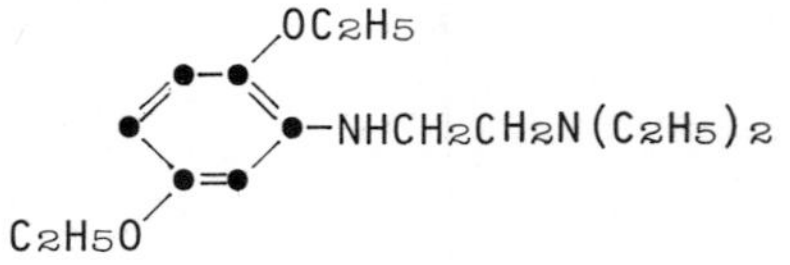
OC2H5
NHCH2CH2N(C2H5)2
C2H5O

→

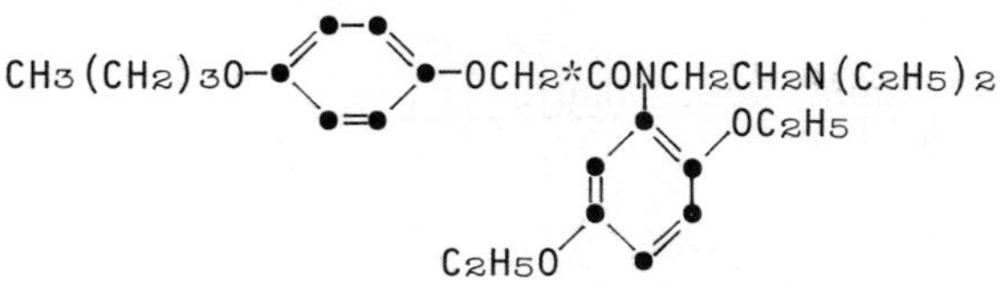

(89%; last two steps)

Fenoxedil
[2-(4-Butoxyphenoxy)-N-(2,5-diethoxyphenyl)-N-[2-(diethylamino)ethyl]acetamide-1-^{14}C]

J. P. Noel, M. Herbert, A. Benakis, and L. Pichat, J. Label. Compound. Radiopharm., 15, 747 (1978).

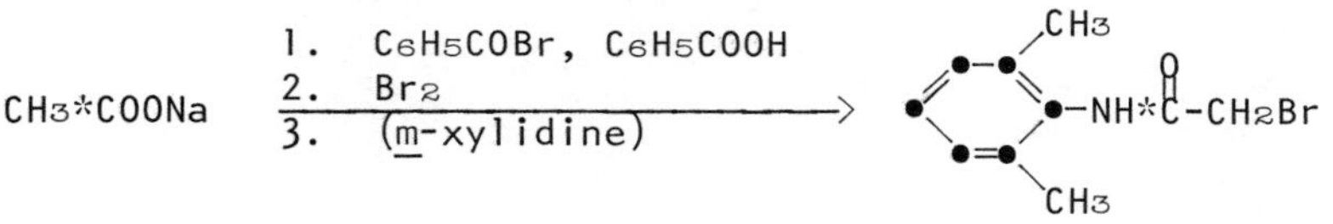

(31%)

2-Bromo-N-(2,6-dimethylphenyl)acetamide-1-^{14}C

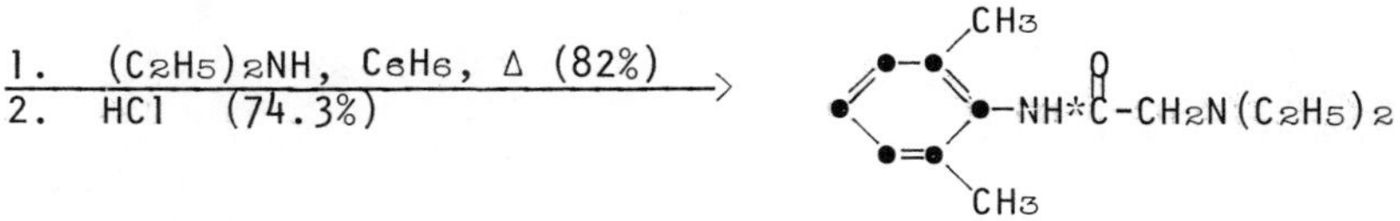

Lidocaine
[2-(Diethylamino)-N-(2,6-dimethylphenyl)acetamide-1-^{14}C]

I. Mezö and I. Teplán, J. Label. Compounds, 8, 359 (1972).

$CH_3{*}CN + Ac_2O \xrightarrow[PtO_2]{H_2} CH_3CONH{*}CH_2CH_3$

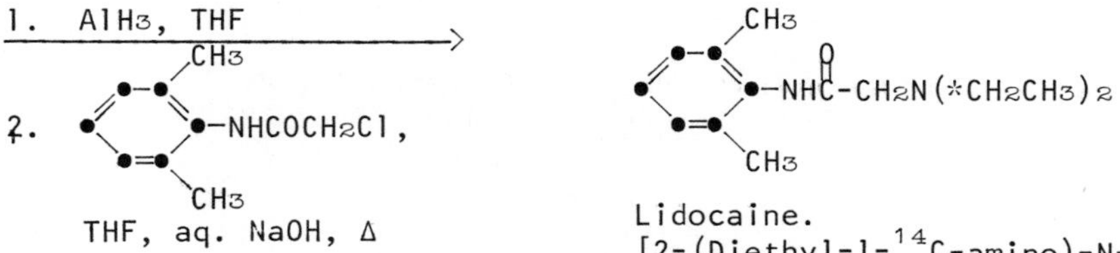

Lidocaine.
[2-(Diethyl-1-^{14}C-amino)-N-(2,6-dimethyl phenyl)acetamide]

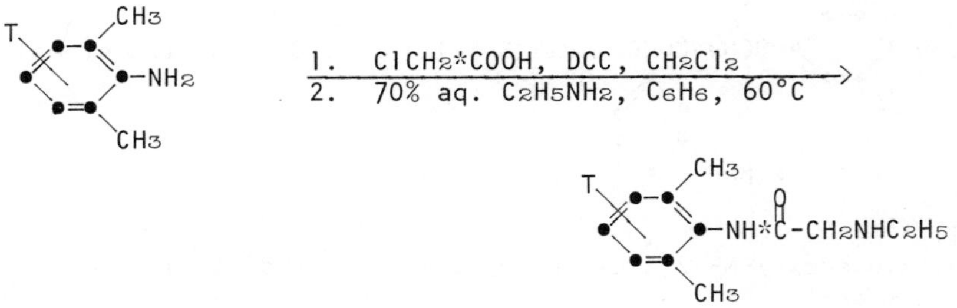
T
CH3
NH2
CH3
1. ClCH2*COOH, DCC, CH2Cl2
2. 70% aq. C2H5NH2, C6H6, 60°C
T
CH3
NH*C-CH2NHC2H5
O
CH3

2-(Ethylamino)-N-(2,6-dimethylphenyl)acetamide-1-^{14}C(ring)-t [metabolite of lidocaine]

S. D. Nelson, G. D. Breck, and W. F. Trager, J. Med. Chem., 16, 1106 (1973).

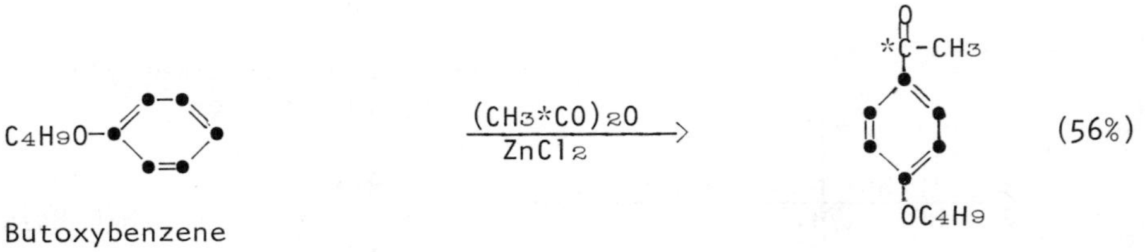
C4H9O
(CH3*CO)2O
ZnCl2
O
*C-CH3
OC4H9
(56%)

Butoxybenzene

1-(4-Butoxyphenyl)ethanone-1-^{14}C

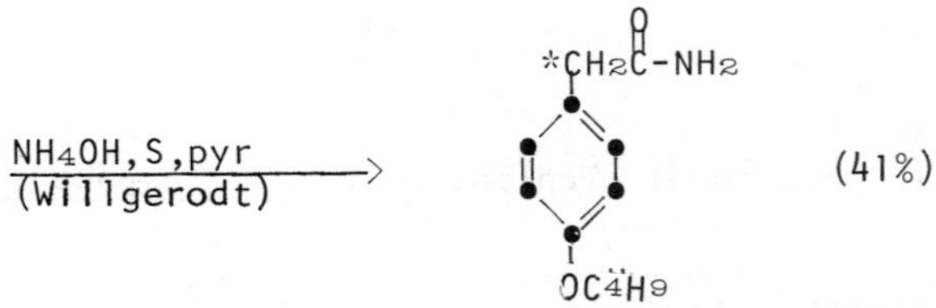
NH4OH,S,pyr
(Willgerodt)
O
*CH2C-NH2
OC4H9
(41%)

4-Butoxybenzeneacetamide-2-^{14}C

C. Gillet, J. Thiriaux, N. P. Buu-Hoi, G. Lambelin, R. Roncucci, and M. J. Simon, J. Label. Compounds, 2, 143 (1966).

$CH_3CHOH{*}COOH$ $\xrightarrow[\text{2. } CH_3CHOHCH_2NH_2,\ CH_3OH,\ \Delta]{\text{1. } CH_2N_2,\ Et_2O}$

dl-Lactic acid
[2-Hydroxypropanoic-
1-^{14}C acid]

$CH_3CHOH{*}\overset{O}{\overset{\|}{C}}-NHCH_2CHOHCH_3$

2-Hydroxy-N-(2-hydroxy-
propyl)propanamide-
1-^{14}C

R. Kupper, D. Nagel, R. Gingell, and G. Brunk, J. Label. Compound. Radiopharm., 15, 175 (1978).

$CH_3{*}\overset{O}{\overset{\|}{C}}-\underset{\underset{\oplus\ \ominus}{N=N}}{\underset{\|}{C}}-\overset{O}{\overset{\|}{C}}-N(C_6H_5)_2$ $\xrightarrow[\text{2. } CH_3COOH,\ EtOH,\ \Delta\ (87\%)]{\text{1. } P(C_6H_5)_3,\ \text{ether}\ (95\%)}$

$CH_3{*}\overset{O}{\overset{\|}{C}}-\underset{N-NH_2}{\underset{\|}{C}}-\overset{O}{\overset{\|}{C}}-N(C_6H_5)_2$

$\xrightarrow[THF]{HCl,\ NaNO_2}$ $CH_3{*}\overset{O}{\overset{\|}{C}}-\overset{O}{\overset{\|}{C}}-\overset{O}{\overset{\|}{C}}-N(C_6H_5)_2$ (71%) $\xrightarrow{NaOH}$

$CH_3{*}CHOH\overset{O}{\overset{\|}{C}}-N(C_6H_5)_2 + CO_2$ (66%)

2-Hydroxy-N,N-diphenyl
propanamide-2-^{14}C

The benzilic acid rearrangement proceeds with migration of the carboxamide group and retention of the labeled carbon.

H. Dahn and S. Karoui, Helv. Chim. Acta, 52, 2491 (1969).

$({*}CH_3)_2NH$ + 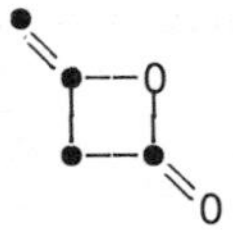 $\xrightarrow{KOH}$ $CH_3COCH_2CON({*}CH_3)_2$ (76-96%)

N-Methylmeth-
anamine-^{14}C

N,N-(Dimethyl-^{14}C)-3-oxo-
butanamide

W. B. Burton, J. Label. Compounds, 7, 111 (1971).

*CN-$(CH_2)_nCOOC_2H_5$ $\xrightarrow[\text{2. } \Delta]{\text{1. HCl, EtOH}}$

n=1; (Cyano-^{14}C)acetic acid ethyl ester
n=2; 3-(Cyano-^{14}C)propanoic acid ethyl ester
n=3; 4-(Cyano-^{14}C)butanoic acid ethyl ester

$H_2N{*}C(=O)-(CH_2)_nCOOC_2H_5$

n=1; (Aminocarbonyl-^{14}C)acetic acid ethyl ester (62%)
n=2; 3-(Aminocarbonyl-^{14}C)propanoic acid ethyl ester (71%)
n=3; 4-(Aminocarbonyl-^{14}C)butanoic acid ethyl ester (46%)

V. Tolman, J. Cabak, and J. Benes, J. Label. Compounds, 10, 39 (1974).

*COOH
OH
*CONH2
O(CH2)5CH3

(67%)

2-Hydroxybenzoic-7-^{14}C acid → 2-Hexyloxybenzamide-7-[14]C

T. Uematsu, Y. Kanaiwa, and A. Hamada, J. Pharm. Soc. Jap., 95, 411 (1975).

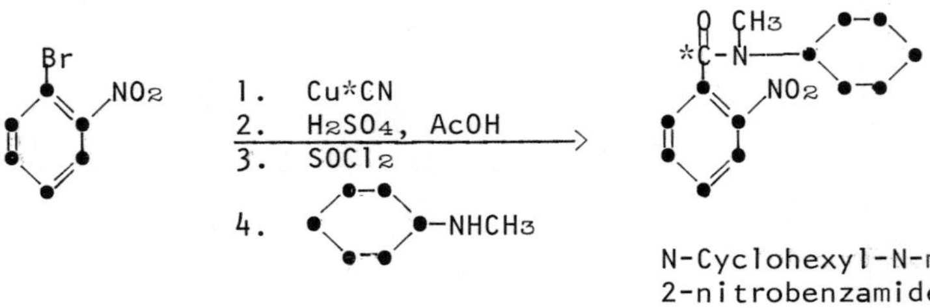
Br
NO2
1. Cu*CN
2. H2SO4, AcOH
3. SOCl2
4.
NHCH3
O
CH3
*C-N
NO2

N-Cyclohexyl-N-methyl-2-nitrobenzamide-7-[14]C

R. Jauch and R. Hankwitz, Arzneim.-Forsch.-(Drug Res.), 25, 1954 (1975).

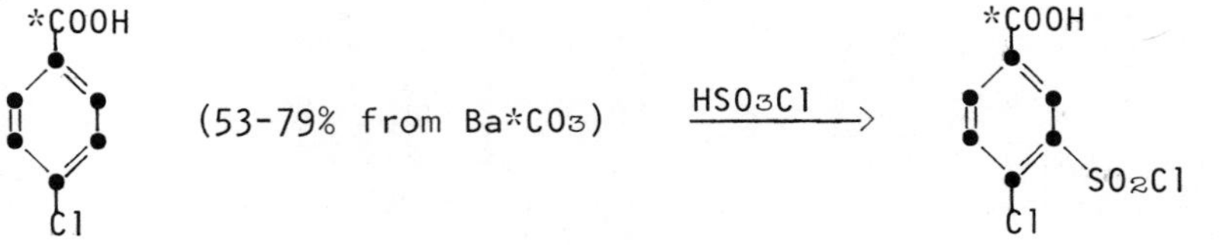

4-Chloro benzoic-7-^{14}C acid

4-Chloro-3-(chlorosulfonyl) benzoic-7-^{14}C acid

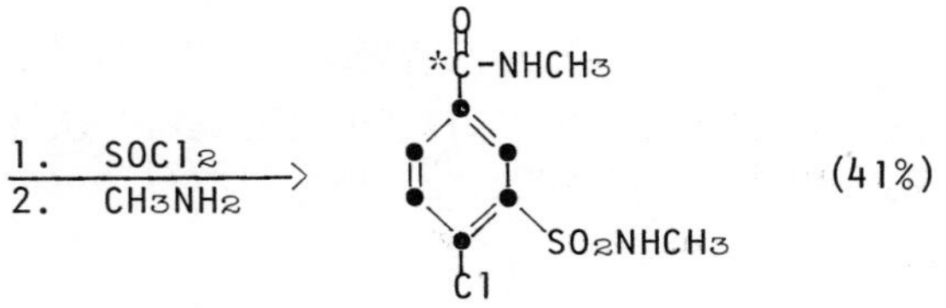

4-Chloro-N-methyl-3-[(methylamino)sulfonyl]-benzamide-7-^{14}C

C. E. Blackburn, M. L. Hoefle, S. F. Chang, G. W. Gwynn, and R. E. Ober, J. Label. Compounds, 2, 402 (1966).

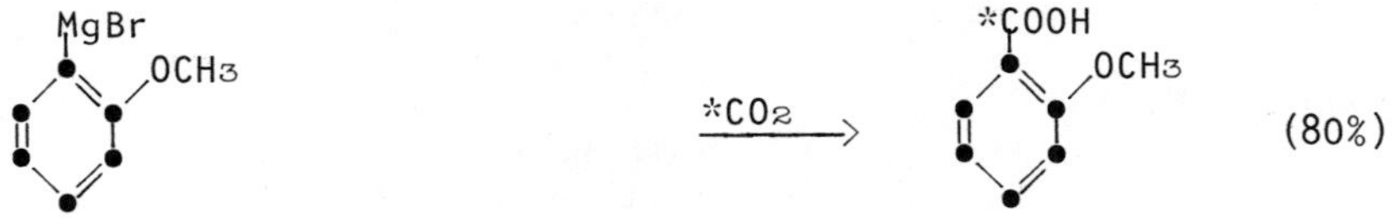

o-Methoxybenzoic acid-7-^{14}C

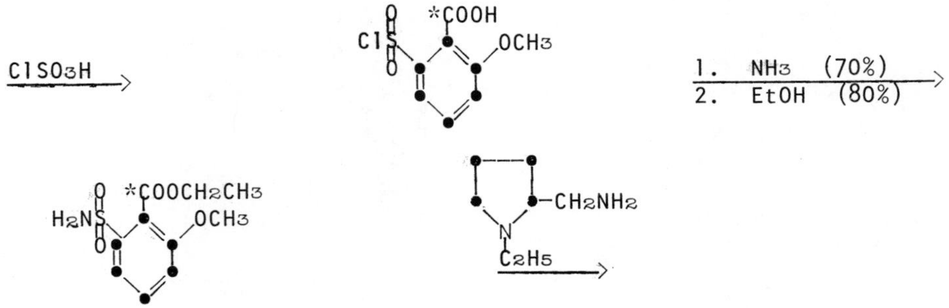

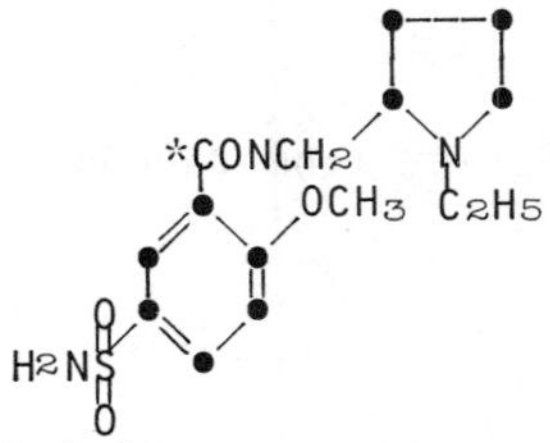
*CONCH2
N
OCH3 C2H5
H2NS
O
O

(73%)

Sulpiride
[5-(Aminosulfonyl)-N-[(l-ethyl-2-pyrrolidinyl)methyl]-2-methoxy-benzamide-7-^{14}C]

J. P. Noël, A. Benakis, M. Herbert, L. Pichat, and M. Thominet, J. Label. Compounds, 8, 665 (1972).

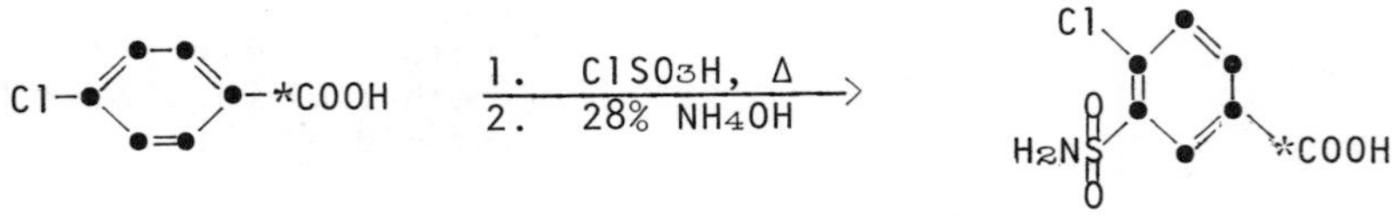
Cl
*COOH
1. ClSO3H, Δ
2. 28% NH4OH
Cl
H2NS
O
O
*COOH

(53%)

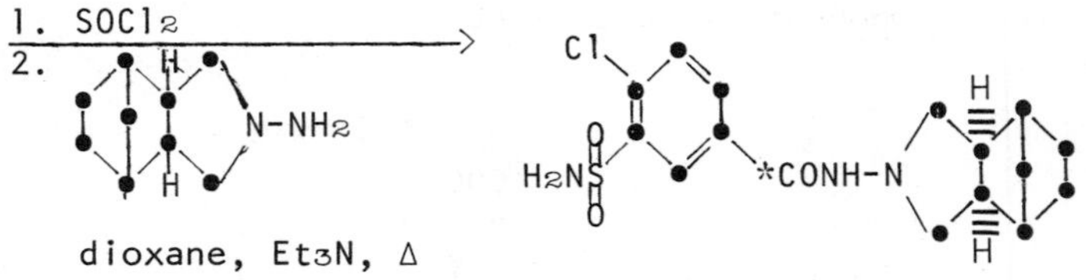
1. SOCl2
2.
H
H
N-NH2
dioxane, Et3N, Δ
Cl
H2NS
O
O
*CONH-N
H
H

(14% overall)

(3aα,7β,7aα)-3-(Aminosulfonyl)-4-chloro-N-(octahydro-4,7-methano-2H-isoindol-2-yl) benzamide-7-^{14}C

T. Nakamura, S. Hamano, and T. Horie, J. Label. Compound. Radiopharm., 14, 191 (1978).

*CH2CH2NH2•HCl
Cl
O
C-N
N
OCH3
(97%)

Benzeneethanamine-β-^{14}C hydrochloride

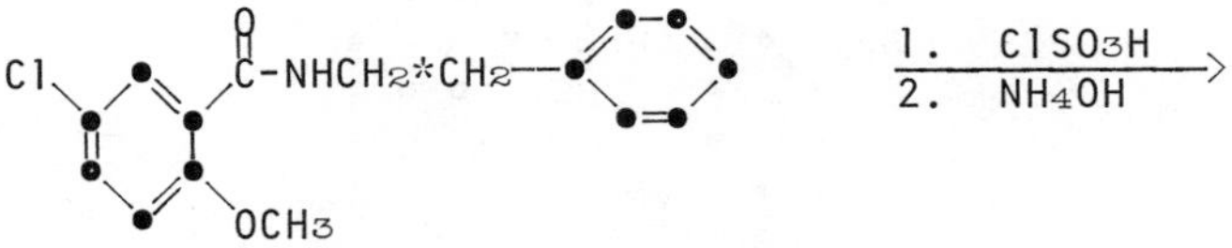
Cl
O
C-NHCH2*CH2
OCH3
1. ClSO3H
2. NH4OH

5-Chloro-2-methoxy-
N-(2-phenylethyl-2-^{14}C)
benzamide

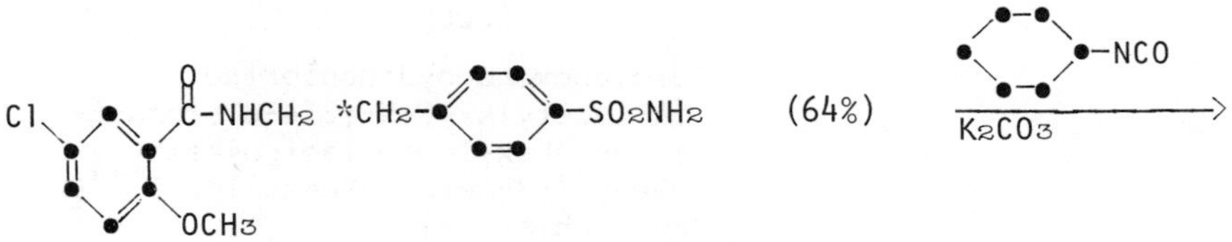
Cl
O
C-NHCH2 *CH2
SO2NH2
OCH3
(64%)
NCO
K2CO3

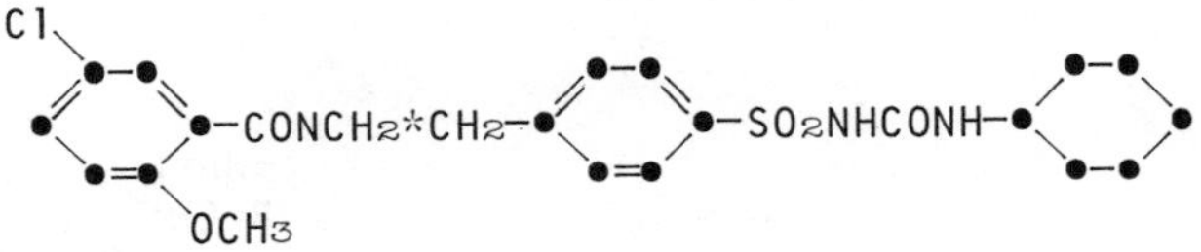
Cl
CONCH2*CH2
SO2NHCONH
OCH3

(60%; 11% overall)

Glyburide
[5-Chloro-N-[2-[4-[[[(cyclohexylamino)carbonyl]amino]sulfonyl]
phenyl]ethyl-2-^{14}C]-2-methoxybenzamide]

R. S. P. Hsi, J. Label. Compound. Radiopharm., 9, 91 (1973).

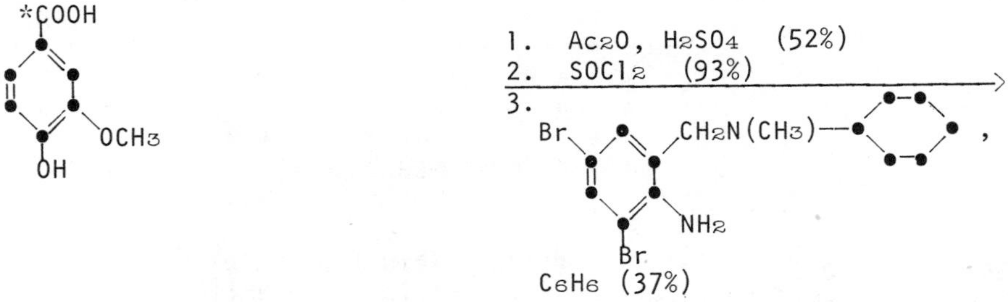
*COOH
OCH3
OH
1. Ac2O, H2SO4 (52%)
2. SOCl2 (93%)
3.
Br
CH2N(CH3)
NH2
Br
C6H6 (37%)

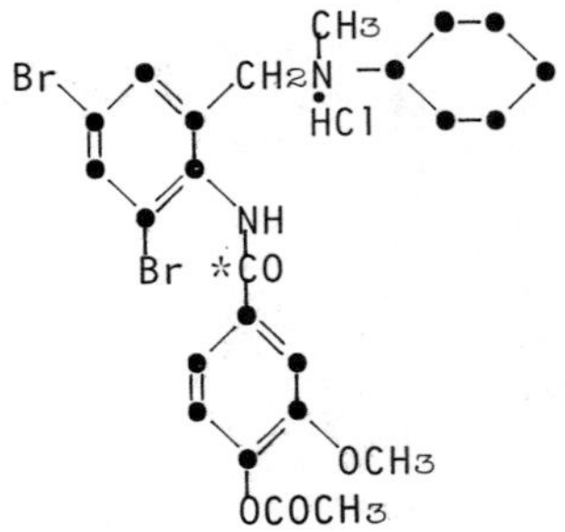
Br
CH3
CH2N
HCl
NH
Br
*CO
OCH3
OCOCH3

(26% overall)

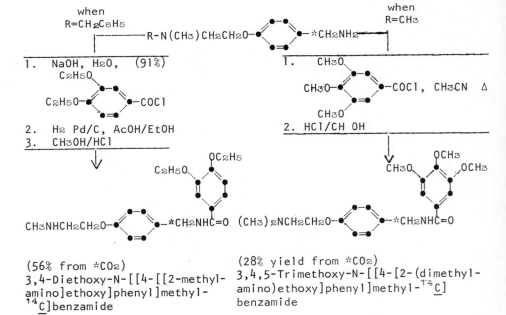

Brovanexine hydrochloride
[4-(Acetyloxy)-N-[2,4-dibromo-6-[(cyclohexylmethylamino)methyl]phenyl]-3-methoxybenzamide-7-^{14}C hydrochloride]

V. Rimbau, J. Label. Compound. Radiopharm., 14, 313 (1978).

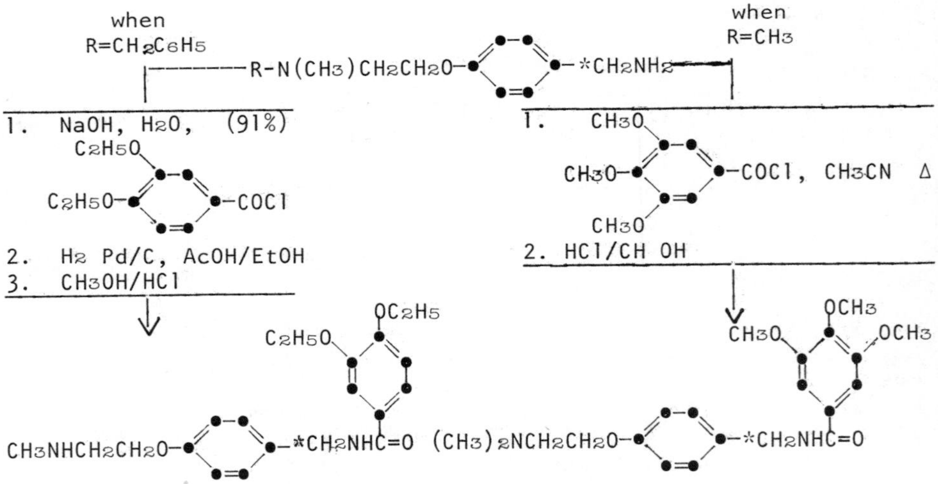
when
R=CH2C6H5
R-N(CH3)CH2CH2O-
-*CH2NH2
when
R=CH3
1. NaOH, H2O, (91%)
C2H5O
C2H5O-
-COCl
2. H2 Pd/C, AcOH/EtOH
3. CH3OH/HCl
1. CH3O
CH3O-
-COCl, CH3CN Δ
CH3O
2. HCl/CH OH
OC2H5
C2H5O
CH3NHCH2CH2O-
-*CH2NHC=O
OCH3
CH3O
OCH3
(CH3)2NCH2CH2O-
-*CH2NHC=O

(56% from *CO_2)
3,4-Diethoxy-N-[[4-[[2-methylamino]ethoxy]phenyl]methyl-^{14}C]benzamide

(28% yield from *CO_2)
3,4,5-Trimethoxy-N-[[4-[2-(dimethylamino)ethoxy]phenyl]methyl-^{14}C]benzamide

R. L. Wineholt, J. D. Johnson, P. J. Heck, and H. H. Kaegi, J. Label. Compounds, 6, 53 (1970).

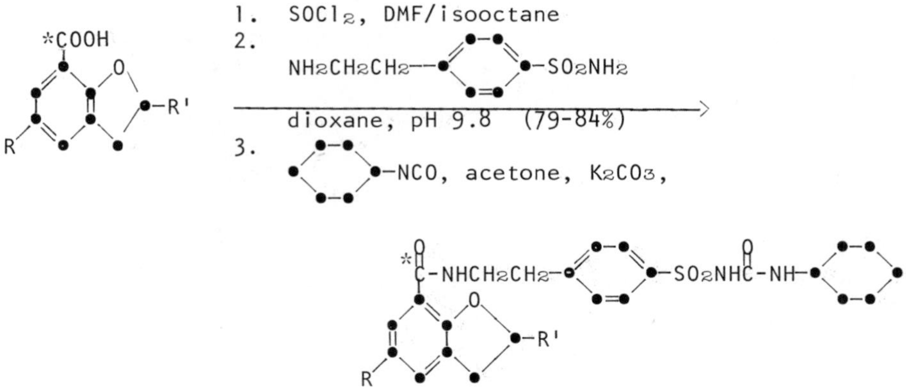

R=R'=H; N-[2-[4-[[[(Cyclohexylamino)carbonyl]amino]sulfonyl]phenyl]ethyl]-2,3-dihydro-7-benzofurancarboxamide-^{14}C (45% overall yield)

R=OCH_3, R'=CH_3; N-[2-[4-[[[(Cyclohexylamino)carbonyl]amino]sulfonyl]phenyl]ethyl]-2,3-dihydro-5-methoxy-2-methyl-7-benzofurancarboxamide-^{14}C (34% overall yield)

L. F. Elsom, D. R. Hawkins, H. Christensen, and F. C. Gronvold, J. Label. Compound. Radiopharm., 13, 75 (1977).

2-11 Thioamides

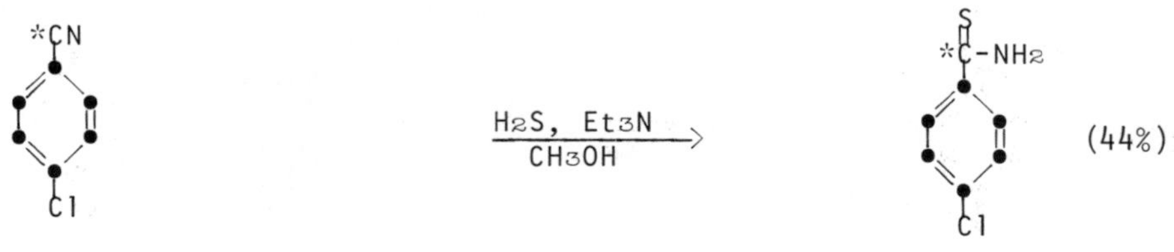

4-Chlorobenzonitrile-(cyano-^{14}C) → 4-Chlorobenzothioamide-7-^{14}C

D. F. White and J. Burns, J. Label. Compound. Radiopharm., 13, 393 (1977).

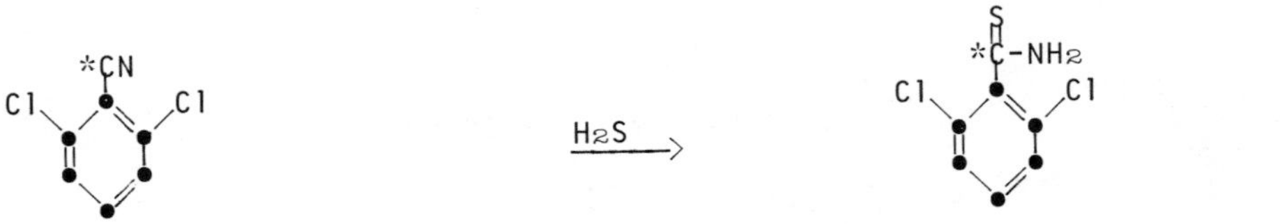

*CN
Cl
Cl
H_2S
S
*C-NH_2
Cl
Cl

2,6-Dichloro benzonitrile-(cyano-^{14}C)

Prefix [2,6-Dichloro-benzothioamide-7-^{14}C]

M. H. Griffiths, J. A. Moss, J. A. Rose, and D. E. Hathaway, Biochem. J., 98, 770 (1966).

2-12 Imides

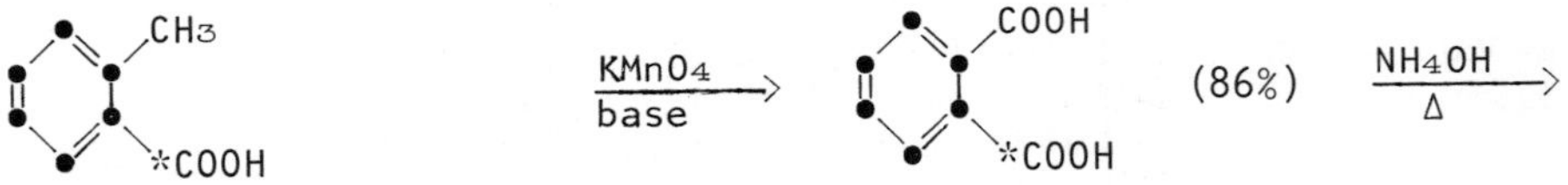

CH_3
*COOH
$KMnO_4$
base
COOH
*COOH
(86%)
NH_4OH
Δ

o-Toluic acid [2-Methylbenzoic-7-^{14}C acid]

1,2-Benzene dicarboxylic acid-(carboxyl-^{14}C)

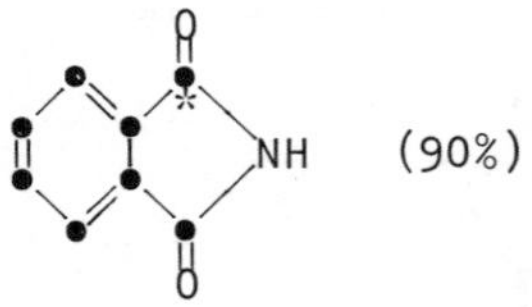

O
*
NH
O
(90%)

1H-Isoindole-1,3(2H)-dione-1-^{14}C

M. A. Leaffer, W. A. Skinner, J. J. Menn, J. B. McBain, and L. W. Fancher, J. Label. Compounds, 3, 334 (1967).

2-13 Hydroxamic Acids

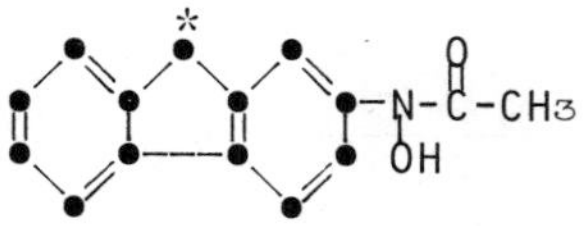

N-9H-Fluoren-2-yl-9-^{14}C N-hydroxyacetamide

Ac_2O, BTEA chloride / CH_2Cl_2, aq. NaOH →

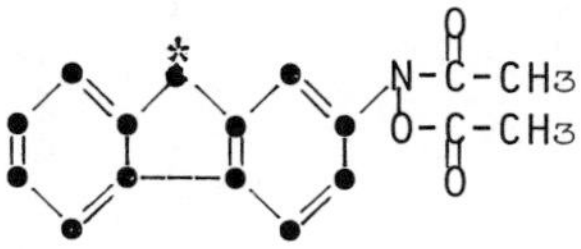

(90-100%)

N-(Acetyloxy)-N-9H-fluoren-2-ylacetamide-9-^{14}C

M. R. Thissen and W. P. Duncan, J. Label. Compound Radiopharm., 15, 59 (1978).

$C_6H_5{}^*COOH$

Benzoic-7-^{14}C acid

1. CH_3OH
2. NH_2OH
3. C_6H_5NCO

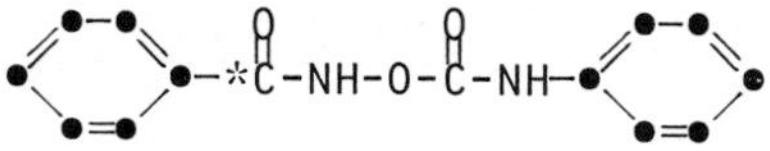

N-[[(Phenylamino)carbonyl]oxy] benzamide-7-^{14}C

E. Zörkendörfer, M. H. Khorgami, and F. Boberg, J. Label. Compounds, 9, 619 (1973).

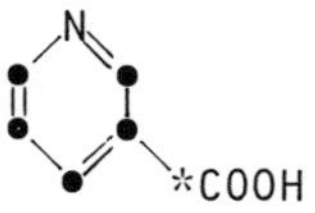

Nicotinic acid [3-Pyridinecarboxylic acid-(carboxyl-^{14}C)]

1. $SOCl_2$
2. CH_3OH
3. $NH_2OH \cdot HCl$, 23% NaOH

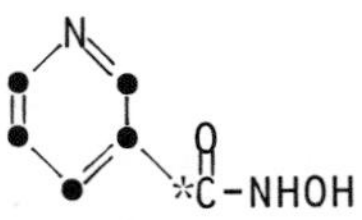

(36% overall)

N-Hydroxy-3-pyridine carboxamide-(carboxyl-^{14}C]

T. Fujita, H. Ejiri, Y. Kodama, and K. Miyao, J. Label. Compounds, 9, 159, 553 (1973).

2-14 Hydrazides

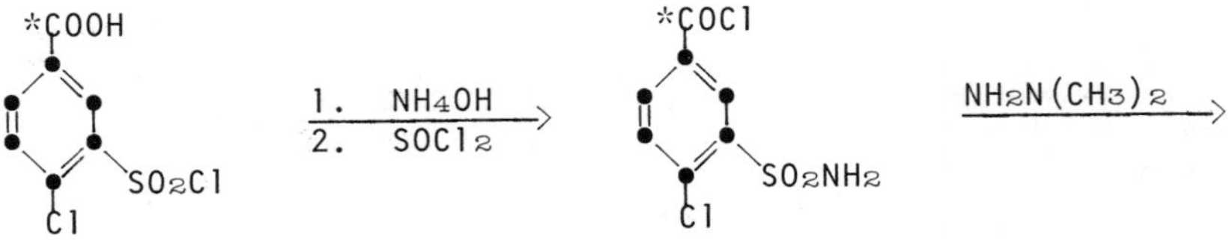
*COOH
SO_2Cl
Cl
1. NH_4OH
2. $SOCl_2$
*COCl
SO_2NH_2
Cl
$NH_2N(CH_3)_2$

4-Chloro-3-(chlorosulfonyl)benzoic-7-^{14}C acid

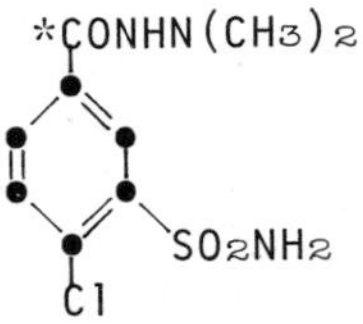
*CONHN$(CH_3)_2$
SO_2NH_2
Cl

(22% from p-chlorobenzoic acid)

3-(Aminosulfonyl)-4-chlorobenzoic-7-^{14}C acid 2,2-dimethyl hydrazide

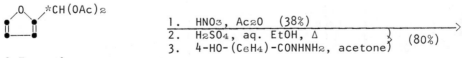

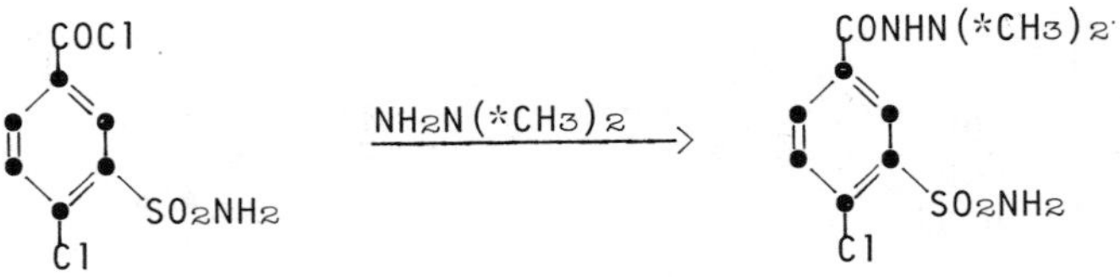
COCl
SO_2NH_2
Cl
$NH_2N(*CH_3)_2$
CONHN$(*CH_3)_2$
SO_2NH_2
Cl

(44%)

3-(Aminosulfonyl)-4-chlorobenzoic acid 2,2-(dimethyl-^{14}C)hydrazide

G. E. Blackburn, M. L. Hoefle, S. F. Chang, G. W. Gwynn, and R. E. Ober, J. Label. Compounds, 2, 402 (1966).

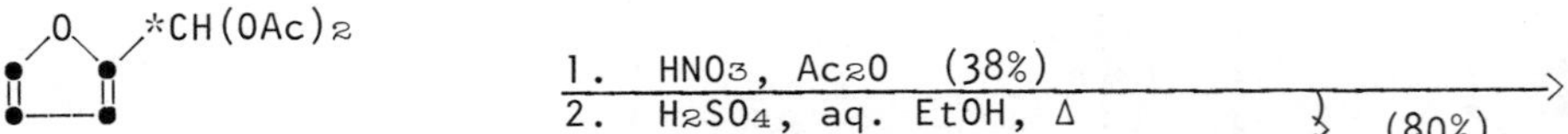
O
*CH$(OAc)_2$

1. HNO_3, Ac_2O (38%)
2. H_2SO_4, aq. EtOH, Δ
3. 4-HO-(C_6H_4)-$CONHNH_2$, acetone
(80%)

2-Furanyl methanediol diacetate-α-^{14}C

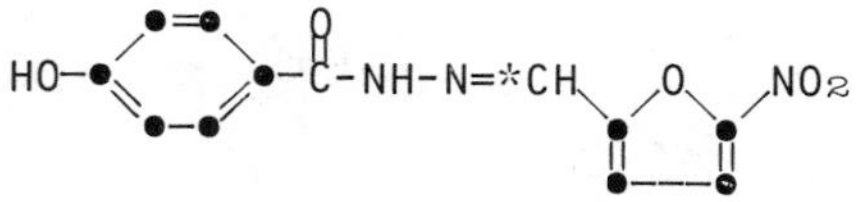
HO
C-NH-N=*CH
O
NO2

(15% from $BaCO_3$)

Nifuroxazide
[4-Hydroxybenzoic acid[(5-nitro-2-furanyl)-methylene-^{14}C]hydrazide]

L. F. Elsom and D. R. Hawkins, J. Label. Compound. Radiopharm., 14, 799 (1978).

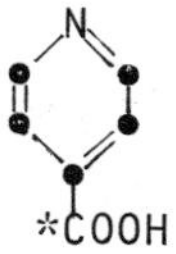
N
*COOH

(50% from K*CN)

1. $SOCl_2$
2. EtOH
3. NH_2NH_2
→

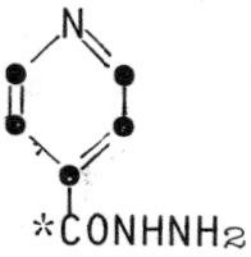
N
*CONHNH2

(99%)

Isonicotinic acid
[4-Pyridinecarboxylic-acid-(carboxyl-^{14}C)]

Isoniazid
[4-Pyridinecarboxylic acid hydrazide-(carboxyl-^{14}C)]

1. C_6Cl_5O-$COCH_2ONH$-Z, DMF (78%)
2. 4N HBr, AcOH (83%)
→

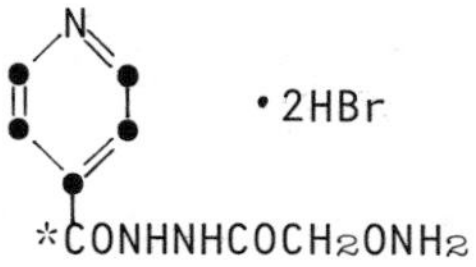
N
*CONHNHCOCH2ONH2

•2HBr

4-Pyridinecarboxylic acid (carboxyl-^{14}C)2-[(amino-oxy)acetyl]hydrazide dihydrobromide

$CH_3{*}COOH$ → Z-$NHOCH_2{*}COOC_6Cl_5$

1. Br_2, P, Δ (83%)
2. $C_6H_5CH_2OCONHOH$, KOH/EtOH (77%)
3. DCC, C_6Cl_5OH, dioxane (12%)

1. isonicotinic hydrazide, DMF
2. 4N HBr, AcOH

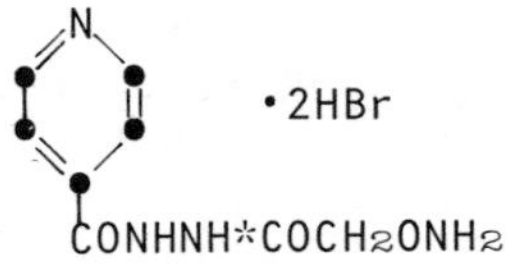

•2HBr (63%)

4-Pyridinecarboxylic acid 2-[(aminooxy)acetyl-1-^{14}C] hydrazide dihydrobromide

E. Koltai, D. Banfi, L. Kisfaludy, and L. Dancsi, J. Label. Compound. Radiopharm., 14, 341 (1978).

2-15 Imidates and Thioimidates

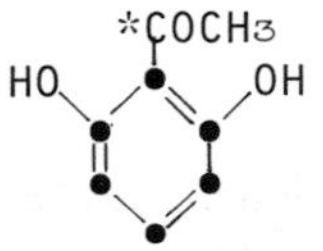

1-(2,6-Dihydroxyphenyl)-ethanone-1-^{14}C

1. CH_2N_2
2. $(CH_3O)_2SO_2$, NaOH, Δ } (34%)
3. NaOCl, NaOH, Δ
4. NaOCl, NaOH room temp. } (49%)

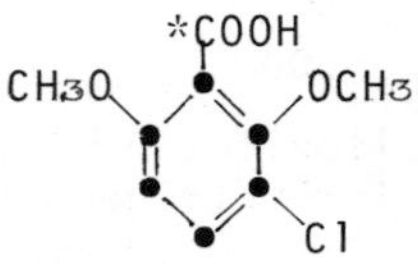

3-Chloro-2,6-dimethoxy benzoic-7-^{14}C acid

1. $SOCl_2$,
2. $CH_3CH_2O\text{-}NH_2$, 8% $NaHCO_3$ toluene } (83%)
3. C_6H_5COCl, $CHCl_3$ aq.NaOH/Et_3N (65%)

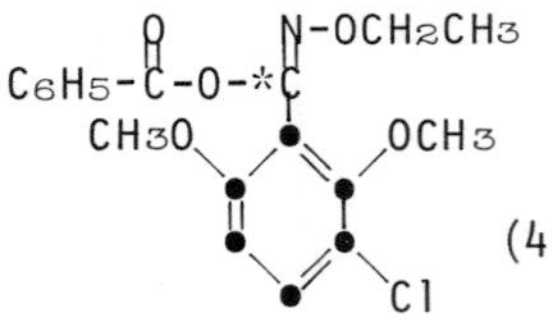

(4% overall)

Benzomate [3-Chloro-N-ethoxy-2,6-dimethoxybenzenecarboximidic-7-^{14}C acid anhydride with benzoic acid]

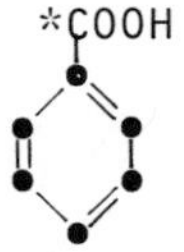

Benzoic-7-^{14}C acid

1. $SOCl_2$, Δ
2. 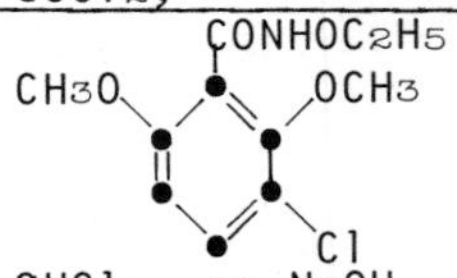
$CHCl_3$, aq.NaOH

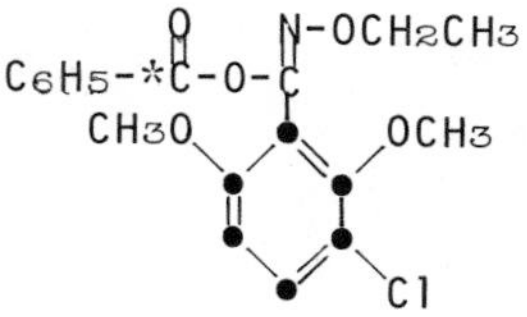
C6H5-*C-O-C
N-OCH2CH3
CH3O
OCH3
Cl

(35%; plus a 53% yield of the N-benzoyl isomer)

3-Chloro-N-ethoxy-2,6-dimethoxybenzenecarboximidic acid anhydride with benzoic-7-^{14}C acid

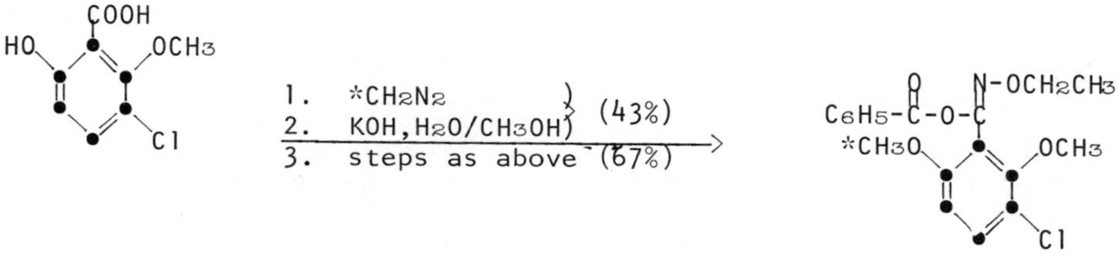
COOH
HO
OCH3
Cl
1. *CH2N2
2. KOH,H2O/CH3OH
(43%)
3. steps as above (67%)
C6H5-C-O-C
N-OCH2CH3
*CH3O
OCH3
Cl

3-Chloro-N-ethoxy 2-methoxy-(6-methoxy-^{14}C)-benzene-carboximidic acid anhydride with benzoic acid

Y. Soeda, S. Kato, D. Takiguchi, R. Sakimoto, and K. Ohkuma, J. Agr. Food Chem., 20, 936 (1972).

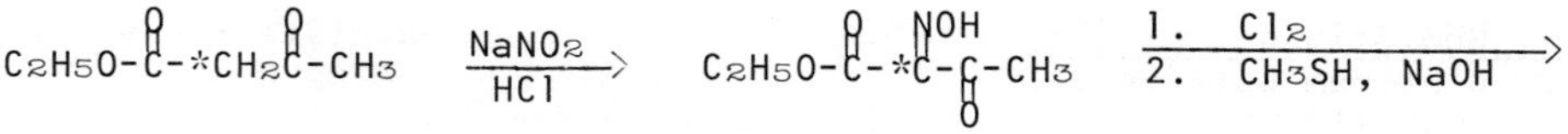
C2H5O-C-*CH2C-CH3
NaNO2
HCl
C2H5O-C-*C-C-CH3
NOH
1. Cl2
2. CH3SH, NaOH

3-Oxobutanoic-2-^{14}C acid ethyl ester

2-(Hydroxyimino)-3-oxobutanoic-2-^{14}C acid ethyl ester

C2H5OOC-*C=NOH
SCH3
1. (CH3)2NH
2. CH3NCO, (C2H5)3N

[(Hydroxyimino)(methylthio)] acetic-2-^{14}C acid ethyl ester

$(CH_3)_2N-\overset{O}{\overset{\|}{C}}-*\underset{SCH_3}{C}=NO\overset{O}{\overset{\|}{C}}-NHCH_3$

2-(Dimethylamino)-N-[[(methylamino)carbonyl]oxy]-2-oxoethanimidothioic-1-^{14}C acid methyl ester

J. Harvey, Jr., J. C.-Y. Han, and R. W. Reiser, J. Agric. Food Chem., 26, 529 (1978).

2-16 Nitriles

$Ba*CO_3 + NH_3 \longrightarrow BaN*CN \xrightarrow[2.\ 800°C]{1.\ Na,\ 330°C} Na*CN$ (90%)

Barium cyanimide-^{14}C

Sodium cyanide-^{14}C

P. Vercier, J. Label. Compounds, 4, 91, (1968).

$Ba*CO_3 \xrightarrow[1100°C]{900-} *CO_2 \xrightarrow[\text{nickel catalyst}]{H_2,\ 300-350°C} *CH_4$

Methane-^{14}C

$\xrightarrow{1.\ NH_3,\ -70°C}$ K*CN (quantitative yields from $BaCO_3$)

2. platinum catalyst, 1000-1100°C
3. KOH, CH_3OH

Potassium cyanide-^{14}C

D. Bánfi, S. Mlinkó, and T. Palágyi, J. Label. Compounds, 7, 221 (1971).

$ClCH_2*COOH \xrightarrow[2.\ NH_4OH\ (50\%)]{1.\ EtOH,\ H_2SO_4\ (81\%)} ClCH_2*CN$

3. P_2O_5 (84%)

Chloroacetic-1-^{14}C acid

Chloroacetonitrile-1-^{14}C

N. Hayashi, T. Toga, and T. Murata, J. Label. Compounds, 10, 609 (1974).

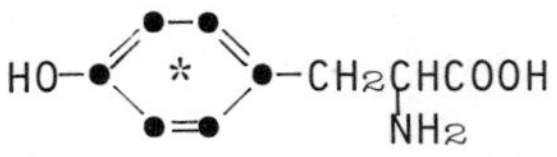

L-Tyrosine
[β-(4-Hydroxyphenyl)alanine-ring-^{14}C]

1. L-amino acid oxidase catalase, pH 7.2
2. $NH_2OH \cdot HCl$, pH 7·2
3. $NaBH_3CN$
→

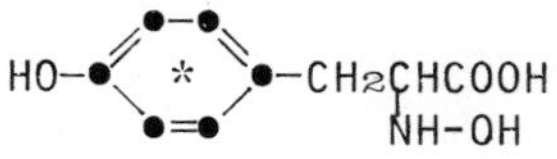

(90% from tyrosine)

DL-N-Hydroxytyrosine-ring-[14]C

1. NH_4OH
2. $SOCl_2$, C_6H_6, Δ
→

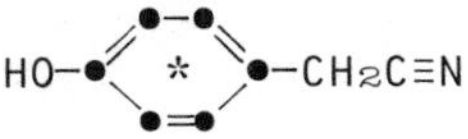

(72%; 51% from tyrosine)

4-Hydroxybenzeneacetonitrile-ring-[14]C

B. L. Moller, J. Label. Compound. Radiopharm., 14, 663 (1978).

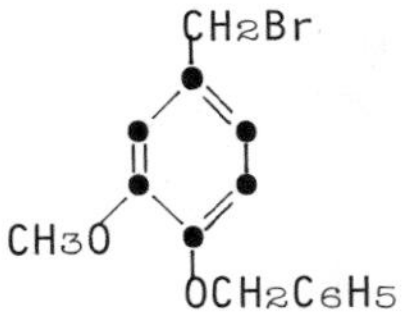

Na*CN / DMF →

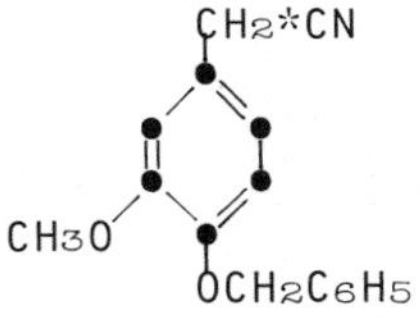

(86%)

3-Methoxy-4-(phenylmethoxy)benzeneacetonitrile-(cyano-^{14}C)

P. R. Borkowski, J. S. Horn, and H. Rapoport, J. Amer. Chem. Soc., 100, 276 (1978).

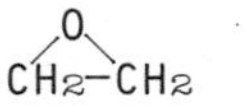

1. K*CN
2. $-H_2O$
→

$CH_2=CH{*}CN$ (60%)

Acrylonitrile
[2-Propenenitrile-1-^{14}C]

A. Kolodziejczyk and A. Arendt, J. Label. Compounds, 11, 385 (1975).

$CH_3{*}COOH$ $\xrightarrow[\text{2. } B_2H_6 \text{ (51\%)}]{\text{1. } Cl_2 \text{ (89\%)}}$ $ClCH_2{*}CH_2OH$ $\xrightarrow{NaCN}$

$HO{*}CH_2CH_2CN$ (80%) $\xrightarrow[\Delta]{KOAc}$ ${*}CH_2{=}CHCN$ (82%) $\xrightarrow{Cl_2}$

3-Hydroxypropane nitrile-3-^{14}C

Acrylonitrile [2-Propenenitrile-3-^{14}C]

$Cl{*}CH_2{-}CCl_2CN$ (90%) $\xrightarrow{Mg-MgI}$ ${*}CH_2{=}C(Cl)CN$ (48%)

2-Chloro-2-propenenitrile-3-^{14}C

C. C. Lee, F. L. Kung, B. Hahn, and A. J. Robson, J. Label. Compounds, 7, 46 (1971); J. Label. Compounds, 8, 77 (1972).

$ClCH_2COOCH_3$ $\xrightarrow{Na{*}CN}$ ${*}CN{-}CH_2COOCH_3$

Cyanoacetic acid methyl ester-(cyano-^{14}C)

G. B. Barlin and W. Pfleiderer, Chem. Ber., 104, 3069 (1971).

$R(CH_2)nCOOC_2H_5$ $\xrightarrow[\text{DMSO; } \Delta \text{ (or EtOH)}]{K{*}CN}$ ${*}CN{-}(CH_2)nCOOC_2H_5$

R=Br, n-1; Bromoacetic acid ethyl ester
R=Cl, n=2; 3-Chloropropanoic acid ethyl ester
R=Br, n=3; 4-Bromobutanoic acid ethyl ester

n=1; (Cyano-^{14}C) acetic acid ethyl ester (43%)
n=2; 3-(Cyano-^{14}C) propanoic acid ethyl ester (66%)
n=3; 4-(Cyano-^{14}C) butanoic acid ethyl ester (93%)

V. Tolman, J. Cabak, and J. Benes, J. Label. Compounds, 10, 39 (1974).

$C_6H_5CH_2CH_2Cl$ —— K^*CN, DMSO / 18-crown-6-ether ——> $C_6H_5CH_2CH_2{}^*CN$ (81%)

Benzenepropane nitrile-(cyano-^{14}C)

C. R. Partington and M. P. Mertes, J. Label. Compound.Radiopharm., 14, 223 (1978).

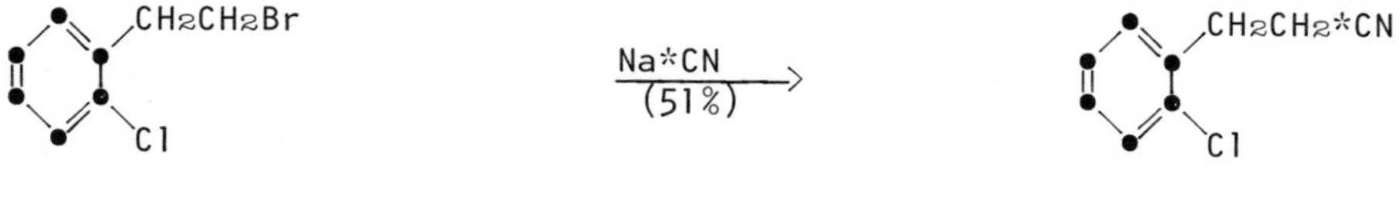

2-Chlorobenzene-propanenitrile-(cyano-^{14}C)

A. G. Sakhabutdinov, V. G. Lipovich, and I. V. Kalechits, Zh. Org. Khim., 11, 1728 (1975).

$ClCH_2COOH$ ——>

1. Na^*CN, $NaHCO_3$, H_2O
2. CH_2N_2, ether
3. NH_3, CH_3OH
4. silica, LiI, P_2O_5

——> $^*CNCH_2{}^*CN$

Malononitrile [propanedinitrile-(cyano-^{14}C)]

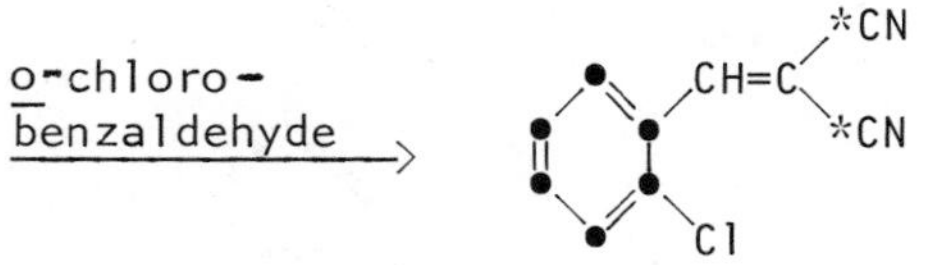

(22% from NaCN)

[(2-Chlorophenyl)methylene] propanedinitrile-(cyano-^{14}C)

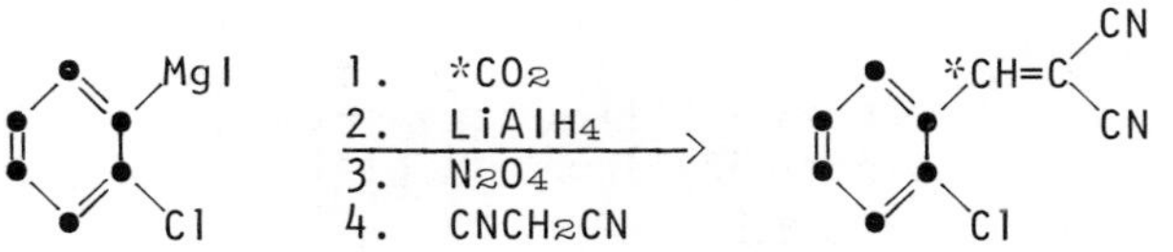

(13% from $BaCO_3$)

[(2-Chlorophenyl)(methylene-^{14}C)]θ propanedinitrile

Using methyl cyanoacetate-2-^{14}C, o-chlorobenzylidene malononitrile-2-^{14}C was prepared in 28% overall yield from cyanoacetamide.

J. M. Harrison, T. D. Inch, I. W. Lawston, R. V. Ley, and G. L. Sainsbury, J. Label. Compound. Radiopharm., 14, 141 (1978).

$C_2H_5OCH_2CH_2Br$ $\xrightarrow[\text{2. } HCOOC_2H_5,\ NaOMe,\ EtOH/C_6H_6]{\text{1. } Na^*CN,\ EtOH/H_2O,\ \Delta}$ $C_2H_5OCH_2CH(^*CN)CH(OC_2H_5)_2$

3,3-Diethoxy-2-(ethoxymethyl)propanenitrile-1-^{14}C

H. Morimoto, N. Hayashi, T. Naka, and S. Kato, Chem. Ber., 106, 893 (1973).

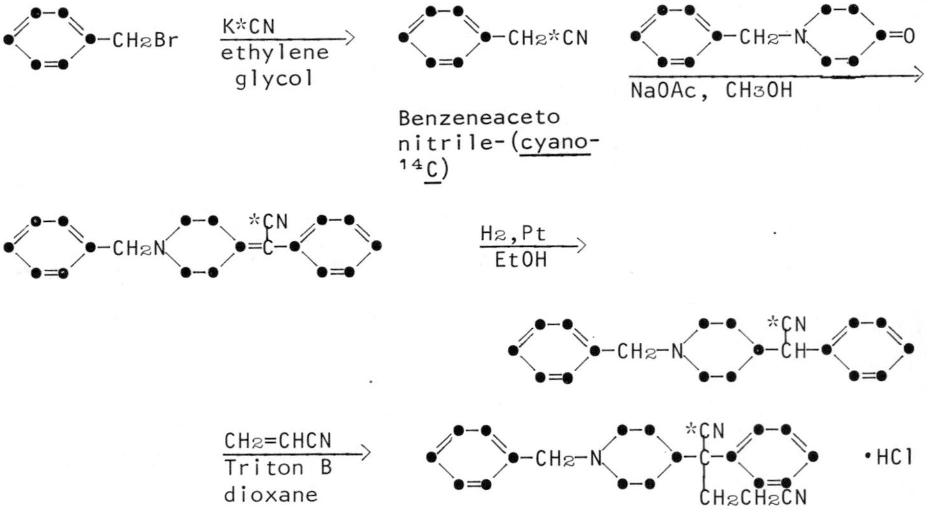
-CH2Br
K*CN
ethylene glycol
-CH2*CN
-CH2-N
=O
NaOAc, CH3OH
-CH2N
*CN
H2,Pt
EtOH
-CH2-N
*CN
CH2=CHCN
Triton B
dioxane
-CH2-N
*CN
CH2CH2CN
•HCl

Benzeneacetonitrile-(cyano-^{14}C)

2-Phenyl-2-[1-(phenylmethyl)-4-piperidinyl]pentane dinitrile-(1-cyano-^{14}C)

I. Van Wijngaarden and W. Sondijn, J. Label. Compounds, 1, 207 (1965).

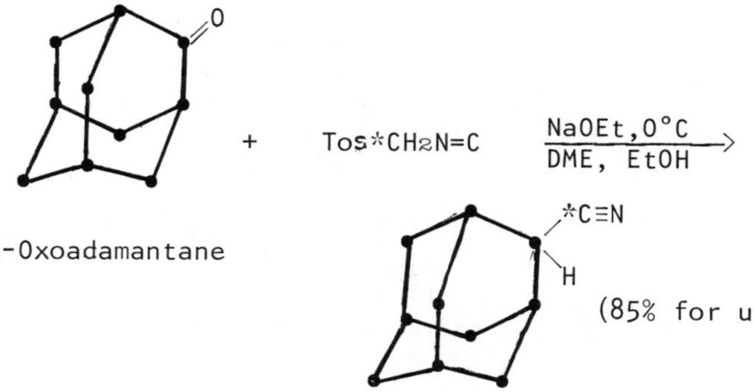
O
+
Tos*CH2N=C
NaOEt,0°C
DME, EtOH
*C≡N
H

2-Oxoadamantane

(85% for unlabeled reaction)

2-(Cyano-^{14}C)adamantane
Tricyclo[3.3.1.1^{3,7}]decane-
2-carbonitrile(cyano-^{14}C)]

A 2-oxazoline intermediate is proposed to account for the loss of the isocyano carbon and not the methylene carbon.

O. H. Oldenziel and A. M. van Leusen, Tetrahedron Lett., 1357 (1973).

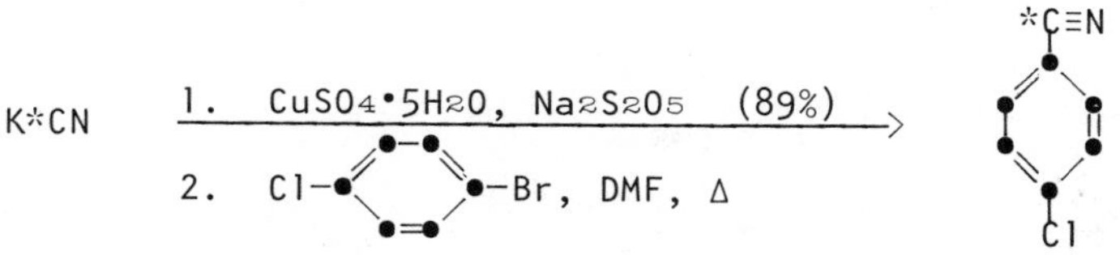
K*CN
1. CuSO4•5H2O, Na2S2O5 (89%)
2. Cl– –Br, DMF, Δ
*C≡N
Cl

4-Chlorobenzonitrile-
(cyano-^{14}C)

D. F. White and J. Burns, J. Label. Compound. Radiopharm., 13, 393 (1977).

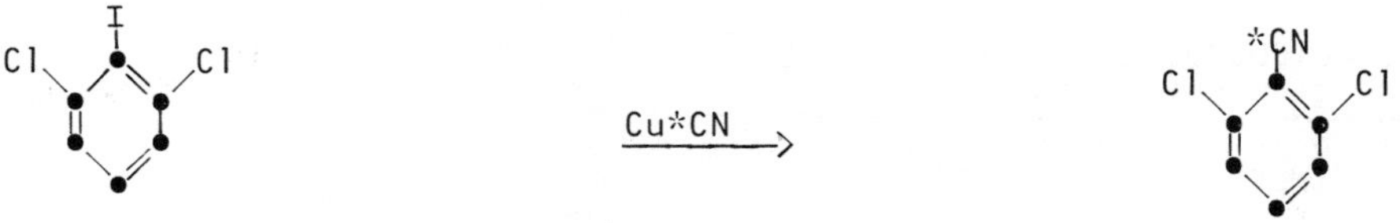
I
Cl
Cl
Cu*CN
*CN
Cl
Cl

2,6-Dichloro
benzonitrile-
(cyano-^{14}C)

M. H. Griffiths, J. A. Moss, J. A. Rose, and D. E. Hathaway, Biochem. J., 98, 770 (1966).

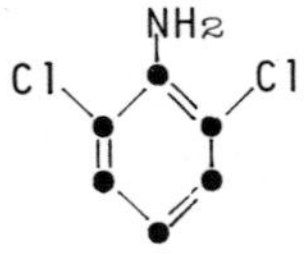

1. $NaNO_2$, H_2SO_4, AcOH
2. K*CN, CuCN, $NaHCO_3/H_2O$

→

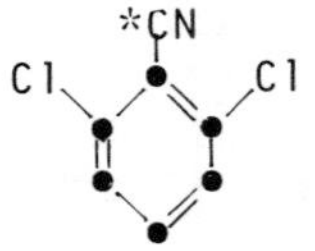

(91%)

2,6-Dichlorobenzonitrile-(cyano-^{14}C)

S. F. Sisenwine, C. O. Tio, and J. Ahern, J. Label. Compound. Radiopharm., 12, 501 (1976).

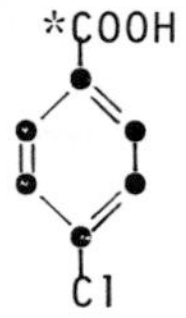

4-Chlorobenzoic-7-^{14}C acid

1. KNO_3, H_2SO_4, (82%)
2. PCl_5, C_6H_6 } (96%)
3. NH_4OH, C_6H_6 }

→

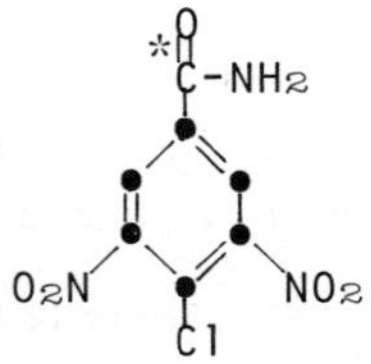

4-Chloro-3,5-dinitrobenzamide-7-^{14}C

1. $POCl_3$, Δ (92%)
2. $SnCl_2$, HCl (97%)

→

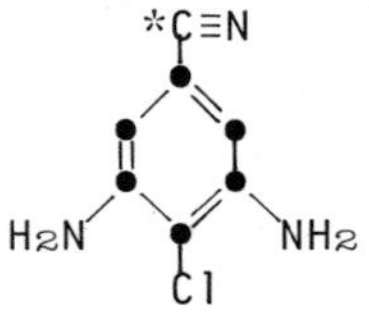

3,5-Diamino-4-chlorobenzonitrile-(cyano-^{14}C)

1. $ClCOCOOC_2H_5$, Et_3N, DMF (82%)
2. aq.NaOH (91%)
3. HCl } (77%)
4. $(HOCH_2)_3CNH_2$ }

→

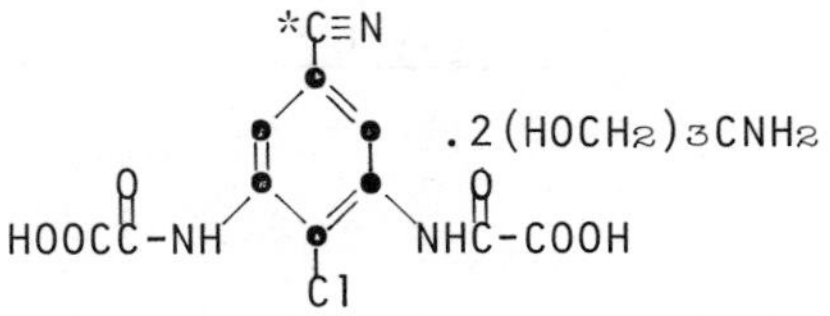
*C≡N
.2(HOCH2)3CNH2
HOOCC-NH
NHC-COOH
Cl

(40% overall)

2,2'-[2-Chloro-5-cyano-^{14}C-1,3-phenylene) diimino]bis[2-oxoacetic acid]-2-amino-2-(hydroxymethyl)-1,3-propanediol(1:2) salt

R. S. P. Hsi and T. D. Johnson, J. Label. Compound. Radiopharm., 14, 861 (1978).

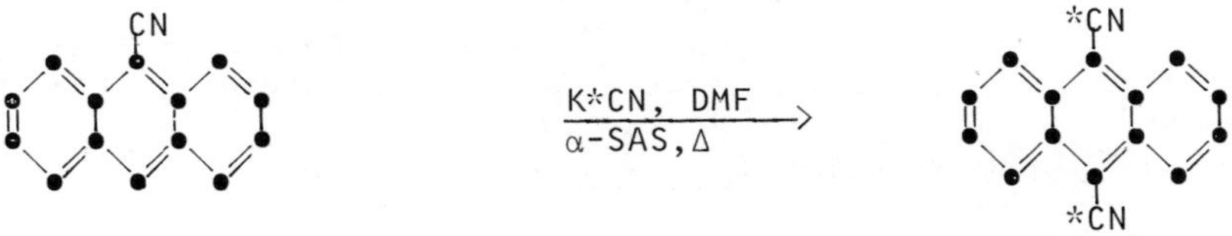
CN
K*CN, DMF
α-SAS,Δ
*CN
*CN

(80%)

9,10-Anthracene dicarbonitrile-(cyano-^{14}C)

A number of cyanations of substituted aromatic and unsaturated compounds is reported.

R. B. Chapas, R. F. Nystrom, and H. R. Snyder, J. Org. Chem., 37, 314 (1972).

2-17 Nitrile Derivatives

KCNO + $^{*}CO_2$ $\xrightarrow[\text{30-120 min, sealed tube}]{\text{390-440°C}}$ K*CNO + $^{*}CO_2$

Potassium cyanate-^{14}C

Complete exchange was observed, ∿50% label in product.

J. Ratusky and R. Tykva, J. Label. Compounds, 3, 50 (1967).

$CH_3CH_2{*}COCl$ —(NaN_3, diglyme)→ $CH_3CH_2N{*}CO$ (55%)

Propanoyl-1-^{14}C chloride

Ethyl isocyanate-1-^{14}C [(Isocyanato-^{14}C)ethane]

D. T. Witiak and F. D. Cazer, J. Label. Compounds, 11, 605 (1975).

K*CN —(1. HCHO; 2. C_6H_5COCl)→ $C_6H_5COOCH_2{*}CN$ (100%) —(1. $LiAlH_4$, THF; 2. H_2O, HCl)→

$HOCH_2{*}CH_2NH_2 \cdot HCl$ (50%) —(1. $SOCl_2$; 2. $COCl_2$)→ $ClCH_2{*}CH_2NCO$ (48%)

1-Chloro-2-isocyanato ethane-2-^{14}C

J. W. Faigle and H. Keberle, J. Label. Compounds, 5, 173 (1969).

K*CN —(S; CH_3COCH_3, Δ)→ KS*CN

Potassium thiocyanate-^{14}C

G. Zólyomi, L. Toldy, and D. Bánfi, J. Label. Compounds, 9, 243 (1973).

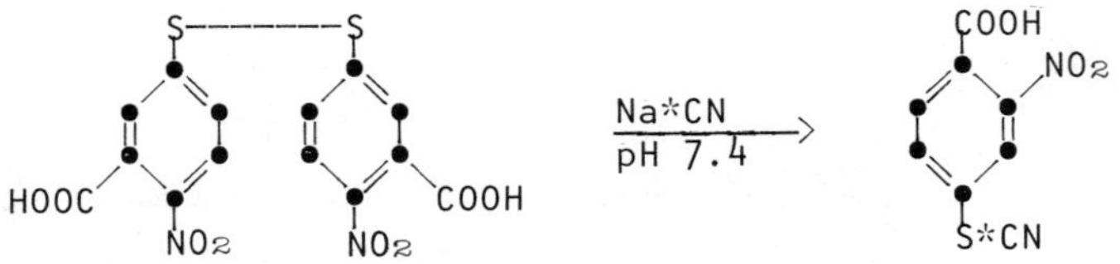
S
S
HOOC
NO2
NO2
COOH
Na*CN
pH 7.4
COOH
NO2
S*CN

2-Nitro-5-thio(cyanato-^{14}C) benzoic acid

RSH ⟶ RS*CN

Thiocyanates-^{14}C

R=β-mercaptoethanol, cysteine, papain.

Y. Degani, H. Neumann, and A. Patchornik, J. Amer. Chem. Soc., 92, 6969 (1970).

$$^{*}CH_3NH_2 \cdot HCl \xrightarrow[2.\ ClCOOC_2H_5]{1.\ CS_2,\ aq.\ NaOH} {}^{*}CH_3N{=}C{=}S \quad (48\%)$$

Isothiocyanatomethane-$^{14}\underline{C}$

J. I. DeGraw, J. S. Engstrom, and E. Willis, J. Pharm. Sci., 64, 1700 (1975).

$$CH_3CH{=}CHCH_2Cl \xrightarrow[DMF,\ \Delta]{KS^{*}CN} CH_3CH{=}CHCH_2S^{*}CN$$

1-Chloro-2-butene → 1-Thiocyanato-$^{14}\underline{C}$-2-butene

$$\xrightarrow{\Delta} CH_2{=}CHCH(CH_3)N^{*}CS$$

3-Isothiocyanato-$^{14}\underline{C}$-3-methyl-1-propene

V. J. Feil, P. W. Aschbacher, and C. H. Lamoureux, J. Label. Compounds, 6, 401 (1970).

$$KS^{*}CN \xrightarrow{C_6H_5COCl} C_6H_5{-}C({=}O){-}N{=}{}^{*}C{=}S$$

Benzoyl-(isothiocyanate-$^{14}\underline{C}$)

G. Zólyomi, L. Toldy, and D. Bánfi, J. Label. Compounds, 9, 243 (1973).

3

Carbonyl Compounds

Aldehydes

3-1 Aliphatic Aldehydes

$H{*}C{\equiv}{*}CH$ → (1. HBr (91%); 2. KOAc, AcOH (97%); 3. $NaOCH_3$, CH_3OH) → $HO{-}{*}CH_2{*}CH_2{-}OH$
Ethylene glycol-1-2-^{14}C

→ (HIO_4) → $H{*}CHO$
Formaldehyde-^{14}C

E. Schreier, Helv. Chim. Acta, 59, 585 (1976).

CH_2OH–${*}CHOH$–CH_2OH → (HCl/HOAc, Δ) → CH_2Cl–${*}CHOH$–CH_2OH (80%) → ($NaIO_4$, H_2O) → $ClCH_2{*}CHO$ (47%)

Glycerol [1,2,3-Propane-triol-2-^{14}C]

Chloroacetaldehyde-1-^{14}C

The chloroacetaldehyde-1-^{14}C was used to form etheno-bridged adenine and cytosine nucleotides.

J. C. Greenfield, N. J. Leonard, and R. F. Nystrom, J. Label. Compound. Radiopharm., 12, 545 (1976).

$*CH_3*CHO$ $\xrightarrow[95°]{Cl_2,\ H_2O}$ $*CCl_3*CHO \cdot H_2O$ (47%)

Acetaldehyde-1,2-^{14}C → Chloral hydrate [Trichloroacetaldehyde-1,2-^{14}C hydrate]

L. E. Weaner, G. L. Burghard, D. W. Blackburn, and W. L. Mendelson, J. Label. Compound. Radiopharm., 13, 141 (1977).

HOO*C-*COOH $\xrightarrow[\text{pH } 1.5-2]{1.2\%\ Na-Hg}$ HOO*C-*CHO

Oxalic-1,2-^{14}C acid → Glyoxylic acid [Oxacetic-1,2-^{14}C acid]

W. S. Saari and W. C. Lumma, Jr., J. Label. Compound. Radiopharm., 14, 349 (1978).

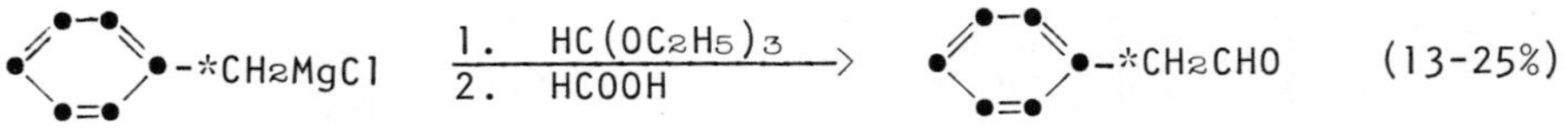

-*CH2MgCl
1. HC(OC2H5)3
2. HCOOH
-*CH2CHO
(13-25%)

Benzeneacetaldehyde-α-^{14}C

W. Y. Cobb, J. Label. Compounds, 5, 378 (1969).

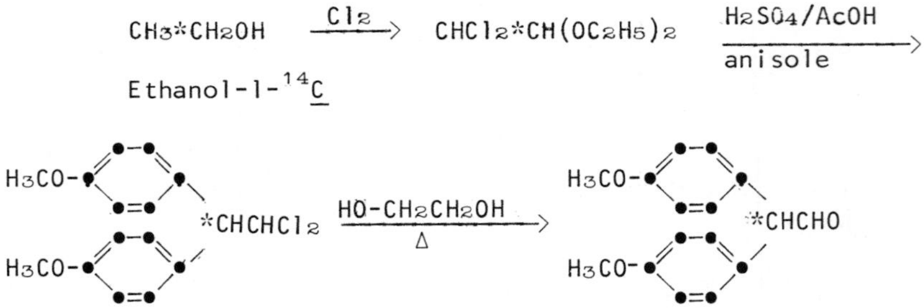

CH3*CH2OH
Cl2
CHCl2*CH(OC2H5)2
H2SO4/AcOH
anisole
Ethanol-1-14C
H3CO-
H3CO-
*CHCHCl2
HO-CH2CH2OH
Δ
H3CO-
H3CO-
*CHCHO

4-Methoxy-α-(4-methoxyphenyl) benzeneacetaldehyde-α-^{14}C

W. Tadros, R. R. Tadros, and S. B. Awad, Helv. Chim. Acta, 59, 355 (1976).

$*CH_3OH + CH_3CHO \xrightarrow[0°C]{CaCl_2} CH_3CH(O*CH_3)_2$ (32%)

1,1-(Dimethoxy-^{14}C) ethane

M. J. Molera, J. A. Garcia Dominquez, and J. M. Santiuste, An. Quim, 74, 853 (1978).

$(CH_3)_2CH*COOH \xrightarrow[2.\ EtOH]{1,\ P, Br_2} (CH_3)_2CBr*COOC_2H_5$ (85%)

2-Methylpropanoic-1-^{14}C acid

$\xrightarrow[2.\ LiAlH_4,\ Et_2O,\ 0°C\ (50\%)]{1.\ C_6H_5\text{-}N(C_2H_5)_2\ (56\%)} CH_2{=}C(CH_3)\text{-}*CH_2OH$

$\xrightarrow{H_2SO_4} (CH_3)_2CH*CHO$ (73%)

2-Methylpropanal-1-^{14}C

F. P. Schmook and O. E. Polansky, Monatsh. Chem. 100, 1640 (1969).

$C_6H_5\text{-}*COCH_3 \xrightarrow[NaNH_2]{ClCH_2COOC_2H_5} C_6H_5\text{-}*C(CH_3)\text{-}CH\text{-}COOC_2H_5$ (epoxide, –O– bridging) (62%)

Phenylethanone-1-^{14}C

$\xrightarrow[2.\ HCl]{1.\ C_2H_5ONa} CH_3*CH(C_6H_5)CHO$ (65%)

2-Phenylpropanal-2-^{14}C

The product was used in mechanistic studies of the elimination of the corresponding E- and Z-vinyl triflates.

P. J. Stang, D. P. Fox, C. J. Collins, and C. R. Watson, Jr., J. Org. Chem., 43, 364 (1978).

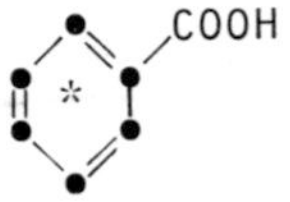

Benzoic acid-(ring-^{14}C)

1. $SOCl_2$
2. H_2, 10% Pd/$BaSO_4$, xylene

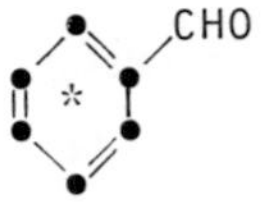

(58%)

Benzaldehyde-(ring-^{14}C)

C_6H_{11}-N=$CHCH_2Li$ / Et_2O →

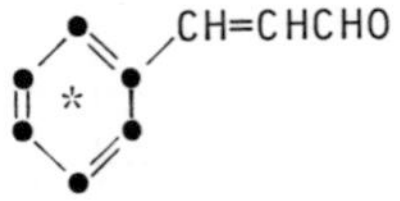

(47%)

Cinnamaldehyde
[(E)-3-Phenyl-2-propenal-(ring-^{14}C)]

A. Heesing and H.-W. Schneeberger, Chem. Ber., 105, 2447 (1972).

C_6H_6 —(1. CH_3*COONa, $AlCl_3$; 2. SO_2Cl_2)→ C_6H_5-*$COCHCl_2$ —(1. CH_3MgBr; 2. piperidine)→

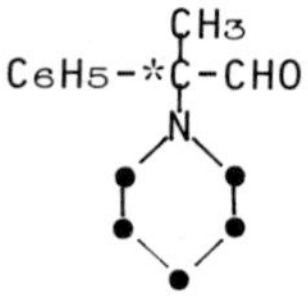

(54%)

α-Methyl-α-phenyl-1-piperidineacetaldehyde-α-^{14}C

R. Nouri-Bimorghi and L. Pichat, Bull. Soc. Chim. Fr., 4057 (1969).

$(CH_3)_2CHCH_2$*COOH (96% from Ba*CO_3)

Isovaleric acid
[3-methylbutanoic-1-^{14}C acid]

1. 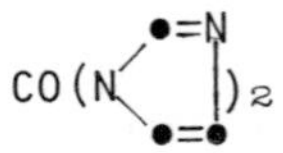
2. $LiAlH_4$, Et_2O →

$(CH_3)_2CHCH_2{}^*CHO$

3-Methylbutanal-^{14}C

L. Pichat, P. Nhuliem, and J.-P. Guermont, Bull. Soc. Chim. Fr., 837 (1971).

$$CH_3\text{-}CH{=}^*CH_2 \xrightarrow[Co_2(CO)_8]{CO,\ H_2} {}^*CH_3CH_2{}^*CH_2CHO + ({}^*CH_3)_2CHCHO$$

Propene-1-^{14}C

Product composition: n-butanal-2-^{14}C (48%), n-butanal-4-^{14}C (32%), and 2-methylpropanal-3-^{14}C (20%). The mechanism proposed involves an olefin-catelyst intermediate undergoing hydrogen transfer along with a double bond shift prior to formation of an acetyl-cobalt carbonyl.

F. Piacenti, M. Bianchi, P. Frediani, V. Matteoli, and A. LoMoro, J. Chem. Soc., Chem. Commun., 789 (1976).

$$CH_3(CH_2)_{10}{}^*COOH \xrightarrow[2.\ H_2,Pd]{1.\ SOCl_2} CH_3(CH_2)_{10}{}^*CHO \quad (42\%)$$

Dodecanoic-1-^{14}C acid → Dodecanal-1-^{14}C

G. B. Calleja and P. Rogers, J. Label. Compounds, 6, 135 (1970).

$$C_{15}H_{31}\text{-}{}^*COOH \xrightarrow[\substack{2.\ LiAlH_4 \\ 3.\ CH_3SO_2Cl,\ pyr \\ 4.\ DMSO}]{1.\ CH_2N_2} C_{15}H_{31}{}^*CHO$$

Hexadecanoic-1-^{14}C acid → Hexadecanal-1-^{14}C

By treatment with p-toluenesulfonic acid in glycerol/benzene, hexadecanal-1-^{14}C was converted in quantitative yield to a mixture of cis- and trans-1,3-dioxanes and cis-and trans-1,3-dioxolanes. All isomers were separable by chromatography.

K. L. Su, W. J. Baumann, T. H. Madson, and H. H. O. Schmid, J. Lipid Res., 15, 39 (1974).

3-2 Aromatic Aldehydes

$C_6H_5MgBr \xrightarrow[\text{2. } LiAlH_4 \text{ 3. air, DMSO}]{\text{1. } {}^{*}CO_2} C_6H_5{}^{*}CHO$ (92%)

Benzaldehyde-7-^{14}C

A. Yoshitake, Y. Makari, K. Kawahara, and M. Endo, J. Label. Compounds, 9, 537 (1973).

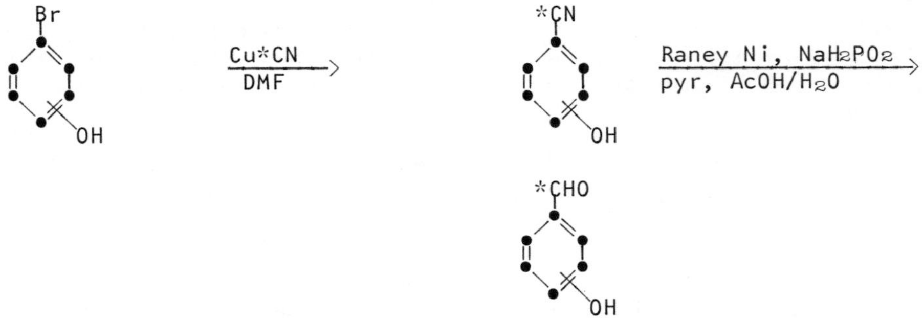

Compounds (yields) prepared in this manner: 2-hydroxybenzaldehyde (63%); 3-hydroxybenzaldehyde (48%); 4-hydroxybenzaldehyde (45%); 2,4-dihydroxybenzaldehyde (49%); 4-hydroxy-3-methoxybenzaldehyde (41%); 3-hydroxy-4-methoxybenzaldehyde (48%).

G. Billek, H. Kindl, A. Schimpl, and F. P. Schmook, J. Label. Compounds, 5, 3 (1969).

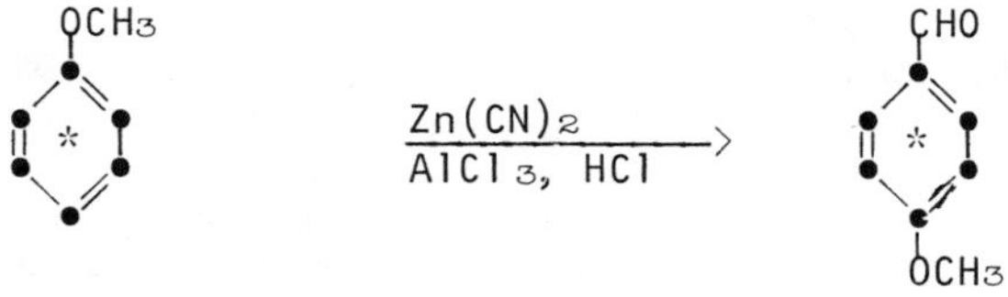

(80% yield of para/ortho mixture from which a 42% yield of para is obtained)

4-Methoxybenzaldehyde-(ring-^{14}C)

M. Herbert, L. Pichat, and Y. Langourieux, J. Label. Compounds, 10, 89 (1974).

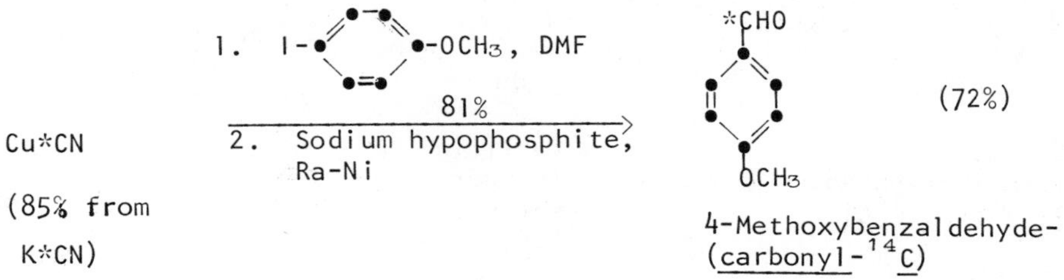
Cu*CN
(85% from K*CN)
1. I-C6H4-OCH3, DMF
81%
2. Sodium hypophosphite, Ra-Ni
*CHO
OCH3
(72%)
4-Methoxybenzaldehyde-(carbonyl-14C)

B. Chabannes, B. Duperray, and H. Pacheo, Bull. Soc. Chim. Fr., 801 (1972).

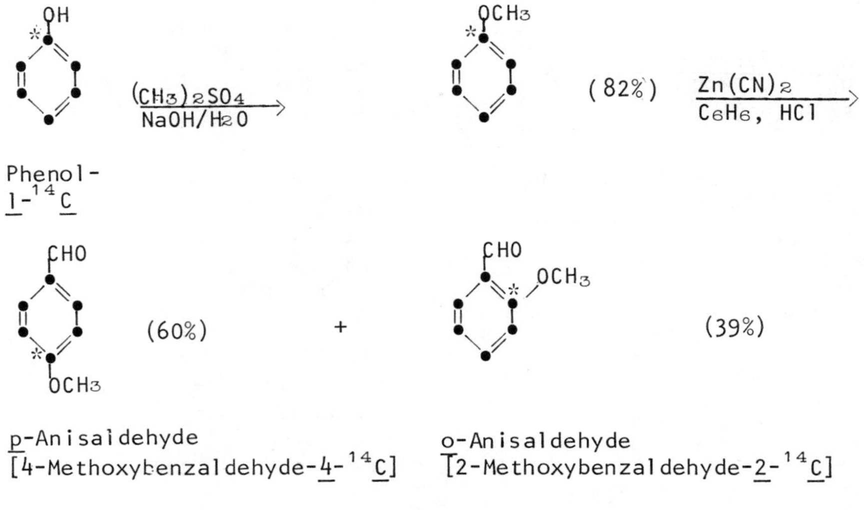
OH
Phenol-1-14C
(CH3)2SO4
NaOH/H2O
OCH3
(82%)
Zn(CN)2
C6H6, HCl
CHO
OCH3
(60%)
+
CHO
OCH3
(39%)
p-Anisaldehyde
[4-Methoxybenzaldehyde-4-14C]
o-Anisaldehyde
[2-Methoxybenzaldehyde-2-14C]

J. H. Kim, C. R. Creger, and J. R. Couch, J. Label. Compounds, 5, 35 (1969).

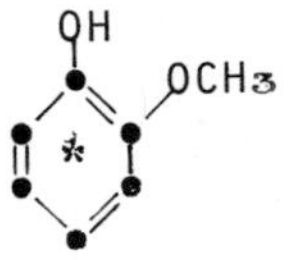

$\xrightarrow[CH_2Cl_2,\ SnCl_2]{CH_3SCHCl_2}$

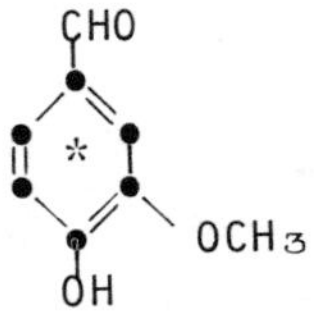

(80% total yield: 63% para; 15% meta; 2% ortho; mixture separable by chromatography)

Guaiacol
[2-Methoxyphenol-1,2, or 5-^{14}C]

Vanillin
[4-Hydroxy-3-methoxybenzaldehyde-3,4, or 6-^{14}C]

K. Kratzl and F. W. Vierhapper, Monatsh. Chem., 102, 425 (1971).

$*CH_3COCH_2OCH_3$ $\xrightarrow[NaOH]{CHO\text{-}CHNO_2\text{-}CHO}$

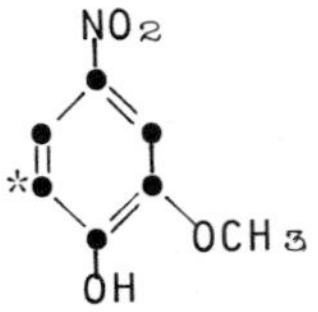

(65%)

(Prepared by addition of $*CH_3MgI$ to CH_3OCH_2CN followed by hydrolysis)

1. Ac_2O, pyr (91%)
2. H_2, 10% Pd/C, EtOH (94%)

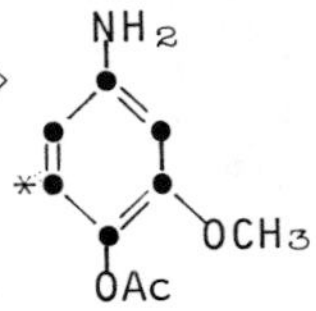

1. $NaNO_2$, HCl } 80%
2. CuCN, KCN }
3. NaH_2PO_2, Raney Ni } 80%
4. KOH, Δ }

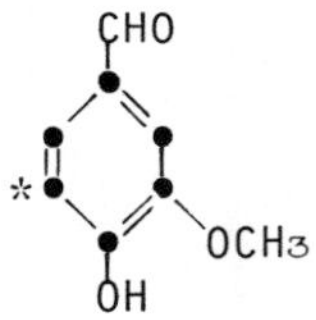

Vanillin
[4-Hydroxy-3-methoxybenzaldehyde-5-^{14}C]

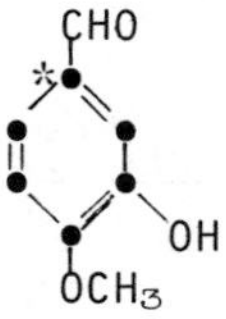

1. $(CH_3)_2SO_2$, DMF, K_2CO_3, Δ (94%)
2. $AlCl_3$, benzene, Δ (80%)

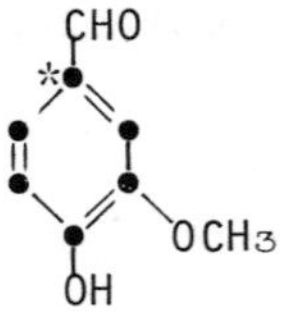

Isovanillin-1-[14]C
(from previous work)

Vanillin
[4-Hydroxy-3-methoxybenzaldehyde-1-^{14}C]

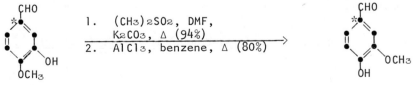

Isovanillin (unlabeled) —— 1. *CH_3I, NaOH, DMSO (80%); 2. $AlCl_3$, benzene, Δ (78%) ——>

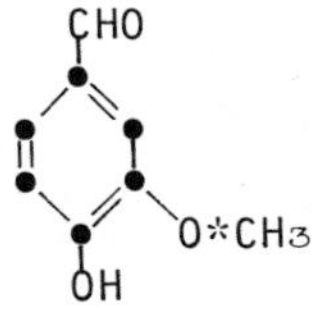

Vanillin
[4-Hydroxy-3-(methoxy-^{14}C)-benzaldehyde]

Vanillin-(1,5- or methoxy-^{14}C) ——> Bicreosol-(1,5- or methoxy-^{14}C)

K. Kratzl, F. W. Vierhapper, and E. Tengler, Monatsh. Chem., 106, 321 (1975).

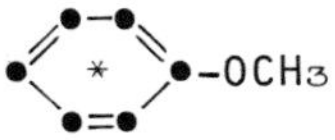

(80%) —— HNO_3, Ac_2O (96%) ——>

Anisole
[Methoxybenzene-ring-U-^{14}C]

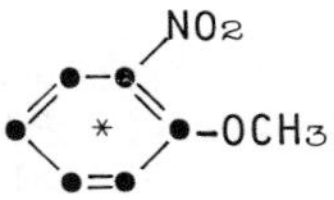

(82%)

1-Methoxy-2-nitrobenzene-(ring-^{14}C) (plus 11% p-isomer)

—— $SnCl_2$, HCl ——>

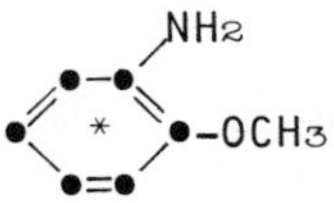

(78%)

2-Methoxybenzenamine-(ring-^{14}C)

—— H_2SO_4, $NaNO_2$ ——>

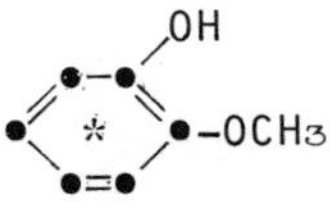

(91%)

Guaiacol
[2-Methoxyphenol-(ring-^{14}C)]

—— CH_3-S-$CHCl_2$, $SnCl_4$ ——>

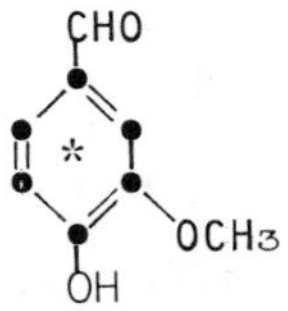

(60%) ——>

Vanillin
[4-Hydroxy-3-methoxybenzaldehyde-(ring-^{14}C)]

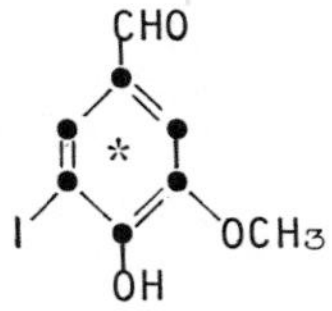

(64%)

4-Hydroxy-3-iodo-5-methoxybenzaldehyde-(ring-^{14}C)

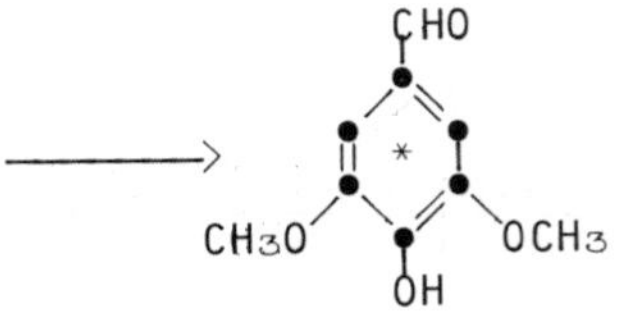
CHO
*
CH3O
OCH3
OH

(54%)

Syringaldehyde
[4-Hydroxy-3,5-dimethoxy-benzaldehyde-(ring-^{14}C)]

K. Haider, J. Label. Compounds, 2, 174 (1966).

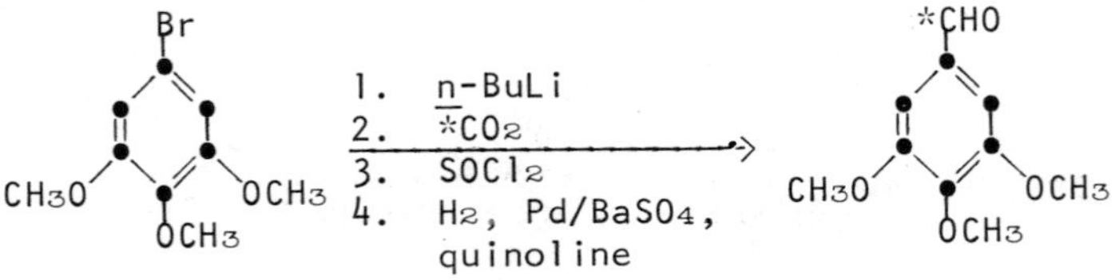
Br
CH3O
OCH3
OCH3
1. n-BuLi
2. *CO2
3. SOCl2
4. H2, Pd/BaSO4, quinoline
*CHO
CH3O
OCH3
OCH3

3,4,5-Trimethoxybenzaldehyde-(carbonyl-^{14}C)

G. Hardy, I. P. Sword, and D. E. Hathway, J. Label. Compounds, 8, 221 (1972).

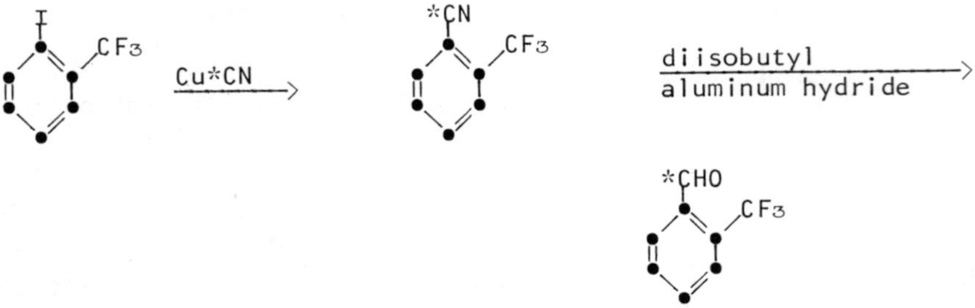
I
CF3
Cu*CN
*CN
CF3
diisobutyl
aluminum hydride
*CHO
CF3

2-Trifluoromethylbenzaldehyde-(carbonyl-^{14}C)

S. Walkenstein, A. P. Intoccia, T. L. Flanagan, B. Hwang, D. Flint, J. Weinstock, A. J. Villani, D. Blackburn, and H. Green, J. Pharm. Sci., 62, 580 (1973).

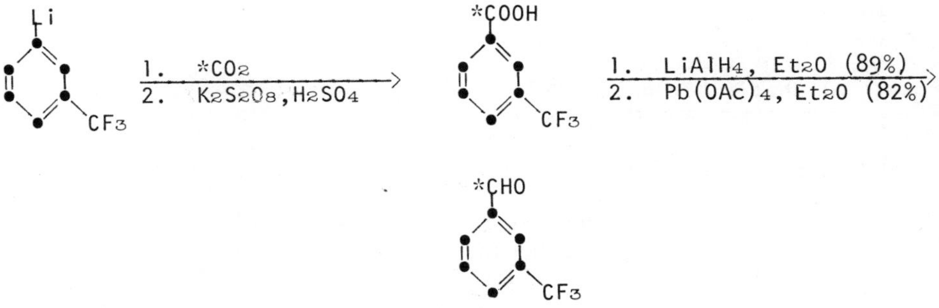
Li
1. *CO2
2. K2S2O8, H2SO4
*COOH
CF3
1. LiAlH4, Et2O (89%)
2. Pb(OAc)4, Et2O (82%)
*CHO
CF3

3-Trifluoromethylbenzaldehyde-(carbonyl-^{14}C)

G. Ronco, H. Renault, J. R. Rapin, and P. Compagnon, J. Label. Compound. Radiopharm, 14, 549 (1978).

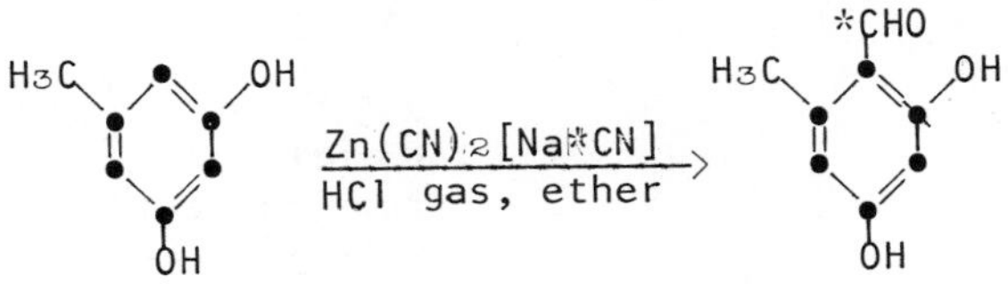
H3C
OH
OH
Zn(CN)2 [Na*CN]
HCl gas, ether
*CHO
H3C
OH
OH

2,4-Dihydroxy-6-methylbenzaldehyde-(carbonyl-^{14}C)

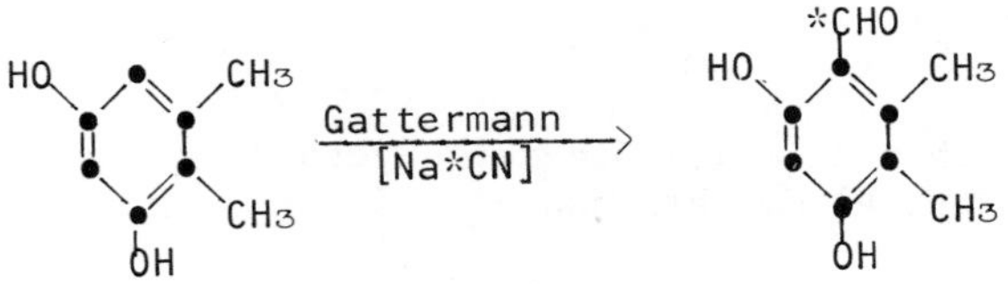
HO
CH3
CH3
OH
Gattermann
[Na*CN]
*CHO
HO
CH3
CH3
OH

(90%)

4,6-Dihydroxy-2,3-dimethylbenzaldehyde-(carbonyl-^{14}C)

J. Better and S. Gatenbeck, Acta Chem. Scand. B, 31, 391 (1977).

Ketones

3-3 Aliphatic Ketones

$(*CH_3CO)_2O \xrightarrow{\Delta} *CH_2CO$ (more than 99.5% of label remained in the methylene position)

Ketene
[Ethenone-2-^{14}C]

D. C. Montague and F. S. Rowland, J. Amer. Chem. Soc., 93, 5381 (1971).

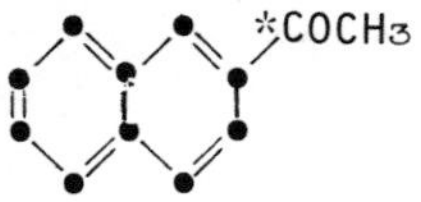

1. NaOBr, H_2O (quant.)
2. Na, isoamyl alcohol, Δ (98%)

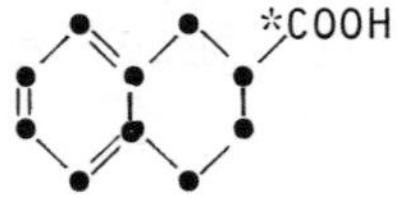

1-(2-Naphthalenyl)ethanone-1-[14]C

1,2,3,4-Tetrahydro-2-naphthalene carboxylic acid-(carboxyl-^{14}C)

1. $SOCl_2$
2. CH_2N_2, ether
3. HCl gas

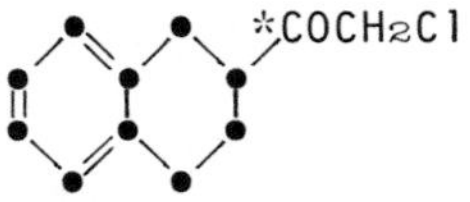

(76%)

2-Chloro-1-(1,2,3,4-tetrahydro-2-naphthalenyl)ethanone-1-[14]C

H. Minato, T. Nagasaki, Y. Katsuyama, T. Yokoshima, K. Suga, and T. Ueda, J. Label. Compound. Radiopharm., 13, 103 (1977).

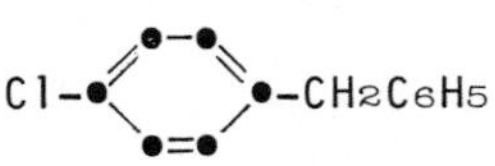

1. n-BuLi, TMEDA/THF
2. $*CO_2$

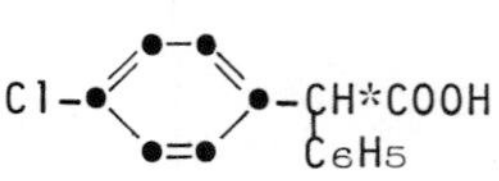

(85%)

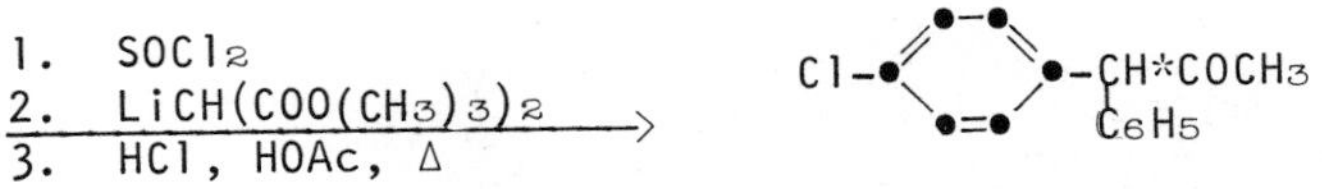

1. SOCl2
2. LiCH(COO(CH3)3)2
3. HCl, HOAc, Δ
Cl
CH*COCH3
C6H5

(72% from $*CO_2$)

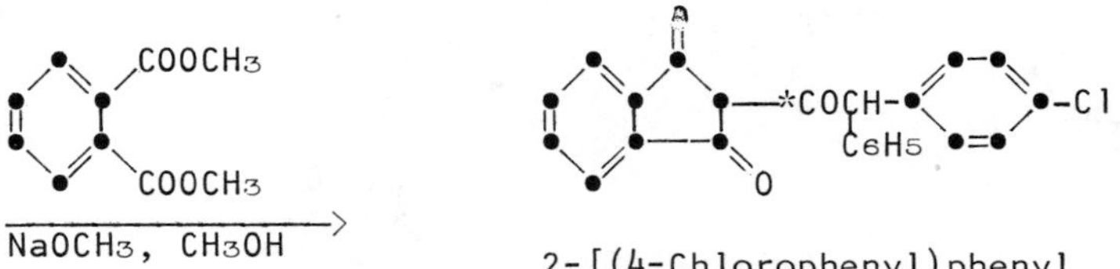

COOCH3
COOCH3
NaOCH3, CH3OH
O
*COCH-
C6H5
Cl
O

(50%; 36% from $*CO_2$)

2-[(4-Chlorophenyl)phenyl(acetyl-1-^{14}C)]-1H-indene-1,3(2H)-dione

L. Pichat, J. Tostain, and E. Boschetti, J. Label. Compound. Radiopharm., 15, 23 (1978).

CH_2OH
$C(OCH_3)_2$
$CH_2OCH_2C_6H_5$

1. $Br{-}{*}CH_2(CH_2)_{16}CH_3$, KOH, C_6H_6 (89%)
2. H_2, Pd, hexane (66%)
3. HCl

→

$CH_2O{-}{*}CH_2(CH_2)_{16}CH_3$
$C{=}O$
CH_2OH

1-Hydroxy-3-(octadecyloxy-1-^{14}C)-2-propanone

C. Piantadosi, K. Chae, K. S. Ishaq, and F. Snyder, J. Pharm. Sci., 62, 320 (1973).

$Cl{*}CH_2COOH$ ⟶ $C_6H_5S{-}{*}CH_2COCl$ —diazomethane / ether→ $C_6H_5S{-}{*}CH_2{-}CO{-}CH_2Cl$ (92%)

α-Chloroacetic-α-^{14}C acid

1-Chloro-3-(phenylthio)-2-propanone-3-[14]C

V. Rosnati, F. Sannicolo, and G. Pagani, Gazz. Chim. Ital., 99, 152 (1969); V. Rosnati, F. Sannicolo, and G. Zecchi, Tetrahedron Lett., 599 (1970).

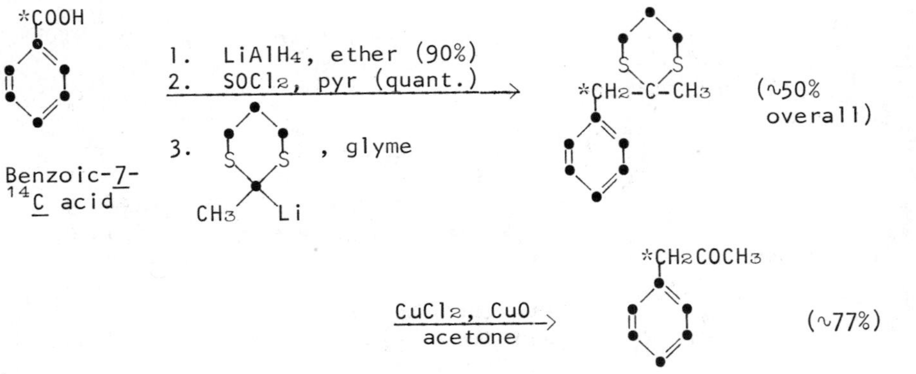
*COOH
Benzoic-7-^{14}C acid
1. LiAlH4, ether (90%)
2. SOCl2, pyr (quant.)
3. , glyme
CH3 Li
S S
*CH2-C-CH3
(~50% overall)
*CH2COCH3
CuCl2, CuO
acetone
(~77%)

1-Phenyl-2-propanone-1-^{14}C

L. Pichat and J.-P. Beaucourt, J. Label. Compound. Radiopharm., 12, 31 (1976).

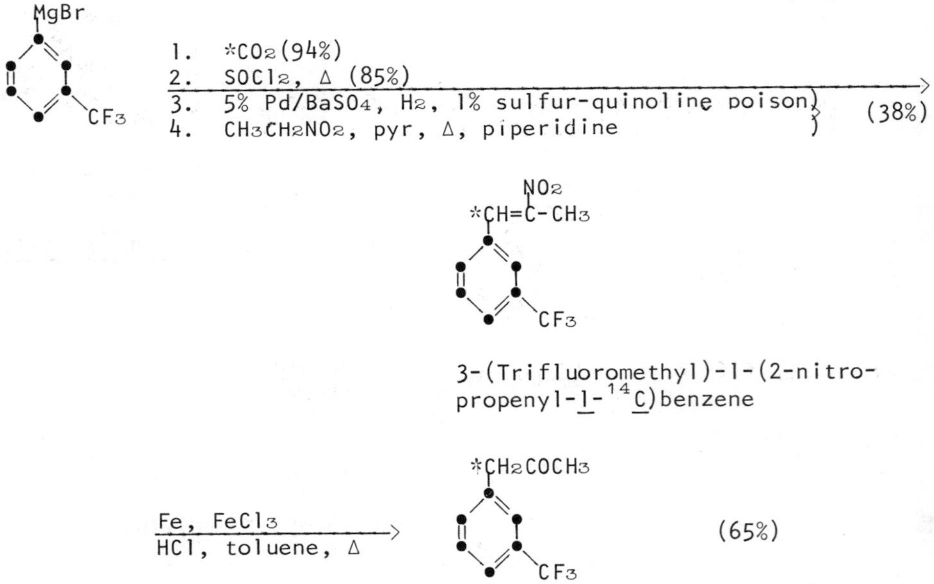
MgBr
CF3
1. *CO2 (94%)
2. SOCl2, Δ (85%)
3. 5% Pd/BaSO4, H2, 1% sulfur-quinoline poison
4. CH3CH2NO2, pyr, Δ, piperidine
(38%)
NO2
*CH=C-CH3
CF3
3-(Trifluoromethyl)-1-(2-nitropropenyl-1-^{14}C)benzene
*CH2COCH3
Fe, FeCl3
HCl, toluene, Δ
(65%)
CF3

1-(3-Trifluoromethylphenyl)-2-propanone-1-^{14}C

D. R. Hawkins and I. Midgley, J. Label. Compounds, 10, 663 (1974).

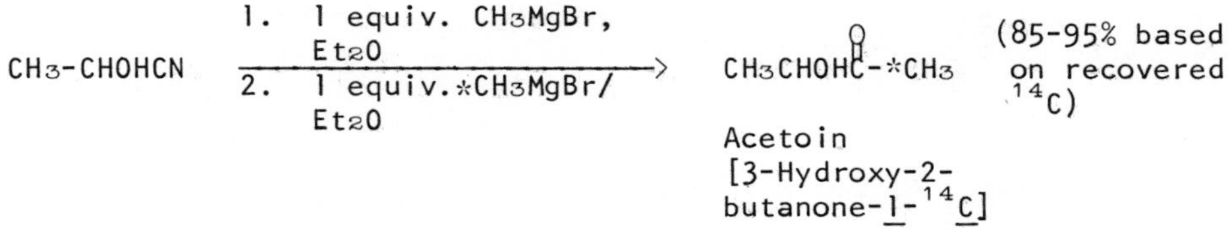
CH3-CHOHCN
1. 1 equiv. CH3MgBr, Et2O
2. 1 equiv.*CH3MgBr/ Et2O
CH3CHOHC(O)-*CH3
(85-95% based on recovered 14C)
Acetoin [3-Hydroxy-2-butanone-1-14C]

Using C_2H_5MgBr-^{14}C, labeled 2-hydroxy-3-pentanone was prepared in 65-75% yield.

J. L. Rabinowitz, J. Label. Compounds, 11, 453 (1975).

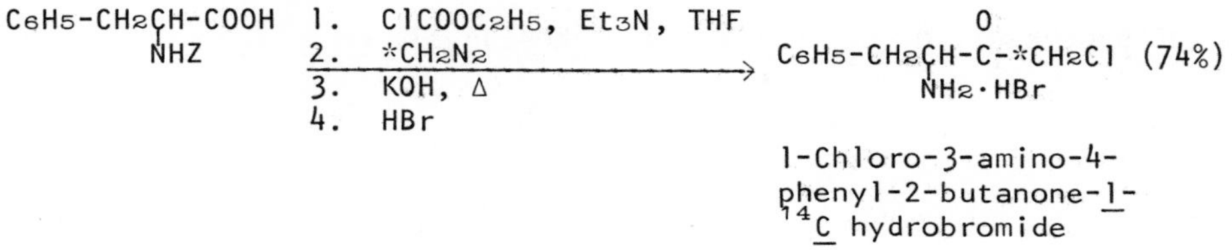
C6H5-CH2CH(NHZ)-COOH
1. ClCOOC2H5, Et3N, THF
2. *CH2N2
3. KOH, Δ
4. HBr
C6H5-CH2CH(NH2·HBr)-C(O)-*CH2Cl (74%)
1-Chloro-3-amino-4-phenyl-2-butanone-1-14C hydrobromide

S. Fittkau, J. Prakt. Chem., 315, 1037 (1973).

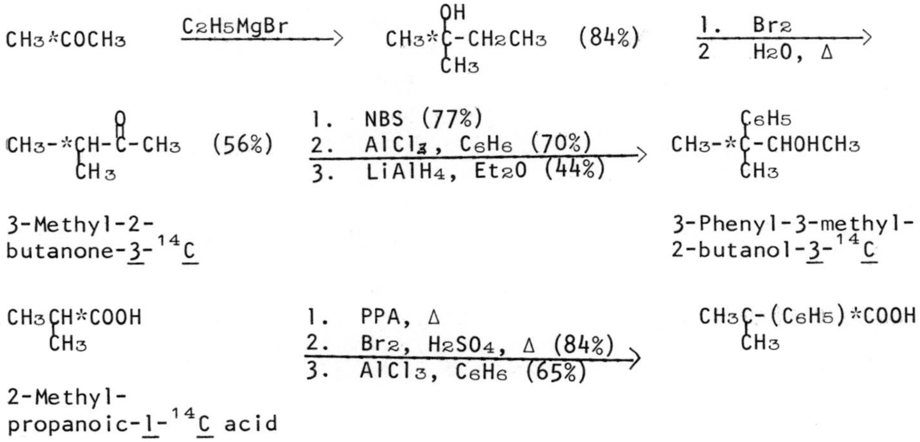
CH3*COCH3
C2H5MgBr
CH3*C(OH)(CH3)-CH2CH3 (84%)
1. Br2
2 H2O, Δ
CH3-*CH(CH3)-C(O)-CH3 (56%)
1. NBS (77%)
2. AlCl3, C6H6 (70%)
3. LiAlH4, Et2O (44%)
CH3-*C(C6H5)(CH3)-CHOHCH3
3-Methyl-2-butanone-3-14C
3-Phenyl-3-methyl-2-butanol-3-14C
CH3CH(CH3)*COOH
1. PPA, Δ
2. Br2, H2SO4, Δ (84%)
3. AlCl3, C6H6 (65%)
CH3C(CH3)-(C6H5)*COOH
2-Methylpropanoic-1-14C acid

$\xrightarrow[\text{2. } CH_3CdCl\ (73\%)]{\text{1. } SOCl_2\ (89\%)}$ $CH_3C(CH_3)(C_6H_5)\text{*}C(=O)\text{-}CH_3$

3-Phenyl-3-methyl-2-butanone-2-^{14}C

J. Laureillard, A. Laurent, and E. Laurent, Bull. Soc. Chim. Fr., part 2, 249 (1973).

$C_6H_5\text{-*}CHO$ $\xrightarrow[\text{HCl gas}]{CH_3COCH_2C_6H_5}$ $C_6H_5\text{*}CH{=}C(C_6H_5)\text{----}C(=O)\text{-}CH_3$ (62%)

Benzaldehyde-(carbonyl -^{14}C)

3,4-Diphenyl-3-buten-2-one-4-^{14}C

S. Goszczynski, M. Lozynski, and M. Kostanski, Rocz. Chem., 50, 499 (1976).

$\text{*}CH_3MgI$ + $CH_3CH_2CH_2CN$ $\xrightarrow{\text{ether}}$ $CH_3CH_2CH_2C(=O)\text{-*}CH_3$ (65%)

2-Pentanone-1-^{14}C

J. L. Rabinowitz and M. Zanger, J. Label. Compounds, 8, 657 (1972).

$(CH_3CO)_2O$ + $CH_3\text{*}COCH_3$ $\xrightarrow{BF_3,\ EtOAc}$

Acetone-2-^{14}C

$CH_3\text{*}C(=O)CH_2\text{*}C(=O)CH_3$ ("inverse addition"; 76% radiochemical yield; 79% chemical yield)

2,4-Pentanedione-2,4-^{14}C

H. E. Doorenbos, W. W. Muelder, and M. N. Wass, J. Label. Compounds, 8, 701 (1972).

$CH_3{*}COCH_3 \xrightarrow[BF_3]{Ac_2O} CH_3{*}\overset{O}{\overset{\|}{C}}-CH_2{*}\overset{O}{\overset{\|}{C}}-CH_3$ (85%)

2,4-Pentanedione-2,4-^{14}C

R. C. Thomas, J. Label. Compound. Radiopharm., 15, 461 (1978).

$CH_3{*}COCH_3 \longrightarrow CH_3{*}\underset{CH_3}{C}{=}CH{*}COCH_3$

Acetone-2-^{14}C

Mesityl oxide
[4-Methyl-3-Penten-2-one-2,4-^{14}C]

H. H. Hatt, G. D. Lichenwalter, and G. H. Riesser, Aust. J. Chem., 23, 561 (1970.

$CH_2{=}CHCH_2CH_2Br \xrightarrow[\text{3. LiOH; 4. } CH_3Li]{\text{1. Mg; 2. } {*}CO_2 \text{ (95\%)}} CH_2{=}CHCH_2CH_2{*}COCH_3$ (70% overall)

5-Hexen-2-one-2-^{14}C

R. L. Ellsworth, G. J. Gatto, H. T. Meriwether, and H. E. Mertel, J. Label. Compound. Radiopharm., 15, 613 (1978).

$(CH_3)_2CHCH_2CH(NH_2){*}COOH \xrightarrow[\text{2. } ClCOOC_2H_5,\ Et_3N,\ Et_2O \text{ (98\%)}]{\text{1. t-BOC-azide, } Et_3N,\ H_2O\text{/dioxane (98\%)}}$

DL-Leucine-1-^{14}C

$(CH_3)_2CHCH_2\underset{NH\text{-}t\text{-}BOC}{CH}-{*}COOC_2H_5 \xrightarrow[\text{2. HCl gas, } Et_2O \text{ (99\%)}]{\text{1. } CH_2N_2,\ Et_2O \text{ (90\%)}}$

$CH_3\underset{CH_3}{C}HCH_2\underset{NH_2\cdot HCl}{CH}-{*}COCH_2Cl$ (86% overall)

3-Amino-1-chloro-5-methylhexan-2-one-2-^{14}C hydrochloride

N. J. Lewis, J. Hes, P. Yip, and F. D. Cazer, J. Label. Compound. Radiopharm., 13, 487 (1977).

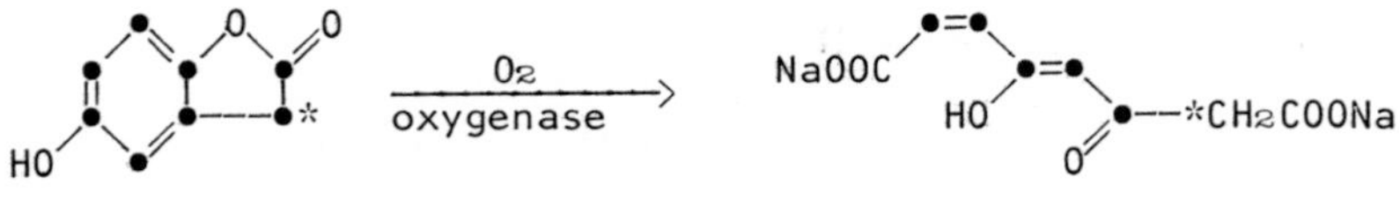

5-Hydroxy-2(3H)-benzofuranone-4-^{14}C

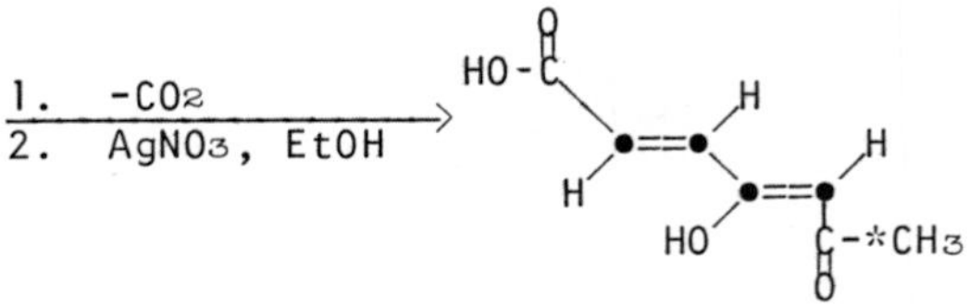

(E,Z)-4-Hydroxy-6-oxo-2,4-heptadienoic-7-^{14}C acid

S. Seltzer, J. Label. Compounds, 9, 643 (1973).

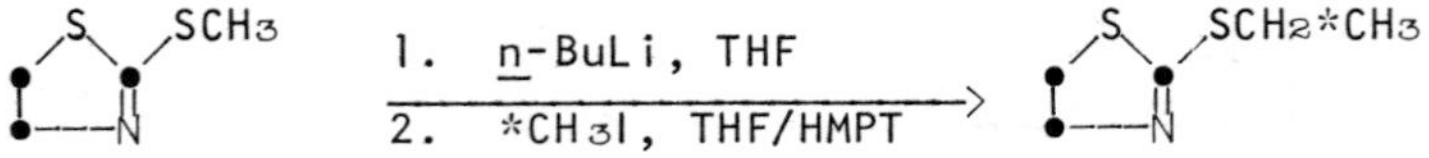

(56%)

$\xrightarrow{C_6H_5CH_2Br}$ $^*CH_3CH_2Br$ $\xrightarrow[2.\ (CH_3)_2NCH(CH_3)CH_2C(C_6H_5)_2CN,\ C_6H_6]{1.\ Mg,\ Et_2O}$

Bromoethane-2-^{14}C

$^*CH_3CH_2COC(C_6H_5)_2$-$CH_2CH(CH_3)N(CH_3)_2$ (14% from $^*CH_3I$)

Methadone
[6-(Dimethylamino)-4,4-diphenyl-3-heptanone-1-^{14}C]

Nguyen-Hoang-Nam, R. Pontikis, H. Hoellinger, and L. Pichat, J. Label. Compound. Radiopharm., 14, 775 (1978).

HC≡C[CH=CH]$_2$-CHO $\xrightarrow[2.\ ^*CH_3\text{-}[C\equiv C]_2H]{1.\ C_2H_5MgBr}$

$^*CH_3$-[C≡C]$_3$-[CH=CH]$_2$-CHOH-CH_2CH_3 (49%)

$\xrightarrow[\text{ether}]{MnO_2}$ $^{*}CH_3-[C{\equiv}C]_3-[CH{=}CH]_2COCH_2CH_3$

Tetradeca-4,6-diene-8,10,12-triyne-3-one-14-^{14}C

F. Bohlmann, W. Karl, and R. Zeisberg, Chem. Ber., 103, 2860 (1970).

3-4 Alicyclic Ketones

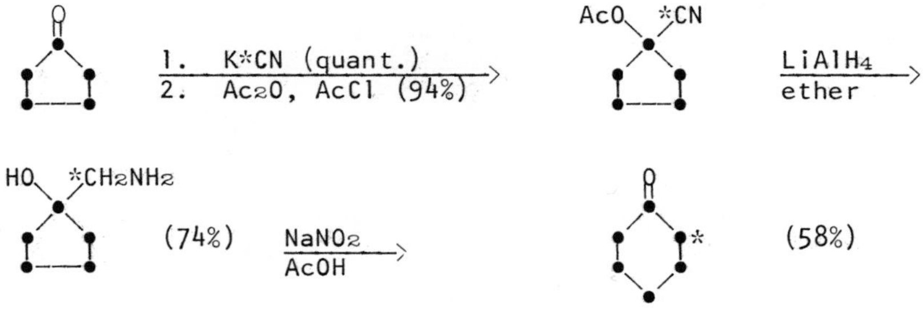
1. K*CN (quant.)
2. Ac2O, AcCl (94%)
AcO *CN
LiAlH4
ether
HO *CH2NH2
(74%)
NaNO2
AcOH
(58%)

Cyclohexanone-2-^{14}C

A. Yoshitake, Y. Makari, K. Kawahara, and T. Doi, J. Label. Compound. Radiopharm., 12, 247 (1976).

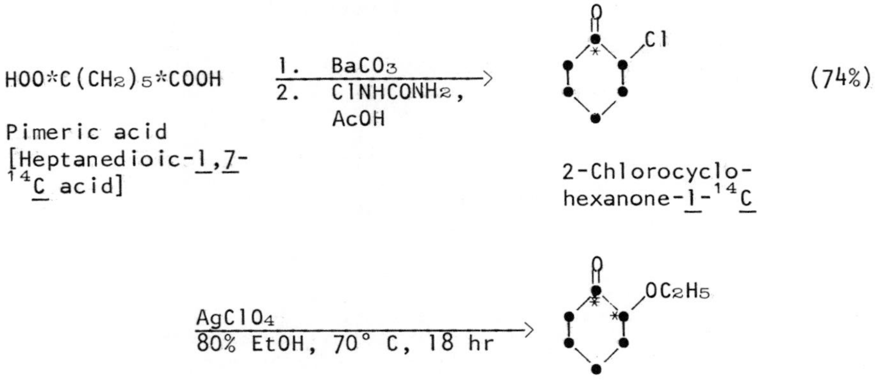
HOO*C(CH2)5*COOH
1. BaCO3
2. ClNHCONH2, AcOH
Cl
(74%)
AgClO4
80% EtOH, 70° C, 18 hr
OC2H5

Pimeric acid [Heptanedioic-1,7-^{14}C acid]

2-Chlorocyclohexanone-1-^{14}C

2-Ethoxycyclohexanone-1,2-^{14}C

A yield of 31% was obtained of material bearing 20-25% of the label in position 2 and 75-80% in position 1. 2-Hydroxycyclohexanone was also isolated in 23% yield. A mechanism involving a 1-ethoxycyclohexene oxide intermediate is proposed.

T. Masuike, N. Furukawa, and S. Oae, Bull. Chem. Soc. Jap., 44, 448 (1971).

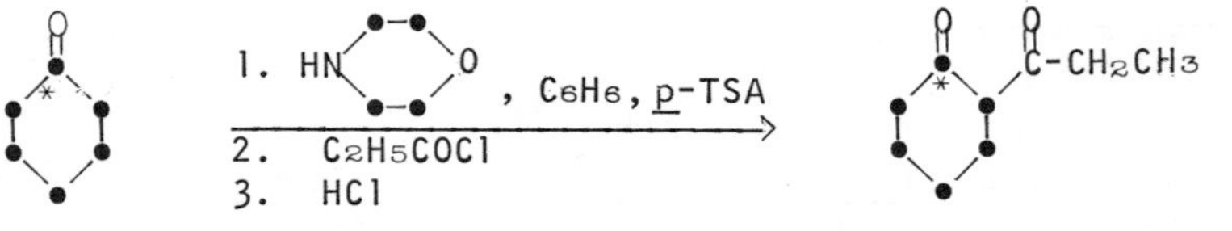
1. HN
O
, C_6H_6, p-TSA
2. C_2H_5COCl
3. HCl
C-CH_2CH_3

(63%)

2-(1-Oxopropyl)-cyclohexanone-1-^{14}C

J. Brugidou, H. Christol, and Y. Langourieux, Bull. Soc. Chim. Fr., 4062 (1970).

HOO*C-$(CH_2)_5$COOC_2H_5 $\xrightarrow[\text{esterification}]{\text{trans}}$ HOO*C-$(CH_2)_5$-COOC$(C_2H_5)_3$

Monoethyl pimelic acid [Heptanedioic-1-^{14}C acid ethyl ester]

Heptanedioic-1-^{14}C acid 1,1-diethylpropyl ester

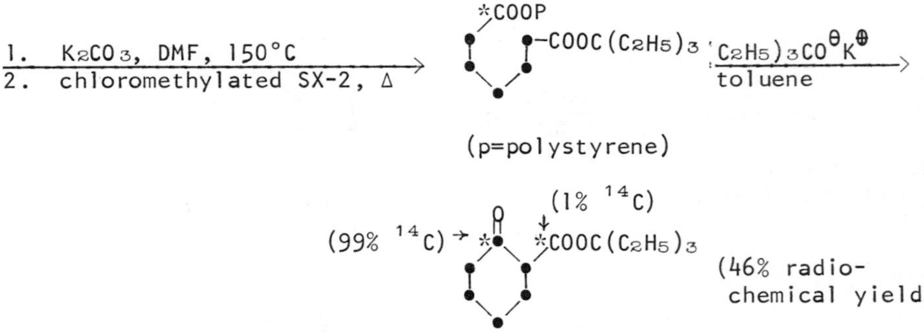
1. K_2CO_3, DMF, 150°C
2. chloromethylated SX-2, Δ
*COOP
-COOC$(C_2H_5)_3$
$(C_2H_5)_3CO^{\ominus}K^{\oplus}$
toluene
(p=polystyrene)
(1% ^{14}C)
(99% ^{14}C)
*COOC$(C_2H_5)_3$

(46% radiochemical yield)

2-Oxocyclohexanecarboxylic-2-^{14}C acid 1,1-diethylpropyl ester

Unidirectional Dieckmann cyclization via solid-phase synthesis

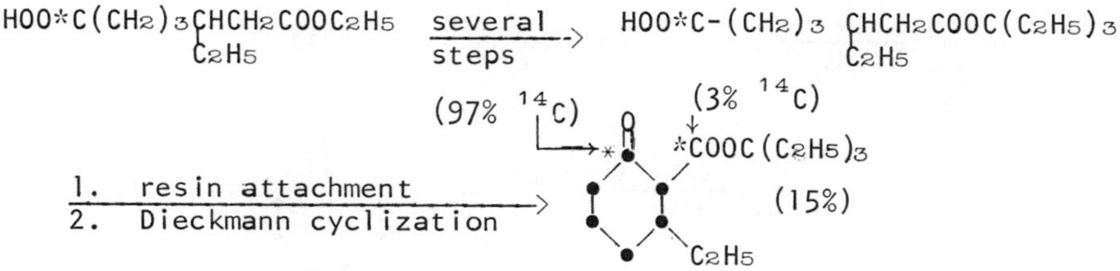
HOO*C(CH2)3CHCH2COOC2H5
C2H5
several steps
HOO*C-(CH2)3 CHCH2COOC(C2H5)3
C2H5
(97% 14C)
(3% 14C)
*COOC(C2H5)3
1. resin attachment
2. Dieckmann cyclization
(15%)
C2H5

2-Ethyl-5-oxocyclohexane-carboxylic-^{14}C acid 1,1-diethylpropyl ester

The position of ^{14}C was determined by decarboxylation to cyclohexanones.

J. I. Crowley and H. Rapoport, J. Amer. Chem. Soc., 92, 6363 (1970).

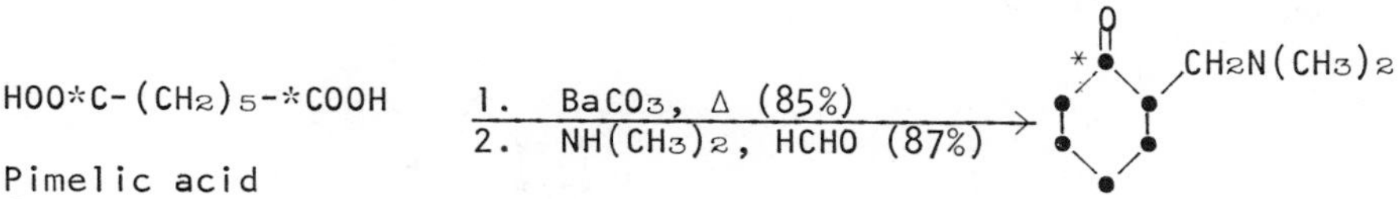
HOO*C-(CH2)5-*COOH
1. BaCO3, Δ (85%)
2. NH(CH3)2, HCHO (87%)
CH2N(CH3)2

Pimelic acid [Heptanedioic-1,7-^{14}C acid]

N-(Dimethylaminomethyl)-2-cyclohexanone-1-^{14}C

J. Brugidou, H. Christol, and Y. Langourieux, Bull. Soc. Chim. Fr., 4062 (1970).

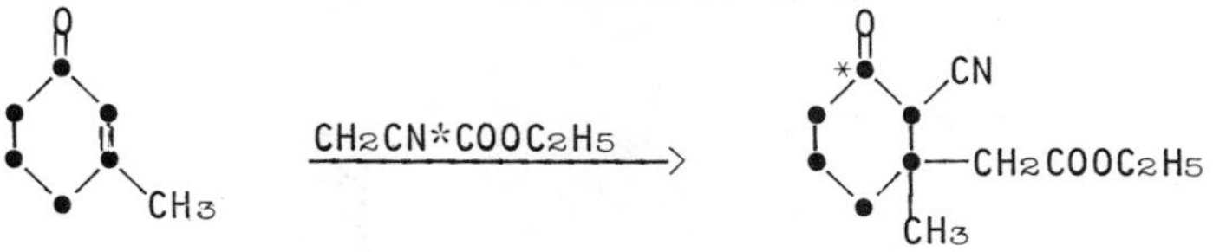
CH3
CH2CN*COOC2H5
CN
CH2COOC2H5
CH3

2-Cyano-1-methyl-3-oxocyclohexaneacetic-3-^{14}C acid ethyl ester

Degradation reactions and ^{13}C labeling indicated the position of the label. Rearrangement via a bicyclo(2.2.2)octane intermediate is proposed.

R. K. Hill and N. D. Ledford, J. Amer. Chem. Soc., 97, 666 (1975).

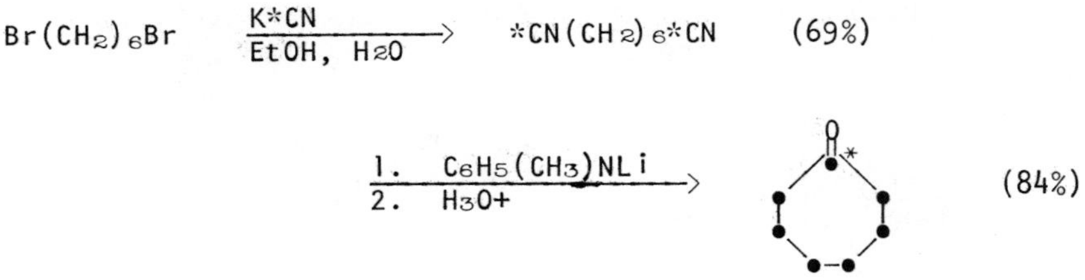
Br(CH2)6Br
K*CN
EtOH, H2O
*CN(CH2)6*CN
(69%)
1. C6H5(CH3)NLi
2. H3O+
O
*
(84%)

Cycloheptanone-1-^{14}C

A. T. Bottini, K. A. Frost II, B. R. Anderson, and V. Dev, Tetrahedron, 29, 1975 (1973).

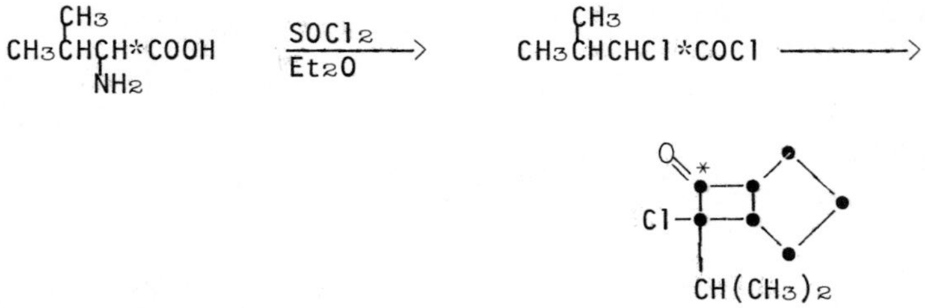
CH3
CH3CHCH*COOH
NH2
SOCl2
Et2O
CH3
CH3CHCHCl*COCl
O
*
Cl
CH(CH3)2

5-Chloro-5(1-methylethyl)-bicyclo[3.2.0] heptan-4-one-4-^{14}C

The product was used for ring contraction studies.

P. R. Brook and D. E. Kitson, J. Chem. Soc., Chem. Commun., 87 (1978).

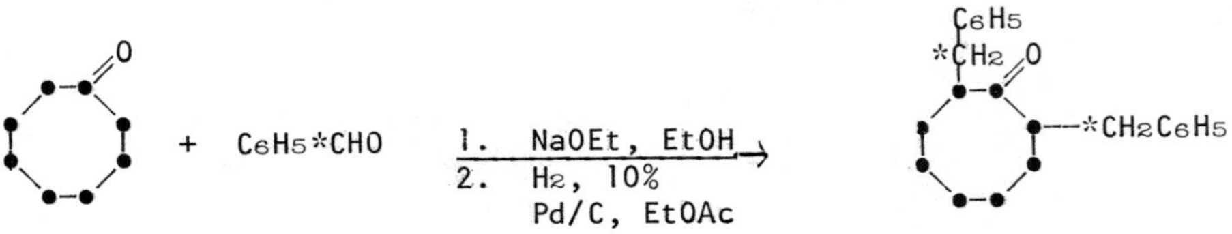
O
+
C6H5*CHO
1. NaOEt, EtOH
2. H2, 10%
Pd/C, EtOAc
C6H5
*CH2
O
*CH2C6H5

2,8-Diphenyl-(methyl-^{14}C)-cyclooctanone

I. H. Hall, R. G. Lamb, M.-H. H. Mar, G. L. Carlson, and C. Piantadosi, J. Pharm. Sci., 64, 235 (1975).

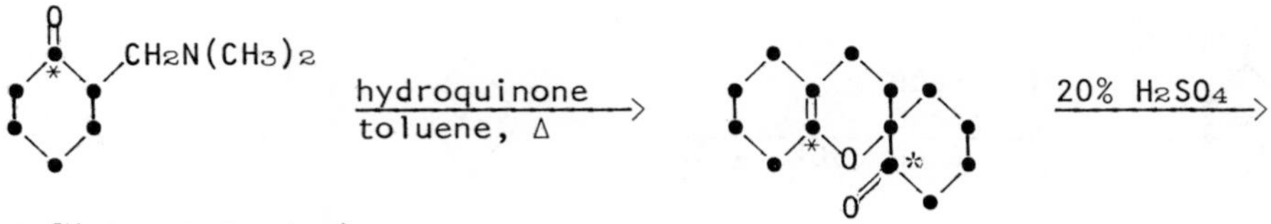
CH2N(CH3)2
hydroquinone
toluene, Δ
20% H2SO4

2-[(Dimethylamino)-methyl]2-cyclohexanone-1-^{14}C

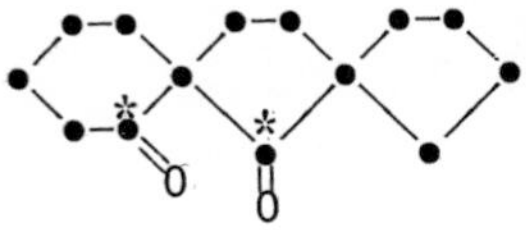

(70% from cyclohexanone derivative)

Dispiro[4.1.5.2]tetradecane-6,8-dione-6,8-^{14}C

J. Brugidou, H. Christol, and Y. Langourieux, Bull. Soc. Chim. Fr., 4062 (1970).

3-5 Aromatic Ketones

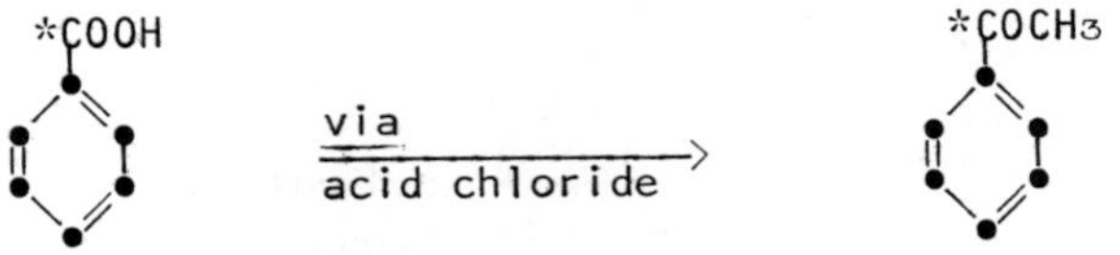
*COOH
via
acid chloride
*COCH3

(89%)

1-Phenylethanone-1-^{14}C

J. Volford and K. Harsanyi, J. Label. Compounds, 9, 219 (1973).

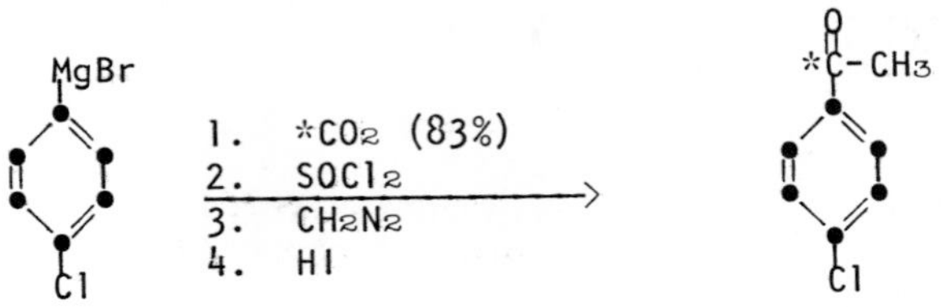
MgBr
Cl
1. *CO2 (83%)
2. SOCl2
3. CH2N2
4. HI
*C-CH3
Cl

1-(4-Chlorophenyl)ethanone-1-^{14}C

J. P. Noël, A. Benakis, R. Valette, M. Herbert, and L. Pichat, J. Label. Compounds, 8, 157 (1972).

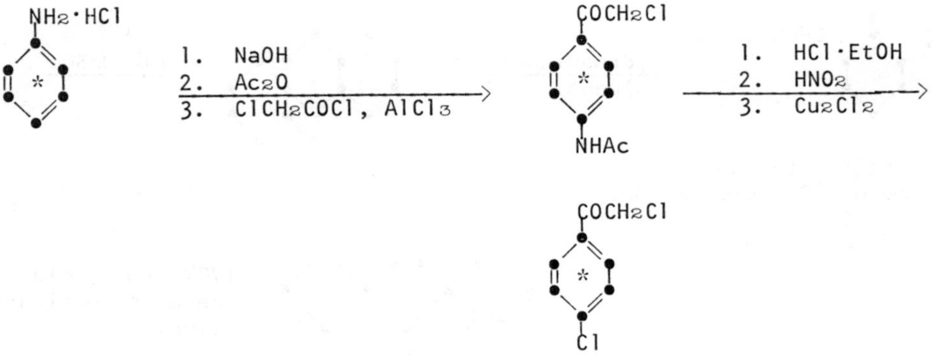
NH2·HCl
1. NaOH
2. Ac2O
3. ClCH2COCl, AlCl3
COCH2Cl
NHAc
1. HCl·EtOH
2. HNO2
3. Cu2Cl2
COCH2Cl
Cl

2-Chloro-1-(4-chlorophenyl)-ring-^{14}C)ethanone

F. S. Tanaka, J. Agr. Food. Chem., 18, 213 (1970).

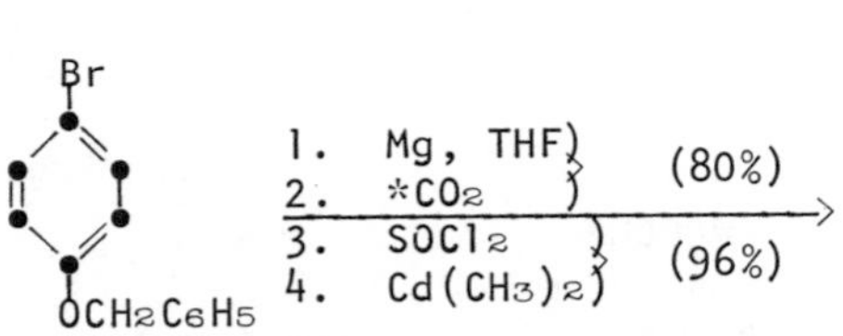
Br
OCH2C6H5
1. Mg, THF
2. *CO2
(80%)
3. SOCl2
4. Cd(CH3)2
(96%)
O
*C-CH3
OCH2C6H5

1-(4-(Phenylmethoxy) phenylethanone-1-^{14}C

K.-H. Schweer, Atompraxis, 12, 85 (1966).

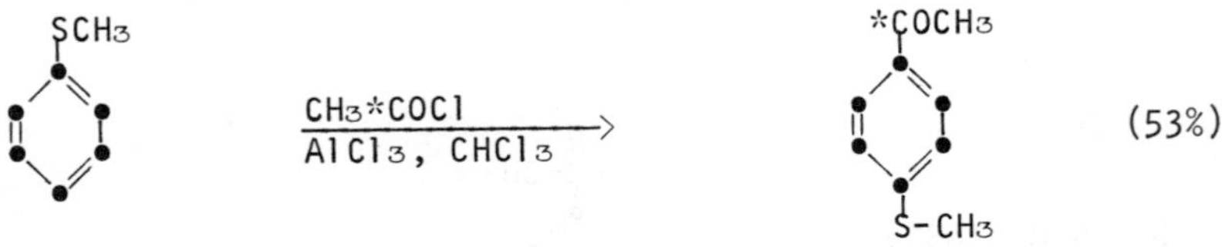
SCH3
CH3*COCl
AlCl3, CHCl3
*COCH3
S-CH3
(53%)

1-(4-Methylthio) phtnylethanone-1-^{14}C

E. Schraven and D. Trottnow, Arzneim.-Forsch.-(Drug Res.), 26, 213 (1976).

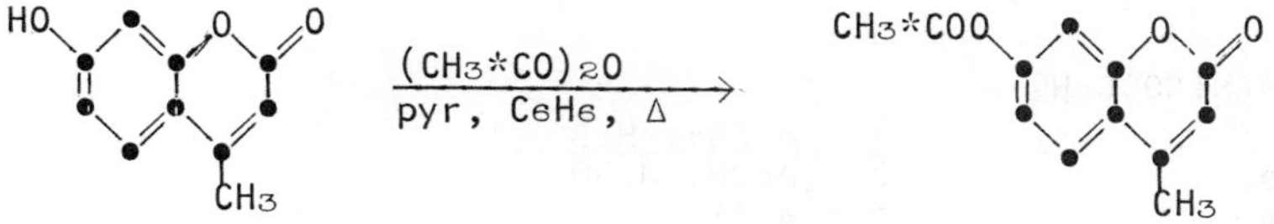
HO
O
O
(CH3*CO)2O
pyr, C6H6, Δ
CH3
CH3*COO
O
O
CH3

7-(Acetyloxy-1-^{14}C)-4-methyl-2H-1-benzopyran-2-one

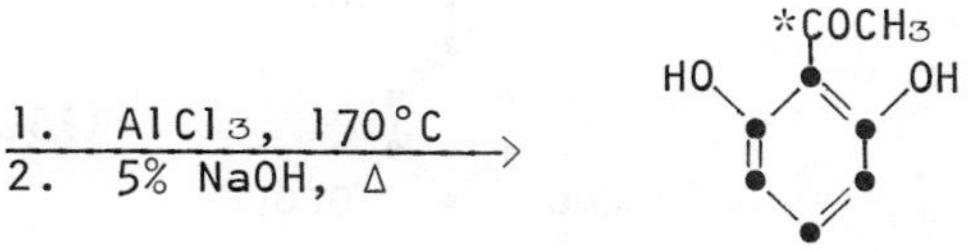
1. AlCl3, 170°C
2. 5% NaOH, Δ
*COCH3
HO
OH

(78%; two steps)

1-(2,6-Dihydroxyphenyl)-ethanone-1-^{14}C

Y. Soeda, S. Kato, D. Takiguchi, R. Sakimoto, and K. Ohkuma, J. Agr. Food. Chem., 20, 936 (1972).

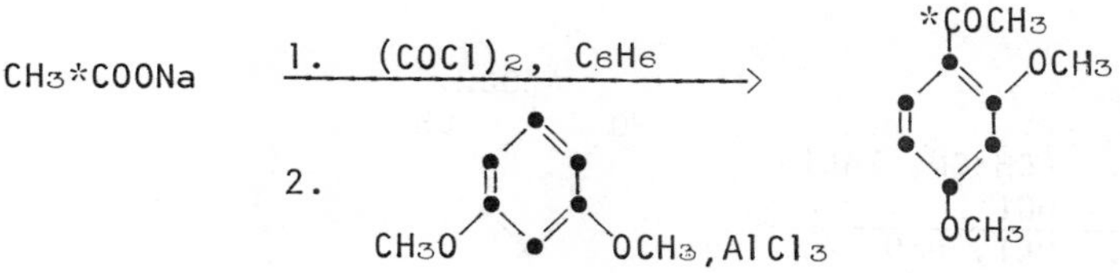
CH3*COONa
1. (COCl)2, C6H6
2.
CH3O
OCH3, AlCl3
*COCH3
OCH3
OCH3

(71%)

1-(2,4-Dimethoxyphenyl)-ethanone-1-^{14}C

B. Chabannes, B. Duperray, and H. Pacheo, Bull. Soc. Chim. Fr., 801 (1972).

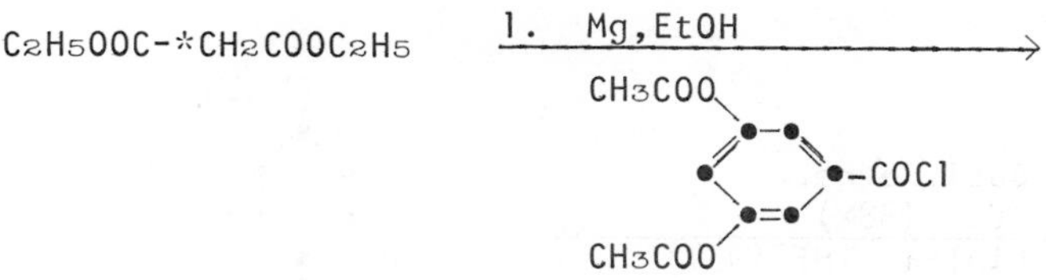
C2H5OOC-*CH2COOC2H5
1. Mg, EtOH
CH3COO
-COCl
CH3COO

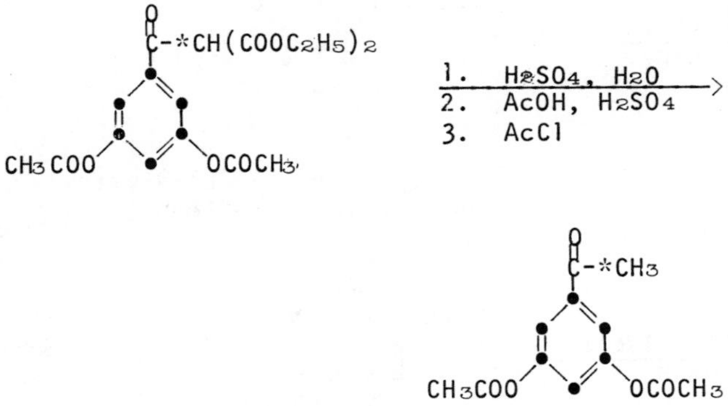
C-*CH(COOC2H5)2
CH3COO
OCOCH3
1. H2SO4, H2O
2. AcOH, H2SO4
3. AcCl
C-*CH3
CH3COO
OCOCH3

(75% overall)

1-[3,5-Bis(acetyloxy)phenyl]-ethanone-2-^{14}C

A. Saus, K. H. Klinger, and E. Bickel, Arzneim.-Forsch-(Drug Res.), 27, 35 (1977).

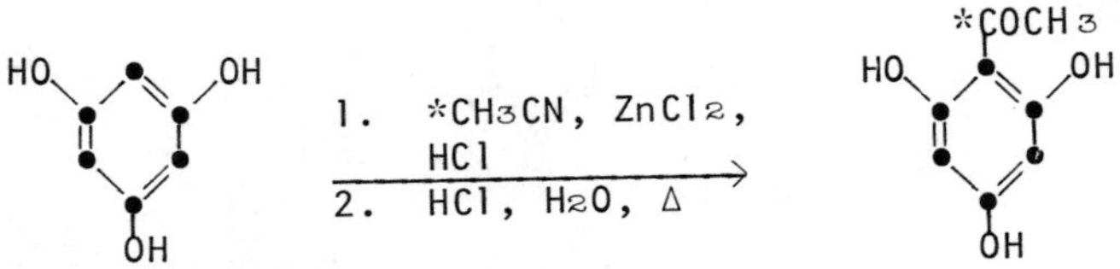
HO
OH
OH
1. *CH3CN, ZnCl2, HCl
2. HCl, H2O, Δ
*COCH3
HO
OH
OH

1-(2,4,6-Trihydroxyphenyl) ethanone-1-^{14}C

T. Honohan, R. L. Hale, J. P. Brown, and R. E. Wingard, Jr., J. Agr. Food Chem., 24, 906 (1976).

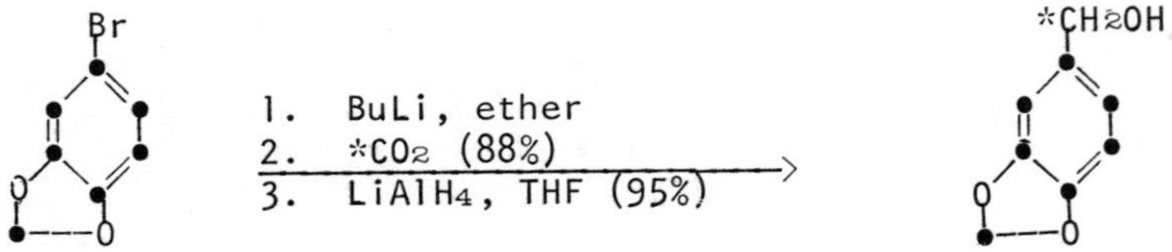
Br
1. BuLi, ether
2. *CO2 (88%)
3. LiAlH4, THF (95%)
*CH2OH

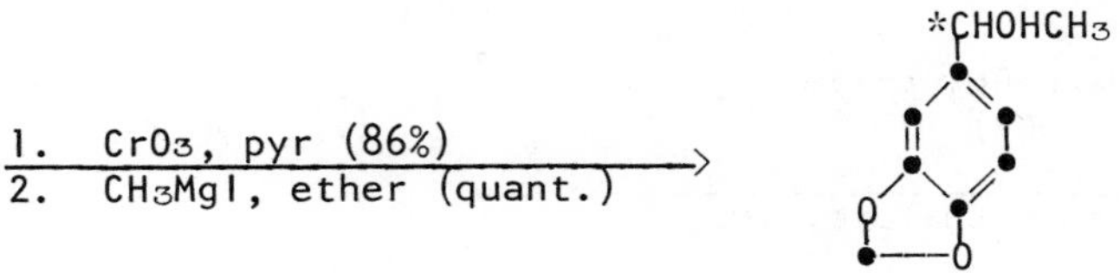

1. CrO3, pyr (86%)
2. CH3MgI, ether (quant.)
*CHOHCH3

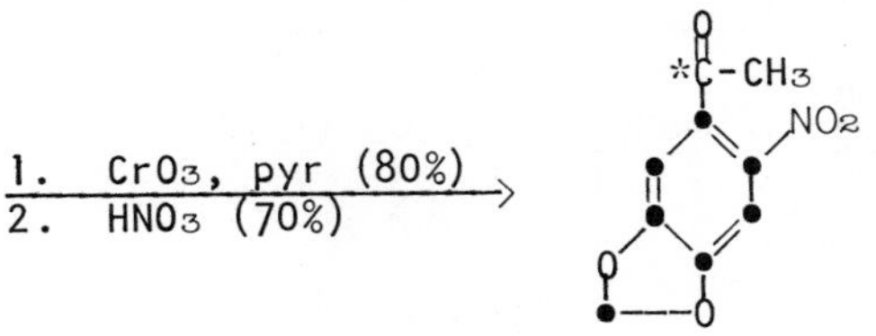

1. CrO3, pyr (80%)
2. HNO3 (70%)
*C-CH3
NO2

1-(6-Nitro-1,3-benzodioxol-5-yl) ethanone-1-^{14}C

T. Nagasaki, Y. Katsuyama, and H. Minato, J. Label. Compound. Radiopharm. 12, 409 (1976).

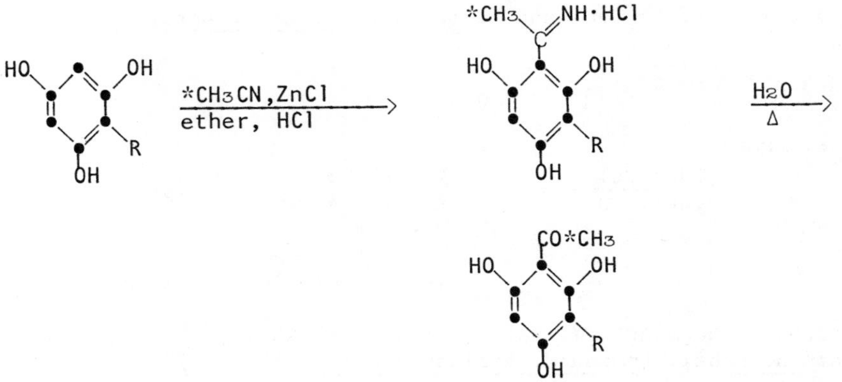

*CH3CN,ZnCl
ether, HCl
*CH3
NH·HCl
H2O
Δ
CO*CH3
HO
OH
R
OH

R = H; 1-(2,4,6-Trihydroxy-phenyl)-ethanone-2-^{14}C
R = CH$_3$; 1-(2,4,6-Trihydroxy-3-methylphenyl)ethanone-2-^{14}C

H. Taguchi, U. Sankawa, and S. Shibata, Chem. Pharm. Bull. (Tokyo), 17, 2054 (1969).

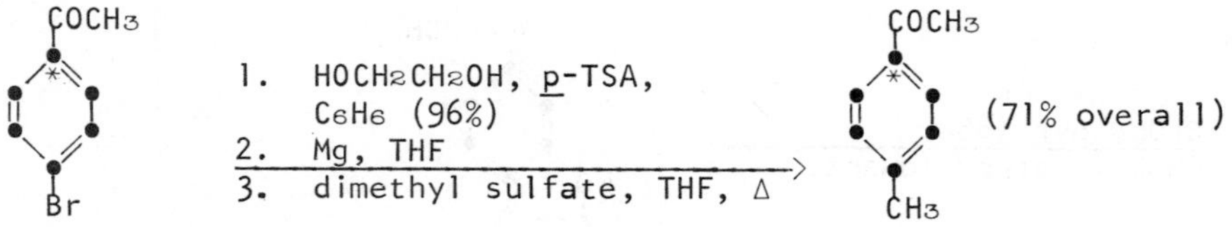
COCH3
Br
1. HOCH2CH2OH, p-TSA, C6H6 (96%)
2. Mg, THF
3. dimethyl sulfate, THF, Δ
COCH3
CH3
(71% overall)

1-(4-Bromophenyl-1-^{14}C)-ethanone

1-(4-Methylphenyl-1-^{14}C)ethanone

B. W. Palmer and A. Fry, J. Label. Compounds, 6, 303 (1970.

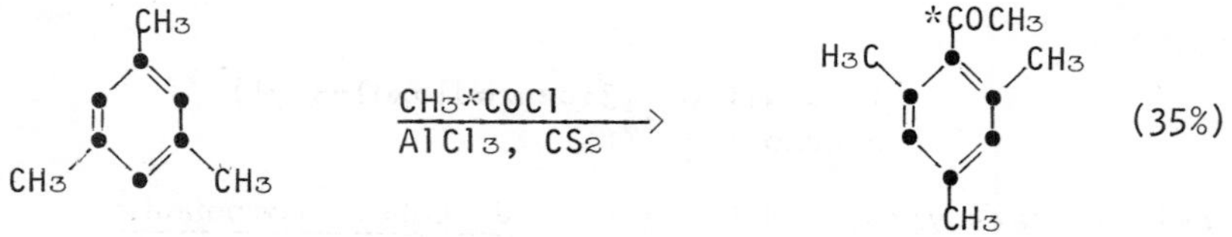
CH3
CH3
CH3
CH3*COCl
AlCl3, CS2
*COCH3
H3C
CH3
CH3
(35%)

1-(2,4,6-Trimethylphenyl)ethanone-1-^{14}C

H. Rodé-Gowal, H. L. Dao, and H. Dahn, Helv. Chim. Acta, 57, 2209 (1974).

MgBr
CH3*COCl
CuCl, Cu
*COCH3
(51%)

1-(2-Naphthalenyl)ethanone-1-^{14}C

H. Minato, T. Nagasaki, Y. Katsuyama, T. Yokoshima, K. Suga, and T. Ueda, J. Label. Compound. Radiopharm., 13, 103 (1977).

$$C_6H_5CH_2{*}COOH \xrightarrow[2.\ AlCl_3,\ C_6H_6]{1.\ PCl_3,\ \Delta} C_6H_5\text{-}{*}\overset{O}{\overset{\|}{C}}\text{-}CH_2C_6H_5 \quad (97\%)$$

Phenyl(phenylmethyl)methanone-α-^{14}C

G. Capozzi, G. Melloni, and G. Modena, J. Chem. Soc. (C), 3018 (1971).

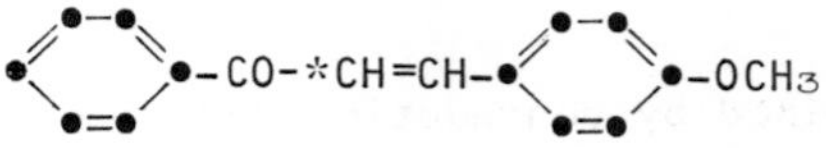

1. $Tl(OAc)_3$, CH_3OH
2. HCl, EtOH

1-Phenyl-3-(4-methoxyphenyl)-2-propen-1-one-2-^{14}C

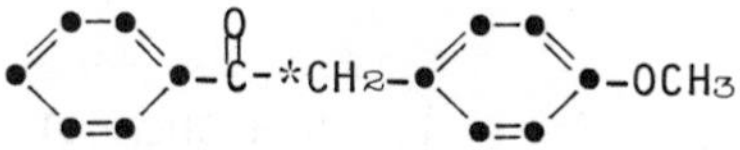

1-Phenyl-2-(4-methoxyphenyl)-ethanone-2-^{14}C

The position of the label in deoxybenzoin was determined by degradation reactions; the position of the label confirms a 1,2-aryl group rearrangement during $Tl(OAc)_3$ oxidation.

W. D. Ollis, K. L. Ormand, and I. O. Sutherland, J. Chem. Soc. (C) (Org.), 119 (1970).

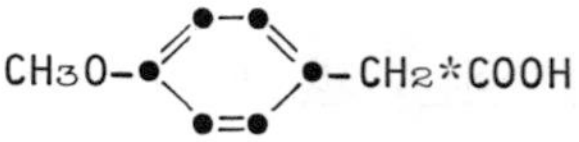

1. $SOCl_2$
2. $C_6H_5OCH_3$, $AlCl_3$ } 63%)

4-Methoxyphenylacetic-1-^{14}C acid

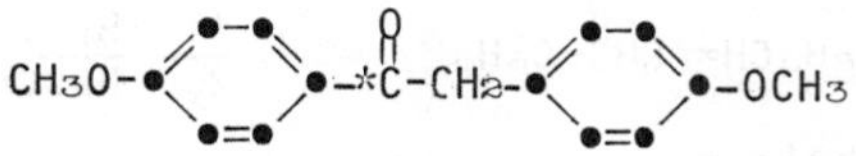

1,2-Bis(4-methoxyphenyl)ethanone-1-^{14}C

R. C. Thomas, J. Label. Compounds, 11, 355 (1975).

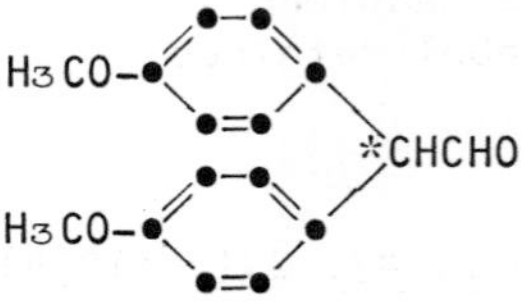

50% H_2SO_4, Δ

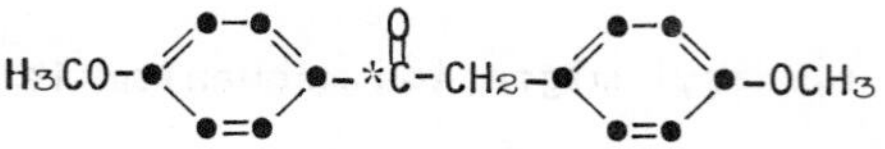

α-(4-Methoxyphenyl)-4-methoxybenzeneacetaldehyde-α-^{14}C

1,2-Bis(4-methoxyphenyl)ethanone-1-^{14}C

The position of the label was determined by degradation reactions.

W. Tadros, R. R. Tadros, and S. B. Awad, Helv. Chim. Acta, 59, 355 (1976).

C_6H_5-*CO-C_6H_5 $\xrightarrow[\text{2. } HCOOH]{\text{1. } C_6H_5CH_2MgCl}$ $(C_6H_5)_2$*C=CHC_6H_5

1,1',1''-[1-(Ethenyl-1-^{14}C)-2-ylidene]trisbenzene

$\xrightarrow[\text{2. } AgNO_3,\ CH_3OH/H_2O]{\text{1. } 5\%\ Br_2/CHCl_3}$ C_6H_5-*C(=O)-CH$(C_6H_5)_2$ (85%)

1,2-Diphenylethanone-1-[14]C

100% Phenyl migration was determined by degradation reactions; a mechanism is proposed.

F. J. Kakis, D. Brase, and A. Oshima, J. Org. Chem., 36, 4117 (1971).

C_6H_5CH=*CHC(=O)-C_6H_5 $\xrightarrow[\text{2. } NaOCH_3\ (62\%)]{\text{1. } Br_2,\ \text{benzene}\ (82\%)}$ C_6H_5C(OH)=*CHC(=O)-C_6H_5

Chalcone
[1,3-Diphenyl-2-propen-1-one-2-^{14}C]

$\xrightarrow[AcOH]{Pb(OAc)_4}$ C_6H_5-*C(=O)-*C(=O)-C_6H_5 (7%)

Benzil
[Diphenylethandione-1,2-^{14}C]
(50% of label retained)

A 1,2-aryl migration mechanism is discussed.

K. Kurosawa and A. Moriyama, Bull. Chem. Soc. Jap., 47, 2717 (1974).

C_2H_5MgI —(1. $*CO_2$ (98%); 2. $AlCl_3$, C_6H_6 (78%))→ C_6H_5-$*COCH_2CH_3$

1-Phenyl-1-propanone-1-^{14}C

—(1. Br_2, CCl_4; 2. CH_3NH_2, C_6H_6)→ $C_6H_5*COCHCH_3$ ($NHCH_3 \cdot HCl$ on CH) (35%)

2-(Methylamino)-1-phenyl-1-propanone-1-^{14}C hydrochloride

Nguyen-Hoang-Nam, M. Herbert, Nguyen-Dat-Xuong, and L. Pichat, J. Label. Compounds, 4, 325 (1968).

H_2N-CH_2*CH_2COOH —(1. TsCl (62%); 2. CH_3I, NaOH (∿47%); 3. HCl, Δ; 4. C_6H_5COCl, NaOH (steps 3–4: 50%))→ $CH_3NCH_2*CH_2COOH$ (COC_6H_5 on N)

β-Alanine-2-^{14}C

—(1. 10% HCl, Δ; 2. H_2, 10% Pd/C, 36% HCHO)→ $(CH_3)_2NCH_2$-$*CH_2COOH$ (91%)

—(1. $SOCl_2$; 2. C_6H_6, $AlCl_3$)→ C_6H_5-C(=O)-$*CH_2CH_2N(CH_3)_2$ (90-100%)

3-(Dimethylamino)-1-phenyl-1-propanone-2-^{14}C

β-Alanine-1-^{14}C was similarly treated to give the corresponding 1-^{14}C labeled product.

A. A. Liebman, B. F. Mundy, and H. Rapoport, J. Amer. Chem. Soc., 89, 664 (1967).

$C_6H_5COCH_3$ —($H*CHO$; $NH(CH_3)_2 \cdot HCl$)→ C_6H_5C(=O)-$CH_2*CH_2N(CH_3)_2 \cdot HCl$

3-(Dimethylamino)-1-phenyl-1-propanone-3-^{14}C

L. A. Holt and B. Milligan, Aust. J. Biol. Sci., 27, 23 (1974); Aust. J. Chem., 30, 2277 (1977).

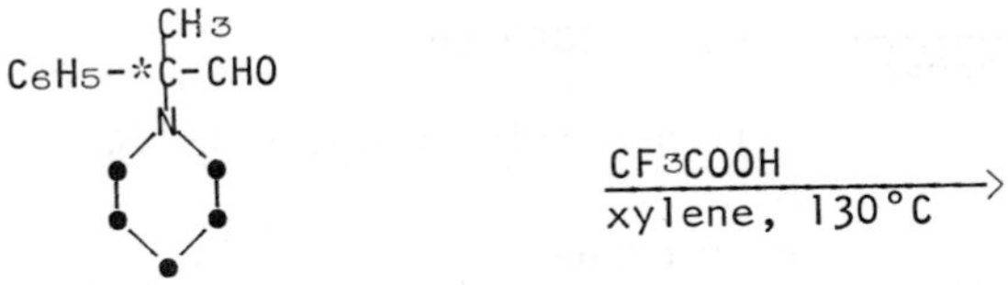

C_6H_5-*C-CHO
CH_3
N
CF_3COOH
xylene, 130°C

α-Methyl-α-phenyl-1-piperidineacetaldehyde-α-^{14}C

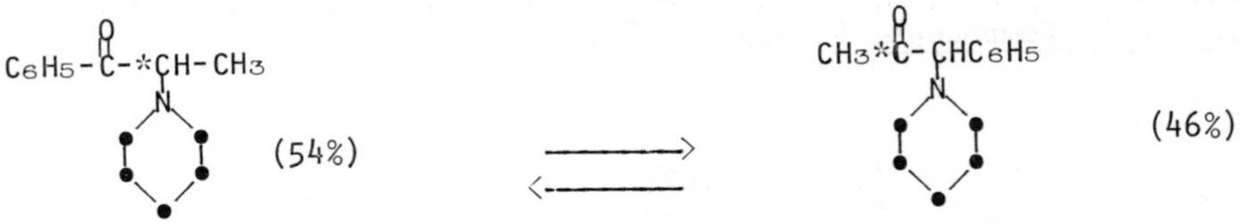

C_6H_5-C-*CH-CH_3
(54%)
CH_3*C-CHC_6H_5
(46%)

1-Phenyl-2-(1-piperidinyl)-1-propanone-2-^{14}C

1-Phenyl-1-(1-piperidinyl)-2-propanone-2-^{14}C

The mixture was separable by chromatography; exclusive phenyl migration was indicated by the position of the label, which was determined by degradation studies.

R. Nouri-Bimorghi and L. Pichat, Bull. Soc. Chim. Fr., 4057 (1969).

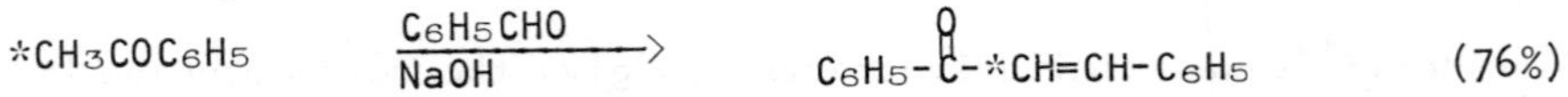

*$CH_3COC_6H_5$
C_6H_5CHO
NaOH
C_6H_5-C-*CH=CH-C_6H_5
(76%)

Chalcone
[1,3-Diphenyl-2-propen-1-one-2-^{14}C]

A 1,2-aryl migration mechanism is discussed.

K. Kurosawa and A. Moriyama, Bull. Chem. Soc. Jap., 47, 2717 (1974).

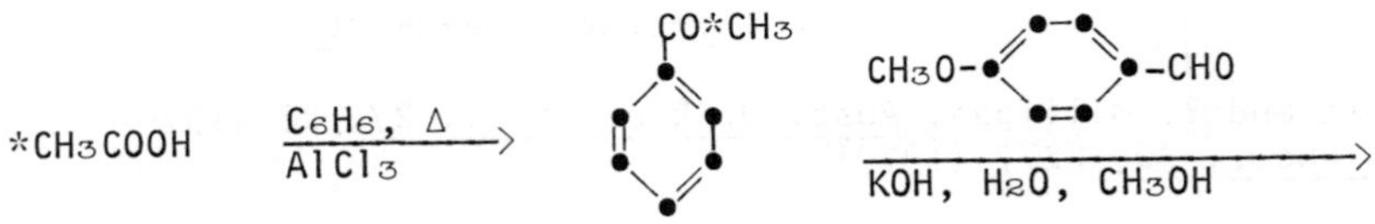

*CH_3COOH
C_6H_6, Δ
$AlCl_3$
CO*CH_3
CH_3O-
-CHO
KOH, H_2O, CH_3OH

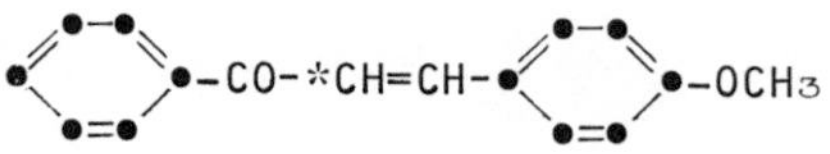

3-(4-Methoxyphenyl)-1-phenyl-2-propen-1-one-2-^{14}C

W. D. Ollis, K. L. Ormand, and I. O. Sutherland, J. Chem. Soc. (C) (Org.), 119 (1970).

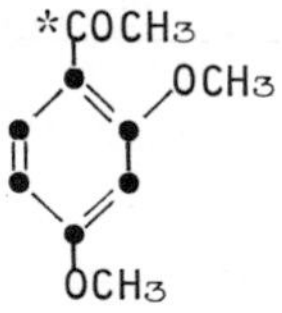

+

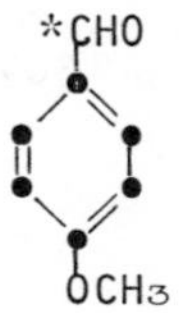

NaOH, EtOH →

1-(2,4-Dimethoxyphenyl) ethanone-1-^{14}C

4-Methoxybenzaldehyde (carbonyl-^{14}C)

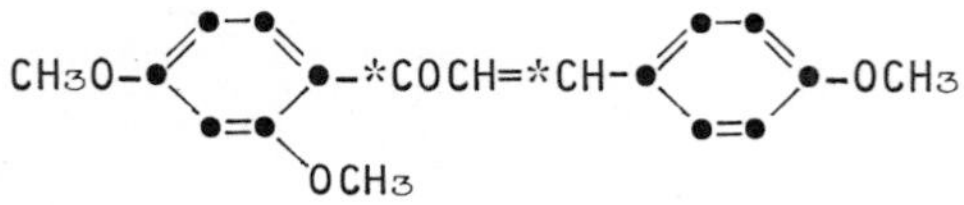

1-(2,4-Dimethoxyphenyl)-3-(4-methoxyphenyl)-2-propen-1-one-1,3-^{14}C

B. Chabannes, B. Duperray, and H. Pacheo, Bull. Soc. Chim. Fr., 801 (1972).

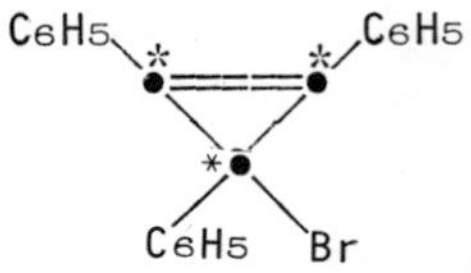

(8% from Ba*CO_3)

20% KOH / 80°C →

1,1',1''-(3-Bromo-1-cyclopropene-1,2,3-^{14}C-1,2,3-triyl)trisbenzene

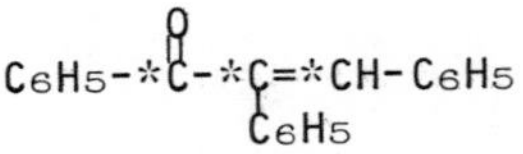
C6H5-*C-*C=*CH-C6H5
O
C6H5

(53%)

1,2,3-Triphenyl-2-propene-1-one-1,2,3-[14]C

The uniform distribution of label among the three nonbenzoid carbon atoms was attributed to be delocalized charge distribution in triphenylcyclopropenyl cation; the positions of label were determined by degradation studies.

A. D'yakonov, R. R. Kostikov, and A. P. Molchanov, Zh. Org. Khim., 6, 316 (1970); English translation, p. 304.

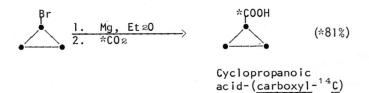

($\underline{i}$-C_3H_7)$NCH_2{}^*CH_2Cl$ (60% from Ba^*CO_3)

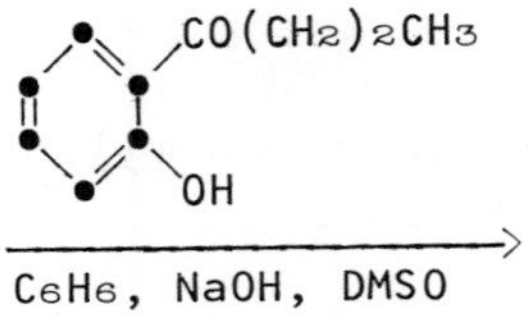
CO(CH2)2CH3
OH
C6H6, NaOH, DMSO

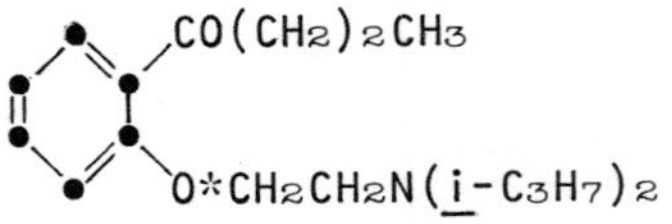
CO(CH2)2CH3
O*CH2CH2N(i-C3H7)2

(57%; 12% overall)

Ketocaine
[1-(2-(2-(Bis(1-methylethyl)amino)-ethoxy-1-^{14}C)phenyl)-1-butanone]

T. Gosztonyi, K. E. Domeij, and R. Sandberg, J. Label. Compound. Radiopharm., 14 639 (1978).

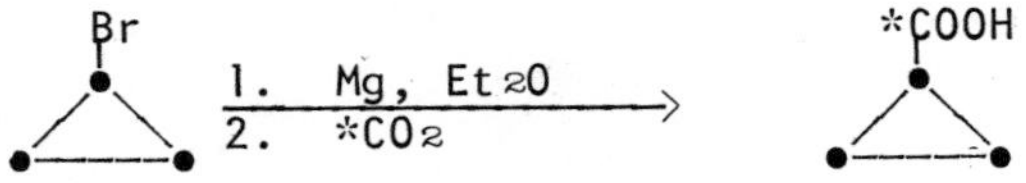
Br
1. Mg, Et2O
2. *CO2
*COOH

(*81%)

Cyclopropanoic acid-(carboxyl-^{14}C)

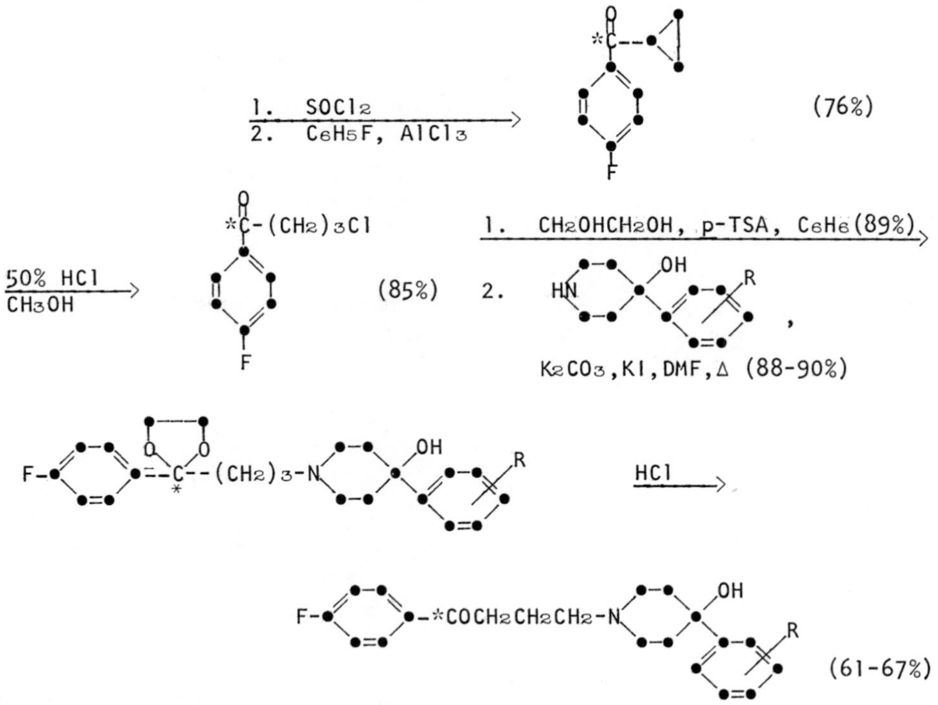
1. SOCl2
2. C6H5F, AlCl3
(76%)
50% HCl
CH3OH
*C-(CH2)3Cl
(85%)
1. CH2OHCH2OH, p-TSA, C6H6 (89%)
2.
HN
OH
R
K2CO3, KI, DMF, Δ (88-90%)
F
O
(CH2)3-N
HCl
F-
-*COCH2CH2CH2-N
(61-67%)

R=4-Cl, Haloperidol-1-^{14}C (31% overall) [4-[4-(4-Chlorophenyl)-4-hydroxy-1-piperidinyl]-1-(4-fluorophenyl)-1-butanone-1-^{14}C];
R=3-CF$_3$, Trifluoroperidol-1-^{14}C (27% overall) [1-(4-Fluorophenyl)-4-[4-hydroxy-4-[3-(trifluoromethyl)phenyl]-1-piperidinyl]-1-butanone-1-^{14}C]

I. Nakatsuka, K. Kawahara, T. Kamada, and A. Yoshitake, J. Label. Compound. Radiopharm., 14, 133 (1978).

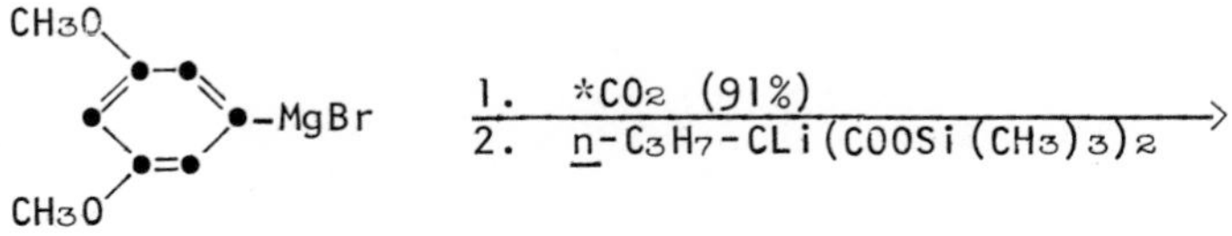
CH3O
-MgBr
CH3O
1. *CO2 (91%)
2. n-C3H7-CLi(COOSi(CH3)3)2

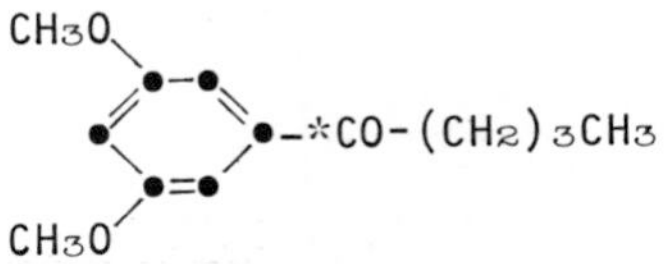

1-(3,5-Dimethoxyphenyl)-1-pentanone-1-^{14}C

Nguyen-Hoang-Nam, J. P. Beaucourt, H. Hoellinger, and L. Pichat, Bull. Soc. Chim. Fr., Part 2, 1367 (1974).

$CH_3CH_2CH_2CH_2{}^*COONa$ → 1. $SOCl_2$; 2. $AlCl_3$, toluene

Pentanoic-1-^{14}C acid sodium salt

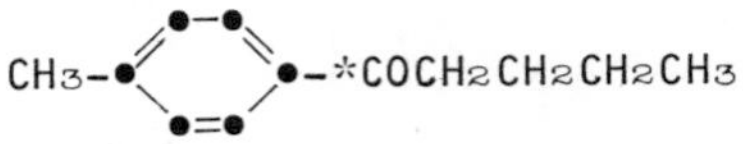

1. Br_2, $CHCl_3$
2. 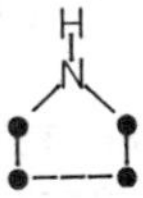 Δ, C_6H_6
3. HCl

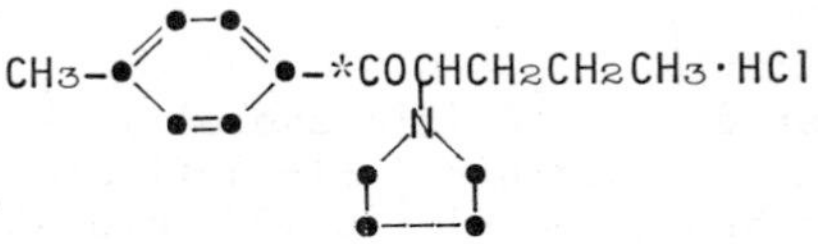

(~40% from sodium valerate)

Pyrovalerone
[1-(4-Methylphenyl)-2-(1-pyrrolidinyl)-1-pentanone-1-^{14}C hydrochloride]

W. Michaelis, J. H. Russel, and O. Schindler, J. Med. Chem., 13, 497 (1970).

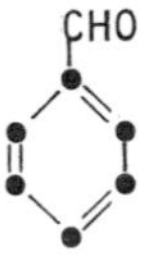

1. $^*CH_3MgI$, Et_2O
2. CrO_3, pyr, CH_2Cl_2 } (50%)
3. 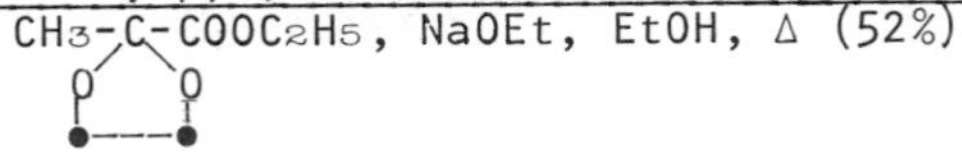 NaOEt, EtOH, Δ (52%)

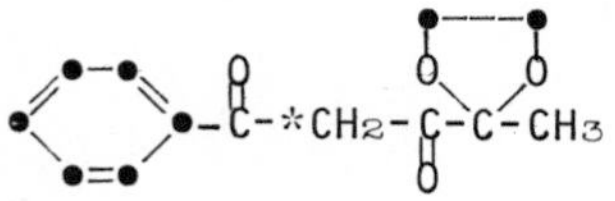
O
O
O
C-*CH2-C-C-CH3
O

(52%)

1-(2-Methyl-1,3-dioxolan-2-yl)-3-phenyl-1,3-propanedione-2-^{14}C

H. Minato, T. Nagasaki, T. Yokoskima, K. Suga, and M. Yamaguchi, J. Label. Compounds, 10, 645 (1974).

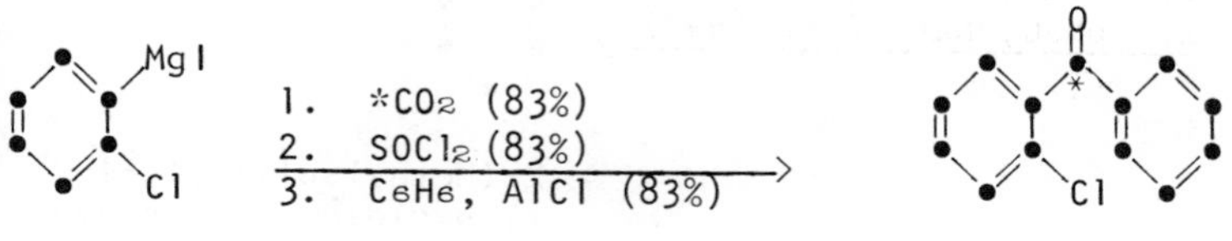
MgI
Cl
1. *CO2 (83%)
2. SOCl2 (83%)
3. C6H6, AlCl (83%)
O
*
Cl

(2-Chlorophenyl)phenylmethanone-α-^{14}C

W. Maul and D. Scherling, J. Label. Compound. Radiopharm., 14, 403 (1978).

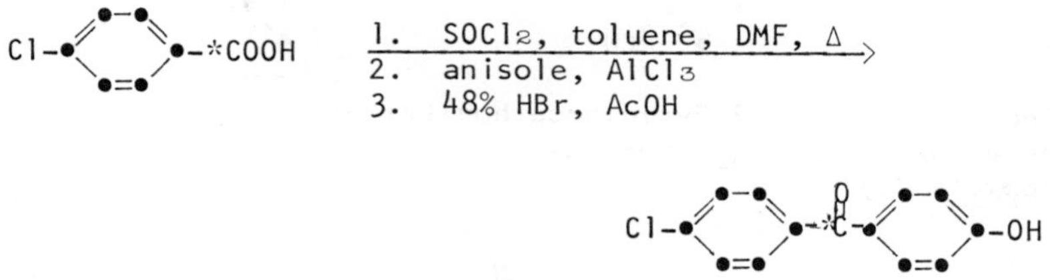
Cl-
-*COOH
1. SOCl2, toluene, DMF, Δ
2. anisole, AlCl3
3. 48% HBr, AcOH
Cl-
O
*C
-OH

(4-Chlorophenyl)(4-hydroxyphenyl)methanone-α-^{14}C

C. Luu Duc, Arzneim.-Forsch.-(Drug Res.), 26, 894 (1976).

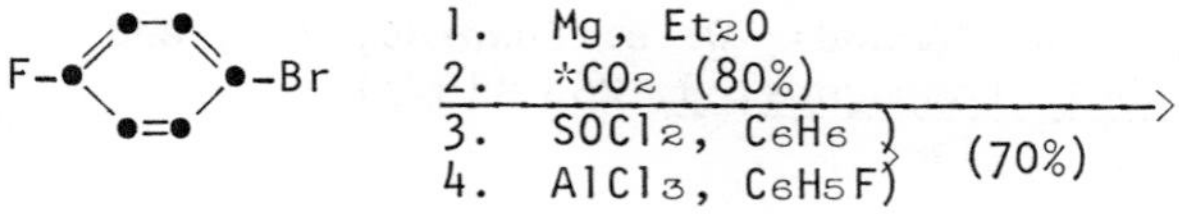
F-
-Br
1. Mg, Et2O
2. *CO2 (80%)
3. SOCl2, C6H6
4. AlCl3, C6H5F
(70%)

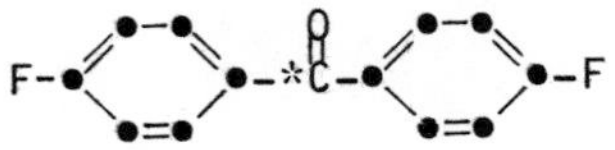

Bis(4-fluorophenyl)methanone-$\underline{\alpha}$-$^{14}\underline{C}$

D. Donnert and K.-H. Schweer, J. Label. Compounds, 9, 405 (1973).

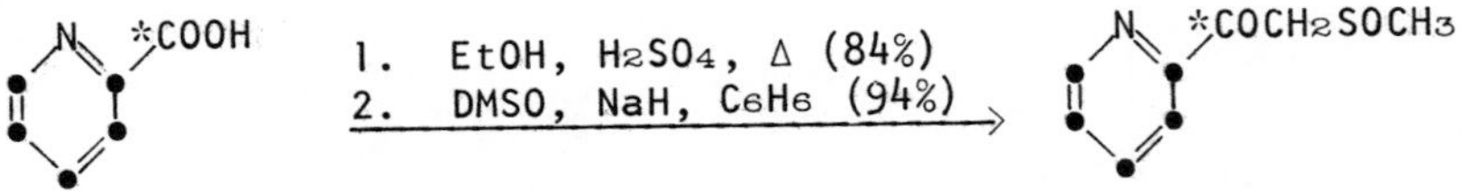
*COOH
1. EtOH, H_2SO_4, Δ (84%)
2. DMSO, NaH, C_6H_6 (94%)
*$COCH_2SOCH_3$

2-(Methylsulfinyl)-1-(2-pyridinyl)ethanone-$\underline{1}$-$^{14}\underline{C}$

E. J. Merrill and G. G. Vernice, J. Label. Compounds, 8, 589 (1972).

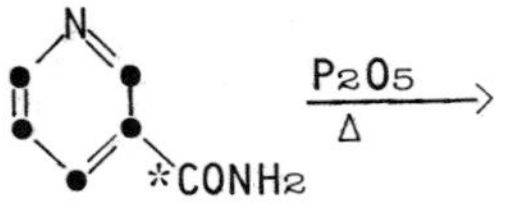
*$CONH_2$
P_2O_5
Δ

Nicotinamide
[3-Pyridinecarboxamide-(carboxyl-$^{14}\underline{C}$)]

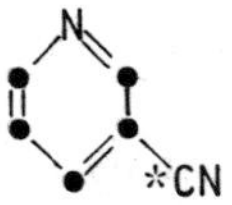
*CN

3-Pyridinecarbonitrile-(cyano-$^{14}\underline{C}$)

(60-80%)

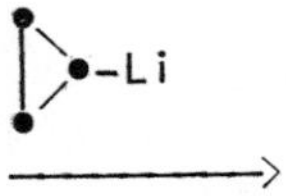
-Li

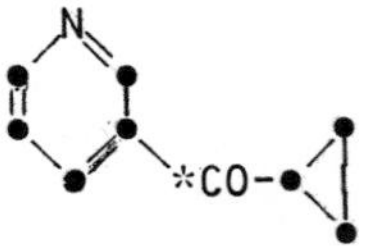
*CO-

(56%)

Cyclopropyl-3-pyridinylmethanone-$\underline{\alpha}$-$^{14}\underline{C}$

R. A. Comes, M. T. Core, M. D. Edmonds, W. B. Edwards, III, and R. W. Jenkins, Jr., J. Label. Compounds, 9, 253 (1973).

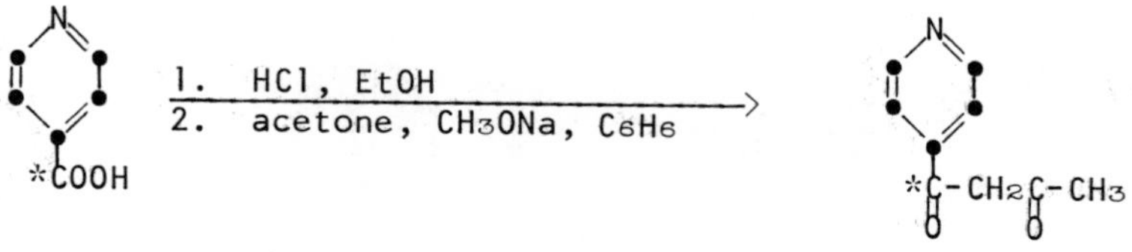
N
*COOH
1. HCl, EtOH
2. acetone, CH3ONa, C6H6
N
*C-CH2C-CH3
O O

(~46%)

1-(4-Pyridinyl)-1,3-butanedione-1-^{14}C

V. J. Bauer and A. E. Lanzilotti, J. Label. Compounds, 5, 87 (1969).

3-6 Cyclic Aromatic Ketones

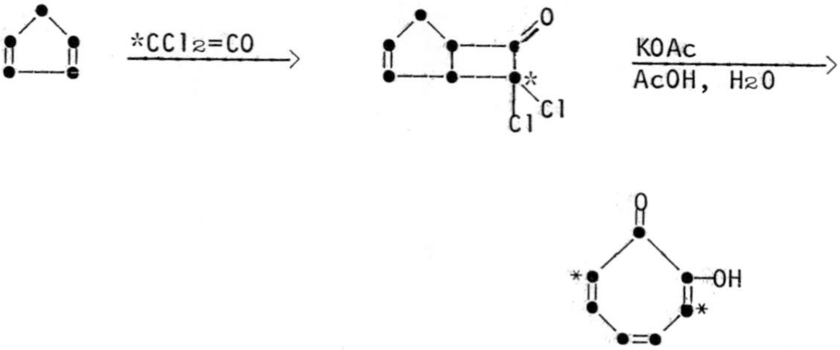
*CCl2=CO
O
*
Cl
Cl
KOAc
AcOH, H2O
O
OH
*
*

Tropolone
[2-Hydroxy-2,4,6-cyclo-heptatrien-1-one-3,7-^{14}C]

All ^{14}C label is located at the C-3 or C-7 positions as determined by degradation reactions; a mechanism is proposed.

T. Asao, T. Machiguchi, and Y. Kitahara, Bull. Chem. Soc. Jap., 43, 2662 (1970).

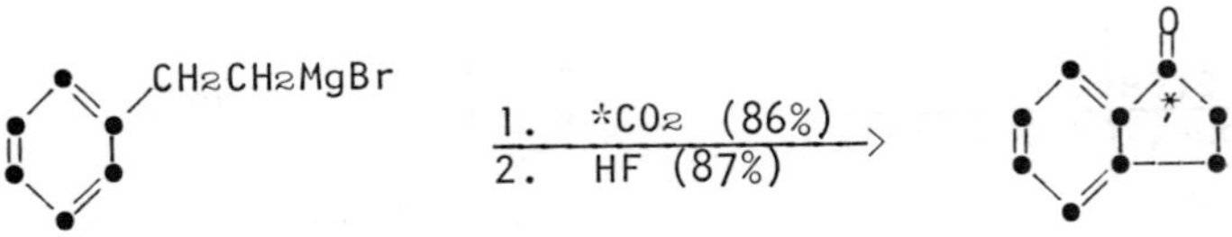
CH2CH2MgBr
1. *CO2 (86%)
2. HF (87%)
O
*

2,3-Dihydro-1H-inden-1-one-1-^{14}C

E. S. Ferdinandi, D. R. Hicks, W. Verbestel, and P. Raman, J. Label. Compound. Radiopharm., 14, 411 (1978).

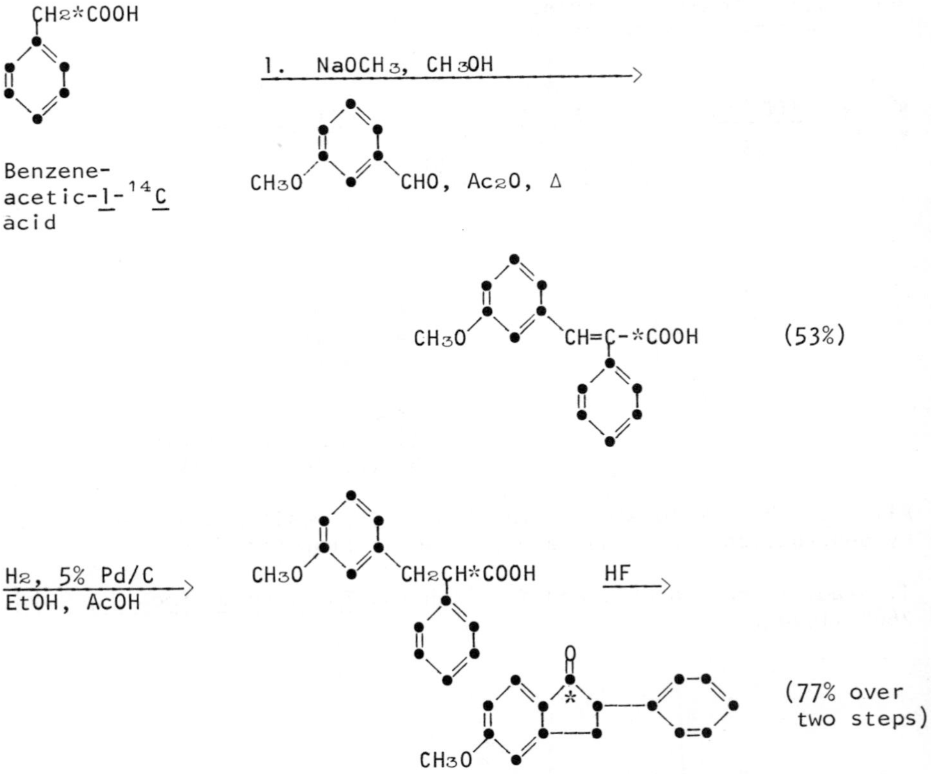
CH2*COOH
1. NaOCH3, CH3OH
CH3O
CHO, Ac2O, Δ
CH3O
CH=C-*COOH
(53%)
H2, 5% Pd/C
EtOH, AcOH
CH3O
CH2CH*COOH
HF
O
*
CH3O
(77% over two steps)

Benzeneacetic-1-^{14}C acid

2,3-Dihydro-5-methoxy-2-phenyl-1H-inden-1-one-1-^{14}C

R. C. Thomas and P. E. Marlatt, J. Label. Compound. Radiopharm., 14, 813 (1978).

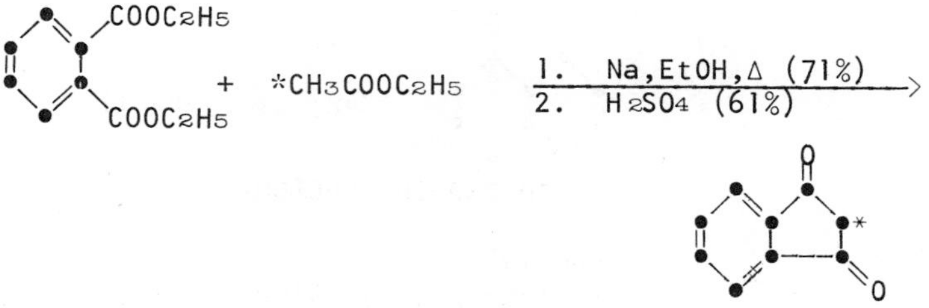

$$\text{COOC}_2\text{H}_5 \text{ / COOC}_2\text{H}_5 \quad + \quad *\text{CH}_3\text{COOC}_2\text{H}_5$$

1. Na, EtOH, Δ (71%)
2. H₂SO₄ (61%)

1H-Indene-1,3(2H)-dione-2-^{14}C

K. Ezoe and K. Kurosawa, Bull. Soc. Chem. Jap., 50, 443 (1977).

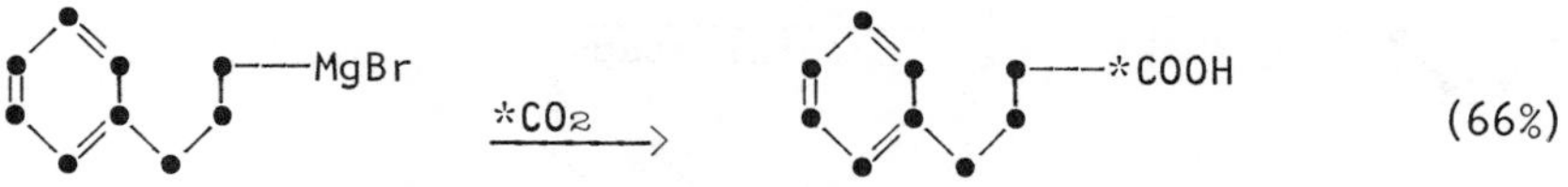

Benzenebutanoic-1-^{14}C acid

NaCl / AlCl₃ ⟶ (61%)

1. K₂S₂O₈, H₂SO₄, CH₃OH
2. aq. NaOH, Δ ⟶

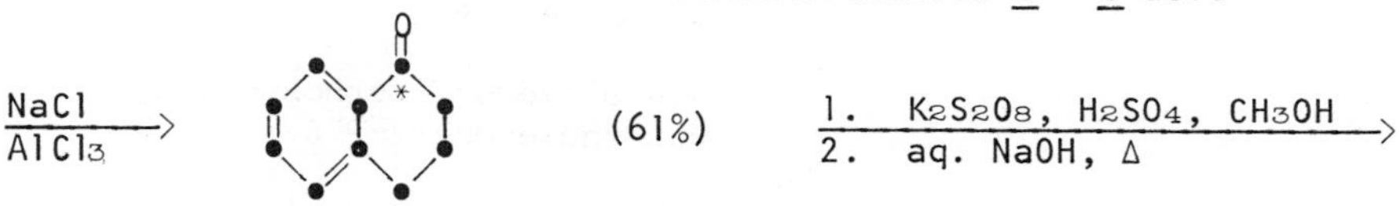

α-Tetralone
[3,4-Dihydro-1(2H)-naphthalenone-1-^{14}C]

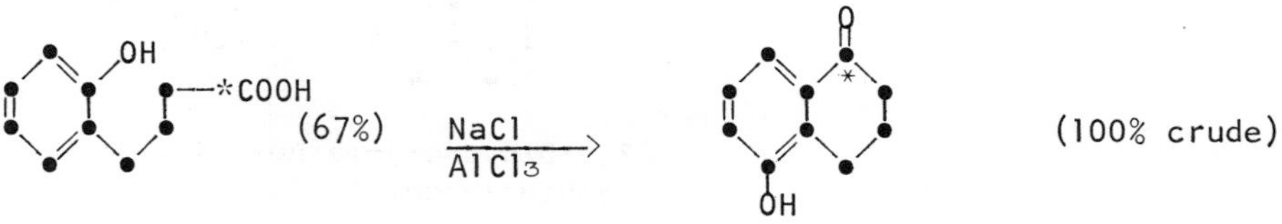

3,4-Dihydro-5-hydroxy-1(2H)-naphthalenone-1-^{14}C

1. $ClCH_2CH(O)CH_2$ (epoxide), NaOH, EtOH (51%)
2. $(CH_3)_3CNH_2$, EtOH, Δ (71%)
3. gaseous HCl, $CHCl_3$
→

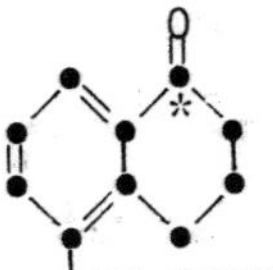

(54%; 6% overall)

$OCH_2CHOHCH_2$-$NHC(CH_3)_3$·HCl

Bunolol
[(±)-5-[3-[(1,1-Dimethylethyl)
amino]-2-hydroxypropoxy]-3,4-
dihydro-1(2H)-naphthalenone-1-^{14}C]

E. J. Merrill, J. Pharm. Sci., 60, 1589 (1971).

CH_3O- 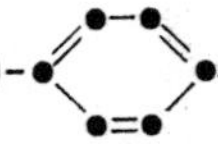 -CH_2CH_2MgBr

1. $*CO_2$
2. several steps →

CH_3O- 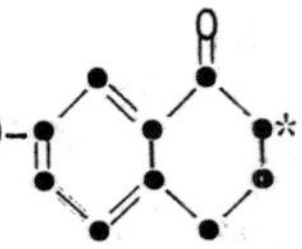 (63% overall)

3,4-Dihydro-7-methoxy-1(2H)-
naphthalenone-2-[14]C

CH_3O- 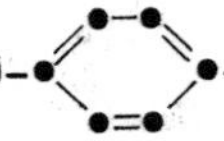 -$CH_2CH_2CH_2MgBr$

1. $*CO_2$
2. steps as before →

CH_3O 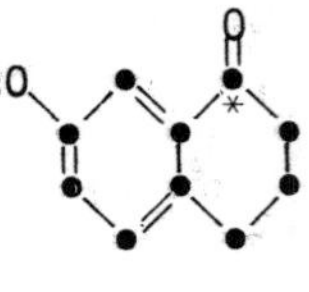 (86% from $*CO_2$)

3,4-Dihydro-7-methoxy-1(2H)-
naphthalenone-1-[14]C

P. J. van der Jagt, W. den Hollander, and B. van Zanten, Tetrahedron, 28, 1779 (1972); Tetrahedron, 27, 1049 (1971).

Cl- 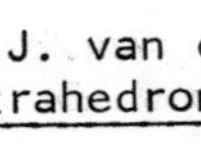 -$CH_2CH_2*CH_2COOH$ $\xrightarrow[(95\%)]{PPA,\Delta}$

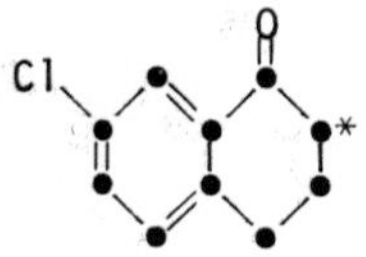
Cl
O
*

7-Chloro-3,4-dihydro-1(2H)-naphthalenone-2-^{14}C

W. Den Hollander, P. J. van der Jagt, and V. van Zanten, J. Label. Compounds, 8, 3 (1972).

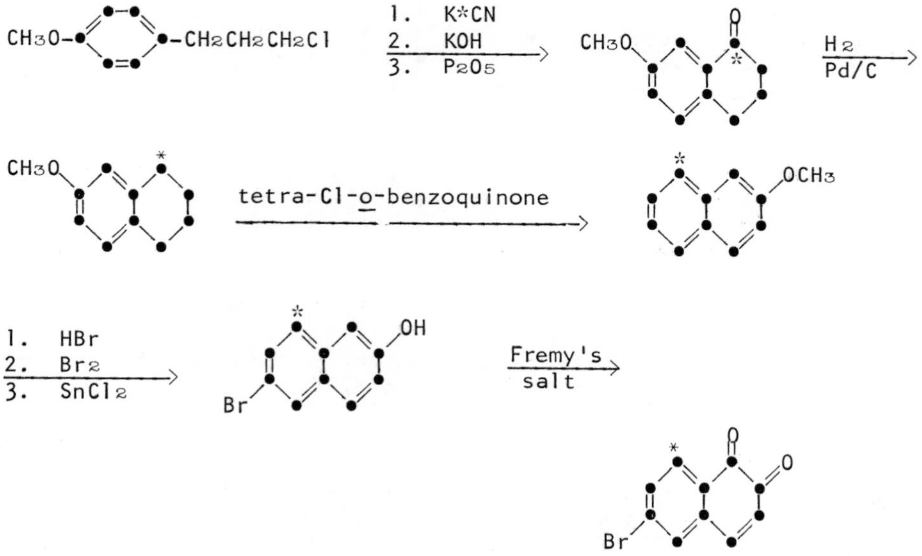
CH3O
CH2CH2CH2Cl
1. K*CN
2. KOH
3. P2O5
CH3O
O
*
H2
Pd/C
CH3O
*
tetra-Cl-o-benzoquinone
*
OCH3
1. HBr
2. Br2
3. SnCl2
*
OH
Br
Fremy's salt
O
*
O
Br

Bonaphthone
[6-Bromo-1,2-naphthalene-dione-8-^{14}C]

A. D. Bulat, L. N. Kivokurt Seva, and N. Y. Kozarinskaya, Khim.-Farm. Zh., 10, 20 (1976).

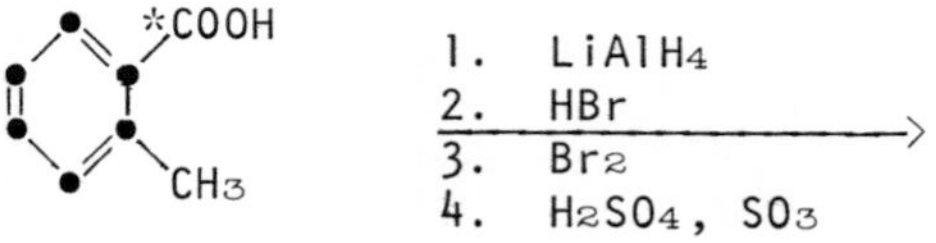
*COOH
CH3
1. LiAlH4
2. HBr
3. Br2
4. H2SO4, SO3

*CHO
*CHO
O
O
O
O

Oxolin
[1,2,3,4-Naphthalenetetrone-
1,4-^{14}C]

A. D. Bulat, Y. Y. Usaevich, A. A. Ginesina, and N. Y. Kozarinskaya, Khim.-Farm. Zh., 7, 12 (1973).

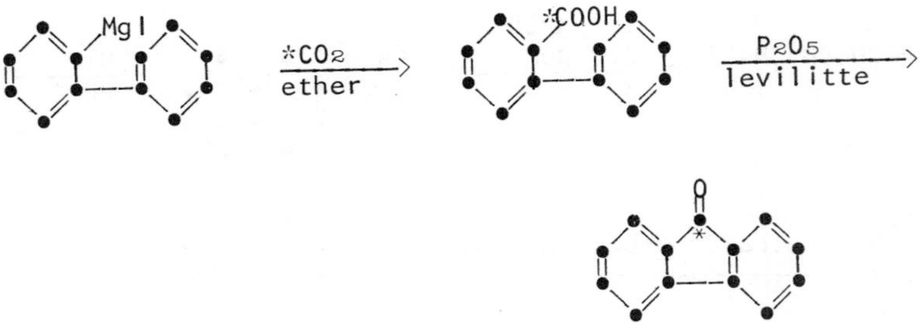
MgI
*CO2
ether
*COOH
P2O5
levilitte
O

9H-Fluoren-9-one-9-^{14}C

Nguyen-Hoang-Nam, H. Hoellinger, M. Herbert, Nguyen-Dat-Xuong, and L. Pichat, J. Label. Compounds, 6, 99 (1970).

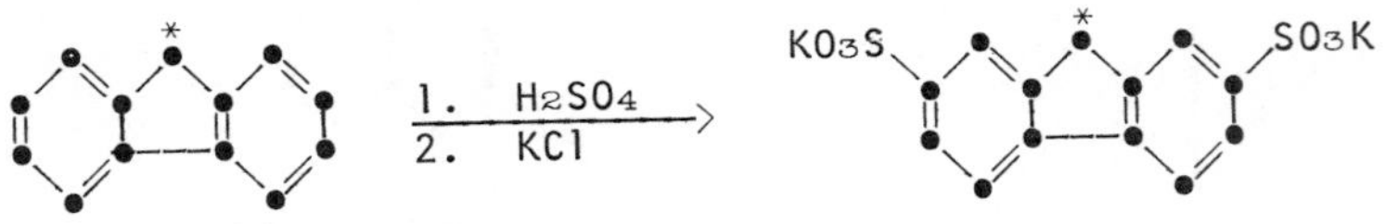
1. H2SO4
2. KCl
KO3S
SO3K

(60%; 2 steps)

Fluorene-9-^{14}C

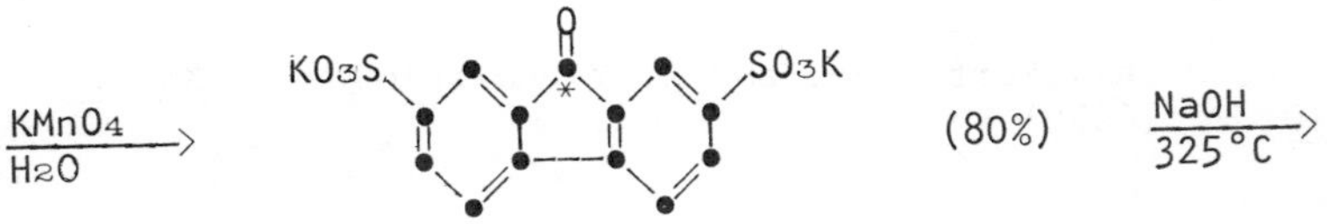
KMnO4
H2O
KO3S
O
SO3K
(80%)
NaOH
325°C

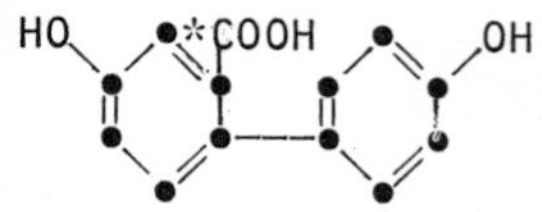

(68%)

ZnCl, 225°C →

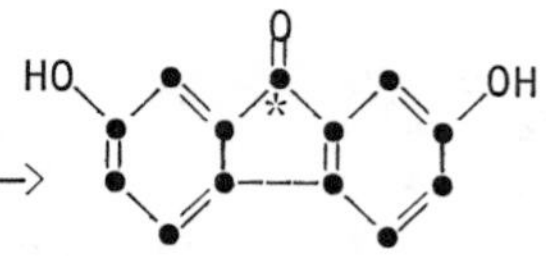

(80%)

$(C_2H_5)_2NCH_2CH_2Cl$ / KOH, toluene →

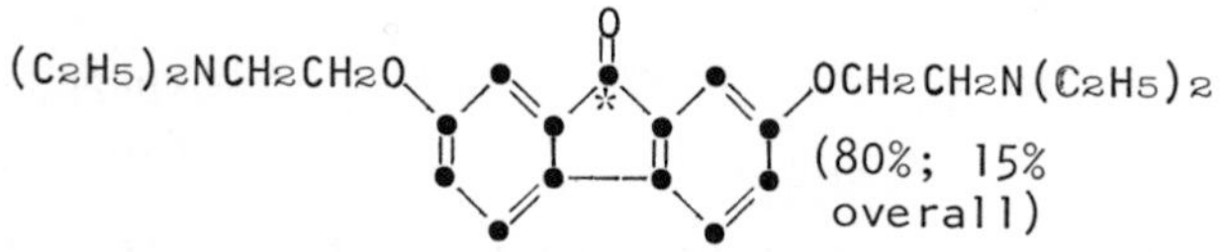

(80%; 15% overall)

Tilorone
[2,7-Bis[2-(diethylamino)ethoxy]-9H-fluoren-9-one-9-^{14}C]

V. P. Gaur and A. Wacker, J. Label. Compounds, 9, 281 (1973).

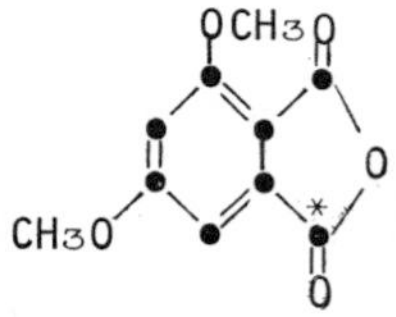

+

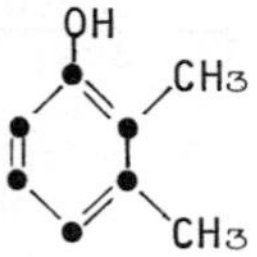

Friedel-Crafts →

4,6-Dimethoxy-1,3-isobenzofurandione-1-^{14}C

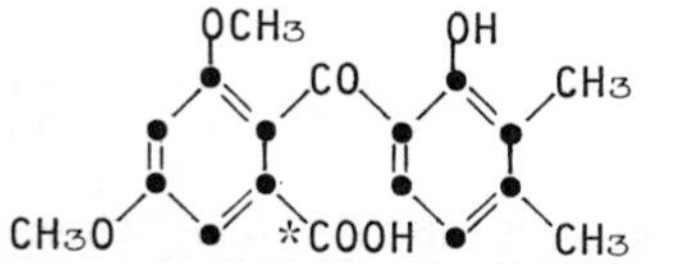

1. boric acid
2. KI, H_3PO_4 →

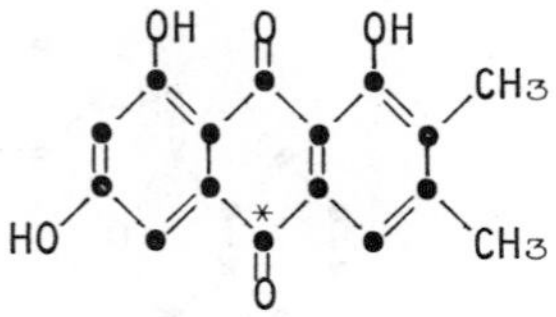

(25% from phthalic anhydride)

1,6,8-Trihydroxy-2,3-dimethyl-9,10-anthracenedione-10-^{14}C

B. Franck, V. Ohnsorge, and H. Flasch, Tetrahedron Lett., 3773 (1970).

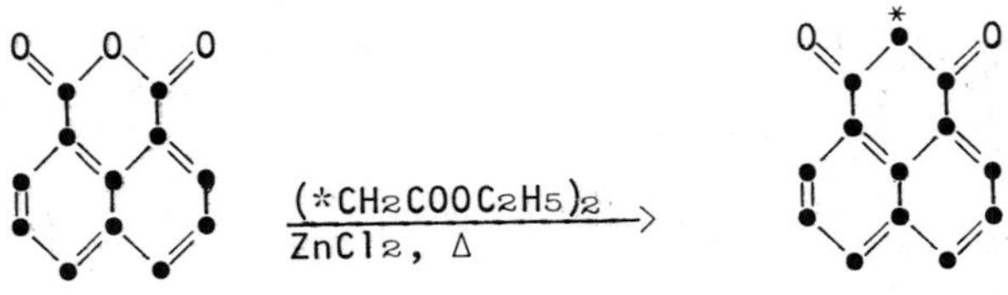

(*CH2COOC2H5)2
ZnCl2, Δ

(81%)

1H-Phenalene-1,3(2H)-dione-2-^{14}C

The mechanism of the reaction of the above-labeled compound with lead tetracetate is discussed.

K. Ezoe and K. Kurosawa, Bull. Soc. Chem. Jap., 50, 443 (1977).

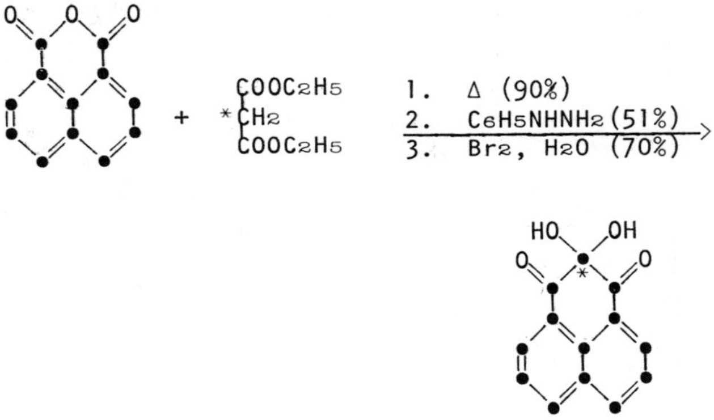

COOC2H5
*CH2
COOC2H5
1. Δ (90%)
2. C6H5NHNH2 (51%)
3. Br2, H2O (70%)
HO
OH

2,2-Dihydroxy-1H-phenalene-1,3(2H)-dione-2-^{14}C

G. Kollenz, Justus Liebig's Ann. Chem., 1666 (1978)

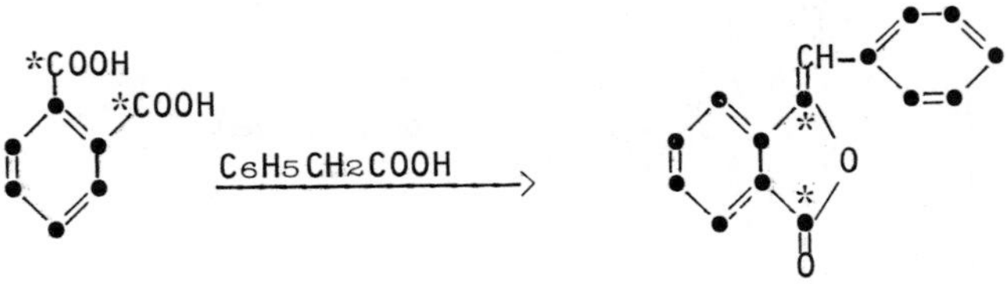

*COOH
*COOH
C6H5CH2COOH
CH-

(77%)

Phthalic acid
[1,2-Benzenedicarboxylic acid-(carboxyl-^{14}C)]

1. NaOH
2. H_2,Pd/C

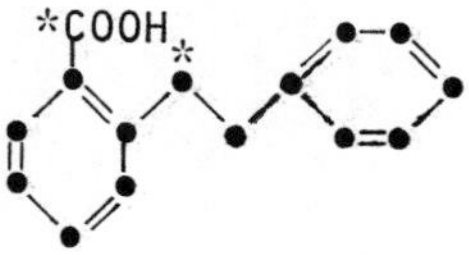

(91%) H_3PO_4

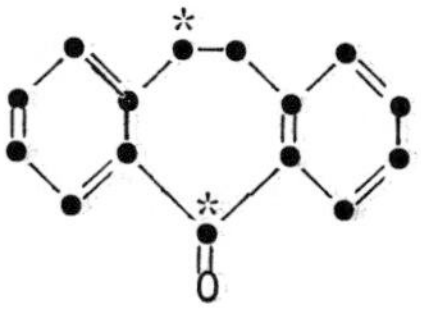

(80%)

10,11-Dihydro-5H-dibenzo[a,d]-cyclohepten-5-one-5,10-^{14}C

W. Maul, J. Label. Compounds, 5, 250 (1969).

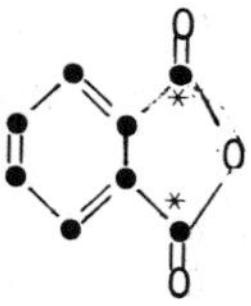

$AlCl_3$, C_6H_6
70°C

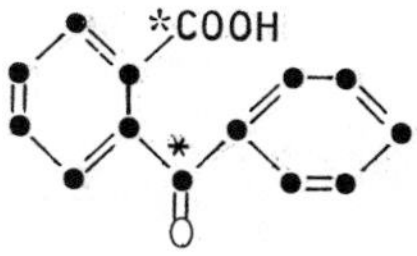

(87%) H_2SO_4

Phthalic anhydride
[1,3-Isobenzofurandione-1-^{14}C]

2-Benzoylbenzoic acid
(carbonyl, carboxyl-^{14}C)

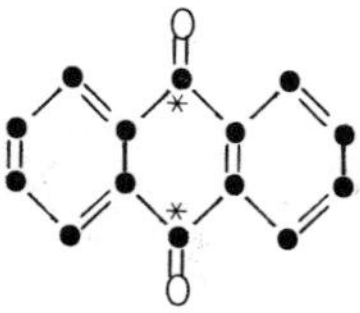

(quant.)

1. H_2SO_4
2. glycerol, H_2O, Δ

9,10-Anthracenedione-
9,10-^{14}C

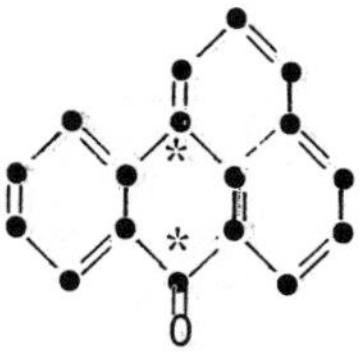

(68%)

Benzanthrone
[7H-Benz[de]anthracen-7-one-7,11b-^{14}C]

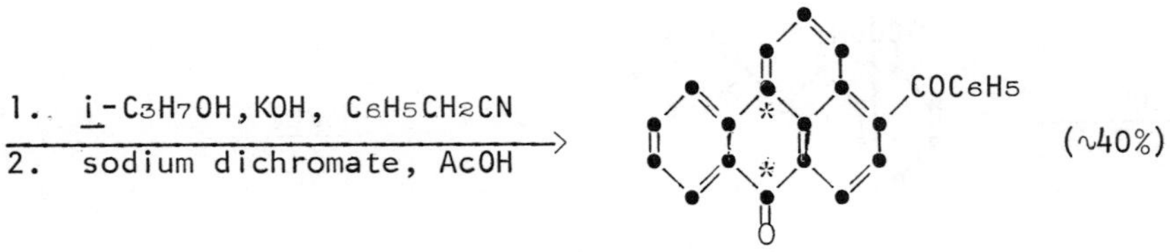
1. i-C3H7OH,KOH, C6H5CH2CN
2. sodium dichromate, AcOH
COC6H5
O
(~40%)

4-Benzoyl-7H-benz[de]anthracen-7-one-7,11b-^{14}C

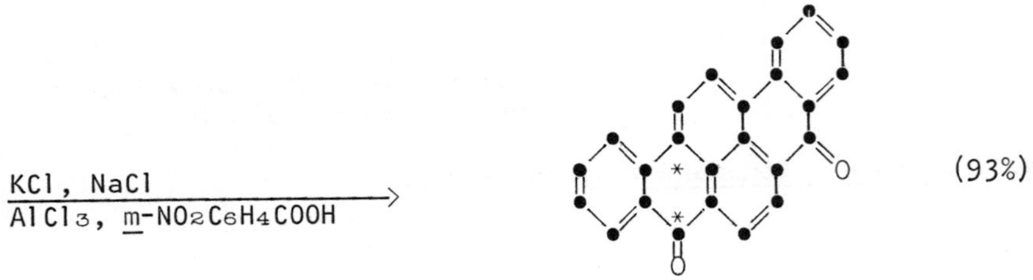
KCl, NaCl
AlCl3, m-NO2C6H4COOH
O
O
(93%)

Benzo[rst]pentaphene-5,8-dione-8,12b-^{14}C

E. Boger and P. Bernfeld, J. Label. Compounds, 1, 109 (1965)

4

Hydroxy Compounds

4-1 Aliphatic Alcohols

$CH_3{*}COONa$ $\xrightarrow[\text{3. } LiAlH_4\text{, ether (70\%)}]{\text{1. } HCl,\ Cl_2,\ CH_3COCl,\ P_2I_2;\ \text{2. } CH_2N_2\ (56\%)}$ $ClCH_2{*}CH_2OH$

2-Chloroethanol-1-[14]C

J. Lintermans, A. Benakis, and J. Williams, J. Label. Compounds, 7, 533 (1971).

$H_2N\text{-}CH_2{*}COOH$ $\xrightarrow[\text{2. } LiAlH_4]{\text{1. } CH_3OH/H_2O,\ Pd}$ $(CH_3)_2NCH_2{*}CH_2OH$

2-(Dimethylamino)ethanol-1-[14]C

Y. Dormard, J. C. Levron, and A. Benakis, Arzneim.-Forsch.-(Drug Res.), 25, 194 (1975).

$BrCH_2{*}COOC_2H_5$ $\xrightarrow[\text{2. } LiAlH_4,\ Et_2O,\ \Delta\ (98\%)]{\text{1. } (C_2H_5)_2NH,\ C_6H_6\ (81\%)}$

$(C_2H_5)_2NCH_2{*}CH_2OH$ (50% from $CH_3{*}COONa$)

2-(Diethylamino)ethanol-1-[14]C

D. Blackburn and G. Burghard, J. Label. Compounds, 1, 226 (1965); see also B. Liedtke and K.-O. Vollmer, J. Label. Compound. Radiopharm., 14, 825 (1978).

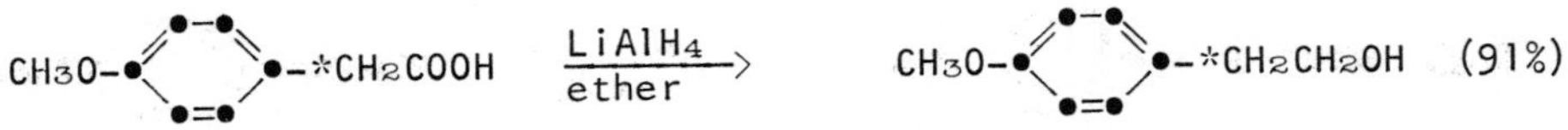
CH3O-
-*CH2COOH
LiAlH4
ether
CH3O-
-*CH2CH2OH
(91%)

4-Methoxybenzeneacetic-$\underline{\alpha}$-$^{14}\underline{C}$ acid

4-Methoxybenzeneethanol-$\underline{\beta}$-$^{14}\underline{C}$

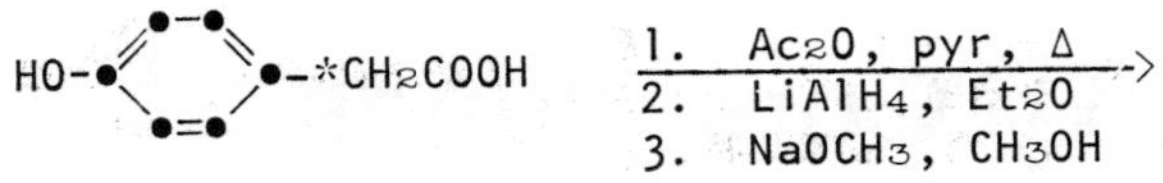
HO-
-*CH2COOH
1. Ac2O, pyr, Δ
2. LiAlH4, Et2O
3. NaOCH3, CH3OH

4-Hydroxybenzeneacetic-$\underline{\alpha}$-$^{14}\underline{C}$ acid

HO-
-*CH2CH2OH
(72%)

Tyrosol
[4-Hydroxybenzeneethanol-$\underline{\beta}$-$^{14}\underline{C}$]

S. Schiefer and H. Kindl, J. Label. Compounds, 7, 291 (1971).

C_6H_5-*CH=CH-COOH $\xrightarrow[\text{2. LiAlH}_4\text{, AlCl}_3\text{, ether}]{\text{1. CH}_2\text{N}_2}$ C_6H_5-*CH=CH-CH_2OH

Cinnamic acid
[3-Phenyl-2-propenoic-$\underline{3}$-$^{14}\underline{C}$ acid]

Cinnamyl alcohol
[3-Phenyl-2-propen-1-ol-$\underline{3}$-$^{14}\underline{C}$]
(no attack on double bond)

Nguyen-Hoang-Nam, H. Hoellinger, and L. Pichat, J. Label. Compounds, 11, 521 (1975).

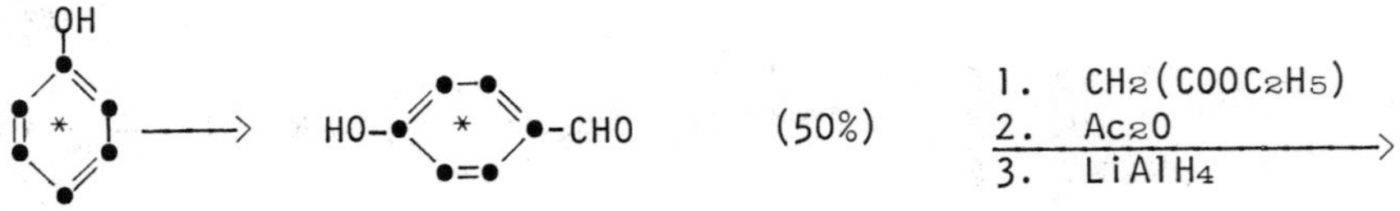
OH
HO-
-CHO
(50%)
1. CH2(COOC2H5)
2. Ac2O
3. LiAlH4

4-Hydroxybenzaldehyde-($\underline{\text{ring}}$-$\underline{U}$-$^{14}\underline{C}$)

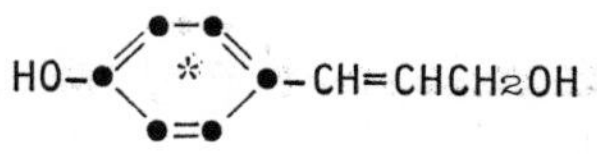

(72%; 18% from $Ba^{*}CO_3$)

p-Coumaralcohol
[4-(3-Hydroxy-1-propenyl)phenol-(ring-^{14}C)]

K. Haider, J. Label. Compounds, 2, 174 (1966).

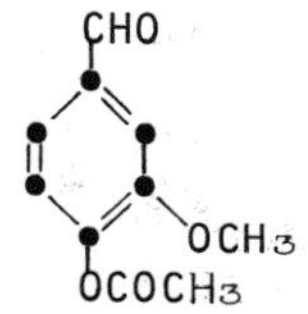

4-(Acetyloxy)-3-methoxybenzaldehyde

1. $*CH_2(COOH)_2$, pyr, piperidine, Δ
2. CH_2N_2 (66%)
3. Vitride, toluene, Δ

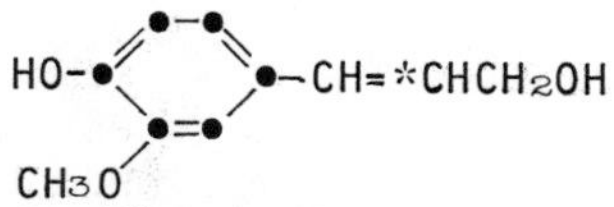

Coniferyl alcohol
[4-(3-Hydroxy-1-propenyl-2-^{14}C)-2-methoxyphenol]

(Knoevenagal condensation; Dolbner modification)

Coniferyl-γ-^{14}C alcohol was prepared starting with malonic-1-^{14}C acid. A Perkin reaction using acetic anhydride-1-^{14}C and acetylvanillin gave only a 1% yield of product.

H. M. Balba and G. G. Still, J. Label. Compound. Radiopharm., 15, 309 (1978).

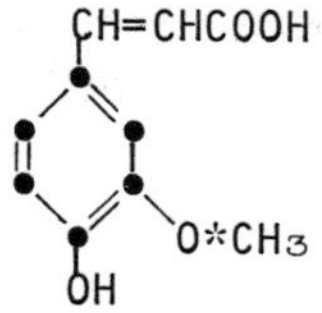

Ferulic acid
[3-(4-Hydroxy-3-(methoxy-^{14}C)phenyl)-2-propenoic acid]

1. Ac_2O
2. $SOCl_2$
3. $LiAlH_4$

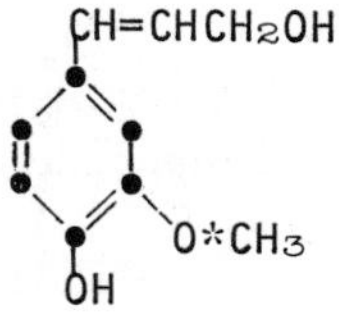

Coniferyl alcohol
[4-(3-Hydroxy-1-propenyl)-2-(methoxy-^{14}C)phenol]

(15% from $*CH_3I$ consumed)

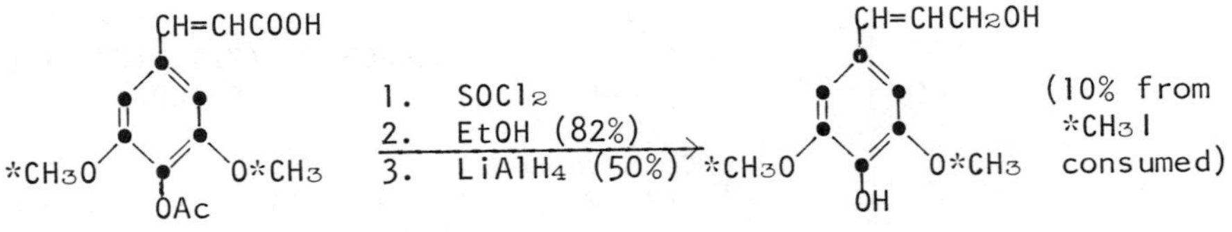
CH=CHCOOH
*CH3O
O*CH3
OAc
1. SOCl2
2. EtOH (82%)
3. LiAlH4 (50%)
CH=CHCH2OH
*CH3O
O*CH3
OH
(10% from *CH3I consumed)

3-[4-(Acetyloxy)-3,5-(dimethoxy-$^{14}\underline{C}$)]-2-phenylpropenoic acid

Sinapin alcohol
[4-(3-Hydroxy-1-propenyl)-2,6-(dimethoxy-$^{14}\underline{C}$)phenol]

K. Haider and S. Lim, J. Label. Compounds, 1, 294 (1965).

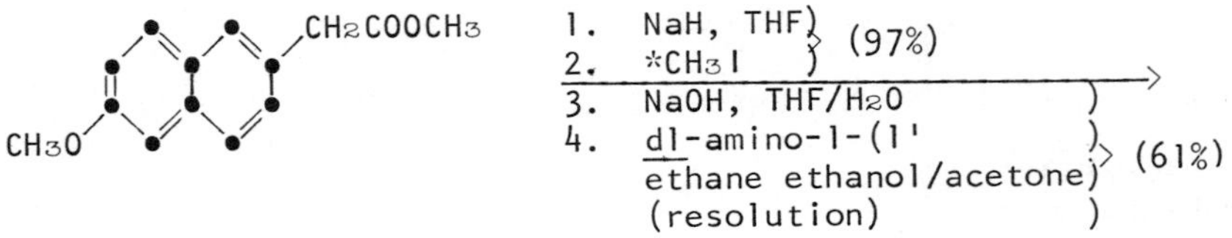
CH2COOCH3
CH3O
1. NaH, THF
2. *CH3I
(97%)
3. NaOH, THF/H2O
4. dl-amino-1-(1' ethane ethanol/acetone (resolution)
(61%)

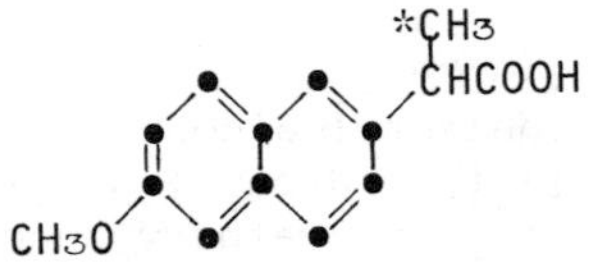
*CH3
CHCOOH
CH3O

Naproxen
[(+)-6-Methoxy-α-(methyl-$^{14}\underline{C}$-)2-naphthaleneacetic acid]

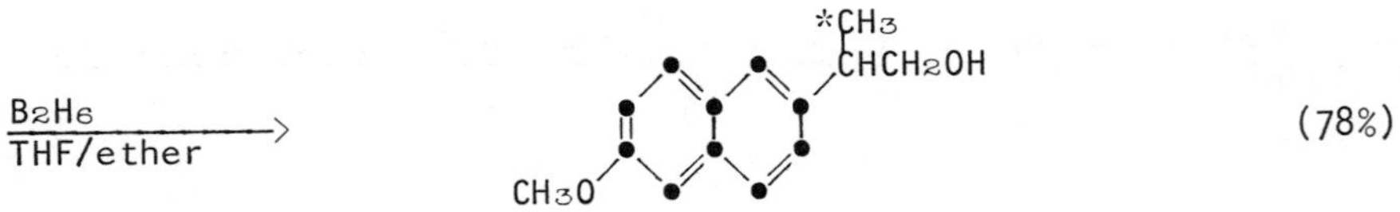
B2H6
THF/ether
*CH3
CHCH2OH
CH3O
(78%)

Naproxol
[(+)-6-Methoxy-α-(methyl-$^{14}\underline{C}$)-2-naphthalenethanol]

W. Hafferl and A. Hary, J. Label. Compounds, 9, 293 (1973).

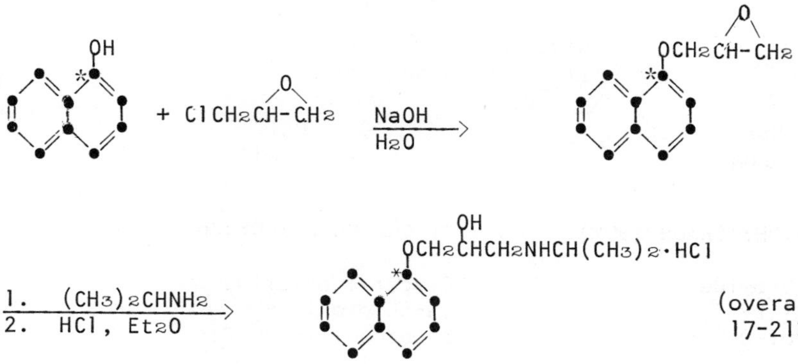
OH
+ ClCH2CH-CH2
O
NaOH
H2O
OCH2CH-CH2
O
1. (CH3)2CHNH2
2. HCl, Et2O
OH
OCH2CHCH2NHCH(CH3)2·HCl

(overall yields 17-21%)

Propranolol
[1-((1-Methylethyl)amino)-3-(naphthalenyloxy-1-^{14}C)-2-propanol]

J. Burns, J. Label. Compounds, 6, 45 (1970).

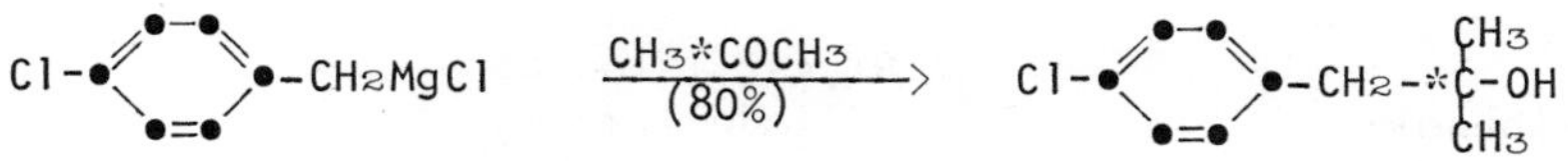
Cl-
-CH2MgCl
CH3*COCH3
(80%)
Cl-
-CH2-*C-OH
CH3
CH3

2-(4-Chlorophenylmethyl)-propan-2-ol-2-^{14}C

J. Engler and L. Pallos, J. Label. Compounds, 9, 81 (1973).

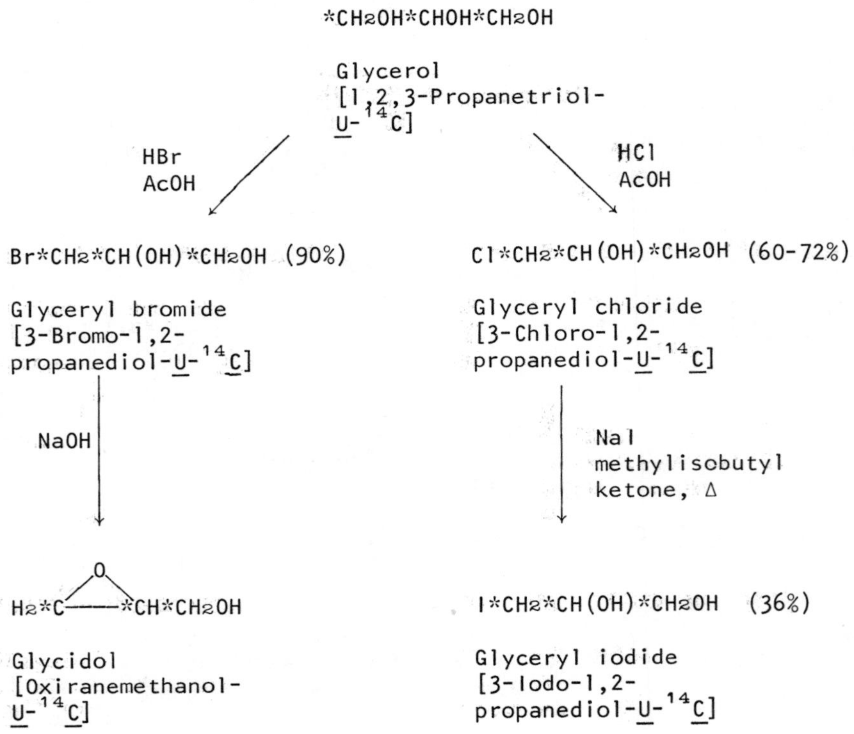
*CH2OH*CHOH*CH2OH
Glycerol
[1,2,3-Propanetriol-U-14C]
HBr
AcOH
HCl
AcOH
Br*CH2*CH(OH)*CH2OH (90%)
Glyceryl bromide
[3-Bromo-1,2-propanediol-U-14C]
Cl*CH2*CH(OH)*CH2OH (60-72%)
Glyceryl chloride
[3-Chloro-1,2-propanediol-U-14C]
NaOH
NaI
methylisobutyl
ketone, Δ
O
H2*C——*CH*CH2OH
Glycidol
[Oxiranemethanol-U-14C]
I*CH2*CH(OH)*CH2OH (36%)
Glyceryl iodide
[3-Iodo-1,2-propanediol-U-14C]

A. R. Jones, J. Label. Compounds, 9, 697 (1973).

$CH_2{=}CH{-}{*}COOH \xrightarrow[3.\ LiAlH_4{-}AlCl_3,\ -80°C]{1.\ Br_2;\ 2.\ CH_2N_2} CH_2BrCHBr{*}CH_2OH$

Acrylic acid
[2-Propenoic-1-^{14}C acid]

$\xrightarrow[2.\ OH^-]{1.\ KOAc} {*}CH_2OHCHOH{*}CH_2OH$ (35% based on Ba*CO_3)

Glycerol
[1,2,3-Propanetriol-1,3-^{14}C]

L. Pichat, M. Herbert, and F. Aubert, J. Label. Compounds, 1, 66 (1965).

$CH_2{=}CHCH_2Cl \xrightarrow[3.\ CH_2N_2;\ 4.\ LiAlH_4\ (75\%)]{1.\ Mg;\ 2.\ {*}CO_2\ (53\%)} CH_2{=}CHCH_2{*}CH_2OH$

3-Buten-1-ol-1-^{14}C

T. Nagasaki, Y. Katsuyama, and H. Minato, J. Label. Compound. Radiopharm., 12, 7 (1976).

$BrCH_2{*}COOC_2H_5 \xrightarrow[3.\ CH_3COCH_3]{1.\ (C_6H_5)_3P;\ 2.\ NaOH} (CH_3)_2C{=}CH{*}COOC_2H_5 \xrightarrow[Et_2O]{LiAlH_4}$

$(CH_3)_2C{=}CH{*}CH_2OH$

3-Methyl-2-buten-1-ol-1-^{14}C

A. O. Colonna and E. G. Gros, J. Label. Compounds, 7, 84 (1971).

$ClCH_2{-}C{\equiv}C{-}CH_2Cl \xrightarrow[NaNH_2,\ NH_3Fe(NO_3)_3]{[H{*}CHO]n,\ Et_2O} HC{\equiv}C{-}C{\equiv}C{-}{*}CH_2OH$ (47%)

Penta-2,4-diyn-1-ol-1-^{14}C

A. G. Fallis, M. T. W. Hearn, Sir Ewart R. H. Jones, V. Thaller, and J. L. Turner, J. Chem. Soc., Perkin Trans. 1, 743 (1973).

$BrCH_2{*}COOCH_3$ → 1. $(C_6H_5)_3P$; 2. CH_3CH_2COCl; 3. Δ → $CH_3CH_2C{\equiv}C\text{-}{*}COOCH_3$

→ 1. NaOH; 2. CH_2N_2; 3. $LiAlH_4$ → $CH_3C{\equiv}CCH_2{*}CH_2OH$

3-Pentyn-1-ol-1-^{14}C

3-Pentyn-1-ol-3-^{14}C was prepared using unlabeled methyl bromoacetate and propionyl-1-^{14}C chloride.

C. J. Collins, B. M. Benjamin, M. Hanack, and H. Stutz, J. Amer. Chem. Soc., 99, 1669 (1977).

$C_3H_7C{\equiv}CH$ → 1. C_2H_5MgBr; 2. ${*}CO_2$; 3. $LiAlH_4$, THF → $C_3H_7CH{=}CH{*}CH_2OH$

(E)-2-Hexen-1-ol-1-^{14}C

$CH_3{*}CH_2Br$ → 1. Mg; 2. HCHO; 3. HBr, H_2SO_4 → $CH_3{*}CH_2CH_2Br$

Bromopropane-2-^{14}C

→ 1. $HC{\equiv}CNa$, NH_3; 2. C_2H_5MgBr; 3. CO_2; 4. $LiAlH_4$ → $CH_3{*}CH_2CH_2CH{=}CH\text{-}CH_2OH$

(E)-2-Hexen-1-ol-5-^{14}C

M. Hamada, Y. Nagata, and A. Hatanaka, Agr. Biol. Chem., 36, 324 (1972).

$Br{*}CH_2COOC_2H_5$ → 1. $P(OC_2H_5)_3$ (89-90%); 2. NaH, DME; 3. $CH_3COCH_2CH_2CH_3$ (steps 2–3: 58-89%); 4. $LiAlH_4$ (95-99%) →

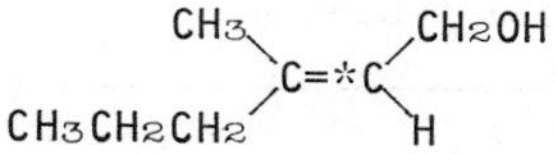

(85/15 ratio of trans/cis)

(E)-3-Methyl-2-hexen-1-ol-2-^{14}C

J. L. Rabinowitz and M. Zanger, J. Label. Compounds, 8, 657 (1972).

$HC{\equiv}C[CH{=}CH]_2{-}CHOHCH{=}CH_2 \xrightarrow[CuCl,\ NH_4Cl,\ CH_3OH{-}H_2O]{{*}CH_3{-}[C{\equiv}C]_2H}$

${*}CH_3{-}[C{\equiv}C]_3{-}[CH{=}CH]_2{-}CHOHCH{=}CH_2$ (51%)

Tetradeca-1,4,6-triene-8,10,12-triyne-3-ol-14-^{14}C

F. Bohlmann, W. Karl, and R. Zeisberg, Chem. Ber., 103, 2860 (1970).

$CH_3(CH_2)_{15}{-}CH_2Br \xrightarrow[3.\ SOCl_2\ (81\%)]{1.\ Mg,\ Et_2O;\ 2.\ {*}CO_2(99\%)} CH_3(CH_2)_{16}{-}{*}COCl$

1-Bromoheptadecane

Stearoyl chloride [Octadecanoyl chloride-1-^{14}C]

$\xrightarrow[Et_2O]{CH_3COCHNaCOOC_2H_5} CH_3(CH_2)_{16}{-}{*}C({=}O){-}CH(COCH_3){-}COOC_2H_5$ (59%)

2-Acetyl-3-oxoeicosanoic-3-^{14}C acid ethyl ester

$\xrightarrow[2.\ Zn,\ Ac_2O,\ AcOH\ (90\%)]{1.\ C_6H_5N_2Cl,\ EtOH,\ CH_3COONa\ (81\%)} CH_3(CH_2)_{16}{-}{*}C({=}O){-}CH(NHCOCH_3)COOC_2H_5$

2-(Acetylamino)-3-oxoeicosanoic-3-^{14}C acid ethyl ester

1. $NaBH_4$, CH_3OH, Et_2O (quant.)
2. HCl, CH_3OH (83%)
3. $LiAlH_4$, THF (90%)
4. crystallization as N-dichloroacetyl derivative (25%)

→ $CH_3(CH_2)_{16}$-*CHOHCH(NH_2)CH_2OH

[R-(R*,S*)]-2-Amino-1,3-eicosanediol-3-^{14}C

W. Stoffel and A. Scheid, Hoppe-Seyler's Z. Physiol. Chem., 350, 1593 (1969).

$(CH_3)_2CHCH_2CHOHCH_2CH(CH_3)CH_2CH(CH_3)_2$ — NaH, dioxane / $ClCH_2$*COOH →

2,6,8-Trimethyl-4-nonanol (TMNOH)

TMNOCH_2*COOH (83%)

1. B_2H_6, THF (97%)
2. $SOCl_2$, pyr, ether (98%)
3. NaH, DMSO, H(OCH_2CH_2)nOH, 75-80°C, 16 hr

→ TMNOCH_2*CH_2(OCH_2CH_2)nOH

[n=5; 86% yield (42% overall);
n=8; 68% yield (33% overall)]

F. S. Tanaka, R. G. Wien, and G. E. Stolzenberg, J. Label. Compound. Radiopharm., 12, 107 (1976).

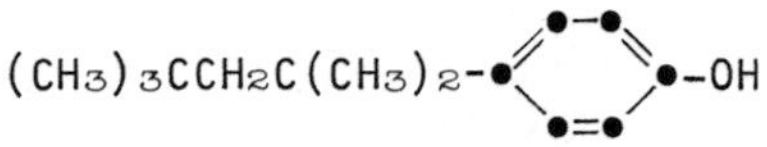

(CH3)3CCH2C(CH3)2-
-OH

$ClCH_2$*COOH / NaH, diglyme, 120°C →

tert-Octylphenol=TOPOH
[4-(1,1,3,3-Tetramethylbutyl)phenol]

TOPOCH_2*COOH (97%)

1. B_2H_6, THF (93%)
2. $SOCl_2$, pyr (96%)
3. H(OCH_2CH_2)nOH, NaH, DMSO, 21°C, 4-5 days

→ TOPOCH_2*CH_2(OCH_2CH_2)nOH

[n=5, 50% yield (42% overall);
n=8, 40% yield (33% overall)]

F. S. Tanaka and R. G. Wien, J. Label Compound. Radiopharm., 12, 97 (1976).

4-2 Alicyclic Alcohols

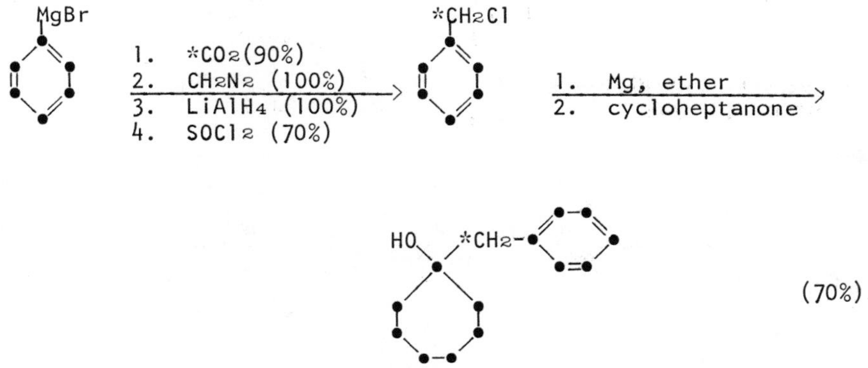
MgBr
1. *CO_2(90%)
2. CH_2N_2 (100%)
3. $LiAlH_4$ (100%)
4. $SOCl_2$ (70%)
*CH_2Cl
1. Mg, ether
2. cycloheptanone
HO
*CH_2-
(70%)

1-[Phenyl(methyl-^{14}C)]-cycloheptan-1-ol

D. Bánfi, J. Volfard, L. Pallos, and G. Zólyomi, J. Label. Compounds, 7, 62 (1971).

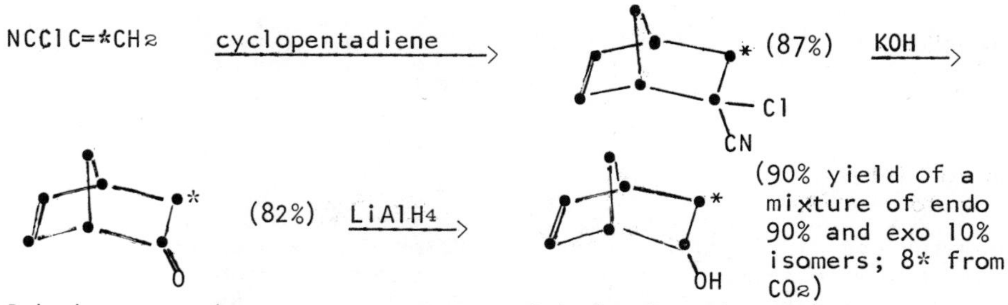
NCClC=*CH_2
cyclopentadiene
(87%)
KOH
Cl
CN
(82%)
$LiAlH_4$
O
OH
(90% yield of a mixture of endo 90% and exo 10% isomers; 8* from CO_2)

Dehydronorcamphor
[Bicyclo[2.2.1]hept-5-en-en-2-one-3-^{14}C]

Dehydro-2-norborneols
[Bicyclo[2.2.1]hept-5-en-2-ol-3-^{14}C]

Subsequent degradation studies revealed that the label was scrambled between position 2 (30%) and position 3 (70%). A mechanism involving a symmetrical ethylene oxide intermediate was proposed during the conversion of chloroethanol to cyanoethanol. The mass spectra of deuterated analogs confirmed the scrambling at this point.

C. C. Lee, F. L. Kung, B. Hahn, and A. J. Robson, J. Label. Compounds, 7, 46 (1971); J. Label. Compounds, 8, 77 (1972).

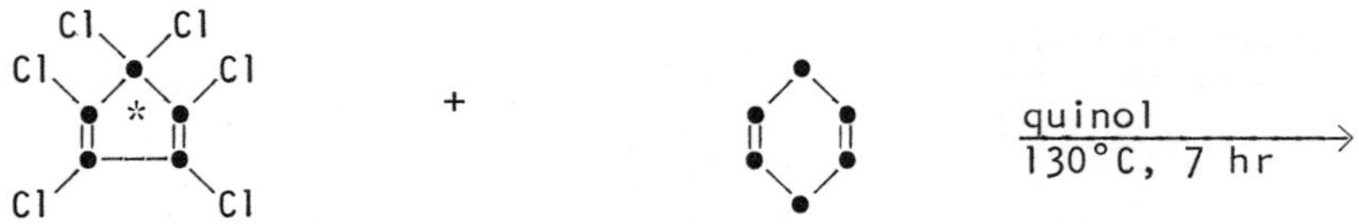
quinol
130°C, 7 hr

Hexachlorocyclopentadiene-
U-^{14}C

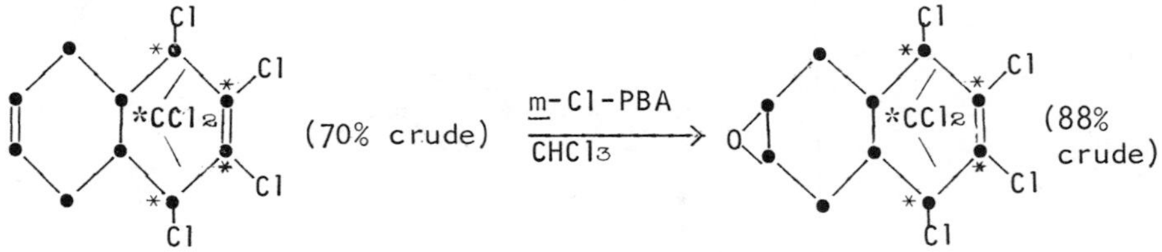
(70% crude)
m-Cl-PBA
$CHCl_3$
(88% crude)

Desmethylene aldrin (^{14}C at chlorinated carbons)

Desmethylene dieldrin (^{14}C at chlorinated carbons)

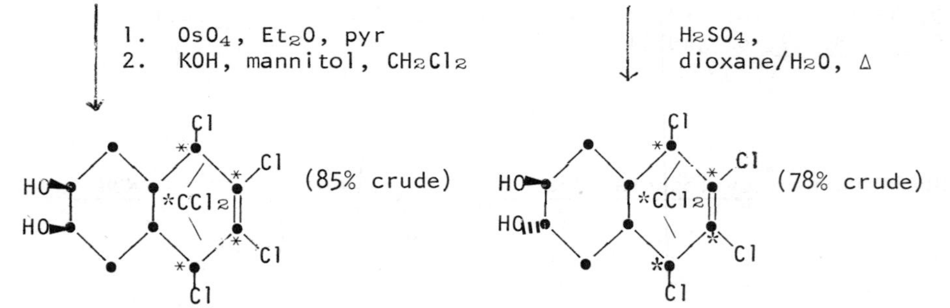
1. OsO_4, Et_2O, pyr
2. KOH, mannitol, CH_2Cl_2
H_2SO_4,
dioxane/H_2O, Δ
(85% crude)
(78% crude)

Desmethylene aldrin-cis-dihydrodiol [cis-1,2,3,4,9,9-Hexachloro-1,4,4a,5,6,7,8,8a-octahydro-1,4-methanonaphthalene-6,7-diol-1,2,3,4,9,9-^{14}C]

Desmethylene aldrin-trans-dihydrodiol [trans-1,2,3,4,9,9-Hexachloro-1,4,4a,5,6,7,8,8a-octahydro-1,4-methanonaphthlalene-6,7-diol-1,2,3,4,9,9-^{14}C]

M. P. Walker, J. D. McKinney, and V. G. Mudgal, J. Label. Compound. Radiopharm., 12, 23 (1976).

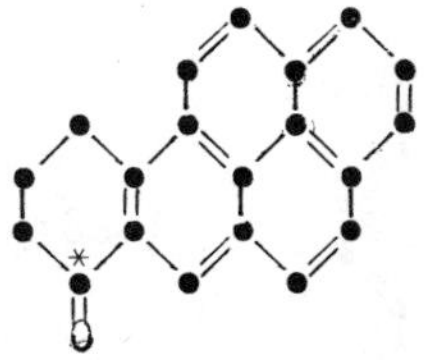

9,10-Dihydrobenzo[a]pyren-7(8H)-one-7-^{14}C

(64% from K*CN)

1. $NaBH_4$, EtOH, Δ
2. HCl/AcOH, Δ
→

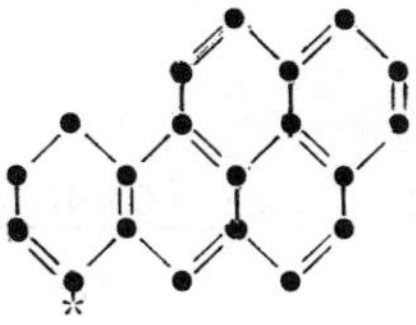

(91%)

$BzOAg$, I_2 / C_6H_6, Δ →

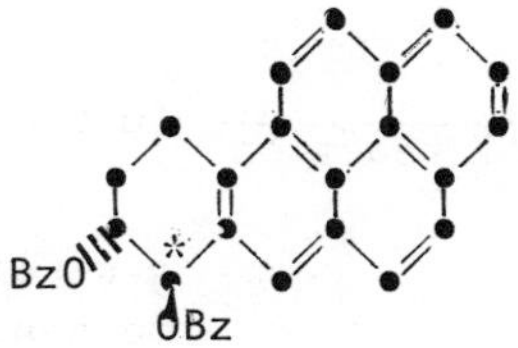
BzO
OBz

(73%)

1. NBS, Bz_2O_2, CCl_4, Δ
2. xylene, Δ
3. $NaOCH_3$, CH_3OH/THF
→

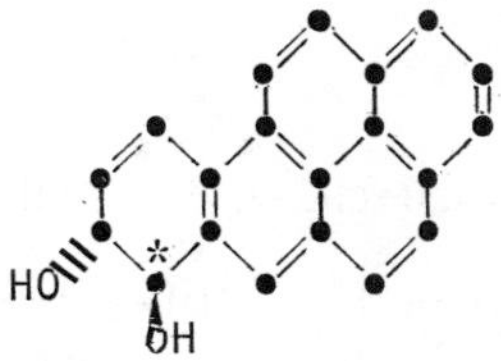
HO
OH

trans-7,8-Dihydrobenzo[a]pyrene-7,8-diol-7-^{14}C

(42%; 18% overall)

m-ClPBA / THF →

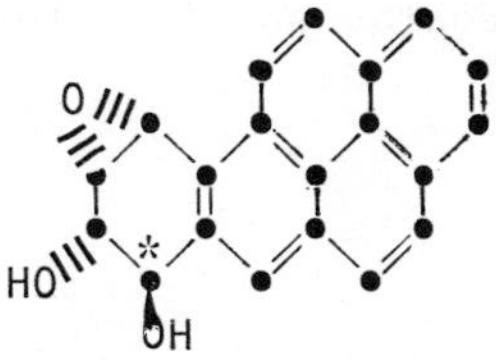
O
HO
OH

(40%; 7% overall)

(7α,8β,8aα,9aα)(+)-Tetrahydrobenzo[10,11]chryseno[3,4b]oxirene-7,8-diol-7-^{14}C

D. J. McCaustland, W. P. Duncan, and J. F. Engel, J. Label. Compound. Radiopharm., 12, 443 (1976)

4-3 Aromatic Alcohols

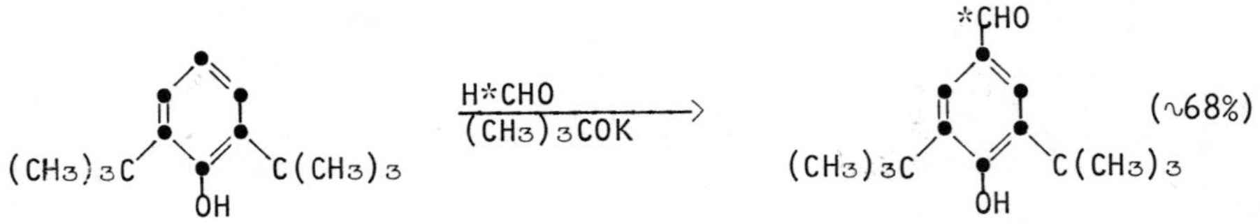
H*CHO
(CH3)3COK
(CH3)3C
C(CH3)3
OH
*CHO
(~68%)

3,5-Di-(1,1-dimethylethyl)-4-hydroxybenzaldehyde-7-^{14}C

K. Figge, J. Label. Compounds, 5, 122 (1969)

$C_3H_7CH{=}CH{*}CH_2OH$ —(Na, Δ; leaf alcohol reaction)→

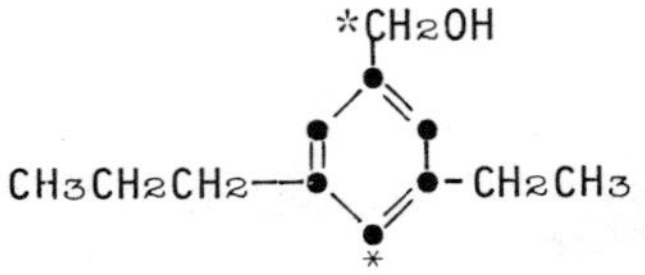
*CH2OH
CH3CH2CH2
CH2CH3
*

(Z)-2-Hexen-1-ol-1-^{14}C

3-Ethyl-5-propylbenzene-methanol-α,4-^{14}C

$CH_3{*}CH_2CH_2CH{=}CHCH_2OH$ —(Na, Δ)→

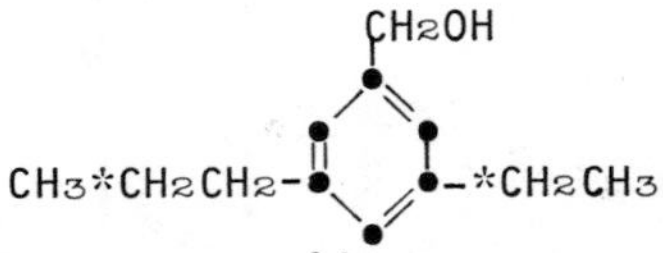
CH2OH
CH3*CH2CH2-
-*CH2CH3

3-(Ethyl-1-^{14}C)-5-(propyl-2-^{14}C)benzenemethanol

The positions of the label were deduced from degradative studies; a condensation pattern is suggested.

M. Hamada, Y. Nagata, and A. Hatanaka, Agr. Biol. Chem., 36, 324 (1972).

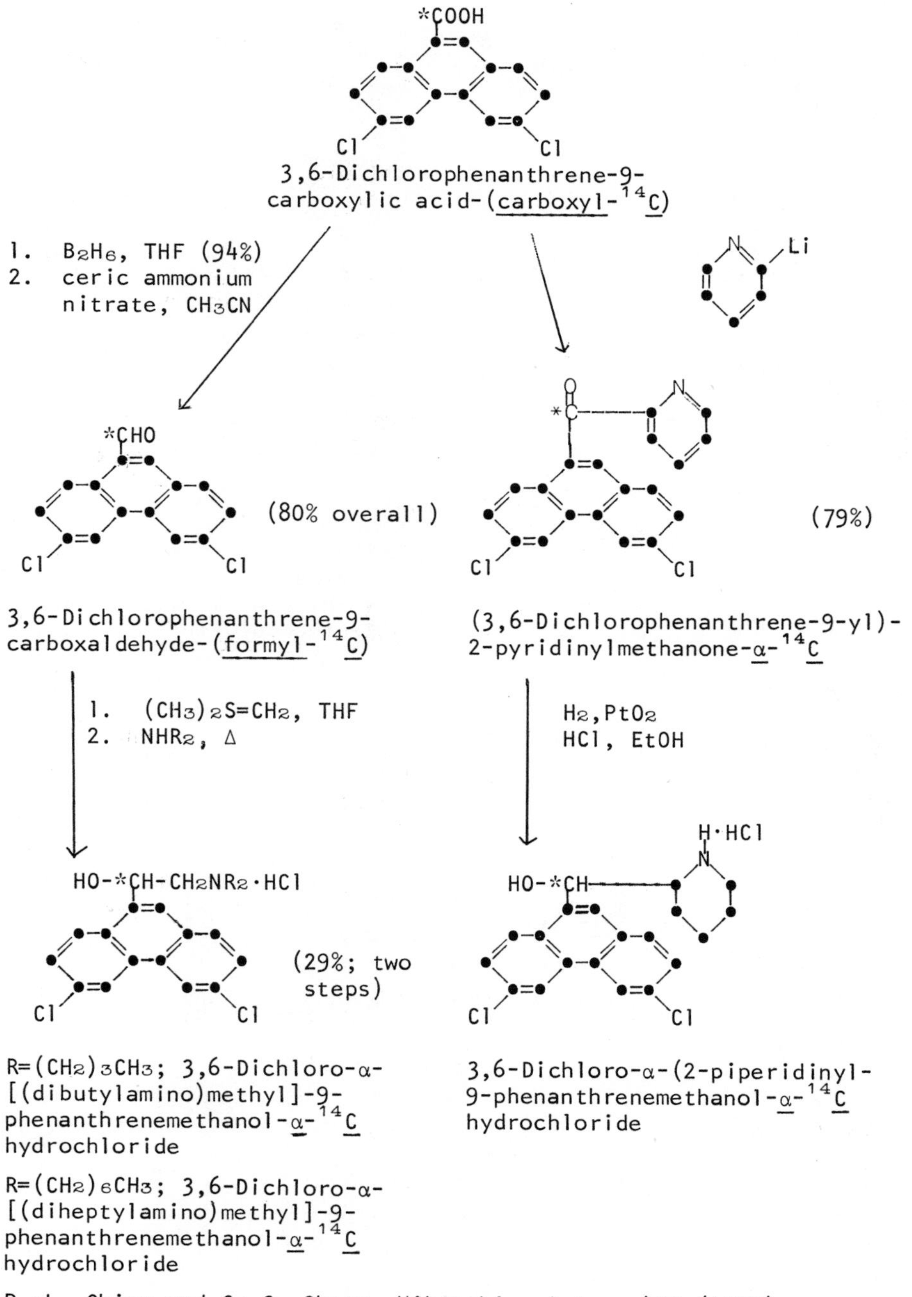
*COOH
Cl
Cl
3,6-Dichlorophenanthrene-9-carboxylic acid-(carboxyl-^{14}C)
1. B_2H_6, THF (94%)
2. ceric ammonium nitrate, CH_3CN
N
Li
*CHO
(80% overall)
O
*C
N
(79%)
3,6-Dichlorophenanthrene-9-carboxaldehyde-(formyl-^{14}C)
(3,6-Dichlorophenanthrene-9-yl)-2-pyridinylmethanone-α-^{14}C
1. $(CH_3)_2S=CH_2$, THF
2. NHR_2, Δ
H_2,PtO_2
HCl, EtOH
HO-*CH-CH_2NR_2·HCl
(29%; two steps)
H·HCl
N
HO-*CH
R=$(CH_2)_3CH_3$; 3,6-Dichloro-α-[(dibutylamino)methyl]-9-phenanthrenemethanol-α-^{14}C hydrochloride
R=$(CH_2)_6CH_3$; 3,6-Dichloro-α-[(diheptylamino)methyl]-9-phenanthrenemethanol-α-^{14}C hydrochloride
3,6-Dichloro-α-(2-piperidinyl-9-phenanthrenemethanol-α-^{14}C hydrochloride

P.-L. Chien and C. C. Cheng, Mikrochim. Acta., 401 (1973).

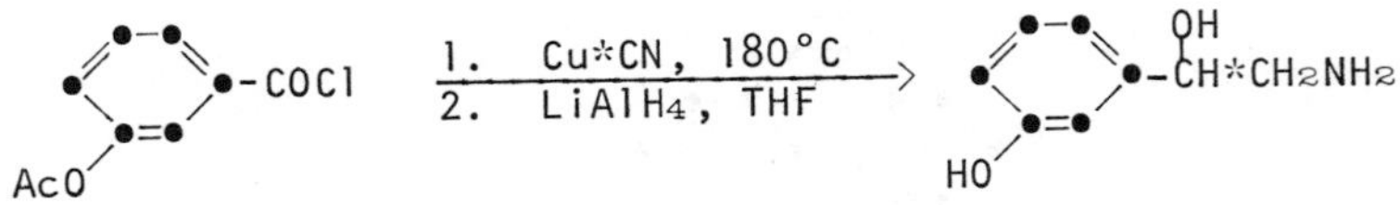
-COCl
AcO
1. Cu*CN, 180°C
2. LiAlH4, THF
OH
-CH*CH2NH2
HO

(47% from Cu*CN)

Norfenefrine
[α-(Aminomethyl-^{14}C)-3-hydroxybenzenemethanol]

K.-O. Vollmer and B. Liedtke, J. Label. Compounds, 9, 347 (1973).

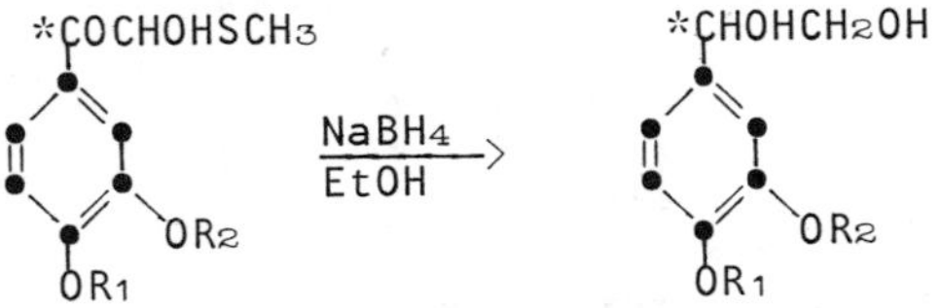
*COCHOHSCH3
OR2
OR1
NaBH4
EtOH
*CHOHCH2OH
OR2
OR1

(60-64% from vanillic and isovanillic acids)

R_1=H, R_2=CH_3; 1-(4-Hydroxy-3-methoxyphenyl)-1,2-ethanediol-1-[14]C

R_1=CH_3, R_2=H; 1-(3-Hydroxy-4-methoxyphenyl)-1,2-ethanediol-1-[14]C

Similarly:

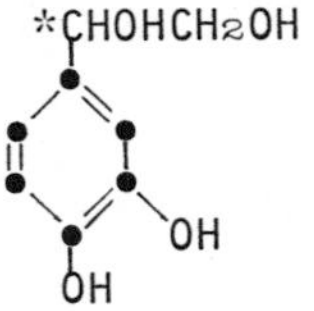
*CHOHCH2OH
OH
OH

(64% overall)

4-(1,2-Dihydroxyethyl-1-^{14}C)-1,2-benzenediol

L. Pichat and J. Tostain, J. Label. Compound. Radiopharm., 13, 587 (1977).

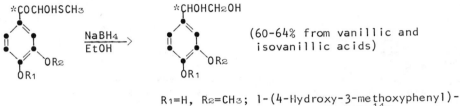

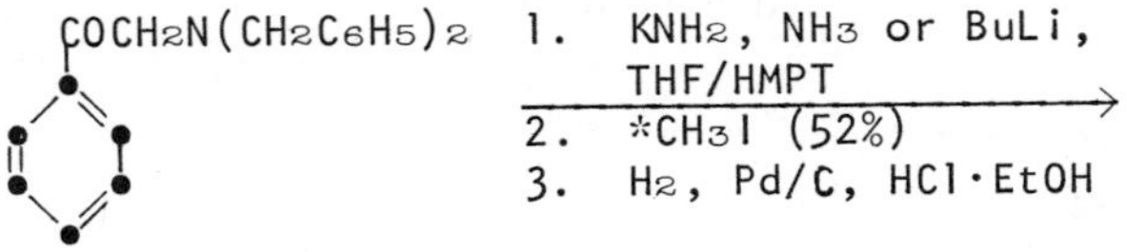
COCH2N(CH2C6H5)2
1. KNH2, NH3 or BuLi, THF/HMPT
2. *CH3I (52%)
3. H2, Pd/C, HCl·EtOH

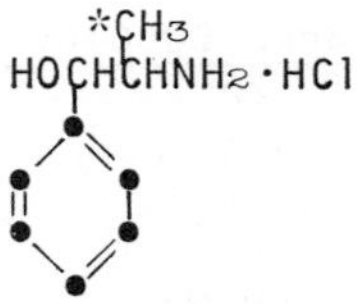

(42% from *CH_3I; 31% from Ba*CO_3)

dl-Norephedrine
[α-(1-Aminoethyl-2-^{14}C) benzenemethanol]

Nguyen-Hoang-Nam, P. Lucas, and L. Pichat, J. Label. Compounds, 10, 49 (1974).

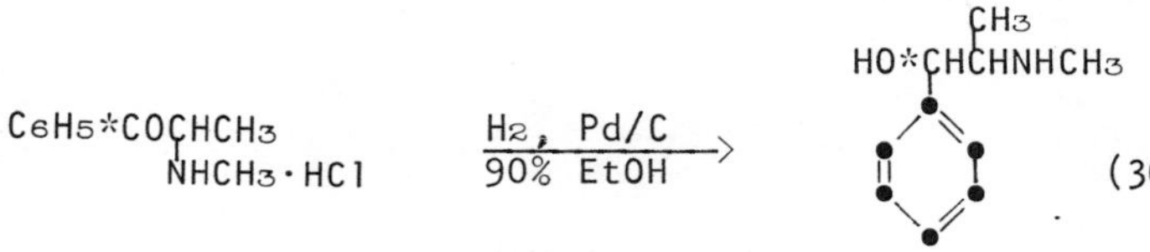

(30% from Ba*CO_3)

Ephedrine
[α-(1-Methylaminoethyl) benzenemethanol-α-^{14}C]

Nguyen-Hoang-Nam, M. Herbert, Nguyen-Dat-Xuong, and L. Pichat, J. Label. Compounds, 4, 325 (1968).

C_6H_5*COC_6H_5 (66% from $BaCO_3$) $\xrightarrow[\text{2. } LiAlH_4]{\text{1. } CH_3CH_2CN,\ NaNH_2}$

$(C_6H_5)_2$*C(OH)--CH(CH_3)CH_2NH_2 (39%)

dl-3-Amino-2-methyl-1,1-diphenylpropanol-1-[14]C

Resolution of the isomers with d-tartaric acid gave a 36% yield of the l-isomer and a 37% yield of the d-isomer; yield was 10% overall from $BaCO_3$.

R. C. Thomas, J. Label. Compound. Radiopharm., 15, 591 (1978).

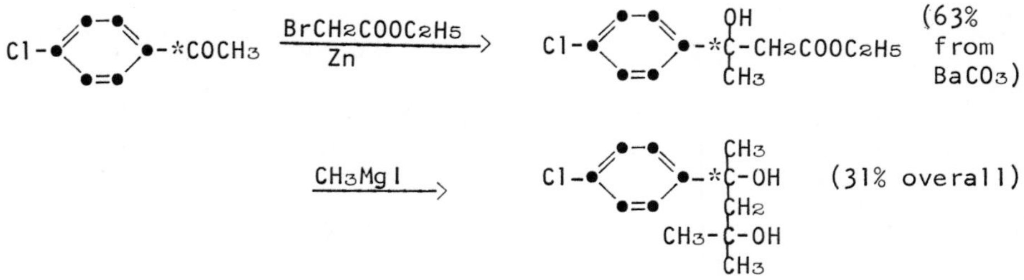
Cl-
-*COCH3
BrCH2COOC2H5
Zn
OH
-*C-CH2COOC2H5
CH3
(63% from BaCO3)
CH3MgI
CH3
-*C-OH
CH2
CH3-C-OH
CH3
(31% overall)

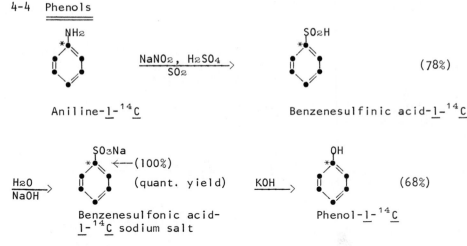

Fenpentadiol
[2-(4-Chlorophenyl)-4-methyl-2,4-pentanediol-2-^{14}C]

J. P. Noël, A. Benakis, R. Valette, M. Herbert, and L. Pichat, J. Label. Compounds, 8, 157 (1972).

4-4 Phenols

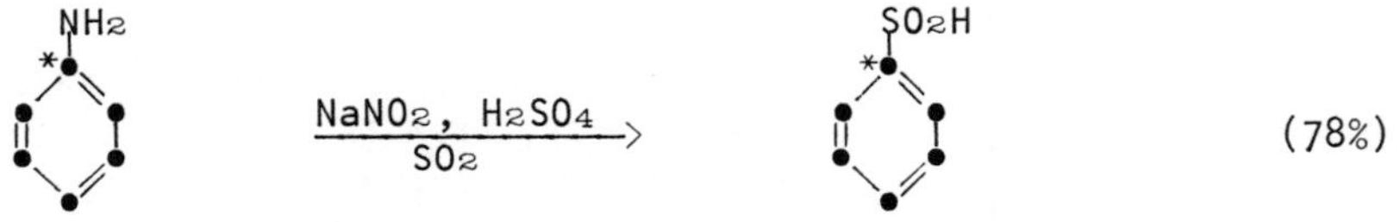
NH2
NaNO2, H2SO4
SO2
SO2H
(78%)

Aniline-1-^{14}C

Benzenesulfinic acid-1-^{14}C

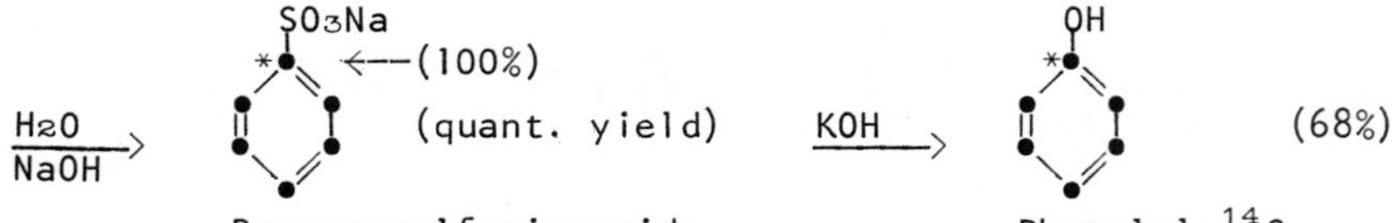
H2O
NaOH
SO3Na
(100%)
(quant. yield)
KOH
OH
(68%)

Benzenesulfonic acid-1-^{14}C sodium salt

Phenol-1-^{14}C

From degratation reactions, 97.2% of the label was found to be in position 1 and 2.1% at position 2. The mechanism is assumed to be a simple aromatic S_{N2}-type substitution.

S. Oae, N. Furukawa, M. Kise, and M. Kawanishi, Bull. Chem. Soc. Jap., 39, 1212 (1966).

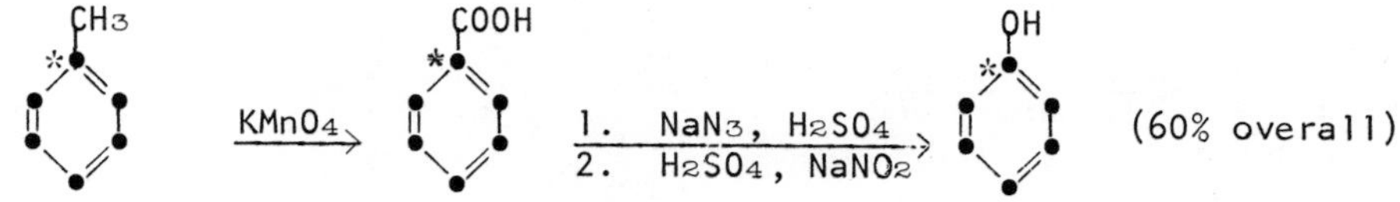
CH3
COOH
OH
KMnO4
1. NaN3, H2SO4
2. H2SO4, NaNO2
(60% overall)

Toluene-1-^{14}C Phenol-1-^{14}C

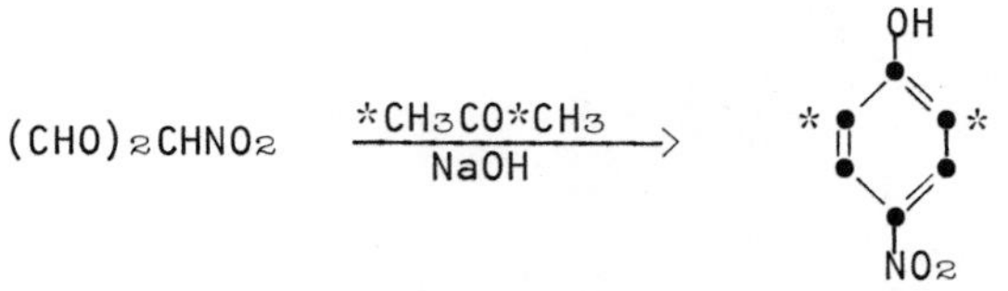
(CHO)2CHNO2
*CH3CO*CH3
NaOH
OH
NO2

4-Nitrophenol-2,6-^{14}C

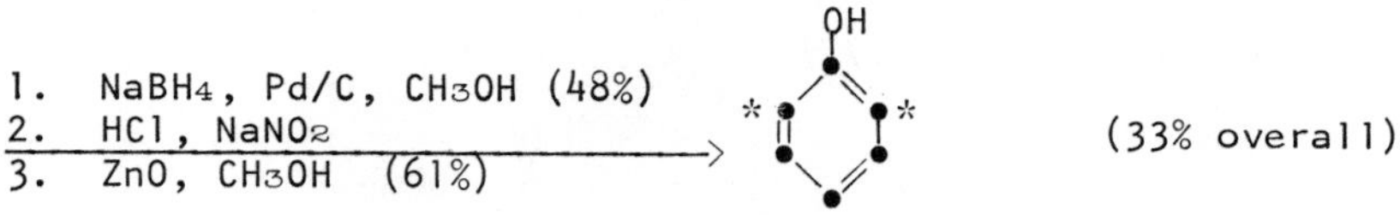
1. NaBH4, Pd/C, CH3OH (48%)
2. HCl, NaNO2
3. ZnO, CH3OH (61%)
OH
(33% overall)

Phenol-2,6-^{14}C

B. Bettens and J. M. Gonze, J. Label. Compounds, 7, 23 (1971)

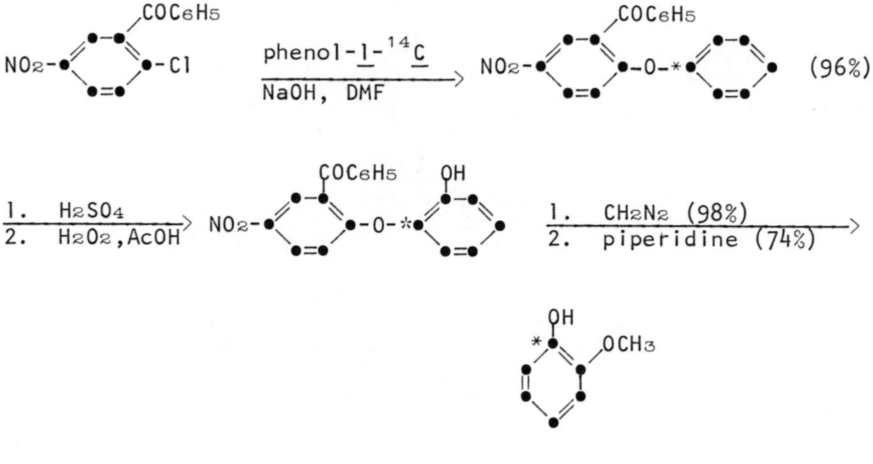
COC6H5
NO2-
-Cl
phenol-1-14C
NaOH, DMF
-O-*
(96%)
1. H2SO4
2. H2O2,AcOH
OH
1. CH2N2 (98%)
2. piperidine (74%)
OCH3

Guaiacol
[2-Methoxyphenol-1-^{14}C]

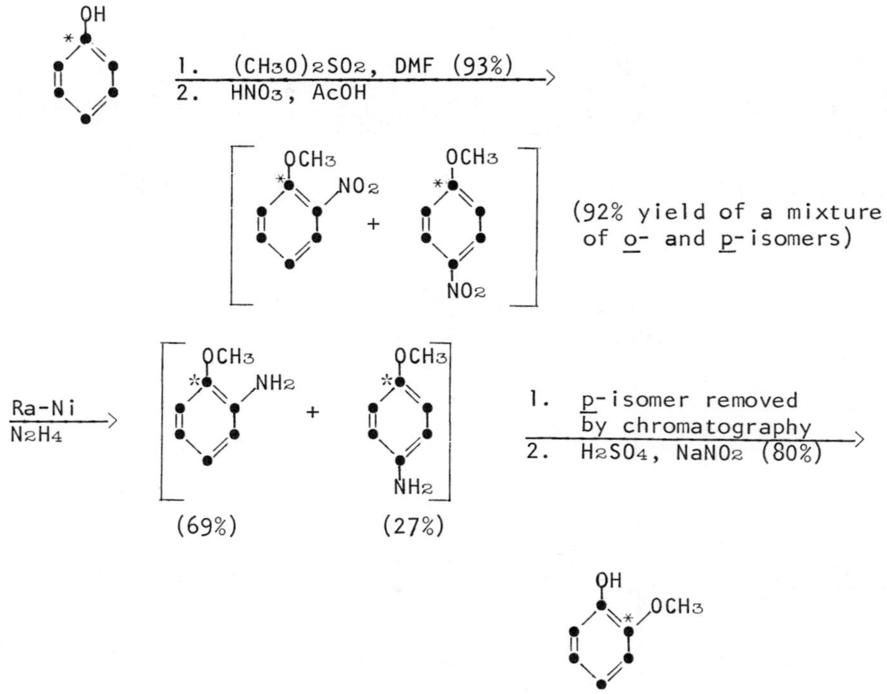
OH
1. (CH3O)2SO2, DMF (93%)
2. HNO3, AcOH
OCH3
NO2
OCH3
NO2
(92% yield of a mixture of o- and p-isomers)
Ra-Ni
N2H4
OCH3
NH2
OCH3
NH2
(69%)
(27%)
1. p-isomer removed by chromatography
2. H2SO4, NaNO2 (80%)
OH
OCH3

Guaiacol
[2-Methoxyphenol-2-^{14}C]

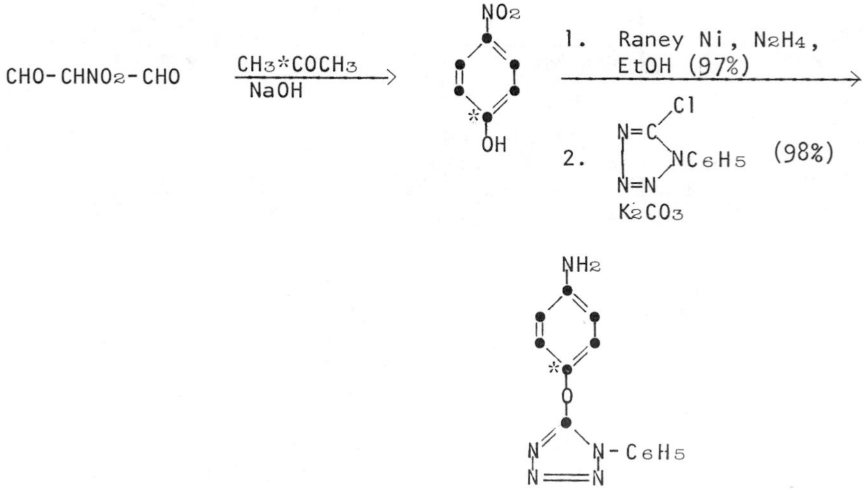
CHO-CHNO2-CHO
CH3*COCH3
NaOH
NO2
OH
1. Raney Ni, N2H4, EtOH (97%)
2.
Cl
N=C
NC6H5
N=N
K2CO3
(98%)
NH2
O
N
N-C6H5
N
N

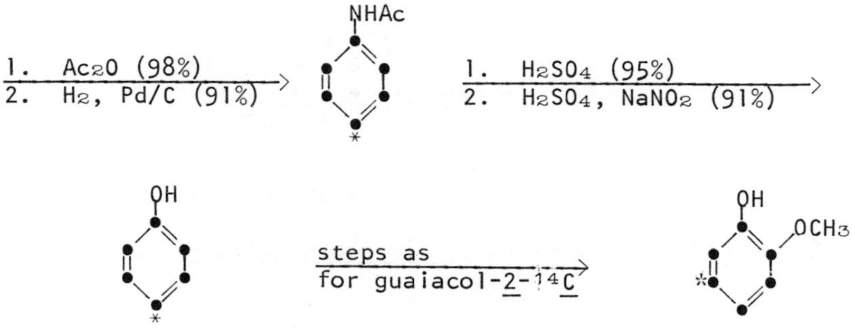
NHAc
1. Ac_2O (98%)
2. H_2, Pd/C (91%)
1. H_2SO_4 (95%)
2. H_2SO_4, $NaNO_2$ (91%)
OH
steps as for guaiacol-2-^{14}C
OCH3

Guaiacol
[2-Methoxyphenol-5-^{14}C]

Routes to guaiacol-3-^{14}C and -4-^{14}C were carried out using unlabeled material.

K. Kratzl and F. W. Vierhapper, Monatsh. Chem., 102 224 (1971).

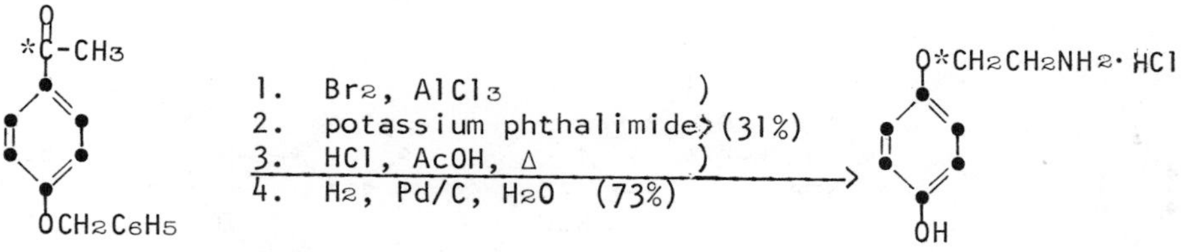
*C-CH3
OCH2C6H5
1. Br_2, $AlCl_3$
2. potassium phthalimide (31%)
3. HCl, AcOH, Δ
4. H_2, Pd/C, H_2O (73%)
O*CH2CH2NH2·HCl
OH

4-(2-Aminoethoxy-1-^{14}C)phenol hydrochloride

K.-H. Schweer, Atompraxis, 12, 85 (1966).

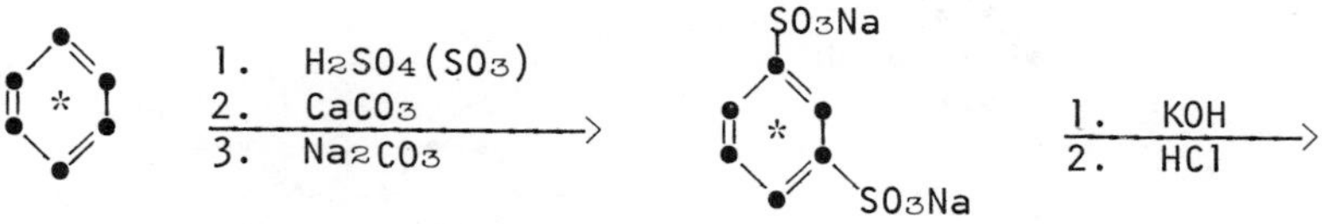
1. $H_2SO_4(SO_3)$
2. $CaCO_3$
3. Na_2CO_3
SO3Na
SO3Na
1. KOH
2. HCl

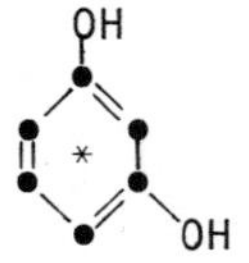
OH
OH

1,3-Benzenediol-U-^{14}C

Y. A. Usaevich and L. I. Vekshina, Khim.-Farm. Zh., 11, 30 (1977).

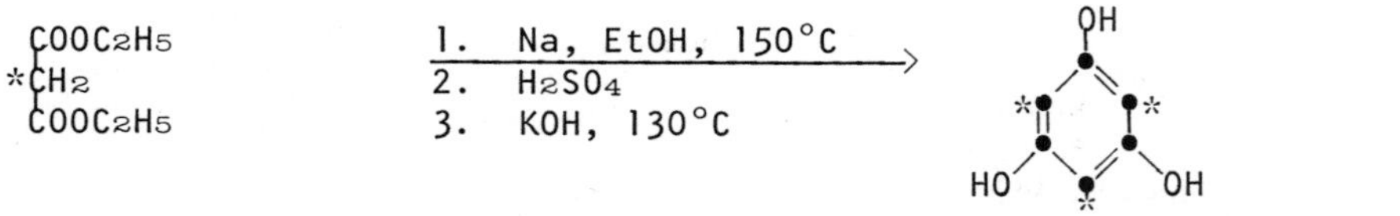
COOC2H5
*CH2
COOC2H5
1. Na, EtOH, 150°C
2. H2SO4
3. KOH, 130°C
OH
HO
OH

Malonic-2-^{14}C acid diethyl ester

Phloroglucinol [1,3,5-Benzenetriol-2,4,6-^{14}C]

S. Johne, H. Bernasch, and D. Gröger, Pharmazie, 25, 777 (1970).

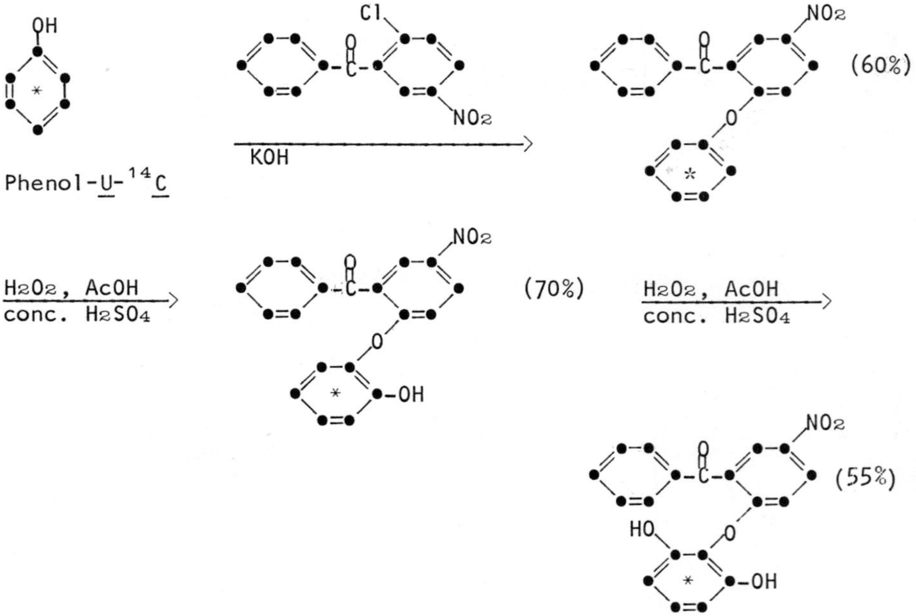
OH
Cl
NO2
KOH
NO2
(60%)
O
H2O2, AcOH
conc. H2SO4
NO2
O
OH
(70%)
H2O2, AcOH
conc. H2SO4
NO2
(55%)
HO
O
OH

Phenol-U-^{14}C

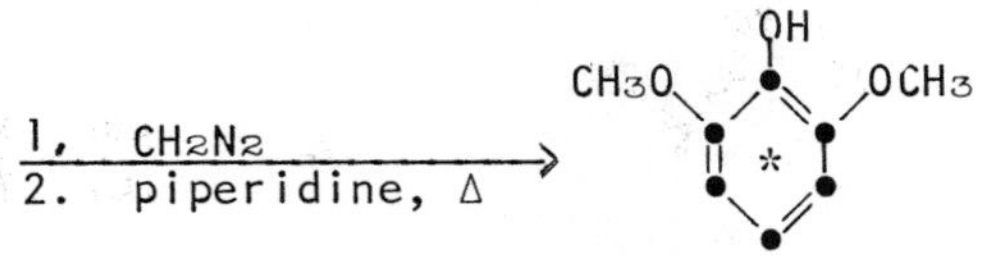

(5-10% overall)

2,6-Dimethoxyphenol-(ring-^{14}C)

J. J. Miller, A. H. Olavesen, and C. G. Curtis, J. Label. Compounds, 10, 151 (1974).

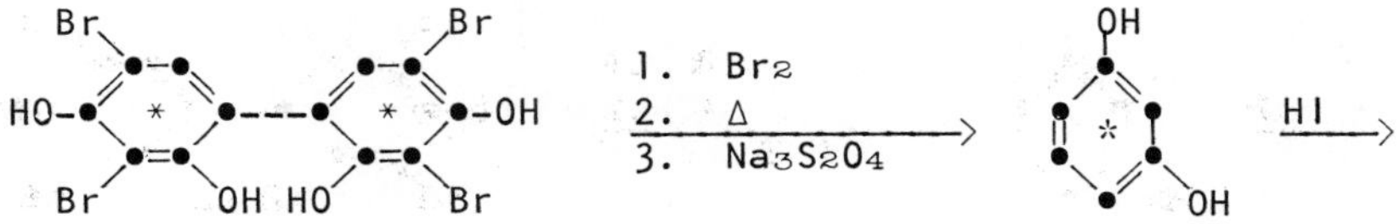

Tebrofen
[3,3'5,5'-Tetrabromo-(1,1'-biphenyl)-2,2',4,4'-tetrol-U-^{14}C]

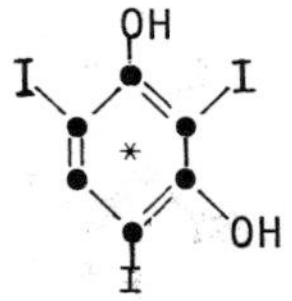

Riodoxol
[2,4,6-Triiodo-1,3-benzenediol-U-^{14}C]

Y. A. Usaevich and L. I. Vekshina, Khim.-Farm. Zh., 11, 30 (1977).

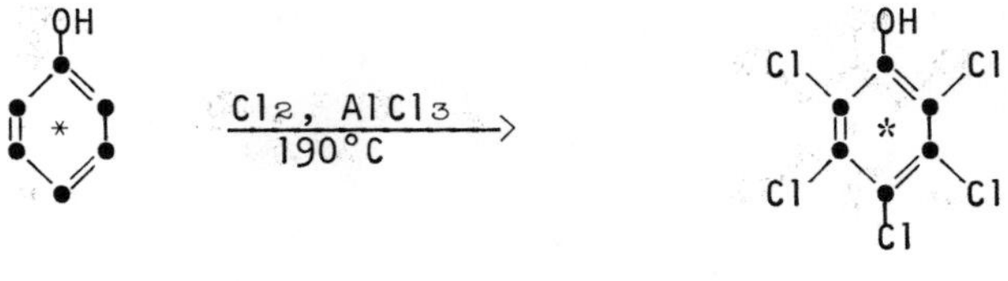

(47%)

Pentachorophenol-U-^{14}C

R. R. Rogers, J. E. Christian, J. E. Etzel, and G. S. Born, J. Label. Compounds, 7, 149 (1971).

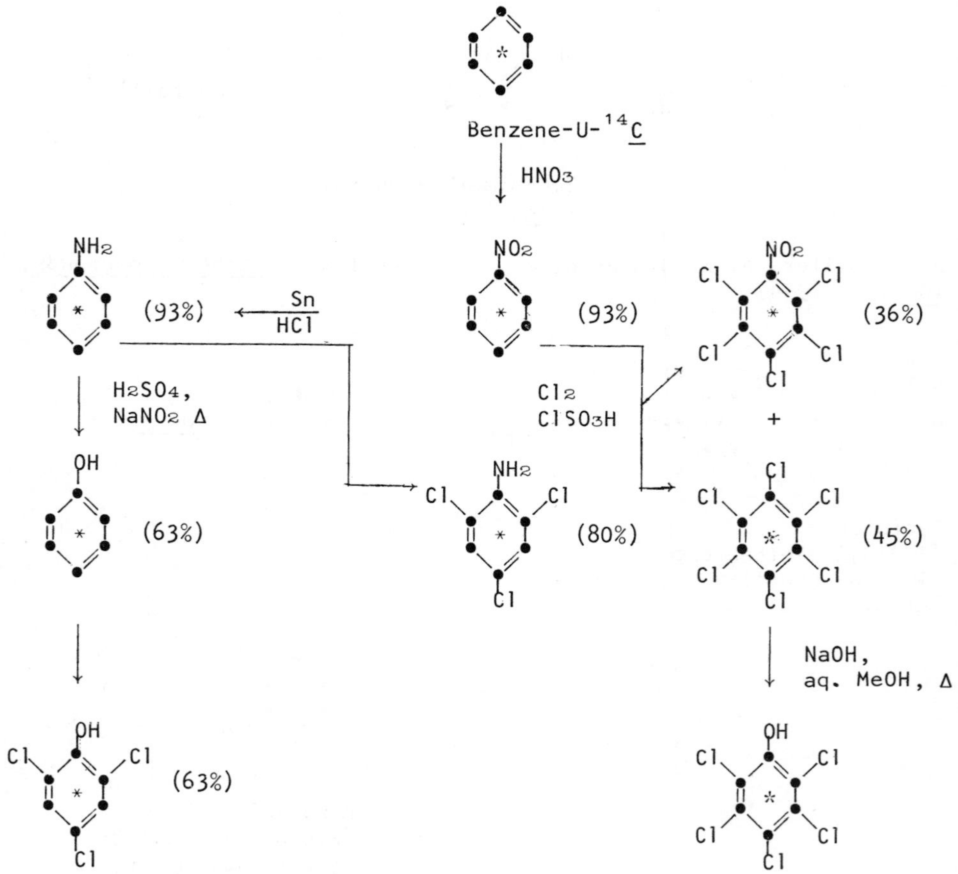
Benzene-U-14C
HNO3
NH2
(93%)
Sn
HCl
NO2
(93%)
NO2
Cl
Cl
Cl
Cl
Cl
(36%)
H2SO4,
NaNO2 Δ
Cl2
ClSO3H
+
OH
(63%)
NH2
Cl
Cl
Cl
(80%)
Cl
Cl
Cl
Cl
Cl
Cl
(45%)
NaOH,
aq. MeOH, Δ
OH
Cl
Cl
Cl
(63%)
OH
Cl
Cl
Cl
Cl
Cl

2,4,6-Trichlorophenol-U-^{14}C

Pentachlorophenol-U-^{14}C

K. Sandrock, A. Attar, D. Bieniek, W. Klein, and F. Korte, J. Label. Compound. Radiopharm., 14, 197 (1977).

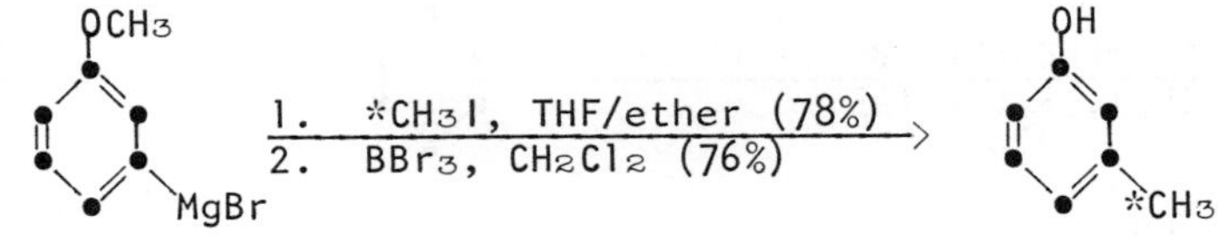
OCH3
MgBr
1. *CH3I, THF/ether (78%)
2. BBr3, CH2Cl2 (76%)
OH
*CH3

3-(Methyl-^{14}C)phenol

A. Yoshitake, K. Kawahara, T. Kamada, and M. Endo, J. Label. Compound. Radiopharm., 13, 323 (1977).

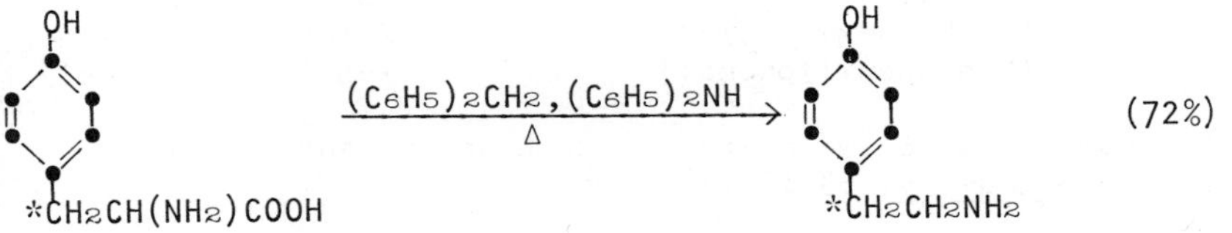
OH
*CH2CH(NH2)COOH
(C6H5)2CH2,(C6H5)2NH
Δ
OH
*CH2CH2NH2
(72%)

DL-Tyrosine-3-^{14}C

Tyramine
[4-(2-Aminoethyl-1-^{14}C)phenol]

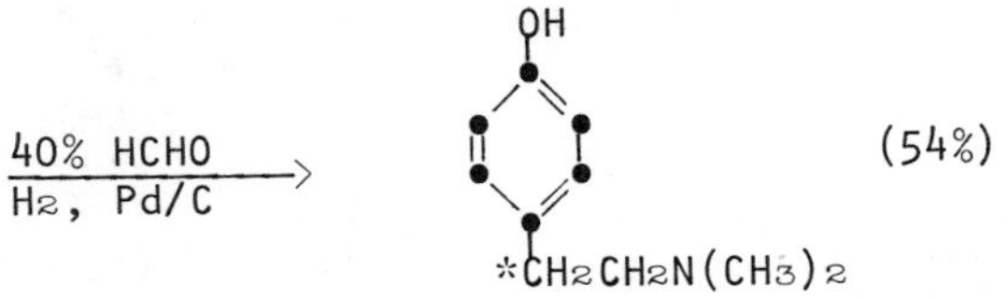
40% HCHO
H2, Pd/C
OH
*CH2CH2N(CH3)2
(54%)

Hordenine
[4-(2-Dimethylaminoethyl-1-^{14}C)phenol]

G. A. Digenis, J. W. Burkett, and V. Mihranian, J. Label. Compounds, 8, 231 (1972).

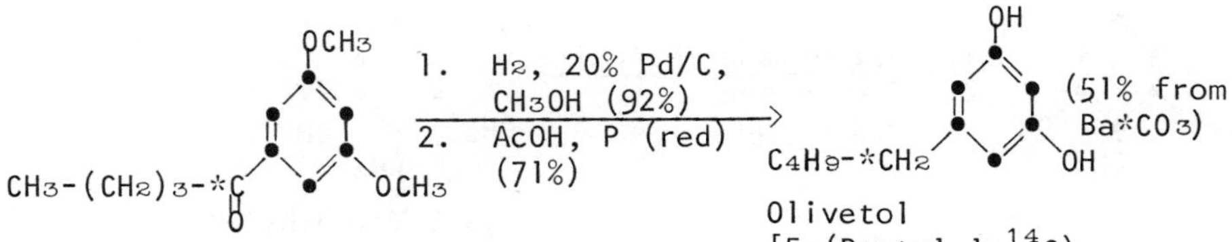
OCH3
CH3-(CH2)3-*C
O
OCH3
1. H2, 20% Pd/C, CH3OH (92%)
2. AcOH, P (red) (71%)
OH
C4H9-*CH2
OH
(51% from Ba*CO3)

Olivetol
[5-(Pentyl-1-^{14}C)-1,3-benzenediol]

Nguyen-Hoang-Nam, J. P. Beaucourt, H. Hoellinger, and L. Pichat, Bull. Soc. Chim. Fr., Part 2, 1367 (1974)

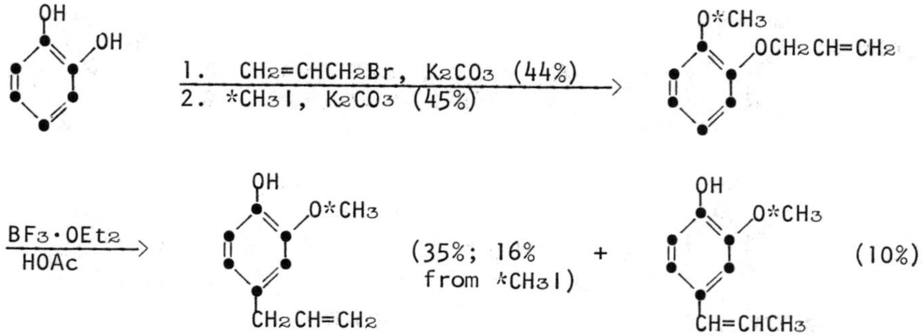
OH
OH
1. CH2=CHCH2Br, K2CO3 (44%)
2. *CH3I, K2CO3 (45%)
O*CH3
OCH2CH=CH2
BF3·OEt2
HOAc
OH
O*CH3
CH2CH=CH2
(35%; 16% from *CH3I)
+
OH
O*CH3
CH=CHCH3
(10%)

Eugenol
[2-(Methoxy-^{14}C)-4-(2-propenyl)phenol]

Isoeugenol
[2-(Methoxy-^{14}C)-4-(1-propenyl)phenol]

J. L. Rabinowitz, J. E. Weinberg, A. R. Gennaro, and M. Zanger, J. Label. Compounds, 9, 53 (1973).

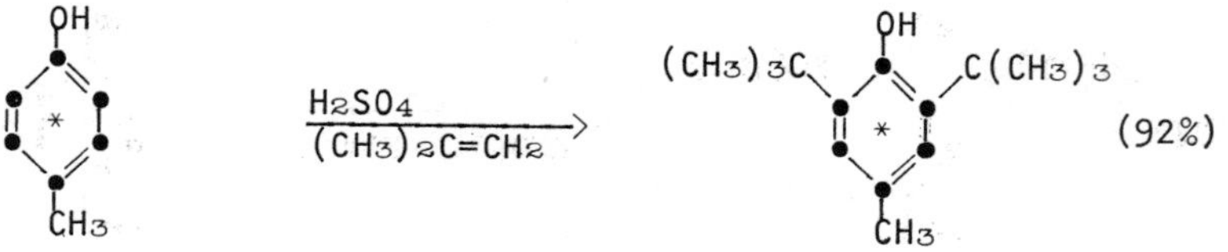
OH
CH3
H2SO4
(CH3)2C=CH2
OH
(CH3)3C
C(CH3)3
CH3
(92%)

Cresol
[4-Methylphenol-(ring-^{14}C)]

BHT
[2,6-Bis(1,1-dimethylethyl)-4-methylphenol-(ring-^{14}C)]

B. D. Shipp, J. B. Data, and J. E. Christian, J. Label. Compounds, 9, 127 (1973).

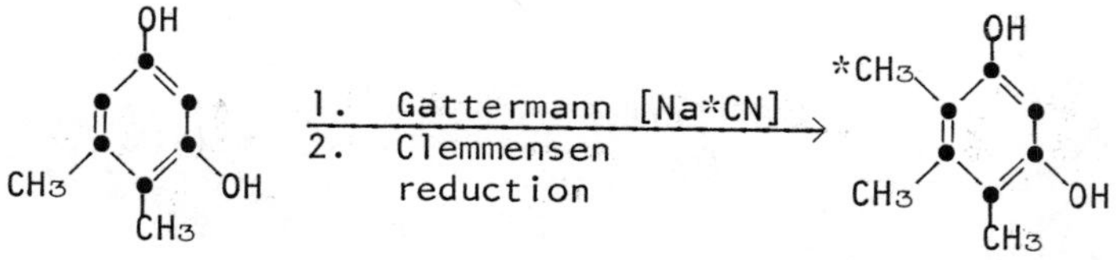
OH
CH3
OH
CH3
1. Gattermann [Na*CN]
2. Clemmensen reduction
OH
*CH3
CH3
OH
CH3

4,5,6-Trimethyl-1,3-benzenediol-(6-methyl-^{14}C)

The 5-ethyl derivative was prepared in a similar manner.

J. Better and S. Gatenbeck, Acta Chem. Scand. B, 31, 391 (1977).

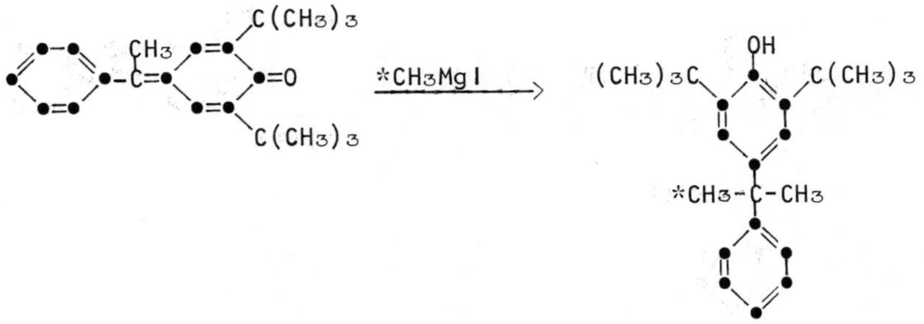
C(CH3)3
CH3
=O
*CH3MgI
C(CH3)3
OH
(CH3)3C
C(CH3)3
*CH3-C-CH3

2,6-Bis(1,1-dimethylethyl)-4-[1-(methyl-^{14}C)-1-phenylethyl]phenol

O. B. Shekhter, A. A. Drabkina, A. A. Lure, A. A. Volodkin, and Y. S. Tsizin, Zh. Org. Khim., 14, 2233 (1978).

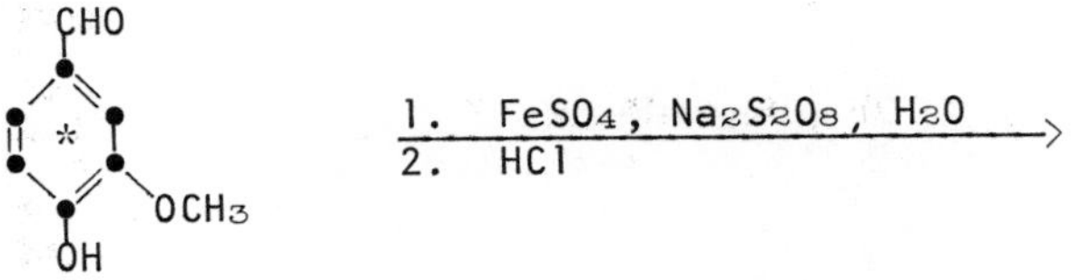
CHO
OCH3
OH
1. FeSO4, Na2S2O8, H2O
2. HCl

Vanillin
[3-Methoxy-4-hydroxy-benzaldehyde-3,4- or -6-^{14}C]

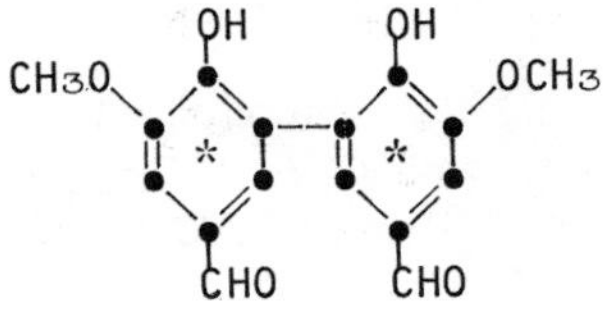
OH
OH
CH3O
OCH3
CHO
CHO

(95%)

6,6'-Dihydroxy-5,5'-dimethoxy-[1,1-biphenyl-3,3'-dicarbox-aldehyde-2,2',-3,3',- or -6,6'-^{14}C]

1. $NH_2NH_2 \cdot H_2O$
2. $N(CH_2CH_2OH)_3$, KOH, Δ →

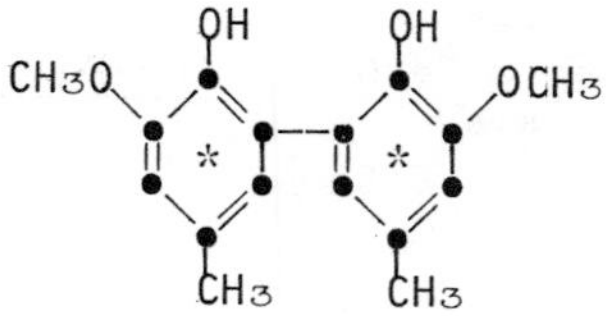

OH
OH
CH_3O
OCH_3
CH_3
CH_3

(75%)

Bicreosol
[3,3'-Dimethoxy-5,5'-dimethyl-[1,1'-biphenyl]-2,2'-,3,3'-, or -6,6'-^{14}C]

K. Kratzl and F. W. Vierhapper, Monatsh. Chem., 102 425 (1971).

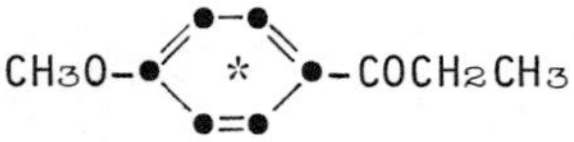

CH_3O
$COCH_2CH_3$

1. 1 eq. $LiAlH_4$, 2 eq. $TiCl_3$
2. NaOH, $HOCH_2CH_2OH$ →

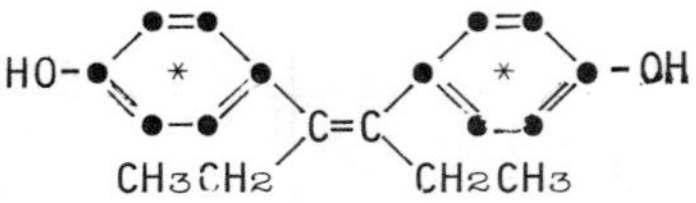

HO
OH
CH_3CH_2
CH_2CH_3

(E)-4,4'-(1,2-Diethyl-1,2-ethenediyl)bisphenol-(ring-^{14}C)

A mixture of the cis and trans isomers was obtained together with some hexestrol side product.

V. J. Feil, P. W. Aschbacher, C. H. Lamoureux, E. R. Mansager, J. G. Ahern, and I. Ary, Science, 198, 510 (1977); J. E. McMurray and M. P. Fleming, J. Amer. Chem. Soc., 96, 4708 (1974).

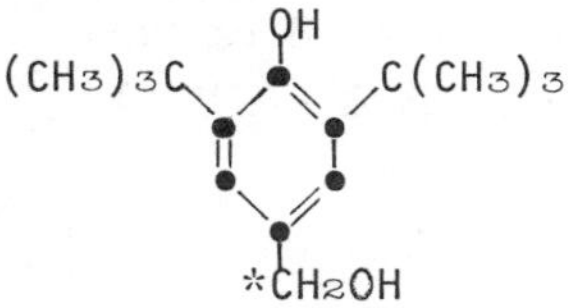

OH
$(CH_3)_3C$
$C(CH_3)_3$
*CH_2OH

Al_2O_3, P_2O_5
1,3,4-trimethylbenzene →

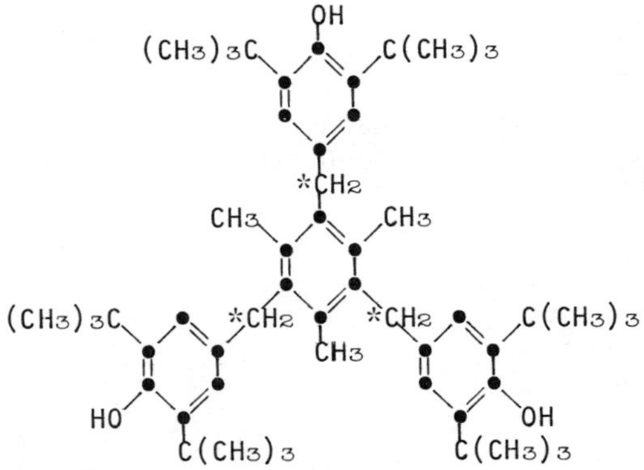
OH
(CH3)3C
C(CH3)3
*CH2
CH3
CH3
(CH3)3C
*CH2
*CH2
C(CH3)3
CH3
HO
OH
C(CH3)3
C(CH3)3

(48% from $*CH_2O$)

4,4',4''-[(2,4,6-Trimethyl-1,3,5-benzenetriyl) tris(methylene-^{14}C)]-[2,6-bis(1,1-dimethylethyl)] phenol

K. Figge, J. Label. Compounds, 5, 122 (1969).

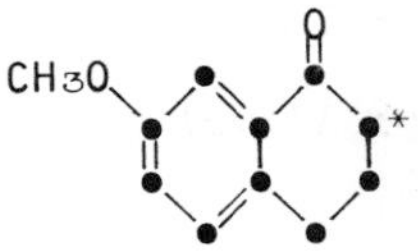
CH3O
O
*

H_2, 10% Pd/C
EtOH
→

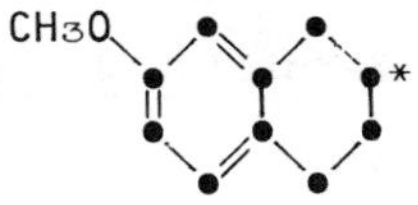
CH3O
*

(59% from $*CO_2$)

3,4-Dihydro-7-methoxy-1(2H)-naphthalenone-2-^{14}C

1,2,3,4-Tetrahydro-7-methoxynaphthalene-2-^{14}C

1. DDQ, C_6H_6, (70%)
2. BBr_3, CH_2Cl_2 (92%)
→

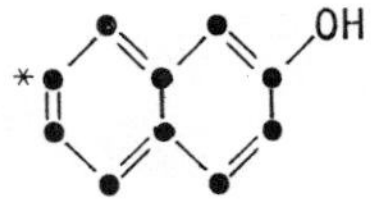
OH
*

H_2, copper chromite catalyst
EtOH, Δ, 150-170 atm
→

2-Naphthalenol-7-^{14}C

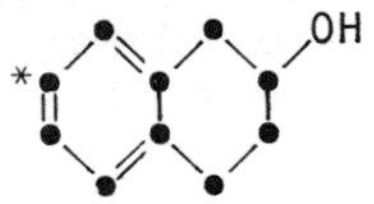
OH
*

(80%)

1,2,3,4-Tetrahydro-2-naphthalenol-7-^{14}C

P. J. van der Jagt, W. den Hollander, and B. van Zanten, Tetrahedron, 28, 1779 (1972); Tetrahedron, 27, 1049 (1971).

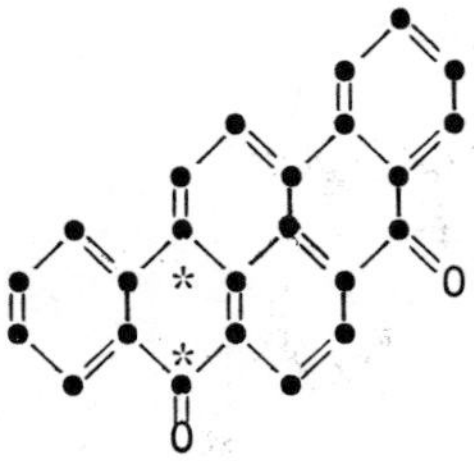

(93%) NaOAc / Ac_2O, Zn →

Benzo[rst]pentaphene-5,8-dione-5,15-^{14}C

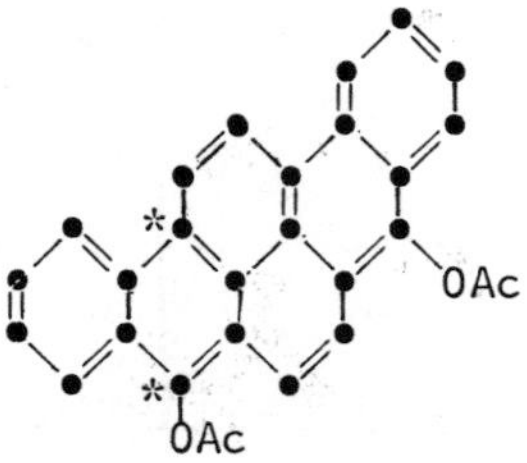

(78%)

Benzo[rst]pentaphene-5,8-diol diacetate-5,15-^{14}C

E. Boger and P. Bernfeld, J. Label. Compounds, 1, 109 (1965).

4-5 Quinones

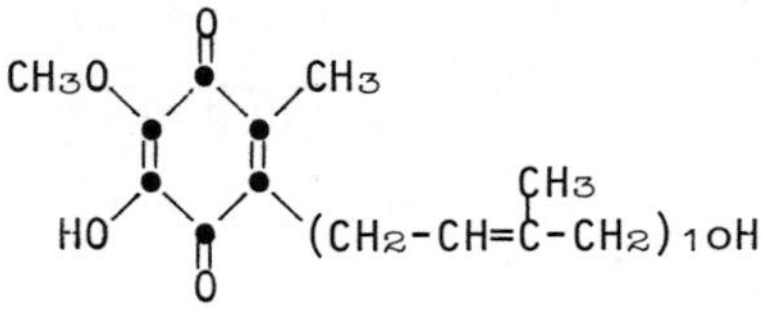

$^*CH_3I$, K_2CO_3 / acetone, Δ →

(All-E)-2-(3,7,11,15,19,23,27,31,35,3a-Decamethyl-2,6,10,14,18,22,26,30,34,38-tetracontadecaenyl)-5-hydroxy-6-methoxy-2,5-cyclohexadiene-1,4-dione

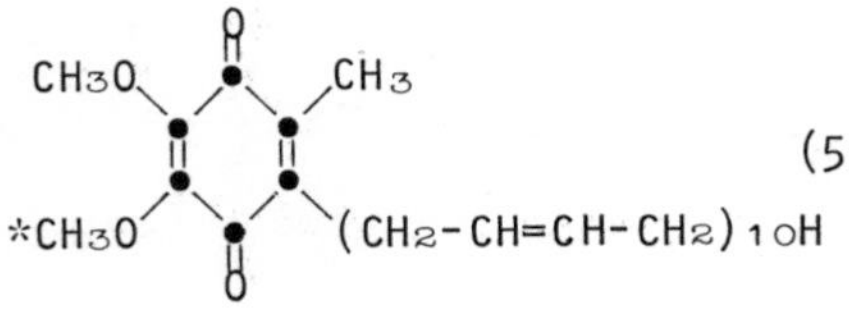

(55%)

(All-E)-2-(3,7,11,15,19,23,27,31,35,3a-Decamethyl-2,6,10,14,18,22,26,30,34,38-tetracontadecaenyl)5,6-dimethoxy-3-methyl-2,5-cyclohexadiene-1,4-dione-(5-methoxy-^{14}C)

H. M. Cheng and J. E. Casida, J. Label. Compounds, 6, 66 (1970).

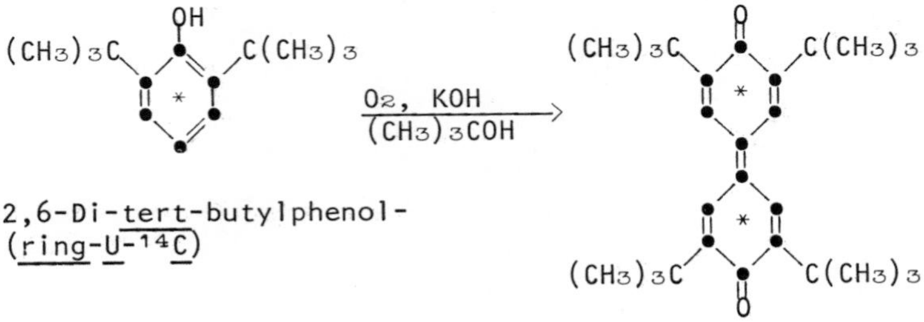

(64%)

2,6-Di-*tert*-butylphenol-(ring-U-^{14}C)

4-[3,5-Bis(1,1-dimethylethyl)-4-oxo-2,5-cyclohexadien-1-ylidene]-2,6-bis(1,1-dimethylethyl)-2,5-cyclohexadien-1-one-U,U-^{14}C

J. F. Heeg, G. S. Born, and H. C. White, J. Label. Compounds, 7, 165 (1971).

5

Ether Compounds

5-1 Ethers

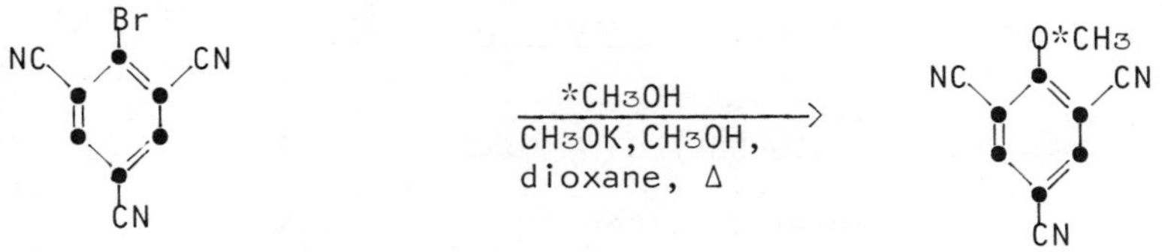
Br
NC
CN
CN
*CH3OH
CH3OK,CH3OH,
dioxane, Δ
O*CH3
NC
CN
CN

2-(Methoxy-^{14}C)-1,3,5-benzenetricarbonitrile

E. J. Fendler, W. Ernsberger, and J. H. Fendler, J. Org. Chem., 36, 2333 (1971).

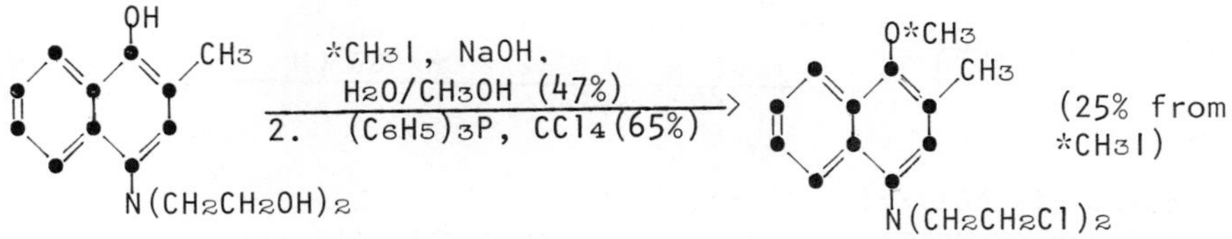
OH
CH3
N(CH2CH2OH)2
*CH3I, NaOH,
H2O/CH3OH (47%)
2. (C6H5)3P, CCl4(65%)
O*CH3
CH3
N(CH2CH2Cl)2
(25% from
*CH3I)

N,N-Bis-(2-chloroethyl)-4-(methoxy-^{14}C)-3-methyl-naphthalenamine

The N,N-bis(2-chloroethyl-1,2-^{14}C) derivative was also prepared.

J.-C. Madelmont, M.-F. Moreau, and D. Godeneche, J. Label. Compound. Radiopharm., 14, 281 (1978).

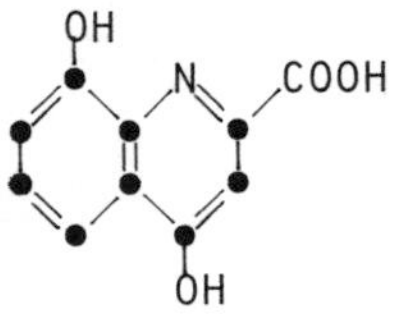

1. $(*CH_3)_2SO_4$, NaOH, CH_3OH, Δ
2. 28% NH_4OH

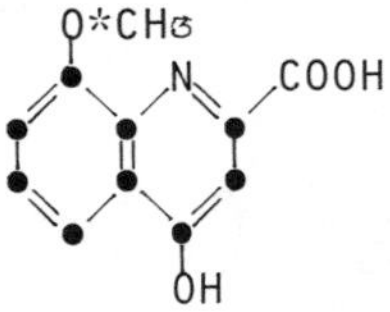

(3% from $(CH_3)_2SO_4$)

Xanthurenic acid methyl ether
[4-Hydroxy-8-(methoxy-^{14}C)-2-quinolinecarboxylic acid]

Ketolization of the 4-hydroxy group allows the selective methylation at position 8.

G. M. Lower, Jr. and G. T. Bryan, J. Label. Compounds, 4, 283 (1968).

$*CH_3CH_2OH$ —(H_2SO_4, Δ)→ $(*CH_3CH_2)_2O$ (66%)

Diethyl ether
[1,1'-Oxybisethane-2,2'-^{14}C]

F. Micheel and O.-E. Brodde, Liebigs Ann. Chem., 1107 (1975).

CH_2OK / CHO / CH_2O (ring with $C(CH_3)_2$) + $CH_3(CH_2)_{14}*CH_2OSO_2CH_3$ —(1. benzene, Δ; 2. HCl, CH_3OH)→

Hexadecanol-1-^{14}C methanesulfonate

$CH_2O-*CH_2(CH_2)_{14}CH_3$
$CHOH$
CH_2OH

[[(Hexadecyl-1-^{14}C)oxy]methyl]-1,2-ethanediol

—(2 equiv. $CH_3(CH_2)_{10}CH_2OSO_2CH_3$, KOH, xylene, Δ)→

$CH_2O-*CH_2(CH_2)_{14}CH_3$
$CHO-CH_2(CH_2)_{10}CH_3$
$CH_2O-CH_2(CH_2)_{10}CH_3$

1,2-Bis(dodecyloxy)-3-[(hexadecyl-1-^{14}C)oxy]propane

R. G. H. Morgan and A. F. Hofmann, J. Lipid Res., 11, 223 (1970); W. J. Baumann and H. K. Mangold, J. Org. Chem., 29, 3055 (1964), J. Org. Chem., 31, 498 (1966).

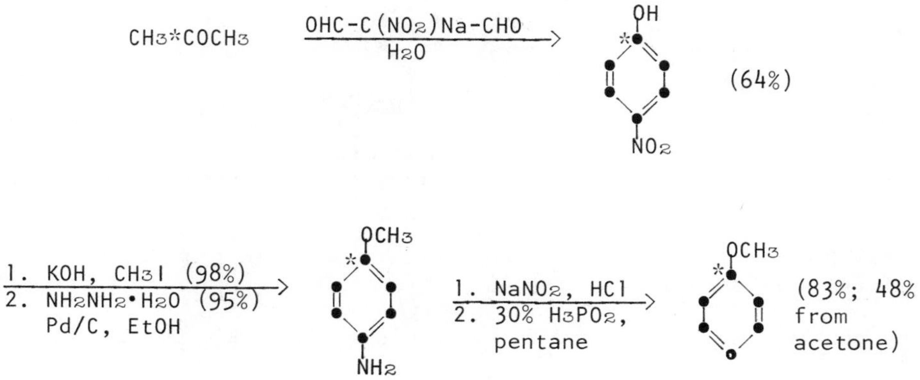
CH3*COCH3
OHC-C(NO2)Na-CHO
H2O
OH
NO2
(64%)
1. KOH, CH3I (98%)
2. NH2NH2·H2O (95%)
Pd/C, EtOH
OCH3
NH2
1. NaNO2, HCl
2. 30% H3PO2,
pentane
OCH3
(83%; 48%
from
acetone)

Anisole
[Methoxybenzene-
1-^{14}C]

N. J. Hales and H. Heaney, Tetrahedron Lett., 4075 (1975).

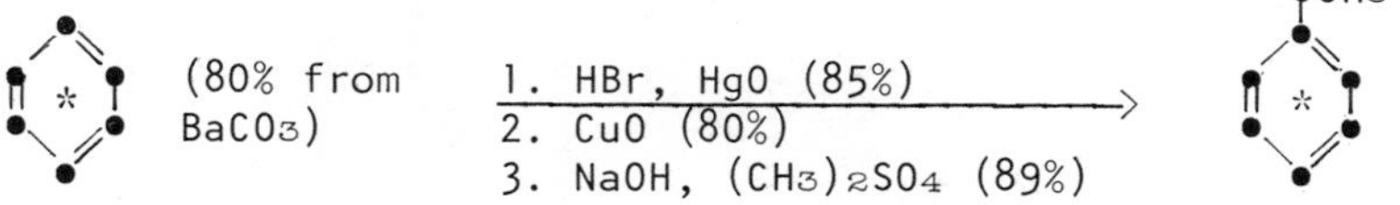
(80% from
BaCO3)
1. HBr, HgO (85%)
2. CuO (80%)
3. NaOH, (CH3)2SO4 (89%)
OCH3

Benzene-U-^{14}C

Anisole
[Methoxybenzene-
ring-^{14}C]

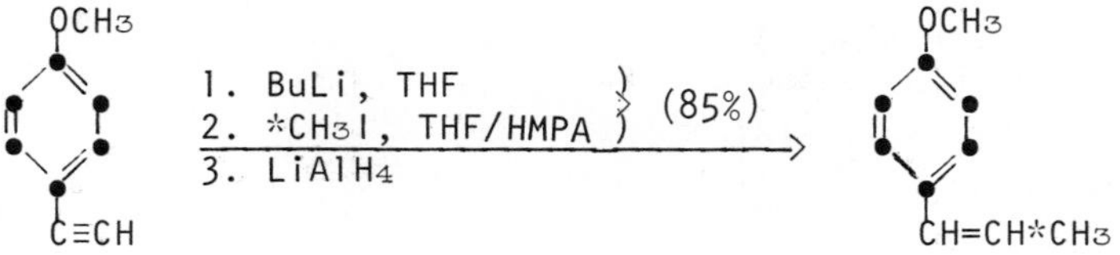
OCH3
C≡CH
1. BuLi, THF
2. *CH3I, THF/HMPA
(85%)
3. LiAlH4
OCH3
CH=CH*CH3

Anethole
[1-Methoxy-4-(1-propenyl-
3-^{14}C) benzene]

55% yield of isomers (85% trans, 15% cis); 20% yield of trans isomer (from *CH_3I) after prep GC.

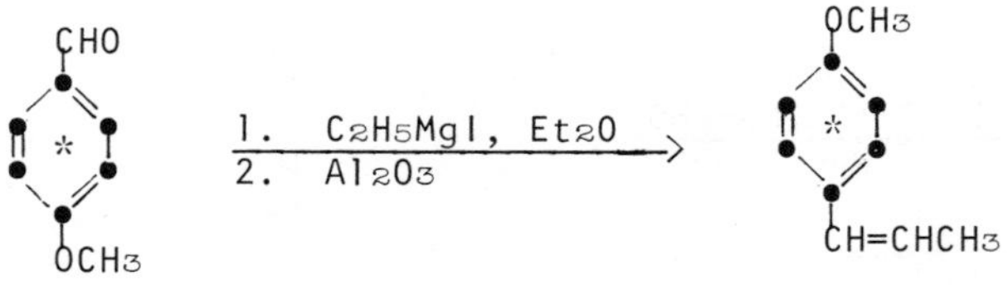
CHO
1. C2H5MgI, Et2O
2. Al2O3
OCH3
OCH3
CH=CHCH3

Anethole
[1-Methoxy-4-(1-propenyl)benzene-(ring-^{14}C)]

(80/20 mixture of trans/cis from which a 5% yield from $BaCO_3$ of trans is obtained by prep GC.)

M. Herbert, L. Pichat, and Y. Langourieux, J. Label. Compounds, 10, 89, (1974).

$$^{*}C_6H_5OH \quad + \quad ClCH_2CH_2OH \xrightarrow[EtOH]{NaOH} {}^{*}C_6H_5\text{-}O\text{-}CH_2CH_2OH \quad (35\%)$$

2-(Phenoxy-U-^{14}C)ethanol

W. Schweers, Tetrahedron Lett., 255 (1970).

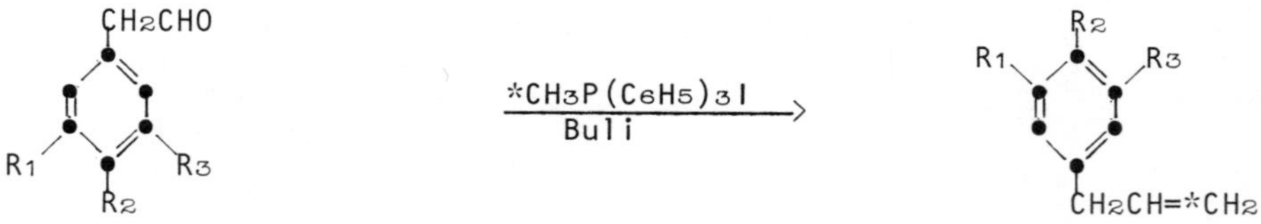
CH2CHO
R1
R3
R2
*CH3P(C6H5)3I
BuLi
R2
R1
R3
CH2CH=*CH2

R_1=R_2=-OCH_2O-, R_3=H, Safrole (37%)
[5-(2-Propenyl-3-^{14}C)-1,3-benzodioxole]

R_1=R_2=-OCH_2O-, R_3=OCH_3, Myristicin (12%)
[4-Methoxy-6-(2-propenyl-3-^{14}C)-1,3-benzodioxole]

R_1=R_2=R_3=OCH_3, Elemicin (24%)
[1,2,3-Trimethoxy-5-(2-propenyl-3-^{14}C)benzene]

Yields are based on n-butyl lithium.

M. Walker, J. McKinney, and E. Oswald, J. Label. Compounds, 10, 405 (1974).

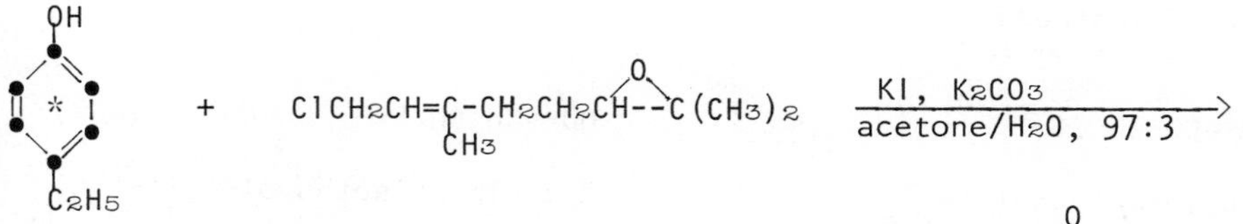
KI, K_2CO_3
acetone/H_2O, 97:3

4-Ethylphenol-(ring-^{14}C)

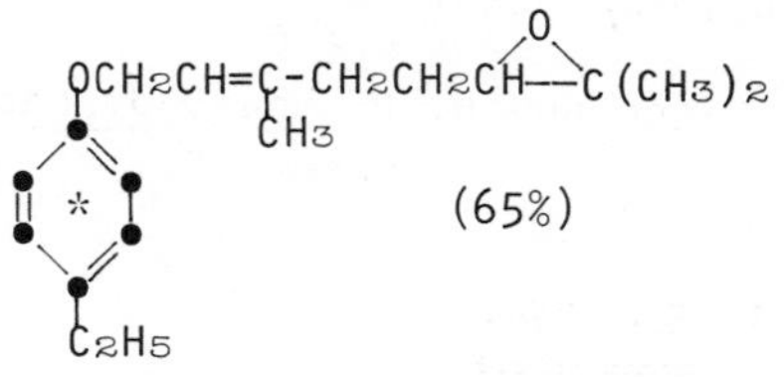

2,2-Dimethyl-3-[5-(4-ethylphenoxy)-3-methyl-3-pentenyl] oxirane-(ring-^{14}C)

J. Kalbfeld, L. J. Hoffman, J. H. Chan, and D. A. Hermann, J. Label. Compounds, 9, 615 (1973).

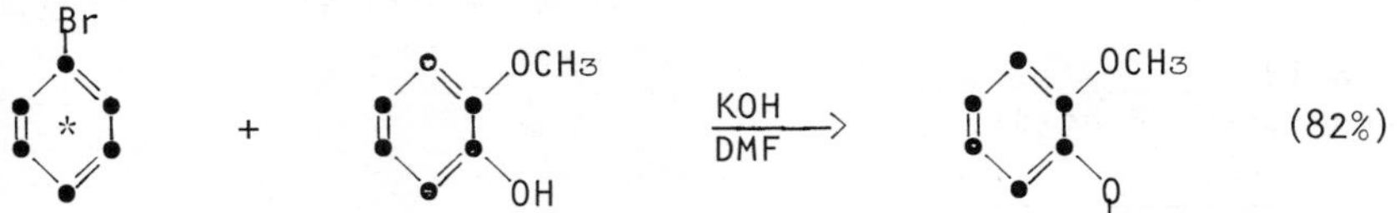
KOH
DMF
(82%)

Bromobenzene-U-^{14}C

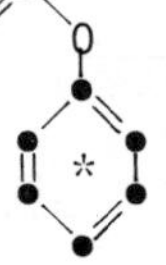

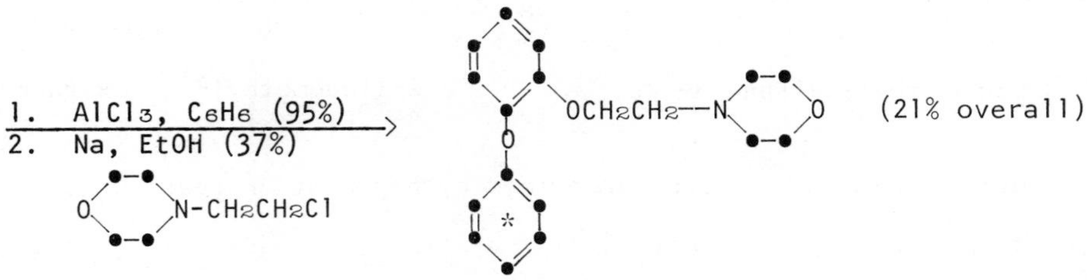
1. $AlCl_3$, C_6H_6 (95%)
2. Na, EtOH (37%)
(21% overall)

4-[2-[2-(2-Phenoxy-U-^{14}C)phenoxy] ethyl] morpholine

T. Horie and T. Fujita, J. Label. Compounds, 8, 581 (1972).

5-2 Thioethers

$HO\text{-*}CH_2CH_2Cl$ $\xrightarrow{Na_2S}$ $HO\text{-*}CH_2CH_2SCH_2\text{*}CH_2OH$ (88%)

2-Chloroethanol-1-^{14}C → 2,2'-Thiobisethanol-1,1'-^{14}C

K. Figge and H. P. Voss, J. Label. Compounds, 9, 23 (1973).

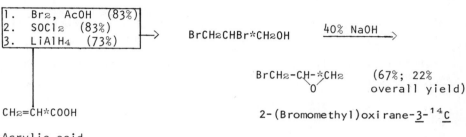

5-3 Epoxides

$CH_2{=}CH\text{*}COOH$

Acrylic acid
[2-Propenoic-1-^{14}C acid]

1. Br_2, AcOH (83%)
2. $SOCl_2$ (83%)
3. $LiAlH_4$ (73%)

→ $BrCH_2CHBr\text{*}CH_2OH$ $\xrightarrow{40\%\ NaOH}$ $BrCH_2\text{-}CH\text{-*}CH_2$ (epoxide, O) (67%; 22% overall yield)

2-(Bromomethyl)oxirane-3-^{14}C

1. Cl_2, AcOH (64%)
2. $SOCl_2$ (77%)
3. $LiAlH_4$, ether (66%)

→ $ClCH_2CHCl\text{*}CH_2OH$ $\xrightarrow{40\%\ NaOH}$ $Cl\text{-}CH_2\text{-}CH\text{—*}CH_2$ (epoxide, O) (57%; 12% overall)

2-(Chloromethyl)oxirane-3-^{14}C

$\xrightarrow[\text{acetone}]{NaI}$ $I\text{-*}CH_2\text{-}CH\text{—*}CH_2$ (epoxide, O) (47%; 6% overall)

2-(Iodomethyl-^{14}C)oxirane-3-^{14}C

The positions of label were determined by degradation reactions.

F. Asinger, A. Saus, B. Fell, and J. Pfeifer, J. Prakt. Chem., 314, 80 (1972).

$C_6H_5\text{*}CHO$ + $ClCH_2COOC_2H_5$ $\xrightarrow[\text{2. NaOH}]{\text{1. t-BuOK}}$ $C_6H_5\text{*}CH\text{—}CHCOOH$ (epoxide, O)

Benzaldehyde-7-^{14}C → 3-Phenyloxirane-3-^{14}C carboxylic acid

J. Domagala and J. Wemple, Tetrahedron Lett., 1179 (1973).

$C_6H_5{*}CHO$ + $BrCH(C_6H_5)COOC_2H_5$ $\xrightarrow[\underline{t}\text{-BuOH}]{\underline{t}\text{-BuOK}}$

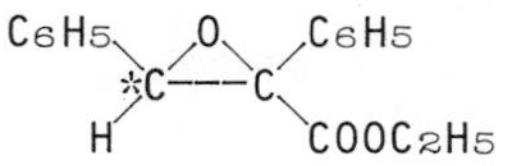

2,3-Diphenyloxirane-3-^{14}C carboxylic acid ethyl ester

R. A. Gorski, D. J. Gagli, and J. Wemple, J. Amer. Chem. Soc., 98, 4588 (1976).

$C_6H_5{*}COCH_3$ $\xrightarrow[NaNH_2]{ClCH_2COOC_2H_5}$

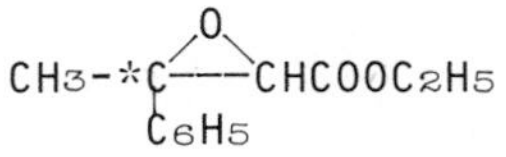

(62%)

3-Methyl-3-phenyloxirane-3-^{14}C carboxylic acid ethyl ester

P. J. Stang, D. P. Fox, C. J. Collins, and C. R. Watson, Jr., J. Org. Chem., 43, 364 (1978).

$C_6H_5{*}COCH_3$ + $CH_3CHBrCOOC_2H_5$ $\xrightarrow[\text{condensation}]{\text{Darzens}}$

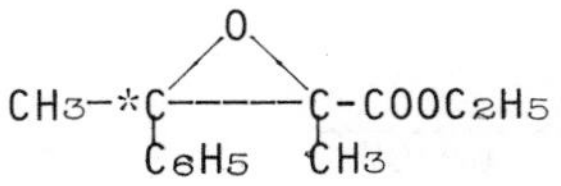

(65% E; 35% Z)

2,3-Dimethyl-3-phenyloxirane-3-^{14}C carboxylic acid ethyl ester

The product was used to determine ethoxycarbonyl migration in the rearrangement of epoxides with $BF_3{\cdot}(C_2H_5)_2O$.

J. Kagan, D. A. Agdeppa, Jr., S. P. Singh, D. A. Mayers, C. Boyajian, C. Poorker, and B. E. Firth, J. Amer. Chem. Soc., 98, 4581 (1976).

${*}CH_3CO{*}CH_3$ + C_6H_5OH $\xrightarrow[\text{toluene, } H_2SO_4\text{, 40°C, 3 hr.}]{\text{thioglycolic acid}}$

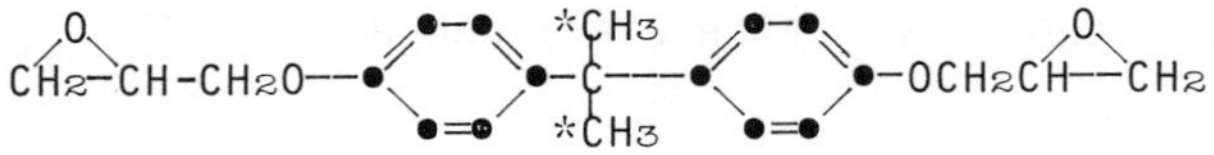
*CH3
CH2-CH-CH2O
*CH3
OCH2CH—CH2

2,2'-[(1-Methyl-^{14}C-ethylidene-1-^{14}C)bis(4,1-phenyleneoxymethylene)]bisoxirane

Similarly, 2,2'-[(1-methylethylidene)bis(4,1-phenylene-(ring-^{14}C)-oxymethylene)]bisoxirane was prepared starting with phenol-U-^{14}C.

D. P. Bishop and D. A. Smith, J. Appl. Polym. Sci., 14, 205 (1970); J. I. DeJong and F. H. D. Dethmers, Rec. Trav. Chim., 84, 460 (1965).

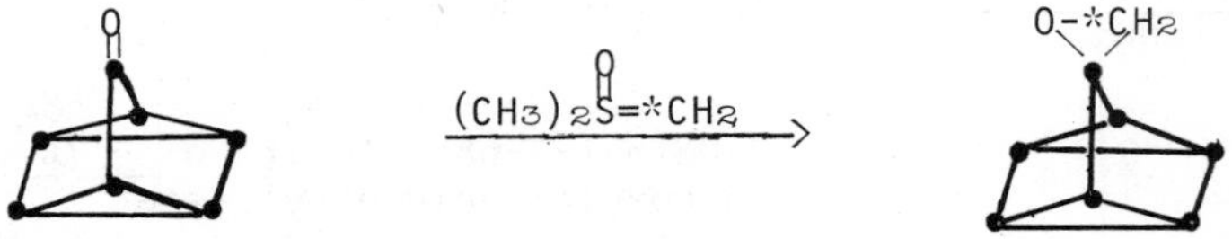
(CH3)2S=*CH2
O-*CH2

(39% from the ketone)

Spiro[oxirane-2,3']-tetracyclo[3.2.0.0^{2,7}.0^{4,6}]heptane-3-^{14}C

R. W. Hoffmann and R. Schüttler, Chem. Ber., 108, 844 (1975).

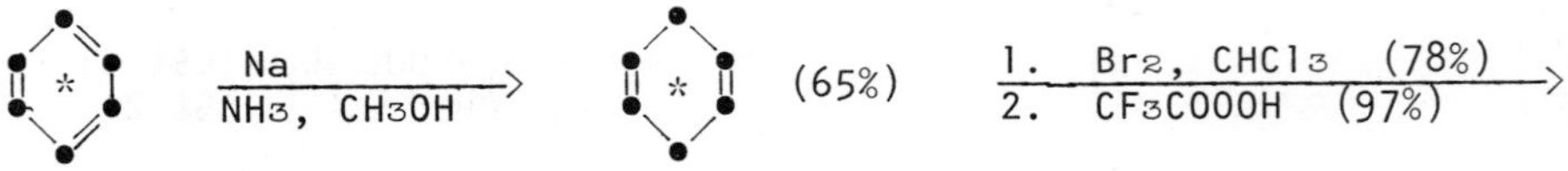
Na
NH3, CH3OH
(65%)
1. Br2, CHCl3 (78%)
2. CF3COOOH (97%)

1,4-Cyclohexadiene-U-^{14}C

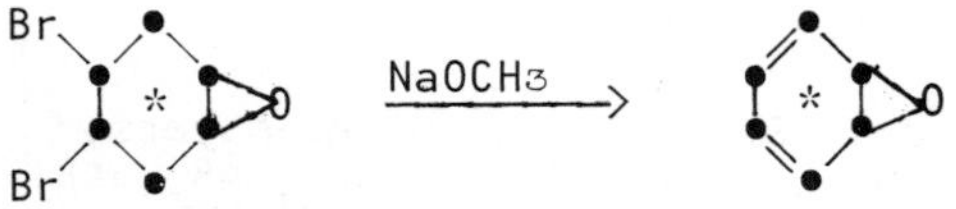
Br
Br
NaOCH3

(60%; 30% overall)

Benzene oxide
[7-Oxabicyclo[4.1.0]hepta-2,4-diene-U-^{14}C]

K. L. Platt and F. Oesch, J. Label. Compound. Radiopharm., 13, 471 (1977).

6

Organic Nitrogen Compounds

6-1 Aliphatic Amines

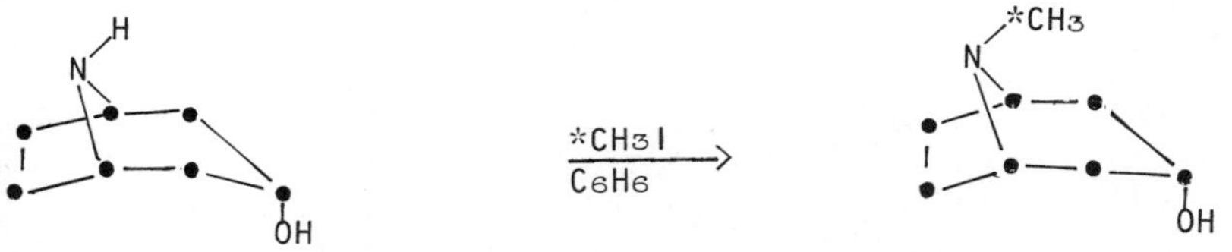

Nortropine
(prepared by reaction of tropine with phenyl chloroformate followed by hydrolysis with KOH)

Tropine
[endo-8-(Methyl-^{14}C)-8-azabicyclo[3.2.1]octan-3-ol]

E. Leete, Phytochemistry, 11, 1713 (1972); see also E. Leete and D. H. Lucast, Tetrahedron Lett., 3401 (1976).

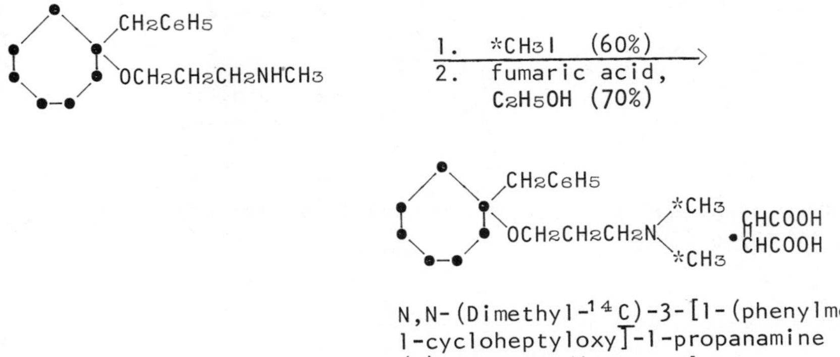

N,N-(Dimethyl-^{14}C)-3-[1-(phenylmethyl)-1-cycloheptyloxy]-1-propanamine (Z)-2-butenedioate salt

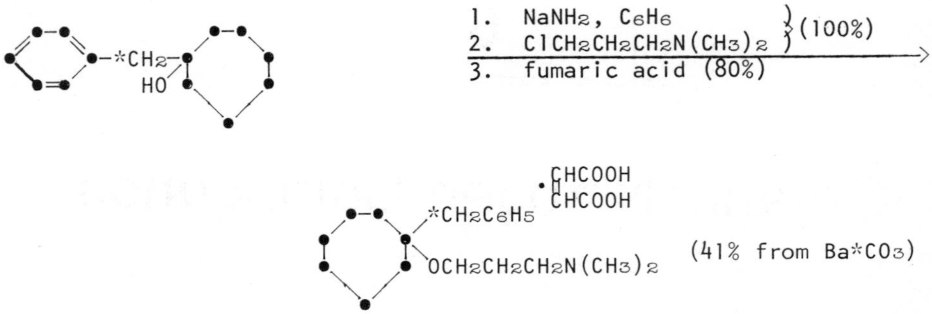

*CH2
HO
1. NaNH2, C6H6
2. ClCH2CH2CH2N(CH3)2
(100%)
3. fumaric acid (80%)
CHCOOH
CHCOOH
*CH2C6H5
OCH2CH2CH2N(CH3)2
(41% from Ba*CO3)

N,N-Dimethyl-3-[1-(phenyl(methyl-^{14}C))-1-cycloheptyloxy]-1-propanamine (Z)-2-butenedioate salt.

D. Bánfi, J. Volfard, L. Pallos, and G. Zolyomi, J. Label. Compounds, 7, 62 (1971).

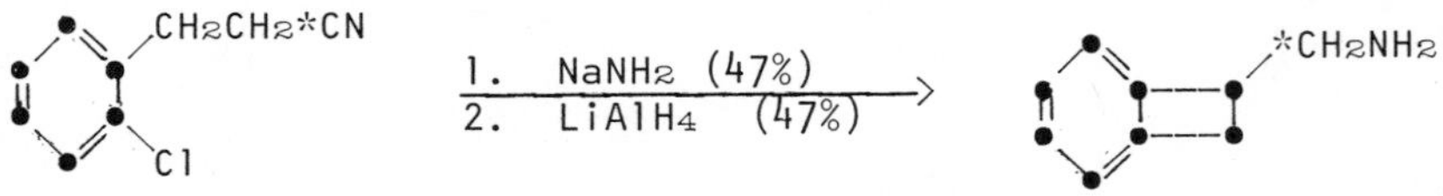

CH2CH2*CN
Cl
1. NaNH2 (47%)
2. LiAlH4 (47%)
*CH2NH2

Bicyclo[4.2.0]octa-1,3,5-triene-7-methanamine-α-^{14}C

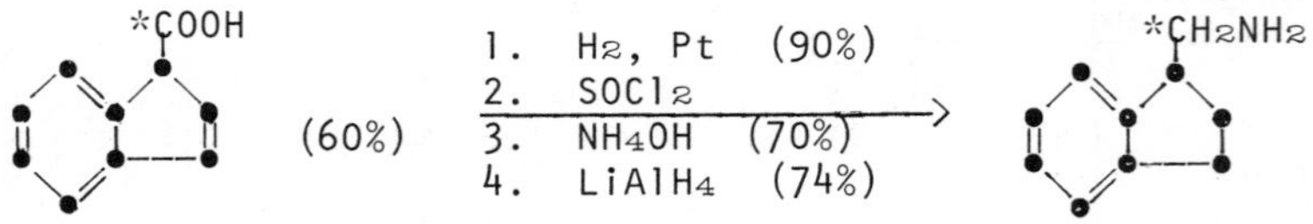

*COOH
(60%)
1. H2, Pt (90%)
2. SOCl2
3. NH4OH (70%)
4. LiAlH4 (74%)
*CH2NH2

2,3-Dihydro-1H-inden-1-methanamine-α-^{14}C

A. G. Sakhabutdinov, V. G. Lipovich, and I. V. Kalechits, Zh. Org. Khim., 11, 1728 (1975).

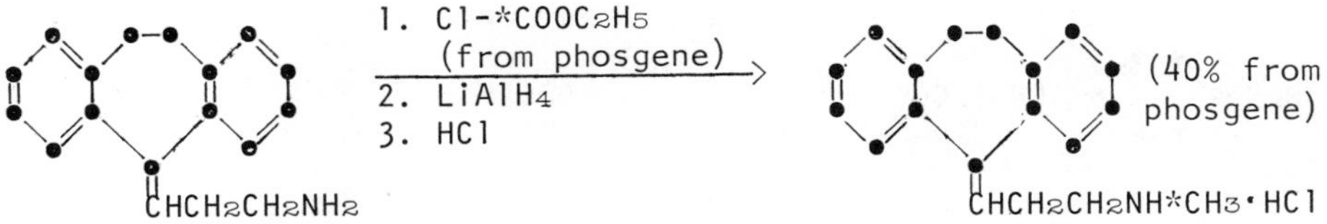

CHCH2CH2NH2
1. Cl-*COOC2H5 (from phosgene)
2. LiAlH4
3. HCl
(40% from phosgene)
CHCH2CH2NH*CH3·HCl

Nortriptyline
[3-(10,11-Dihydro-5H-dibenzo[a,d]-cyclohepten-5-ylidene)-N-(methyl-^{14}C)-1-propanamine hydrochloride]

Similarly:

$C_6H_5CH_2CH_2CH_2NH_2$ ⟶ $C_6H_5CH_2CH_2CH_2NH{*}CH_3{\cdot}HCl$ (31% from phosgene)

N-(Methyl-^{14}C)-3-phenyl-1-propanamine

F. J. Marshall and R. E. McMahon, J. Label. Compounds, 6, 261 (1970).

$CH_3{*}COONa$ —(1. $SOCl_2$, Et_2O; 2. $C_2H_5NH_2$; 3. $LiAlH_4$)⟶ $CH_3{*}CH_2NHC_2H_5$ (32%)

N-Ethylethanamine-1-^{14}C

R. D. Barnes, J. Label. Compounds, 10, 207 (1974).

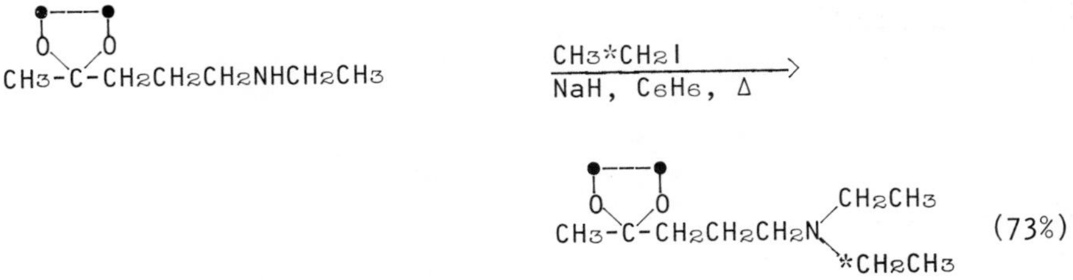

CH3-C-CH2CH2CH2NHCH2CH3
CH3*CH2I
NaH, C6H6, Δ
CH3-C-CH2CH2CH2N
CH2CH3
*CH2CH3
(73%)

N-Ethyl-N-(ethyl-1-^{14}C)-2-methyl-1,3-dioxolane-2-propanamine

H. Minato, Y. Katsuyama, and T. Nagasaki, J. Label. Compound. Radiopharm., 13, 513 (1977).

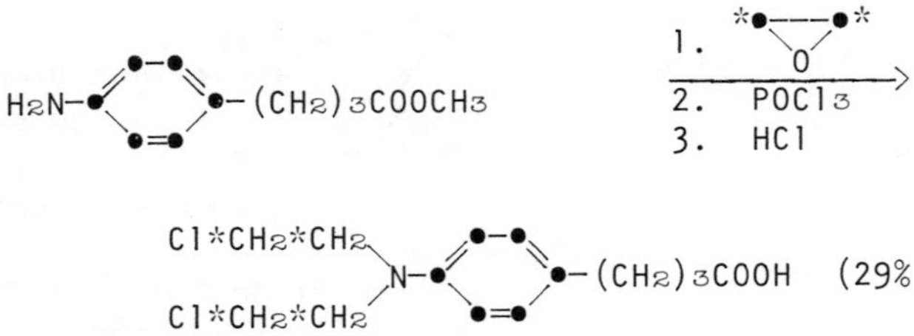
H2N
(CH2)3COOCH3
1.
O
2. POCl3
3. HCl
Cl*CH2*CH2
N
Cl*CH2*CH2
(CH2)3COOH

(29% from ethylene oxide)

4-[Bis(2-chloroethyl-1,2-^{14}C)-amino]benzenebutanoic acid

J. Moreau and J.-C. Madelmont, J. Label. Compounds, 10, 271 (1974).

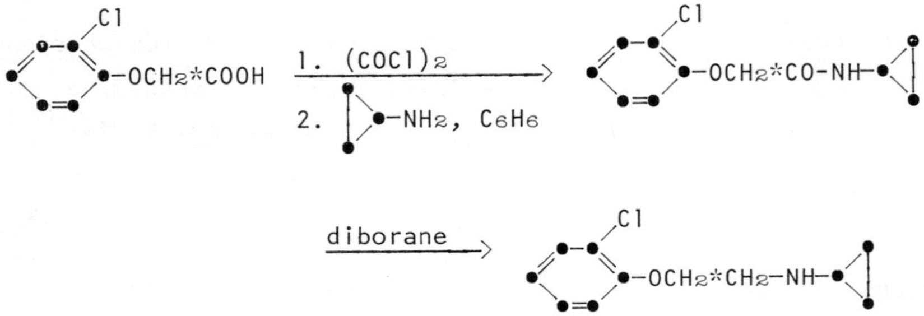
Cl
OCH2*COOH
1. (COCl)2
2.
NH2, C6H6
Cl
OCH2*CO-NH
diborane
Cl
OCH2*CH2-NH

(73%)

(61%)

N-[2-(2-Chlorophenoxy)ethyl-1-^{14}C]cyclopropanamine

Similarly prepared:

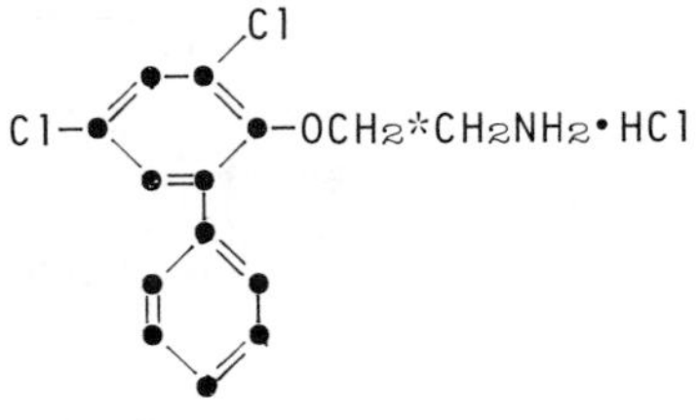
Cl
Cl
OCH2*CH2NH2•HCl

2-(2,4-Dichloro-6-phenylphenoxy)-ethanamine-1-^{14}C hydrochloride

F. J. Marshall, R. E. McMahon, and W. B. Lacefield, J. Label. Compounds, 8, 461 (1972).

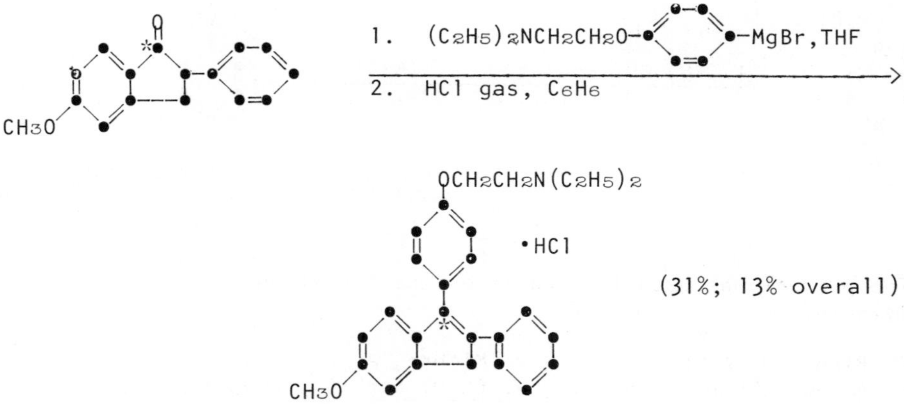
CH3O
1. (C2H5)2NCH2CH2O- -MgBr,THF
2. HCl gas, C6H6
OCH2CH2N(C2H5)2
•HCl
(31%; 13% overall)
CH3O

2-[4-(6-Methoxy-2-phenyl-1H-indan-3-yl-3-^{14}C)phenoxy]-N,N-diethylethanamine hydrochloride

R. C. Thomas and P. E. Marlatt, J. Label. Compound.Radiopharm., 14, 813 (1978).

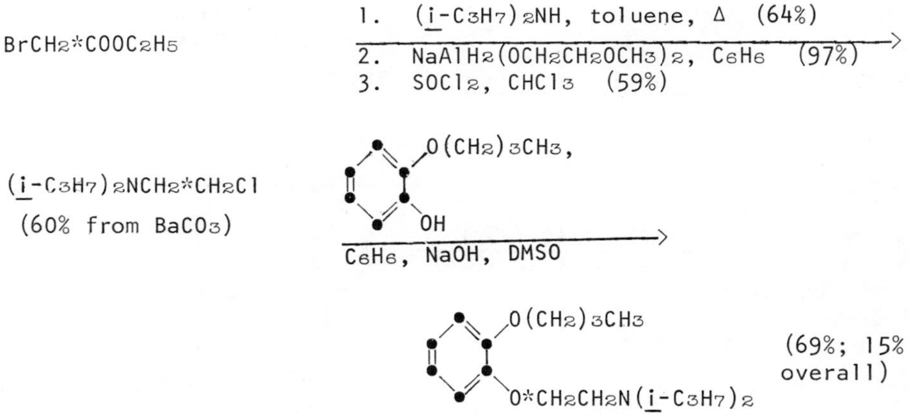
BrCH2*COOC2H5
1. (i-C3H7)2NH, toluene, Δ (64%)
2. NaAlH2(OCH2CH2OCH3)2, C6H6 (97%)
3. SOCl2, CHCl3 (59%)
(i-C3H7)2NCH2*CH2Cl
(60% from BaCO3)
O(CH2)3CH3,
OH
C6H6, NaOH, DMSO
O(CH2)3CH3
O*CH2CH2N(i-C3H7)2
(69%; 15% overall)

2-(2-Butoxyphenoxy)-N,N-bis-(1-methylethyl)ethanamine-2-^{14}C hydrochloride

T. Gosztonyi, K. E. Domeij, and R. Sandberg, J. Label. Compound. Radiopharm., 14, 639 (1978).

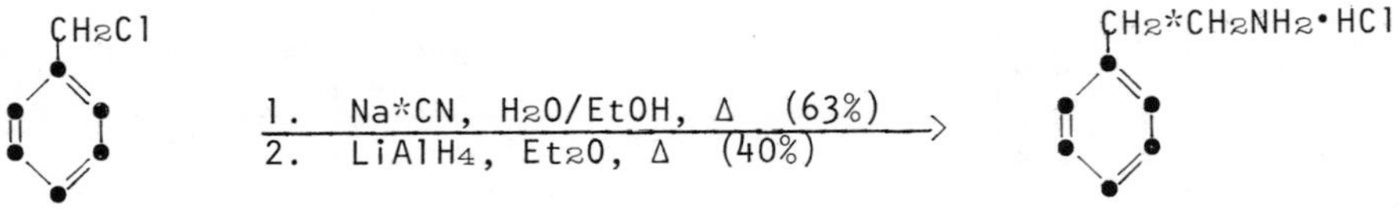
CH_2Cl
1. Na^*CN, $H_2O/EtOH$, Δ (63%)
2. $LiAlH_4$, Et_2O, Δ (40%)
$CH_2{}^*CH_2NH_2 \cdot HCl$

Benzeneethanamine-α-^{14}C hydrochloride

The product was used in studies on the formation of dopamine-melanin.

F. Binns, J. A. G. King, S. N. Mishra, A. Percival, N. C. Robson, G. A. Swan, and A. Waggott, J. Chem. Soc. (C), 2063 (1970).

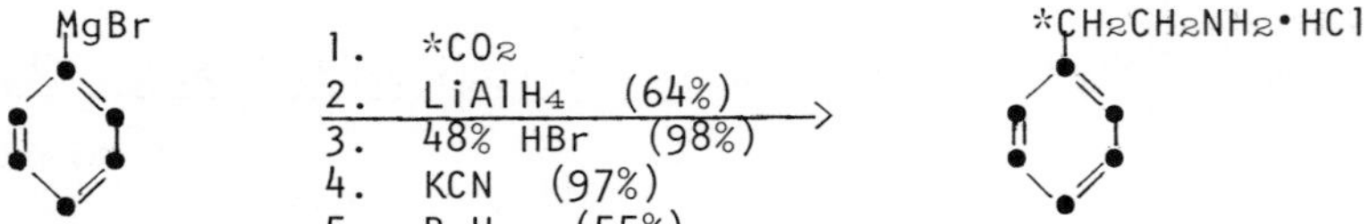
MgBr
1. $^*CO_2$
2. $LiAlH_4$ (64%)
3. 48% HBr (98%)
4. KCN (97%)
5. B_2H_6 (55%)
$^*CH_2CH_2NH_2 \cdot HCl$

Benzeneethanamine-β-^{14}C hydrochloride

R. S. P. Hsi, J. Label. Compounds, 9, 91 (1973).

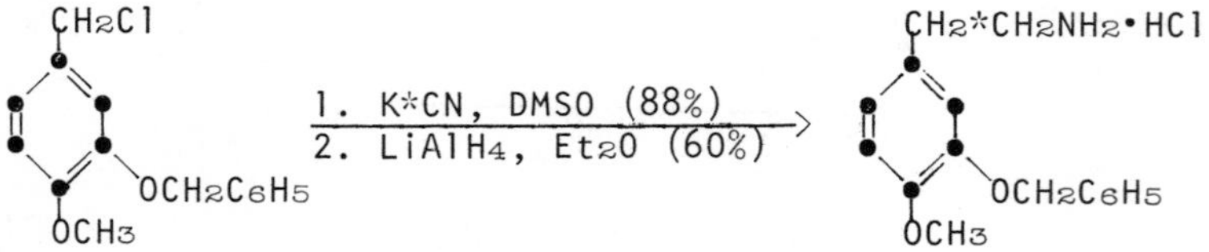
CH_2Cl
$OCH_2C_6H_5$
OCH_3
1. K^*CN, DMSO (88%)
2. $LiAlH_4$, Et_2O (60%)
$CH_2{}^*CH_2NH_2 \cdot HCl$
$OCH_2C_6H_5$
OCH_3

4-Methoxy-3-(phenylmethoxy)-benzeneethanamine-α-^{14}C hydrochloride

The product was subsequently converted to N-norprotosinomeine-3-^{14}C.

D. H. R. Barton, R. B. Boar, and D. A. Widdowson, J. Chem. Soc. (C), 1213 (1970). See also, D. H. R. Barton, R. James, G. W. Kirby, D. W. Turner, and D. A. Widdowson, J. Chem. Soc. (C), 1529 (1968); D. H. R. Barton, A. J. Kirby, and G. W. Kirby, J. Chem. Soc. (C), 929 (1968).

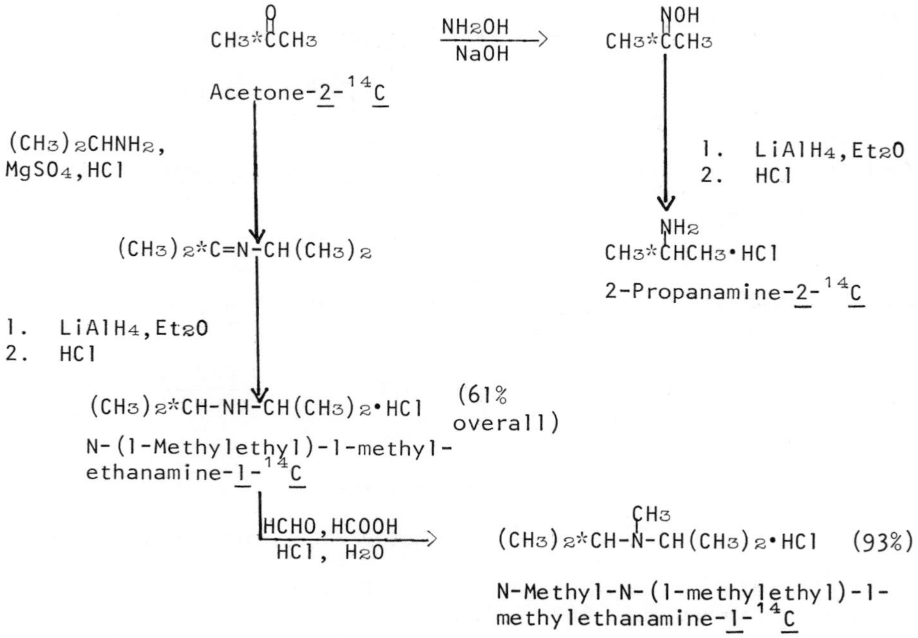
CH3*CCH3
Acetone-2-14C
NH2OH
NaOH
NOH
CH3*CCH3
(CH3)2CHNH2,
MgSO4,HCl
1. LiAlH4,Et2O
2. HCl
NH2
CH3*CHCH3•HCl
2-Propanamine-2-14C
(CH3)2*C=N-CH(CH3)2
1. LiAlH4,Et2O
2. HCl
(CH3)2*CH-NH-CH(CH3)2•HCl
(61% overall)
N-(1-Methylethyl)-1-methyl-
ethanamine-1-14C
HCHO,HCOOH
HCl, H2O
CH3
(CH3)2*CH-N-CH(CH3)2•HCl
(93%)
N-Methyl-N-(1-methylethyl)-1-
methylethanamine-1-14C

C. Colombini, M. Terbojevich, and E. Peggion, J. Label. Compounds, 1, 195 (1965).

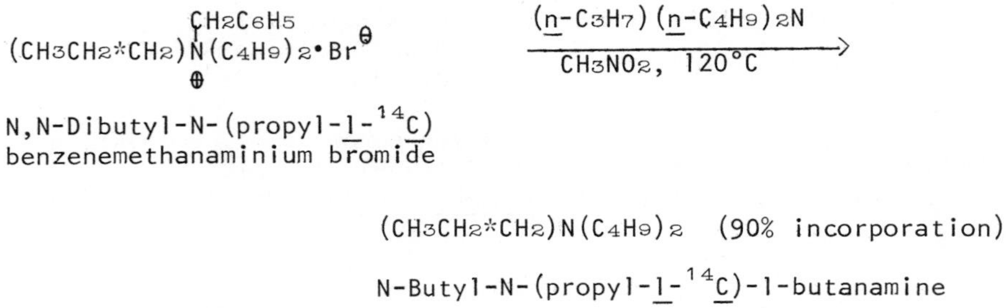
CH2C6H5
(CH3CH2*CH2)N(C4H9)2•Br
N,N-Dibutyl-N-(propyl-1-14C)
benzenemethanaminium bromide
(n-C3H7)(n-C4H9)2N
CH3NO2, 120°C
(CH3CH2*CH2)N(C4H9)2
(90% incorporation)
N-Butyl-N-(propyl-1-14C)-1-butanamine

H. Elias, K. Lotzsch, and K. Weimer, Chem. Ber., 104, 683 (1971).

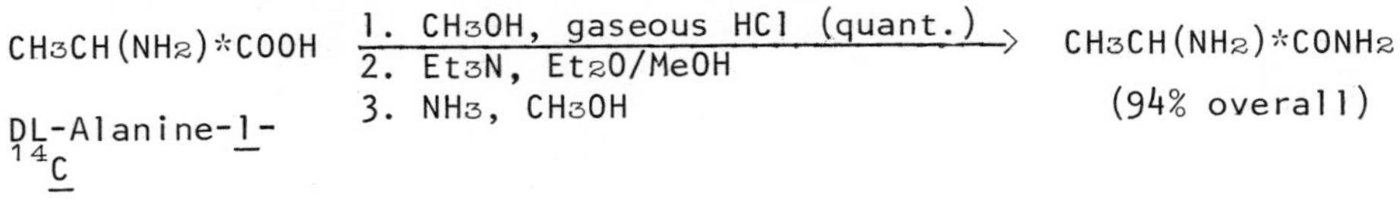
CH3CH(NH2)*COOH
DL-Alanine-1-14C
1. CH3OH, gaseous HCl (quant.)
2. Et3N, Et2O/MeOH
3. NH3, CH3OH
CH3CH(NH2)*CONH2
(94% overall)

$\xrightarrow[\text{2. HCl}]{\text{1. Red-Al, } C_6H_6}$ $CH_3CH(NH_2)-{}^*CH_2NH_2 \cdot 2HCl$ (44%)

1,2-Propanediamine-1-^{14}C dihydrochloride

Y.-T. Lin, M. A. Leaffer, and M. Tanabe, J. Label. Compound. Radiopharm., 12, 591 (1976).

$C_6H_6CH_2N(CH_3)CH_2CH_2Cl$ $\xrightarrow[EtOH/H_2O]{K^*CN}$ $C_6H_6CH_2N(CH_3)CH_2CH_2{}^*CN$ (90%)

$\xrightarrow[Et_2O]{LiAlH_4}$ $C_6H_6CH_2N(CH_3)CH_2CH_2{}^*CH_2NH_2$ (86%) $\xrightarrow[CH_3OH,\ HCl]{H_2, Pd/C}$

$CH_3NHCH_2CH_2{}^*CH_2NH_2$ (82%)

N'-Methyl-1,3-propanediamine-3-^{14}C

S. K. Figdor, M. S. von Wittenau, J. K. Faulkner, and A. M. Monro, J. Label. Compounds, 6, 362 (1970).

$(CH_3)_2NCHCH_2Cl$ $\xrightarrow[\text{3. HCl}]{\text{1. K*CN, EtOH; 2. Na, EtOH}}$ $(CH_3)_2NCH_2CH_2{}^*CH_2NH_2 \cdot 2HCl$

N',N'-Dimethyl-1,3-propanediamine-3-^{14}C dihydrochloride

J. F. Biernat, B. Stefánska, E. Jereczek-Morawska, T. Umiński, and A. Ledochowski, Rocz. Chem., 43, 1749 (1969); see also A. Kolodziejczyk and A. Arendt, J. Label. Compounds, 11, 385 (1975).

$(CH_3)_2C(OH)-C{\equiv}CH + RNHCH_3$ $\xrightarrow[CuCl,\ \Delta]{H^*CHO,\ dioxane}$ $(CH_3)_2C(OH)-C{\equiv}C-{}^*CH_2-N(CH_3)-R$

$\xrightarrow[\Delta]{KOH}$ $HC{\equiv}C-{}^*CH_2-N(CH_3)-R$

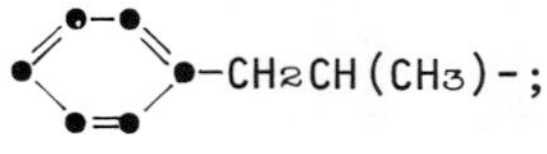
R =
-CH2CH(CH3)-;

N,α-Dimethyl-N-2-propynyl-1-^{14}C-benzeneethanamine (28%)

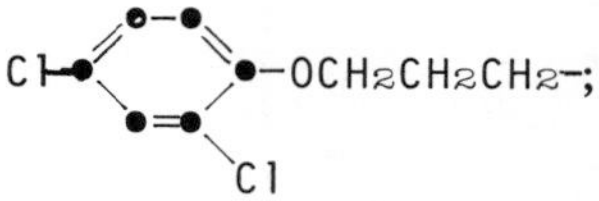
R = Cl
-OCH2CH2CH2-;
Cl

N-[3-(2,4-Dichlorophenoxy)propyl]-N-methyl-2-propyn-amine-1-[14]C (33% overall)

J. S. Fowler, J. Label. Compound.Radiopharm., 14, 435 (1978).

*CH2COCH3
L-(-)-α-methylbenzylamine
C6H6

1-Phenyl-2-propanone-1-[14]C

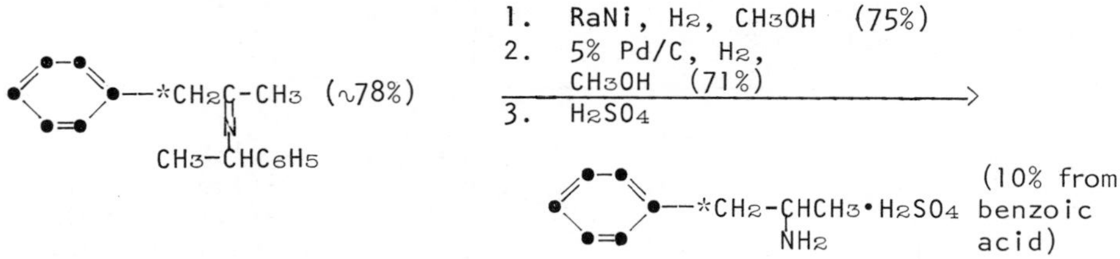
*CH2C-CH3 (~78%)
N
CH3-CHC6H5
1. RaNi, H2, CH3OH (75%)
2. 5% Pd/C, H2, CH3OH (71%)
3. H2SO4
*CH2-CHCH3·H2SO4
NH2
(10% from benzoic acid)

D-(+)-Amphetamine sulfate [(+)-α-Methylbenzeneethanamine-β-^{14}C sulfate]

L. Pichat and J.-P. Beaucourt, J. Label. Compound.Radiopharm., 12, 31 (1976).

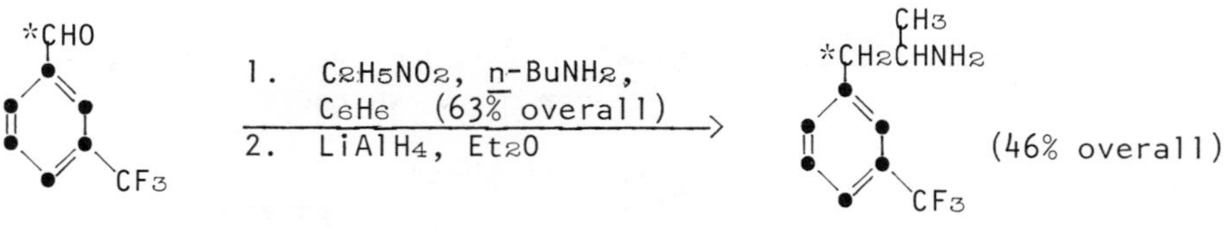
*CHO
CF3
1. C2H5NO2, n-BuNH2, C6H6 (63% overall)
2. LiAlH4, Et2O
CH3
*CH2CHNH2
CF3
(46% overall)

Norfenfluramine [α-Methyl-3-(trifluoro methyl)benzeneethanamine-β-^{14}C]

G. Ronco, H. Renault, J. R. Rapin, and P. Compagnon, J. Label. Compound. Radiopharm, 14, 549 (1978).

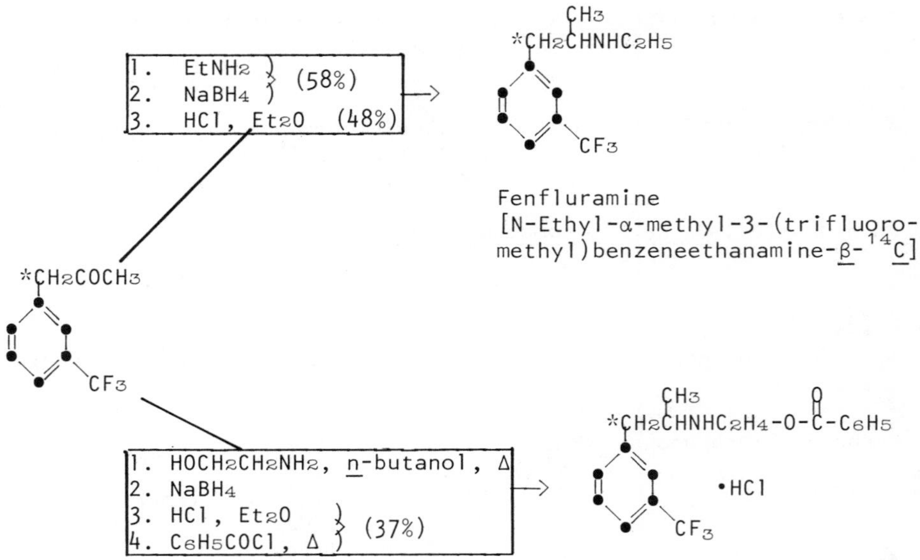
1. EtNH2
2. NaBH4
(58%)
3. HCl, Et2O (48%)
1. HOCH2CH2NH2, n-butanol, Δ
2. NaBH4
3. HCl, Et2O
4. C6H5COCl, Δ
(37%)
·HCl

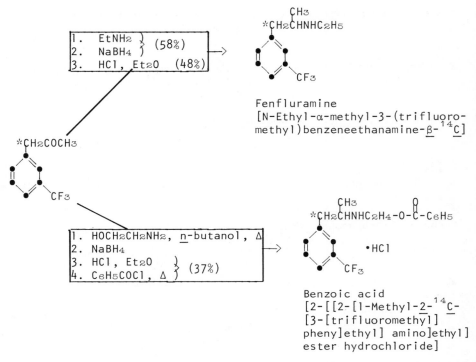

Fenfluramine
[N-Ethyl-α-methyl-3-(trifluoromethyl)benzeneethanamine-β-^{14}C]

Benzoic acid
[2-[[2-[1-Methyl-2-[14]C-
[3-[trifluoromethyl]
pheny]ethyl] amino]ethyl]
ester hydrochloride]

D. R. Hawkins and I. Midgley, J. Label. Compounds, 10, 663 (1974).

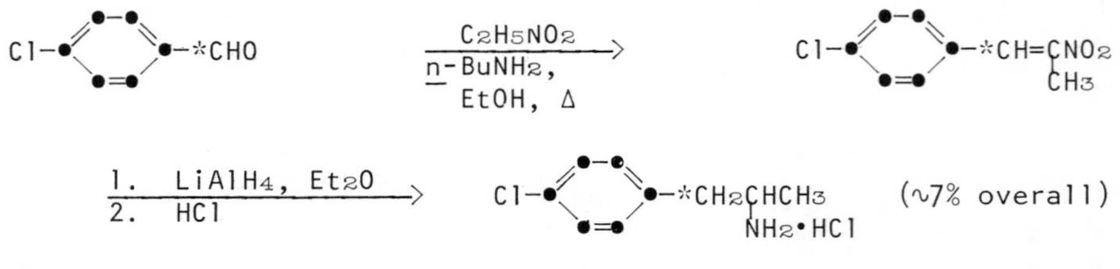
C2H5NO2
n-BuNH2,
EtOH, Δ
1. LiAlH4, Et2O
2. HCl
(~7% overall)

p-Chloroamphetamine
[4-Chloro-α-methylbenzene-
ethanamine-β-^{14}C hydrochloride

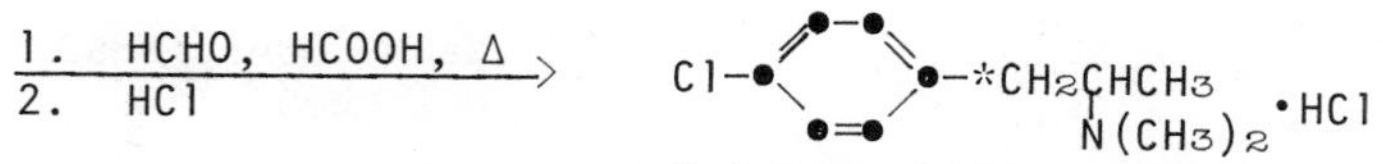
1. HCHO, HCOOH, Δ
2. HCl
Cl
*CH2CHCH3
N(CH3)2
•HCl

N,N-Dimethyl-p-chloroamphetamine
[4-Chloro,N,N,α-trimethylbenzeneethanamine-β-^{14}C hydrochloride]

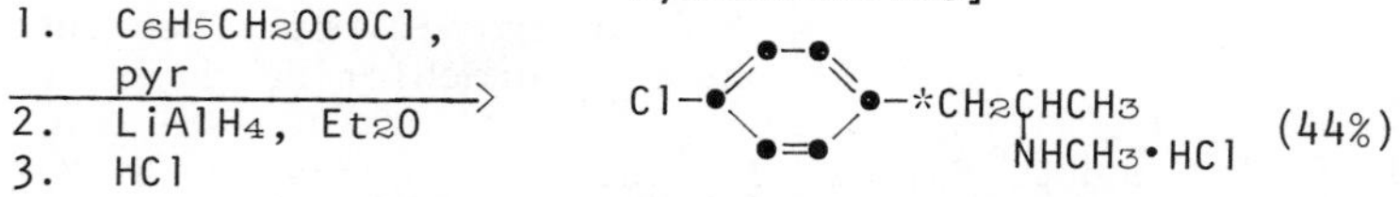
1. C6H5CH2OCOCl, pyr
2. LiAlH4, Et2O
3. HCl
Cl
*CH2CHCH3
NHCH3•HCl
(44%)

N-Methyl-p-chloroamphetamine
[4-Chloro-N,α-dimethylbenzeneethanamine-β-^{14}C hydrochloride]

E. P. Burrows, E. Sanders-Bush, H. J. Sekerke, and H. E. Smith, J. Label. Compound. Radiopharm., 12, 173 (1976).

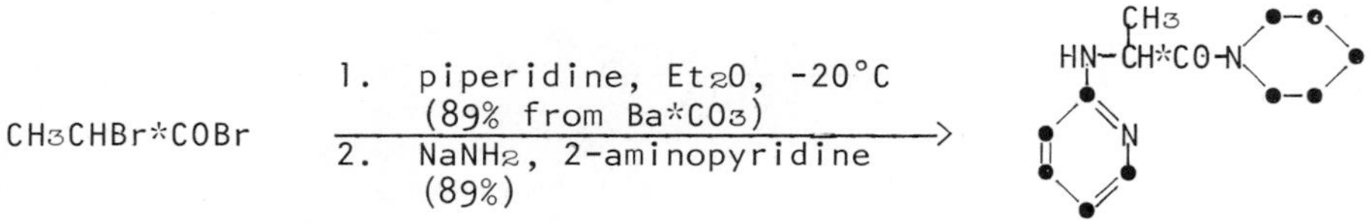
CH3CHBr*COBr
1. piperidine, Et2O, -20°C (89% from Ba*CO3)
2. NaNH2, 2-aminopyridine (89%)
CH3
HN-CH*CO-N
N

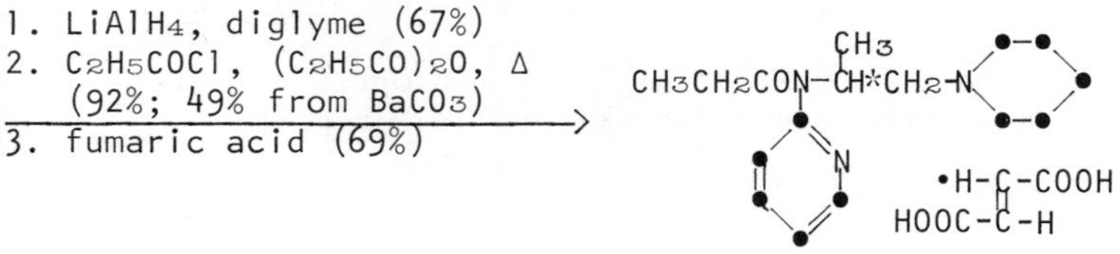
1. LiAlH4, diglyme (67%)
2. C2H5COCl, (C2H5CO)2O, Δ (92%; 49% from BaCO3)
3. fumaric acid (69%)
CH3
CH3CH2CON-CH*CH2-N
N
•H-C-COOH
HOOC-C-H

Propiram fumarate
[N-[1-Methyl-2-(1-piperidinyl)ethyl-2-^{14}C]-N-2-pyridinylpropanamide-(E)-2-butenedioate]

W. Maul, J. Label. Compound. Radiopharm., 12, 181 (1976); see also B. Duhm, W. Maul, H. Medenwald, K. Patzschke, and L. A. Wegner, Arzneim.-Forsch.-(Drug Res.), 24, 632 (1974).

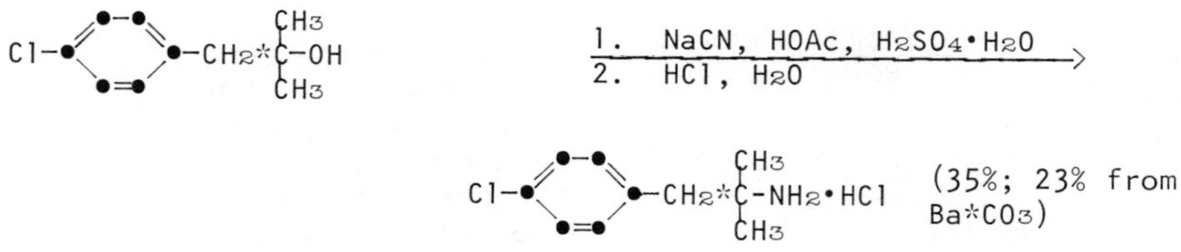
Cl
$CH_2{*}C$–OH
CH_3
CH_3
1. NaCN, HOAc, $H_2SO_4 \cdot H_2O$
2. HCl, H_2O
Cl
$CH_2{*}C-NH_2 \cdot HCl$
CH_3
CH_3
(35%; 23% from $Ba{*}CO_3$)

4-Chloro-α,α-dimethylbenzeneethanamine-α-^{14}C hydrochloride

J. Engler and L. Pallos, J. Label. Compounds, 9, 81 (1973).

C_6H_5MgBr —— 1. $*CO_2$; 2. $LiAlH_4$; 3. $Pb(OAc)_4$ ——> $C_6H_5{*}CHO$ (75% from $*CO_2$)

Benzaldehyde-^{14}C

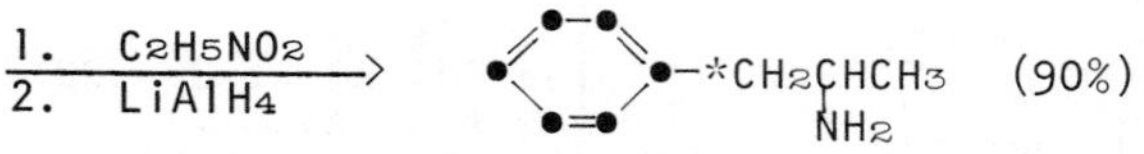
1. $C_2H_5NO_2$
2. $LiAlH_4$
$-{*}CH_2CHCH_3$
NH_2
(90%)

Amphetamine
[(±)-α-Methylbenzene-ethanamine-β-^{14}C]

Resolution of the racemic mixture with the appropriate tartaric acid derivative gave the respective (+) and (-) isomers.

(+)-Amphetamine-β-^{14}C —— 1. o-chlorobenzaldehyde; 2. $NaBH_4$; 3. HCl ——>

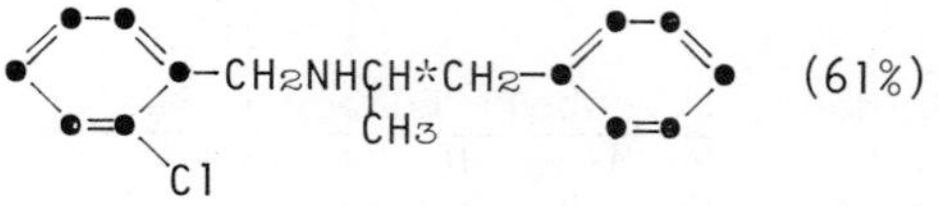
$-CH_2NHCH{*}CH_2-$
CH_3
Cl
(61%)

Clobenzorex
[(+)-N-[(2-Chlorophenyl)methyl)-α-methylbenzeneethanamine-β-^{14}C]

J. Lintermans, A. Benakis, and R. Ratouis, J. Label Compound, 6, 289 (1970)

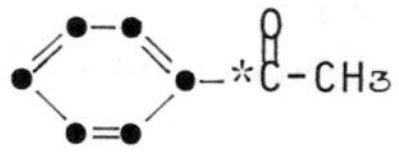

1. $(C_6H_5)_2CHCH_2CH_2NH_2$, EtOH
2. H_2, Pd/C, EtOH
3. HCl

→

$(C_6H_5)_2CHCH_2CH_2NH{*}CH(CH_3)C_6H_5 \cdot HCl$ (25%)

N-(1'-Phenethyl-1'-^{14}C)-3,3-diphenylpropylamine hydrochloride

$BrCH_2COOH$ —(1. $K{*}CN$, H_2O; 2. C_6H_5CHO)→ $C_6H_5CH{=}C({*}CN){-}COOH$ (75%) —(1. Cu, Δ (88%); 2. $AlCl_3$, C_6H_6 (83%); 3. $LiAlH_4$, Et_2O (100%))→

$C_6H_5CH_2CH_2{*}CH_2NH_2$ —(steps as above)→ $(C_6H_5)_2CHCH_2{*}CH_2NHCH(CH_3)C_6H_5 \cdot HCl$

N-(1'-Phenethyl)-3,3-diphenylpropylamine-1-^{14}C hydrochloride

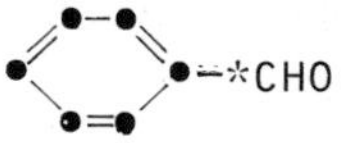

—($CNCH_2COOH$)→ $C_6H_5{*}CH{=}C(CN){-}COOH$ —(steps as above)→

$(C_6H_5)_2{*}CHCH_2CH_2NHCH(CH_3)C_6H_5 \cdot HCl$

N-(1'-Phenethyl)-3,3-diphenylpropylamine-3-^{14}C hydrochloride

$C_6H_5CH_2CH_2{*}CN$

1. KOH, EtOH (100%)
2. $SOCl_2$, C_6H_6 (100%)
3. (−)-α-phenethylamine, Et_3N, CH_2Cl_2 (95%)
4. $LiAlH_4$, Et_2O } (58%)
5. HCl

→

$(C_6H_5)_2CHCH_2{*}CH_2NHCH(CH_3)C_6H_5 \cdot HCl$

(−)-N-(1'-Phenethyl)-3,3-diphenylpropylamine-1-^{14}C hydrochloride

Similarly:

$C_6H_5{*}CH{=}C(CN){-}COOH$ ⟶ $C_6H_5{*}CH_2CH_2CN$ ⟶

$(C_6H_5)_2{}^*CHCH_2CH_2NHCH(CH_3)\text{-}C_6H_5 \cdot HCl$

(-)-N-(1'-Phenethyl)-3,3-diphenylpropylamine-3-^{14}C hydrochloride

J. Volford and K. Harsanyi, J. Label. Compounds, 9, 219 (1973).

$CH_3CH_2CH_2Br$ → 1. Na*CN, glycol (87%); 2. $LiAlH_4$, ether (79%); 3. HCl → $CH_3CH_2CH_2{}^*CH_2NH_2 \cdot HCl$

1-Butanamine-1-^{14}C hydrochloride

G. B. Howarth and A. W. Craig, J. Label. Compounds, 8, 249 (1972).

$(CH_3)_2C{=}CHMgBr$ → 1. $^*CO_2$ (94%); 2. CH_2N_2 (98%); 3. $LiAlH_4$ (46%) → $(CH_3)_2C{=}CH{}^*CH_2OH$

→ 1. PBr_3 (92%); 2. potassium phthalimide (86%); 3. HCl, CH_3OH (54%) → $(CH_3)_2C{=}CH{}^*CH_2NH_2 \cdot HCl$

3-Methyl-2-buten-1-amine-1-^{14}C hydrochloride

Nguyen-Van-Bac, M. Herbert, Nguyen-Hoang-Nam, L. Pichat, and Nguyen-Dat-Xuong, J. Label. Compounds, 7, 319 (1971).

6-2 Aromatic Amines

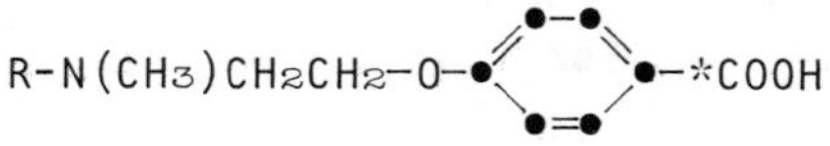

1. $SOCl_2$
2. NH_3
3. $LiAlH_4$, THF, Δ

R=CH_3 or $CH_2C_6H_5$

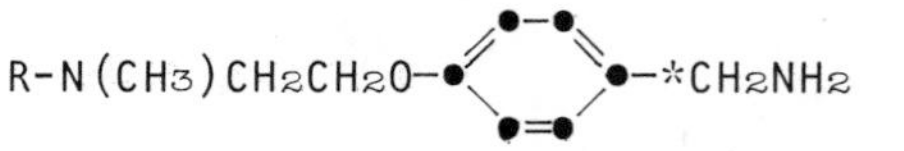

(95%)

R=CH_3; 4-[2-(Dimethylamino)ethoxy]-benzeneemethanamine-α-[14]C

R=$CH_2C_6H_5$; 4-[2-[(Phenylmethyl)amino]ethoxy]benzenemethanamine-α-[14]C

R. L. Wineholt, J. D. Johnson, P. J. Heck, and H. H. Kaegi, J. Label. Compounds, 6, 53 (1970).

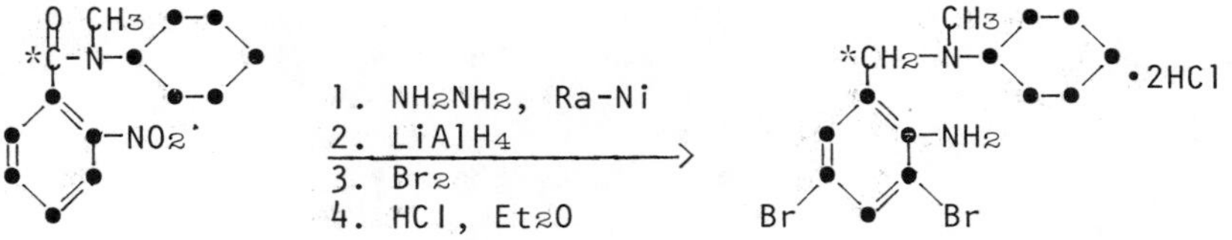
1. NH_2NH_2, Ra-Ni
2. $LiAlH_4$
3. Br_2
4. HCl, Et_2O
•2HCl
NO_2
NH_2
Br
Br

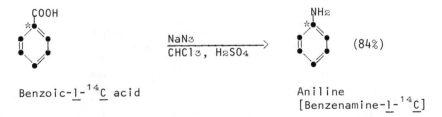

Bisolvon (Bromohexine)
[2-Amino-3,5-dibromo-[N-cyclohexyl-N-methyl]benzenemethanamine-α-^{14}C dihydrochloride]

R. Jauch and R. Hankwitz, Arzneim.-Forsch.-(Drug Res.), 25, 1954 (1975).

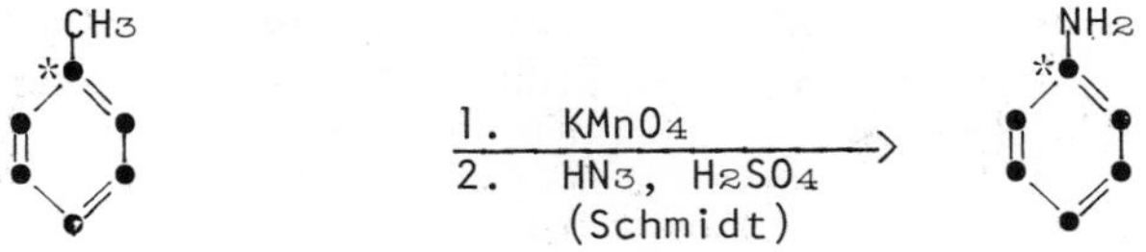
CH_3
1. $KMnO_4$
2. HN_3, H_2SO_4
(Schmidt)
NH_2

Toluene-1-^{14}C

Aniline
[Benzenamine-1-^{14}C]

R. F. C. Brown and M. Butcher, Aust. J. Chem., 25, 149 (1972).

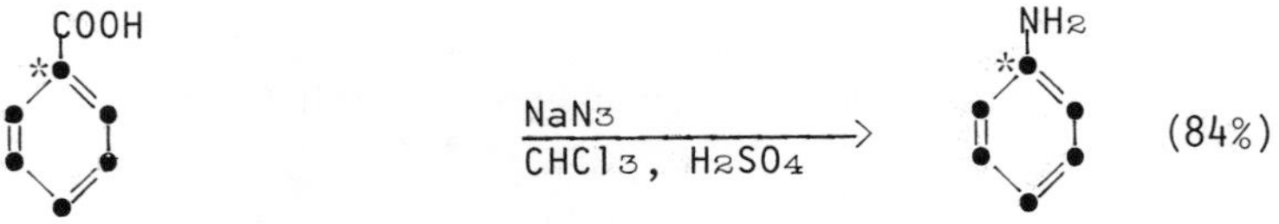
COOH
NaN_3
$CHCl_3$, H_2SO_4
NH_2
(84%)

Benzoic-1-^{14}C acid

Aniline
[Benzenamine-1-^{14}C]

S. Oae, N. Furukawa, M. Kise, and M. Kawanishi, Bull. Chem. Soc. Jap., 39, 1212 (1966).

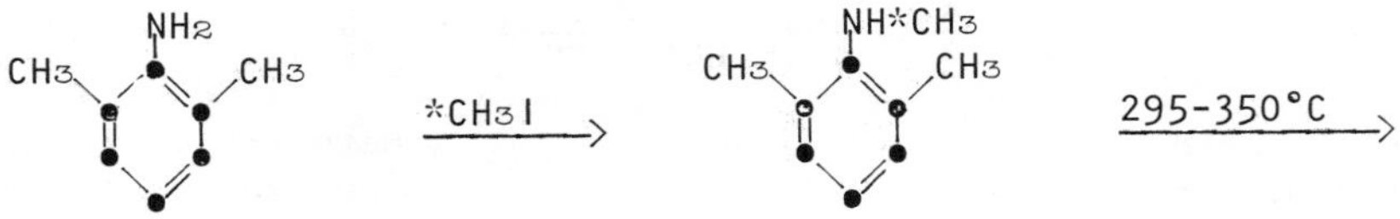
NH_2
CH_3
CH_3
$^*CH_3I$
NH^*CH_3
CH_3
CH_3
295-350°C

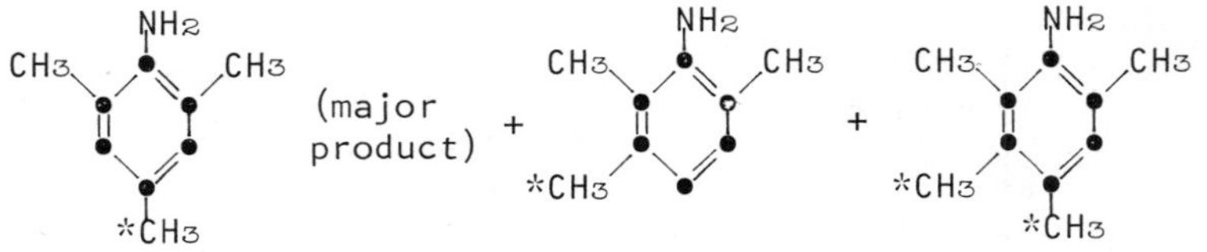

NH2
CH3
CH3
*CH3
(major product)
+
+

Mesidene [2,4,6-Trimethylbenzenamine-(4-methyl-^{14}C)]

2,3,6-Trimethylbenzenamine-(3-methyl-^{14}C)

2,3,4,6-Tetramethylbenzenamine-(3,4-methyl-^{14}C)

The composition of the mixture varied with temperature of the reaction.

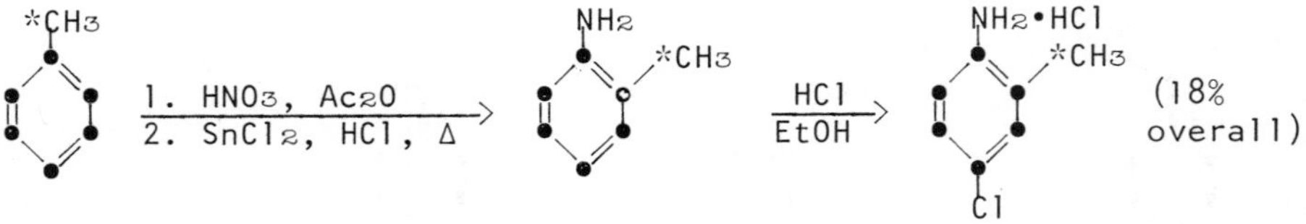

*CH3
1. HNO3, Ac2O
2. SnCl2, HCl, Δ
NH2
*CH3
HCl
EtOH
NH2•HCl
Cl
(18% overall)

(other isomers separated by chromatography)

4-Chloro-2-methyl-^{14}C-benzenamine hydrochloride

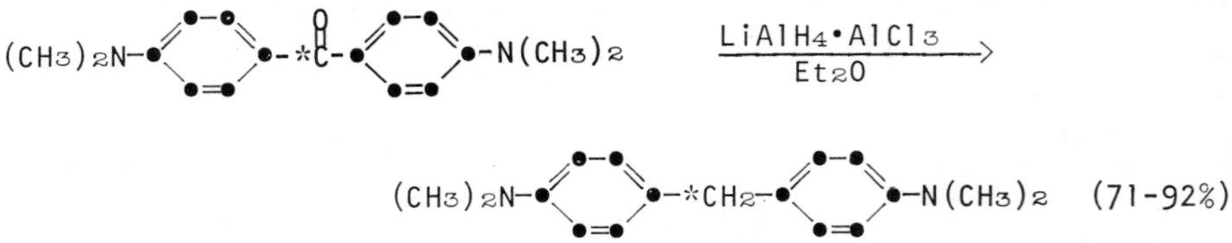

(CH3)2N
N(CH3)2
*C
O
LiAlH4•AlCl3
Et2O
*CH2
(71-92%)

4,4'-(Methylene-^{14}C)bis[N,N-dimethylbenzenamine]

T. P. Johnston, A. T. Shortnacy, and R. H. James, J. Label. Compound. Radiopharm., 15, 599 (1978).

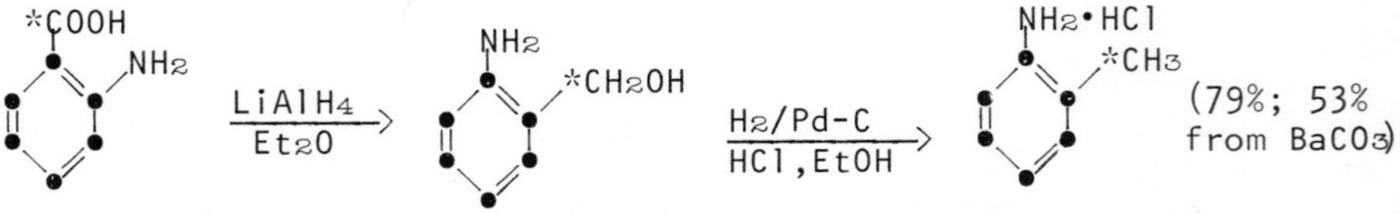

*COOH
NH2
LiAlH4
Et2O
NH2
*CH2OH
H2/Pd-C
HCl, EtOH
NH2•HCl
*CH3
(79%; 53% from BaCO3)

Anthranilic acid [2-Aminobenzoic-7-^{14}C acid

2-Methyl-^{14}C benzenamine hydrochloride

Starting with 2-bromo-3-nitronaphthalene, 3-(methyl-^{14}C)-2-naphtalenamine was prepared in the same manner in 40% overall yield.

L. Weiss, M. Loy, S. S. Hecht, and D. Hoffmann, J. Label. Compound. Radiopharm., 14, 119 (1978).

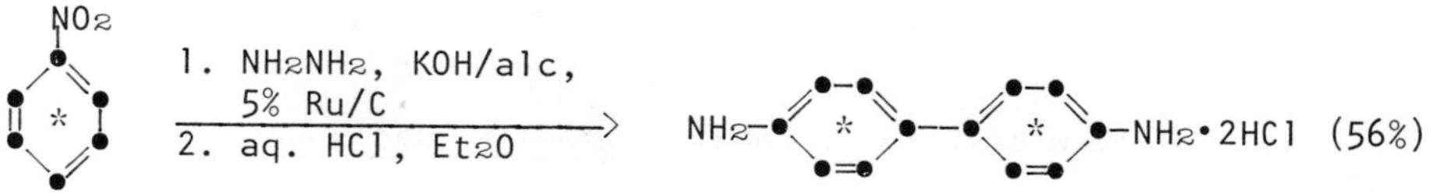
NO2
1. NH2NH2, KOH/alc, 5% Ru/C
2. aq. HCl, Et2O
NH2
NH2·2HCl (56%)

Nitrobenzene-U-^{14}C

Benzidine
[[1,1'-Biphenyl-U-^{14}C]-4,4'-diamine dihydrochloride]

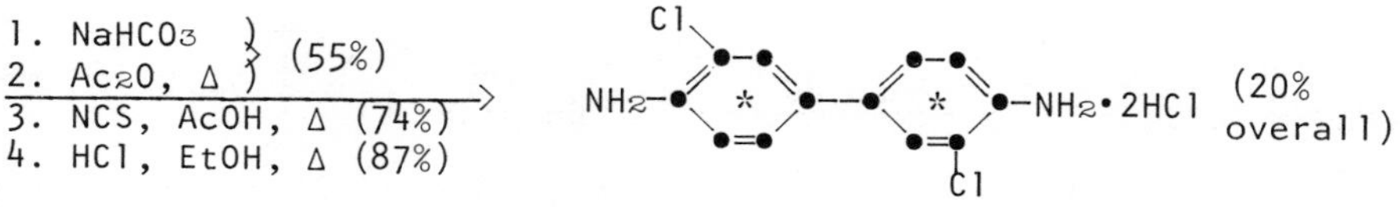
1. NaHCO3
2. Ac2O, Δ
(55%)
3. NCS, AcOH, Δ (74%)
4. HCl, EtOH, Δ (87%)
Cl
NH2
NH2·2HCl
Cl
(20% overall)

[1,1'-Biphenyl-U-^{14}C]-3,3'-dichloro-4,4'-diamine dihydrochloride

W. P. Duncan, J. C. Wiley, Jr., and W. C. Perry, J. Label. Compound. Radiopharm., 13, 305 (1977).

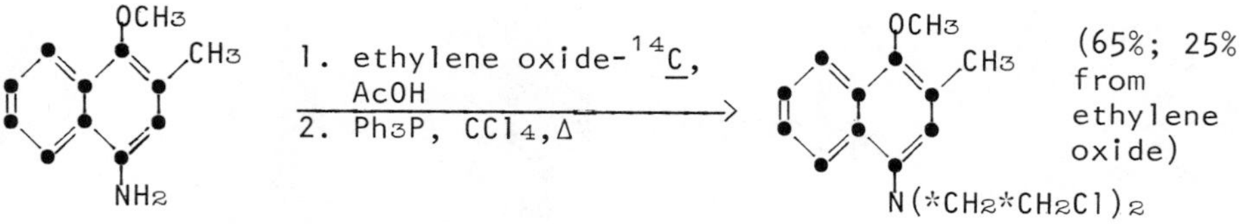
OCH3
CH3
NH2
1. ethylene oxide-14C, AcOH
2. Ph3P, CCl4, Δ
OCH3
CH3
N(*CH2*CH2Cl)2
(65%; 25% from ethylene oxide)

N,N-Bis(2-chloroethyl-^{14}C)-4-methoxy-3-methyl-1-naphthalenamine

The O-methoxy-^{14}C derivative was also prepared.

J.-C. Madelmont, M.-F. Moreau, and D. Godeneche, J. Label. Compound. Radiopharm., 14, 281 (1978).

6-3 Imines

$*RNH_2 \cdot HCl + CH_3CHO \xrightarrow[H_2O]{KOH} *R\text{-}N{=}CHCH_3$

$*R = *CH_3$; N-Ethylidenemethanamine-1-^{14}C

$*R = CH_3*CH_2\text{-}$; N-Ethylideneethanamine-1-^{14}C

H. Braun and M. Wiessler, J. Label. Compound. Radiopharm., 14, 887 (1978).

6-4 Hydroxyl Amines

$*CH_3O\text{-}N(*CH_3)\text{-}COOC_2H_5 \xrightarrow[\Delta]{\text{concd. HCl}} *CH_3O\text{-}NH(*CH_3) \cdot HCl$ (74%)

(Methoxy-^{14}C)(methyl-^{14}C)carbamyl acid ethyl ester

N-(Methoxy-^{14}C)methanamine-^{14}C hydrochloride

K. N. Arjungi, F.-W. Krüger, and M. Wiessler, J. Label. Compound. Radiopharm., 14, 913 (1978).

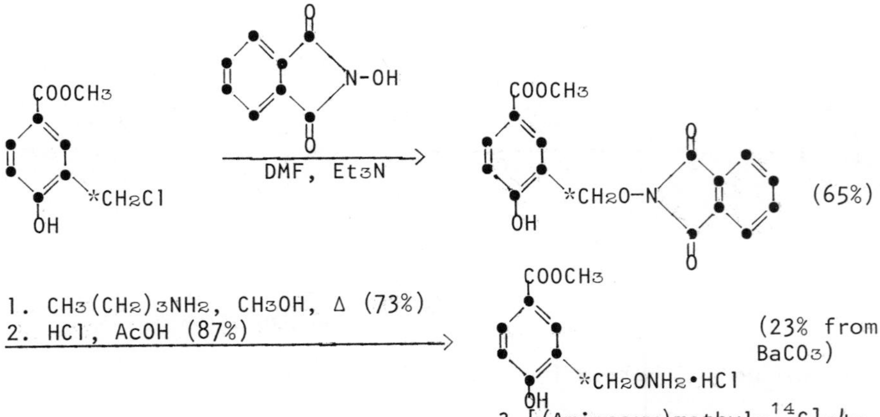
COOCH3
*CH2Cl
OH
N-OH
DMF, Et3N
*CH2O-N
(65%)
1. CH3(CH2)3NH2, CH3OH, Δ (73%)
2. HCl, AcOH (87%)
*CH2ONH2•HCl
(23% from BaCO3)

3-[(Aminooxy)methyl-^{14}C]-4-hydroxybenzoic acid methyl ester hydrochloride

J. Engler and E. Kasztreiner, J. Label. Compounds, 9, 237 (1973).

6-5 Oximes

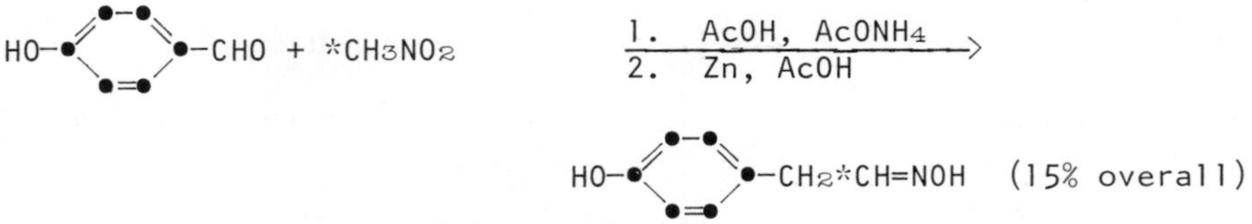
HO–
–CHO + *CH3NO2
1. AcOH, AcONH4
2. Zn, AcOH
HO–
–CH2*CH=NOH
(15% overall)

4-Hydroxybenzeneacetaldehyde-1-^{14}C oxime

H. Kindl and S. Schiefer, Monatsch. Chem., 100, 1773 (1969).

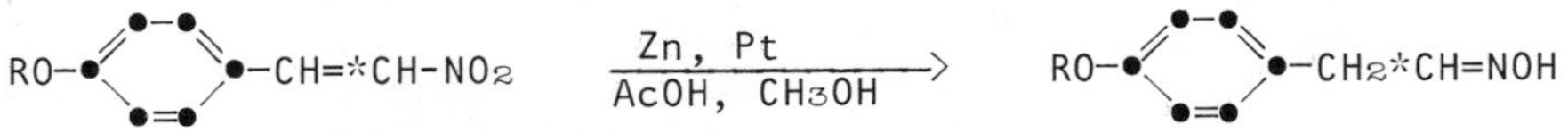
RO–
–CH=*CH-NO2
Zn, Pt
AcOH, CH3OH
RO–
–CH2*CH=NOH

R=H; 4-Hydroxybenzeneacetaldehyde-1-^{14}C oxime (11%)

R=CH_3; 4-Methoxybenzeneacetaldehyde-1-^{14}C oxime (26%)

S. Schiefer and H. Kindl, J. Label. Compounds, 7, 291 (1971).

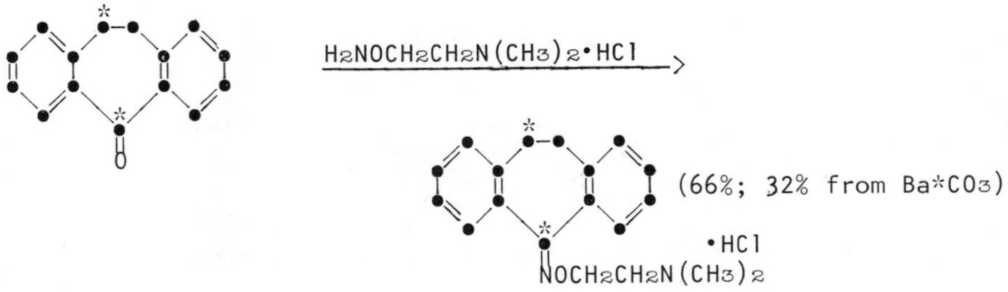
H2NOCH2CH2N(CH3)2·HCl
(66%; 32% from Ba*CO3)
·HCl
NOCH2CH2N(CH3)2

Noxiptilin
[10,11-Dihydro-5H-dibenzo[a,d]cyclohepten-5-one-5,10-^{14}C-O-[2-(dimethylamino)ethyl]oxime]

W. Maul, J. Label. Compounds, 5, 250 (1969).

6-6 Hydrazines

$H_2N-N(CH_3)^{*}CH_2COOH$ —(1N HCl)→ $CH_3NHNH^{*}CH_3$

1-Methylhydrazino-acetic-α-^{14}C acid → 1,2-Dimethylhydrazine-^{14}C

93% of specific activity is retained; a mechanism is proposed.

S. Kondo, S. Shibahara, S. Takahashi, K. Maeda, H. Umezawa, and M. Ohno, J. Amer. Chem. Soc., 93, 6305 (1971).

$C_6H_5-CONNaNHCO-C_6H_5$ —($^{*}CH_3I$ / DMF)→ $C_6H_5-CON^{*}CH_3NHCOC_6H_5$ (85%)

(Methyl-^{14}C)-N,N'-dibenzoylhydrazine

—($(CH_3)_2SO_4$, NaOH / H_2O, 95°C)→ $C_6H_5CON^{*}CH_3N^{*}CH_3COC_6H_5$ (89%)

—(HCl)→ $^{*}CH_3NHNH^{*}CH_3 \cdot 2HCl$ (97%)

1,2-(Dimethyl-^{14}C)-hydrazine hydrochloride

M. Horisberger and H. Matsumoto, J. Label. Compounds, 4, 164 (1968).

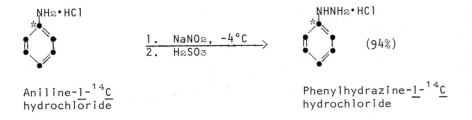

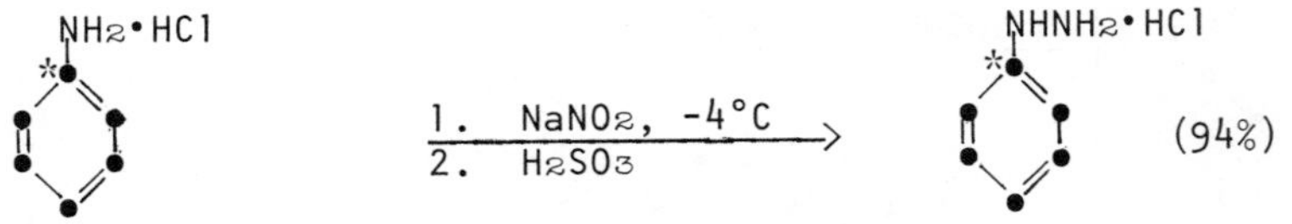
NH2•HCl
1. NaNO2, -4°C
2. H2SO3
NHNH2•HCl
(94%)

Aniline-1-^{14}C hydrochloride → Phenylhydrazine-1-^{14}C hydrochloride

T. F. Burger, J. Label. Compounds, 4, 262 (1968).

6-7 Azo Compounds

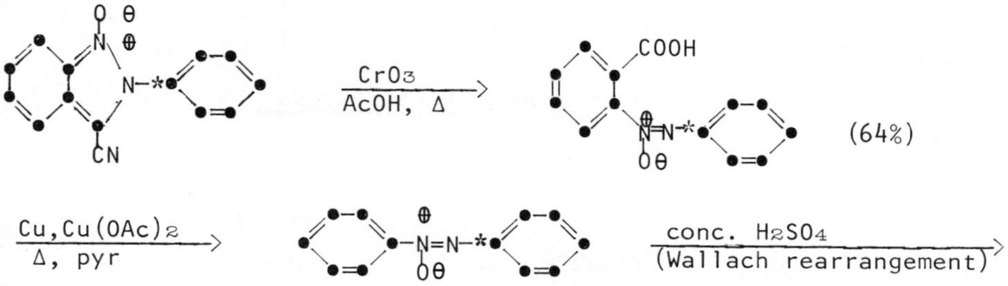

Azoxybenzene
[Diphenyldiazene-1-oxide-1'-^{14}C]

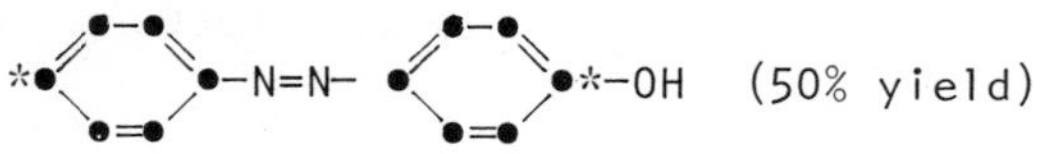

4-Phenylazophenol-1,4'-^{14}C

Approximately equal amounts of label are found at the 4 and 4' positions by degradation reactions; a symmetrical intermediate is proposed.

L. C. Behr and E. C. Hendley, J. Org. Chem., 31, 2175 (1966).

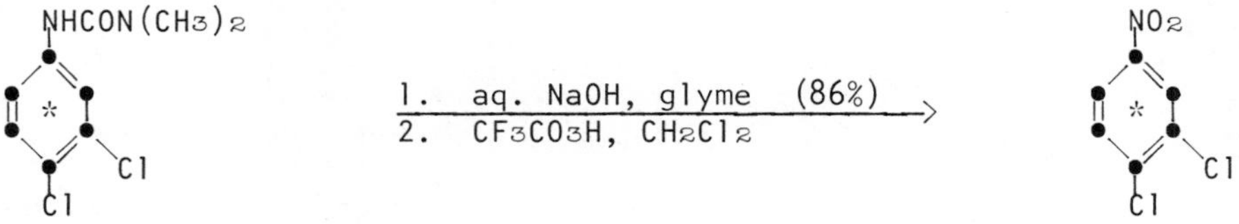

Diuron
[N'-(3,4-Dichlorophenyl-(ring-^{14}C))-N,N-dimethylurea]

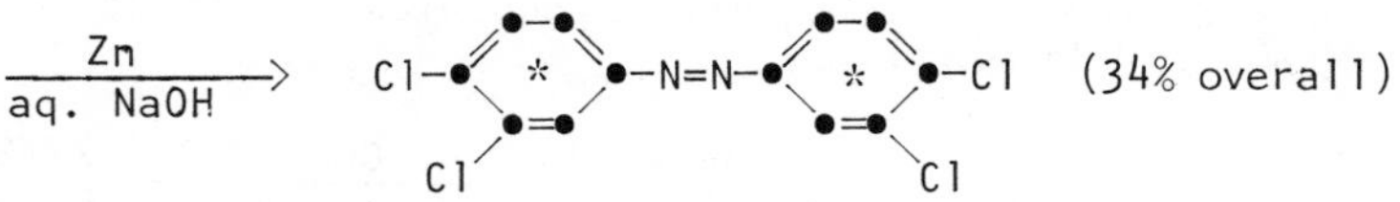

3,3',4,4'-Tetrachloroazobenzene
[Diazenebis(3,4-dichlorophenyl-(ring-^{14}C)]

F. S. Tanaka and R. G. Wien, J. Label. Compounds, 7, 459 (1971).

$*C_6H_5COCl \xrightarrow[NaOH]{N_2H_4,\ H_2SO_4} (*C_6H_5CONH)_2 \xrightarrow[CCl_4]{Br_2} *C_6H_5CO\text{-}N\text{=}N\text{-}CO*C_6H_5$

Benzoyl chloride-(ring-^{14}C) — Dibenzoyldiazene-(ring-^{14}C)

J. C. Bevington and D. J. Stamper, Trans. Faraday Soc., 66, 688 (1970).

$*CH_3NHNH*CH_3 \cdot 2HCl \xrightarrow[2.\ m\text{-}Cl\text{-}PBA]{1.\ HgO} *CH_3\text{-}\overset{\oplus}{N}(O^{\ominus})\text{=}N*CH_3$ (31%)

1,2-Dimethylhydrazine-^{14}C dihydrochloride

$\xrightarrow[2.\ CH_3COOAg]{1.\ NBS,\ CCl_4} *CH_3\text{-}\overset{\oplus}{N}(O^{\ominus})\text{=}N\text{-}*CH_2OCOCH_3$ (27%)

(Methyl-^{14}C-ONN-azoxy)-methanol-^{14}C acetate ester

M. Horisberger and H. Matsumoto, J. Label. Compounds, 4, 164 (1968).

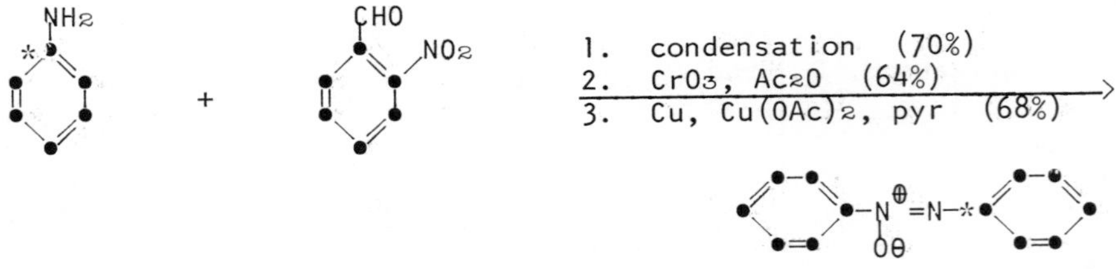
NH2
CHO
NO2
1. condensation (70%)
2. CrO3, Ac2O (64%)
3. Cu, Cu(OAc)2, pyr (68%)
N
=N
O

Diphenyldiazene 1-oxide-1'-^{14}C

The 1-^{14}C-labeled compound was used to study the Wallach transformation of azoxybenzene to p-hydroxyazobenzene. By subsequent degradation reactions, the oxygen atom was found to migrate to the 4 and 4' positions.

L. C. Behr and E. C. Hendly, J. Org. Chem., 31, 2715 (1966); the same compound has been used to study the rearrangements with arenesulfonic anhydrides: S. Oae and T. Maeda, Tetrahedron, 28, 2127 (1972).

6-8 Diazo Compounds

$H_2N\text{-}{*}CH_2COOH$ —(1. HCl, EtOH (98%); 2. KOAc, $NaNO_2$, (93%) H_2O, H_2SO_4)→ ${*}CHN_2COOC_2H_5$

Glycine-2-^{14}C

Diazoacetic-2-^{14}C acid ethyl ester

N. E. Pawlowski, J. E. Nixon, D. J. Lee, and R. O. Sinnhuber, J. Label. Compounds, 10, 45 (1974).

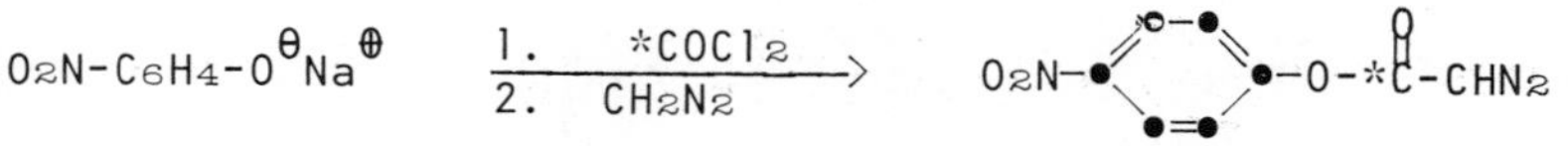

Diazoacetic-1-^{14}C acid 4-nitrophenyl ester

J. Shafer, P. Baronowsky, R. Laursen, F. Finn, and F. H. Westheimer, J. Biol. Chem., 241, 421 (1966).

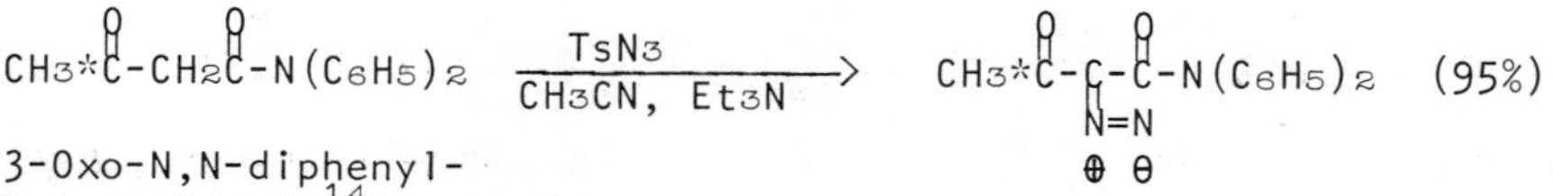

3-Oxo-N,N-diphenyl-butanamide-3-^{14}C

2-Diazo-3-oxo-N,N-diphenylbutanamide-3-^{14}C

H. Dahn and S. Karoui, Helv. Chim. Acta, 52, 2491 (1969).

6-9 Azides

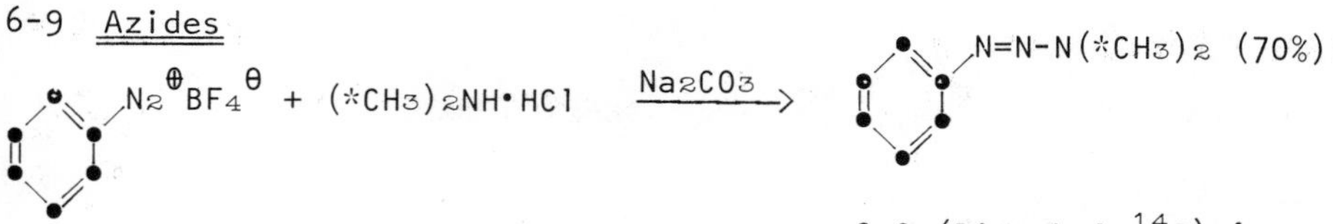

3,3-(Dimethyl-^{14}C)-1-phenyl-1-triazine

G. F. Kolar and Ch. Schweickhardt, J. Label. Compounds, 11, 43 (1975).

6-10 N-Nitrosoamines

$^{*}CH_3O-N(^{*}CH_3)H \cdot HCl \xrightarrow[CH_2Cl_2]{NaNO_2,\ HCl} {}^{*}CH_3O-N(^{*}CH_3)-NO$ (49%)

N-(Methoxy-^{14}C)-methanamine-^{14}C hydrochloride → N-(Methoxy-^{14}C)-N-nitrosomethanamine-^{14}C

K. N. Arjungi, F.-W. Krüger, and M. Wiessler, J. Label. Compound. Radiopharm., 14, 913 (1978).

$^{*}CH_3NH_2 \cdot HCl$ → 1. HCHO, NaOH/H_2O; 2. NOCl, CH_2Cl_2, 0°C; 3. AgOAc → $^{*}CH_3N(NO)-CH_2OC(=O)-CH_3$ (24% overall)

(Methyl-^{14}C)nitrosoaminomethanol acetate (ester)

H. Braun and M. Wiessler, J. Label. Compound.Radiopharm., 13, 379 (1977).

$^{*}CH_3NHCOOC_2H_5 \xrightarrow[NaNO_2]{HNO_3} {}^{*}CH_3-N(NO)-COOC_2H_5$ (36% overall)

(Methyl-^{14}C)nitrosocarbamate acid ethyl ester

A. Alarif, S. Kimball, and S. Epstein, J. Label. Compounds, 10, 161 (1974).

$^{*}CH_3NHCH_2COOH \xrightarrow[H_2O]{HCl,\ NaNO_2} {}^{*}CH_3N(NO)CH_2COOH$ (64%)

Sarcosine [N-(Methyl-^{14}C)glycine] → N-Nitrososarcosine [N-(Methyl-^{14}C)-N-nitrosoglycine]

T. Hansen, W. T. Iwaoka, and M. C. Archer, J. Label. Compounds, 10, 689 (1974).

$*R{-}N{=}CHCH_3$ —(1. NOCl, CH_2Cl_2; 2. AgOAc)→ $CH_3COOCH(CH_3){-}N(NO){-}*R$

$*R = *CH_3$; 1-(Methyl-^{14}C)nitrosoaminoethanol acetate ester (16% yield)

$*R = CH_3*CH_2-$; 1-(Ethyl-1-^{14}C)nitrosoaminoethanol acetate ester (33% yield)

H. Braun and M. Wiessler, J. Label. Compound. Radiopharm., 14, 887 (1978).

$CH_3CHOH*CONHCH_2CHOHCH_3$ —(1. $BH_3 \cdot (CH_3)_2S$, THF, Δ; 2. $NaNO_2$, H_2SO_4)→

$CH_3CH(OH){-}*CH_2{-}N(NO){-}*CH_2CH(OH){-}CH_3$ (45% overall)

1,1'-(Nitrosoimino)bis-2-propanol-1,1'-^{14}C

R. Kupper, D. Nagel, R. Gingell, and G. Brunk, J. Label. Compound. Radiopharm., 15, 175 (1978).

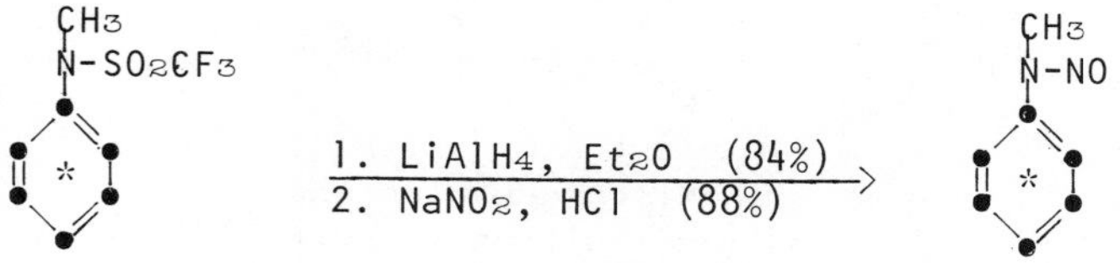
CH3
N-SO2CF3
1. LiAlH4, Et2O (84%)
2. NaNO2, HCl (88%)
CH3
N-NO

(62% overall)

N-Methyl-N-nitrosobenzenamine-(ring-^{14}C)

Use of $*CH_3I$ and nonradioactive aniline gave N-methyl-^{14}C-N-nitrosobenzenamine in similar yield.

C. J. Grandjean, M. C. Eagen, and J. Goldston, J. Label. Compound. Radiopharm., 12, 207 (1976).

$C_6H_5CH_2N(^*CH_3)\text{-}SO_2CF_3 \xrightarrow[\text{2. isoamyl nitrite}]{\text{1. LiAlH}_4\text{, Et}_2\text{O}} C_6H_5CH_2N(^*CH_3)\text{-}NO$ (26% overall)

N-(Methyl-^{14}C)-N-nitroso-benzenemethanamine

$C_6H_5{}^*CH_2N(CH_3)\text{-}SO_2CF_3 \xrightarrow[\text{2. isoamyl nitrite}]{\text{1. LiAlH}_4\text{, Et}_2\text{O}} C_6H_5{}^*CH_2N(CH_3)\text{-}NO$ (24% overall)

N-Methyl-N-nitroso-benzenemethanamine-α-^{14}C

P. L. Skipper, J. Label. Compound. Radiopharm., 15, 575 (1978).

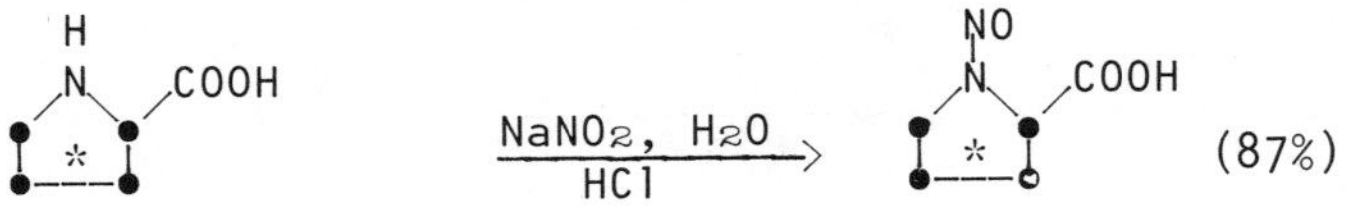
H
N
COOH
NaNO2, H2O
HCl
NO
N
COOH
(87%)

L-Proline-U-^{14}C

1-Nitroso-L-proline [N-Nitroso-2-pyrrolidine-carboxylic-U-^{14}C acid]

T. Hansen, W. T. Iwaoka, and M. C. Archer, J. Label. Compounds, 10, 689 (1974).

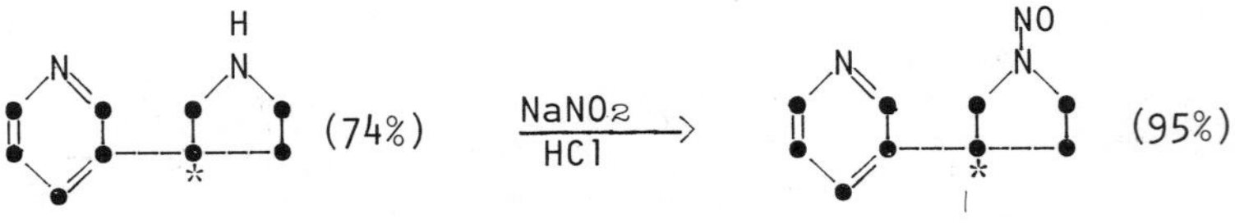
N
H
N
(74%)
NaNO2
HCl
N
NO
N
(95%)

Nornicotine [3-(3-Pyrrolidinyl-3-^{14}C)pyridine]

N-Nitrosonornicotine [3-(1-Nitroso-3-pyrrolidinyl-3-^{14}C)pyridine]

M. W. Hu, W. E. Bondinell, and D. Hoffman, J. Label. Compounds, 10, 79 (1974).

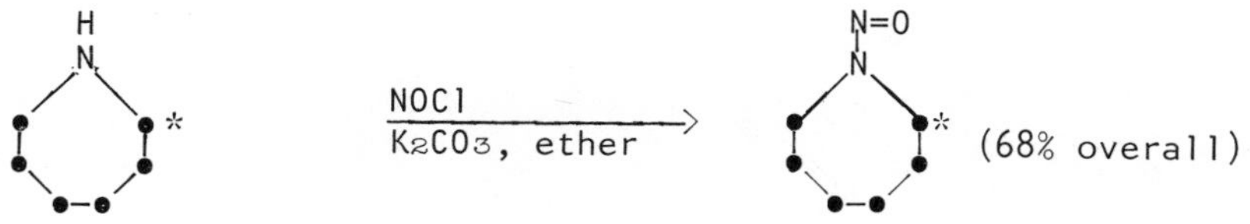

Hexahydro-1H-azepine-2-^{14}C

Hexahydro-1-nitroso-1H-azepine-2-^{14}C

C. J. Grandjean, D. L. Nagel, L. Wallcave, K. Phelps, and G. Charnock, J. Label. Compounds, 9, 419 (1973).

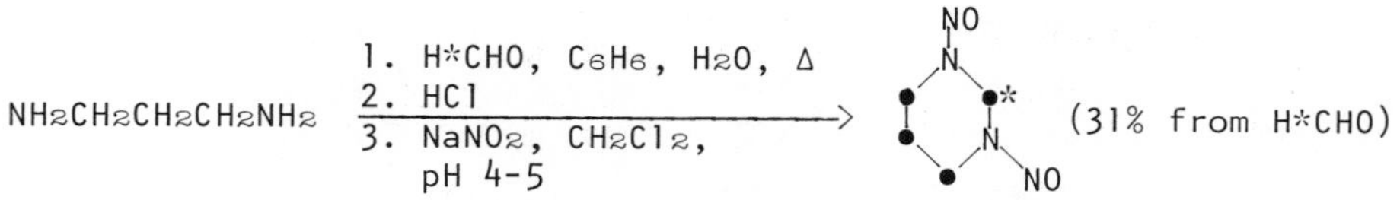

Dinitrosohexahydropyrimidine-2-^{14}C

H. Braun, B. Bertram, and M. Wiessler, J. Label. Compound. Radiopharm., 13, 375 (1977).

6-11 N-Nitroamines

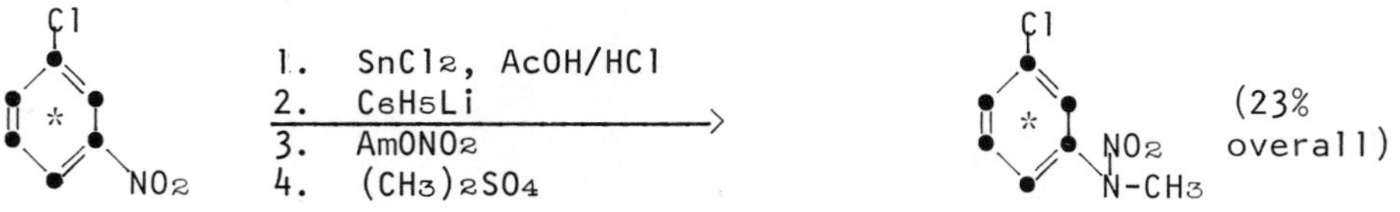

3-Chloro-N-methyl-N-nitrobenzenamine-(ring-^{14}C)

W. N. White and J. R. Klink, J. Org. Chem., 42, 166 (1977).

7

Hydrocarbons

Jnsubstituted Hydrocarbons

7-1 Aliphatic Hydrocarbons

$$HC \equiv CLi{:}NH_2CH_2CH_2NH_2 \xrightarrow[\text{room temp. 6 hr}]{*CH_3I} HC \equiv C\text{-}{*}CH_3$$

(20% based on $*CH_3I$)

Propyne-3-^{14}C

D. C. Myers and F. Schmidt-Bleek, J. Label. Compounds, 3, 62 (1967).

$$*CH_3MgI \quad + \quad CH_2{=}CHCH_2Br \longrightarrow CH_2{=}CHCH_2\text{-}{*}CH_3$$

1-Butene-4-^{14}C

M. Blanchard, H. Delplace, and J.-C. Delgrange, C. R. Acad. Sc. Paris, Ser. C, 269, 1016 (1969).

$$*CH_3\text{-}C{\equiv}C\text{-}(C_3H_7) \xrightleftharpoons{MoO_2\text{-}SiO_2} *CH_3\text{-}C{\equiv}C\text{-}{*}CH_3 \quad + \quad (C_3H_7)\text{-}C{\equiv}C\text{-}(C_3H_7)$$

2-Hexyne-1-^{14}C (prepared from 1-pentyne and $*CH_3I$ in 48% yield)

2-Butyne-1,4-^{14}C

4-Octyne (inactive)

A. Mortreux and M. Blanchard, Bull. Soc. Chim. Fr., 1641 (1972).

$$(C_6H_5)_2CHK + Cl{*}CH_2CH{=}CH_2 \xrightarrow[Et_2O]{NH_3} (C_6H_5)_2CH{-}{*}CH_2CH{=}CH_2$$

1,1-(3-Butenylidene-2-^{14}C) bisbenzene

E. Grovenstein, Jr. and A. B. Cottingham, J. Amer. Chem. Soc., 99, 1881 (1977).

$$H[C{\equiv}C]_2CH(OC_2H_5)_2 \xrightarrow[\text{3. NaOH, } CH_3OH/H_2O \text{ (deformylation)}]{\text{1. } {*}CH_3I,\ LiNH_2/NH_3 \quad \text{2. 2N HCl}} {*}CH_3[C{\equiv}C]_2H \text{ (65\% from } {*}CH_3I)$$

Penta-1,3-diyne-5-^{14}C

A. G. Fallis, M. T. W. Hearn, Sir Ewart R. H. Jones, V. Thaller, and J. L. Turner, J. Chem. Soc., Perkin Trans. I, 743 (1973).

$$\underline{n}\text{-}C_5H_{11}COCl \xrightarrow[\text{2. Na, } N_2H_4,\ O(CH_2OH)_2 \text{ (63\%)}]{\text{1. } ({*}CH_3)_2Cd \text{ (64\%)}} \underline{n}\text{-}C_6H_{13}\text{-}{*}CH_3$$

Heptane-1-^{14}C

$$\underline{n}\text{-}C_5H_{11}MgBr \xrightarrow[\text{3. steps as above}]{\text{1. } {*}CO_2 \quad \text{2. } SOCl_2 \text{ (55\%)}} \underline{n}\text{-}C_5H_{11}\text{-}{*}CH_2CH_3$$

Heptane-2-^{14}C

I. Bally, E. Gârd, E. Ciornei, M. Biltz, and A. T. Balaban, J. Label. Compounds, 11, 63 (1975).

$$C_6H_{13}{*}COOH \xrightarrow[\text{3. Mg} \quad \text{4. } H_2O]{\text{1. } LiAlH_4 \quad \text{2. } PBr_3} CH_3CH_2CH_2CH_2CH_2CH_2{*}CH_3$$

Heptane-1-^{14}C

$$H{*}COOH \xrightarrow[\text{2. } C_3H_7MgBr]{\text{1. EtOH}} C_3H_7{*}CHOHC_3H_7$$

$$\xrightarrow[\text{3. } H_2,\ PtO_2]{\text{1. AcOH} \quad \text{2. 400°C}} CH_3CH_2CH_2{*}CH_2CH_2CH_2CH_3$$

Heptane-4-^{14}C

B. H. Davis and P. B. Venuto, J. Org. Chem., 36, 337 (1971).

$R\text{-}CO\text{-}R(H) + (C_6H_5)_3P{=}{*}CH_2 \longrightarrow R\text{-}C(={*}CH_2)\text{-}R(H)$ (54-75% yields)

carbonyl substrate	olefin product
n-butyraldehyde	1-pentene-1-^{14}C
2-pentanone	2-methyl-1-pentene-1-^{14}C
iso-valeraldehyde	4-methyl-1-pentene-1-^{14}C
n-valeraldehyde	1-hexene-1-^{14}C
n-hexaldehyde	1-heptene-1-^{14}C
cyclohexanone	methylene-^{14}C-cyclohexane
n-heptaldehyde	1-octene-1-^{14}C

M. A. Muhs, J. Label. Compounds, 4, 59 (1968).

$(CH_3)_3C\text{-}CH_2COOC_2H_5$ → $(CH_3)_3CCH_2CH({*}CH_3)_2$

1. ${*}CH_3MgI$ } (43%)
2. I_2, Δ
3. H_2, EtOH, hexachloroplatinic acid } (55%)

Isooctane [2,2,4-Trimethyl-(4-methyl-^{14}C)-pentane-5-^{14}C]

I. Bally and A. T. Balaban, Rev. Roum. Chim., 20, 1471 (1975).

$CH_3(CH_2)_6{*}COOH$ → $CH_3(CH_2)_6{*}CH_2C{\equiv}CH$ (61% overall)

Octanoic-1-^{14}C acid

1. $LiAlH_4$ (87%)
2. HBr (91%)
3. $HC{\equiv}CNa$, DMSO (77%)

1-Decyne-3-^{14}C

W. J. Gensler, K. W. Pober, D. W. Solomon, R. Yanase, and M. B. Floyd, J. Chem. Soc. (D), Chem. Commun., 287 (1970).

7-2 Alicyclic Hydrocarbons

$CH_2{=}CHCH_2\text{-}{*}CH_3$ —V-Mo catalyst mixture→

1-Butene-4-^{14}C

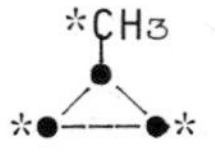

*CH3
*
*

(Methyl-^{14}C)cyclopropane-2-^{14}C

The scrambled label was explained by the catalytic rearrangement of the starting material to 1-butene-1-^{14}C; the position of the label in 1-butene-4-^{14}C was determined by degradation reactions.

M. Blanchard, H. Delplace, and J.-C. Delgrange, C. R. Acad. Sci. Paris, Ser. C, 269, 1016 (1969).

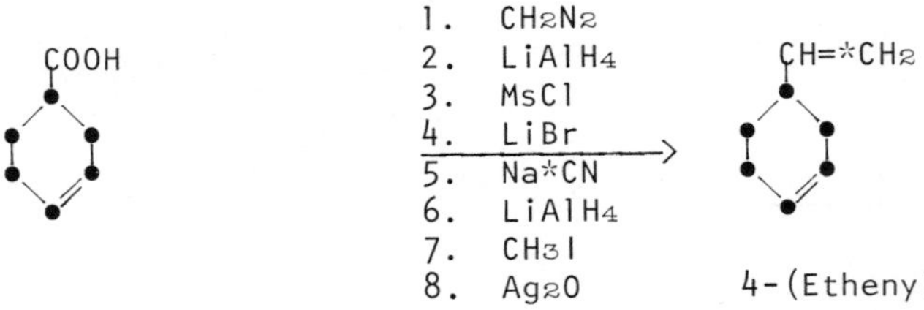
COOH
1. CH_2N_2
2. $LiAlH_4$
3. MsCl
4. LiBr
5. Na*CN
6. $LiAlH_4$
7. CH_3I
8. Ag_2O
CH=*CH_2

4-(Ethenyl-2-^{14}C)cyclohexene

W. von E. Doering and D. M. Brenner, Tetrahedron Lett., 899 (1976).

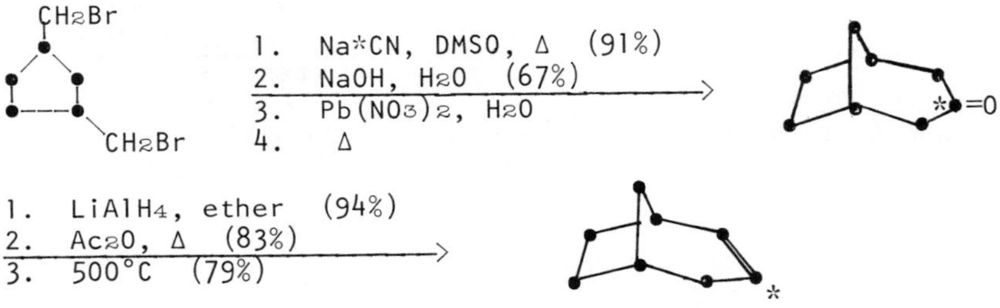
CH_2Br
CH_2Br
1. Na*CN, DMSO, Δ (91%)
2. NaOH, H_2O (67%)
3. $Pb(NO_3)_2$, H_2O
4. Δ
*=O
1. $LiAlH_4$, ether (94%)
2. Ac_2O, Δ (83%)
3. 500°C (79%)
*

Bicyclo[3.2.1]oct-2-ene-3-^{14}C

The product was used in mechanistic studies (thermal rearrangement).

G. Limarola, F. Petit, and M. Evrard, Bull. Soc. Chim. Fr., Part 2, 1295 (1975).

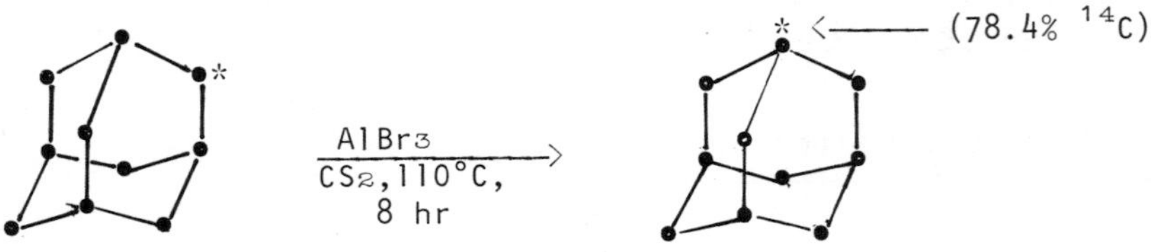
*
$AlBr_3$
CS_2, 110°C,
8 hr
* ←—— (78.4% ^{14}C)

Adamantane-2-^{14}C [Tricyclo[3.3.1.^{3,7}] decane-2-^{14}C]

Adamantane-1-^{14}C

The location of label (scrambling) was determined by degradation reactions.

Z. Majerski, S. H. Liggero, P. von R. Schleyer, and A. P. Wolf, J. Chem. Soc. (D), Chem. Comm., 1596 (1970).

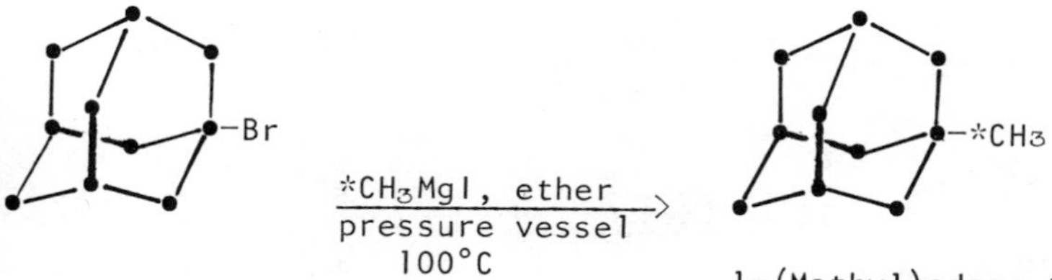

-Br
*CH₃MgI, ether
pressure vessel
100°C
-*CH₃

1-(Methyl)adamantane
[1-(Methyl-^{14}C)-tricyclo
[3.3.1.1^{3,7}] decane]

The methyl group contained 97% of the activity (determined by degradation studies).

E. Osawa, Z. Majerski, and P. von R. Schleyer, J. Org. Chem., 36, 205 (1971).

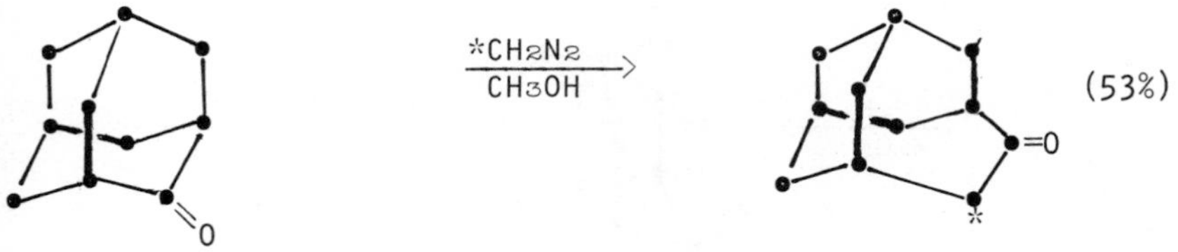

*CH₂N₂
CH₃OH
(53%)
=O
O

Adamantanone

Homoadamantan-4-one
[Tricyclo[4.3.1.1^{3,7}]-
undecan-4-one-5-^{14}C]

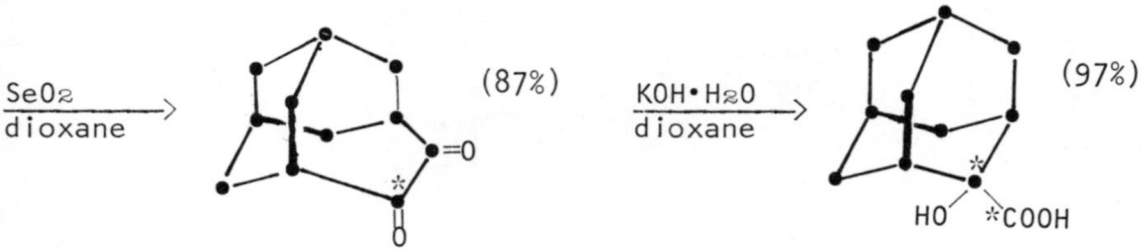

SeO₂
dioxane
(87%)
=O
O
KOH•H₂O
dioxane
(97%)
HO
*COOH

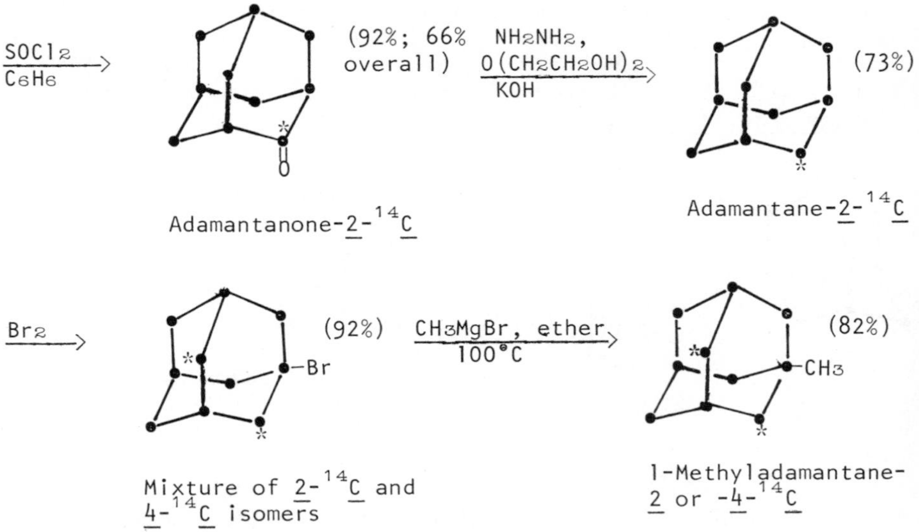

$SOCl_2$
C_6H_6
(92%; 66% overall)
NH_2NH_2,
$O(CH_2CH_2OH)_2$
KOH
(73%)
Adamantanone-2-^{14}C
Adamantane-2-^{14}C
Br_2
(92%)
Br
CH_3MgBr, ether
100°C
(82%)
CH_3
Mixture of 2-^{14}C and 4-^{14}C isomers
1-Methyladamantane-2 or -4-^{14}C

S. H. Liggero, Z. Majerski, P. von R. Schleyer, A. P. Wolf, C. S. Redvanly, H. Wynberg, J. A. Boerma, and J. Strating, J. Label. Compounds, 7, 3 (1971).

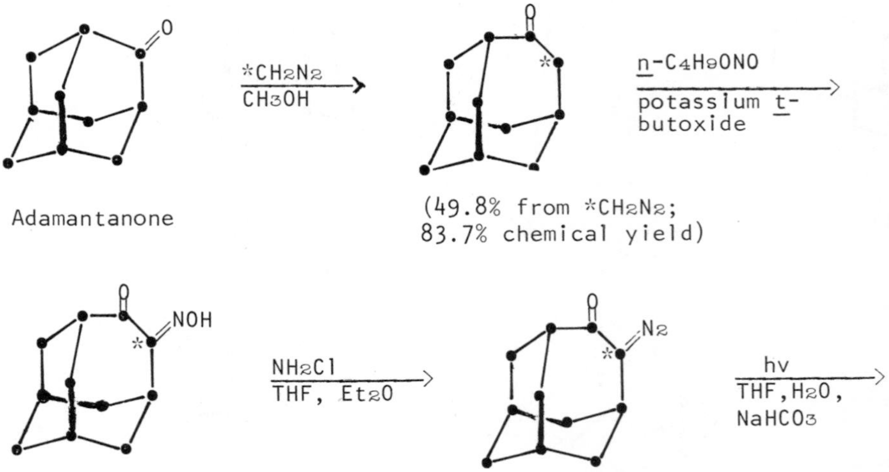

O
$*CH_2N_2$
CH_3OH
n-C_4H_9ONO
potassium t-butoxide
Adamantanone
(49.8% from $*CH_2N_2$; 83.7% chemical yield)
NOH
NH_2Cl
THF, Et_2O
N_2
hv
THF, H_2O, $NaHCO_3$

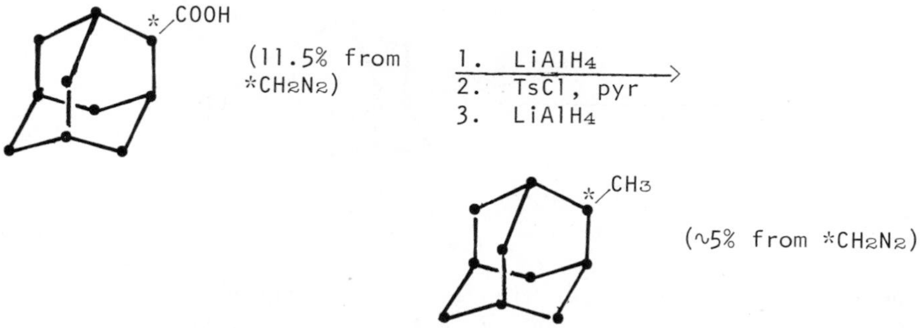
*COOH
(11.5% from *CH2N2)
1. LiAlH4
2. TsCl, pyr
3. LiAlH4
*CH3
(~5% from *CH2N2)

2-Methyladamantane-2-[14]C

Z. Majerski, A. P. Wolf, and P. v. R. Schleyer, J. Label. Compounds, 6, 179 (1970).

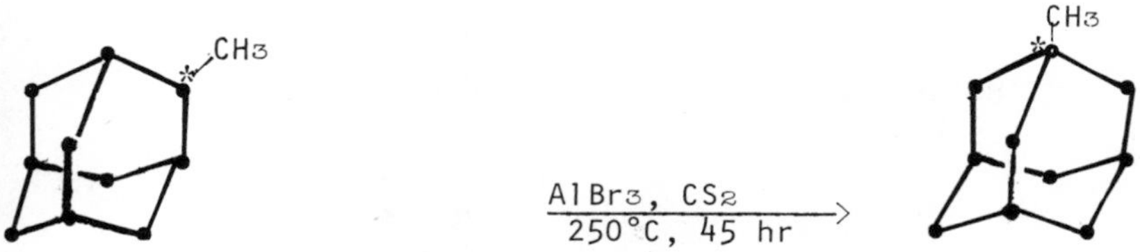
*CH3
AlBr3, CS2
250°C, 45 hr
CH3
*

2-Methyladamantane-2-[14]C

1-Methyl-
adamantane-1-[14]C

The position of the label was determined by degradation reactions; 90±2% of the activity was found in position 1 and no activity was found in the methyl group; a mechanism is postulated.

Z. Majerski, P. v. R. Schleyer, and A. P. Wolf, J. Amer. Chem. Soc., 92, 5731 (1970).

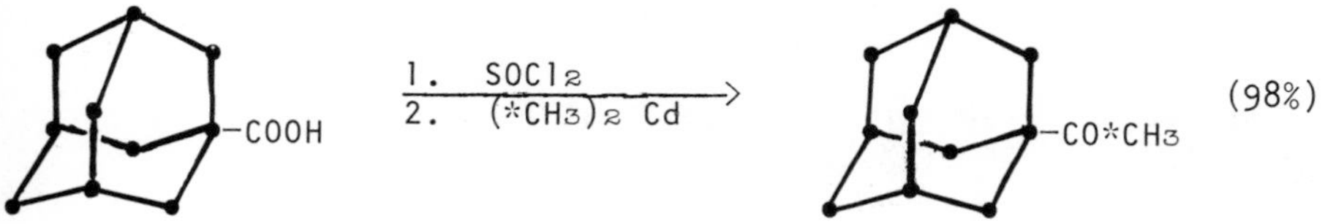
-COOH
1. SOCl2
2. (*CH3)2 Cd
-CO*CH3
(98%)

1-(Tricyclo[3.3.1.1^{3,7}]
dec-1-yl)ethanone-2-[14]C

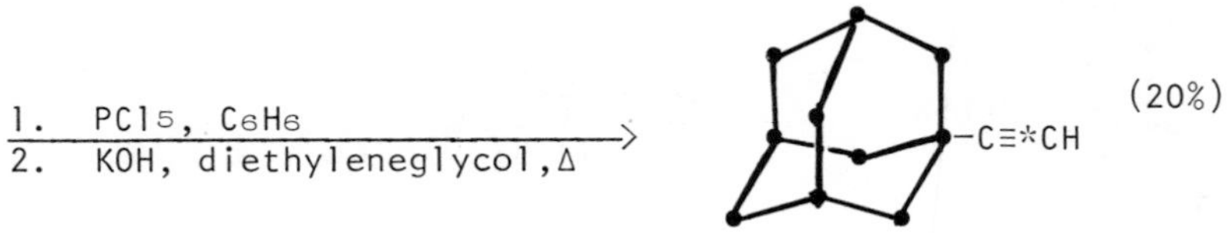
1. PCl5, C6H6
2. KOH, diethyleneglycol,Δ
—C≡*CH
(20%)

1-(Ethynyl-2-^{14}C)-tricylo [3,3,1,1^{3,7}]-decane

The acetylene compound was cleaved with permanganate to adamantane-1-carboxylic acid, which showed no activity, thus confirming the label to be in position 2. Pyrolysis of the acetylene compound (740-780°C) scrambles the label over positions 1 and 2; a mechanism is proposed.

R. F. C. Brown, F. W. Eastwood, and G. P. Jackman, Aust. J. Chem., 30, 1757 (1977).

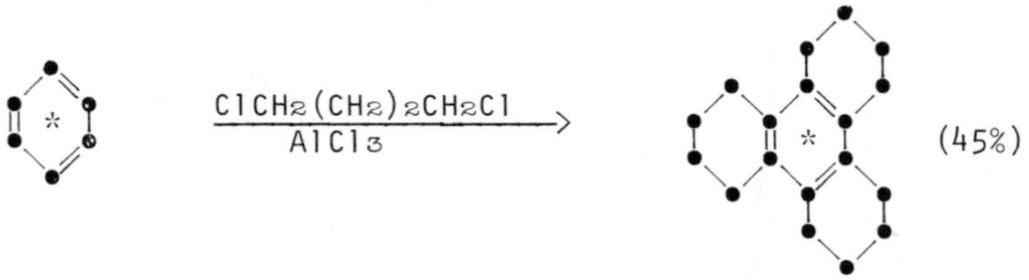
ClCH2(CH2)2CH2Cl
AlCl3
(45%)

Dodecahydrotriphenylene-^{14}C

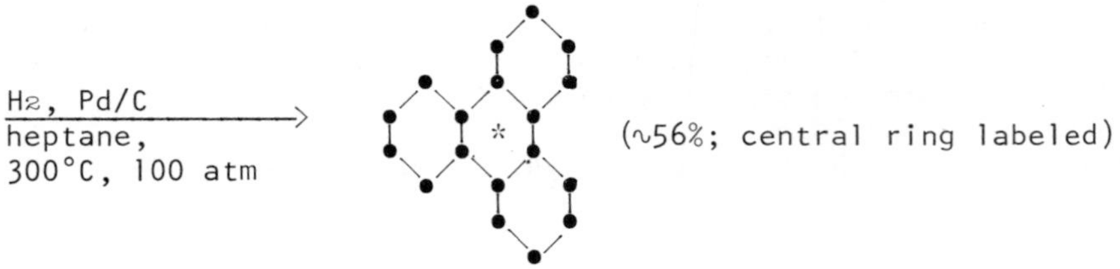
H2, Pd/C
heptane,
300°C, 100 atm
(∿56%; central ring labeled)

Perhydrotriphenylene-^{14}C (PHTP) [Octadecahydrotriphenylene]

M. Farina, U. Pedretti, M. T. Gramegna, and G. Audisio, Macromolecules, 3, 475 (1970).

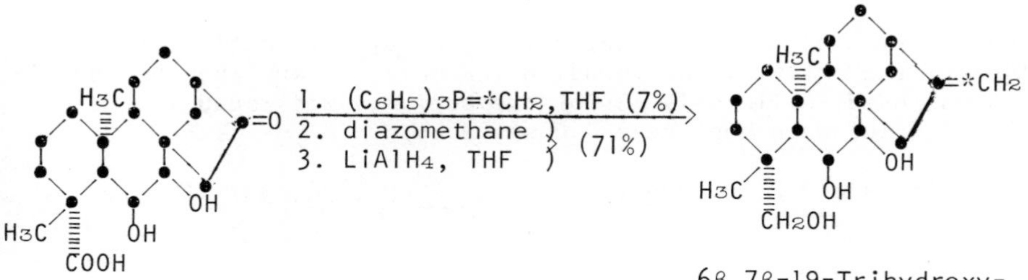
H3C
=O
OH
H3C
OH
COOH
1. (C6H5)3P=*CH2,THF (7%)
2. diazomethane
3. LiAlH4, THF
(71%)
H3C
=*CH2
OH
H3C
OH
CH2OH

6β,7β-19-Trihydroxy-kaur-16-ene-17-[14]C

B. E. Cross and J. C. Stewart, Phytochemistry, 9, 1065 (1970).

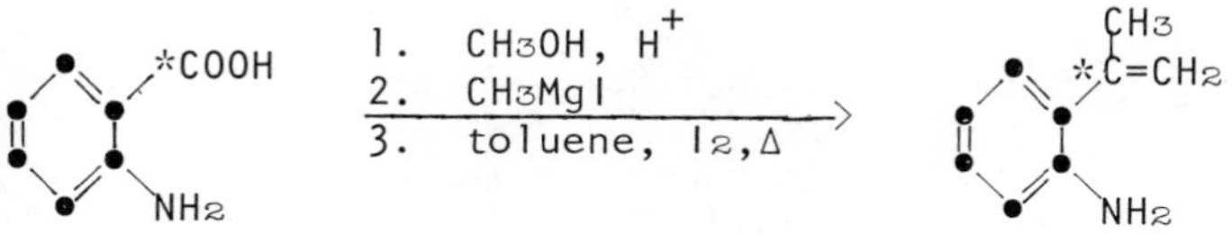
*COOH
NH2
1. CH3OH, H+
2. CH3MgI
3. toluene, I2,Δ
CH3
*C=CH2
NH2

2-(1-Methyl-ethenyl-1-^{14}C)-benzeneamine

H. C. van der Plas, D. J. Buurman, and C. M. Vos, Rec. Trav. Chim. J. Roy. Neth. Chem., 97, 50 (1978).

7-3 Mononuclear Aromatic Hydrocarbons

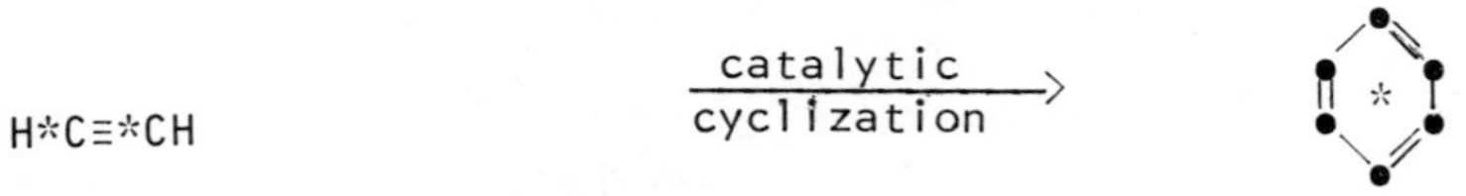
H*C≡*CH
catalytic
cyclization
*

Benzene-U-[14]C

A number of procedures are reported for this cyclization: see L. L. McDowell and M. E. Ryan, Int.J.Appl. Radiat.Isotopes, 17, 175 (1966); F. Pietig and H. W. Scharpenseel, Proc. Int. Conf. Prep. Stor. Labelled Compds., 57 (1968); M. A. Tamers, Int. J. Appl. Radiat. Isotopes, 26, 676 (1975).

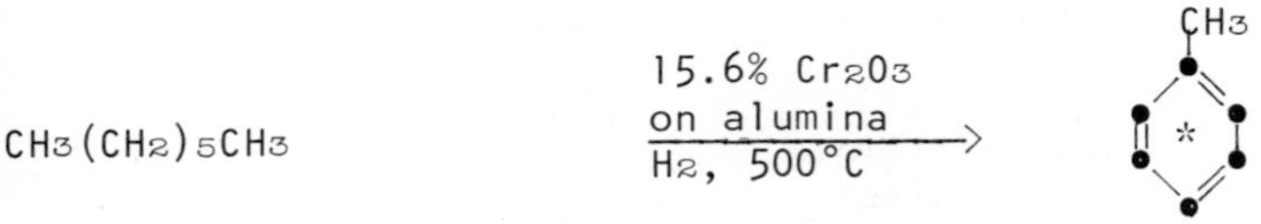
CH3(CH2)5CH3
15.6% Cr2O3
on alumina
H2, 500°C
CH3
*

n-Heptane-1 or -4-[14]C

Toluene-[14]C
[Methylbenzene-^{14}C]

The position of the label was determined by degradation reactions; ~40% of the activity was found in the methyl group when heptane-1-^{14}C was used, while only ~3% of the activity was found in the methyl group when heptane-4-^{14}C was used.

B. H. Davis and P. B. Venuto, J. Org. Chem., 36, 337 (1971).

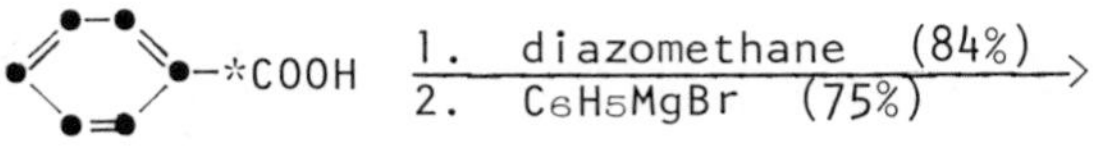
-*COOH
1. diazomethane (84%)
2. C6H5MgBr (75%)
(C6H5)3*COH

Triphenylcarbinol-α-^{14}C

1. $C_6H_5NH_2 \cdot HCl$, AcOH, Δ
2. $NaNO_2$, H_3PO_2, AcOH
→ $(C_6H_5)_4{*}C$ (17% overall)

Tetraphenylmethane-α-^{14}C
[1,1',1'',1'''-(Methane-^{14}C)tetrayltetrabis benzene]

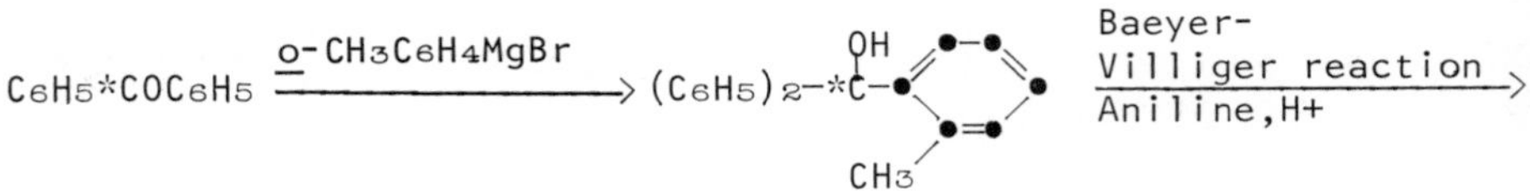
C6H5*COC6H5
o-CH3C6H4MgBr
(C6H5)2-*C-
OH
CH3
Baeyer-Villiger reaction
Aniline,H+

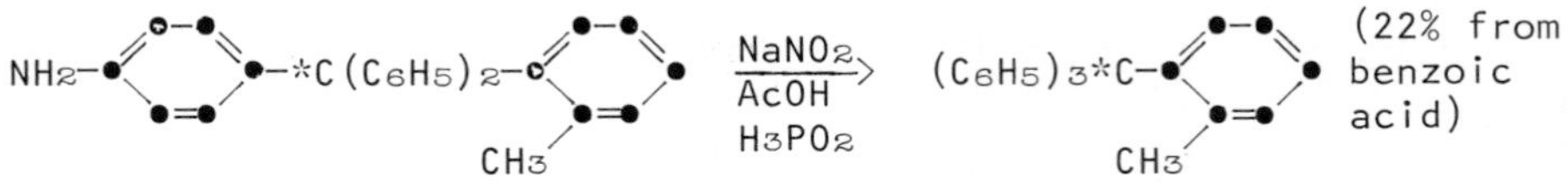
NH2-
-*C(C6H5)2-
CH3
NaNO2
AcOH
H3PO2
(C6H5)3*C-
CH3
(22% from benzoic acid)

o-Methyltetraphenylmethane-α-^{14}C

Similarly:

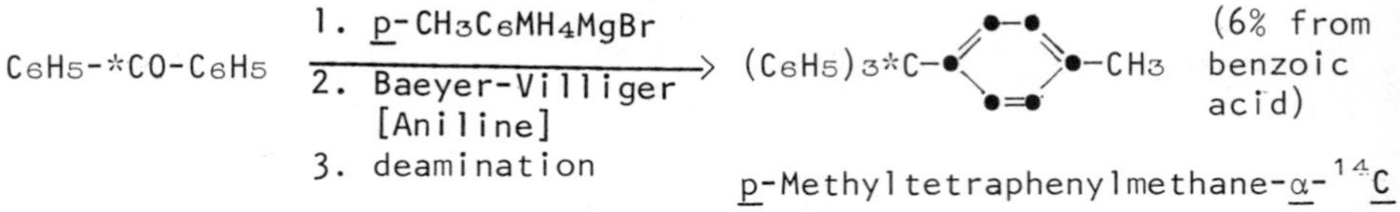
C6H5-*CO-C6H5
1. p-CH3C6MH4MgBr
2. Baeyer-Villiger [Aniline]
3. deamination
(C6H5)3*C-
-CH3
(6% from benzoic acid)

p-Methyltetraphenylmethane-α-^{14}C

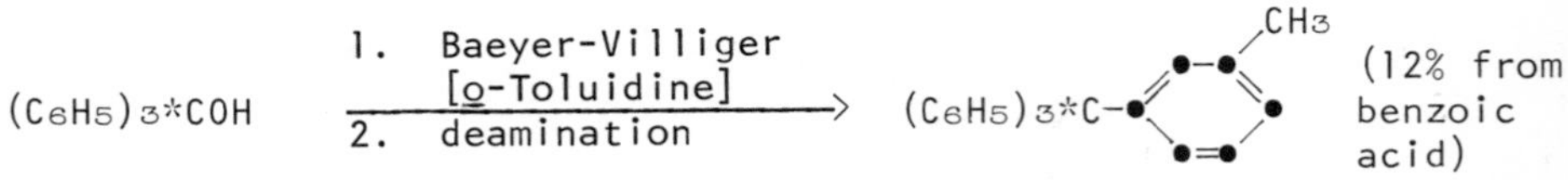
(C6H5)3*COH
1. Baeyer-Villiger [o-Toluidine]
2. deamination
(C6H5)3*C-
CH3
(12% from benzoic acid)

Triphenylcarbinol-α-^{14}C

m-Methyltetraphenylmethane-α-^{14}C

Other compounds similarly prepared:

o-Methoxytetraphenylmethane-α-^{14}C (3% from benzoic acid-7-^{14}C)
m-Methoxytetraphenylmethane-α-^{14}C (14%)
p-Methoxytetraphenylmethane-α-^{14}C (17%)
o-Chlorotetraphenylmethane-(phenyl-U-^{14}C) (31% from the carbinol)
m-Chlorotetraphenylmethane-α-^{14}C (39%)
p-Chlorotetraphenylmethane-α-^{14}C (24%)

T. Suehiro, A. Kanoya, T. Yamauchi, T. Komori, and S. Igeta, Tetrahedron, 24, 1551 (1968); Tetrahedron, 26, 963 (1970).

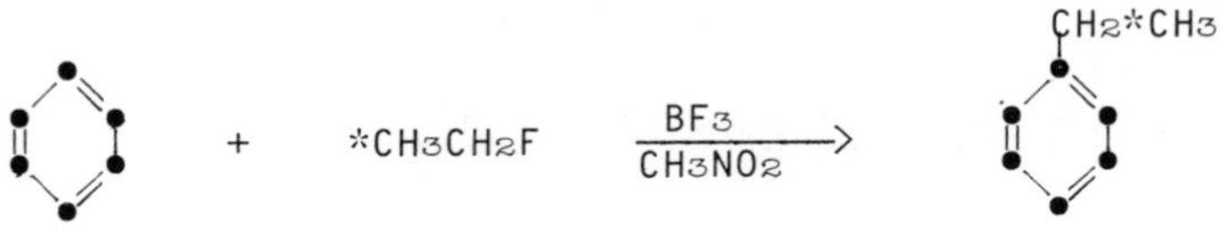
+
*CH3CH2F
BF3
CH3NO2
CH2*CH3

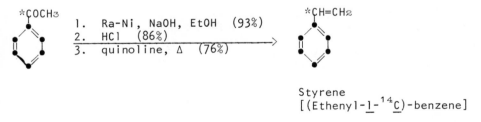

(Ethyl-2-^{14}C)-benzene

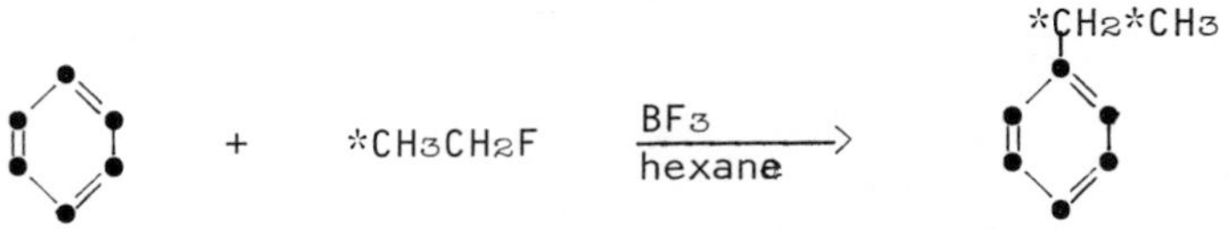
+
*CH3CH2F
BF3
hexane
*CH2*CH3

(Ethyl-1,2-^{14}C)-benzene

A. Natsubori and R. Nakane, J. Org. Chem., 35, 3372 (1970).

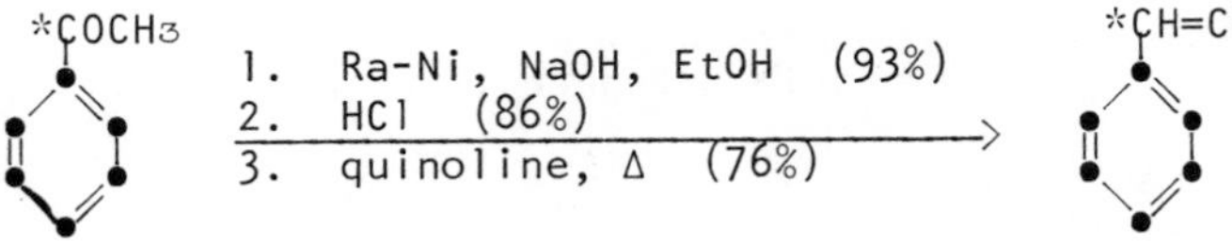
*COCH3
1. Ra-Ni, NaOH, EtOH (93%)
2. HCl (86%)
3. quinoline, Δ (76%)
*CH=CH2

Styrene
[(Ethenyl-1-^{14}C)-benzene]

G. M. Badger, S. D. Jolad, and T. M. Spotswood, Aust. J. Chem., 19, 95 (1966).

$C_6H_5CH{=}P(C_6H_5)_3$ + $H{*}CHO$ $\xrightarrow[\text{hexane}]{\Delta}$ 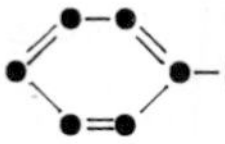 $-CH{=}{*}CH_2$ (31%)

Styrene
[(Ethenyl-2-^{14}C)-benzene]

C. A. Barson and D. K. Burns, J. Label. Compound. Radiopharm., 15, 339 (1978).

$C_6H_5CH_2{*}COOH$ ⟶ $C_6H_5CH_2{*}COC_6H_5$ $\xrightarrow[\text{2. } H_2SO_4 \text{ (52\%)}]{\text{1. } LiAlH_4,\ Et_2O \text{ (98\%)}}$

$C_6H_5{*}CH{=}{*}CHC_6H_5$ $\xrightarrow[\text{2. KOH, EtOH (82\%)}]{\text{1. } Br_2,\ Et_2O \text{ (68\%)}}$ $C_6H_5{*}C{\equiv}{*}CC_6H_5$

Stilbene

1,1'-(1,2-Ethynediyl-^{14}C)-bisbenzene

G. Modena, G. Scorrano, and U. Tonellato, J. Chem. Soc, Perkin Trans. II, 493 (1973).

$(C_6H_5)_3P$ $\xrightarrow[\text{HCl gas}]{H{*}CHO}$ $Cl{*}CH_2\overset{\oplus}{P}(C_6H_5)_3$ $Cl^{\ominus}$ $\xrightarrow{p\text{-}C_6H_5\text{-}C_6H_4COC_6H_5}$

(89% from $P(C_6H_5)_3$)

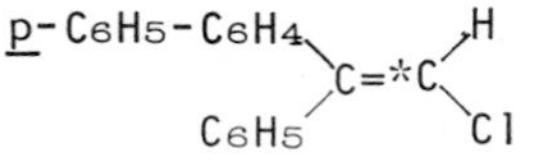
p-C6H5-C6H4
H
C=*C
C6H5
Cl

\+

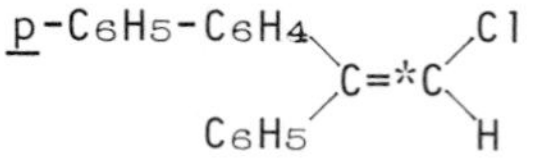
p-C6H5-C6H4
Cl
C=*C
C6H5
H

(E)-2-(4-Biphenyl)-1-chloro-2-phenylethylene-1-[14]C

(Z)-2-(4-Biphenylyl)-1-chloro-2-phenylethylene-1-[14]C

A 95% yield was obtained of a mixture (∿20% trans, ∿69% cis), separable by crystallization.

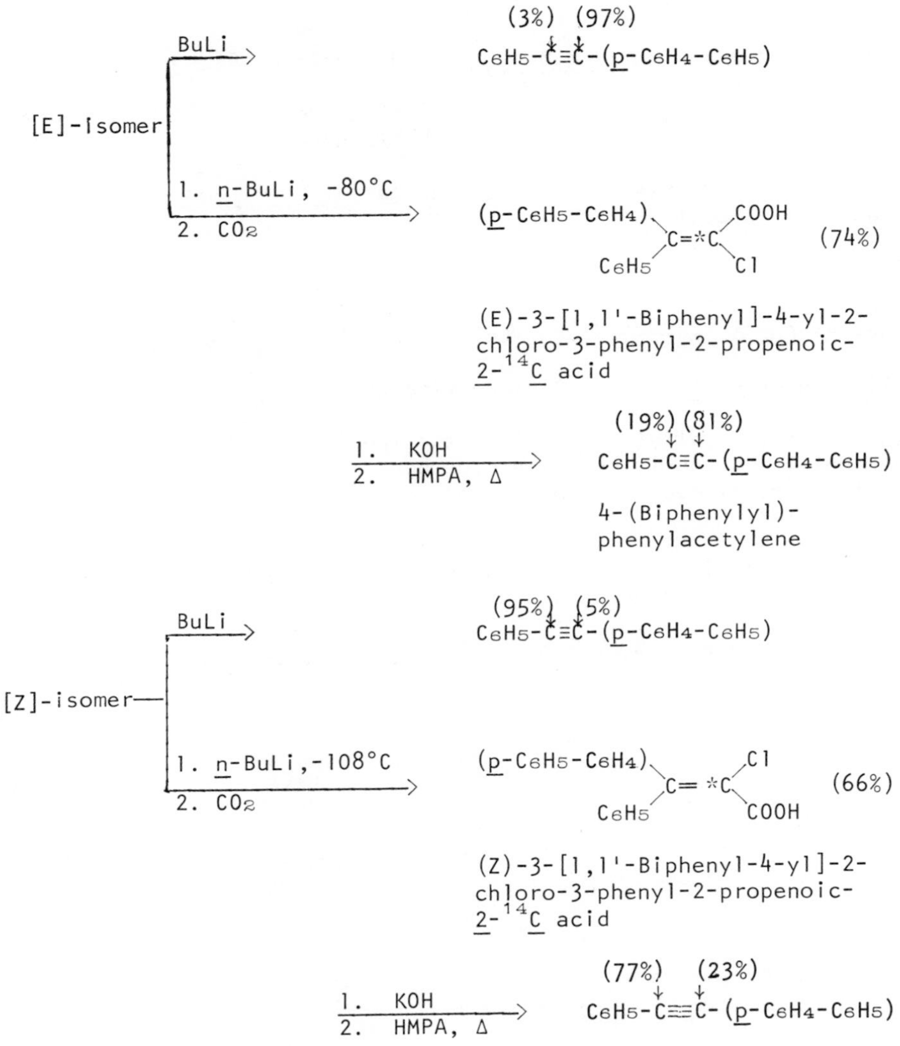

[E]-isomer
BuLi
(3%) (97%)
C6H5-C≡C-(p-C6H4-C6H5)
1. n-BuLi, -80°C
2. CO2
(p-C6H5-C6H4)
C6H5
C=*C
COOH
Cl
(74%)
(E)-3-[1,1'-Biphenyl]-4-yl-2-chloro-3-phenyl-2-propenoic-2-14C acid
1. KOH
2. HMPA, Δ
(19%) (81%)
C6H5-C≡C-(p-C6H4-C6H5)
4-(Biphenylyl)-phenylacetylene
[Z]-isomer
BuLi
(95%) (5%)
C6H5-C≡C-(p-C6H4-C6H5)
1. n-BuLi,-108°C
2. CO2
(p-C6H5-C6H4)
C6H5
C= *C
Cl
COOH
(66%)
(Z)-3-[1,1'-Biphenyl-4-yl]-2-chloro-3-phenyl-2-propenoic-2-14C acid
1. KOH
2. HMPA, Δ
(77%) (23%)
C6H5-C≡C-(p-C6H4-C6H5)

Stereoselective migration of the aryl substituent trans to the halogen atom is observed (position of the label was determined by degradation reactions).

G. Köbrich, G. Reitz, and U. Schumaker, Chem. Ber., 105, 1674 (1972); see also, G. Kobrich, H. Trapp, and I. Hornke, Chem. Ber., 100, 961 (1967).

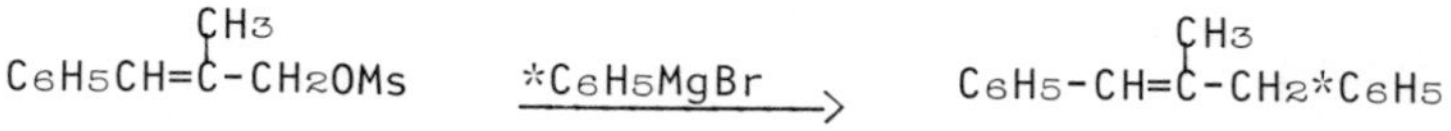

$$CH_3$$
$$C_6H_5CH=C-CH_2OMs \quad \xrightarrow{*C_6H_5MgBr} \quad C_6H_5-CH=C-CH_2*C_6H_5$$
$$CH_3$$

1,1'-(2-Methyl-1,3-propenyldiyl-
bis(benzene-^{14}C)

J. M. Gamboa, C. Sáa, and J. M. Figurea, J. Chem. Soc., Perkin
Trans. II, 2025 (1973).

$$CH_2=CH-*CH_2Cl \quad \xrightarrow[Et_2O]{C_6H_5Li} \quad CH_2=CHCH_2C_6H_5 \ (24\%) \ +$$

$$CH_2$$
$$| \quad CH-C_6H_5 \quad (19\%)$$
$$CH_2$$

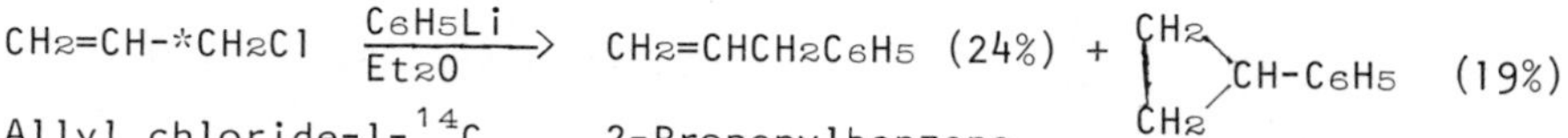

Allyl chloride-1-^{14}C 2-Propenylbenzene   Benzenecyclopropane

(prepared from allyl   (24% of the label   (50% of the label
alcohol-1-^{14}C; position   is at the benzilic   is at the benzilic
of label confirmed by   position)   position)
ozonolysis)

The position of the label was determined by degradation reactions;
cyclopropene intermediates are proposed.

R. M. Magid and J. G. Welch, J. Amer. Chem. Soc., 90, 5211 (1968).

$$\begin{array}{c} CH_3 \\ \diagdown \\ H \diagup \end{array} C=C \begin{array}{c} H \\ \diagup \\ \diagdown CHO \end{array} \quad \xrightarrow{*CH_3MgI} \quad \begin{array}{c} CH_3 \\ \diagdown \\ H \diagup \end{array} C=C \begin{array}{c} H \\ \diagup \\ \diagdown CHOH*CH_3 \end{array}$$

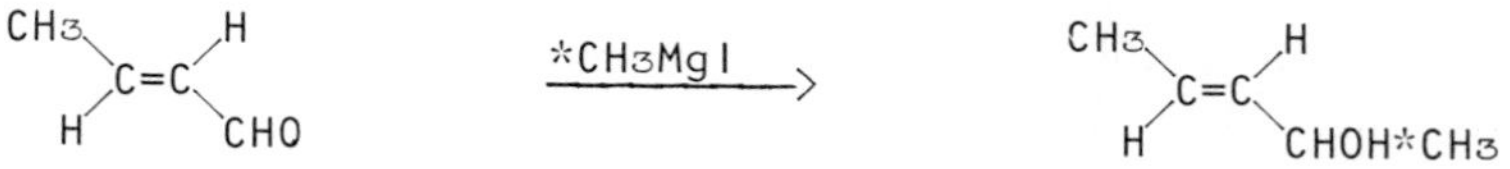

(>99.5% of ^{14}C at position 5
confirmed by ozonolysis)

$$\xrightarrow[pyr]{POCl_3} \quad \begin{array}{c} *CH_3 \\ \diagdown \\ H \diagup \end{array} C=C \begin{array}{c} H \\ \diagup \\ \diagdown CHCl-*CH_3 \end{array} \quad (69\%)$$

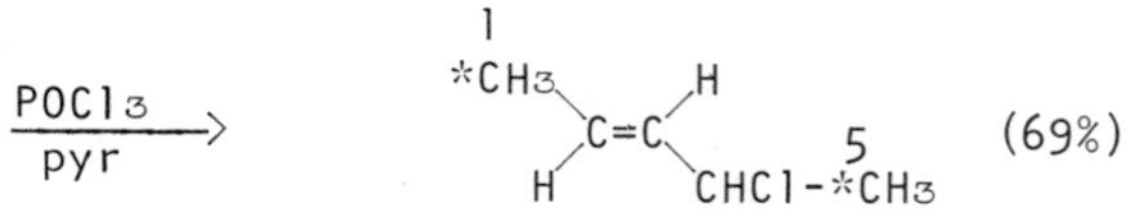

(E)-4-Chloro-2-pentene-1,5-^{14}C

(58.1% of label is at C_5,
41.9% of label is at C_1;
determined by ozonolysis)

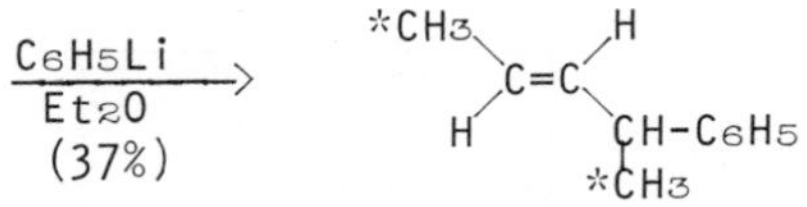

C_6H_5Li
Et_2O
(37%)
*CH_3
H
C=C
H
CH-C_6H_5
*CH_3

(E)-(1-Methyl-^{14}C)-(2-butenyl) benzene-4-^{14}C

(50% of label is at C_1 and 50% at C_5; equal amounts of α and γ attack; a concerted mechanism is suggested.)

R. M. Magid, E. C. Nieh, and R. D. Gandour, J. Org. Chem., 36, 2099 (1971).

7-4 Polynuclear Aromatic Hydrocarbons

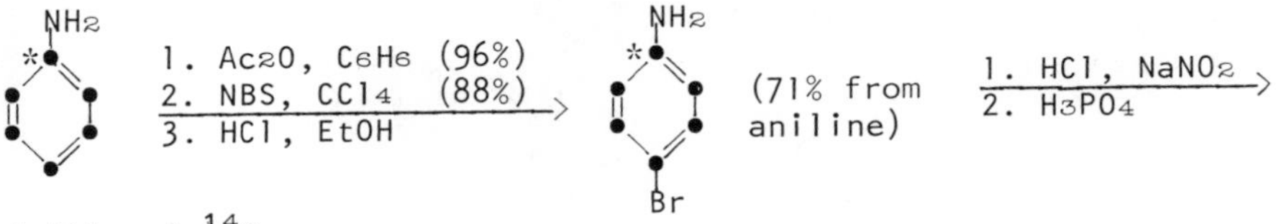

NH_2
1. Ac_2O, C_6H_6 (96%)
2. NBS, CCl_4 (88%)
3. HCl, EtOH
NH_2
Br
(71% from aniline)
1. HCl, $NaNO_2$
2. H_3PO_4

Aniline-1-^{14}C

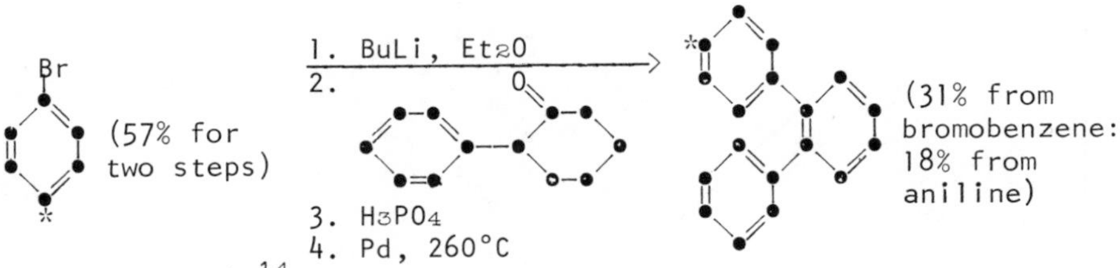

Br
(57% for two steps)
1. BuLi, Et_2O
2.
O
3. H_3PO_4
4. Pd, 260°C
(31% from bromobenzene: 18% from aniline)

Bromobenzene-4-^{14}C

1,1':2':1''-Terphenyl-4-^{14}C

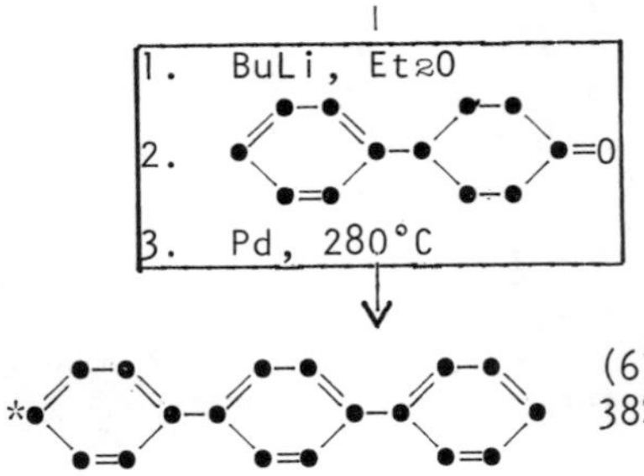

1. BuLi, Et_2O
2.
=O
3. Pd, 280°C

(67% from bromobenzene; 38% from aniline)

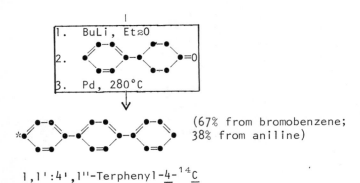

1,1':4',1''-Terphenyl-4-^{14}C

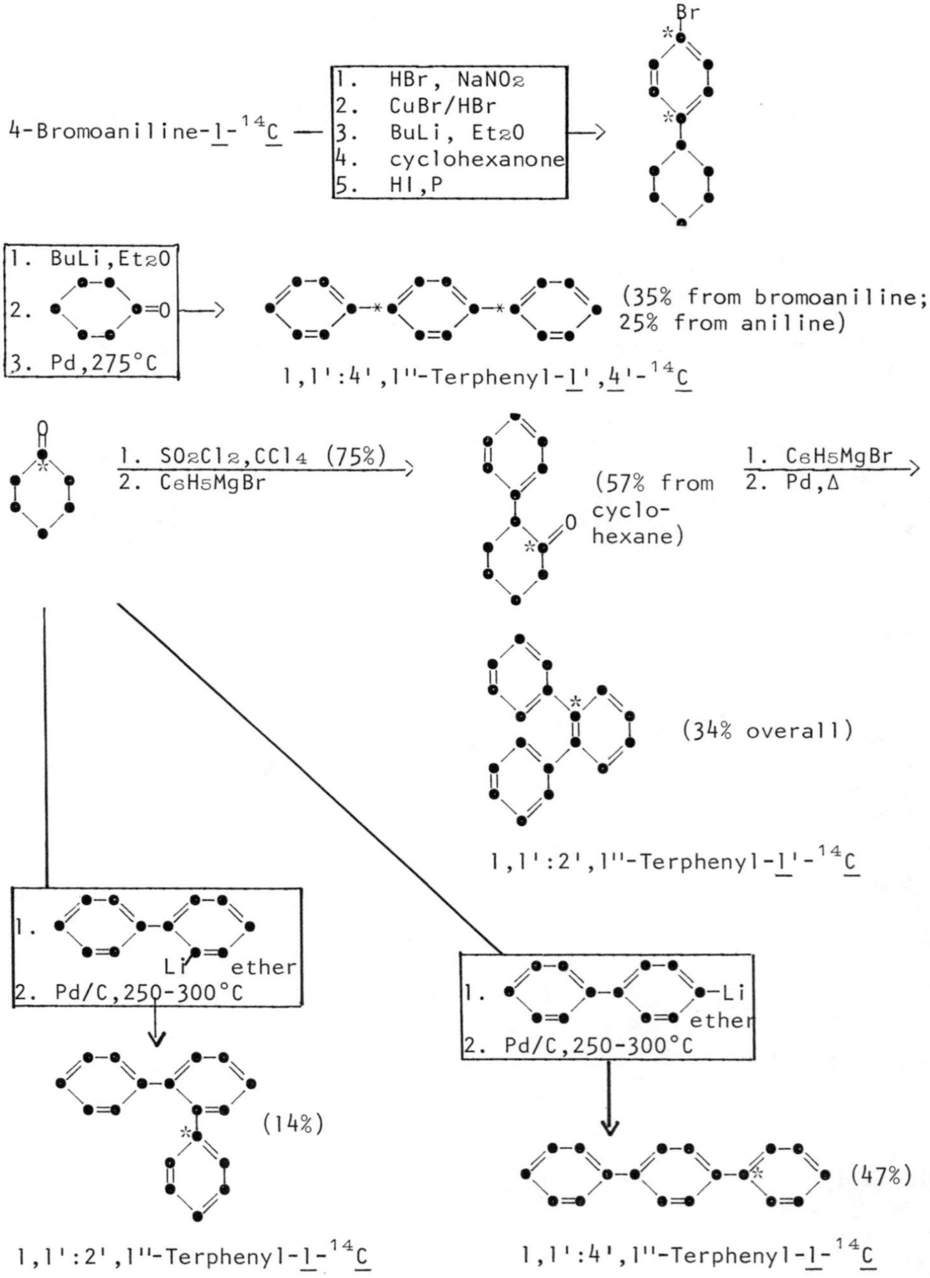
4-Bromoaniline-1-14C
1. HBr, NaNO2
2. CuBr/HBr
3. BuLi, Et2O
4. cyclohexanone
5. HI,P
Br
1. BuLi,Et2O
2.
3. Pd,275°C
(35% from bromoaniline; 25% from aniline)
1,1':4',1''-Terphenyl-1',4'-14C
1. SO2Cl2,CCl4 (75%)
2. C6H5MgBr
(57% from cyclohexane)
1. C6H5MgBr
2. Pd,Δ
(34% overall)
1,1':2',1''-Terphenyl-1'-14C
Li
ether
2. Pd/C,250-300°C
(14%)
1,1':2',1''-Terphenyl-1-14C
Li
ether
2. Pd/C,250-300°C
(47%)
1,1':4',1''-Terphenyl-1-14C

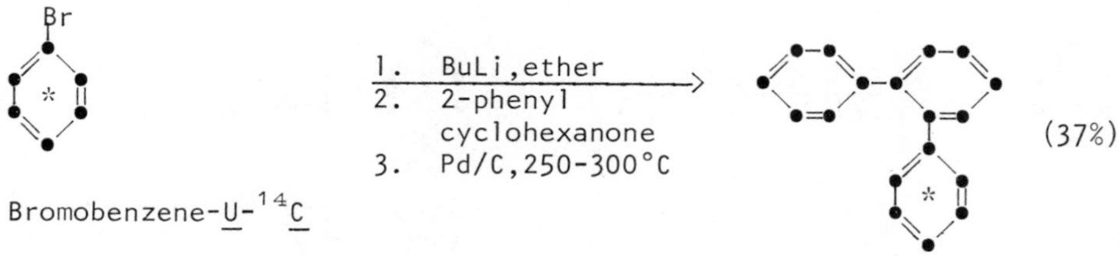
Br
1. BuLi,ether
2. 2-phenyl cyclohexanone
3. Pd/C,250-300°C
(37%)

Bromobenzene-U-^{14}C

1,1':2',1''-Terphenyl-(1,2,3,4,5,6)-^{14}C

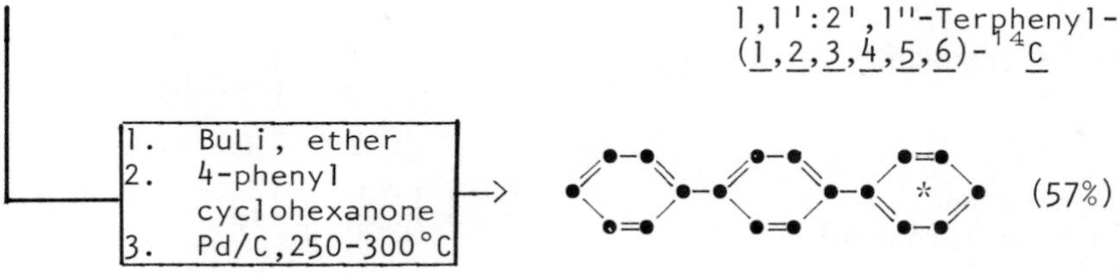
1. BuLi, ether
2. 4-phenyl cyclohexanone
3. Pd/C,250-300°C
(57%)

1,1':4',1''-Terphenyl-(1,2,3,4,5,6)-^{14}C

Similarly:

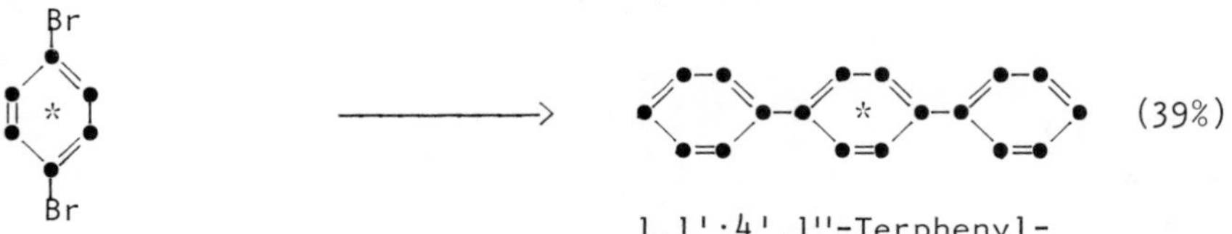
Br
Br
(39%)

1,4-Dibromo benzene-U-^{14}C

1,1':4',1''-Terphenyl-(1',2',3',4',5',6')-^{14}C

W. Hafferl, E. Fischer, and G. Juppe, J. Label. Compounds, 1, 169 (1965); W Hafferl and G. Juppe, J. Label. Compounds, 4, 80 (1968).

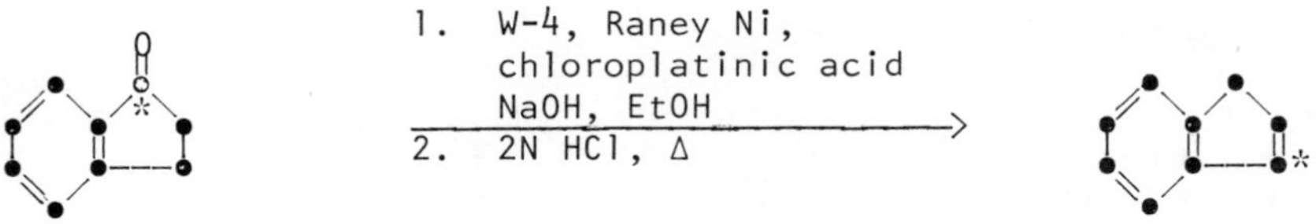
O
1. W-4, Raney Ni, chloroplatinic acid NaOH, EtOH
2. 2N HCl, Δ

1H-Indene-3-^{14}C

G. M. Badger, S. D. Jolad, and T. M. Spotswood, Aust. J. Chem., 19, 85 (1966).

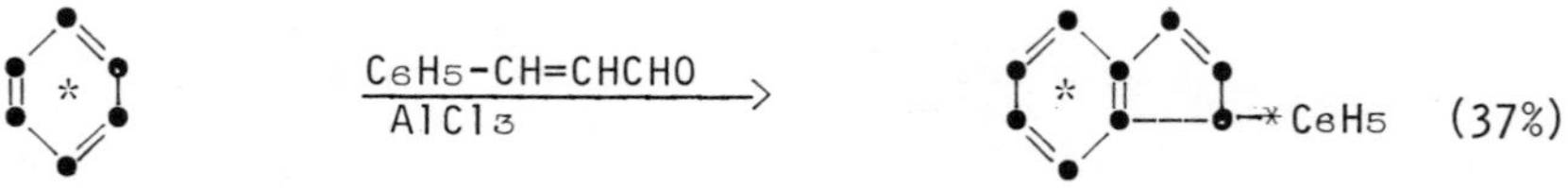
C6H5-CH=CHCHO
AlCl3
C6H5
(37%)

3-(Phenyl-U-^{14}C)-1H-indene-(aryl-U-^{14}C)

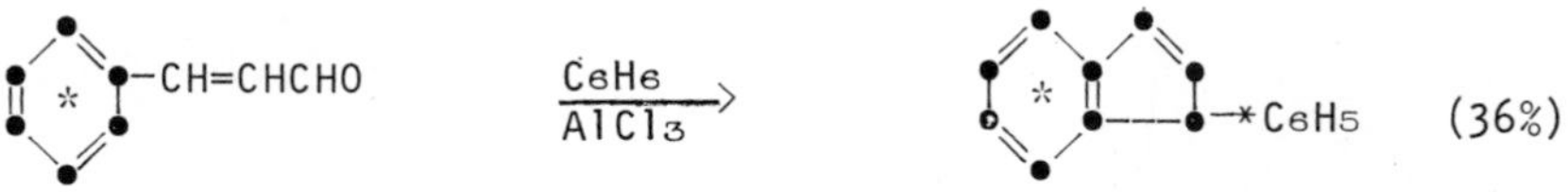
-CH=CHCHO
C6H6
AlCl3
C6H5
(36%)

Cinnamaldehyde [3-Phenylpropenal-(ring-^{14}C)]

3-(Phenyl-U-^{14}C)-1H-indene-(aryl-U-^{14}C)

Both aryl groups in the product become labeled regardless of which labeled starting material is used; a mechanism is proposed.

A. Hessing and H.-W. Schneeberger, Chem. Ber., 105, 2447 (1972).

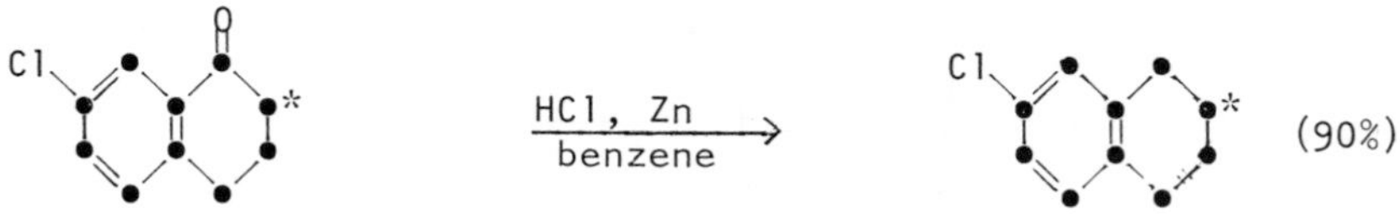
Cl
O
HCl, Zn
benzene
Cl
(90%)

7-Chloro-3,4-dihydro-1(2H)naphthamenone-2-^{14}C

T2,catalyst
(85%)
1. DDQ,C6H6,Δ (80%)
2. T2,catalyst (80%)
T
T

Tetralin [1,2,3,4-Tetrahydronaphthalene-2-^{14}C,7-t]

Naphthalene-2-^{14}C,7-t

Similarly:

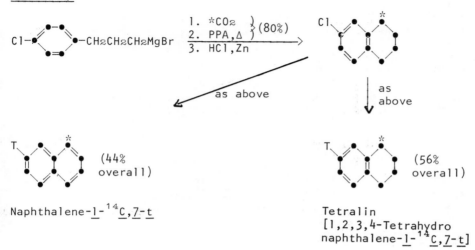

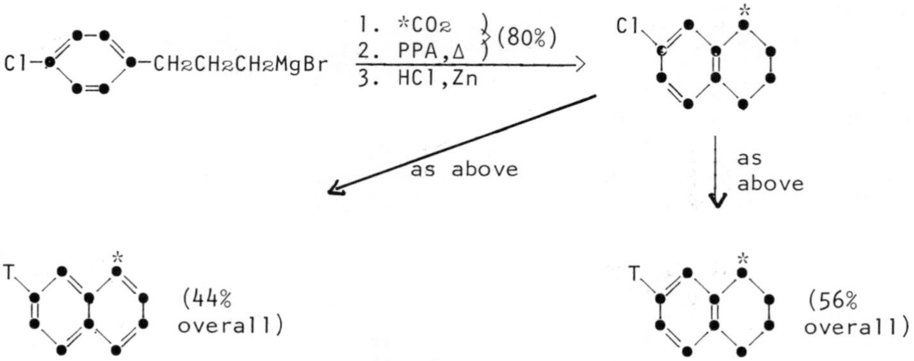
Cl
$CH_2CH_2CH_2MgBr$
1. $*CO_2$
2. PPA,Δ
(80%)
3. HCl,Zn
Cl
as above
as above
T
(44% overall)
T
(56% overall)

Naphthalene-1-^{14}C,7-t

Tetralin [1,2,3,4-Tetrahydro naphthalene-1-^{14}C,7-t]

W. Den Hollander, P. J. van der Jagt, and B. van Zanten, J. Label. Compounds, 8, 3 (1972).

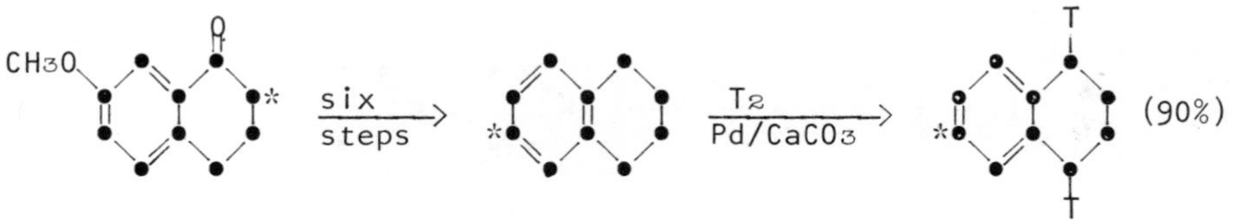
CH_3O
O
six steps
T_2
$Pd/CaCO_3$
T
T
(90%)

3,4-Dihydro-7-methoxy-1(2H)-naphthalenone-2-^{14}C

Tetralin-6-^{14}C

Tetralin-6-^{14}C, 1,4-t

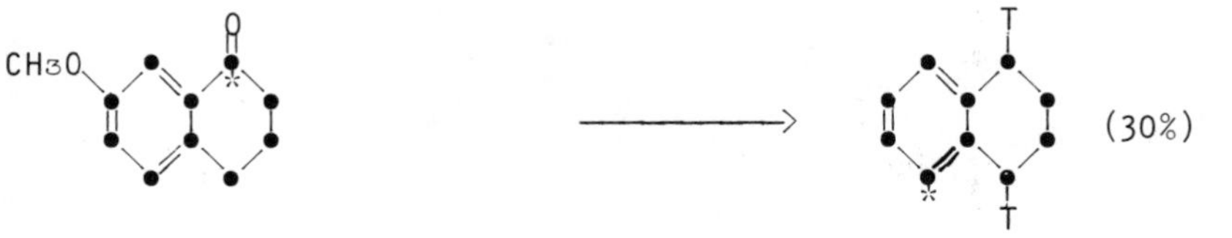
CH_3O
O
T
T
(30%)

3,4-Dihydro-7-methoxy-1(2H)-naphthalenone-1-^{14}C

Tetralin-5-^{14}C,1,4-t

Decalin-1-^{14}C,7-t and decalin-2,7-t were also prepared; the relative positions of label were confirmed by degradation reactions.

P. J. van der Jagt, W. den Hollander, and B. van Zanten, Tetrahedron, 28, 1779 (1972); Tetrahedron, 27, 1049 (1971).

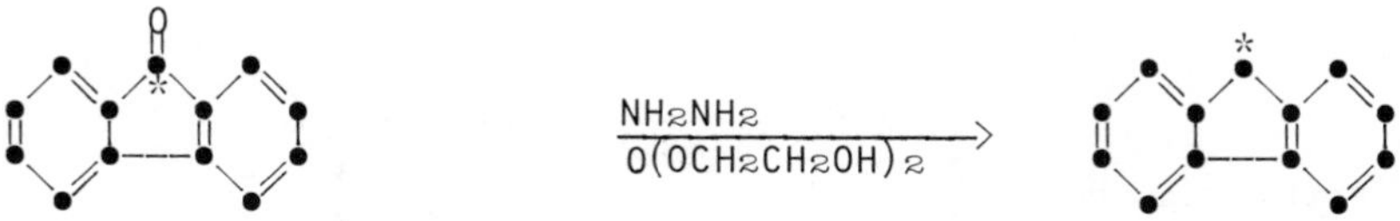
O
*
NH_2NH_2
$O(OCH_2CH_2OH)_2$
*

9H-Fluoren-9-one-9-^{14}C

9H-Fluorene-9-^{14}C

Nguyen-Hoang-Nam, H. Hoellinger, M. Herbert, Nguyen-Dat-Xuong, and L. Pichat, J. Label. Compounds, 6, 99 (1970).

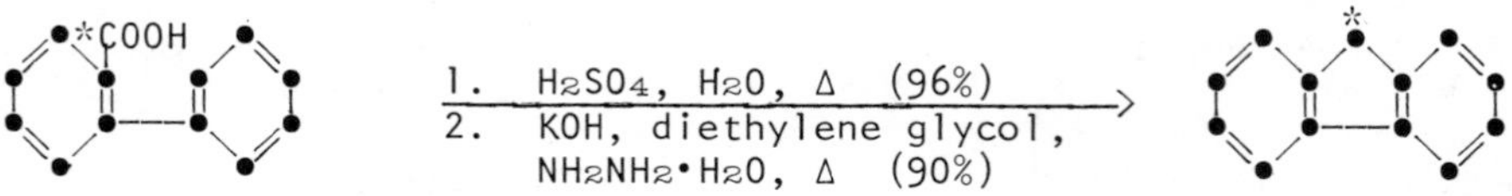
*COOH
1. H_2SO_4, H_2O, Δ (96%)
2. KOH, diethylene glycol, $NH_2NH_2 \cdot H_2O$, Δ (90%)
*

2-Phenylbenzoic-7-^{14}C acid

9H-Fluorene-9-^{14}C

V. P. Gaur and A. Wacker, J. Label. Compounds, 9, 281 (1973).

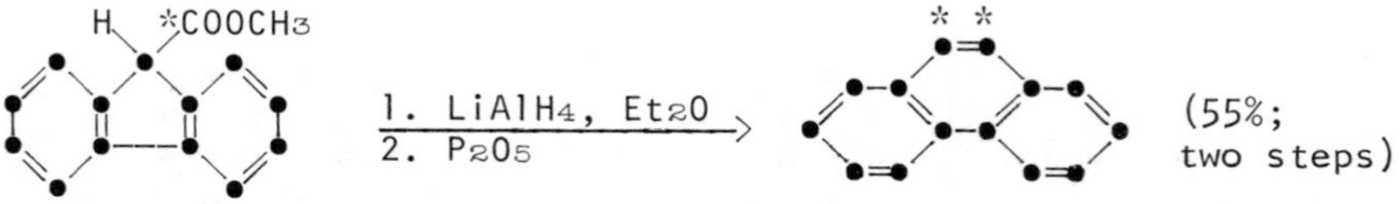
H
*$COOCH_3$
1. $LiAlH_4$, Et_2O
2. P_2O_5
* *
(55%; two steps)

Phenanthrene-9,10-^{14}C

K. D. Göhler and H. R. Schütte, Z. Chem., 10, 190 (1970).

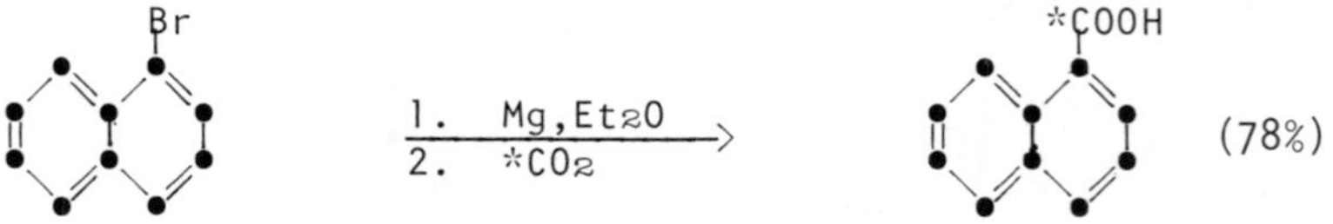
Br
1. Mg, Et_2O
2. *CO_2
*COOH
(78%)

1-Naphthalene carboxylic-^{14}C acid

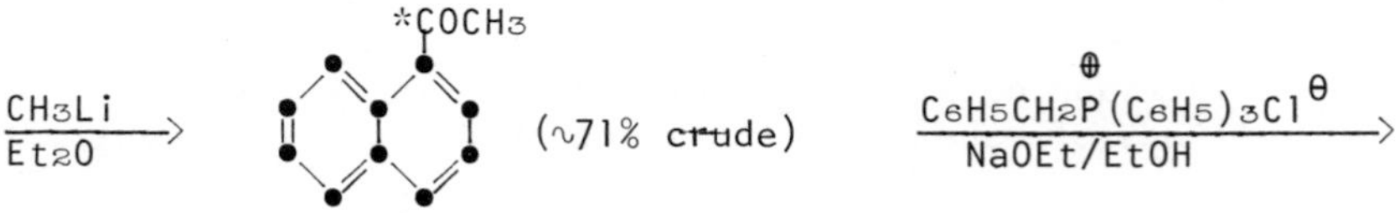
CH_3Li
Et_2O
*$COCH_3$
(~71% crude)
$C_6H_5CH_2\overset{\oplus}{P}(C_6H_5)_3Cl^{\ominus}$
NaOEt/EtOH

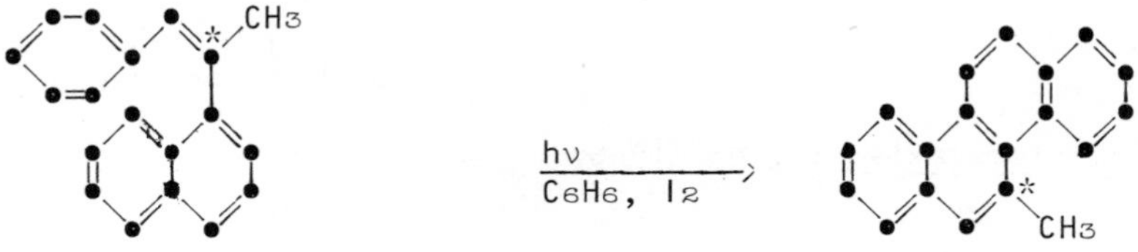
CH3
hν
C6H6, I2
CH3

(30%)

[37% yield of a mixture of cis (79%) and trans (21%) isomers]

5-Methylchrysene-5-^{14}C

L. Weiss, M. Loy, S. S. Hecht, and D. Hoffmann, J. Label. Compound. Radiopharm., 14, 119 (1978).

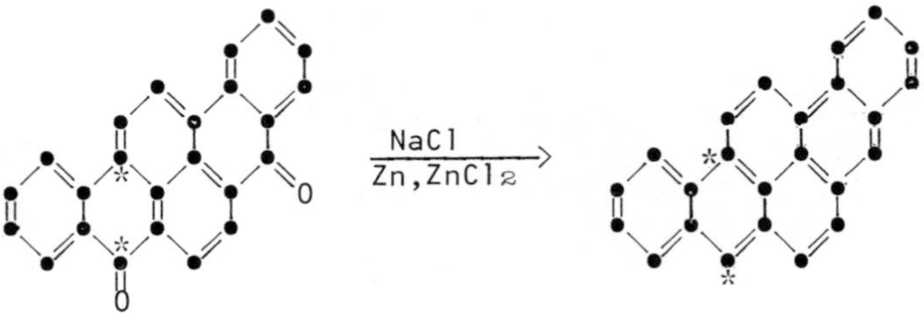
O
NaCl
Zn,ZnCl2
O

(35%; 5% based on phthalic anhydride-7-^{14}C)

Benzo[rst]pentaphene-5,8-dione-8,12b-^{14}C

Benzo[rst]pentaphene-8,12b-^{14}C

E. Boger and P. Bernfeld, J. Label. Compounds, 1, 109 (1965).

Substituted Hydrocarbons

7-5 Aliphatic Halides

$$*CH_3CO*CH_3 \xrightarrow[H_2O,\Delta]{Ca(OCl)_2} *CHCl_3 \quad (\sim 25\%)$$

Chloroform
[Trichloromethane-^{14}C]

$\xrightarrow[\text{dioxane}]{\text{LiAlH}_4}$ $*CH_2Cl_2$ (~70%)

Dichloromethane-^{14}C

H. E. Dobbs, Atompraxis, 12, 83 (1966).

$*CH_3CO*CH_3$ $\xrightarrow[H_2O]{\text{NaI, NaOCl}}$ $*CHI_3$ (96%) $\xrightarrow[H_2O]{Ag_2O_3\text{, NaOH}}$ $*CH_2I_2$ (90%)

Acetone-1,3-^{14}C | Iodoform-^{14}C | Diiodomethane-^{14}C

A. R. Jones, J. Label. Compounds, 11, 77 (1975).

$*CH_2{=}*CH_2 + Cl_2$ $\xrightarrow[CCl_4]{\text{Zn (trace)}}$ $Cl*CH_2*CH_2Cl$ $\xrightarrow[h\nu]{Cl_2}$

1,2-Dichloroethane-1,2-^{14}C

(67% chemical yield;
35% radiochemical yield)

$Cl*CH_2*CHCl_2$

1,1,2-Trichloroethane-1,2-^{14}C

(60% chemical yield;
45% radiochemical yield)

A. P. M. van der Veek and A. C. Besemer, J. Label. Compounds, 11, 149 (1975).

CH_3SCH_3 $\xrightarrow{\text{1. BuLi, TMEDA; 2. }*CO_2\text{ (83\%); 3. LiAlH}_4\text{, Et}_2\text{O; 4. trioctylphosphine, CCl}_4}$ $CH_3SCH_2*CH_2Cl$

1. BuLi, TMEDA
2. $*CO_2$ (83%)
3. $LiAlH_4$, Et_2O
4. trioctylphosphine, CCl_4

1-Chloro-2-(methylthio)ethane-1-^{14}C

L. Pichat and J. P. Beaucourt, J. Label. Compounds, 10, 103 (1974).

$Cl{*}CH_2{*}CH_2Cl$ —(gas chromatographic generator)→ $*CH_2{=}*CHCl$ (∼46%)

1,2-Dichloroethane-^{14}C → Vinyl chloride [Chloroethene-1,2-^{14}C]

E. R. Wagner, W. M. Muelder, P. G. Watanabe, R. E. Hefner, Jr., W. H. Braun, and P. J. Gehring, J. Label. Compounds, 11, 535 (1975).

$*CH_2{=}*CH_2$ —($SbCl_5$)→ $Cl{*}CH_2{*}CH_2Cl$ —(NaOH / MeOH)→ $*CH_2{=}*CHCl$

Chloroethene-U-^{14}C

$*CH{\equiv}*CH$ —($SbCl_5$)→ $Cl_2{*}CH{*}CHCl_2$ —($Ca(OH)_2$, Δ)→ $*CHCl{=}*CCl_2$

Trichloroethene-U-^{14}C

W. J. Criddle, G. S. Park, D. Robertson, and W. H. J. Thomas, J. Label. Compounds, 8, 601 (1972).

$*CCl_3CCl_2{*}CCl_3$ —(Catalytic or thermal cracking)→ $*CCl_2{=}*CCl_2$ + $*CCl_4$

Octachloropropane-1,3-^{14}C → Tetrachloroethylene-^{14}C + Tetrachloromethane-^{14}C

F. Boberg, H. Khalaf, and K. Habenstein, J. Label. Compounds, 7, 155 (1971).

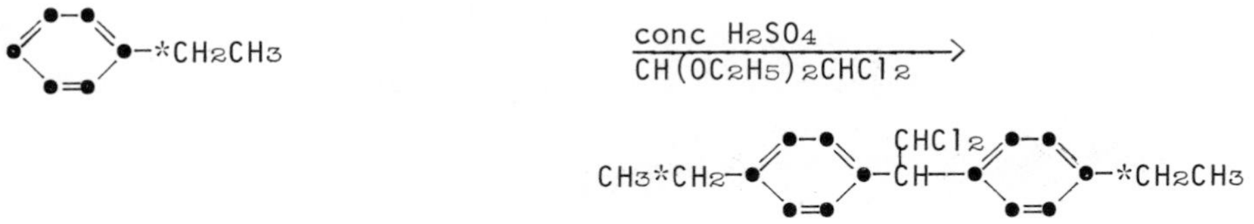

–*CH2CH3
conc H2SO4
CH(OC2H5)2CHCl2
CHCl2
CH3*CH2–
–CH–
–*CH2CH3

Perthane
[1,1'-(2,2-Dichloroethylidene)-bis[4-(ethyl-1-^{14}C)-benzene]

An 88% crude yield was obtained containing 74% p,p'-isomer, 12% o,p'-isomer, and 14% impurities; the p,p'-isomer was obtained in 95% purity in 18% yield by recrystallizations.

S. C. Halladay, W. P. Cahill, and G. W. Ware, J. Agr. Food Chem., 20, 541 (1972).

$CH_3CH_2{*}CH_2Cl \xrightarrow[0°C]{AlCl_3} CH_3CH_2CH_2Cl$ (22%)(7%)(71%) + $CH_3CHClCH_3$ (1.4-3.0%)

1-Chloropropane-^{14}C 2-Chloropropane-^{14}C

The isotopic scrambling data was determined by degradation studies; equilibrating protonated cyclopropane intermediates are proposed.

C. C. Lee and D. J. Woodcock, J. Amer. Chem. Soc., 92, 5992 (1970).

${*}CHCl_3 \xrightarrow[AlCl_3]{CCl_2=CCl_2} Cl_2{*}CHCCl_2CCl_3 \xrightarrow[2.\ Cl_2]{1.\ KOH,\ CH_3OH} {*}CCl_3CCl_2{*}CCl_3$

Chloroform-^{14}C Octachloropropane-1,3-^{14}C

F. Boberg, H. Khalaf, and K. Habenstein, J. Label. Compounds, 7, 155 (1971).

$CH_3{*}CH_2OH \xrightarrow{8\ steps} CCl_3{*}CCl_2CCl_3$

Octachloropropane-2-^{14}C

F. Boberg, K. Habenstein, and R. Voss, Z. Naturforsch., 32b, 668 (1977).

${*}COOC_2H_5{-}CH_2{-}{*}COOC_2H_5 \xrightarrow[Et_2O]{LiAlH_4} {*}CH_2OH{-}CH_2{-}{*}CH_2OH$ (84%) $\xrightarrow[2.\ 48\%\ HBr,\ \Delta]{1.\ Ac_2O,\ \Delta}$

Propane-1,3-diol-1,3-^{14}C

$^*CH_2Br-CH_2-^*CH_2Br$ (87%)

1,3-Dibromopropane-1,3-^{14}C

Diethyl malonate-2-^{14}C or -U-^{14}C can be used to obtain any desired labeled product.

A. R. Jones, J. Label. Compounds, 11, 77 (1975).

$^*CCl_2{=}CCl{-}^*COOH \xrightarrow[Cu/CrO_3]{quinoline} {}^*CCl_2{=}CHCl \xrightarrow[AlCl_3]{CHCl_3} CHCl_2{-}CHCl{-}^*CCl_3$

Trichloroacrylic-1,3-^{14}C acid

$\xrightarrow[MeOH]{KOH} CHCl_2CCl{=}^*CCl_2 \xrightarrow{Cl_2} CHCl_2CCl_2{}^*CCl_3$

$\xrightarrow[MeOH]{KOH} CCl_2{=}CCl{-}^*CCl_3$

Hexachloro-1-propene-3-^{14}C

F. Boberg, H. Khalaf, and K. Kirchnoff, J. Label. Compounds, 7, 247, 255 (1971).

$HC{\equiv}C{-}^*COOH$ → (1. diazomethane; 2. $LiAlH_4$, Et_2O (50%); 3. PBr_3, pyr (50%)) → $HC{\equiv}C{-}^*CH_2Br$

Propynoic-1-^{14}C acid

$\xrightarrow[CH_3COOH]{HBr} {}^*CH_2{=}CBr{-}^*CH_2Br$

2,3-Dibromopropene-1,3-^{14}C

[Label scrambling at this step can be controlled by reaction time (3-hr optimum)]

C. George, E. W. Gill, and J. A. Hudson, J. Chem. Soc. (C), 74 (1970).

$CH_3CH_2CH_2MgCl$ —(1. $*CO_2$; 2. $LiAlH_4$; 3. TsCl; 4. $CaCl_2$, ethylene glycol (75%))→ $CH_3CH_2CH_2{*}CH_2Cl$

1-Chlorobutane-1-^{14}C

Degradation reactions indicated all of the ^{14}C label was located at position 1. Subsequent treatment of the 1-chlorobutane-1-^{14}C with $AlCl_3$ gave isomeric chlorobutanes consisting of the n-butyl (negligible scrambling), sec-butyl (extensive scrambling over all four positions), and small amounts of the t-butyl and iso-butyl isomers. Successive 1,2-hydride shifts were proposed, rather than protonated methyl cyclopropanes, to account for the scrambling.

C. C. Lee and I. Y. Zea Ponce, Can. J. Chem., 50, 3179 (1972).

$(C_6H_5)_2CH{-}{*}CH_2CH{=}CH_2$ —(1. KNH_2, NH_3/Et_2O; 2. CH_2Cl_2)→ $ClCH_2C(C_6H_5)_2{*}CH_2CH{=}CH_2$

1,1'-(3-Butenylidene-2-^{14}C)-bisbenzene → 1,1'-[1-(Chloromethyl)-3-butenylidene-2-^{14}C] bisbenzene

An overall yield of 72% was reported for the unlabeled reactions; degradation reactions indicated 98% of the activity was at the C-2 position. The compound was used in mechanistic studies of the rearrangements of alkali metal salts.

E. Grovenstein, Jr. and A. B. Cottingham, J. Amer. Chem. Soc., 99, 1881 (1977).

$*CCl_2{=}CCl{-}{*}CCl_3$ + $CHCl{=}CHCl$ —($AlCl_3$, CH_2Cl_2)→

Hexachloropropene-1,3-^{14}C (cis)

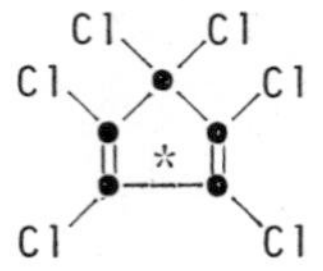
Cl
Cl
Cl
Cl
*
Cl
Cl

Hexachlorocyclopentadiene-U-^{14}C

E. Zörkendörfer, J. Label. Compounds, 9, 463 (1973).

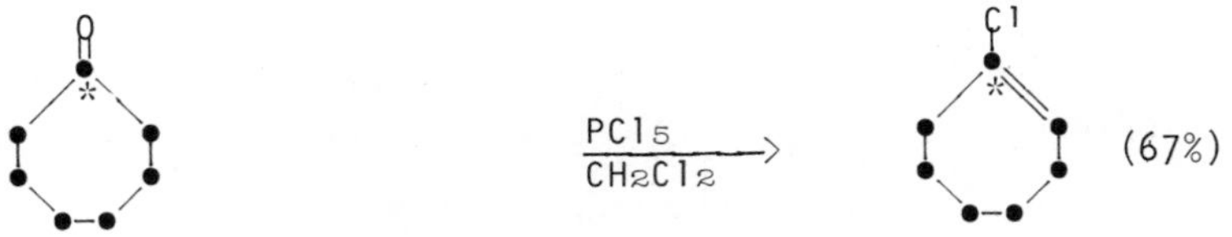
PCl5
CH2Cl2
(67%)

Cycloheptanone-1-^{14}C 1-Chlorocycloheptene-1-^{14}C

A. T. Bottini, K. A. Frost, II, B. R. Anderson, and V. Dev, *Tetrahedron*, **29**, 1975 (1973).

7-6 Aromatic Halides

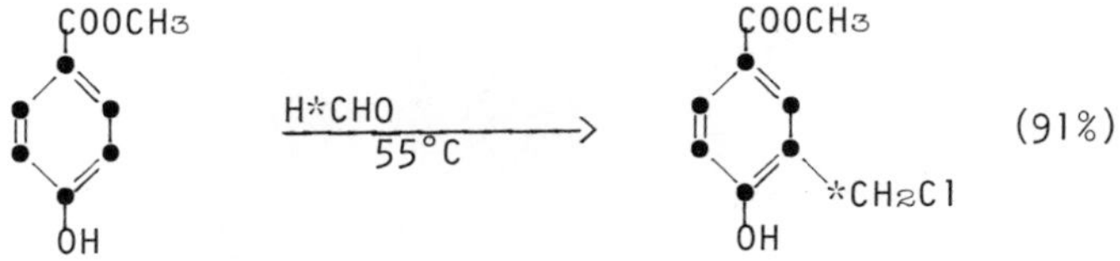
COOCH3
OH
H*CHO
55°C
COOCH3
*CH2Cl
OH
(91%)

3-(Chloromethyl-^{14}C)-4-hydroxy-benzeneacetic acid methyl ester

J. Engler and E. Kasztreiner, *J. Label. Compounds*, **9**, 237 (1973).

$C_6H_5CH_2{*}COOH$ $\xrightarrow[\text{3. } Br_2]{\text{1. } LiAlH_4\text{, ether; 2. KOH, S}}$ $C_6H_5CHBr{*}CH_2Br$

Benzene acetic-1-^{14}C acid

Styrene dibromide [(1,2-Dibromoethenyl-2-^{14}C)-benzene]

C. A. Barson, R. G. C. Henbest, and J. C. Robb, *Trans Faraday Soc.*, **67**, 2365 (1971).

$C_6H_5{*}CHO$ $\xrightarrow[\text{reaction}]{\text{Perkin}}$ $C_6H_5{*}CH{=}CHCOOH$ (50%)

trans

1. Br_2
2. $NaOH/H_2O$

$C_6H_5{}^*CH{=}CHBr$ ⟵ trans ⟶ $C_6H_5{}^*CH{=}CHBr$

1. Br_2
2. $NaHCO_3$, acetone

trans-β-Bromostyrene
[(E)-(2-Bromoethenyl-1-^{14}C)benzene]

cis-β-Bromostyrene
[(Z)-(2-Bromoethenyl-1-^{14}C)benzene]

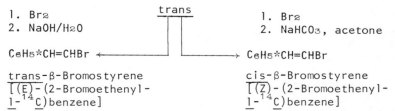

The products were used for hydride-shift mechanistic studies.

C. C. Lee and E. C. F. Ko, J. Org. Chem., 40, 2132 (1975).

$C_6H_5CH_2{}^*COOC_2H_5$ —(1. C_6H_5MgBr, Et_2O, Δ (66%); 2. Br_2, AcOH (60%))⟶ $C_6H_5\text{-}CBr{=}{}^*C(C_6H_5)_2$

Triphenylvinyl-bromide
[1,1',1''-(1-Bromo-1-ethenyl-2-ylidene-2-^{14}C) trisbenzene]

C. C. Lee, A. J. Cessna, B. A. Davis, and M. Oka, Can. J. Chem., 52, 2679 (1974); ibid., 56, 2459 (1978).

$C_6H_5{}^*COOH$ —(1. $SOCl_2$; 2. CH_3OH; 3. NH_2NH_2; 4. $C_6H_5SO_2Cl$, pyr)⟶ $C_6H_5{}^*CONHNHSO_2C_6H_5$ (97%)

—(1. Na_2CO_3, $HOCH_2CH_2OH$, 165°C; 2. $SOCl_2$)⟶ $C_6H_5{}^*CHCl_2$ (37% from benzoic acid)

—(1. t-BuOK; 2. $C_6H_5C{\equiv}CC_6H_5$; 3. t-BuOH, H_2O; 4. HBr)⟶

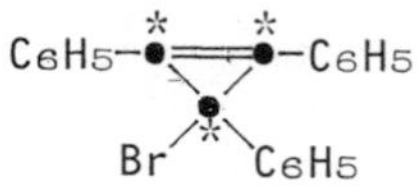
C6H5
C6H5
Br
C6H5

(8% from Ba^*CO_3)

Triphenylcyclopropenyl bromide
[1,1',1''-(3-Bromo-1-cyclopropene-1,2,3-^{14}C)trisbenzene]

A. D'yakonov, R. R. Kostikov, and A. P. Molchanov, Zh. Org. Khim., 6, 316 (1970); English translation p. 304.

*CH_3I — 1. $P(C_6H_5)_3$, Et_2O (94%); 2. BuLi, Et_2O; 3. $(C_6H_5)_2CO$ (78%) → $(C_6H_5)_2C{=}^*CH_2$ — I_2, hν →

1,1-Diphenylethylene
[1,1'-Ethenylidene-
2-^{14}C-bisbenzene]

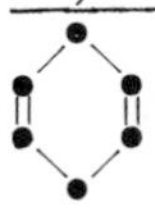

$(C_6H_5)_2CH^*CH_3$ (88%) — $AgSO_4$, I_2 / H_2SO_4 → (p-IC_6H_4)$_2CH^*CH_3$ (31%; 20% from *CH_3I)

1,1-Diphenylethane
[1,1'-Ethylidene-
2-^{14}C-bisbenzene]

1,1-Di-(p-iodophenyl)ethane
[1,1'Ethylidene-2-^{14}C-bis
4-iodobenzene]

H. H. Szmant, J. Colon, and J. Castrillón, J. Org. Chem., 36, 573 (1971).

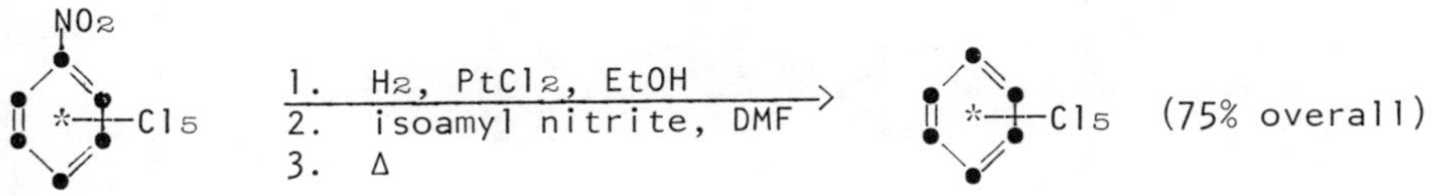

NO2
Cl5
1. H2, PtCl2, EtOH
2. isoamyl nitrite, DMF
3. Δ
Cl5
(75% overall)

Pentachlorobenzene-U-^{14}C

J. P. Müller, A. Attar, H.-J. Kurth, and D. Bieniek, J. Label. Compound. Radiopharm., 15, 499 (1979).

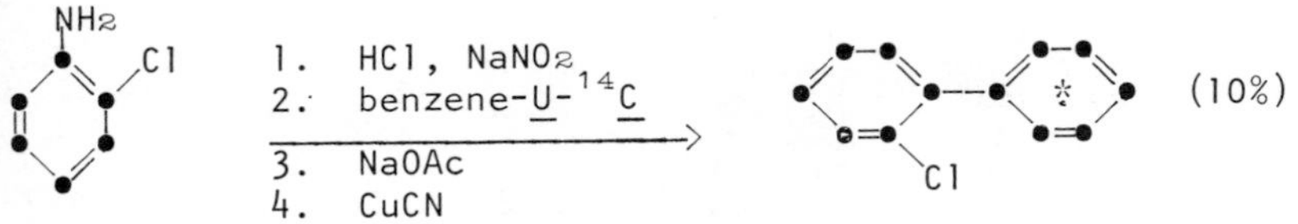

NH2
Cl
1. HCl, NaNO2
2. benzene-U-14C
3. NaOAc
4. CuCN
Cl
(10%)

2-Chloro-1,1'-biphenyl-
1',2',3',4',5',6'-^{14}C

P. B. Reichardt and S. E. Schuttner, J. Label. Compound. Radiopharm., 12, 243 (1976).

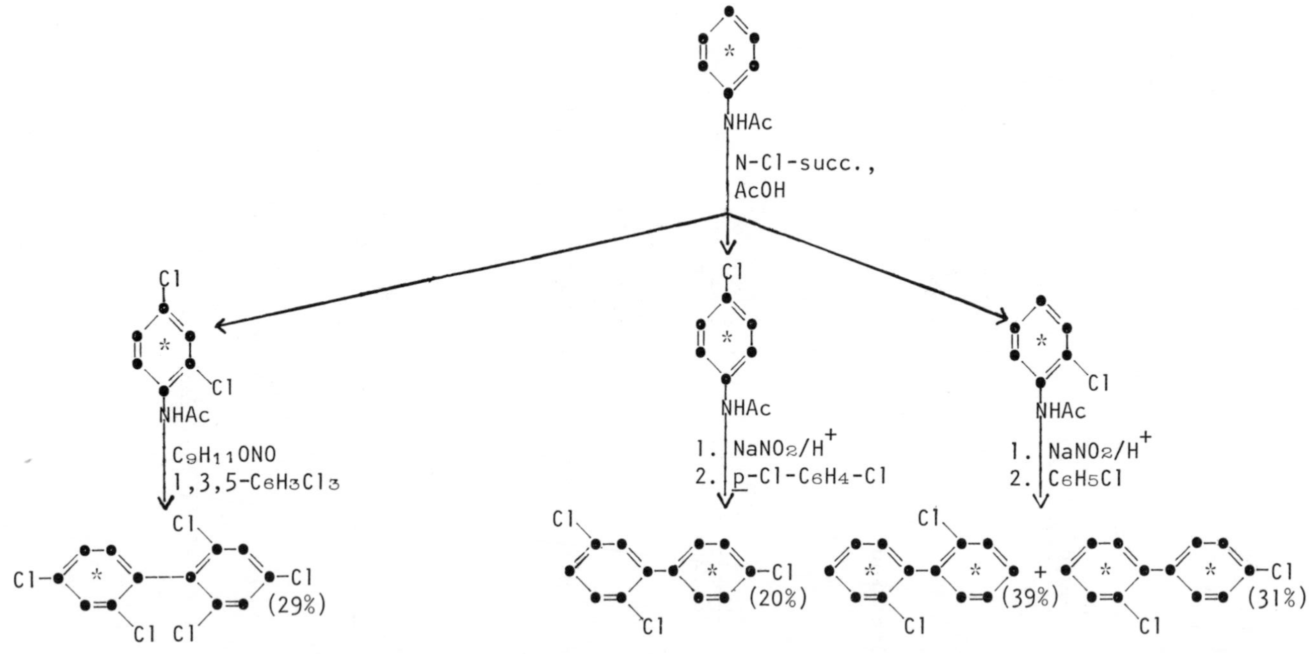
NHAc
N-Cl-succ., AcOH
Cl
Cl
NHAc
$C_9H_{11}ONO$
1,3,5-$C_6H_3Cl_3$
Cl
NHAc
1. $NaNO_2/H^+$
2. p-Cl-C_6H_4-Cl
Cl
NHAc
1. $NaNO_2/H^+$
2. C_6H_5Cl
Cl
Cl
Cl
Cl Cl
(29%)
Cl
Cl
Cl
(20%)
Cl
Cl
(39%)
+
Cl
Cl
(31%)

2,4,6,2',4'-Pentachloro-1,1'-biphenyl-1',2',3',4'-5',6'-^{14}C

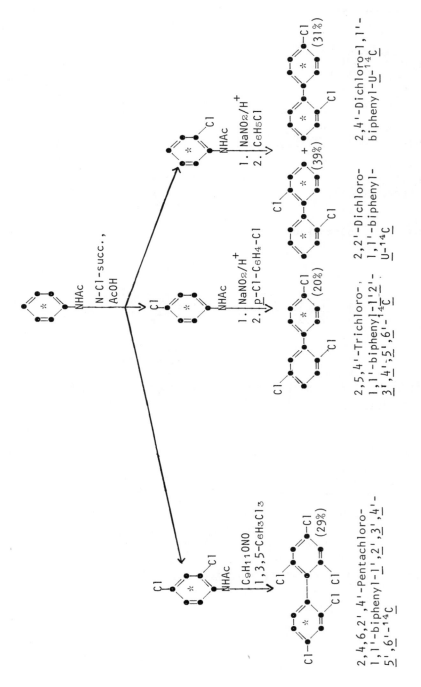

2,5,4'-Trichloro-1,1'-biphenyl-1'2'-3',4',5',6'-^{14}C

2,2'-Dichloro-1,1'-biphenyl-U-^{14}C

2,4'-Dichloro-1,1'-biphenyl-U-^{14}C

K. Sandrock, A. Attar, D. Bienik, W. Klein, and F. Korte, J. Label. Compound.Radiopharm., 14, 197 (1978).

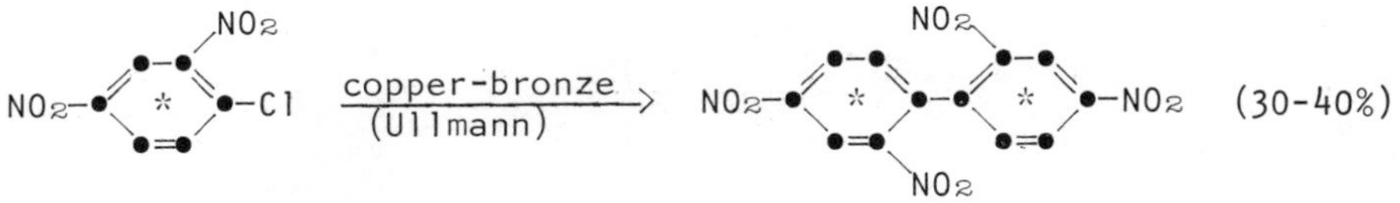
NO2
NO2
Cl
copper-bronze
(Ullmann)
NO2
NO2
NO2
NO2
(30-40%)

1-Chloro-2,4-dinitro-benzene-U-^{14}C

2,4,2',4'-Tetranitro-1,1'-biphenyl-U-^{14}C

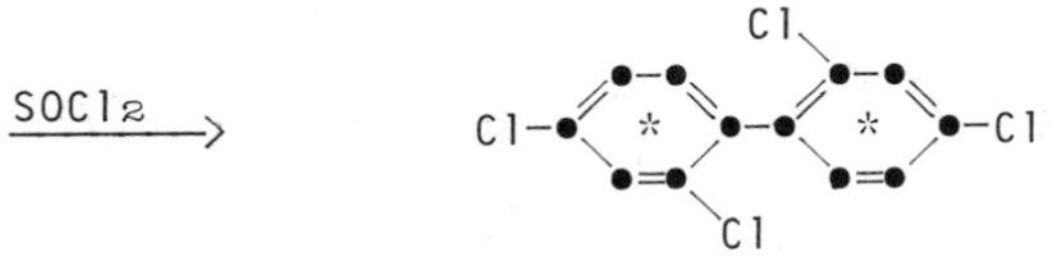
SOCl2
Cl
Cl
Cl
Cl

2,4,2',4'-Tetrachloro-1,1'-biphenyl-U-^{14}C

B. Melvas, J. Label. Compounds, 10, 325 (1974).

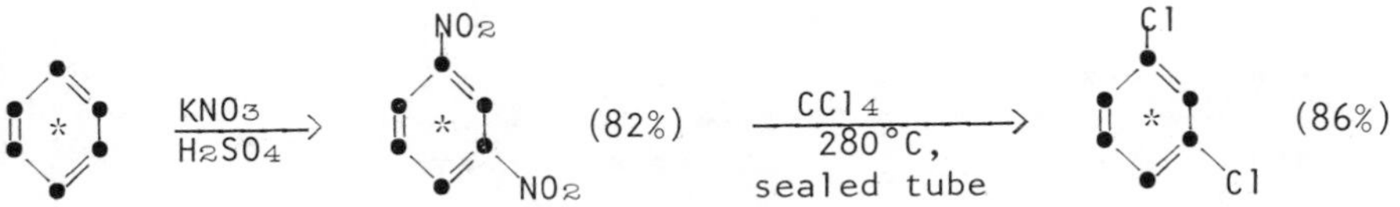
KNO3
H2SO4
NO2
NO2
(82%)
CCl4
280°C,
sealed tube
Cl
Cl
(86%)

Benzene-U-^{14}C

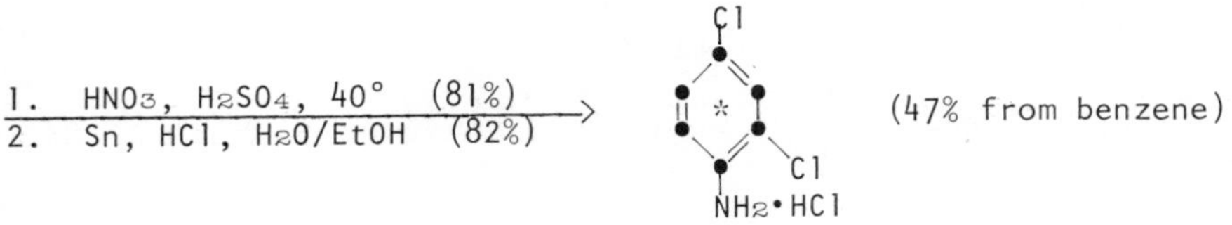
1. HNO3, H2SO4, 40° (81%)
2. Sn, HCl, H2O/EtOH (82%)
Cl
Cl
NH2•HCl
(47% from benzene)

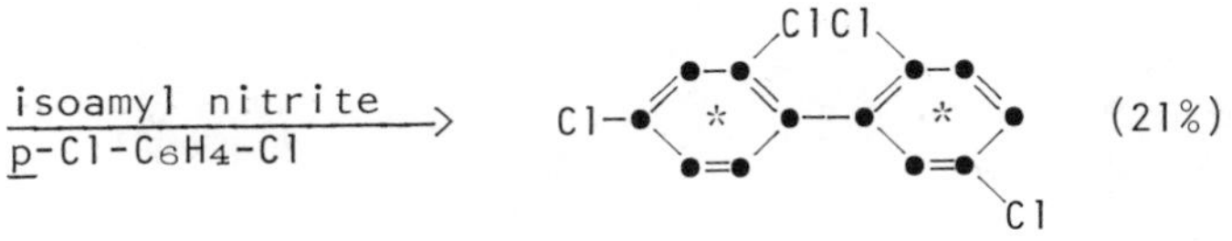
isoamyl nitrite
p-Cl-C6H4-Cl
ClCl
Cl
Cl
(21%)

2,4,2',5'-Tetrachloro-1,1'-biphenyl-U-^{14}C

T. Moriya, J. Label. Compound.Radiopharm., 14, 625 (1978).

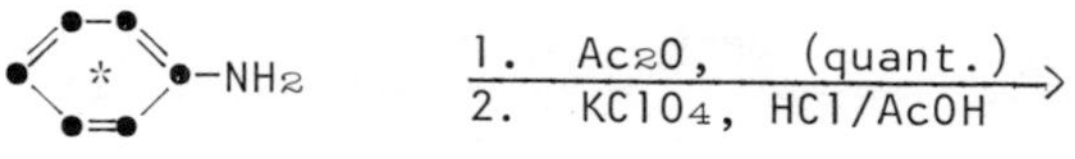
NH2
1. Ac2O, (quant.)
2. KClO4, HCl/AcOH

Aniline-U-^{14}C

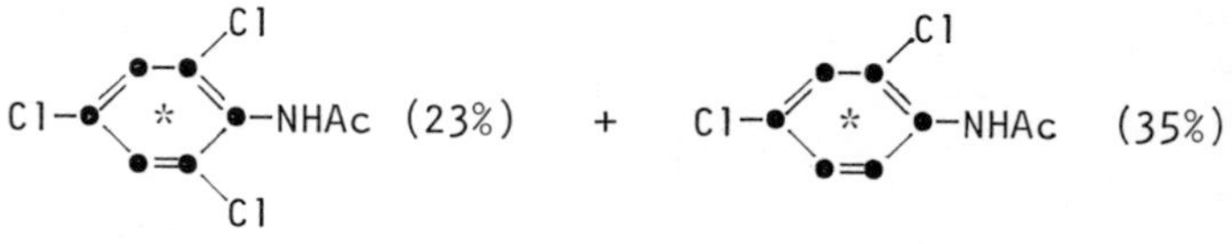
Cl
Cl
NHAc (23%)
+
Cl
Cl
NHAc (35%)
Cl

N-(2,4,6-Trichlorophenyl)-acetamide-(ring-^{14}C)

N-(2,4-Dichlorophenyl)-acetamide-(ring-^{14}C)

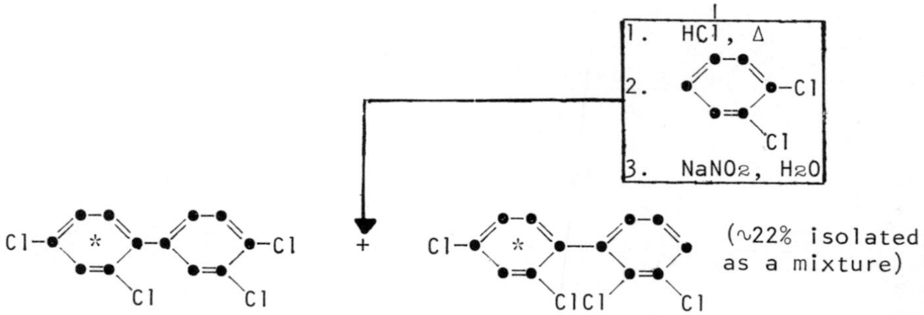
1. HCl, Δ
2.
Cl
Cl
3. NaNO2, H2O
Cl
Cl
Cl
Cl
+
Cl
ClCl
Cl
(~22% isolated as a mixture)

2,3',4,4'-Tetrachloro-1,1'-biphenyl-^{14}C [PCB-^{14}C]

2,2',3',4-Tetrachloro-1,1'-biphenyl-^{14}C [PCB-^{14}C]

M. Moron, G. Sundström, and C. A. Wachtmeister, Acta Chem. Scand., 26, 830 (1972).

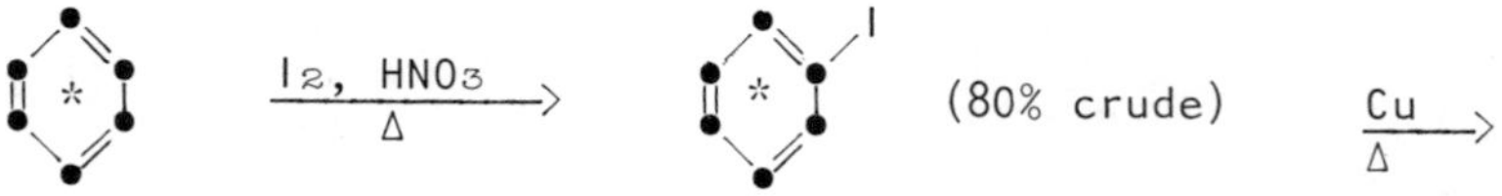
I2, HNO3
Δ
I
(80% crude)
Cu
Δ

Iodobenzene-U-^{14}C

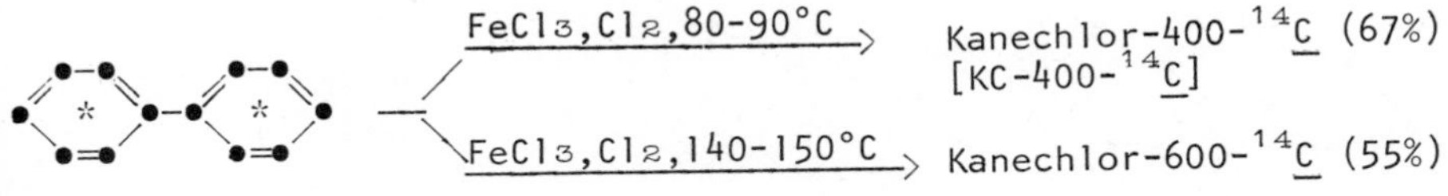
FeCl₃,Cl₂,80-90°C
Kanechlor-400-14C (67%)
[KC-400-14C]
FeCl₃,Cl₂,140-150°C
Kanechlor-600-14C (55%)

Biphenyl-U-^{14}C

(53% overall)

The products are mixtures of tetra- and hexachlorobiphenyls (PCB).

K. Hoizumi and T. Moriya, J. Label. Compounds, 10, 499 (1974).

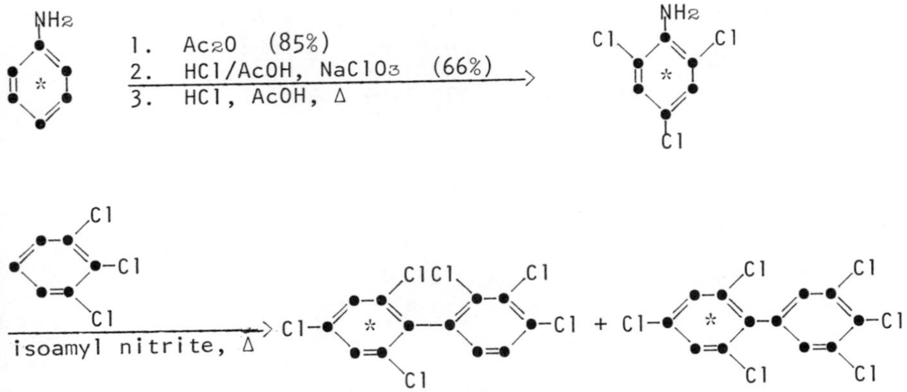
NH₂
1. Ac₂O (85%)
2. HCl/AcOH, NaClO₃ (66%)
3. HCl, AcOH, Δ
NH₂
Cl
Cl
Cl
Cl
Cl
Cl
isoamyl nitrite, Δ
Cl
ClCl
Cl
Cl
Cl
Cl
+
Cl
Cl
Cl
Cl
Cl
Cl

2,2',3,4,4',6'- and 2',3,4,4',5,6'-Hexachloro-1,1'-biphenyl-(ring-U-^{14}C) [PCB]

A 21% yield was obtained of a mixture of isomers (12% yield from aniline). An unlabeled mixture was separated chromatographically.

G. Sundström and C. A. Wachmeister, Acta Chem. Scand., 26, 3816 (1972).

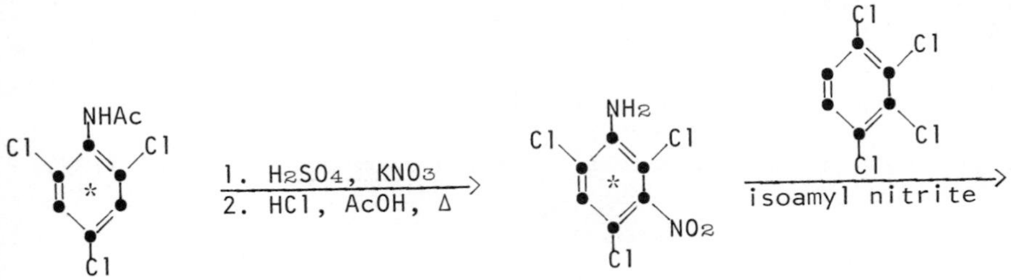
NHAc
Cl
Cl
Cl
1. H₂SO₄, KNO₃
2. HCl, AcOH, Δ
NH₂
Cl
Cl
NO₂
Cl
Cl
Cl
Cl
Cl
isoamyl nitrite

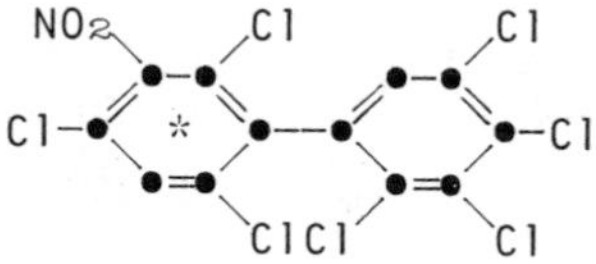

(16% overall) $\xrightarrow[\text{280-290°C, autoclave}]{CCl_4}$

3-Nitro-2,2',3',4,4',5',6-heptachloro-1,1'-biphenyl-(ring-^{14}C)

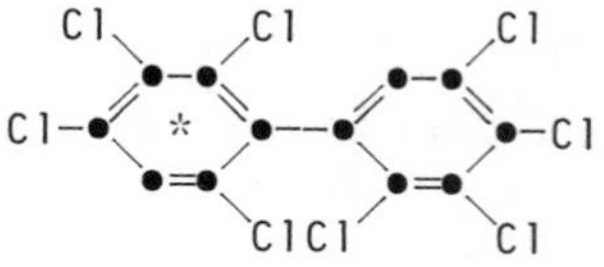

(8% overall)

2,2',3,3',4,4',5,6'-Octachloro-1,1'-biphenyl-(ring-^{14}C)

G. Sundström, Acta Chem. Scand., 27, 1109 (1973).

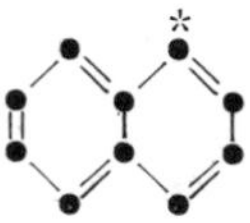

$\xrightarrow[SO_2Cl_2]{Cl_2}$

Naphthalene-1-^{14}C

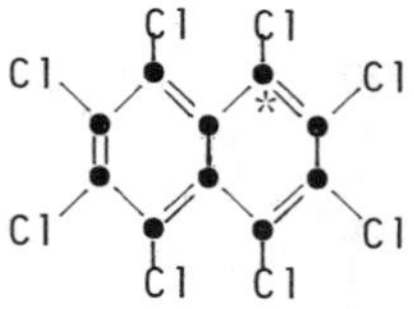

$\xrightarrow{SO_2Cl_2/Cl_2}$

Octachloronaphthalene-1-^{14}C

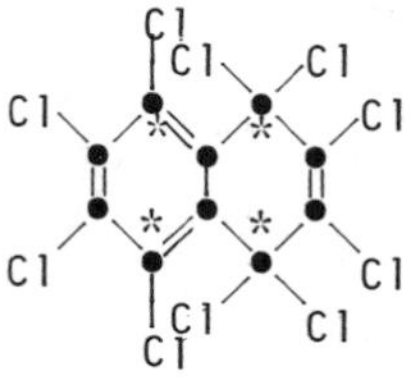

Decachloro-1,4-dihydronaphthalene-1,4,5,8-^{14}C

$\xrightarrow{Cl_2}$

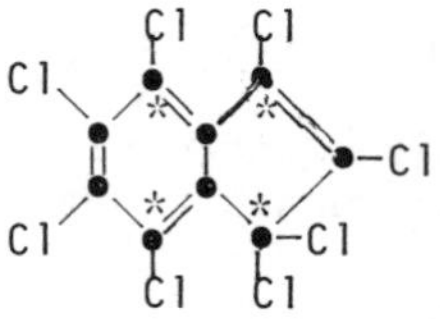

Octachloro-1H-indene-1,3,4,7-^{14}C

$\xrightarrow{Cl_2}$

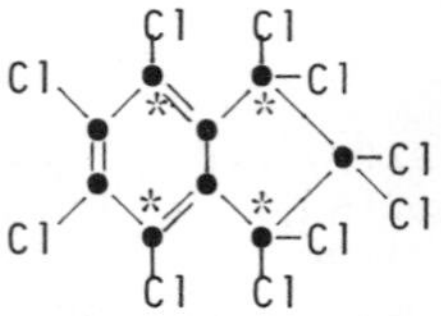

Decachloro-1H-indane-1,3,4,7-^{14}C

The β-carbon was eliminated by chlorolysis.

E. Zörkendörfer and F. Boberg, J. Label. Compounds, 8, 567 (1972).

7-7 Nitro Compounds

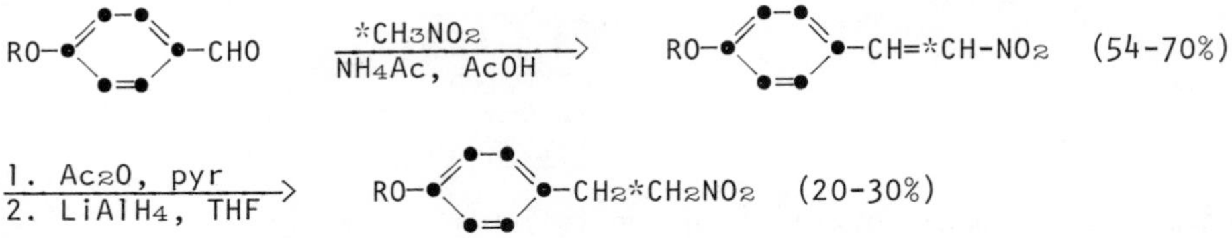
RO
CHO
*CH3NO2
NH4Ac, AcOH
RO
CH=*CH-NO2
(54-70%)
1. Ac2O, pyr
2. LiAlH4, THF
RO
CH2*CH2NO2
(20-30%)

R=H; 4-(2-Nitroethyl-2-^{14}C)phenol
R=CH_3; 1-Methoxy-4-(2-nitroethyl-2-^{14}C)benzene

S. Schiefer and H. Kindl, J. Label. Compounds, 7, 291 (1971).

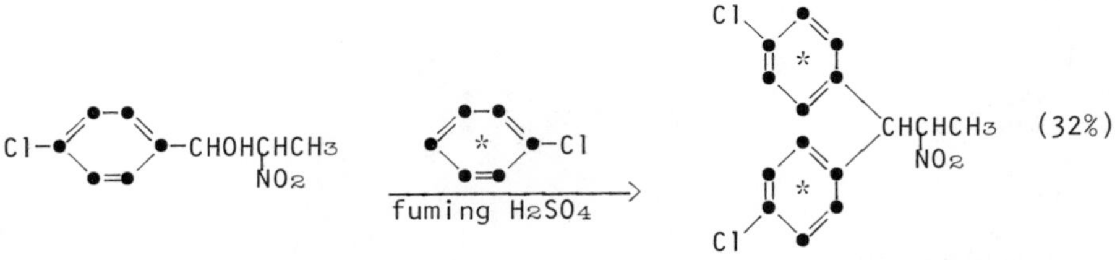
Cl
CHOHCHCH3
NO2
*
Cl
fuming H2SO4
Cl
CHCHCH3
NO2
(32%)
Cl

1,1'-(2-Nitropropylidene) bis-(4-chlorobenzene-(ring-^{14}C))

R. H. Jarboe, Jr., J. B. Data, and J. E. Christian, J. Pharm. Sci., 59, 1019 (1970).

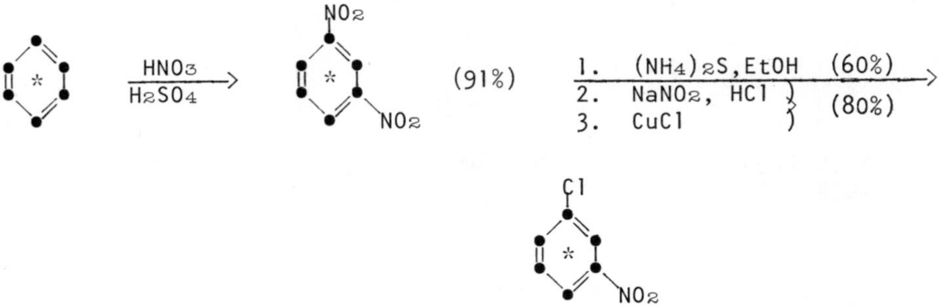
HNO3
H2SO4
NO2
NO2
(91%)
1. (NH4)2S, EtOH (60%)
2. NaNO2, HCl
3. CuCl
(80%)
Cl
NO2

1-Chloro-3-nitrobenzene-U-^{14}C

W. N. White and J. R. Klink, J. Org. Chem., 42, 166 (1977).

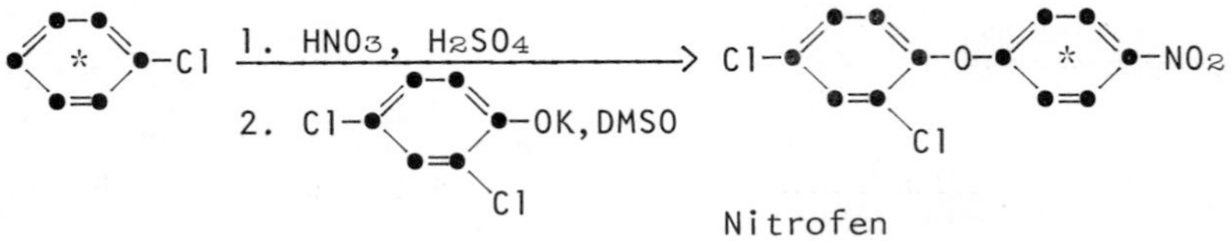

(42% overall)

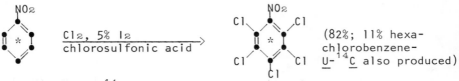

Nitrofen
[2,4-Dichloro-1-(4-nitrophenoxy-1,2,3,4,5,6-^{14}C)benzene]

The crude product mixture had the following composition: nitrofen (58%); the 2'-nitrophenyl isomer (32%); unidentified substance (10%).

A. Unverricht and H. R. Schütte, Z. Chem., 17, 369 (1977).

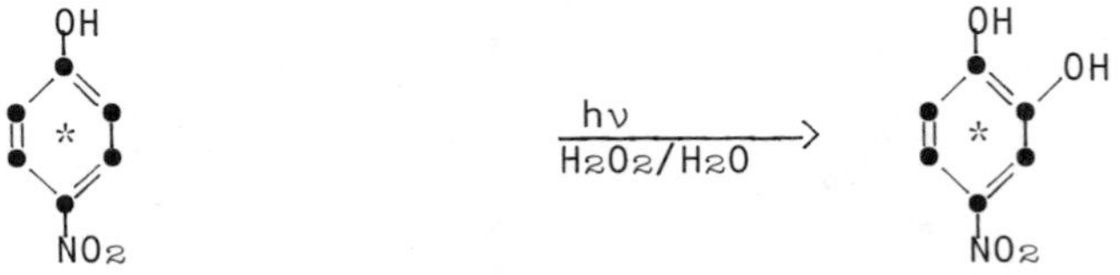

4-Nitrophenol-U-^{14}C

4-Nitrocatechol
[4-Nitro-1,2-benzenediol-U-^{14}C]

F. A. Norris and G. G. Still, J. Label. Compounds, 9, 661 (1973).

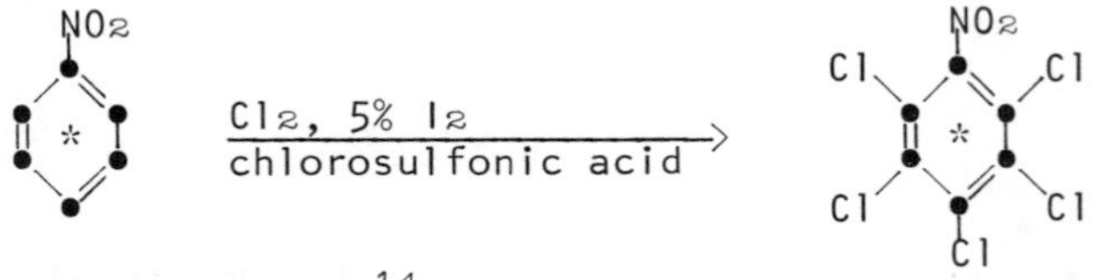

(82%; 11% hexachlorobenzene-U-^{14}C also produced)

Nitrobenzene-U-^{14}C

Pentachloronitrobenzene-U-^{14}C

R. E. Kadunce and G. L. Lamoureux, J. Label. Compound.Radiopharm., 12, 459 (1976).

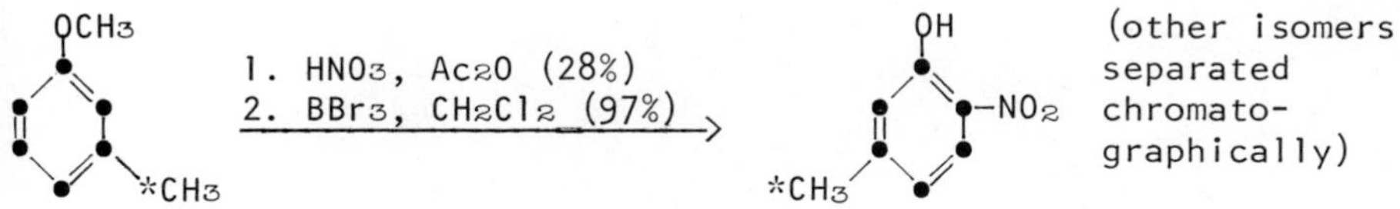
OCH3
1. HNO3, Ac2O (28%)
2. BBr3, CH2Cl2 (97%)
*CH3
OH
NO2
*CH3
(other isomers separated chromatographically)

(5-Methyl-^{14}C)-2-nitrophenol

A. Yoshitake, F. Shono, T. Kamada, and I. Nakatsuka, J. Label. Compound. Radiopharm., 13, 333 (1977).

8

Carbonic Acid Derivatives

8-1 Carbonic Acid Derivatives

$$*CH_3I \xrightarrow[300\text{-}325°C]{P_2S_5} *CS_2 \quad \text{(quant.)}$$

Carbon disulfide-[14]C

C. W. Perry and W. Burger, J. Label. Compound. Radiopharm., 13, 113 (1977).

$$Ba*CO_3 \xrightarrow[2.\ \text{dil. } H_2SO_4]{1.\ NH_3,\ 840°C} H_2N*CN \quad (83\%)$$

Cyanamide-[14]C

R. S. P. Hsi, J. Label. Compounds, 8, 407 (1972).

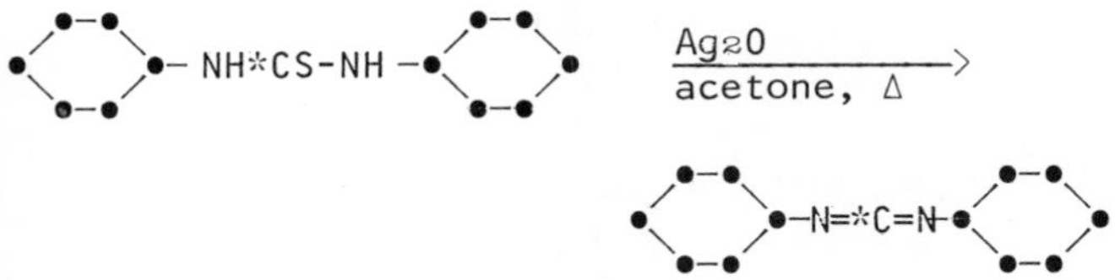

NH*CS-NH
Ag2O
acetone, Δ
N=*C=N

(54% from $*CH_3I$)

N,N'-Dicyclohexylcarbodiimide (DCC)
[N,N'-(Methanetetrayl-^{14}C)-biscyclohexanamine]

C. W. Perry and W. Burger, J. Label Compound. Radiopharm., 13, 113 (1977).

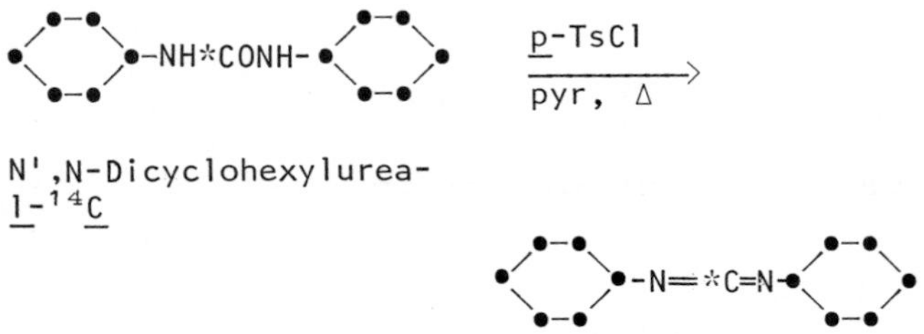
-NH*CONH-
p-TsCl
pyr, Δ
-N=*C=N-

N',N-Dicyclohexylurea-1-^{14}C

(21% from urea)

N',N-Dicyclohexylcarbodiimide-1-^{14}C

R. B. Merrifield, B. F. Gisin, and A. N. Bach, J. Org. Chem., 42, 1291 (1977).

$$Ba^*CO_3 \xrightarrow[H_2O]{AgNO_3} Ag_2{}^*CO_3 \quad (95\text{-}100\%) \xrightarrow[DMF]{C_2H_5I,\ Et_3N} C_2H_5O\text{-}{}^*C(=O)\text{-}OC_2H_5$$

Carbonic-^{14}C acid diethyl ester (60-85% from Ba*CO$_3$)

W. R. Porter, L. A. Spitznagle, and W. F. Trager, J. Label. Compound. Radiopharm., 12, 577 (1976).

$$C_2H_5O^-K + {}^*CO_2 \longrightarrow C_2H_5O\text{-}{}^*C(=O)\text{-}O^-K^+ \xrightarrow{C_2H_5O\text{-}C(=O)\text{-}Cl} C_2H_5O\text{-}{}^*C(=O)\text{-}O\text{-}{}^*C(=O)\text{-}OC_2H_5$$

Dicarbonic-^{14}C acid diethyl ester (54%)

$$CH_3{}^*CH_2O^-K^+ + CO_2 \longrightarrow CH_3{}^*CH_2O\text{-}C(=O)\text{-}O^-K^+ \xrightarrow{C_2H_5O\text{-}C(=O)\text{-}Cl} CH_3{}^*CH_2\text{-}O\text{-}C(=O)\text{-}O\text{-}C(=O)\text{-}OC_2H_5$$

Dicarbonic acid (diethyl-1-^{14}C) ester (33%)

E. Fischer and R. Schelenz, J. Label. Compounds, 5, 333 (1969).

8-2 Guanidines

$CH_3(CH_2)_7NH_2 + NH_2\text{-}{*}CN \xrightarrow[\text{2. } H_2SO_4]{\text{1. AcOH, } CH_3OH,\ \Delta}$

$\left[CH_3(CH_2)_7NH{*}C(=NH)NH_3\right]_2\ SO_4$

Octylguanidine-(carbamyl-^{14}C) sulfate

M. Salmón, M. T. de Gómez Puyon, and A. G. Puyou, Chem. Ind., (London), 852 (1976).

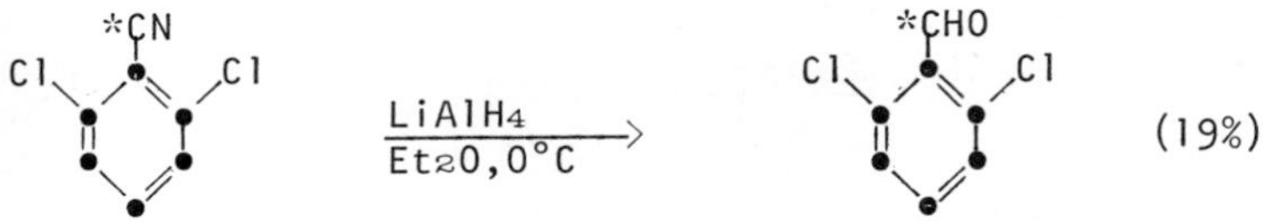

2,6-Dichlorobenzonitrile-(cyano-^{14}C) → 2,6-Dichlorobenzaldehyde-(carbonyl-^{14}C)

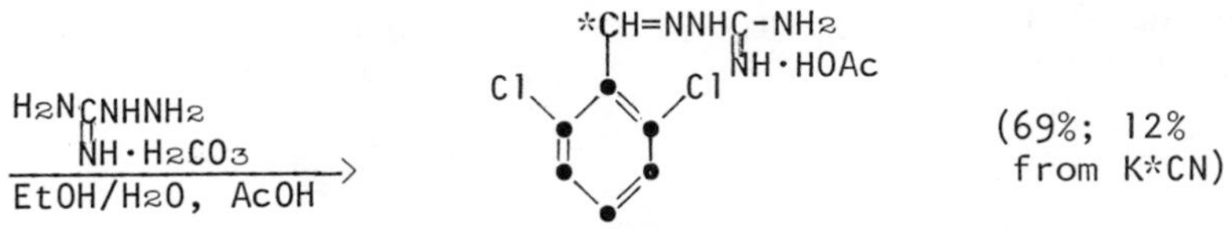

2-[(2,6-Dichlorophenyl)-methylene-^{14}C]hydrazinecarboximidamide acetic acid salt

S. F. Sisenwine, C. O. Tio, and J. Ahern, J. Label. Compound. Radiopharm., 12, 501 (1976).

8-3 Ureas

$K{*}CNO \xrightarrow[H_2O]{CH_3NH_3Cl} NH_2\text{-}{*}CONHCH_3$ (96-98%)

Methylurea-(carbonyl-^{14}C)

J. Knabe, H. Junginger, D. Straus, and H.-L. Schmidt, Arch. Pharm., 305, 277 (1972); Arch. Pharm., 306, 306 (1973).

$C_2H_5NH_2 \cdot HCl \xrightarrow[H_2O,\ \Delta]{K^*CNO} C_2H_5NH^*CONH_2$

Ethylurea-(carbonyl-^{14}C)

R. Kaul, B. Hempel, and W. Schäfer, Arzneim. Forsch.-(Drug Res.), 26, 489 (1976).

$CH_3CH_2CH_2{}^*CH_2NH_2 \cdot HCl \xrightarrow[2.\ HONO]{1.\ NH_2CONH_2,\ H_2O,\ \Delta}$

$CH_3CH_2CH_2{}^*CH_2N(NO)CONH_2$ (48%; 32% from NaCN)

(N-Butyl-1-^{14}C)-N-nitrosourea

G. B. Howarth and A. W. Craig, J. Label. Compounds, 8, 249 (1972).

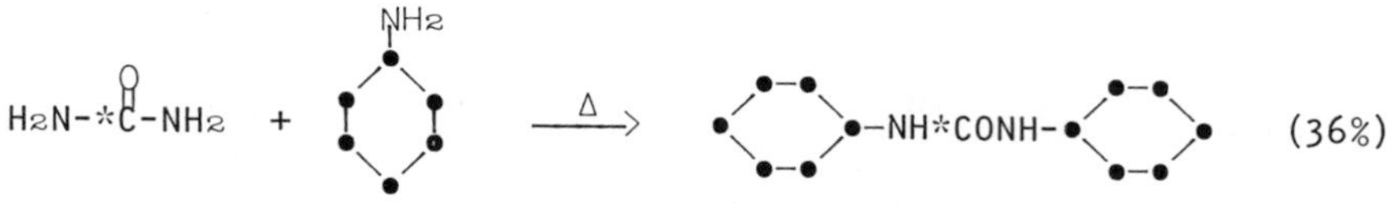

N,N'-Dicylohexylurea-1-^{14}C

R. B. Merrifield, B. F. Gisin, and A. N. Bach, J. Org. Chem., 42, 1291 (1977).

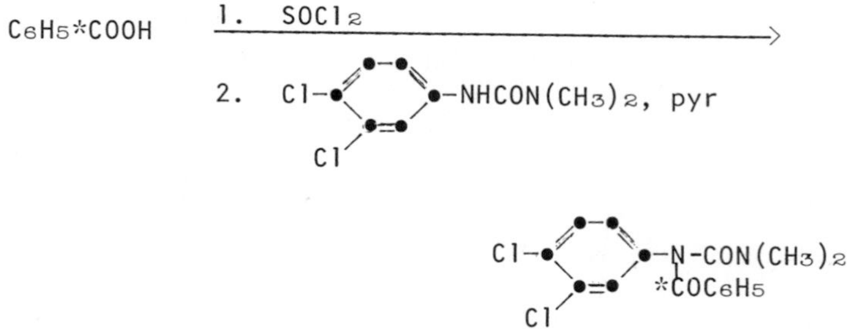

Phenobenzuron
[N-(3,4-Dichlorophenyl)-N-(dimethylamino)carbonylbenzamide-7-^{14}C]

J. Lintermans and A. Benakis, J. Label. Compounds, 7, 561 (1971).

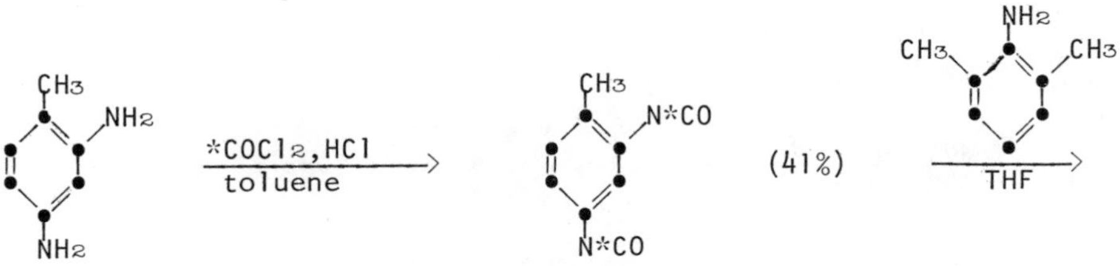

2,4-(Diisocyanato-^{14}C)-1-methylbenzene

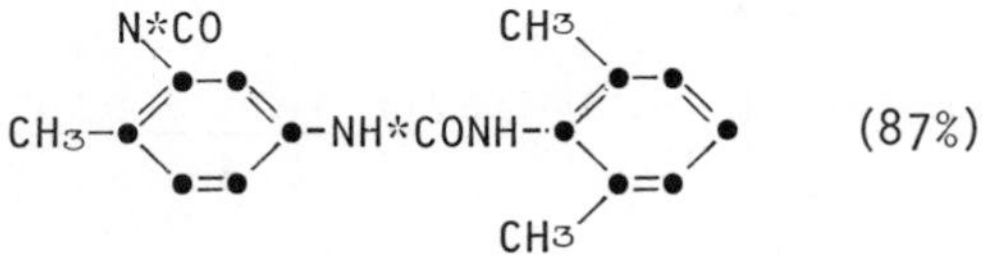

N-(2,6-Dimethylphenyl)-N'-(3-(isocyanato-^{14}C)-4-methylphenyl)-urea-1-^{14}C

The ^{14}C distribution was determined by selective hydrolysis of the isocyanate groups.

E. F. Kopka, N. Sue Rapp, and J. D. Ingham, J. Label. Compounds, 1, 214 (1965).

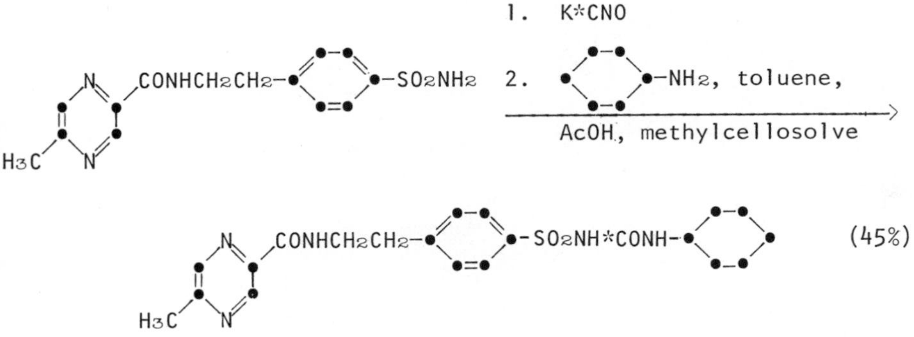

Glipizide
[1-Cyclohexyl-3-[[p-[2-(5-methylpyrazinecarboxamido)ethyl]phenyl]sulfonyl]urea-1-^{14}C]

G. C. Goldaniga, C. Maraone, E. Pianezzola, G. Valzelli, and V. Ambrogi, Arzneim.-Forsch.-(Drug Res.), 23, 242 (1973).

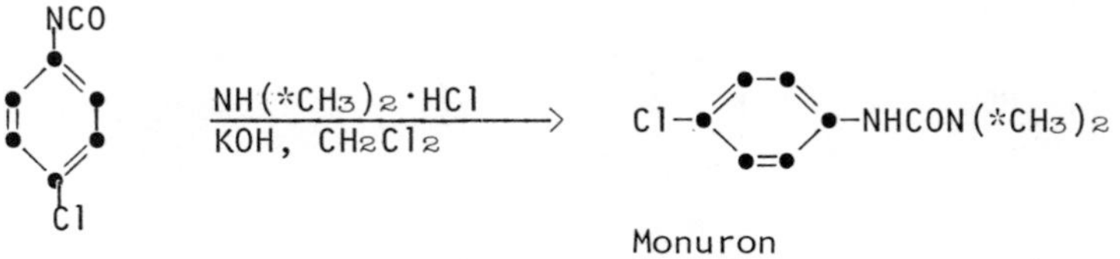
NCO
Cl
NH(*CH3)2·HCl
KOH, CH2Cl2
Cl
NHCON(*CH3)2

(92%)

Monuron
[N'-(4-Chlorophenyl)-N,N-(dimethyl-^{14}C)-urea]

Other compounds prepared in a similar manner: diuron (85%), fenuron (98%), and chloroxuron (72%).

M. Look and L. R. White, J. Agr. Food Chem., 18, 745 (1970).

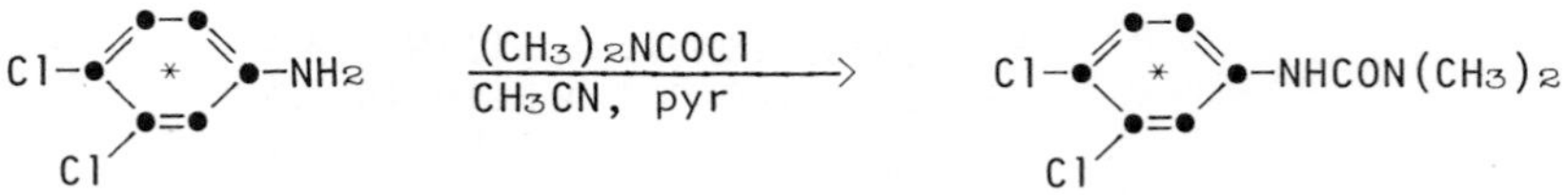
Cl
NH2
Cl
(CH3)2NCOCl
CH3CN, pyr
Cl
NHCON(CH3)2
Cl

(71%)

Diuron
[3-(3,4-(Dichlorophenyl-U-^{14}C) 1,1-dimethylurea]

V. A. Elder and B. L. Koch, J. Agr. Food Chem., 25, 973 (1977).

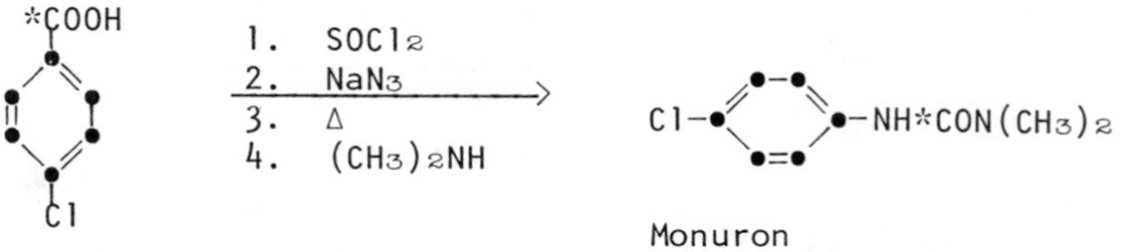
*COOH
Cl
1. SOCl2
2. NaN3
3. Δ
4. (CH3)2NH
Cl
NH*CON(CH3)2

(54% overall)

Monuron
[N'-(4-Chlorophenyl)-N,N-dimethylurea-1-^{14}C]

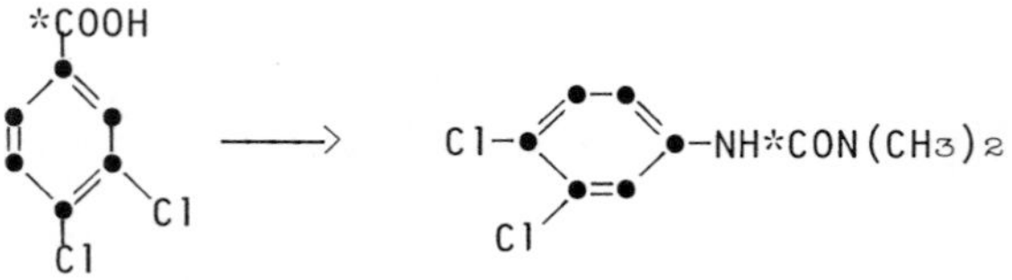
*COOH
Cl
Cl
Cl
NH*CON(CH3)2
Cl

(22% overall yield)

Diuron
[3-(3,4-Dichlorophenyl)-1,1-dimethylurea-1-^{14}C]

In a similar manner, N,N-dimethyl-^{14}C-labeled diuron (92%) and monuron (94%) were prepared, as were ring-^{14}C-labeled diuron (22%) and monuron (54%).

F. S. Tanaka, J. Agr. Food Chem., 18, 213 (1970).

8-4 Thioureas

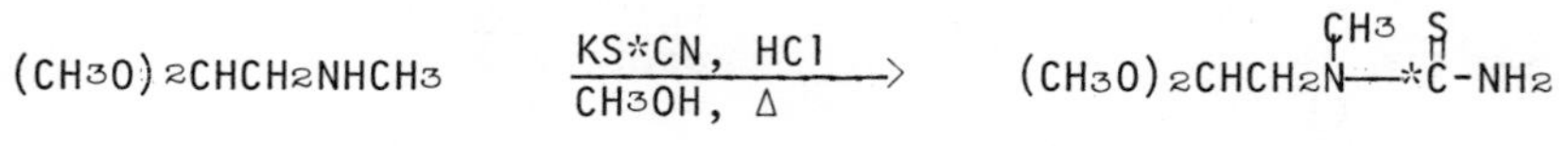

N-[2-(Dimethoxy)ethyl]-N-methyl-(thiourea-^{14}C)]

P. W. Lee, M. J. Gudzinowicz, and R. A. Neal, J. Label. Compound. Radiopharm., 14, 633 (1978).

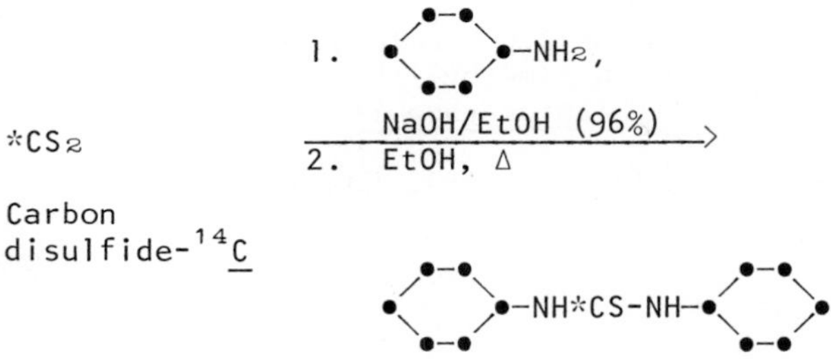

Carbon disulfide-^{14}C

(77% overall yield)

N,N'-Dicyclohexyl-(thiourea-^{14}C)

C. W. Perry and W. Burger, J. Label. Compound. Radiopharm., 13, 113 (1977).

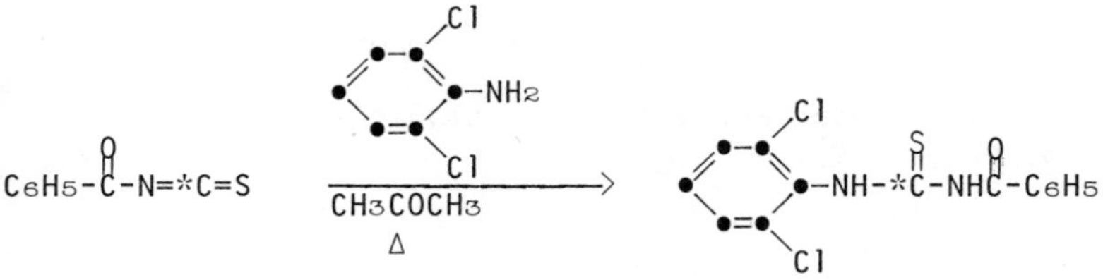

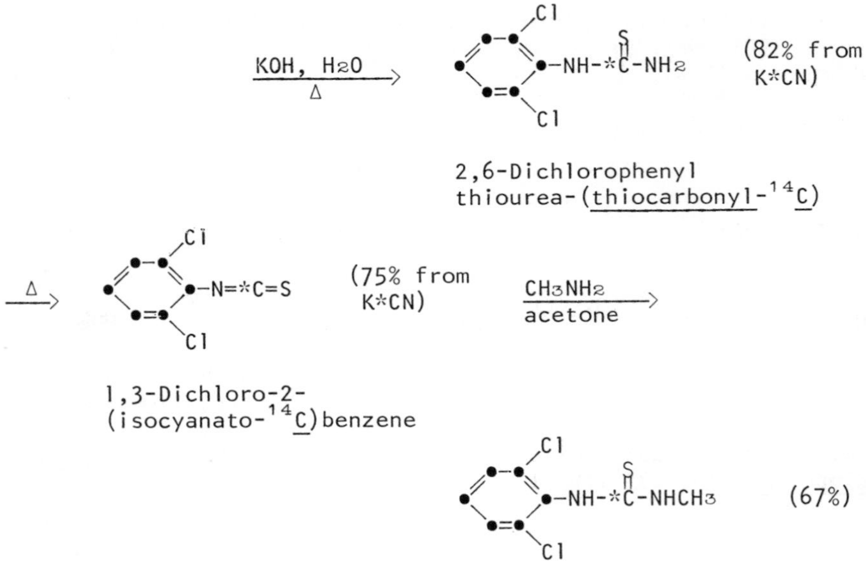
KOH, H2O
Δ
Cl
S
NH-*C-NH2
(82% from K*CN)
Δ
N=*C=S
(75% from K*CN)
CH3NH2
acetone
NH-*C-NHCH3
(67%)

2,6-Dichlorophenyl thiourea-(thiocarbonyl-^{14}C)

1,3-Dichloro-2-(isocyanato-^{14}C)benzene

N-(2,6-Dichlorophenyl)-N'-(methyl)thiourea-(thiocarbonyl-^{14}C)

G. Zólyomi, L. Toldy, and D. Bánfi, J. Label. Compounds, 9, 243 (1973).

$CH_2{=}CHCH(CH_3)N{=}{}^*C{=}S$ $\xrightarrow[\text{DMF, EtOH, }\Delta]{CH_3NHC(S)NHNH_2}$ $CH_2{=}CHCH(CH_3)NH{}^*C(S)NHNHC(S)NHCH_3$ (~17% from KS*CN)

(3-Isothiocyanato-^{14}C)-3-methyl-1-propene

N-Methyl-N'-(1-methyl-2-propenyl)-1,2-hydrazinedicarbothioamide-(2-thioxo-^{14}C)

V. J. Feil, P. W. Aschbacher, and C. H. Lamoureux, J. Label. Compounds, 6, 401 (1970).

8-5 Carbamates

$$*CH_3NH_2 \cdot HCl \xrightarrow{ClCOOC_2H_5} *CH_3NHC(=O)-OC_2H_5$$

(Methyl-^{14}C)carbamic acid ethyl ester

A. Alarif, S. Kimball, and S. Epstein, J. Label. Compounds, 10, 161 (1974).

$$HO-NHC(=O)-OC_2H_5 \xrightarrow[2.\ (*CH_3O)_2SO_2]{1.\ 15\%\ KOH} *CH_3O-N(*CH_3)-C(=O)-OC_2H_5 \quad (83\%)$$

(Methoxy-^{14}C)-(methyl-^{14}C)-carbamic acid ethyl ester

K. N. Arjungi, F.-W. Krüger, and M. Wiessler, J. Label. Compound. Radiopharm., 14, 913 (1978).

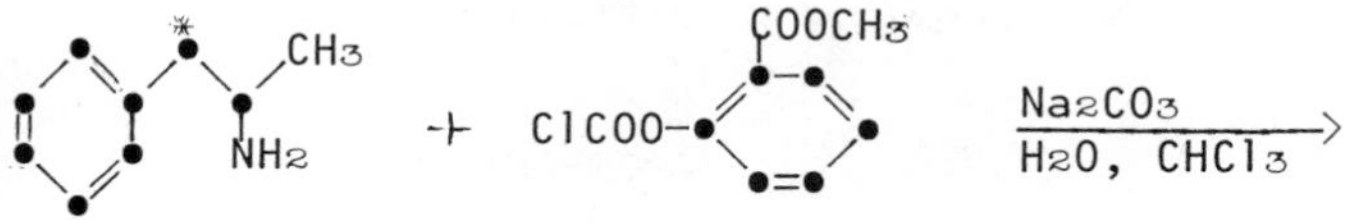
CH3
NH2
COOCH3
ClCOO
Na2CO3
H2O, CHCl3

d-Amphetamine [α-Methylbenzene-ethanamine-β-^{14}C]

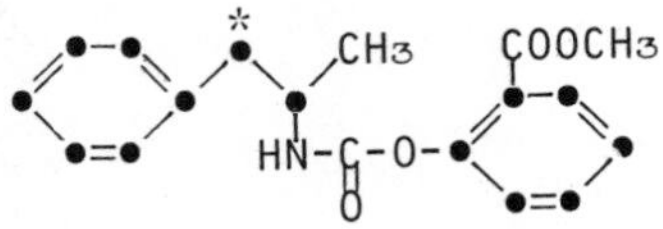
CH3
COOCH3
HN-C-O-
O

(87%)

2-[[[[2-(1-Methyl-2-phenyl)-ethyl-2-^{14}C]amino]carbonyl]-oxy]benzoic acid methyl ester

Similarly prepared was o-nitrophenyl-d-α-methylphen(ethyl-β-^{14}C) carbamate.

A. J. Verbiscar and L. G. Abood, J. Med. Chem., 13, 1176 (1970).

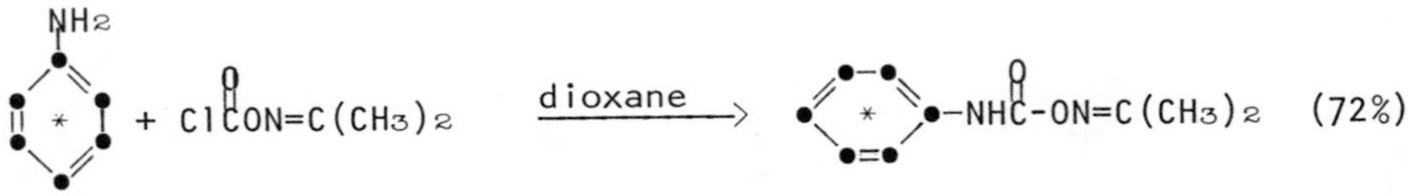
NH2
+ ClCON=C(CH3)2
dioxane
NHC-ON=C(CH3)2
(72%)

Proximpham
[2-Propanone-O-
[(phenylamino)carbonyl]-
oxime-(ring-^{14}C)]

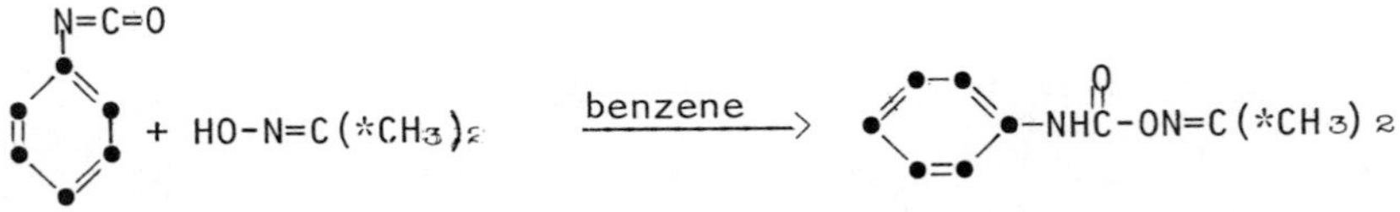
N=C=O
+ HO-N=C(*CH3)2
benzene
NHC-ON=C(*CH3)2

Proximpham-1,3-^{14}C

H. R. Schütte, C. Beyer, A. Jumar, K. Sieber, and P. Held, Z. Chem., 15, 220 (1975).

Condensation of methyl isocyanate-(carbonyl-^{14}C) with the appropriate phenol or oxime gave the following insecticides (carbonyl) labeled) in 85-95% yields:

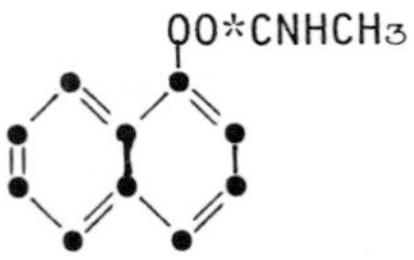
OO*CNHCH3

Carbaryl
[1-Naphthalenol methyl-
(carbamate-^{14}C)]

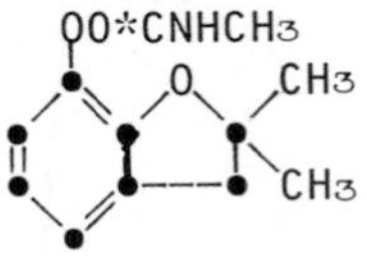
OO*CNHCH3
O
CH3
CH3

Carbofuran
[2,3-Dihydro-2,2-dimethyl-
7-benzofuranol methyl
(carbamate-^{14}C)]

$CH_3C(SCH_3)=NO^*C(=O)NHCH_3$

Methomyl
[N-[[(Methylamino)carbonyl
-^{14}C]oxy]ethanimidothioic
acid methyl ester]

$CH_3SC(CH_3)_2CH=NO^*CONHCH_3$

Aldicarb
[2-Methyl-2-(methylthio)
propanal-O-[(methylamino)
carbonyl-^{14}C)oxime]

H. E. Hurst and H. W. Dorough, J. Label. Compound. Radiopharm., 14, 11 (1978).

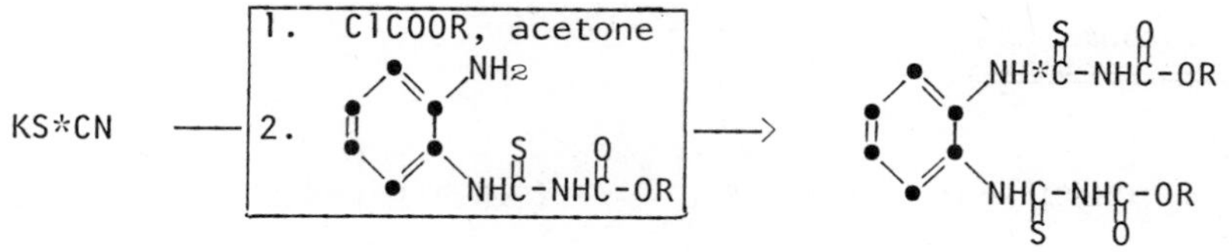
KS*CN
1. ClCOOR, acetone
2.
NH2
NHC-NHC-OR
NH*C-NHC-OR
NHC-NHC-OR

R=C_2H_5; Thiophanate (61%)
[[[2-[[(Ethoxycarbonyl)amino]thioxomethyl]amino]phenyl]-aminothioxomethyl-^{14}C]carbamic acid ethyl ester]
R=CH_3; Methyl thiophanate-^{14}C (59%)

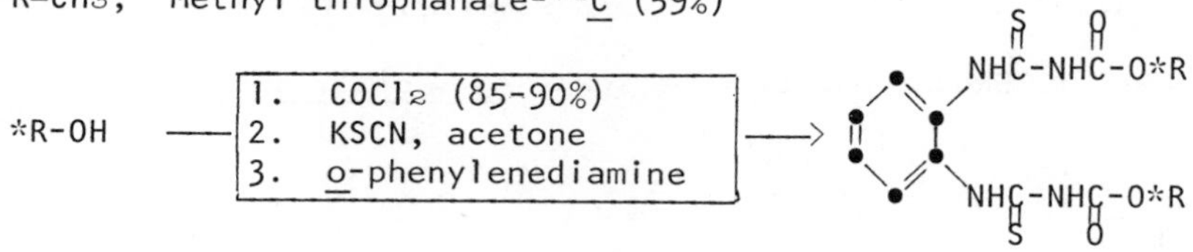
*R-OH
1. COCl2 (85-90%)
2. KSCN, acetone
3. o-phenylenediamine
NHC-NHC-O*R
NHC-NHC-O*R

R=ethyl-1-^{14}C; Thiophanate-(diethyl-1-^{14}C ester) (34%)
R=methyl-^{14}C; Methyl thiophanate-(dimethyl-^{14}C ester) (22%)

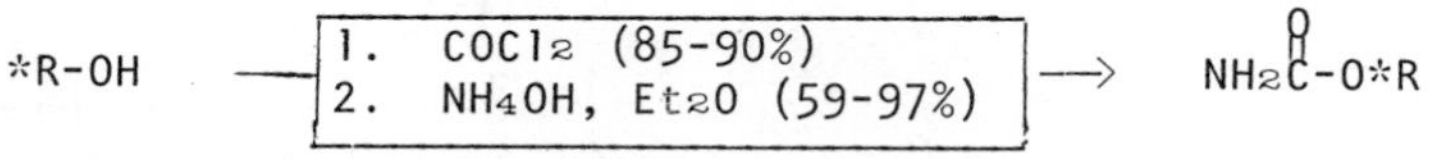
*R-OH
1. COCl2 (85-90%)
2. NH4OH, Et2O (59-97%)
NH2C-O*R

R=ethyl-1-^{14}C; Carbamic acid-(ethyl-1-^{14}C) ester
R=methyl-^{14}C; Carbamic acid-(methyl-^{14}C) ester

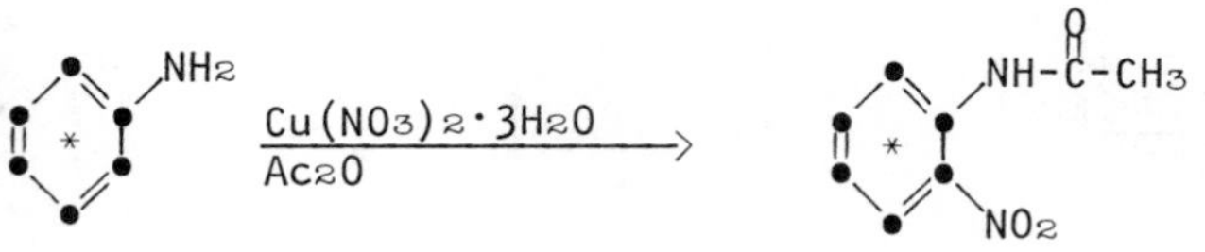
NH2
Cu(NO3)2·3H2O
Ac2O
NH-C-CH3
NO2

(69%; the yield of p-isomer was 23%, separable by chromatography)

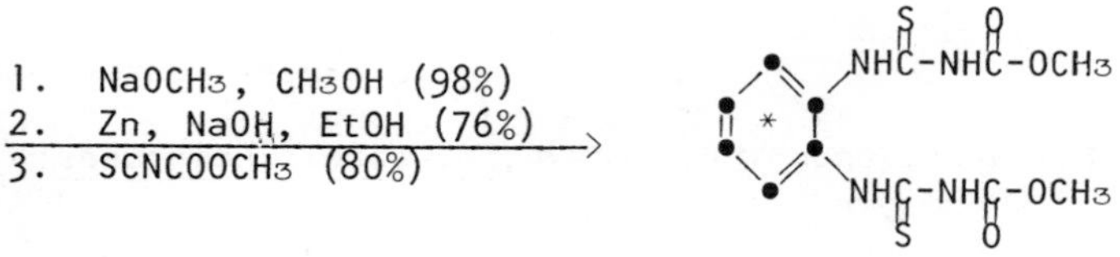
1. NaOCH3, CH3OH (98%)
2. Zn, NaOH, EtOH (76%)
3. SCNCOOCH3 (80%)
NHC-NHC-OCH3
NHC-NHC-OCH3

Methyl thiophanate-(ring-^{14}C)

Y. Soeda, D. Takiguchi, S. Kosaka, and T. Noguchi, J. Agr. Food. Chem., 20, 940 (1972).

8-6 Thiocarbamates

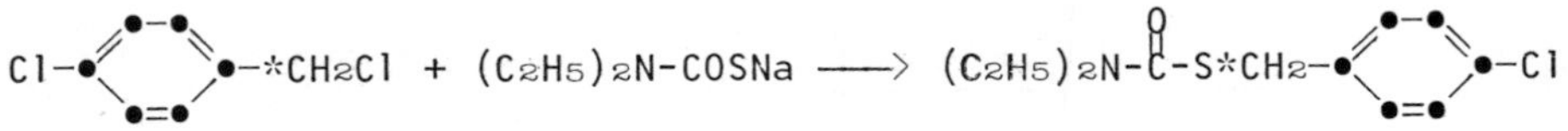
Cl
*CH2Cl + (C2H5)2N-COSNa
(C2H5)2N-C-S*CH2-
O
Cl

1-Chloro-4-(chloromethyl-^{14}C)benzene
[from 4-Chlorobenzoic acid-7-^{14}C]

Benthiocarb
[Carbamothioic acid diethyl-S-[(4-chlorophenyl)-(methyl-^{14}C)] ester]

K. Ishikawa, I. Okuda, and S. Kuwatsuka, Agr. Biol. Chem., 37, 165 (1973).

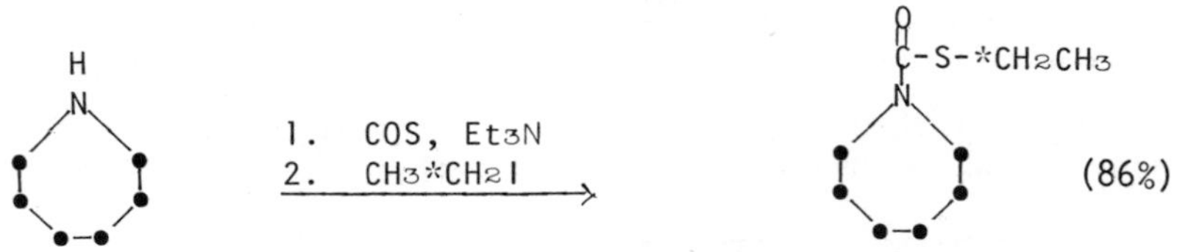
H
N
1. COS, Et3N
2. CH3*CH2I
O
C-S-*CH2CH3
N
(86%)

Hexahydro-1H-azepine-1-carbothioic acid S-ethyl-1-^{14}C ester

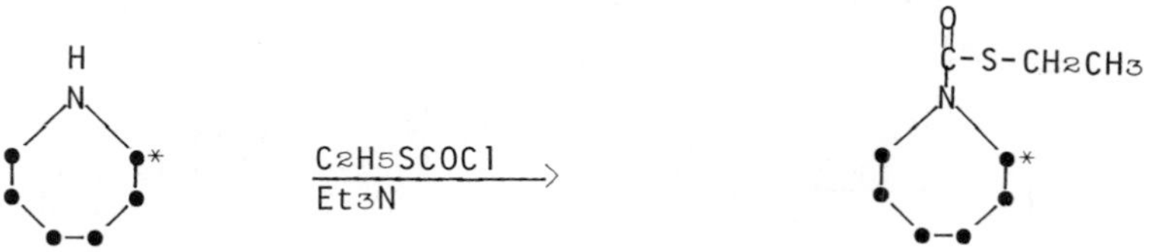
H
N
*
C2H5SCOCl
Et3N
O
C-S-CH2CH3
N
*

Hexahydro-1H-azepine-2-^{14}C

Hexahydro-1H-azepine-2-^{14}C 1-carbothioic acid S-ethyl ester

A. D. Gutman, D. R. Baker, and M. E. Brokke, J. Label. Compounds, 2, 219 (1966).

$NH_2{*}CH_2{*}CH_2NH_2 \cdot 2HCl$ $\xrightarrow[\text{dioxane}]{CS_2,\ NaOH}$ $NaSC(=S)NH\text{-}{*}CH_2{*}CH_2\text{-}NHC(=S)SNa$ (52%)

1,2-Ethanediamine-1,2-^{14}C dihydrochloride

Nabam
[(1,2-Ethanediyl-1,2-^{14}C) biscarbamodithioic acid disodium salt]

H. A. Selling, J. Berg, and A. C. Besemer, J. Label. Compounds, 10, 671 (1974).

9

Heterocyclic Compounds

Compounds with One Heteroatom

9-1 Three-Membered Rings

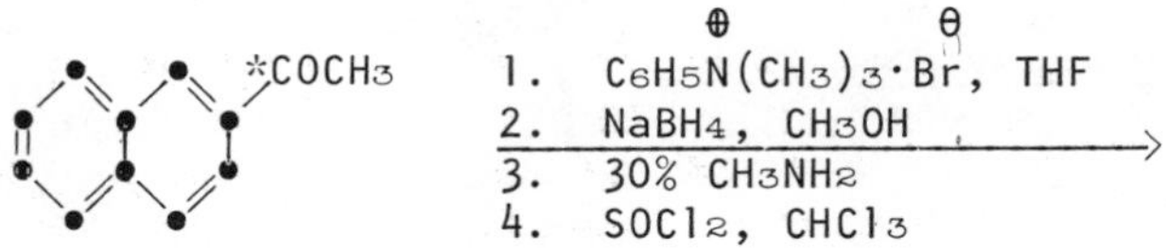
*COCH3
1. C6H5N(CH3)3·Br, THF
2. NaBH4, CH3OH
3. 30% CH3NH2
4. SOCl2, CHCl3

1-(2-Naphthalenyl)-ethanone-1-^{14}C

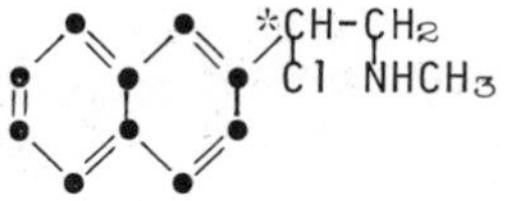
*CH-CH2
Cl NHCH3

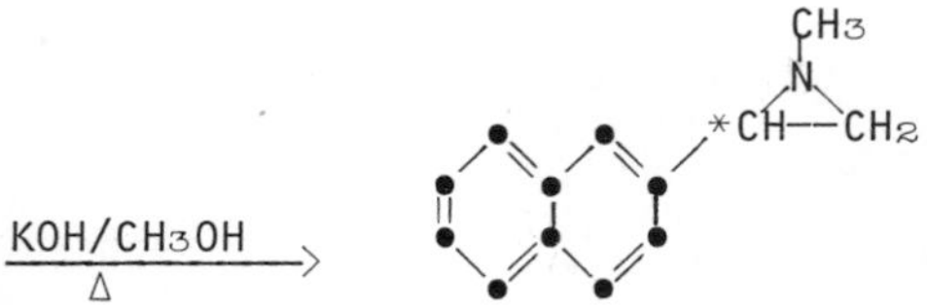
KOH/CH3OH
Δ
CH3
N
*CH—CH2

(32% overall)

1-Methyl-2-(2-naphthalenyl)-aziridine-2-^{14}C

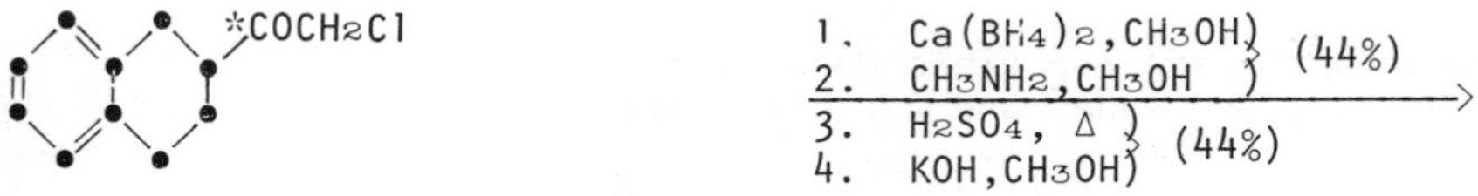
*COCH2Cl
1. Ca(BH4)2,CH3OH
2. CH3NH2,CH3OH
(44%)
3. H2SO4, Δ
4. KOH,CH3OH
(44%)

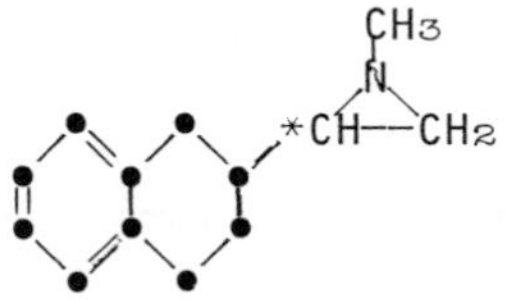
CH3
N
*CH
CH2

(14% overall from ketone)

1-Methyl-2-(1,2,3,4-tetrahydro-2-naphthalenyl)aziridine-2-^{14}C

H. Minato, T. Nagasaki, Y. Katsuyama, T. Yokoshima, K. Suga, and T. Ueda, J. Label. Compound. Radiopharm., 13, 103 (1977).

9-2 Five-Membered Rings

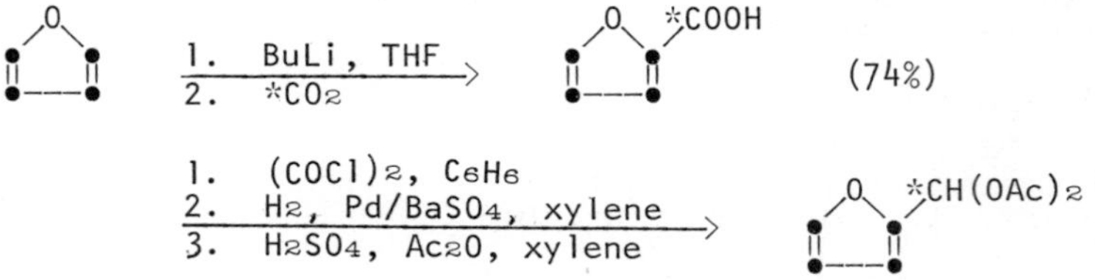
O
1. BuLi, THF
2. *CO2
*COOH
1. (COCl)2, C6H6
2. H2, Pd/BaSO4, xylene
3. H2SO4, Ac2O, xylene
*CH(OAc)2

(74%)

(68% for three steps)

2-Furan(methane-^{14}C)-diol diacetate

L. F. Elsom and D. R. Hawkins, J. Label. Compound. Radiopharm., 14, 799 (1978).

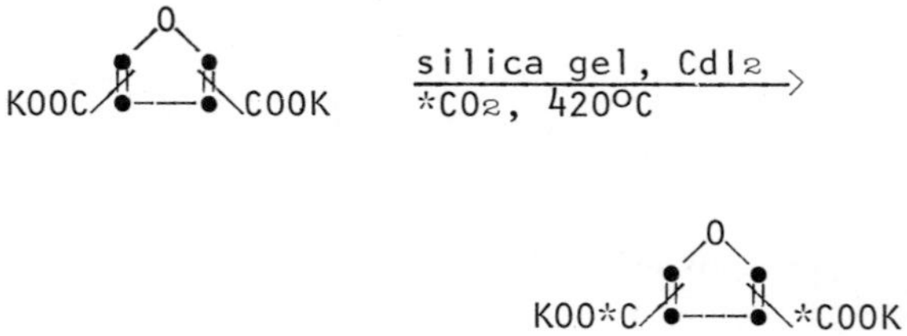
O
KOOC
COOK
silica gel, CdI2
*CO2, 420°C
KOO*C
*COOK

(40-59% recovery; 62-95% incorporation of radioactivity)

Transcarboxylation reactions were carried out on a number of naphthalene, pyridine, and furan systems.

J. Ratusky and R. Tykva, J. Label. Compounds, 5, 211 (1969).

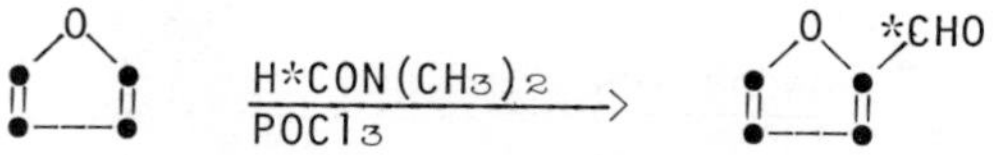

(60-66%)

Furfural
[2-Furancarboxaldehyde-(carbonyl-^{14}C)]

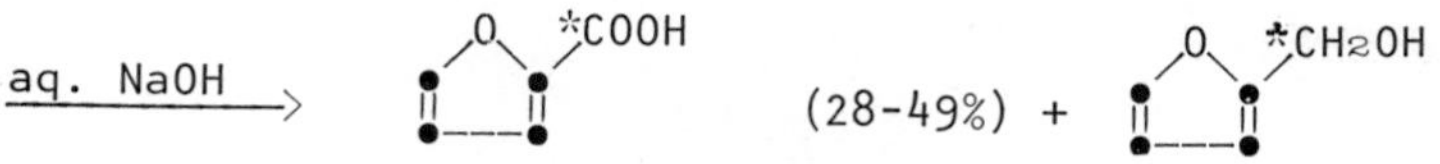

(28-49%) + (30-32%)

2-Furancarboxylic acid-(carboxyl-^{14}C)

2-Furan-(methanol-^{14}C)

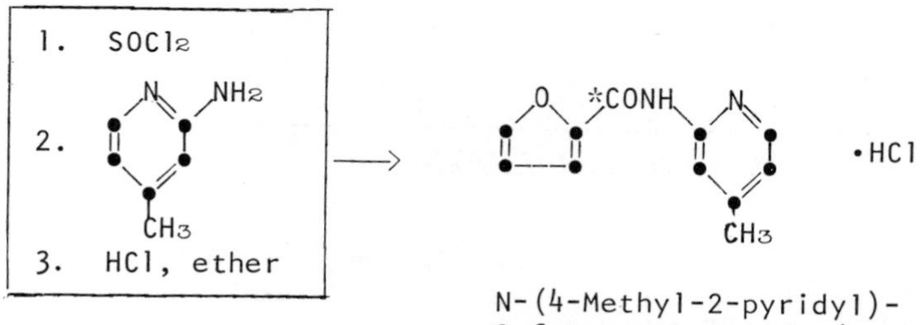

(49-54%)

N-(4-Methyl-2-pyridyl)-2-furancarboxamide-(carboxyl-^{14}C) hydrochloride

Z. Ozdowska, J. Label. Compound. Radiopharm., 14, 361 (1978).

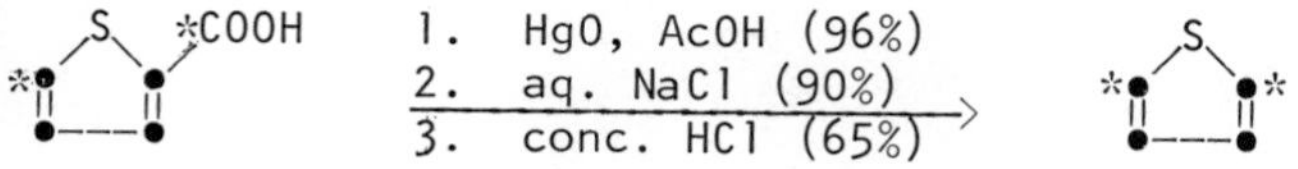

Thiophene-2,5-^{14}C

J. L. Chanal, M.-T. Calmette, B. Bonnaud, and H. Cousse, Eur. J. Med. Chem.-Chim. Ther., 9, 641 (1974).

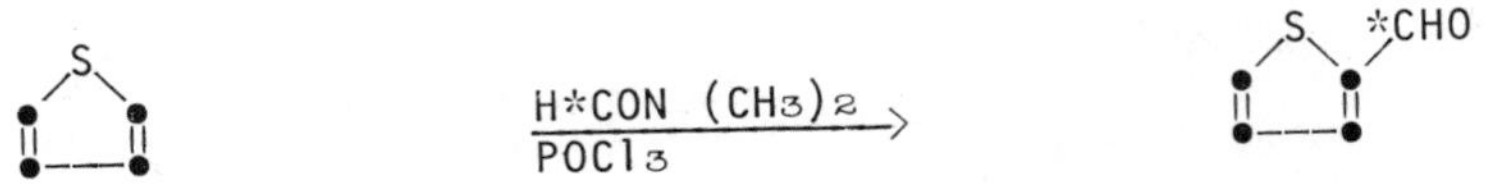

2-Thiophene
carboxaldehyde-
(carbonyl-^{14}C)

S. K. Figdor, M. S. von Wittenau, J. K. Faulkner, and A. M. Monro, J. Label. Compounds, 6, 362 (1970).

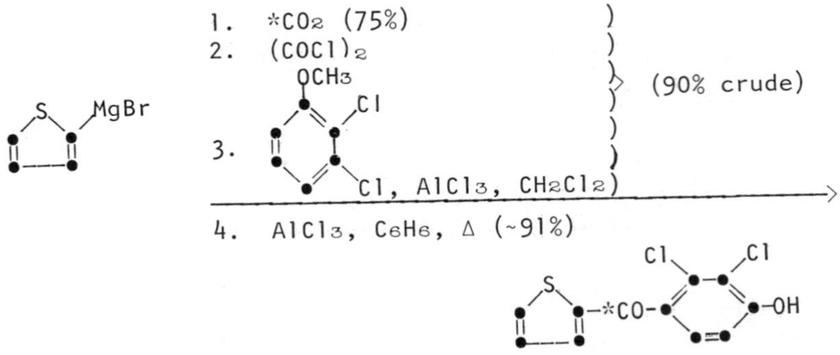

(2,3-Dichloro-4-hydroxyphenyl)-
2-thienylmethanone-^{14}C

M. Herbert and L. Pichat, J. Label. Compound.Radiopharm., 12, 437 (1976).

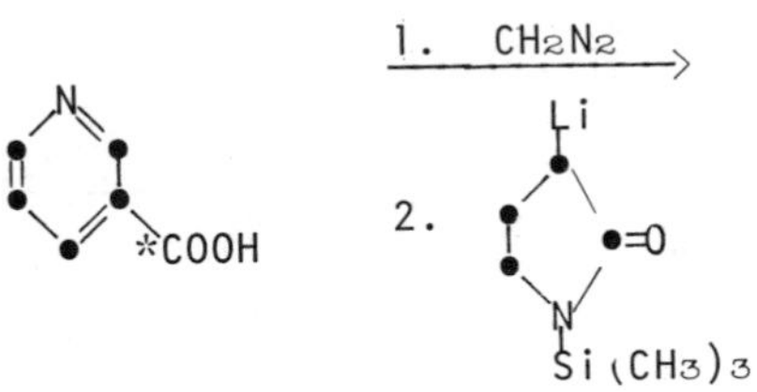

Nicotinic acid
[3-Pyridinecarboxylic-^{14}C acid]

3-(3-Pyridinylcarbonyl-^{14}C)-
1-(trimethylsilyl)-2-
pyrrolidone

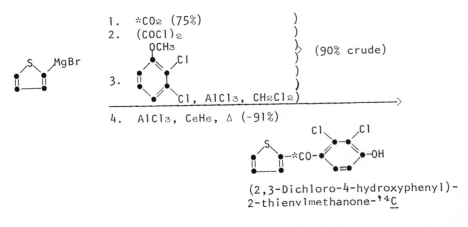

conc. HCl, Δ →

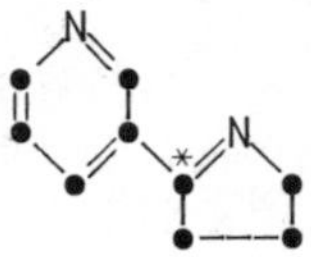

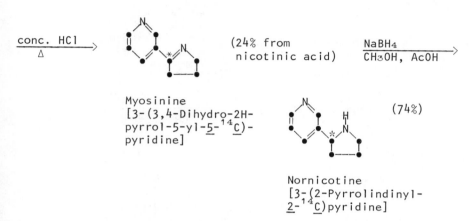

(24% from nicotinic acid)

NaBH₄ → CH₃OH, AcOH

Myosinine
[3-(3,4-Dihydro-2H-pyrrol-5-yl-5-^{14}C)-pyridine]

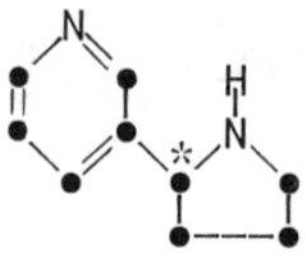

(74%)

Nornicotine
[3-(2-Pyrrolindinyl-2-^{14}C)pyridine]

M. W. Hu, W. E. Bondinell, and D. Hoffman, J. Label. Compounds, 10, 79 (1974).

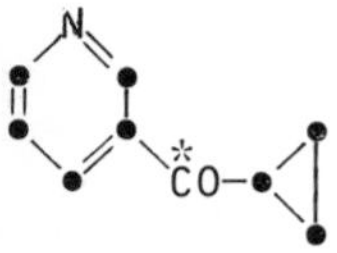

$HCONHCH_3$, $MgCl_2$ →

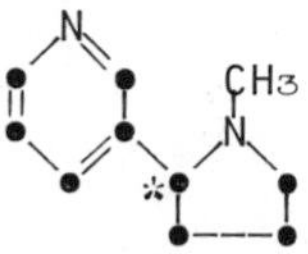

(32%)

DL-Nicotine
[3-(1-Methyl-2-pyrrolidinyl-2-^{14}C) pyridine]

R. A. Comes, M. T. Core, M. D. Edmonds, W. B. Edwards, III, and R. W. Jenkins, Jr., J. Label. Compounds, 9, 253 (1973).

$C_6H_5CHCH_2COOH$
*COOH .2NH₃

1. 210-220°C
2. $LiAlH_4$, ether/dioxane →

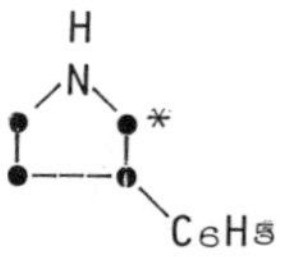

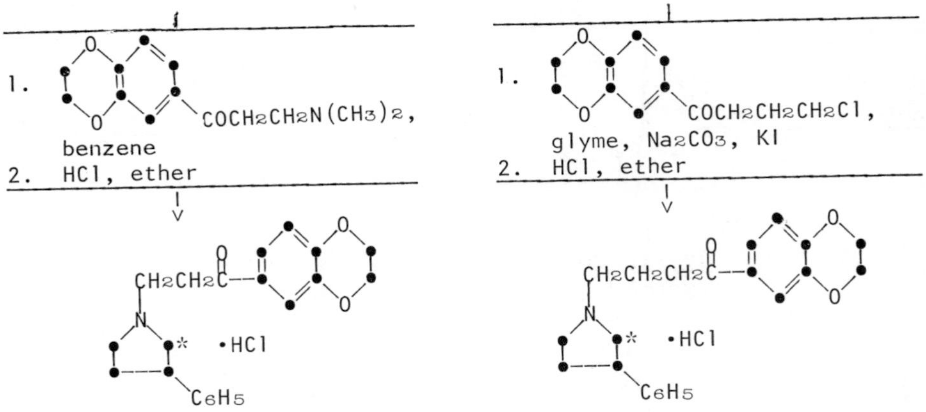

1.
$COCH_2CH_2N(CH_3)_2$,
benzene
2. HCl, ether
CH_2CH_2C
•HCl
C_6H_5
1.
$COCH_2CH_2CH_2Cl$,
glyme, Na_2CO_3, KI
2. HCl, ether
$CH_2CH_2CH_2C$
•HCl
C_6H_5

Pyrroxane
[1-(2,3-Dihydro-1,4-benzodioxin-6-yl)-3-(3-phenyl-1-pyrrolidinyl-2-^{14}C)-1-propanone hydrochloride]

Butiroxane
[1-(2,3-Dihydro-1,4-benzodioxin-6-yl)-3-(3-phenyl-1-pyrrolidinyl-2-^{14}C)-1-butanone hydrochloride]

B. Z. Askinazi, S. M. Chizhik, and N. Y. Kozarinskaya, Khim.-Farm. Zh., 12, 82 (1978).

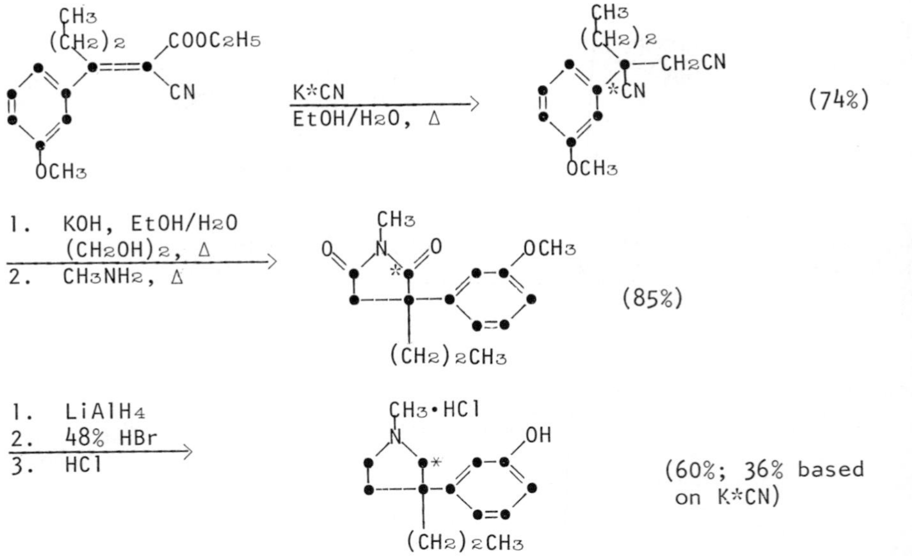

CH_3
$(CH_2)_2$
$COOC_2H_5$
CN
OCH_3
K*CN
EtOH/H_2O, Δ
CH_2CN
*CN
(74%)
1. KOH, EtOH/H_2O
$(CH_2OH)_2$, Δ
2. CH_3NH_2, Δ
OCH_3
$(CH_2)_2CH_3$
(85%)
1. $LiAlH_4$
2. 48% HBr
3. HCl
CH_3•HCl
OH
$(CH_2)_2CH_3$
(60%; 36% based on K*CN)

Profadol
[3-(1-Methyl-3-propyl-3-pyrrolidinyl-2-^{14}C)phenol hydrochloride]

C. E. Blackburn, J. Label. Compounds, 6, 21 (1970).

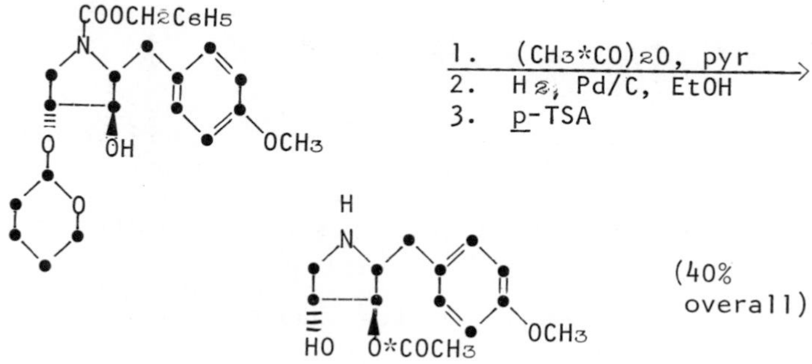
COOCH2C6H5
N
OH
O
O
OCH3
1. (CH3*CO)2O, pyr
2. H2, Pd/C, EtOH
3. p-TSA
H
N
HO
O*COCH3
OCH3

(40% overall)

Anisomycin
[[2S-(3α,4β)]-2-[(4-Methoxyphenyl) methyl]-3,4-pyrrolidinediol-3-(acetate-1-^{14}C)]

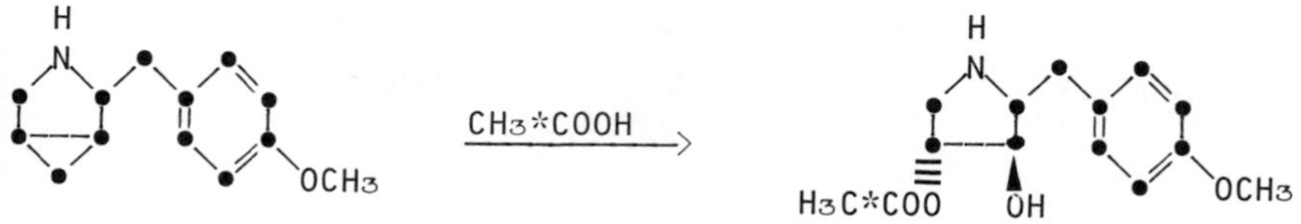
H
N
OCH3
CH3*COOH
H
N
H3C*COO
OH
OCH3

Isoanisomycin
[[2S-(3α,4β)]-2-[(4-Methoxyphenyl)methyl]-3,4-pyrrolidinediol-4-(acetate-1-^{14}C)]

Acetylation of the above two products gives a mixture which after mild hydrolysis gives radioactive N-acetyldeacetylanisomycin; 30% of acetate-1-^{14}C from anisomycin became incorporated into the N-acetyl product while only 7% of the labeled acetate from isoanisomycin was incorporated. Internal transacetylation via bicyclic intermediates is postulated.

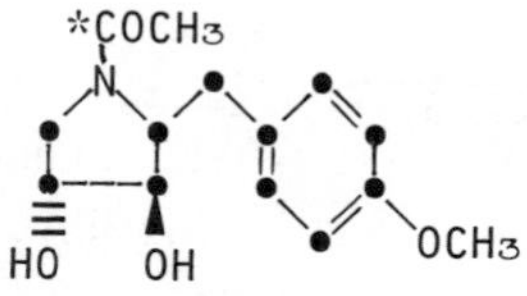
*COCH3
N
HO
OH
OCH3

N-(Acetyl)deacetylanisomycin
[[2S-(3α,4β)]-1-(Acetyl-1-^{14}C)-2-[(4-methoxyphenyl)methyl]-3,4-pyrrolidinediol]

K. Butler, J. Org. Chem., 33, 2136 (1968).

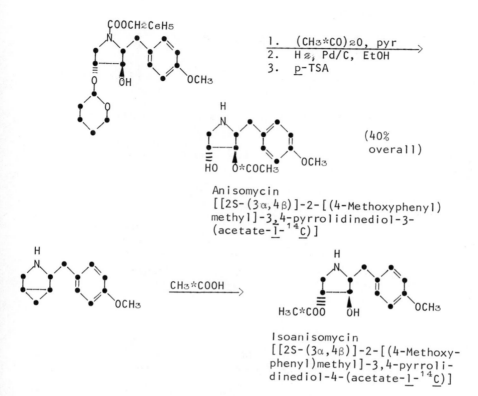

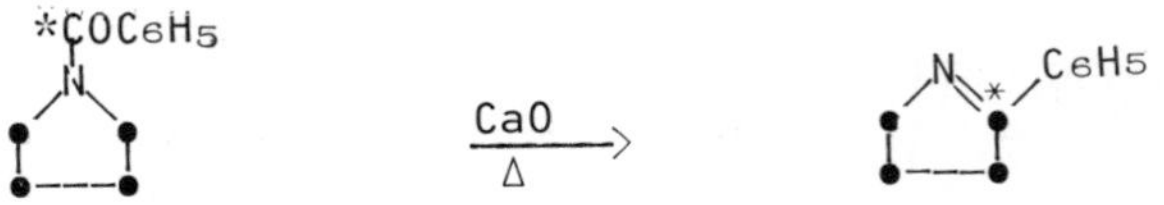
*COC6H5
N
CaO
Δ
N
C6H5

3,4-Dihydro-5-phenyl-2H-pyrrole-5-^{14}C

The label is assumed to be at the 5 position; a mechanism is proposed.

B. P. Mundy, K. B. ipkowitz, M. Lee, and B. R. Larsen, J. Org. Chem., 39, 1963 (1974).

$H_2N^*CH_2CH_2CH_2COOH$

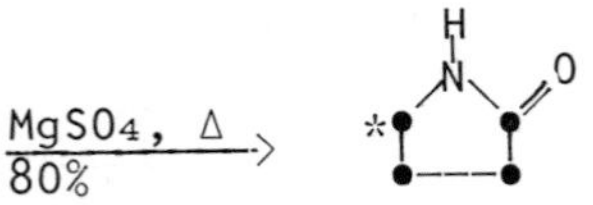
MgSO4, Δ
80%
H
N
O

(70-80% from 3-cyanopropionate; 56% overall)

4-Aminobutanoic-4-^{14}C acid

2-Pyrrolidinone-5-^{14}C

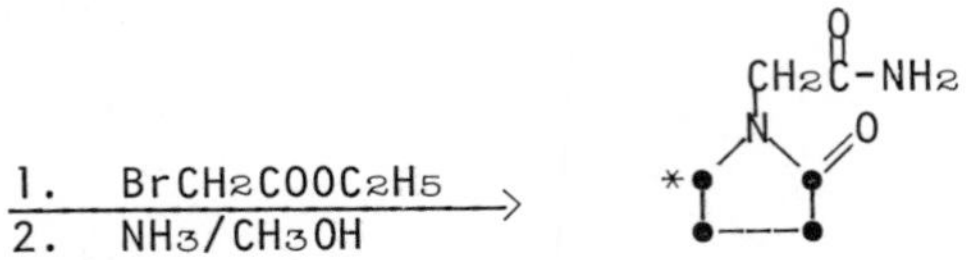
1. BrCH2COOC2H5
2. NH3/CH3OH
O
CH2C-NH2
N
O

(29%)

2-Oxo-1-pyrrolidine acetamide-5-^{14}C

A. J. Villani, W. L. Mendelson, and D. W. Blackburn, J. Label. Compounds, 9, 269 (1973).

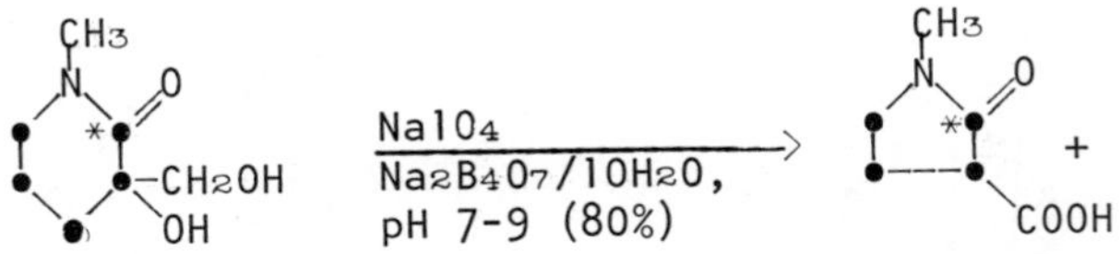
CH3
N
O
CH2OH
OH
NaIO4
Na2B4O7/10H2O,
pH 7-9 (80%)
CH3
N
O
COOH

\+ HCHO (<0.02% activity)

3-Hydroxy-3-hydroxymethyl-1-methyl-2-piperidinone-2-^{14}C

1-Methyl-2-oxopyrrolidine-3-carboxylic-2-^{14}C acid

Decarboxylation indicated that 0.6% of the activity was in the evolved CO_2 leaving 99.2% of the activity in the resulting 1-methyl-2-pyrrolidinone. The label was therefore assumed to be at the 2-position; a mechanism for the major and minor pathways was proposed. Yields given are for unlabeled reactions.

M. L. Rueppel and H. Rapoport, J. Amer. Chem. Soc., 94, 3877 (1972).

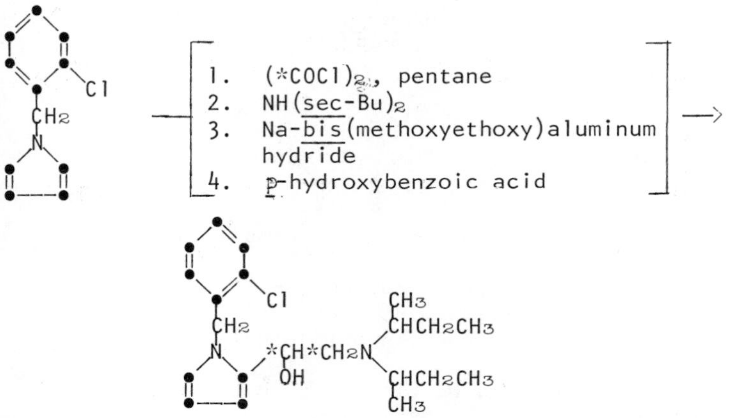
Cl
CH2
N
1. (*COCl)2, pentane
2. NH(sec-Bu)2
3. Na-bis(methoxyethoxy)aluminum hydride
4. p-hydroxybenzoic acid
Cl
CH3
CHCH2CH3
CH2
N
*CH*CH2N
OH
CHCH2CH3
CH3

Viminol
[α-[[Bis(1-methylpropyl)amino]methyl-^{14}C]-1-[(2-chlorophenyl)methyl]-1H-pyrrole-2-methanol-^{14}C]

B. D. Cameron, L. F. Chasseaud, G. Hardy, J. D. Lewis, V. H. Saggers, and I. P. Sword, Arzneim.-Forsch.-(Drug Res.), 23, 708 (1973).

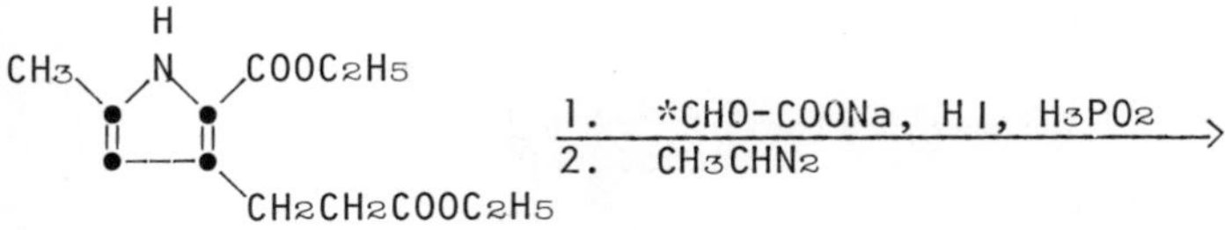
H
CH3
N
COOC2H5
1. *CHO-COONa, HI, H3PO2
2. CH3CHN2
CH2CH2COOC2H5

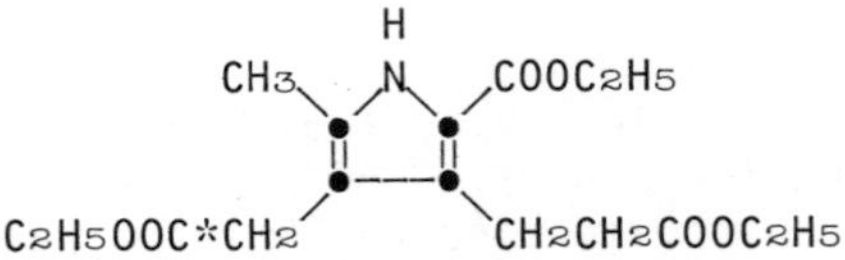

2-(Ethoxycarbonyl)-4-(2-ethoxy-2-oxy-1-^{14}C-ethyl)-5-methyl-1H-pyrrole-3-propanoic acid ethyl ester

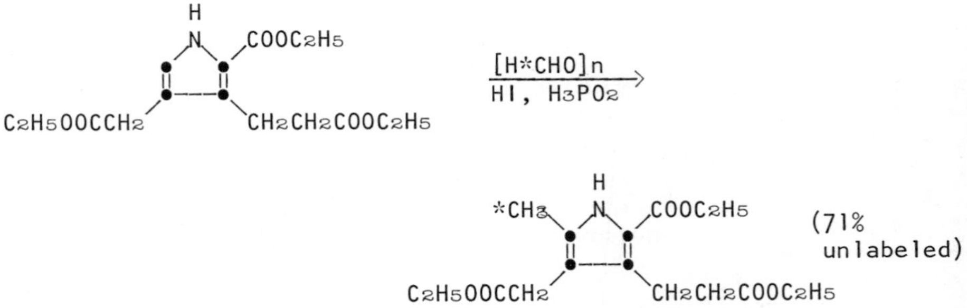
[H*CHO]n
HI, H_3PO_2
(71%
unlabeled)

2-(Ethoxycarbonyl)-4-(2-ethoxy-2-oxyethyl)-5-(methyl-^{14}C)-1H-pyrrole-3-propanoic acid ethyl ester

A. R. Battersby, D. A. Evans, K. H. Gibson, E. McDonald, and L. Nixon, J. Chem. Soc., Perkin Trans.I, 1546 (1973).

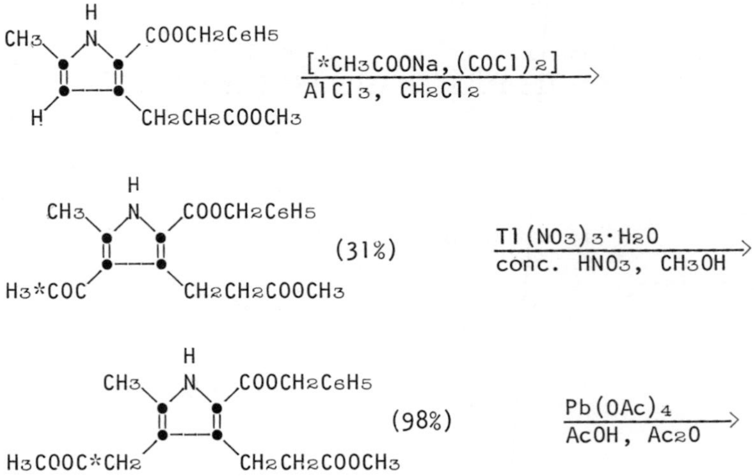
[*CH_3COONa, $(COCl)_2$]
$AlCl_3$, CH_2Cl_2
(31%)
$Tl(NO_3)_3\cdot H_2O$
conc. HNO_3, CH_3OH
(98%)
$Pb(OAc)_4$
AcOH, Ac_2O

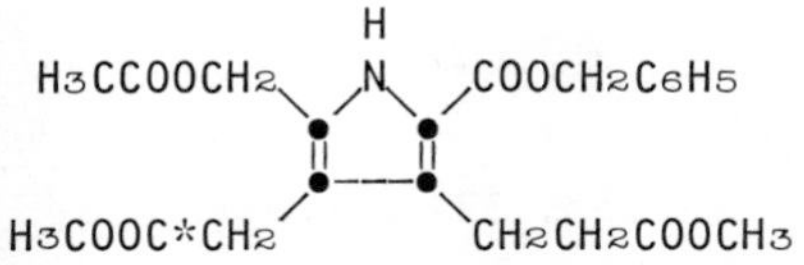

(92%)

1. Potassium phthalimide DMSO (85%)
2. 10% H_2SO_4, CF_3COOH, anisole (60%)

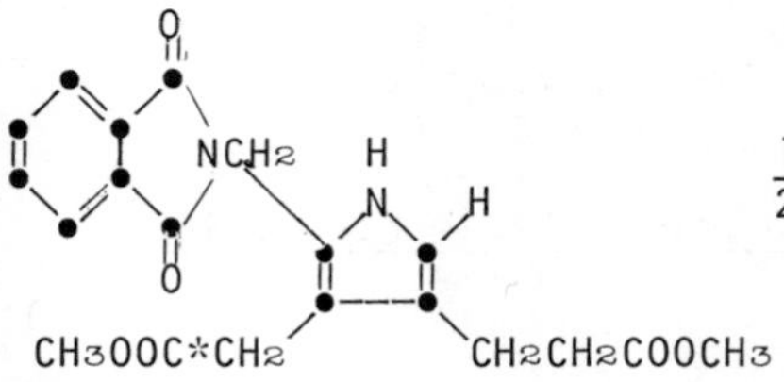

1. NH_2OH, THF (62% for unlabeled)
2. 2N KOH (66%)

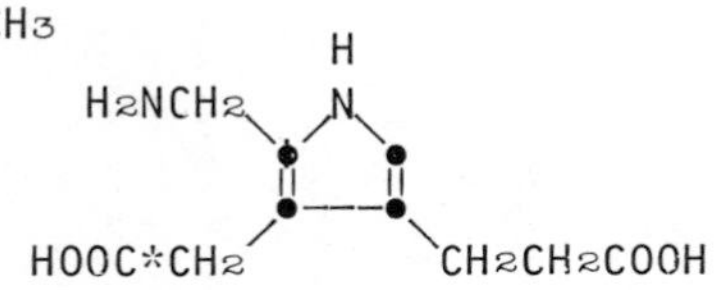

Porphobilinogen-PBG
[5-(Aminomethyl)-4-carboxymethyl-^{14}C)
1H-pyrrole-3-propanoic acid]

G. W. Kenner, J. Rimmer, K. M. Smith, and J. F. Unsworth, J. Chem. Soc., Perkin Trans. I, 332 (1977); J. Chem. Soc., Chem. Commun., 43 (1973).

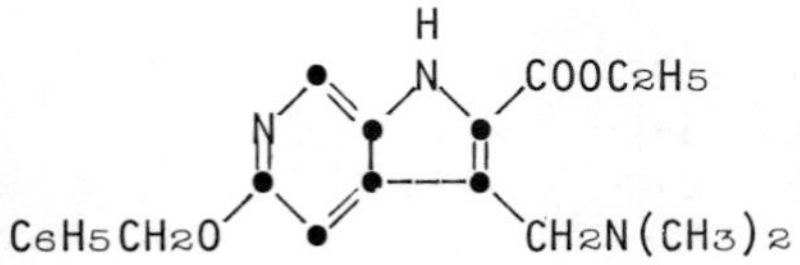

*$CH_2(COOC_2H_5)_2$
Na, decalin, Δ

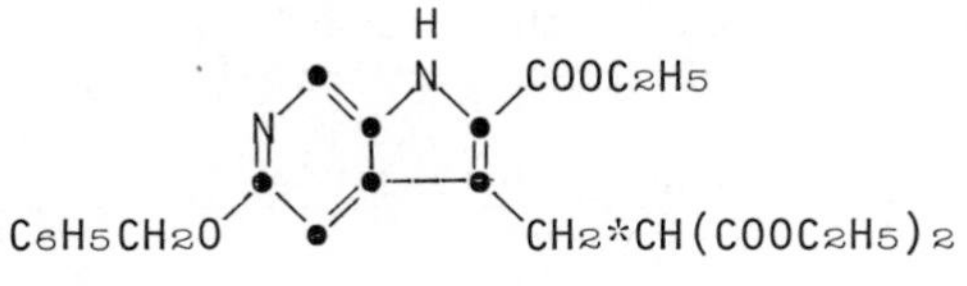

(50%)

1. conc. HCl, Δ (94%)
2. H_2, 10% Pd/C, aq. Na_2CO_3 (90%)
3. H_2O, Δ (95%)

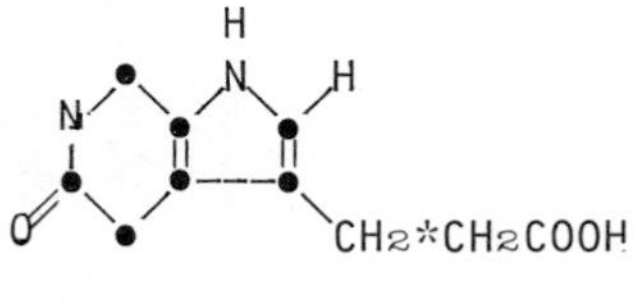

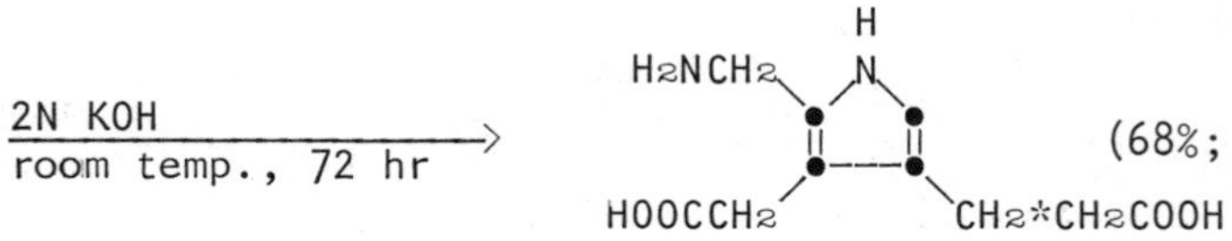
2N KOH
room temp., 72 hr
H
H2NCH2
N
HOOCCH2
CH2*CH2COOH

(68%; 27% overall)

Porphobilinogen
[5-(Aminomethyl)-4-(carboxymethyl)-1H-pyrrole-3-propanoic-2-^{14}C acid]

A. Valasinas and L. Diaz, J. Label. Compound. Radiopharm., 15, 549 (1978).

$^{*}C_6H_5Br$ + $C_6H_5NH_2$ $\xrightarrow[\Delta]{K}$ $(^{*}C_6H_5)_2NH$ (34%)

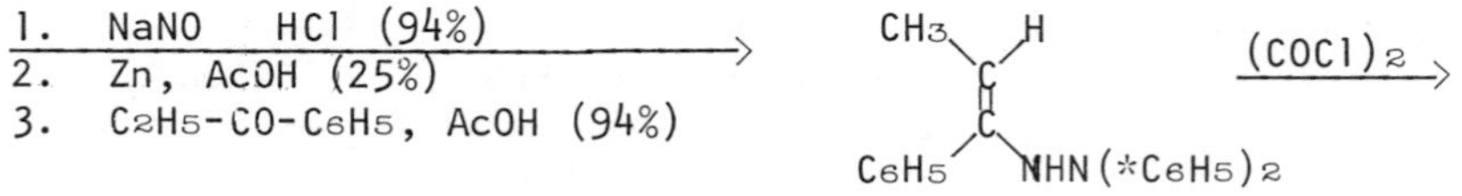
1. NaNO HCl (94%)
2. Zn, AcOH (25%)
3. C2H5-CO-C6H5, AcOH (94%)
CH3
H
C
C
C6H5
NHN(*C6H5)2
(COCl)2

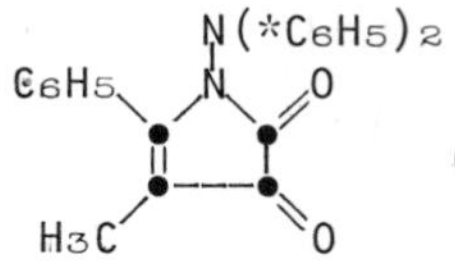
N(*C6H5)2
C6H5
N
O
H3C
O

(62%; 3% overall)

1-(Diphenyl-U-^{14}C-amino)-4-methyl-5-phenyl-1H-pyrrole-2,3-dione

The product was used in the mechanistic study of the rearrangement (intramolecular proposed) to pyrrolo[2,3b]indole.

G. Kollenz and C. Labes, Justus Liebigs Ann. Chem., 174 (1976).

9-3 Six-Membered Rings

*COOH
*COOH

1. EtOH, CCl_4 (76%)
2. NaOEt, CH_3COCH_3
3. HCl, Δ

→

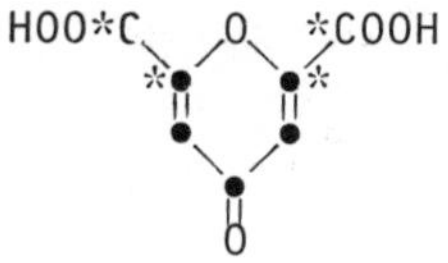

(46% based on oxalic acid)

Chelidonic acid
[4-oxo-4H-pyran-2,6-(dicarboxylic-^{14}C)-2,6-^{14}C acid]

J. Bergman and J. R. Gear, J. Label. Compounds, 11, 485 (1975).

$NH_2(CH_2)_4$*$CHNH_2COOH$•HCl

dl-Lysine•HCl-2-^{14}C

1. NBS, H_2O
2. CH_2=$CHCH_2MgCl$, THF

→

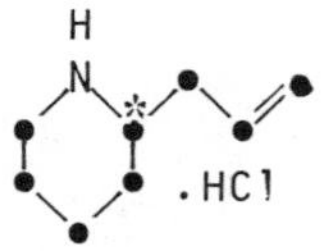

(8%)

2-(2-Propenyl) piperidine-2-^{14}C hydrochloride

M. Preiss and I. D. Spenser, Chem. Ber., 104, 1967 (1971).

Ts-N(CH_2CH_2Cl)$_2$

$C_6H_5CH_2$*CN
NaH, toluene, Δ

→

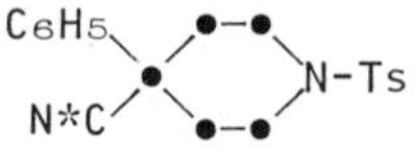

(57%)

1. 75% H_2SO_4
2. EtOH
3. NaOH
4. HCl gas

→

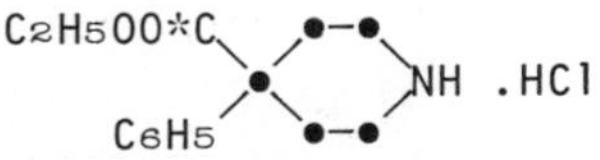

(41%)

Norpethidine hydrochloride
[4-Phenyl-4-piperidine-carboxylic-^{14}C acid ethyl ester hydrochloride]

1. [HCHO]n, C6H5COCH3,
EtOH, Δ (63%)
2. NaBH4, CH3OH (29%)
HOCHCH2CH2-N
C6H5
*COOC2H5
C6H5
•HCl

DL-Phenoperidine
[1-(3-Hydroxy-3-phenylpropyl)-4-piperidinecarboxylic-^{14}C acid ethyl ester hydrochloride]

C. Luu Duc, Cl. Charlon, Cl. Agnius Delord, J. Cros, and B. Monsarrat, J. Label. Compound. Radiopharm., 15, 693 (1978).

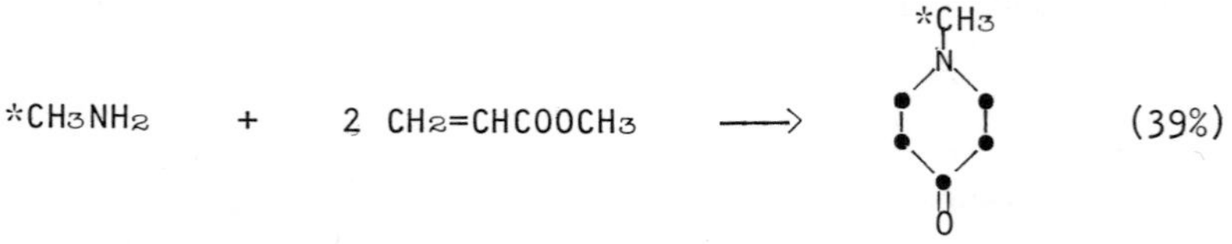
*CH3NH2
+
2 CH2=CHCOOCH3
*CH3
N
O
(39%)

(1-Methyl-^{14}C)-4-piperidinone

N. G. Tsyshkova and F. A. Trofimov, Khim.-Farm. Zh., 5, 14 (1971).

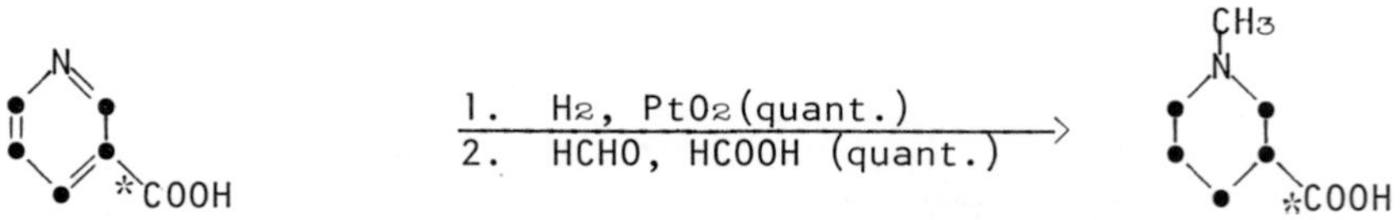
N
*COOH
1. H2, PtO2 (quant.)
2. HCHO, HCOOH (quant.)
CH3
N
*COOH

Nicotinic-^{14}C acid

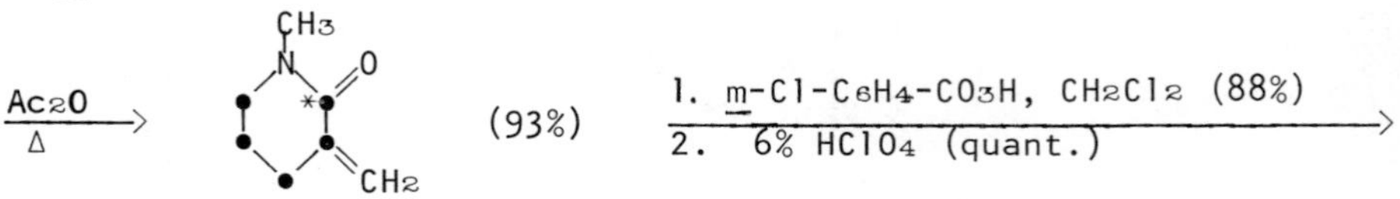
Ac2O
Δ
CH3
N
O
CH2
(93%)
1. m-Cl-C6H4-CO3H, CH2Cl2 (88%)
2. 6% HClO4 (quant.)

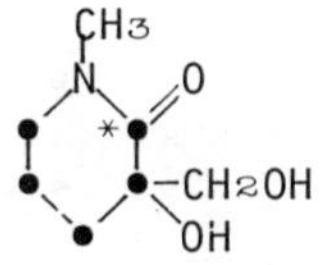
CH3
N
O
*
CH2OH
OH

3-Hydroxy-3-hydroxymethyl-1-methyl-2-piperidinone-2-^{14}C

M. L. Reuppel and H. Rapoport, J. Amer. Chem. Soc., 94, 3877 (1972).

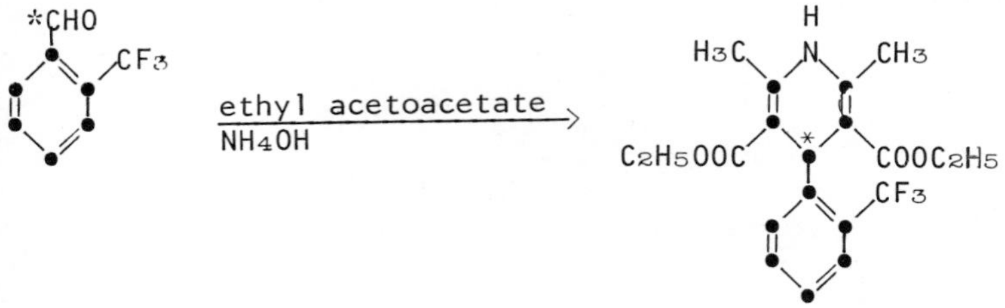
*CHO
CF3
ethyl acetoacetate
NH4OH
H
H3C
N
CH3
C2H5OOC
*
COOC2H5
CF3

2,6-Dimethyl-4-[2-trifluoromethylphenyl]-1,4-dihydropyridine-3,5-dicarboxylic-4-^{14}C acid diethyl ester

S. S. Walkenstein, A. P. Intoccia, T. L. Flanagan, B. Hwang, D. Flint, J. Weinstock, A. J. Villani, D. Blackburn, and H. Green, J. Pharm. Sci., 62, 580 (1973).

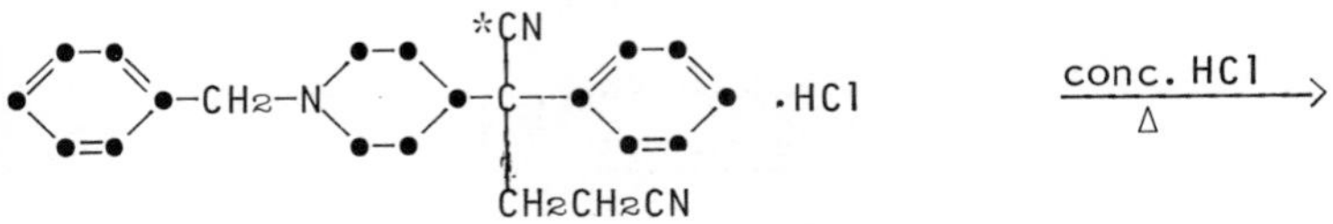
*CN
CH2–N
C
CH2CH2CN
.HCl
conc. HCl
Δ

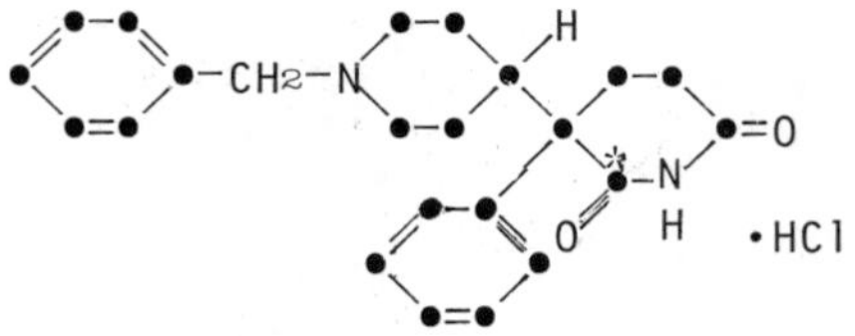
CH2
N
H
O
N
H
O
•HCl

(38% from K*CN)

Benzetimide
[3-Phenyl-3-[1-(phenylmethyl)-
4-piperidinyl]-2,6-piperidinedione-
2-^{14}C hydrochloride]

I. van Wijngaarden and W. Sondijn, J. Label. Compounds, 1, 207 (1965).

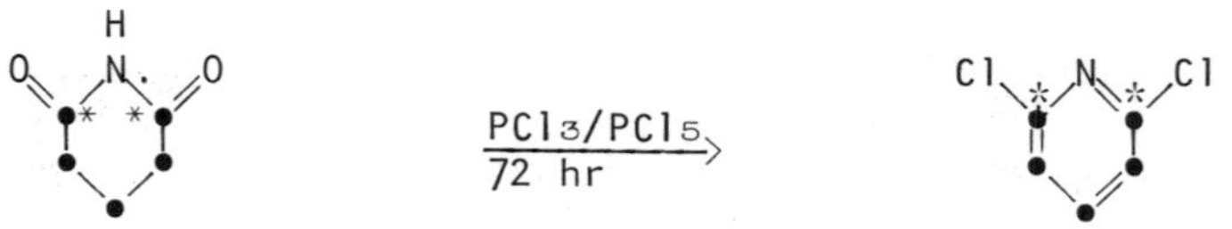
H
O
N
O
PCl3/PCl5
72 hr
Cl
N
Cl

(78%)

2,6-Dichloropyridine-
2,6-^{14}C

L. H. McKendry and W. W. Muelder, J. Label. Compound.Radiopharm., 15, 87 (1978).

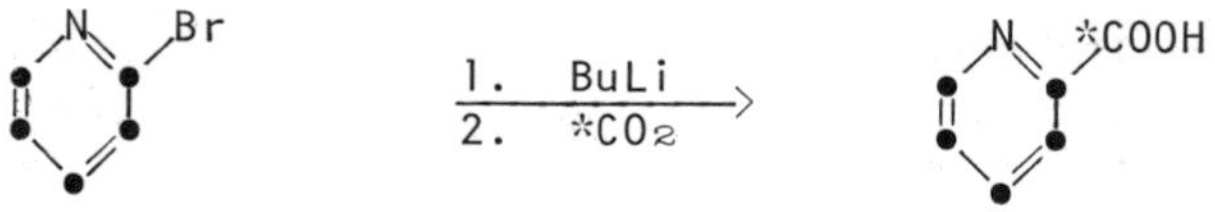
N
Br
1. BuLi
2. *CO2
N
*COOH

(31%)

2-Pyridinecarboxylic acid
(carboxyl-^{14}C)

E. J. Merril and G. G. Vernice, J. Label. Compounds, 8, 589 (1972).

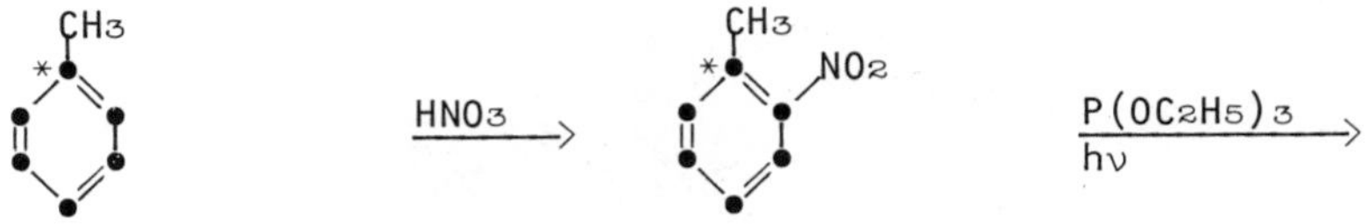

Toluene-1-^{14}C

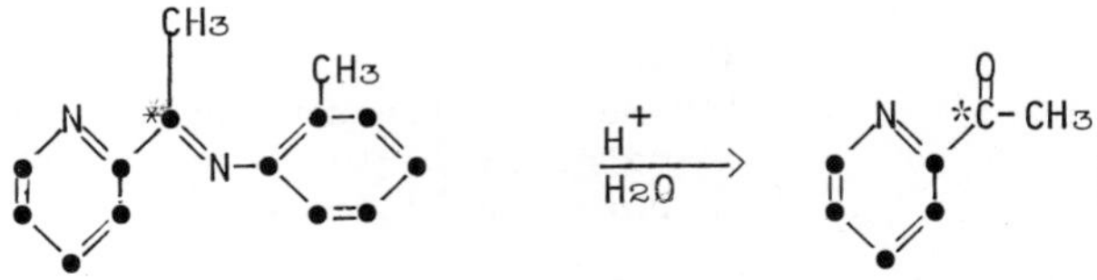

(14%) (plus other products)

1-(2-Pyridinyl)-ethanone-1-^{14}C

R. J. Sundberg and S. R. Suter, J. Org. Chem., 35, 827 (1970).

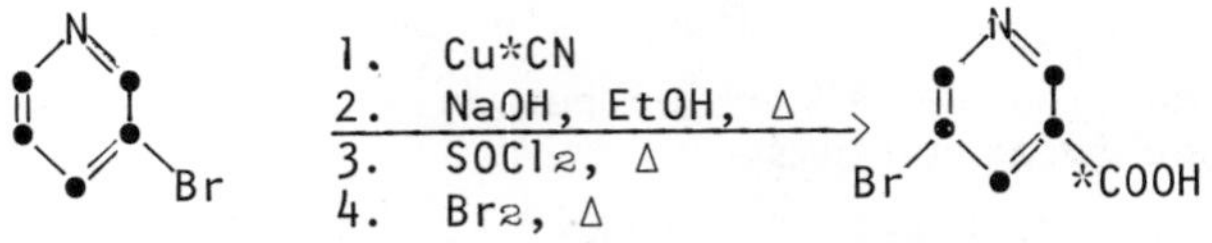

(37% overall)

5-Bromonicotinic acid [5-Bromo-3-pyridinecarboxylic acid-(carboxyl-^{14}C)]

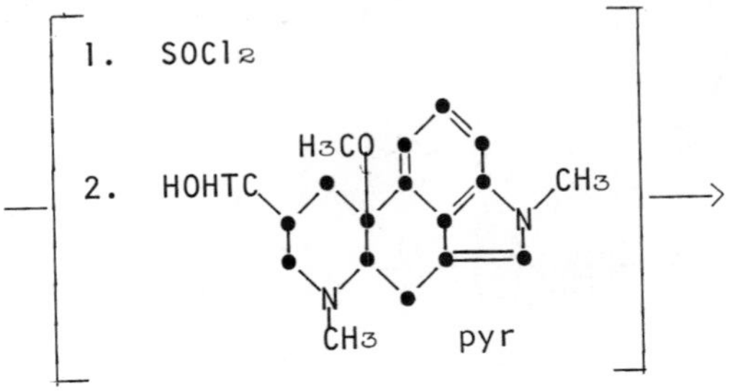

1. SOCl2
2. HOHTC
H3CO
CH3
N
CH3
pyr

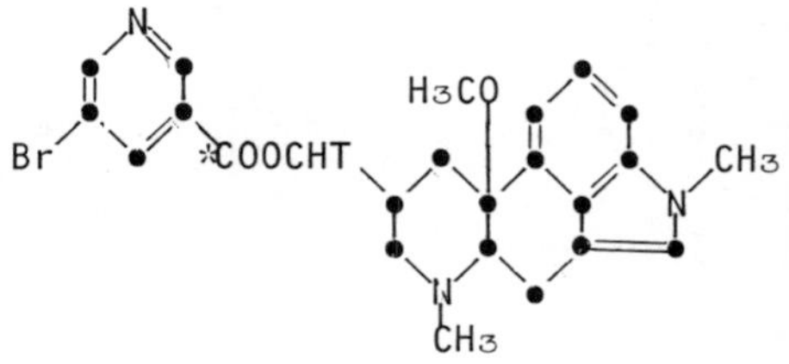

Nicargoline
[10-Methoxy-1,6-dimethylergoline 8β-methanol-17-t-5-bromopyridinecarboxylate-^{14}C(ester)]

G. P. Vicario, G. C. Perucca, P. G. Ramella, and F. Arcamone, J. Label. Compound. Radiopharm., 15, 353 (1978).

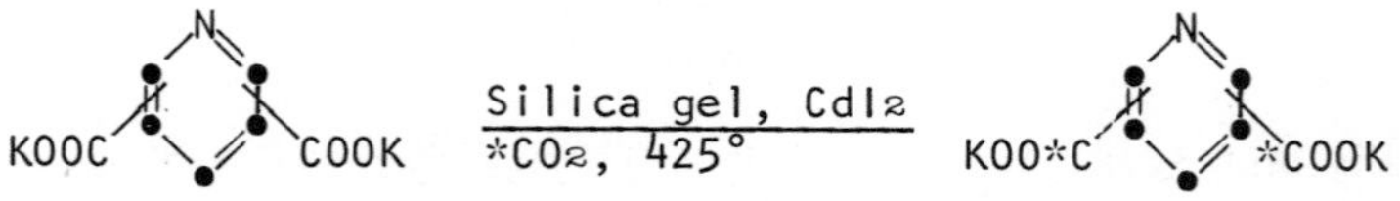

(46-59% recovery; incorporations of 65-94% radioactivity)

Pyridinedicarboxylic-^{14}C acids dipotassium salts

Transcarboxylation reactions were carried out on a number of naphthalene, pyridine, and furan systems.

J. Ratusky and R. Tykva, J. Label. Compounds, 5, 211 (1969).

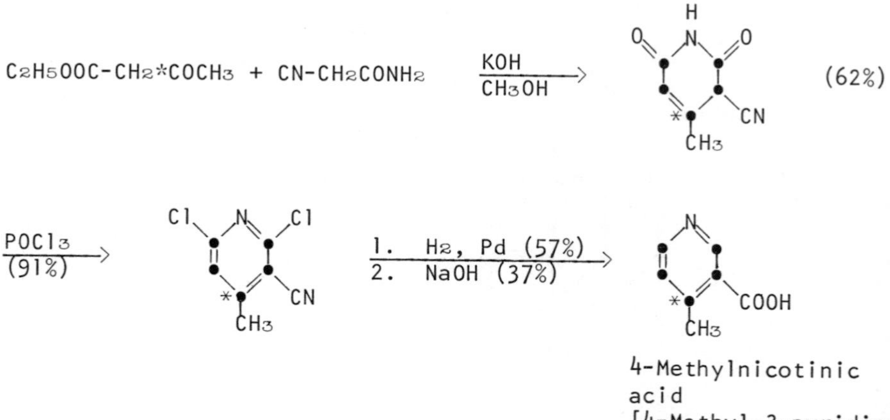

4-Methylnicotinic acid
[4-Methyl-3-pyridinecarboxylic-4-^{14}C]

E. Leete and S. A. S. Leete, J. Org. Chem., 43, 2122 (1978).

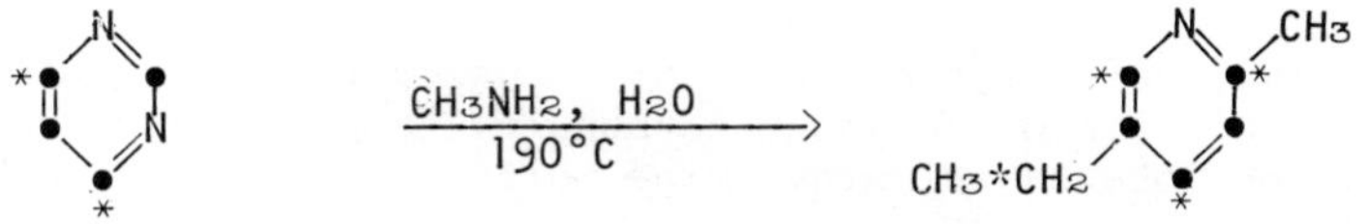
CH3NH2, H2O
190°C
CH3
CH3*CH2

(25%)

Pyrimidine-4,6-^{14}C

5-(Ethyl-1-^{14}C)-2-methylpyridine-2,4,6-^{14}C

Similarly:

*CH3
*CH3CH2

5-(Ethyl-2-^{14}C)-2-methyl-^{14}C)pyridine-3,5-^{14}C

A mechanism is proposed.

E. A. Oostveen and H. C. van der Plas, Rec. Trav. Chim., J. Roy. Neth. Chem., 95, 104 (1976).

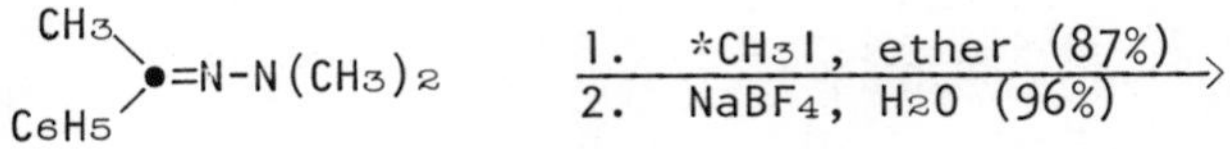
CH3
C6H5
=N-N(CH3)2
1. *CH3I, ether (87%)
2. NaBF4, H2O (96%)

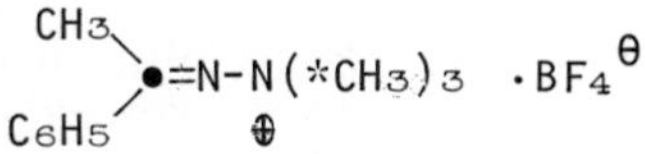
CH3
C6H5
=N-N(*CH3)3 ·BF4
⊕

(1,1,1-Trimethyl-^{14}C)-2-(1-phenyl)-ethylidene) hydrazinium tetrafluoroborate

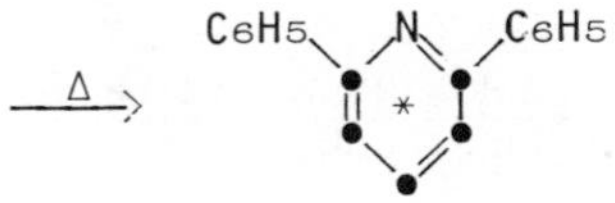
Δ
C6H5
C6H5

(55%; yields are for unlabeled reactions)

2,6-Diphenyl(pyridine-U-^{14}C)

The ratio of activity of starting material to product is 1:2.96, supporting a mechanism in which the γ carbon in the pyridine ring originates from the labeled trimethylamine moiety.

G. R. Newkome and D. L. Fishel, J. Org. Chem., 37, 1329 (1972).

C_2H_5OOC-*CH=*CH-$COOC_2H_5$ + 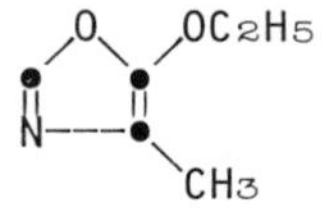

Fumaric-2,3-^{14}C acid diethyl ester

⟶ 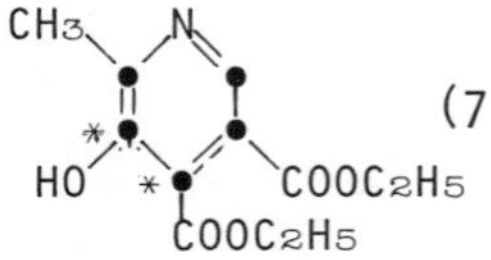 (71%)

5-Hydroxy-6-methyl-3,4-pyridinedicarboxylic acid-4,5-^{14}C diethyl ester

1. $LiAlH_4$
2. HCl
⟶ 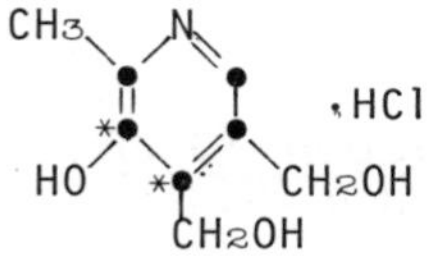 (60%; 43% from fumarate, 16% from $BaCO_3$)

Pyridoxine hydrochloride
[5-Hydroxy-6-methyl-3,4-pyridinedimethanol-4,5-^{14}C -hydrochloride]

C. Colombini and E. Celon, Gazz. Chim. Ital., 99, 526 (1969).
C. E. Colombini and E. E. McCoy, Biochemistry, 9, 533 (1970).

CH_3*$COCH_2COOC_2H_5$ —— 1. CH_3CHO, EtOH, NH_4OH (65%); 2. $NaNO_2$, AcOH (70%) ⟶

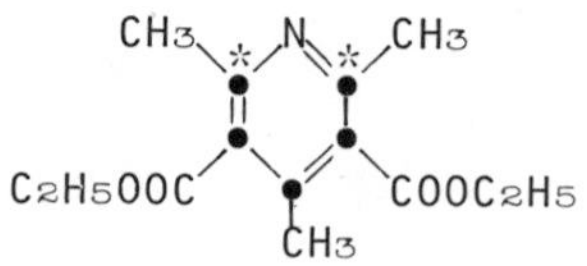

2,4,6-Trimethyl-3,5-pyridinedicarboxylic acid-2,6-^{14}C diethyl ester

$CH_3{*}COCH_2COOC_2H_5$ → 1. HCHO, EtOH, NH_4OH (65%); 2. $NaNO_2$, AcOH →

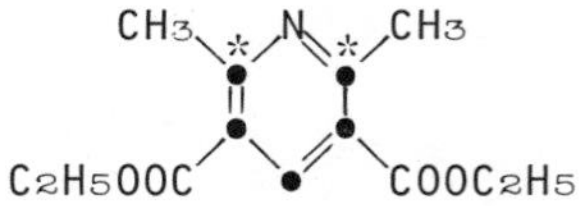

2,6-Dimethyl-3,5-pyridinedicarboxylic acid-2,6-^{14}C acid diethyl ester

W. J. Racz and G. S. Marks, Biochem. Pharmacol., 21, 143, 1511 (1972).

$C_2H_5OO{*}C-CH_2{*}COOC_2H_5$ → $CH_2=CHCN$ → $CN-CH_2CH_2CH({*}COOC_2H_5)_2$

Ethyl malonate-1,3-^{14}C

→ H_2, Ra-Ni; $(C_2H_5)_3N$, EtOH →

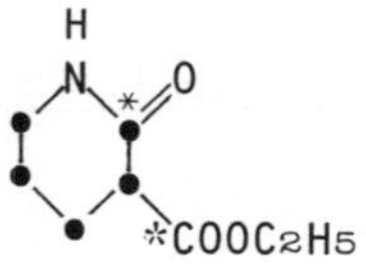

→ 1. $(C_2H_5)_3O^{\oplus}BF_4^{\ominus}$, CH_2Cl_2; 2. $NaHCO_3$, Na_2CO_3, H_2O; 3. $NaBH_4$, EtOH →

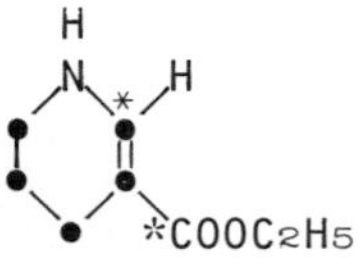

→ 1. DDQ, ether; 2. 6N HCl, Δ →

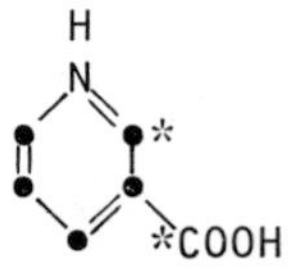
H
N
*
*COOH

(23% overall)

Nicotinic acid
[3-Pyridinecarboxylic acid-(2,carboxyl-^{14}C)]

Similarly, using ethyl malonate-2-^{14}C:

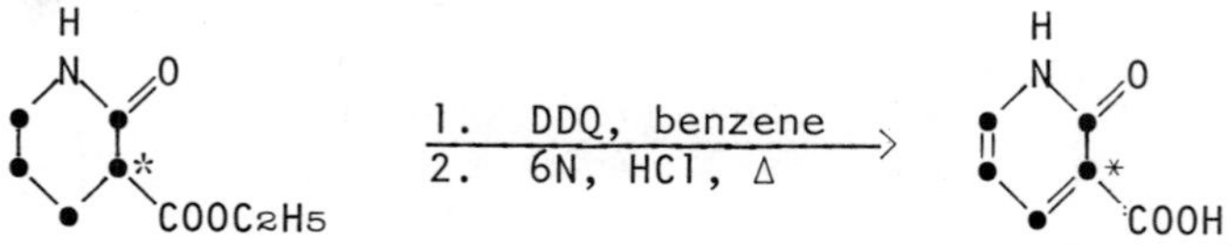
H
N
O
*
COOC2H5
1. DDQ, benzene
2. 6N, HCl, Δ
H
N
O
*
COOH

(12% overall)

1,2-Dihydro-2-oxo-3-pyridinecarboxylic-3-^{14}C acid

A. A. Liebman, D. H. Malarek, A. M. Dorsky, and H. H. Kaegi, J. Heterocycl. Chem., 11, 1105 (1974).

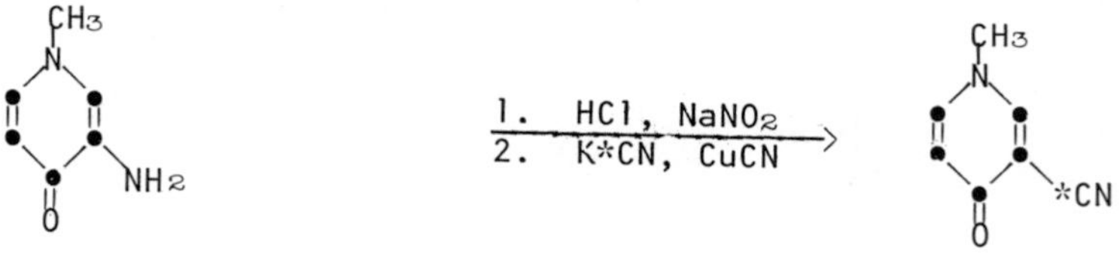
CH3
N
NH2
O
1. HCl, NaNO2
2. K*CN, CuCN
CH3
N
*CN
O

(from 4-hydroxypyridine)

1-Methyl-4-oxo-3-pyridinecarbonitrile-(cyano-^{14}C)

H. E. Johnson and G. R. Waller, J. Label. Compounds, 4, 289 (1968).

9-4 Seven-Membered Rings

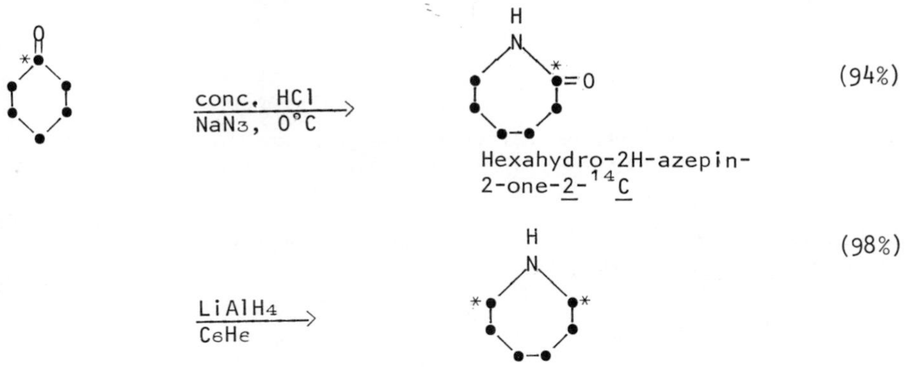
conc. HCl
NaN3, 0°C
(94%)
LiAlH4
C6H6
(98%)

Hexahydro-2H-azepin-2-one-2-^{14}C

Hexahydro-1H-azepine-2,6-^{14}C

A. D. Gutman, D. R. Baker, and M. E. Brokke, J. Label. Compounds, 2, 219 (1966); see also C. J. Grandjean, D. L. Nagel, L. Wallcave, K. Phelps, and G. Charnock, J. Label. Compounds, 9, 419 (1973).

9-5 Bicyclic Compounds

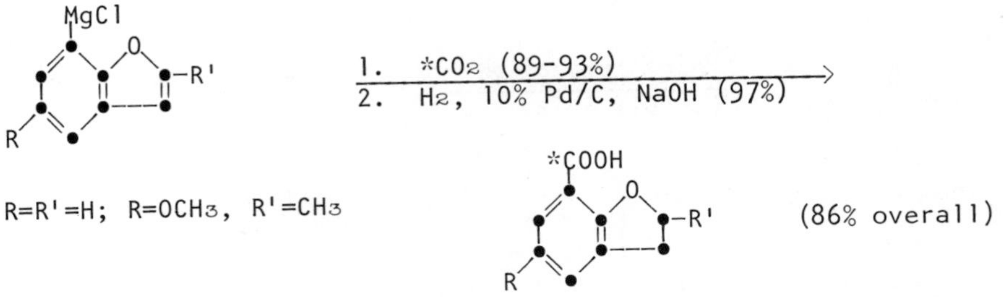
MgCl
R'
R
1. *CO2 (89-93%)
2. H2, 10% Pd/C, NaOH (97%)
R=R'=H; R=OCH3, R'=CH3
*COOH
(86% overall)

2,3-Dihydro-5-methoxy-2-methyl-7-benzofurancarboxylic-^{14}C acid [when R=OCH_3, R'=CH_3]

L. F. Elsom, D. R. Hawkins, H. Christensen, and F. C. Grønvold, J. Label. Compound. Radiopharm., 13, 75 (1977).

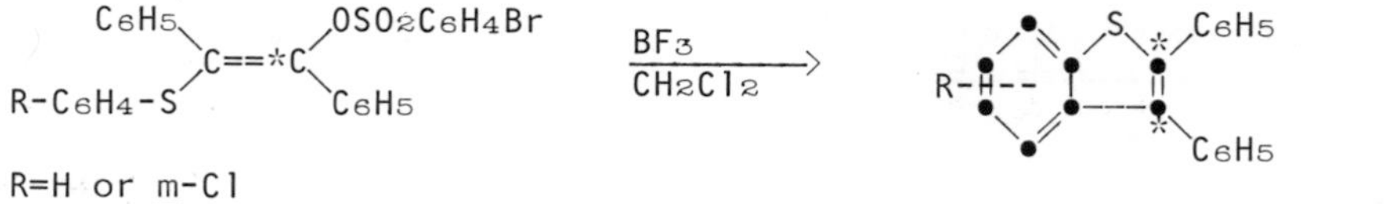
C6H5
OSO2C6H4Br
C==*C
R-C6H4-S
C6H5
BF3
CH2Cl2
S
C6H5
R-H--
C6H5

R=H or m-Cl

2,3-Diphenylbenzo[b]-
thiophene-2,3-^{14}C

The scrambled label was explained by the intermediacy of a thiirenium cation; the positions of label were determined by degradation studies.

G. Capozzi, G. Melloni, G. Modena, and U. Tonellato, J. Chem. Soc. (D) Chem. Commun., 1520 (1969).

H*COOH
1.
CH3
NH2,Δ
2. (CH3)3COK, Δ
H
N
(19% overall)

1H-Indole-2-^{14}C

L. J. King, D. V. Parke, and R. T. Williams, Biochem. J., 98, 226 (1966).

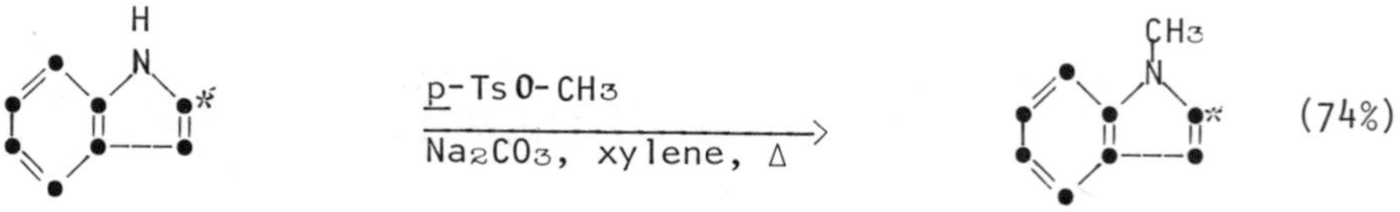
H
N
p-TsO-CH3
Na2CO3, xylene, Δ
CH3
N
(74%)

1H-indole-
2-^{14}C

1-Methyl-1H-
indole-2-^{14}C

D. Hoffman and G. Rathkamp, Anal. Chem., 42, 366 (1970).

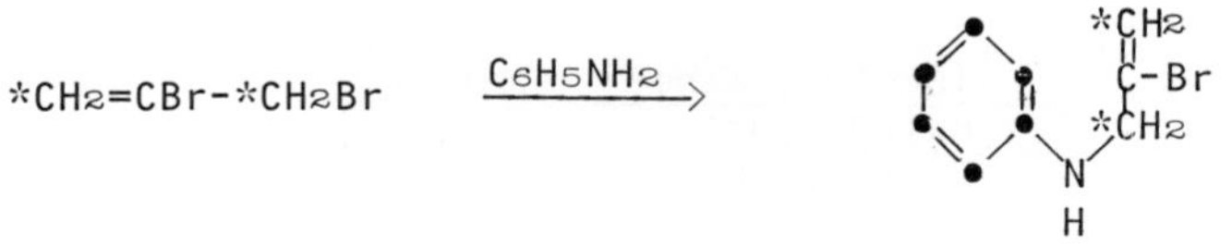

N-(2-Bromo-2-propenyl-1,3-^{14}C)benzeneamine (72% of the label was at C-1 and 28% at C-3)

(59%)

2-(Methyl-^{14}C)-1H-indole-3-^{14}C

The label became even more scrambled after the cyclization reaction; two competing mechanisms are proposed.

C. George, E. W. Gill, and J. A. Hudson, J. Chem. Soc. (C), 74 (1970).

2-Oxopropanoic-3-^{14}C acid sodium salt

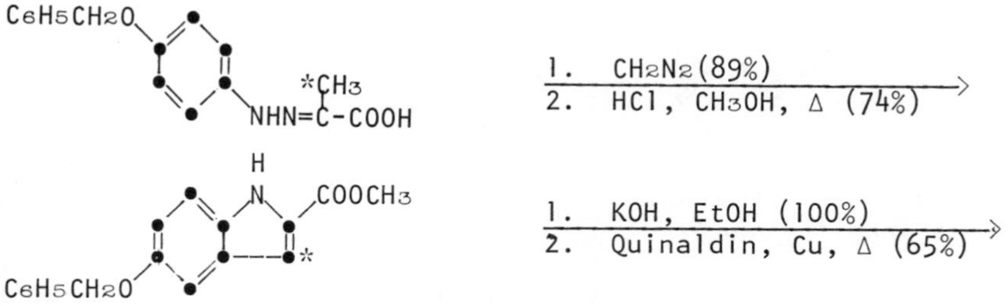

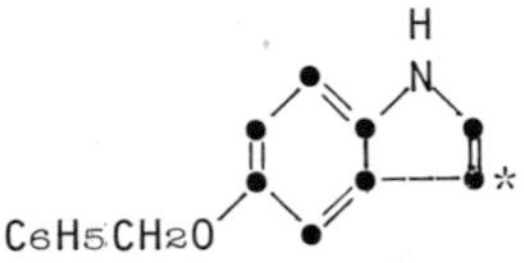

1. $(COCl)_2$, ether
2. $NH(CH_2C_6H_5)_2$
3. $LiAlH_4$, THF, Δ

5-(Phenylmethoxy)-
1H-indole-3-^{14}C

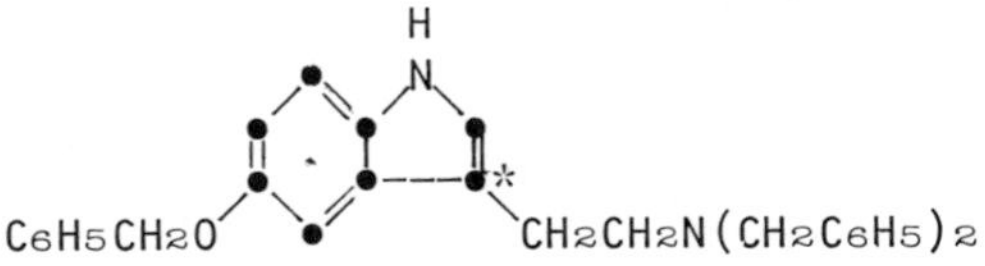

(46% from 3 steps)

1. H_2, 10% Pd/$BaSO_4$, CH_3OH
2. creatinine, H_2SO_4

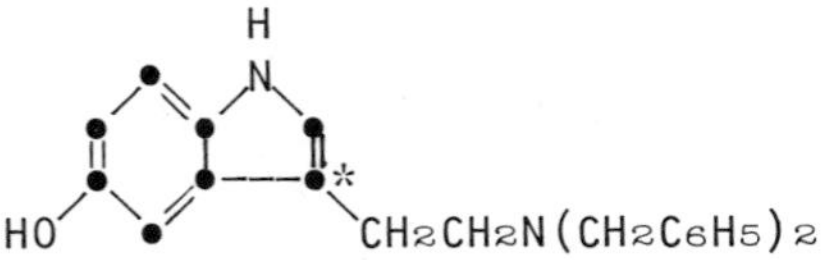

(72%; 10% from pyruvic acid-3-^{14}C)

Serotonin
[3-[2-Di-(phenylmethyl)amino-
ethyl]-1H-indol-5-ol-3-^{14}C]

D. Keglević and L. Stančić, J. Label Compounds, 3, 144 (1967).

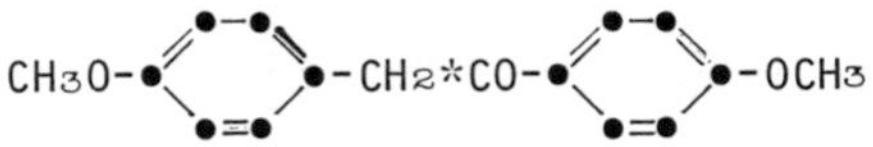

1. $C_6H_5NHNH_2$, AcOH, C_6H_6, Δ
2. HCl/EtOH, Δ

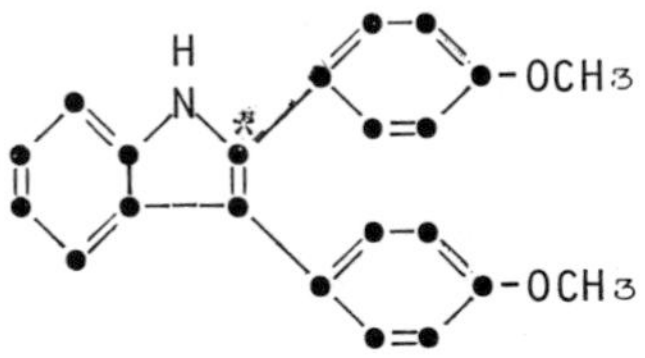

(47%; 23% from $BaCO_3$)

2,3-Bis(4-methoxyphenyl)-
1H-indole-2-^{14}C

R. C. Thomas, J. Label. Compounds, 11, 355 (1975).

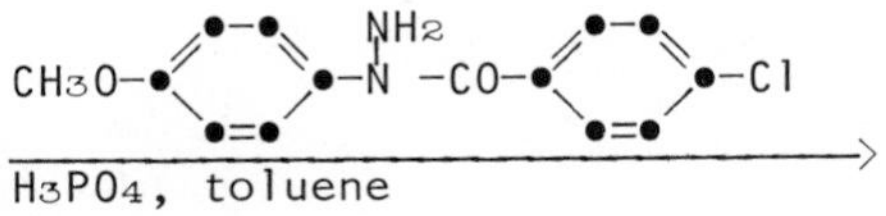
NH2
CH3O-
-N -CO-
-Cl
H3PO4, toluene

$CH_3{*}COCH_2CH_2COOH$

Levulinic acid
[4-Oxopentanoic-4-^{14}C acid]

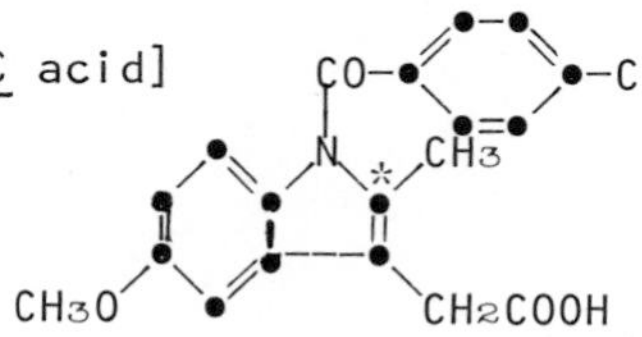
CO-
-Cl
N
CH3
CH3O
CH2COOH

(82% crude)

Indomethacin
[1-(4-Chlorobenzoyl)-5-methoxy-2-methyl-1H-indole-2-^{14}C-3-acetic acid]

R. L. Ellsworth, G. J. Gatto, H. T. Meriwether, and H. E. Mertel, J. Label. Compound.Radiopharm. 15, 613 (1978).

$CH_3{*}COCH_2CH_2COOH$

Levulinic acid
[4-Oxopentanoic-4-^{14}C acid]

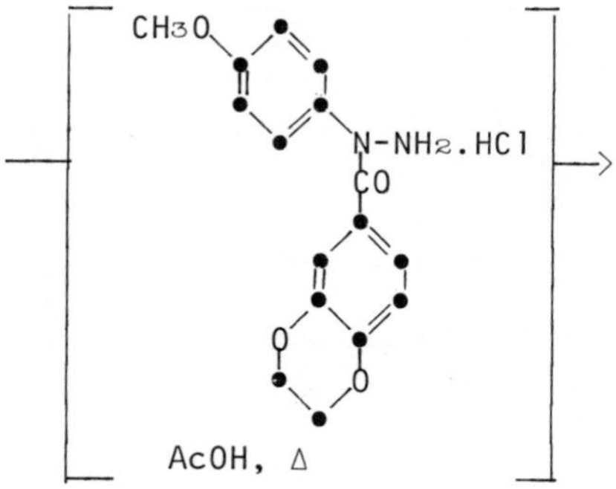
CH3O
N-NH2.HCl
CO
O
O
AcOH, Δ

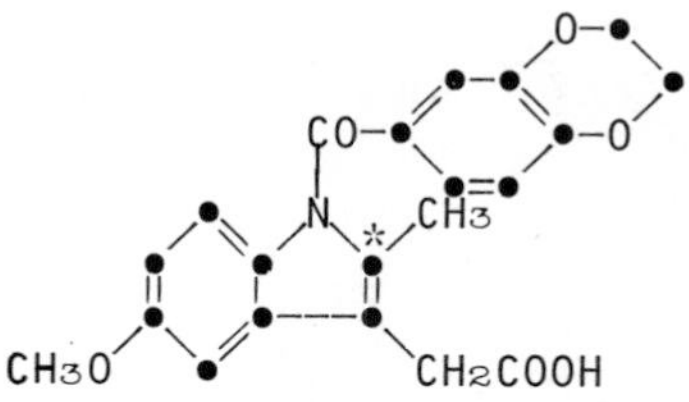
O
CO-
O
N
CH3
CH3O
CH2COOH

(58%; 25% from sodium acetate-1-^{14}C)

1-[(2,3-Dihydro-1,4-benzodioxin-6-yl)carbonyl]-5-methoxy-2-methyl-1H-indole-2-^{14}C-3-acetic acid

I. Nakatsuka, M Hazue, Y. Makari, K. Kawahara, M. Endo, and A. Yoshitake, J. Label. Compound.Radiopharm., 12, 395 (1976).

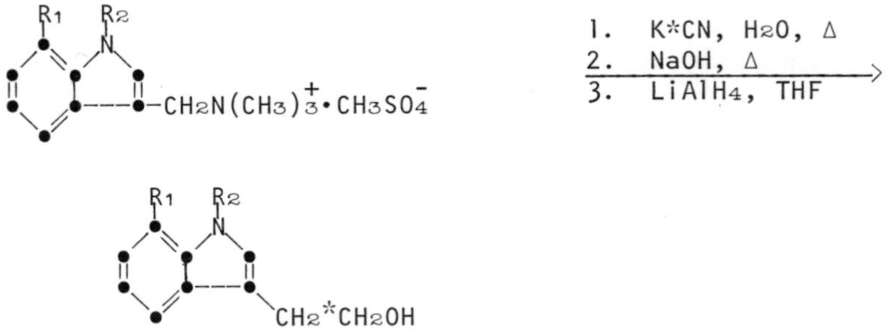
R1
R2
N
$CH_2N(CH_3)_3^+ \cdot CH_3SO_4^-$
1. K*CN, H_2O, Δ
2. NaOH, Δ
3. $LiAlH_4$, THF
R1
R2
N
$CH_2{}^*CH_2OH$

$R_1=R_2=H$; 1H-Indole-3-ethanol-<u>1</u>-^{14}<u>C</u> (80% overall)
$R_1=C_2H_5$, $R_2=H$; 7-Ethylindole-3-ethanol-<u>1</u>-^{14}<u>C</u> (95% overall)
$R_1=H$, $R_2=C_2H_5$; 1-Ethylindole-3-ethanol-<u>1'</u>-^{14}<u>C</u> (59% overall)

E. S. Ferdinandi, D. R. Hicks, W. Verbestel, and P. Raman, <u>J. Label. Compound. Radiopharm.</u>, <u>14</u>, 411 (1978).

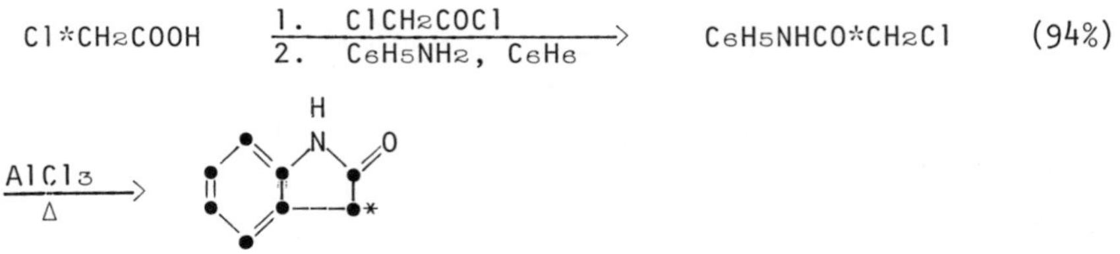
Cl*CH_2COOH
1. $ClCH_2COCl$
2. $C_6H_5NH_2$, C_6H_6
$C_6H_5NHCO{}^*CH_2Cl$
(94%)
$AlCl_3$
Δ
H
N
O
*

1,3-Dihydro-2H-indol-2-one-<u>3</u>-^{14}<u>C</u>

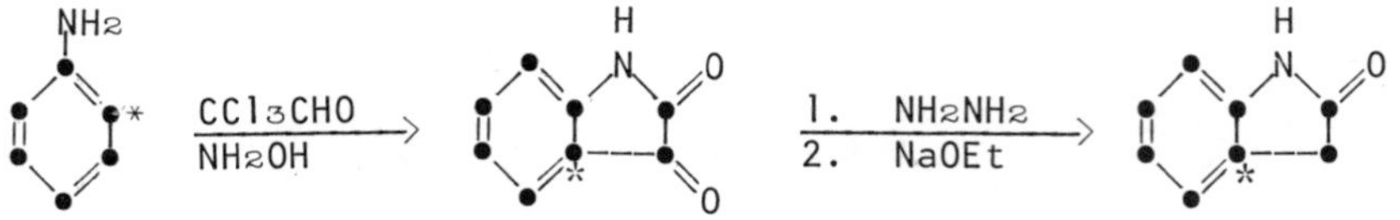
NH_2
*
CCl_3CHO
NH_2OH
H
N
O
O
*
1. NH_2NH_2
2. NaOEt
H
N
O
*

1,3-Dihydro-2H-indol-2-one-<u>3a</u>-^{14}<u>C</u>

R. F. C. Brown and M. Butcher, <u>Aust. J. Chem.</u>, <u>25</u>, 149 (1972).

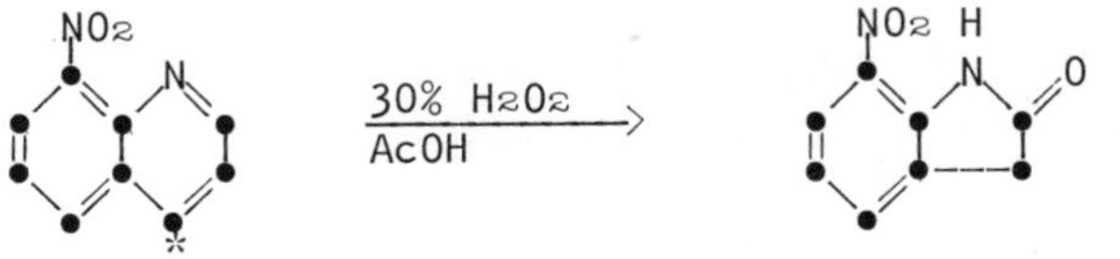

(20%)

8-Nitroquinoline-4-^{14}C

1,3-Dihydro-7-nitro-2H-indol-2-one-^{14}C

The specific activity of the 4-^{14}C product was the same as the starting material while the specific activity of the similarly prepared 2,4-^{14}C product was half that of the starting material. A mechanism for the loss of carbon-2 was proposed.

H. C. van der Plas and D. J. Buurman, Chem. Pharm. Bull., 23, 2682 (1975).

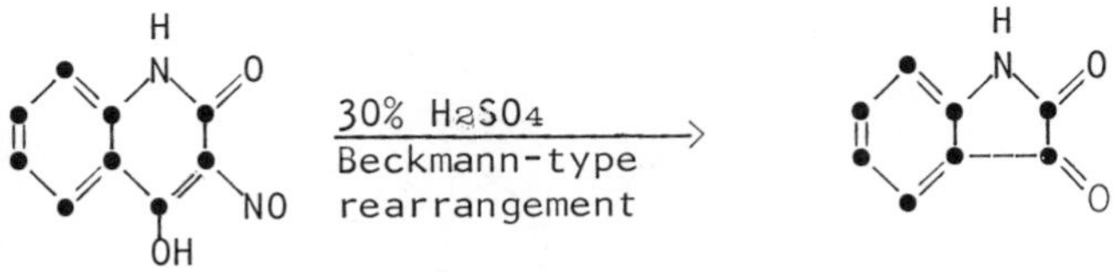

Isatin
[1H-Indol-2,3-dione-^{14}C]

plus

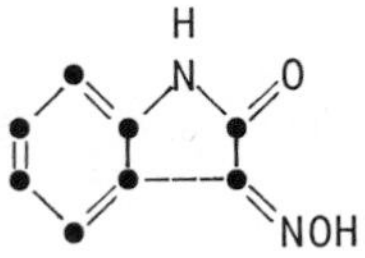

Isatoxime
[1H-Indol-2,3-dione-
-3-oxime-^{14}C]

Variously labeled precursors were used (∿30% yield of each product obtained). Carbon dioxide was lost from C-2 and carbon monoxide appears to be from C-4. Several reaction mechanisms are proposed.

R. H. Prager and K. Y. Ting, Aust. J. Chem., 25, 1229 (1972).

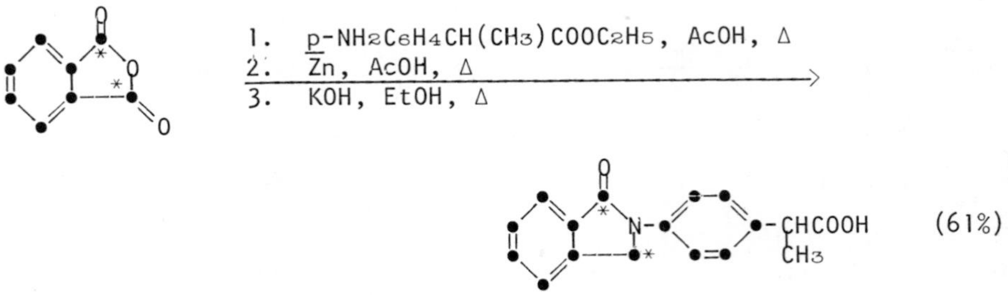
1. p-NH2C6H4CH(CH3)COOC2H5, AcOH, Δ
2. Zn, AcOH, Δ
3. KOH, EtOH, Δ
CHCOOH
CH3
(61%)

4-(1,3-Dihydro-1-oxo-2H-isoindol-2-yl-1,3-^{14}C)-α-methylbenzeneacetic acid

G. C. Goldaniga, E. Pianezzola, and G. Valzelli, Arzneim.-Forsch- (Drug Res.), 24, 1603 (1974).

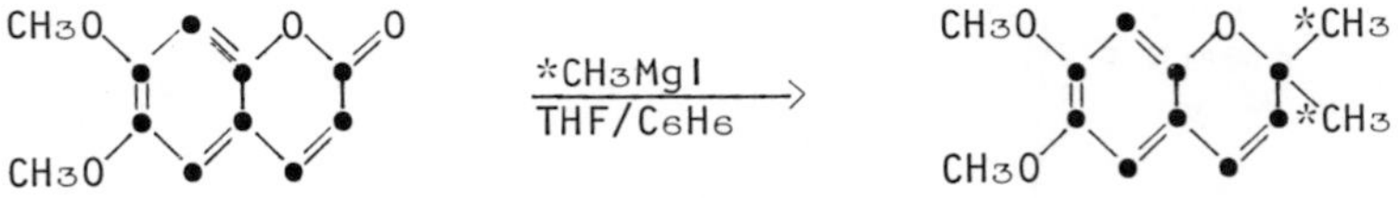
CH3O
CH3O
*CH3MgI
THF/C6H6
*CH3
*CH3

Precocene
[6,7-Dimethoxy-(2,2-dimethyl-[14]-C)-2H-1-benzopyran]

T. Ohta, R. J. Kuhr, and W. S. Bowers, J. Agr. Food. Chem., 25, 478 (1977).

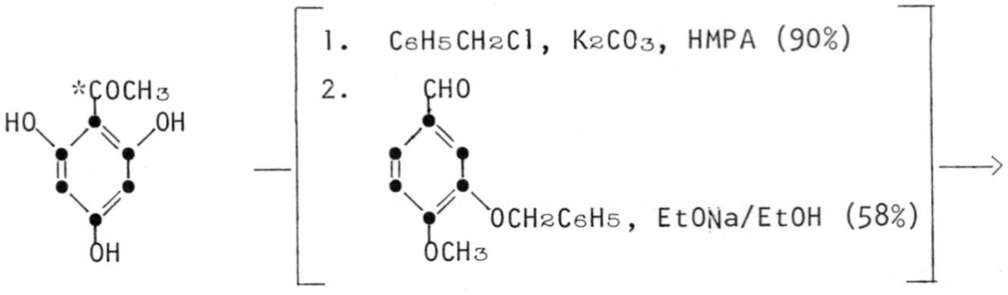
*COCH3
HO
OH
OH
1. C6H5CH2Cl, K2CO3, HMPA (90%)
2.
CHO
OCH2C6H5, EtONa/EtOH (58%)
OCH3

1-(2,4,6-Trihydroxy-phenyl)ethanone-1-[14]C

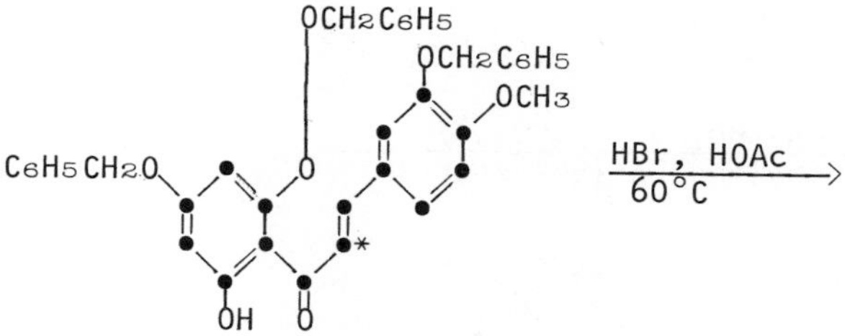
OCH2C6H5
OCH2C6H5
OCH3
C6H5CH2O
O
OH
O
*
HBr, HOAc
60°C

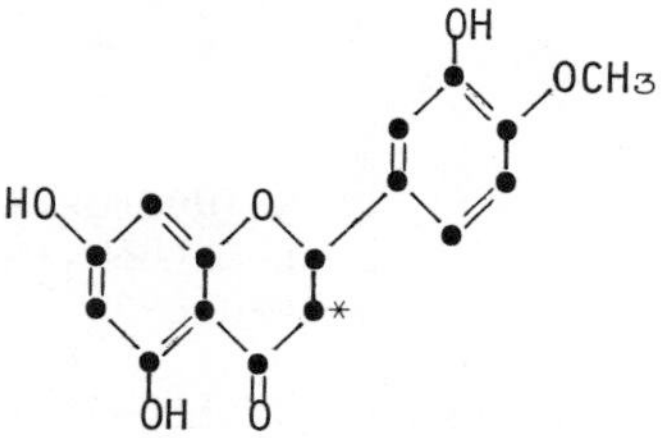
OH
OCH3
HO
O
*
OH
O

(8% overall)

Hesperetin
[2,3-Dihydro-5,7-dihydroxy-2(3-hydroxy-4-methoxyphenyl)-4H-1-benzopyran-4-one-3-^{14}C]

T. Honohan, R. L. Hale, J. P. Brown, and R. E. Wingard, Jr., J. Agr. Food Chem., 24, 906 (1976).

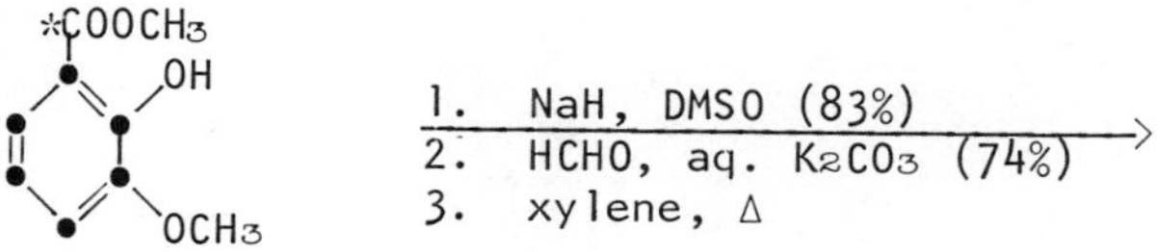
*COOCH3
OH
OCH3
1. NaH, DMSO (83%)
2. HCHO, aq. K2CO3 (74%)
3. xylene, Δ

2-Hydroxy-3-methoxybenzoic-^{14}C acid methyl ester

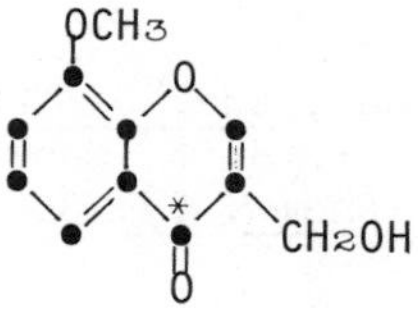
OCH3
O
*
CH2OH
O

(27% overall based on $^*CO_2$ consumed)

3-(Hydroxymethyl)-8-methoxy-4H-1-benzopyran-4-one-4-^{14}C

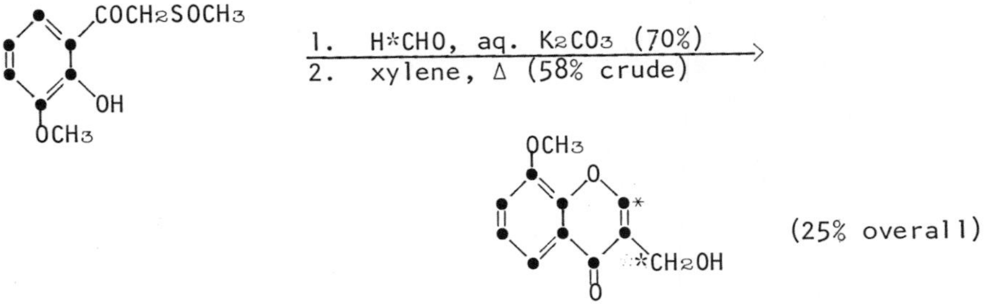
COCH2SOCH3
OH
OCH3
1. H*CHO, aq. K2CO3 (70%)
2. xylene, Δ (58% crude)
OCH3
O
*
*CH2OH
O
(25% overall)

3-(Hydroxymethyl-^{14}C)-8-methoxy-4H-1-benzopyran-4-one-2-^{14}C

E. J. Merrill and A. D. Lewis, J. Label. Compound. Radiopharm., 13, 385 (1977).

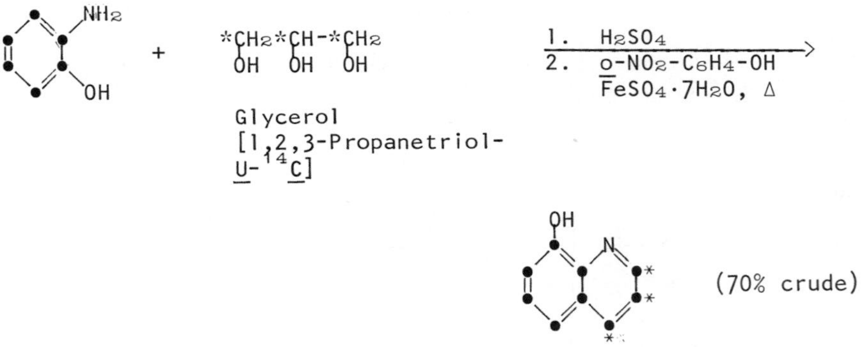
NH2
OH
+
*CH2*CH-*CH2
OH OH OH
Glycerol
[1,2,3-Propanetriol-U-14C]
1. H2SO4
2. o-NO2-C6H4-OH
FeSO4·7H2O, Δ
OH
N
*
*
*
(70% crude)

8-Quinolinol-2,3,4-^{14}C

A. Corsini and J. Abraham, Can. J. Chem., 48, 2360 (1970); Can. J. Chem., 47, 1435 (1969); R. H. F. Manske, A. E. Ledingham, and W. R. Ashford, Can. J. Chem., 27, 359 (1949).

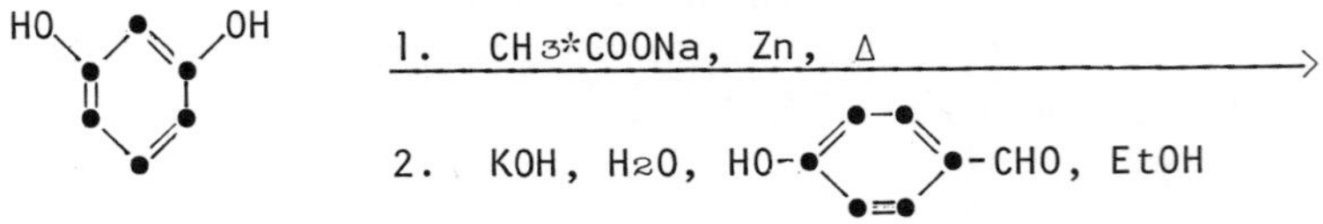
HO
OH
1. CH3*COONa, Zn, Δ
2. KOH, H2O, HO-
-CHO, EtOH

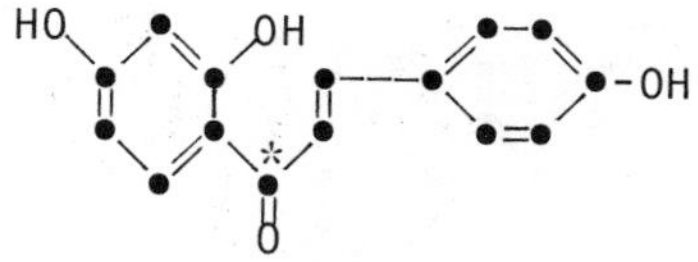

Isoliquiritigenin
[1-(2,4-Dihydroxyphenyl)-3-(4-hydroxyphenyl)-2-propen-1-one-1-^{14}C]

The 2-^{14}C derivative was also prepared using sodium acetate-2-^{14}C.

HCl / EtOH →

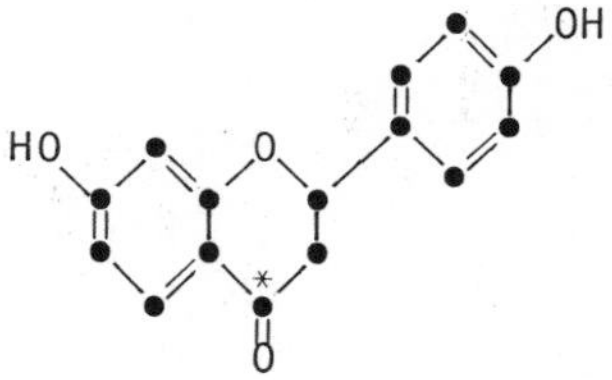

(∿57%)

(±)-Liquiritigenin
[2,3-Dihydro-7-hydroxy-2-(4-hydroxyphenyl)-4H-1-benzopyran-4-one-4-^{14}C]

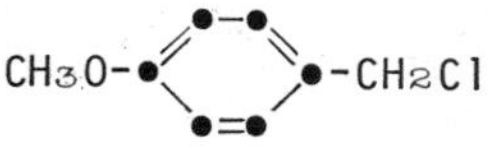

1. K*CN, KI, acetone, Δ
2. resorcinol, $ZnCl_2$, HCl gas
3. H_2O, (HCl), Δ →

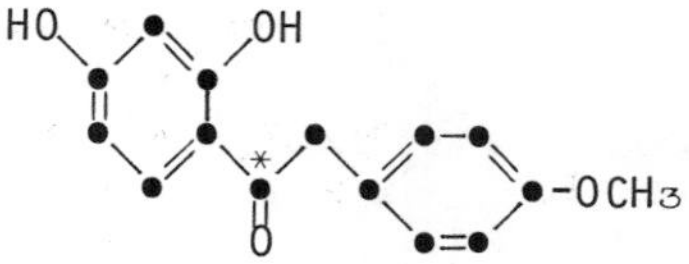

$HC(OC_2H_5)_3$, pyr, Δ / piperidine →

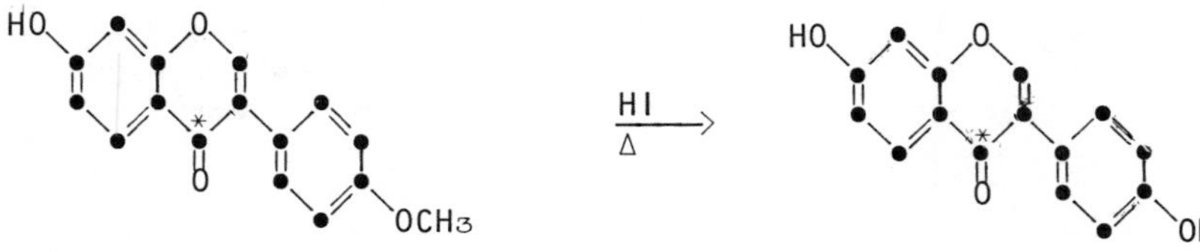
HO
O
*
O
OCH3
HI
Δ
HO
O
*
O
OH

Formononetin
[7-Hydroxy-3-(4-methoxyphenyl)-4H-1-benzopyran-4-one-4-^{14}C]

Daidzein
[7-Hydroxy-3-(4-hydroxyphenyl)-4H-1-benzopyran-4-one-4-^{14}C]

T. Inoue and M. Fujita, Chem. Pharm. Bull. (Tokyo), 25, 3226 (1977); P. M. Dewick, W. Barz and H. Grisebach, Phytochem., 9, 775 (1970); W. Barz, Ch. Adamek, and J. Berlin, Phytochem., 9, 1735 (1970).

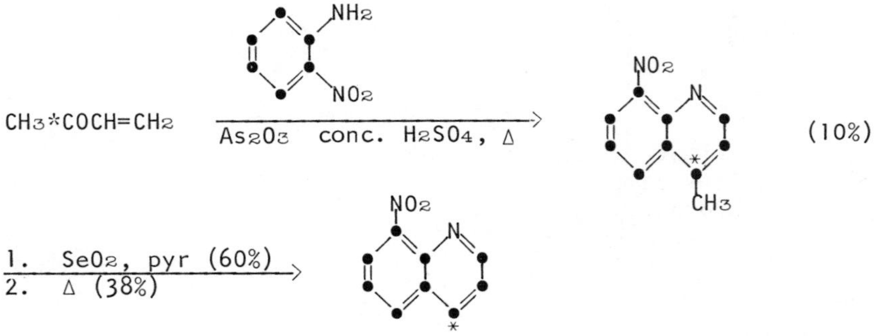
NH2
NO2
CH3*COCH=CH2
As2O3 conc. H2SO4, Δ
NO2
N
*
CH3
(10%)
1. SeO2, pyr (60%)
2. Δ (38%)
NO2
N
*

8-Nitroquinoline-4-^{14}C

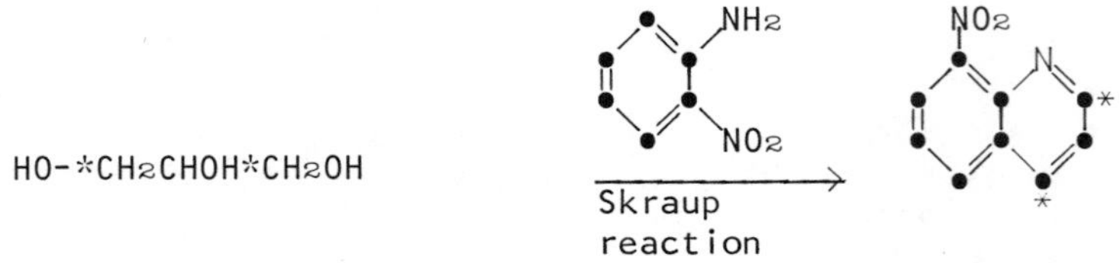
NH2
NO2
HO-*CH2CHOH*CH2OH
Skraup
reaction
NO2
N
*
*

8-Nitroquinoline-2,4-^{14}C

H. C. van der Plas and D. J. Buurman, Chem. Pharm. Bull., 23, 2682 (1975).

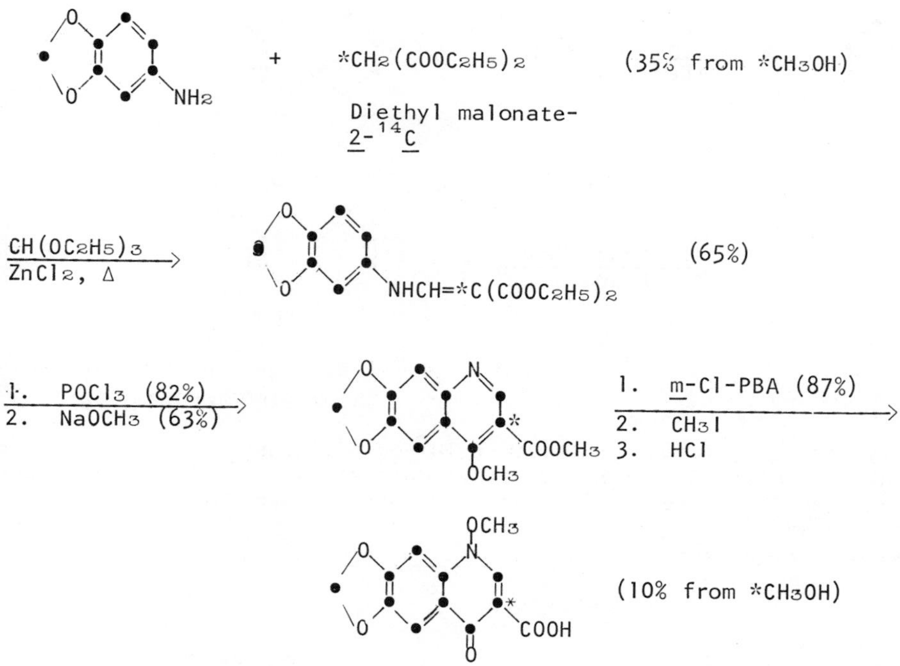
NH2
+
*CH2(COOC2H5)2
(35% from *CH3OH)
Diethyl malonate-2-14C
CH(OC2H5)3
ZnCl2, Δ
NHCH=*C(COOC2H5)2
(65%)
1. POCl3 (82%)
2. NaOCH3 (63%)
N
COOCH3
OCH3
1. m-Cl-PBA (87%)
2. CH3I
3. HCl
OCH3
N
COOH
(10% from *CH3OH)

5,8-Dihydro-5-methoxy-8-oxo-1,3-dioxolo[4,5g]-quinoline-7-^{14}C-7-carboxylic acid

A. Yoshitake, Y. Makari, and M. Endo, J. Label. Compounds, 10, 589 (1974).

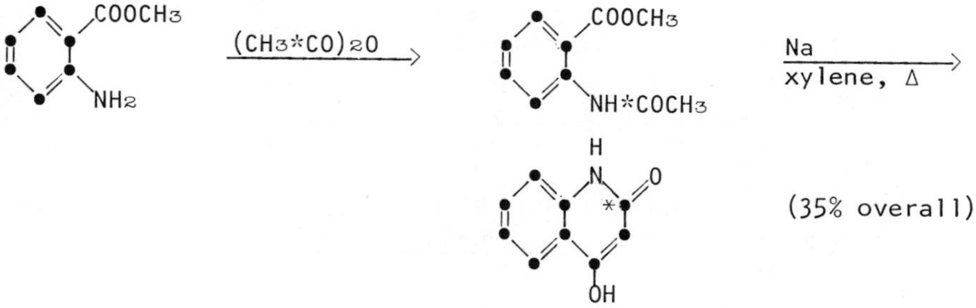
COOCH3
NH2
(CH3*CO)2O
COOCH3
NH*COCH3
Na
xylene, Δ
H
N
O
OH
(35% overall)

4-Hydroxy-2(1H)-quinolinone-2-^{14}C

4-Hydroxy-2(1H)-quinolinone-3-^{14}C was prepared using acetic anhydride-2-^{14}C.

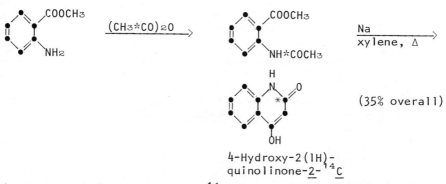

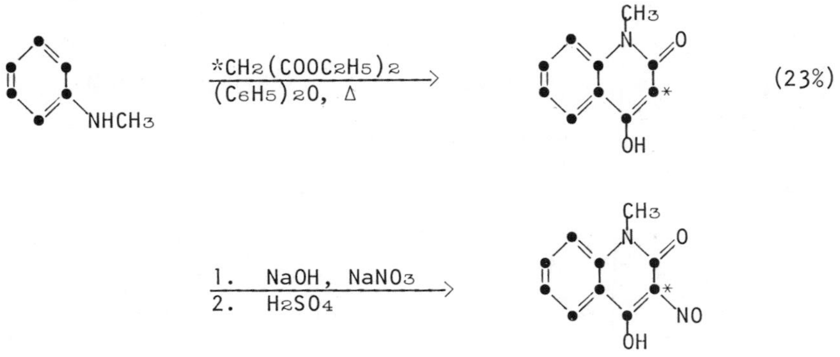
NHCH3
*CH2(COOC2H5)2
(C6H5)2O, Δ
CH3
N
O
*
OH
(23%)
1. NaOH, NaNO3
2. H2SO4
CH3
N
O
*
NO
OH

4-Hydroxy-1-methyl-3-nitroso-2(1H)quinolinone-3-^{14}C

Similarly, 4-hydroxy-3-nitroso-2(1H)-quinolinone-3-^{14}C was prepared in 83% yield. Starting with ethyl malonate-1,3-^{14}C, the corresponding 2,4-^{14}C labeled derivatives were prepared in 75% yields.

R. H. Praeger and K. Y. Ting, Aust. J. Chem., 25, 1229 (1972).

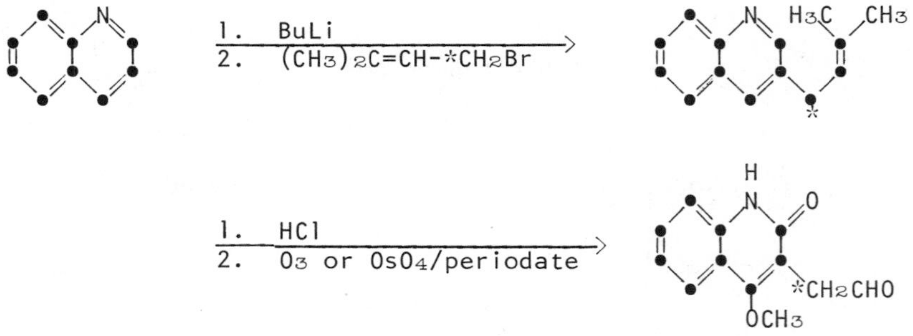
N
1. BuLi
2. (CH3)2C=CH-*CH2Br
N
H3C
CH3
*
H
N
O
1. HCl
2. O3 or OsO4/periodate
*CH2CHO
OCH3

1,2-Dihydro-4-methoxy-2-oxo-3-quinoline acetaldehyde-α-^{14}C

J. F. Collins, W. J. Donnelly, M. F. Grundon, D. M. Harrison, and C. G. Spyropoulos, J. Chem. Soc., Chem. Commun., 1029 (1972).

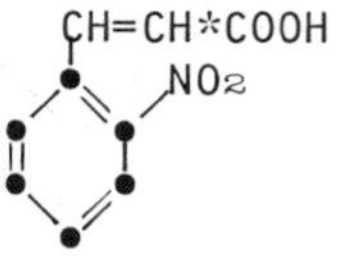

1. PCl_5, $POCl_3$
2. NH_3, C_6H_6
3. P_2O_5

→

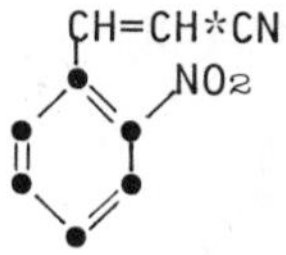

(E)-(2-Nitrophenyl)-2-propenoic-^{14}C acid

$NaOCH_3$, CH_3OH (quant.) →

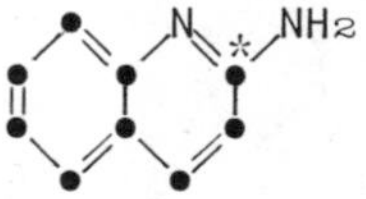

2-Quinolinamine-2-^{14}C

1. Cl-$COOC_2H_5$, pyr
2. H_2O_2, AcOH

→

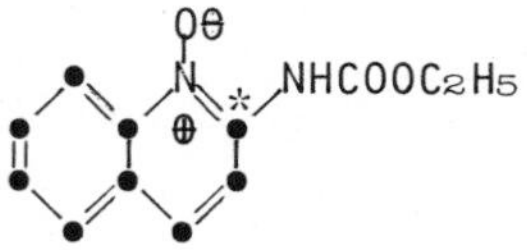

(57%)

2-Quinolinylcarbamic acid-2-^{14}C-N-oxide ethyl ester

R. F. C. Brown and R. J. Smith, Aust. J. Chem., 25, 607 (1972).

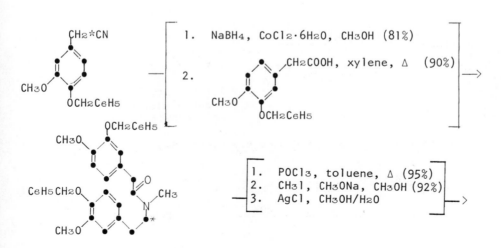

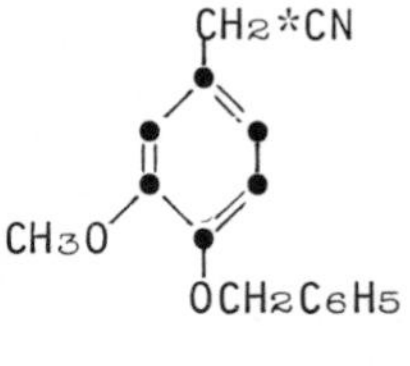

1. $NaBH_4$, $CoCl_2 \cdot 6H_2O$, CH_3OH (81%)
2. 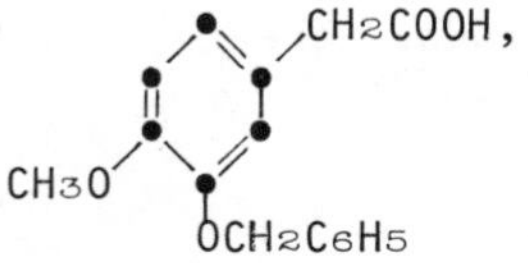 xylene, Δ (90%)

→

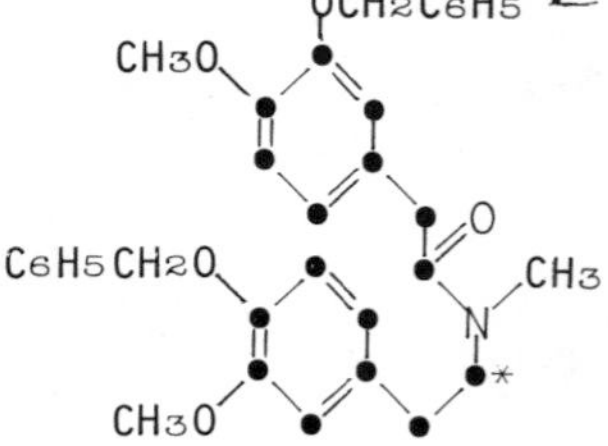

1. $POCl_3$, toluene, Δ (95%)
2. CH_3I, CH_3ONa, CH_3OH (92%)
3. AgCl, CH_3OH/H_2O

→

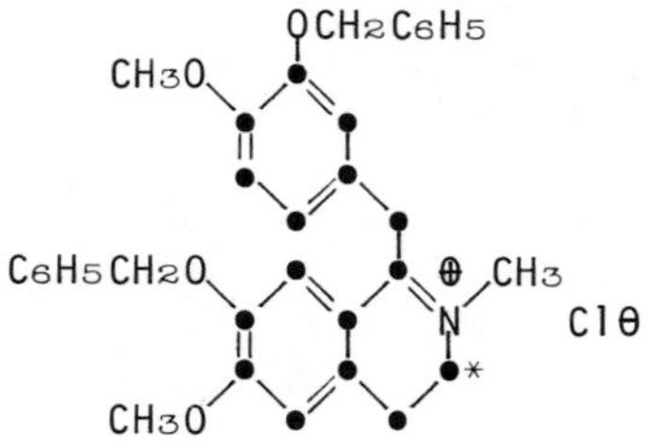
OCH2C6H5
CH3O
C6H5CH2O
CH3
N
Cl
CH3O
*

[1. HCl gas, EtOH (98%)
2. $NaBH_4$, CH_3OH (97%)] ⟶

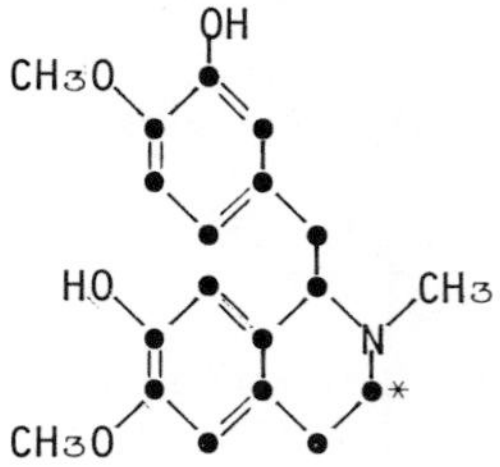
OH
CH3O
HO
CH3
N
CH3O
*

Reticuline
[(S)-1,2,3,4-Tetrahydro-1-[(3-hydroxy-4-methoxyphenyl)methyl]-6-methoxy-2-methyl-7-isoquinolinol-3-^{14}C]

The yields given are for unlabeled reactions.

P. R. Borkowski, J. S. Horn, and H. Rapoport, J. Amer. Chem. Soc., 100, 276 (1978).

$CH_3{*}CH_2OH$ —— 1. $COCl_2$; 2. quinoline; 3. Na_2CO_3, C_6H_6, CH_3CH_3OH ⟶

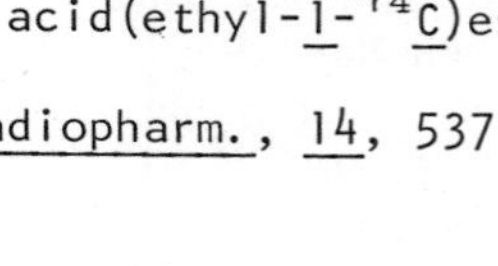
COO*CH2CH3
N
OCH2CH3

(72% from ethanol)

1,2-Dihydro-2-ethoxy-1-quinolinecarboxylic acid(ethyl-1-^{14}C)ester

W. T. Robinson, J. Label. Compound. Radiopharm., 14, 537 (1978).

$C_6H_5{*}CH{=}C(C_6H_5)COCH_3$ —— 1. NH_2OH (53%); 2. C_6H_5-COCl, Et_2O (61%) ⟶ $C_6H_5{*}CH{=}C(C_6H_5)C({=}N{-}O{-}COC_6H_5){-}CH_3$

Δ / nitrobenzene →

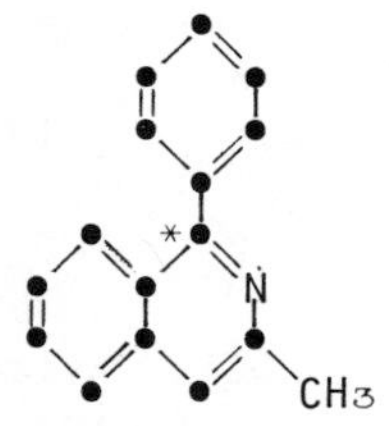

(11%)

3-Methyl-1-phenyl-isoquinoline-1-^{14}C

The position of label was determined by degradation reactions; a hydrogen migration mechanism is proposed.

S. Goszczyński, M. Lozyński, and M. Kostański, Rocz. Chem., 50, 499 (1976).

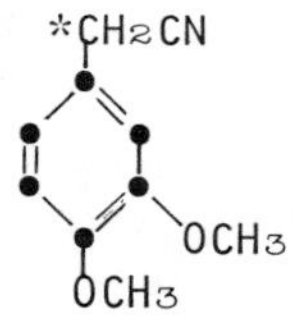

3,4-Dimethoxybenzene-acetonitrile-α-^{14}C

→

1. $LiAlH_4$, Et_2O (96%)
2. 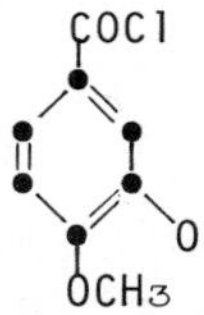 , Et_2O (89%)
3. $POCl_3$, toluene
4. Tetralin, 10% Pd/pumice (91%)

→

↓ KOH/H_2O, $HOCH_2CH_2OH$

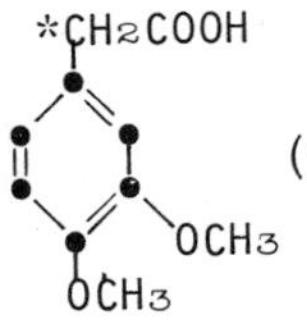

(95%)

Homoveratric acid
[3,4-Dimethoxy-benzeneacetic-α-^{14}C acid]

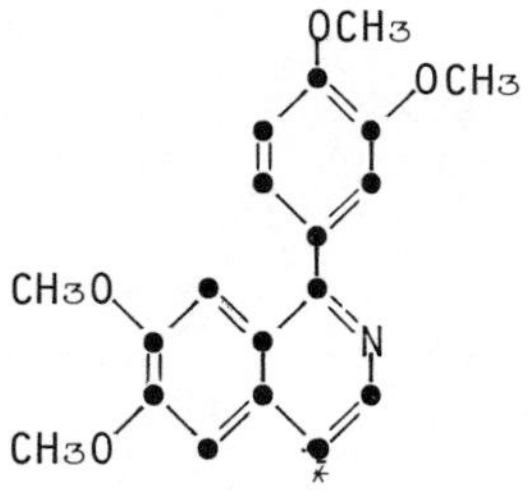

Quinopavine
[1-(3,4-Dimethoxyphenyl)-6,7-dimethoxyisoquinoline-4-^{14}C]

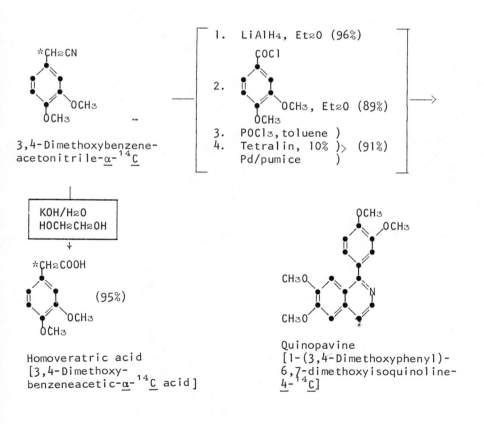

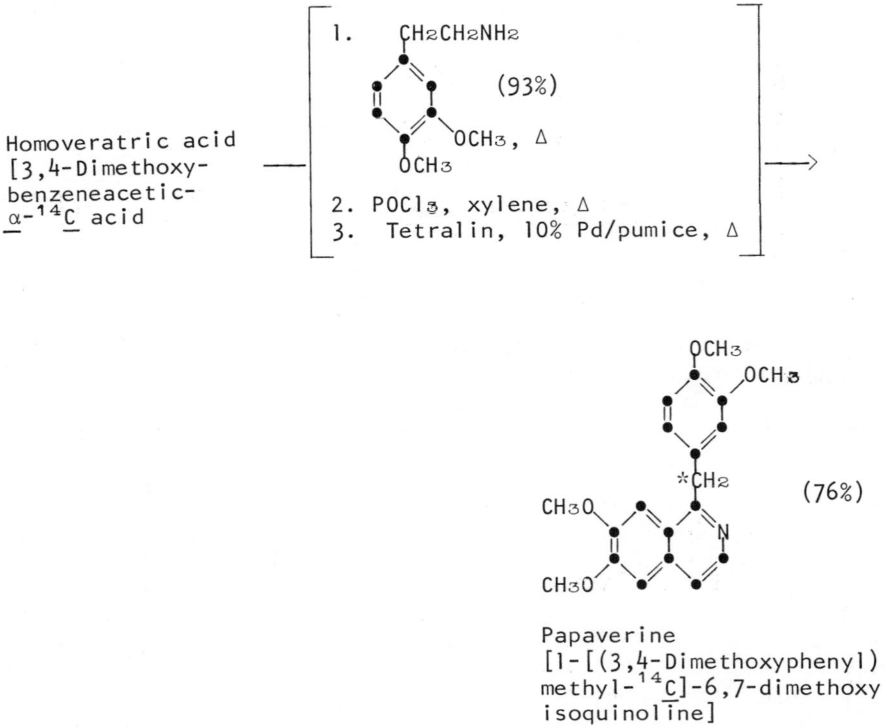
Homoveratric acid
[3,4-Dimethoxy-
benzeneacetic-
α-14C acid
1. CH2CH2NH2
OCH3, Δ
OCH3
(93%)
2. POCl3, xylene, Δ
3. Tetralin, 10% Pd/pumice, Δ
OCH3
OCH3
*CH2
CH3O
CH3O
N
(76%)
Papaverine
[1-[(3,4-Dimethoxyphenyl)
methyl-14C]-6,7-dimethoxy
isoquinoline]

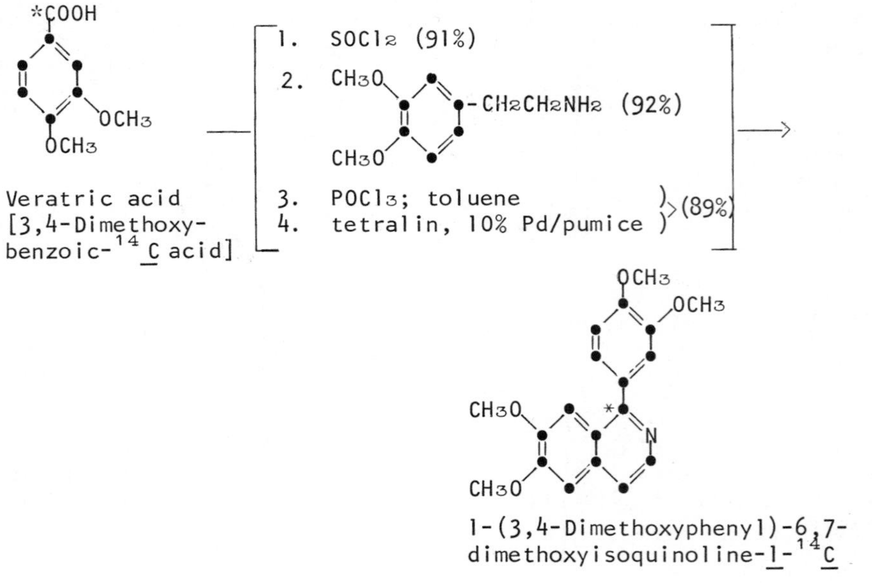
*COOH
OCH3
OCH3
Veratric acid
[3,4-Dimethoxy-
benzoic-14C acid]
1. SOCl2 (91%)
2. CH3O
CH3O
-CH2CH2NH2 (92%)
3. POCl3; toluene
4. tetralin, 10% Pd/pumice
(89%)
OCH3
OCH3
CH3O
CH3O
*
N
1-(3,4-Dimethoxyphenyl)-6,7-
dimethoxyisoquinoline-1-14C

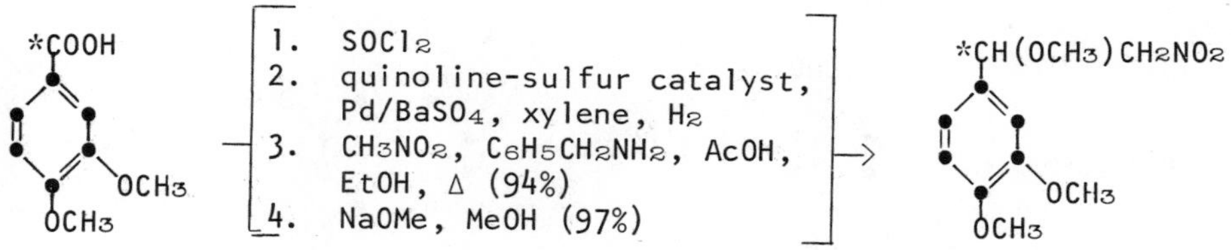
*COOH
OCH3
OCH3
1. SOCl2
2. quinoline-sulfur catalyst, Pd/BaSO4, xylene, H2
3. CH3NO2, C6H5CH2NH2, AcOH, EtOH, Δ (94%)
4. NaOMe, MeOH (97%)
*CH(OCH3)CH2NO2
OCH3
OCH3

Veratric acid
[3,4-Dimethoxybenzoic-^{14}C acid]

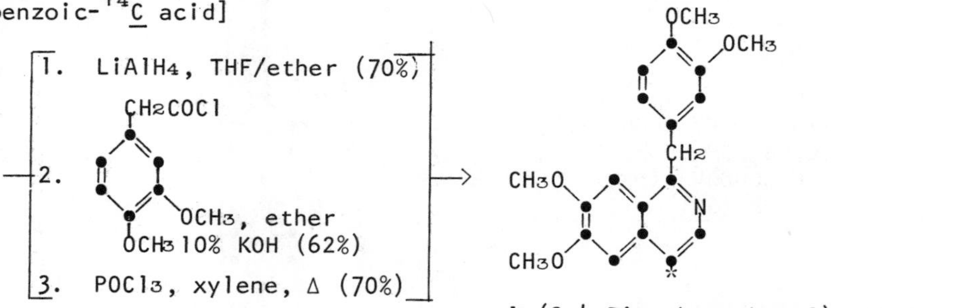
1. LiAlH4, THF/ether (70%)
CH2COCl
2.
OCH3, ether
OCH3 10% KOH (62%)
3. POCl3, xylene, Δ (70%)
OCH3
OCH3
CH2
CH3O
N
CH3O
*

1-(3,4-Dimethoxyphenyl)methyl-6,7-dimethoxyisoquinoline-4-^{14}C

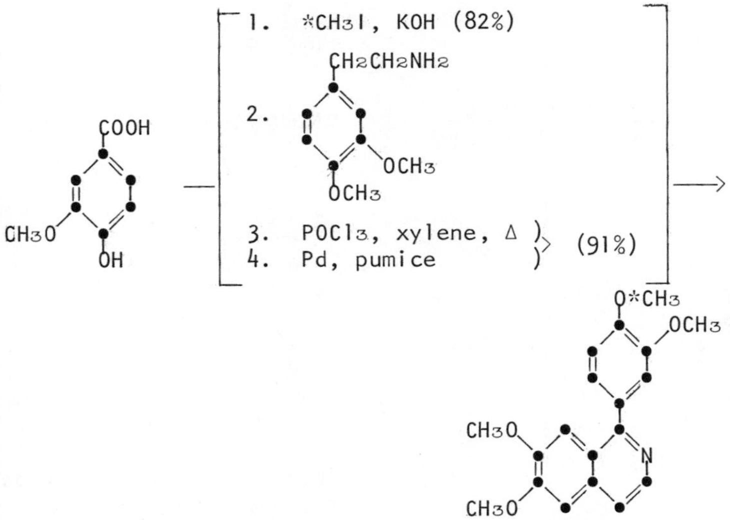
COOH
CH3O
OH
1. *CH3I, KOH (82%)
CH2CH2NH2
2.
OCH3
OCH3
3. POCl3, xylene, Δ
4. Pd, pumice
(91%)
O*CH3
OCH3
CH3O
N
CH3O

1-(3-Methoxy-(4-methoxy-^{14}C)-phenyl)-6,7-dimethoxyisoquinoline

S. D. Ithakissios, G. Tsatsas, J. Nikokavouras, and A. Tsolis, J. Label. Compounds, 10, 369 (1974).

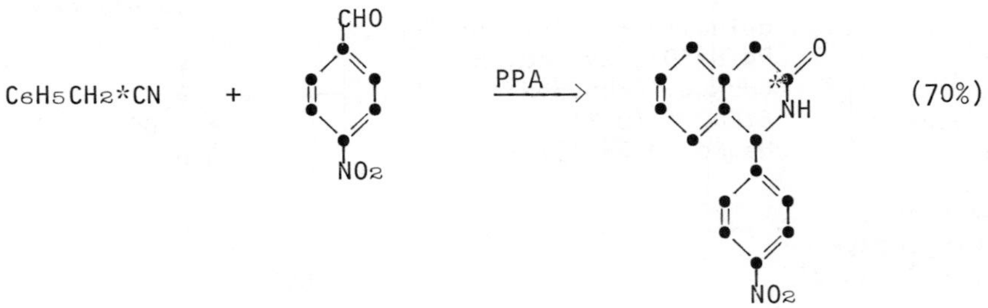
C6H5CH2*CN
+
CHO
NO2
PPA
O
NH
NO2
(70%)

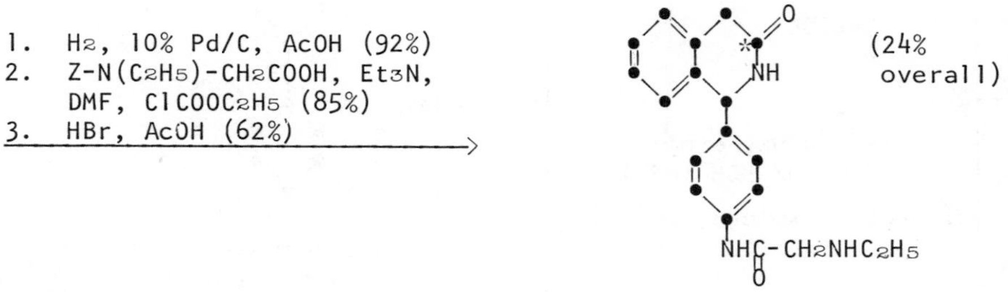
1. H2, 10% Pd/C, AcOH (92%)
2. Z-N(C2H5)-CH2COOH, Et3N, DMF, ClCOOC2H5 (85%)
3. HBr, AcOH (62%)
O
NH
NHC-CH2NHC2H5
O
(24% overall)

2-(Ethylamino)-N-[4-(1,2,3,4-tetrahydro-3-oxo-1-isoquinyl-3-^{14}C)phenyl] acetamide

$BrCH_2{}^*COOH$ $\xrightarrow[\text{2. Z-Cl, NaOH}]{\text{1. } C_2H_5NH_2,\ H_2O,\ \Delta}$ $Z\text{-}N(C_2H_5)CH_2{}^*COOH$ (66%)

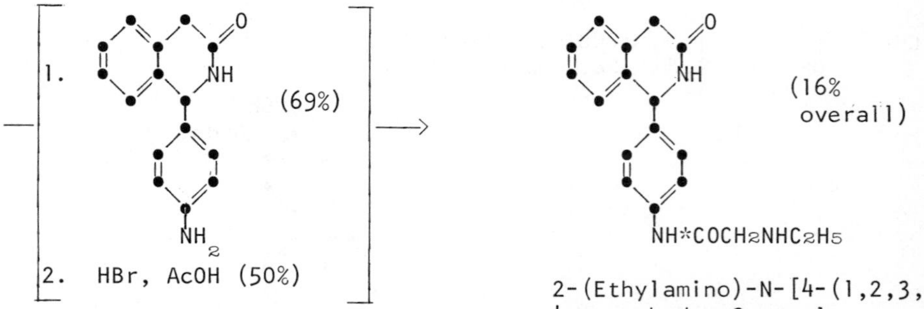
1.
O
NH
NH2
(69%)
2. HBr, AcOH (50%)
O
NH
NH*COCH2NHC2H5
(16% overall)

2-(Ethylamino)-N-[4-(1,2,3,4-tetrahydro-3-oxo-1-isoquinyl)phenyl]acetamide-1-^{14}C

E. Koltai, D. Bánfi, L. Hazai, and Gy. Deák, J. Label. Compound. Radiopharm., 15, 331 (1978).

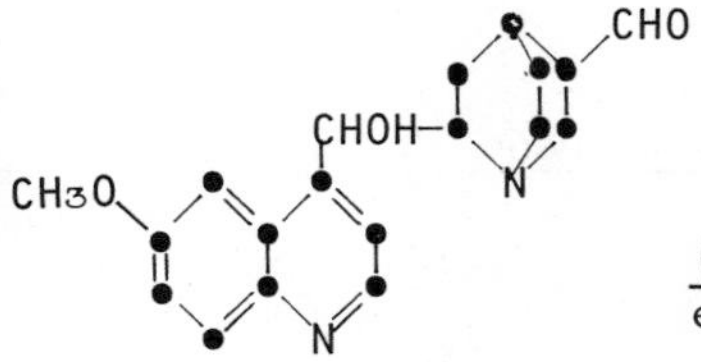

$\underline{(C_6H_5)_3P{=}^*CH_2}$ →
ether / THF

Quinidinal
(from OsO_4 oxidation
of quinidine)

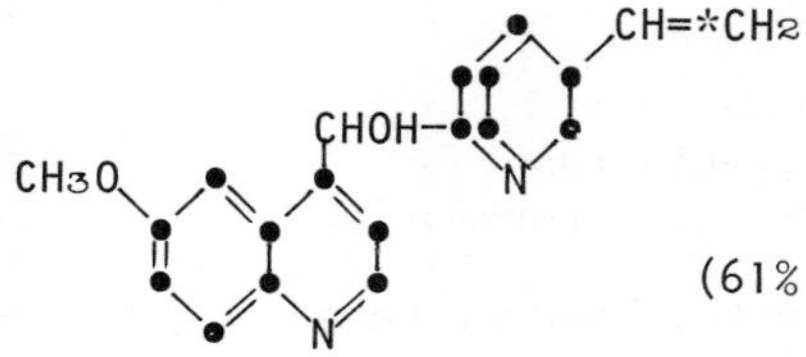

(61% from $^*CH_3I$)

$\underline{CH_3COOH}$ →
CH_3OH, Δ

Quinidine-$^{14}\underline{C}$

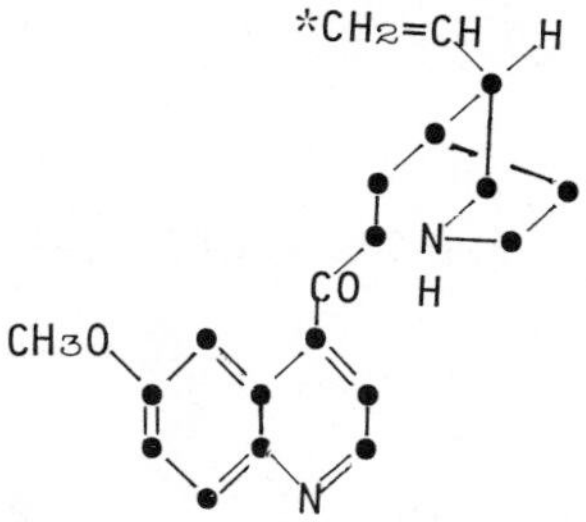

(17%)

Viquidil (Quinicine)
[(3R-cis)-3-(3-Ethenyl-$\underline{2}$-$^{14}\underline{C}$-4-piperidinyl)-1-(6-methoxy-4-quinolinyl)-1-propanone]

C. Guérémy, A. Uzan, and J.-C. Tamen, Arzneim.-Forsch.-(Drug Res.), 22, 1336 (1972).

9-6 Tricyclic Compounds

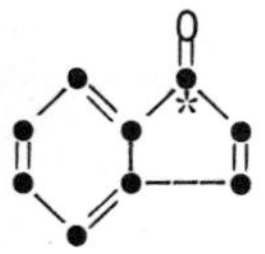

1. $NaBH_4$, CH_3OH
2. Amberlyst 15, cyclohexane →
3. C_2H_5MgBr, toluene)
4. ethylene oxide, Et_2O) (67%)
5. KOH, CH_3OH, Δ)

2,3-Dihydro-1H-inden-1-one-$\underline{1}$-$^{14}\underline{C}$

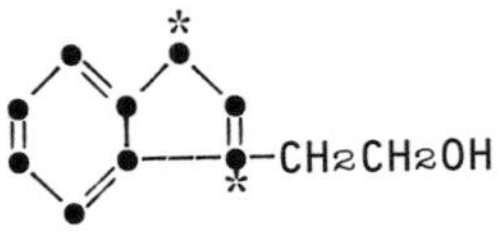

1. 1-(N,N-dimethylamino)-butan-3-one, BF_3, toluene
2. HCl, Et_2O

1H-Indene-1,3-[14]C 3-ethanol

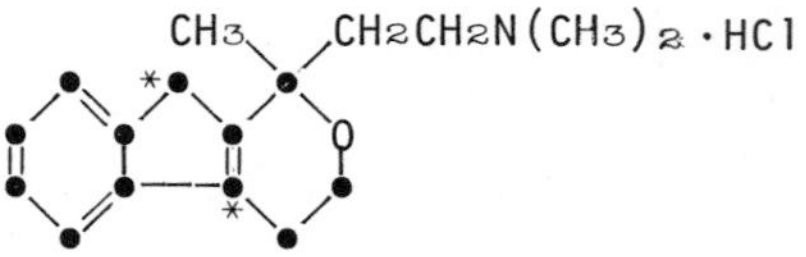

(5% from Ba^*CO_3)

Pirandamine
[1,3,4,9-Tetrahydro-N,N-1-trimethylindeno[2,1-C]pyran-1-ethanamine-4a,9-^{14}C hydrochloride]

E. S. Ferdinandi, D. R. Hicks, W. Verbestel, and P. Raman, J. Label. Compound. Radiopharm., 14, 411 (1978).

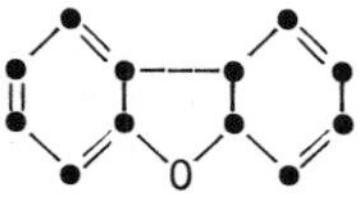

+ $CH_3{}^*COCl$ $\xrightarrow{AlCl_3,\ CH_2Cl_2}$

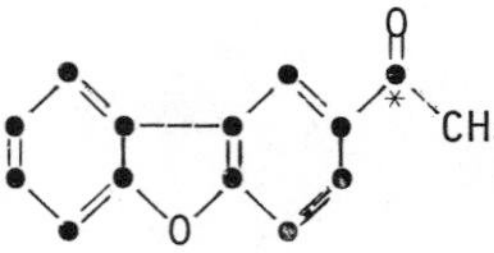

(77%)

1. S, $(NH_4)_2S$, dioxane, Δ
2. KOH, EtOH

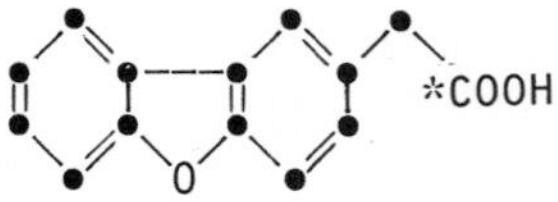

(15% overall)

2-Dibenzofuranacetic acid-(carboxyl-^{14}C)

E. S. Ferdinandi, J. Label. Compound. Radiopharm., 12, 357 (1976).

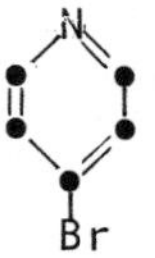

1. C_4H_9Li
2. $^*CO_2$

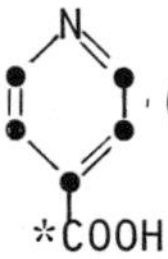

(91%)

$\xrightarrow{benzene,\ AlCl_3}$

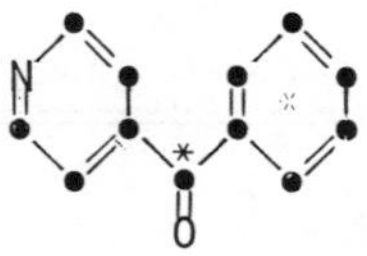

(79%)

Isonicotinic acid
[4-Pyridine-carboxylic-^{14}C acid]

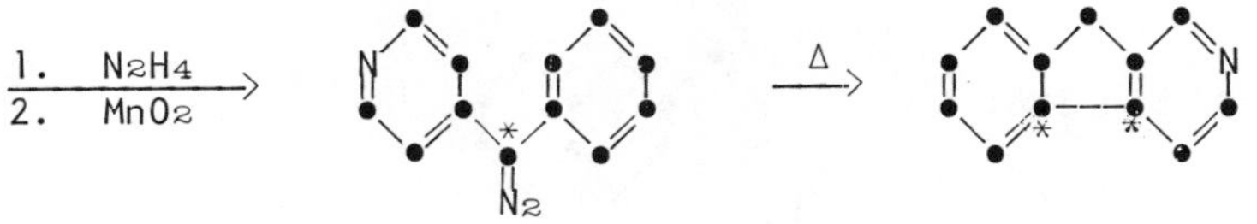

1. N2H4
2. MnO2
N2
Δ

(70%)

2-Azafluorene
[9H-Indenol[2,1-c]-
pyridine-4a,4b-^{14}C]

Degradation reactions showed 91.4% of the label was at the 4a position and 8.6% at 4b; the pyridine ring expansion mechanism is preferred over the benzene ring expansion mechanism.

C. Mayor and C. Wentrup, J. Amer. Chem. Soc., 97, 7467 (1975).

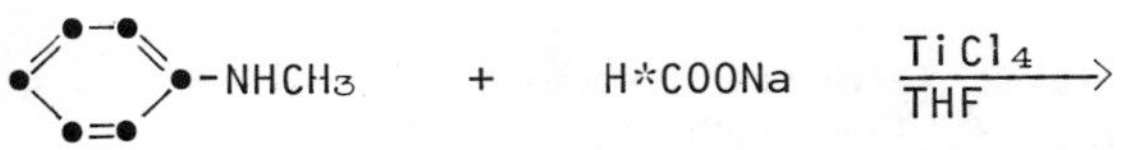

-NHCH3
+
H*COONa
TiCl4
THF
*CHO
-NCH3

(59%)

N-Methyl-N-phenyl-
formamide-[14]C

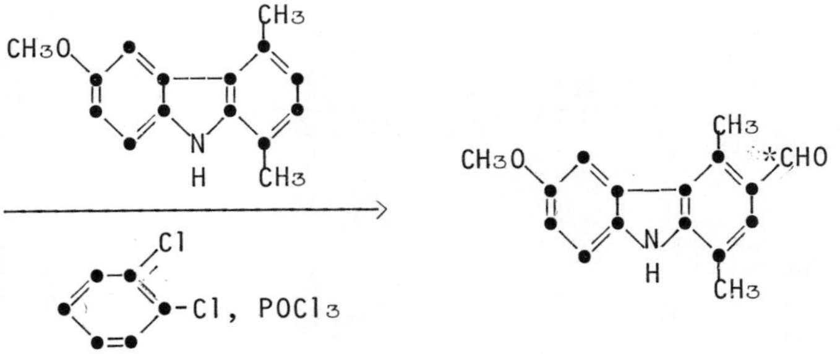

CH3
CH3O
N
H
CH3
Cl
-Cl, POCl3
CH3
*CHO
CH3O
N
H
CH3

(73% crude)

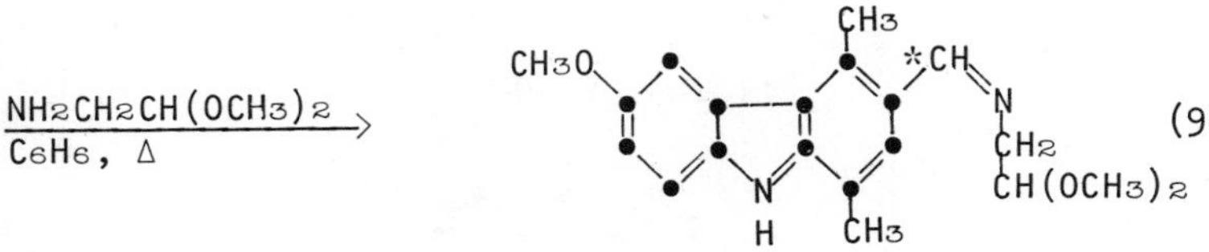

NH2CH2CH(OCH3)2
C6H6, Δ
CH3
CH3O
*CH
N
CH2
CH(OCH3)2
N
H
CH3

(98%)

2,2-Dimethoxy-N-[(6-methoxy-1,4-
dimethyl-9H-carbazol-3-yl)methylene-
[14]C]ethanamine

Nguyen Van-Bac, M. Herbert, L. Pichat, M.-M. Janot, and N. Dat-Xuong, J. Label. Compounds, 11, 241 (1975).

$(CH_3)_2NCH_2CH_2{*}CH_2NH_2 \cdot 2HCl$

N^3,N^3-Dimethyl-1,3-propanediamine-1-^{14}C dihydrochloride

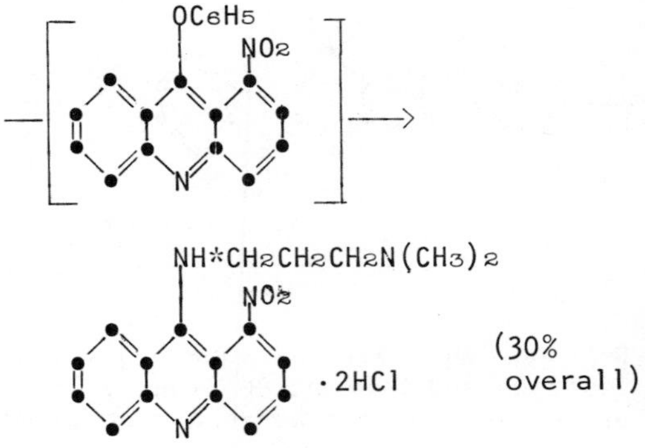
OC6H5
NO2
N
NH*CH2CH2CH2N(CH3)2
NO2
N
·2HCl
(30% overall)

N,N-Dimethyl-N'-(1-nitro-9-acridinyl)-1,3-propaneamine-1-^{14}C dihydrochloride

J. F. Biernat, B. Stefańska, E. Jereczek-Morawaka, T. Umiński, and A. Ledochowski, Rocz. Chem., 43, 1749 (1969); see also A. Kolodziejczyk and A. Arendt, J. Label. Compounds, 11, 385 (1975).

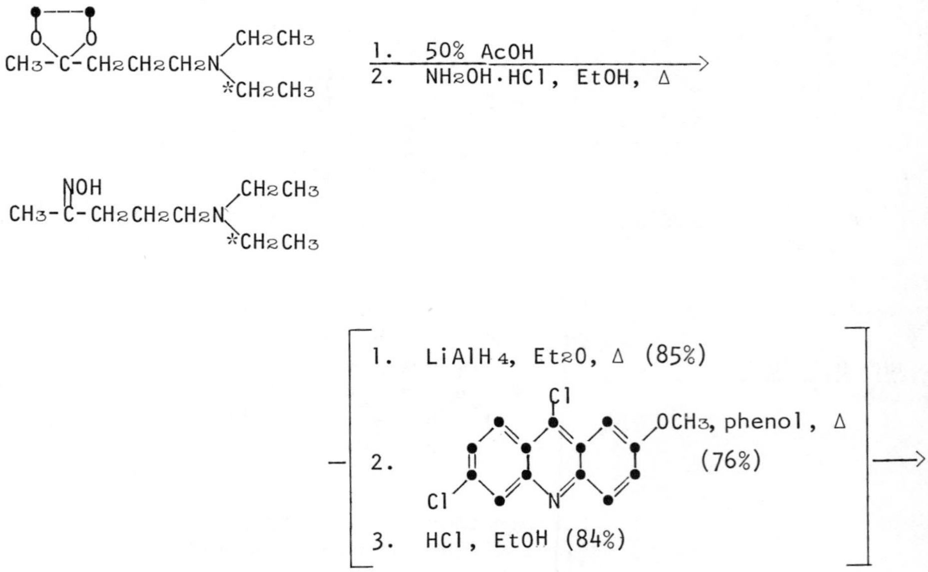
CH3-C-CH2CH2CH2N(CH2CH3)(*CH2CH3)
1. 50% AcOH
2. NH2OH·HCl, EtOH, Δ
NOH
CH3-C-CH2CH2CH2N(CH2CH3)(*CH2CH3)
1. LiAlH4, Et2O, Δ (85%)
Cl
OCH3, phenol, Δ
2.
(76%)
Cl
N
3. HCl, EtOH (84%)

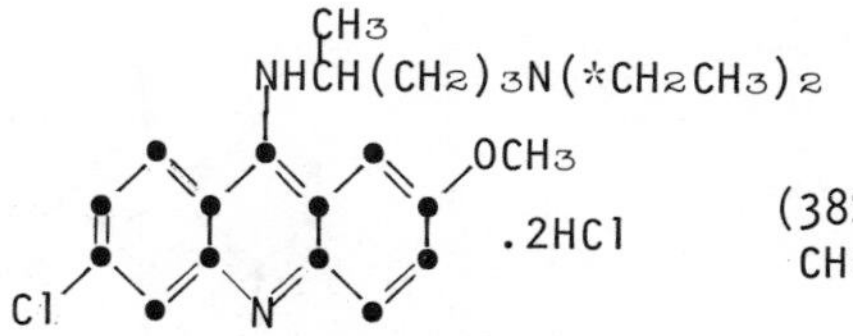

CH_3
$NHCH(CH_2)_3N(^*CH_2CH_3)_2$
OCH_3
.2HCl
Cl
N

(38% from $CH_3{}^*CH_2I$)

Quinacrine hydrochloride
[N⁴-(6-Chloro-2-methoxy-9-acridinyl)-N',N'-(diethyl-1-^{14}C)-1,4-pentanediamine dihydrochloride]

H. Minato, Y. Katsuyama, and T. Nagasaki, J. Label. Compound. Radiopharm., 13, 513 (1977).

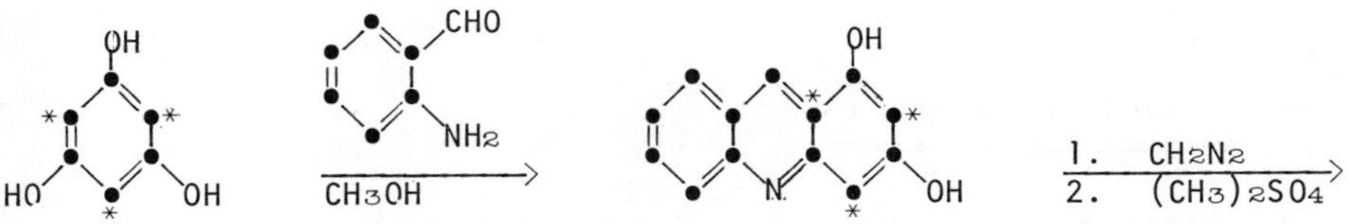

OH
HO
OH
CHO
NH_2
CH_3OH
OH
N
OH
1. CH_2N_2
2. $(CH_3)_2SO_4$

1,3-Acridinediol-2,4,9a-^{14}C

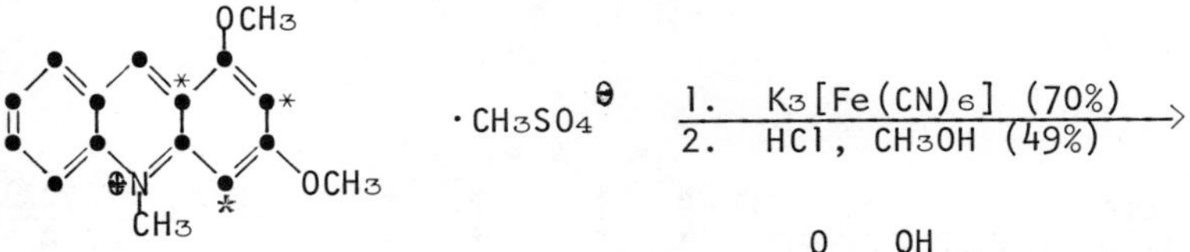

OCH_3
OCH_3
$\oplus$N
CH_3
$\cdot CH_3SO_4^{\ominus}$
1. $K_3[Fe(CN)_6]$ (70%)
2. HCl, CH_3OH (49%)

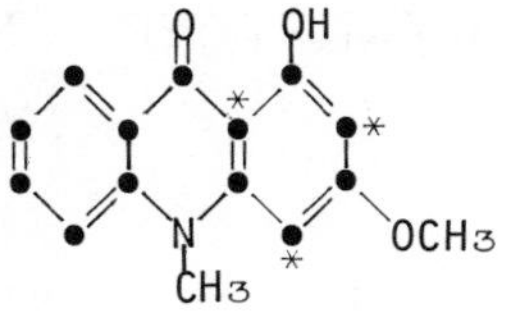

O
OH
N
CH_3
OCH_3

1-Hydroxy-3-methoxy-10-methyl-9(10H)-acridinone-2,4,10-^{14}C

S. Johne, H. Bernasch, and D. Gröger, Pharmazie, 25, 777 (1970).

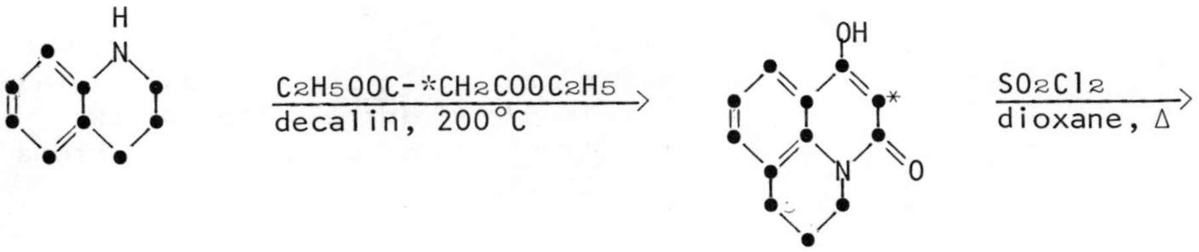

H
N
$C_2H_5OOC-{}^*CH_2COOC_2H_5$
decalin, 200°C
OH
N
O
SO_2Cl_2
dioxane, Δ

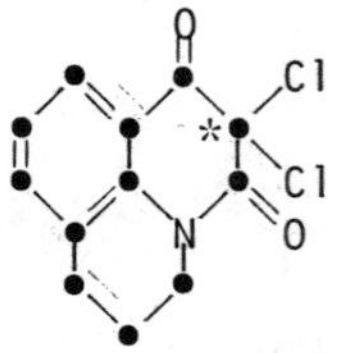
Cl
Cl
N
O

(65%)

2,2-Dichloro-6,7-dihydro-1H,5H-benzo[ij]quinolizine-1,3(2H)-dione-2-[14]C

The mechanism of the subsequent ring contraction reaction is discussed.

G. Kollenz and T. Kappe, Liebigs Ann. Chem., 1634 (1974).

9-7 Pentacyclic Compounds

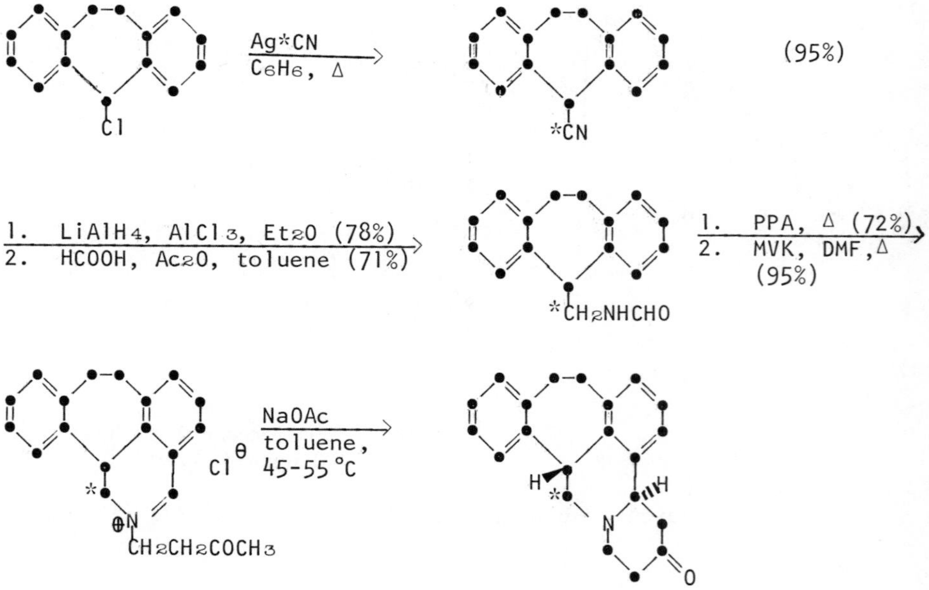
Cl
Ag*CN
C6H6, Δ
*CN
(95%)
1. LiAlH4, AlCl3, Et2O (78%)
2. HCOOH, Ac2O, toluene (71%)
*CH2NHCHO
1. PPA, Δ (72%)
2. MVK, DMF, Δ (95%)
⊕N
CH2CH2COCH3
Cl⊖
NaOAc
toluene, 45-55 °C
H
H
N
O

(Mixture of cis and trans obtained in 57% yield; 43% from Ag*CN; trans isomer separated by chromatography)

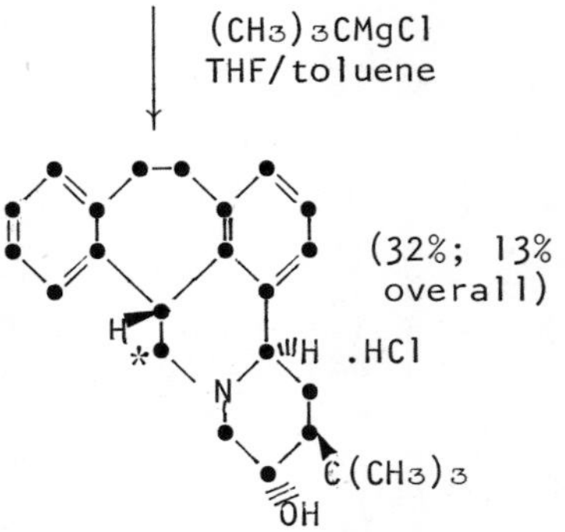
(CH3)3CMgCl
THF/toluene
H
*
H .HCl
N
C(CH3)3
OH

(32%; 13% overall)

Butaclamol hydrochloride
[(3S-(3α,4aα,13bβ)]octahydro-3-(1-methylethyl)-1H-benzo-[6,7]cyclohepta[1,2,3de]pyrido[2,1a]isoquinolin-3-ol-14-^{14}C hydrochloride]

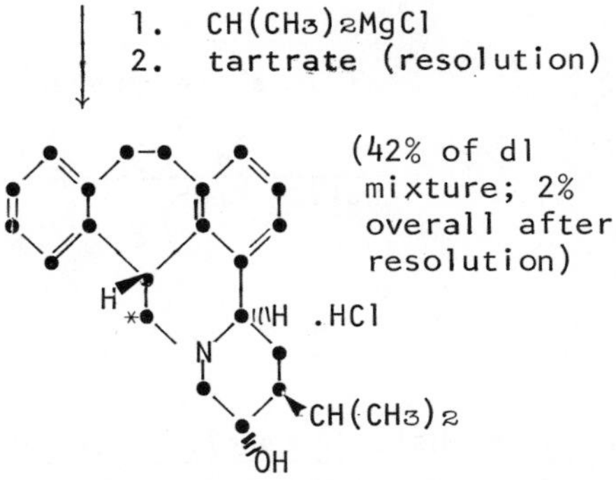
1. CH(CH3)2MgCl
2. tartrate (resolution)
H
*
H .HCl
N
CH(CH3)2
OH

(42% of dl mixture; 2% overall after resolution)

Dexclamol hydrochloride
[3R-(3aα,4aα,13bβ)]-3-(1,1-Dimethylethyl)-2,3,4,4a,8,9,13b,14-octahydro-1H-benzo[6,7]cyclohepta-[1,2,3-de]pyrido[2,1-a]-isoquinolin-3-ol-14-^{14}C hydrochloride]

E. S. Ferdinandi, P. Raman, and V. Ross, J. Label. Compound. Radiopharm. 14, 757 (1978).

Compounds with Two Heteroatoms

9-8 Five-Membered Rings

$(CH_2OH)_2$ $\xrightarrow[H_3PO_4,\ CaCl_2]{H^*CHO}$

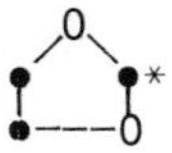
O
*
O

(60%)

1,3-Dioxolane-2-^{14}C

M. J. Molera, J. A. Garcia Dominguez, and A. U. Acuña, An. Quim., 70, 559 (1974).

$C_6H_5{*}COOH$ $\xrightarrow[3.\ (C_2H_5O)_3CH\ (90\%)]{1.\ SOCl_2;\ 2.\ (C_2H_5)_2Cd\ (56\%)}$

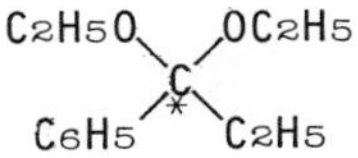
C2H5O
OC2H5
C
*
C6H5
C2H5

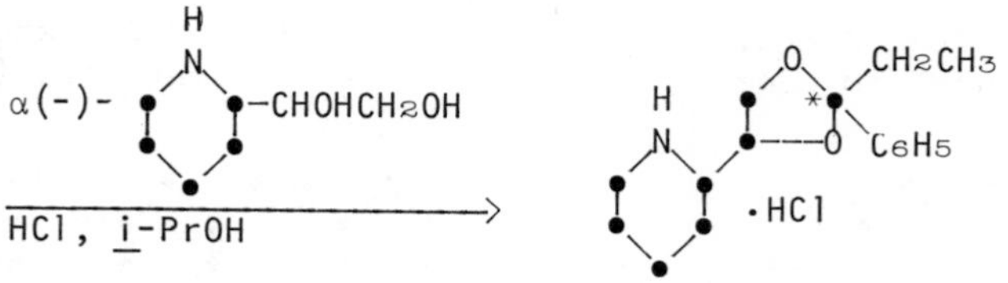
α(-)-
-CHOHCH2OH
HCl, i-PrOH
CH2CH3
C6H5
·HCl

2-(2-Ethyl-2-phenyl-1,3-dioxolan-4-yl-2-^{14}C)-piperidine hydrochloride

R. S. P. Hsi, J. Label. Compounds, 10, 381 (1974).

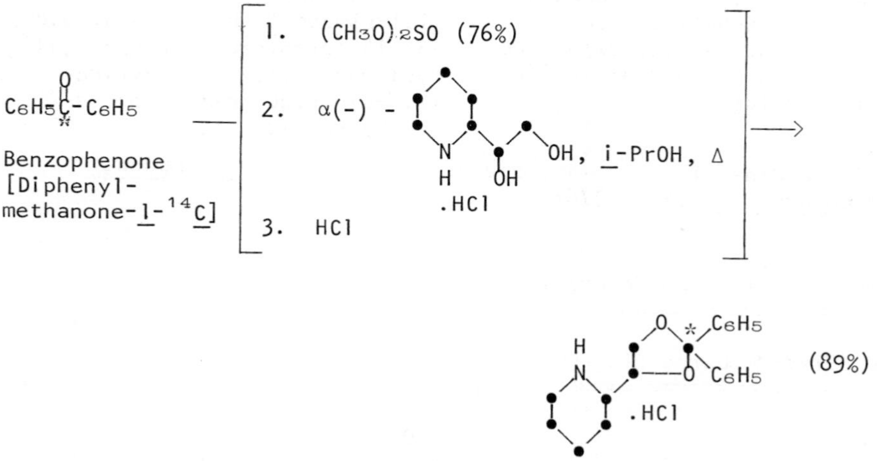
C6H5C-C6H5
1. (CH3O)2SO (76%)
2. α(-) -
OH, i-PrOH, Δ
.HCl
3. HCl
C6H5
C6H5
.HCl
(89%)

Benzophenone [Diphenyl-methanone-1-^{14}C]

Dioxadrol [2-(2,2-Diphenyl-1,3-dioxolan-2-^{14}C)-4-yl-piperidine hydrochloride]

Using the (+)-piperidine derivative, the opposite entaniomer was prepared.

R. S. P. Hsi and R. C. Thomas, Jr., J. Label. Compounds, 9, 425 (1973).

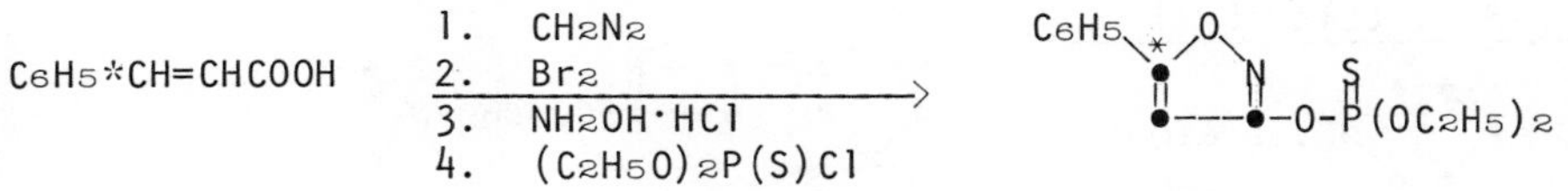
C6H5*CH=CHCOOH
1. CH2N2
2. Br2
3. NH2OH·HCl
4. (C2H5O)2P(S)Cl
C6H5
O
N
S
O-P(OC2H5)2

Isoxathion
[O,O-Diethylphosphorothioic acid O-[5-phenyl (isoxazolyl-5-^{14}C)]ester]

M. Ando, M. Nakagawa, T. Nakamura, and K. Tomita, Agr. Biol. Chem., 39, 803 (1975).

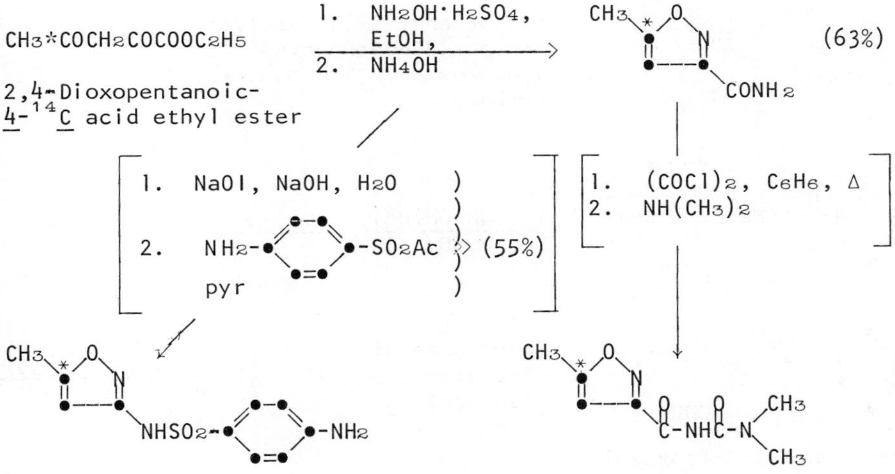
CH3*COCH2COCOOC2H5
1. NH2OH·H2SO4, EtOH,
2. NH4OH
CH3
O
N
(63%)
CONH2
1. NaOI, NaOH, H2O
2. NH2- -SO2Ac
pyr
(55%)
1. (COCl)2, C6H6, Δ
2. NH(CH3)2
NHSO2- -NH2
C-NHC-N
CH3
CH3

2,4-Dioxopentanoic-4-^{14}C acid ethyl ester

4-Amino-N-(5-methyl-3-isoxazolyl-5-^{14}C)benzenesulfonamide

N,N-Dimethyl-N'-(5-methyl-3-isoxazoyl carbonyl-5-^{14}C) urea

H. Minato, T. Nagasaki, and Y. Katsuyama, J. Label. Compounds, 11, 275 (1975).

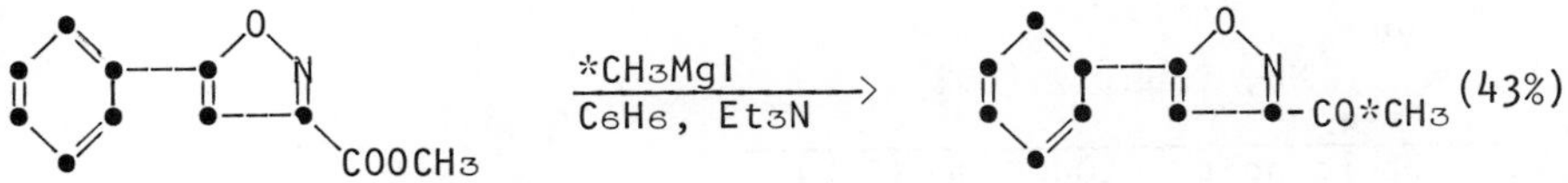
O
N
COOCH3
*CH3MgI
C6H6, Et3N
-CO*CH3
(43%)

1-(5-Phenyl-3-isoxazolyl)ethanone-1-^{14}C

1. Br_2, CCl_4 (85%)

2. 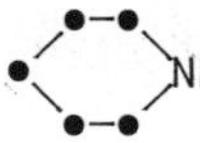NH, acetone (74%)

→

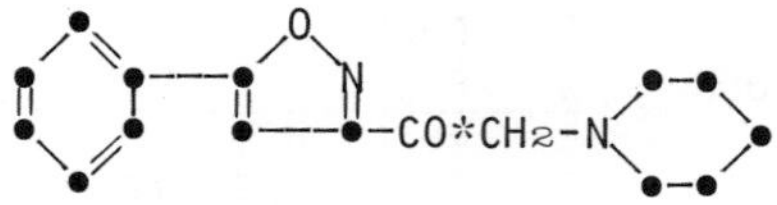

1. $NaBH_4$, CH_3OH (74%)
2. citric acid, CH_3OH, Δ (30%)

→

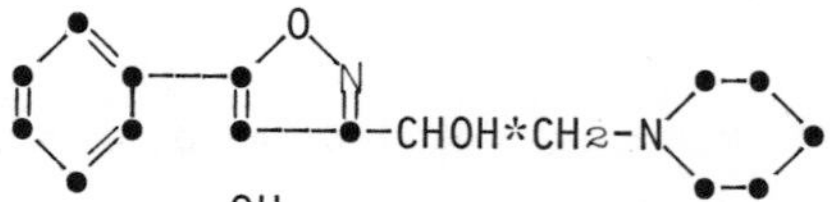

$HOOC-CH_2-C(OH)(COOH)-CH_2COOH$ (27% overall on free base)

α-(5-Phenyl-3-isoxazolyl)-1-piperidineethanol-β-^{14}C 2-hydroxy-1,2,3-propanetricarboxylate

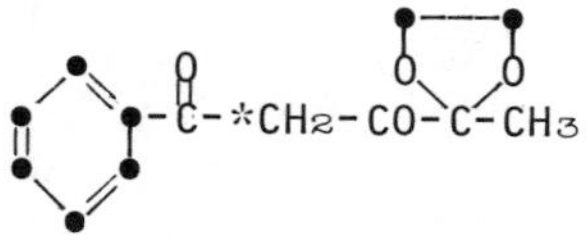

1. $NH_2OH.HCl$, EtOH, Δ
2. H_2SO_4, THF

→

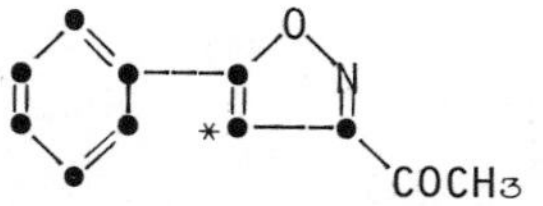

1-(5-Phenyl-3-isoxazolyl-4-^{14}C)ethanone (55% separated by preparative TLC)

(plus some of the 5-acetyl-3-phenylisoxazole-4-^{14}C isomer)

1. Br_2, CCl_4 (83%)
2. $NaBH_4$, CH_3OH (70%)

→

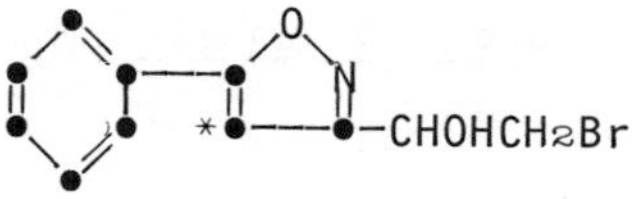

KOH / CH_3OH →

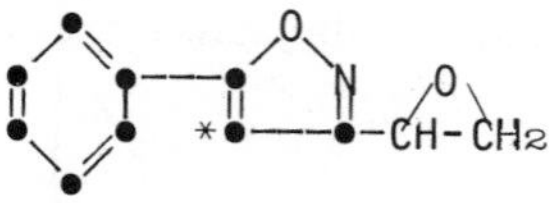

(99%)

1. 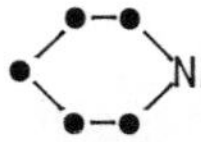NH, C_6H_6, Δ (80%)
2. citric acid, EtOH/C_6H_6 (95%)

→

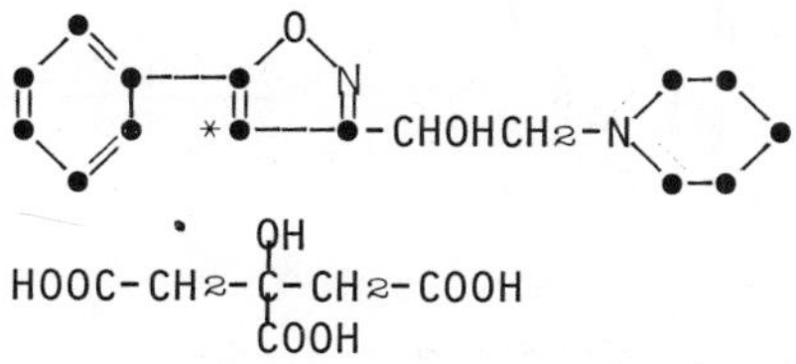

α-(5-Phenyl-3-isoxazolyl-4-^{14}C)-1-piperidineethanol 2-hydroxy-1,2,3-propanetricarboxylate

H. Minato, T. Nagasaki, T. Yokoshima, K. Suga, and M. Yamaguchi, J. Label. Compounds, 10, 645 (1974)

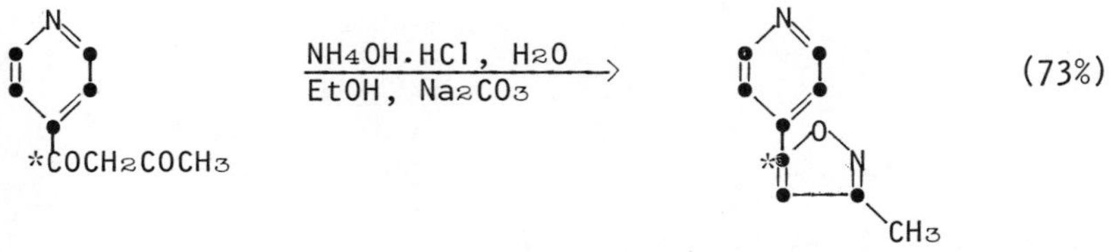

4-(3-Methyl-5-isoxazolyl-5-^{14}C)pyridine

V. J. Bauer and A. E. Lanzilotti, J. Label. Compounds, 5, 87 (1969).

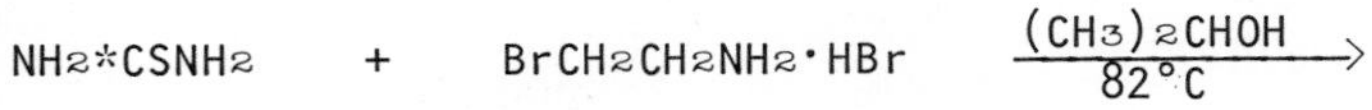

Thiourea-^{14}C

Carbamimidothioic-^{14}C acid 2-aminoethyl ester dihydrobromide

4,5-Dihydro-2-thiazolamine-2-^{14}C hydrobromide

L. Konrád and I. Kozák, J. Label. Compounds, 9, 107 (1973).

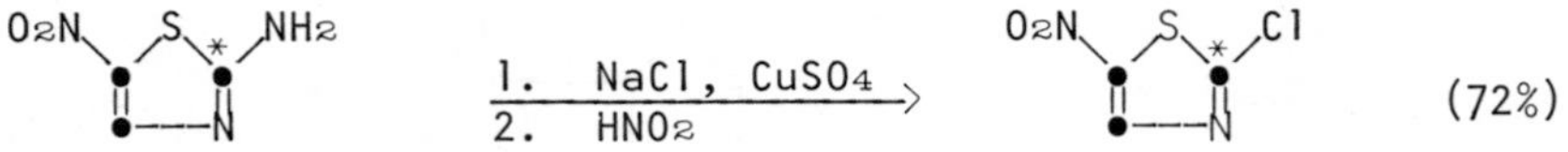
1. NaCl, $CuSO_4$
2. HNO_2
(72%)

2-Chloro-5-nitrothiazole-2-^{14}C

J. W. Faigle and H. Keberle, J. Label. Compounds, 5, 173 (1969).

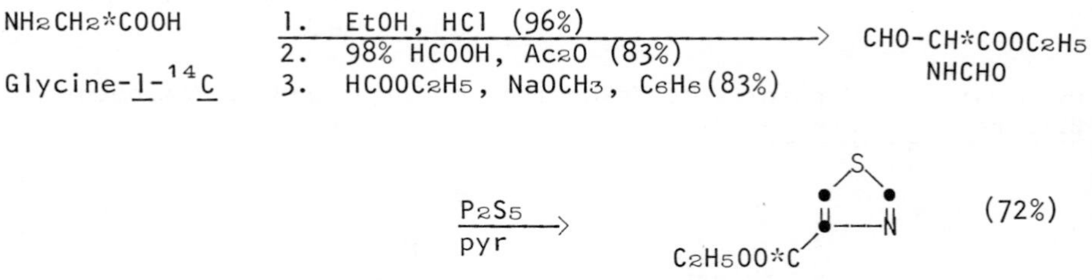
$NH_2CH_2{*}COOH$
Glycine-1-^{14}C
1. EtOH, HCl (96%)
2. 98% HCOOH, Ac_2O (83%)
3. $HCOOC_2H_5$, $NaOCH_3$, C_6H_6 (83%)
$CHO\text{-}CH{*}COOC_2H_5$
NHCHO
P_2S_5
pyr
$C_2H_5OO{*}C$
(72%)

4-Thiazolecarboxylic acid ethyl ester-(carboxyl-^{14}C)

R. L. Ellsworth, H. E. Mertel, and W. J. A. VandenHeuvel, J. Agr. Food Chem., 24, 544 (1976).

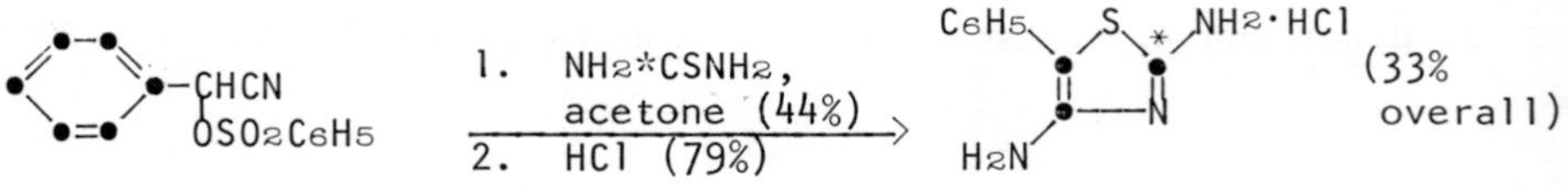
CHCN
$OSO_2C_6H_5$
1. $NH_2{*}CSNH_2$, acetone (44%)
2. HCl (79%)
C_6H_5
$NH_2 \cdot HCl$
H_2N
(33% overall)

Amiphenazole
[5-Phenyl-2,4-thiazolediamine-2-^{14}C hydrochloride]

J. G. Adams, P. J. Nicholls, and H. Williams, J. Label. Compound. Radiopharm., 12, 239 (1976).

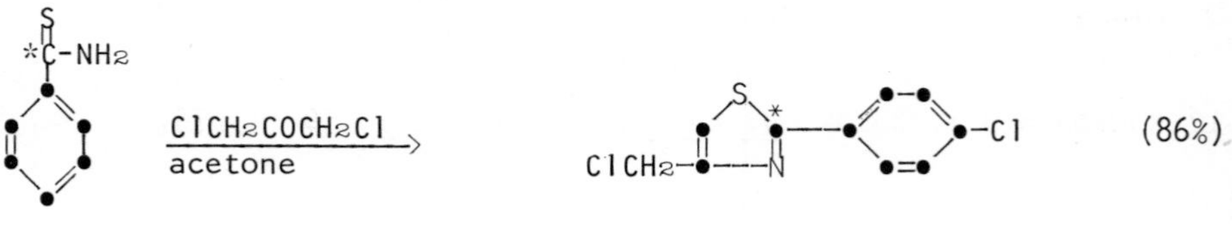
$*C\text{-}NH_2$
$ClCH_2COCH_2Cl$
acetone
$ClCH_2$
Cl
(86%)

1. KCN, DMSO (68%)
2. 6N HCl, dioxane, Δ

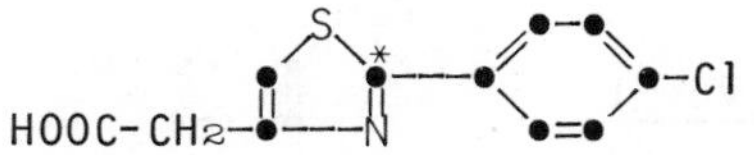

(22% overall)

2-(4-Chlorophenyl)-4-thiazoleacetic acid-2-^{14}C

D. F. White and J. Burns, J. Label. Compound. Radiopharm., 13, 393 (1977).

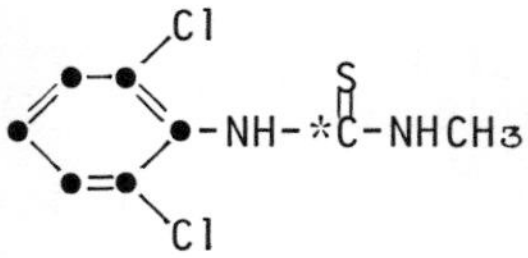

(67%)

$CH_3CHBrCH_2Br$
isoamyl alcohol, Δ

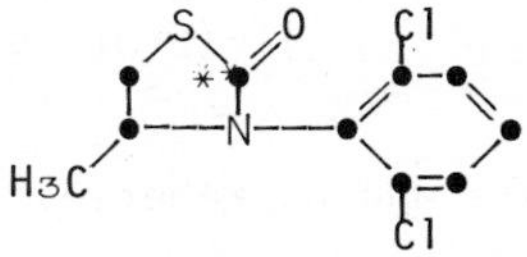

(~25%)

3-(2,6-Dichlorophenyl)-4-methyl-2-thiazolidinone-2-^{14}C

Similarly:

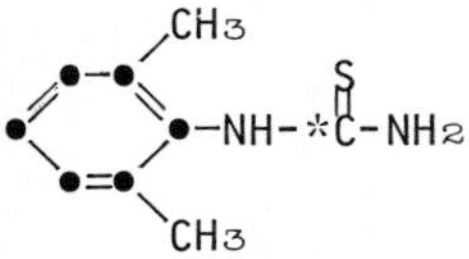

(74% from K*CN)

1. Δ (quant.)
2. $CH_3NHCH_2CH_2OH$ (82%)

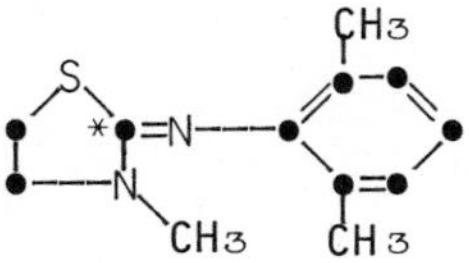

2,6-Dimethyl-N-(3-methyl-2-thiazolidinylidene-2-^{14}C)-benzeneamine

G. Zőlyomi, L. Toldy, and D. Bánfi, J. Label. Compounds, 9, 243 (1973).

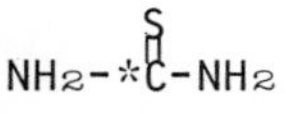

+

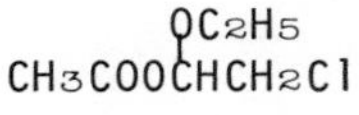

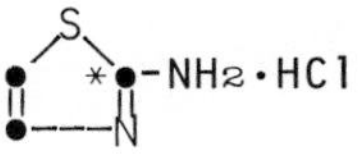

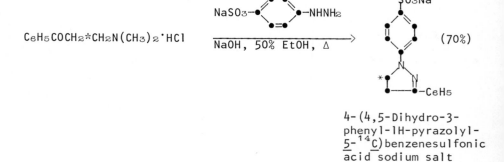

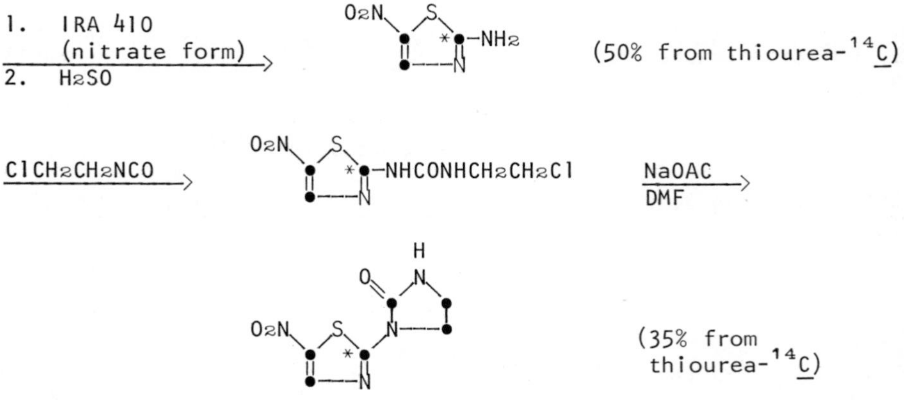
1. IRA 410
(nitrate form)
2. H2SO
O2N
S
NH2
(50% from thiourea-14C)
ClCH2CH2NCO
O2N
S
NHCONHCH2CH2Cl
NaOAC
DMF
H
O
N
O2N
S
N
(35% from thiourea-14C)

Niridazole
[1-(5-Nitro-2-thiazolyl-2-^{14}C)-2-imidazolidinone]

J. W. Faigle and H. Keberle, J. Label. Compounds, 5, 173 (1969).

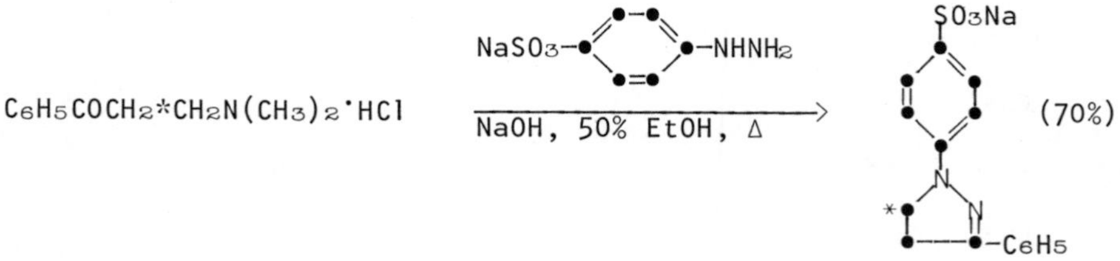
C6H5COCH2*CH2N(CH3)2·HCl
NaSO3
NHNH2
NaOH, 50% EtOH, Δ
SO3Na
(70%)
N
N
C6H5

4-(4,5-Dihydro-3-phenyl-1H-pyrazolyl-5-^{14}C)benzenesulfonic acid sodium salt

L. A. Holt and B. Milligan, Aust. J. Biol. Sci., 27, 23 (1974); Aust. J. Chem., 30, 2277 (1977).

$CH_3{*}COCH_2{*}COCH_3$ $\xrightarrow{NH_2NH_2}$

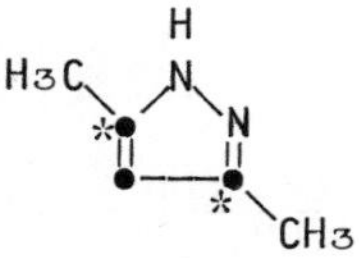

(45%; 38% from acetone-2-^{14}C)

2,4-Pentadione-2,4-^{14}C

3,5-Dimethyl-1H-pyrazole-3,5-^{14}C

$CH_3{*}COCH_2COCOOC_2H_5$ $\xrightarrow[\Delta]{NH_2NH_2}$

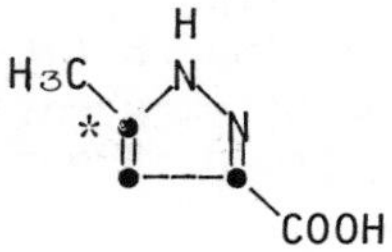

(61%; 46% from acetone-2-^{14}C)

5-Methyl-1H-pyrazole-3-carboxylic acid-5-^{14}C

R. C. Thomas, J. Label. Compound. Radiopharm., 15, 461 (1978).

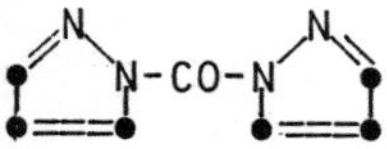

$\xrightarrow[COCl_2,\ THF]{CH_3{*}COCH_3}$

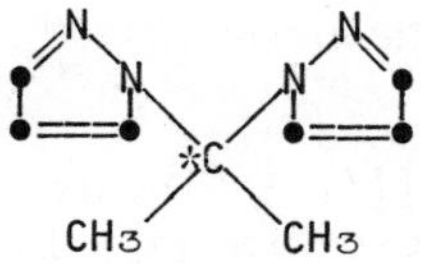

1,1'-(1-Methylethylidene-1-^{14}C)bis-1H-pyrazole

L. K. Peterson, E. Kiehlmann, A. R. Sanger, and K. I. Thé, Can. J. Chem., 52, 2367 (1974).

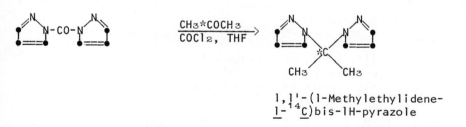

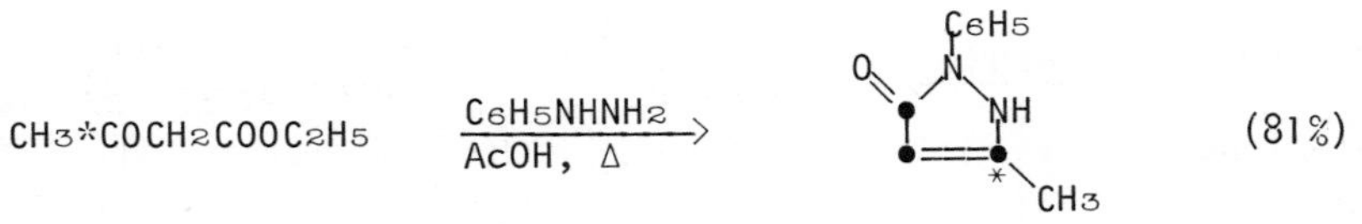

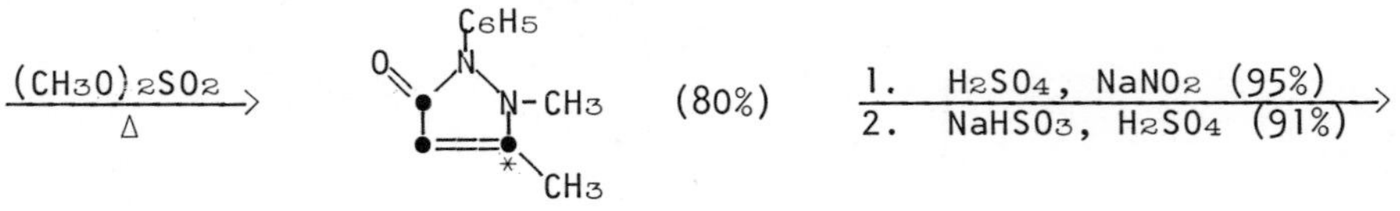

Antipyrine
[1,2-Dihydro-1,5-dimethyl-2-phenyl-3H-pyrazol-3-one-5-^{14}C]

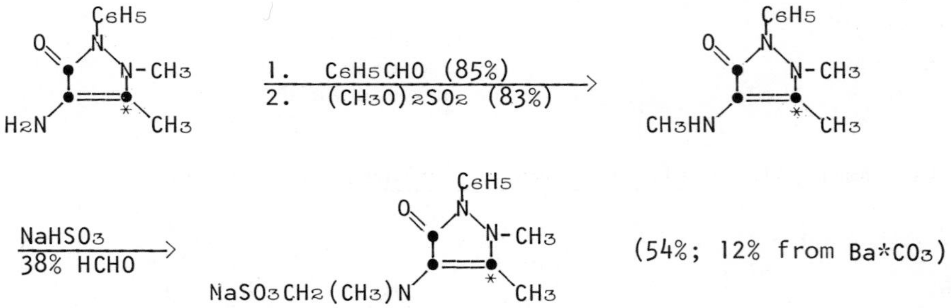

Novolgine
[[(2,3-Dihydro-1,5-dimethyl-3-oxo-2-phenyl-1H-pyrazol-4-yl)methylamino]methanesulfonic-5-^{14}C sodium salt]

O. Christ, H.-M. Kellner, G. Ross, W. Rupp, and A. Schwarz, Arzneim.-Forsch.-(Drug Res.), 23, 1760 (1973).

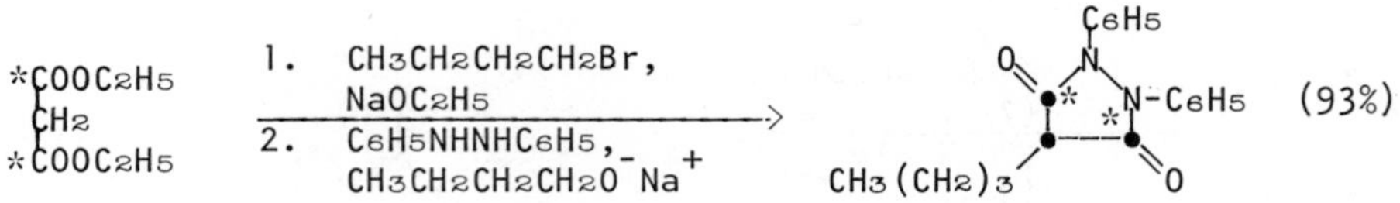

4-Butyl-1,2-diphenyl-3,5-pyrazolidinedione-3,5-^{14}C

S. Stavchansky and K. B. Kostenbauder, J. Label. Compounds, 8, 653 (1972).

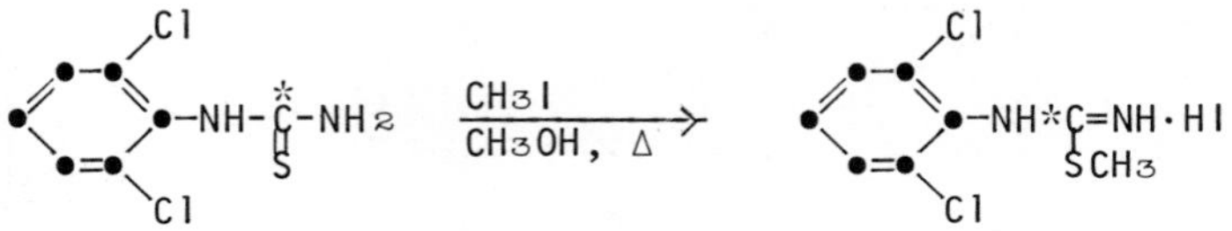

(from K*CN)

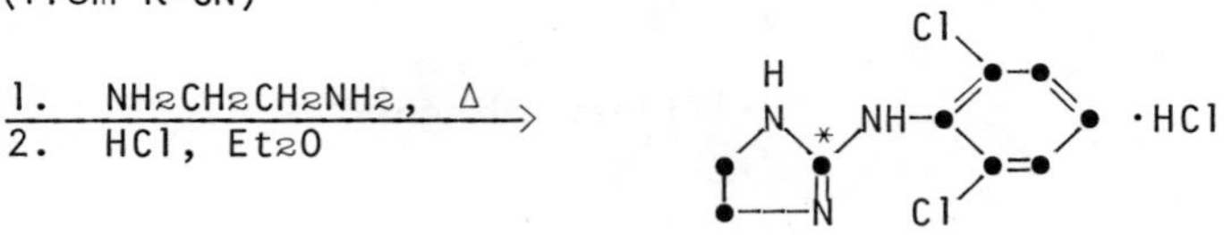

Clonidine
[2-(2,6-Dichloroanilino)-2-imidazoline-2-^{14}C hydrochloride]

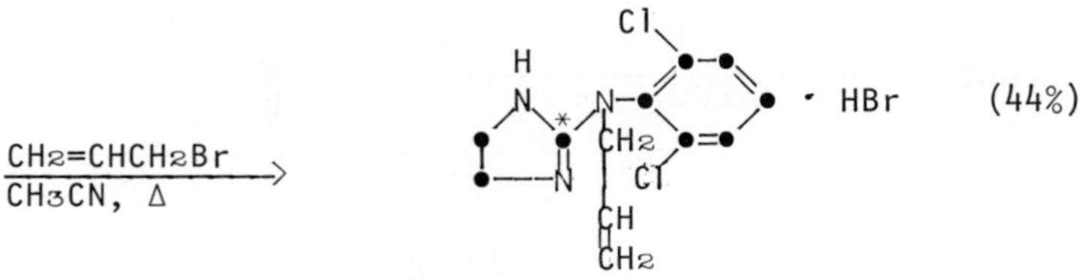

N-(2,6-Dichlorophenyl)-N-2-propenyl-1H-imidazol-2-amine-2-^{14}C hydrobromide

M. Stiasni and H. Stäble, J. Label. Compound. Radiopharm., 14, 51 (1978).

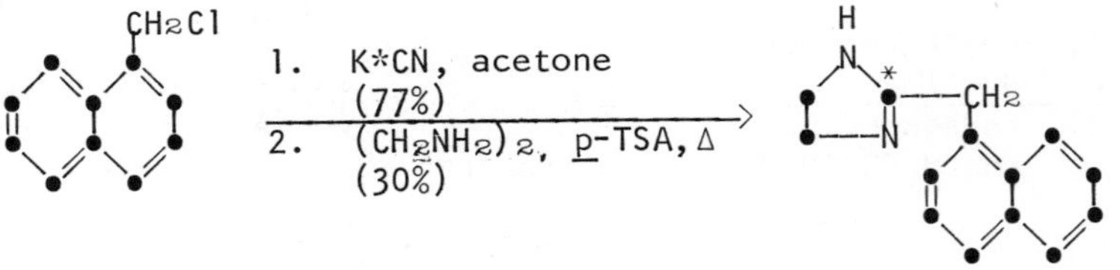
CH2Cl
1. K*CN, acetone
(77%)
2. (CH2NH2)2, p-TSA, Δ
(30%)
H
N
*
CH2
N

(23% overall)

4,5-Dihydro-2-[(1-naphthalenyl)methyl]imidazole-2-[14]C

C. L. Duc, M.-H. Pera, H. Fillion, and C. A. Delord, Bull. Soc. Chim. Fr., Part 2, 555 (1976).

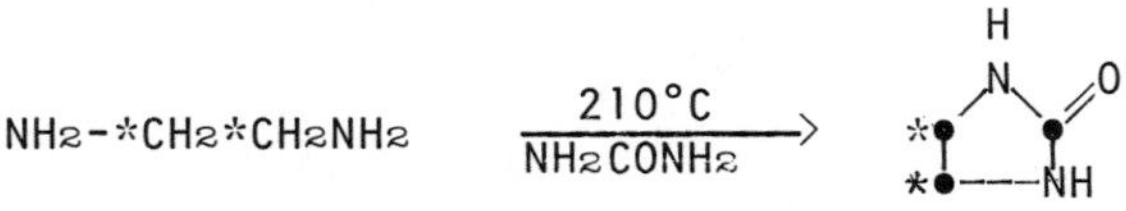
NH2-*CH2*CH2NH2
210°C
NH2CONH2
H
N
O
NH

(54% average yield)

2-Imidazolidinone-4,5-[14]C

W. B. Burton, Microchem. J., 15, 161 (1970).

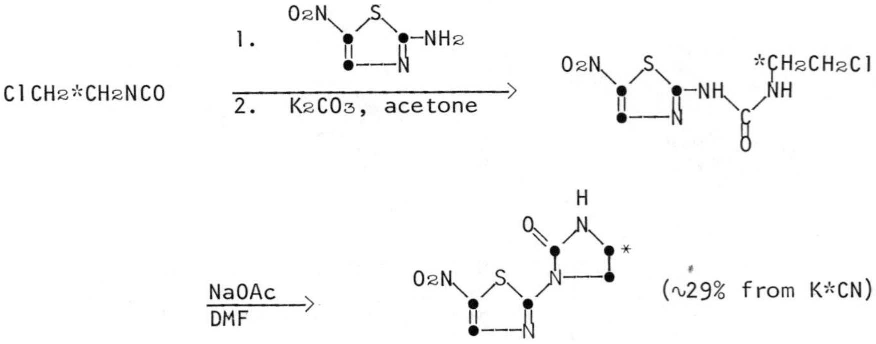
O2N
S
NH2
N
1.
ClCH2*CH2NCO
2. K2CO3, acetone
*CH2CH2Cl
NH
NH
O
NaOAc
DMF
H
N
(~29% from K*CN)

Niridazole
[1-(5-Nitro-2-thiazolyl)-2-imidazolidinone-4-^{14}C]

J. W. Faigle and H. Keberle, J. Label. Compounds, 5, 173 (1969).

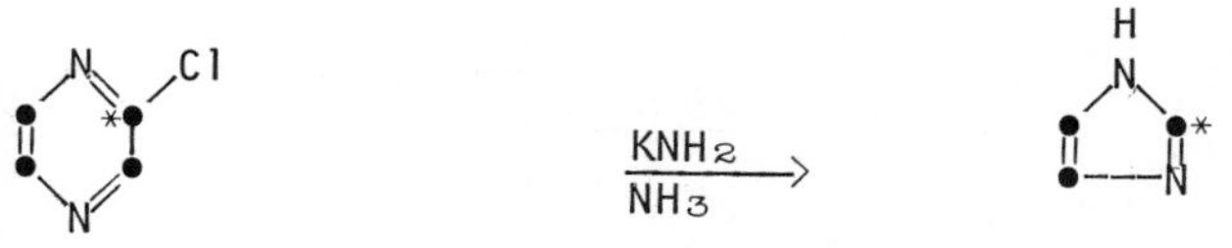
Cl
KNH2
NH3
H

(plus other products)

2-Chloropyrazine-2-^{14}C

1H-Imidazole-^{14}C

The specific activity of imidazole was the same as that of 2-chloropyrazine (the label is presumed to be at position 2 in imidazole). A mechanism is postulated (supported by ^{15}N-labeling studies).

P. J. Lont, H. C. van der Plas, and E. Bosma, Rec. Trav. Chim., J. Roy. Neth. Chem., 91, 1352 (1972).

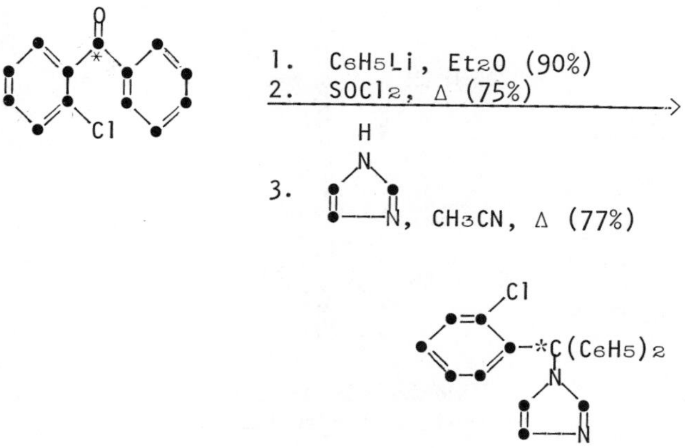
O
Cl
1. C6H5Li, Et2O (90%)
2. SOCl2, Δ (75%)
H
3.
, CH3CN, Δ (77%)
Cl
*C(C6H5)2

(30% from Ba*CO$_3$)

Clotrimazole
[1-[(2-Chlorophenyl)diphenylmethyl-^{14}C]-1H-imidazole]

W. Maul and D. Scherling, J. Label. Compound. Radiopharm., 14, 403 (1978).

$^{*}CH_3N=C=S$
(Methyl-^{14}C)-isothiocyanate

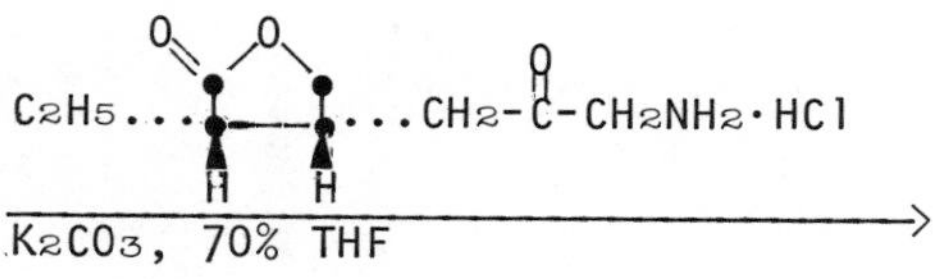
O
O
O
C2H5...
...CH2-C-CH2NH2·HCl
H
H
K2CO3, 70% THF

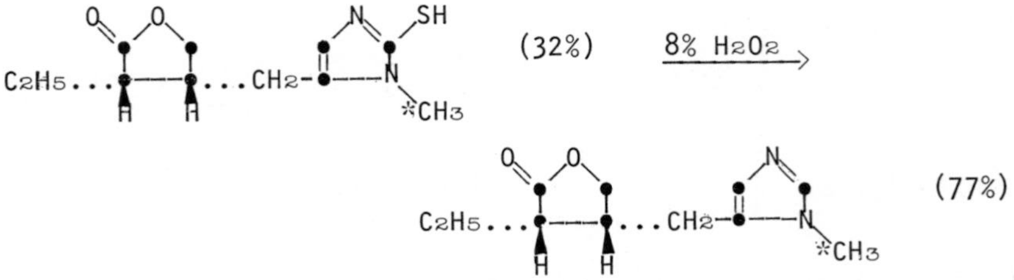

d-Pilocarpine
[(3S-cis)-3-Ethyldihydro-4-[(1-methyl-^{14}C-1H-imidazol-5-yl)methyl]-2-(3H)-furanone]

J. I. DeGraw, J. S. Engstrom, and E. Willis, J. Pharm. Sci., 64, 1700 (1975).

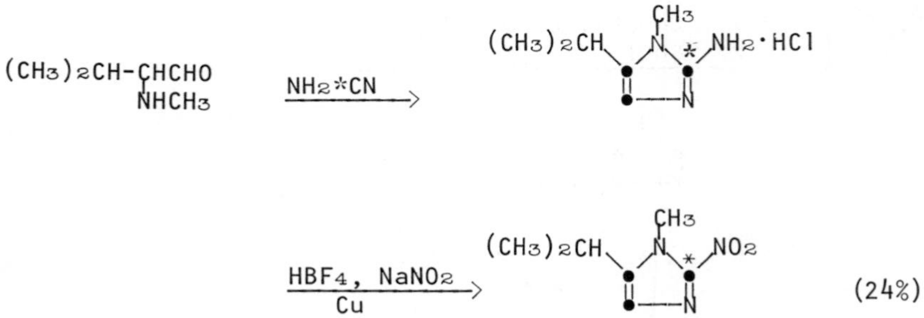

1-Methyl-5-(1-methylethyl)-2-nitro-1H-imidazole-2-^{14}C

Similarly:

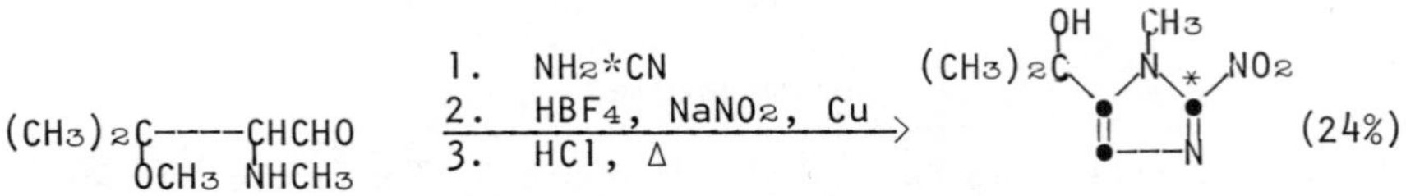

α,α,1-Trimethyl-2-nitro-1H-imidazole-5-methanol-2-^{14}C

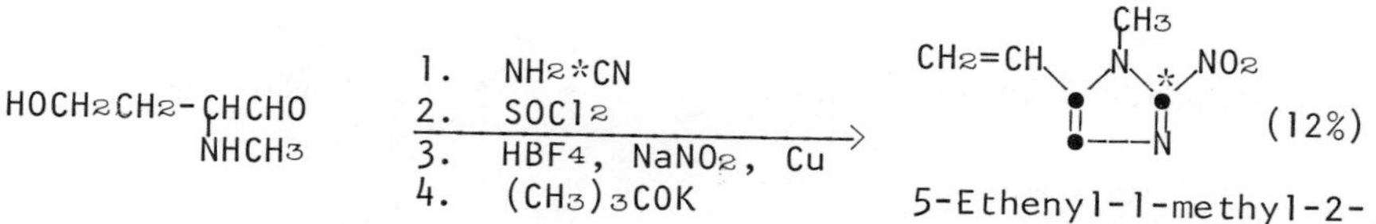
HOCH2CH2-CHCHO
NHCH3
1. NH2*CN
2. SOCl2
3. HBF4, NaNO2, Cu
4. (CH3)3COK
CH3
CH2=CH
NO2
(12%)

5-Ethenyl-1-methyl-2-nitro-1H-imidazole-2-^{14}C

G. Sartori, G. C. Lancini, and B. Cavalleri, J. Label. Compound. Radiopharm., 15, 673 (1978).

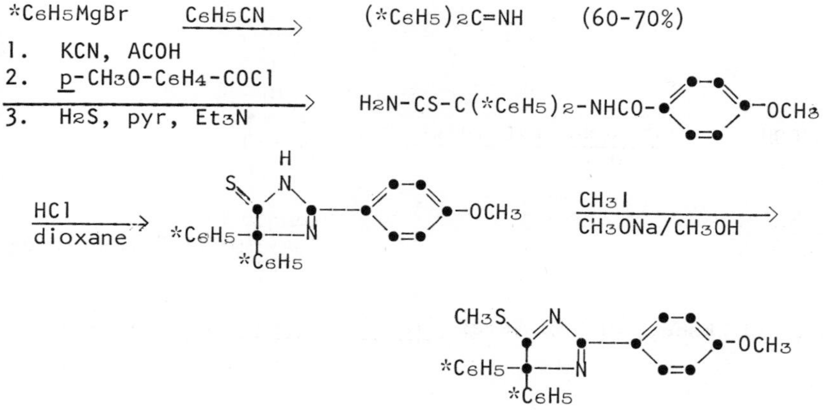
*C6H5MgBr
C6H5CN
(*C6H5)2C=NH
(60-70%)
1. KCN, ACOH
2. p-CH3O-C6H4-COCl
3. H2S, pyr, Et3N
H2N-CS-C(*C6H5)2-NHCO-
OCH3
HCl
dioxane
*C6H5
*C6H5
OCH3
CH3I
CH3ONa/CH3OH
CH3S
*C6H5
*C6H5
OCH3

5-(4-Methoxyphenyl)-2-(methylthio)-3,3-di-(phenyl-^{14}C)-3H-imidazole

The compound was used in mechanistic studies in the thermal rearrangement to 2,4,5-triarylimidazoles.

E. Koltai, J. Nyitrai, K. Lempert, and L. Bursics, Chem. Ber., 107, 1649 (1974).

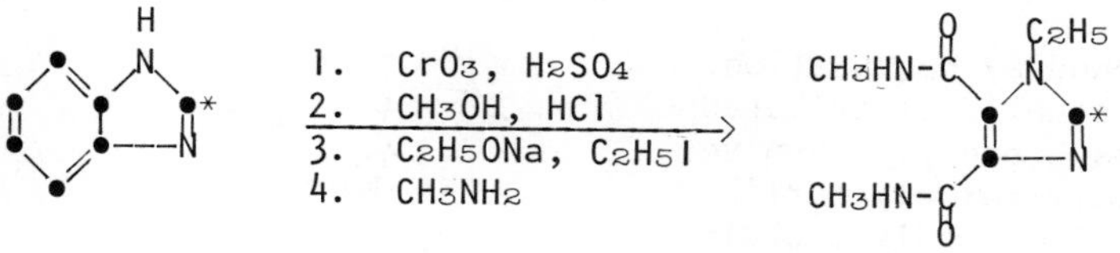
1. CrO3, H2SO4
2. CH3OH, HCl
3. C2H5ONa, C2H5I
4. CH3NH2
CH3HN-C
C2H5
CH3HN-C

Ethymizol
[1-Ethyl-N,N'-dimethyl-1H-imidazole-4,5-dicarboxamide-2-^{14}C]

Y. Y. Usaevich and L. I. Vekshina, Khim.-Farm. Zh., 11, 37 (1977).

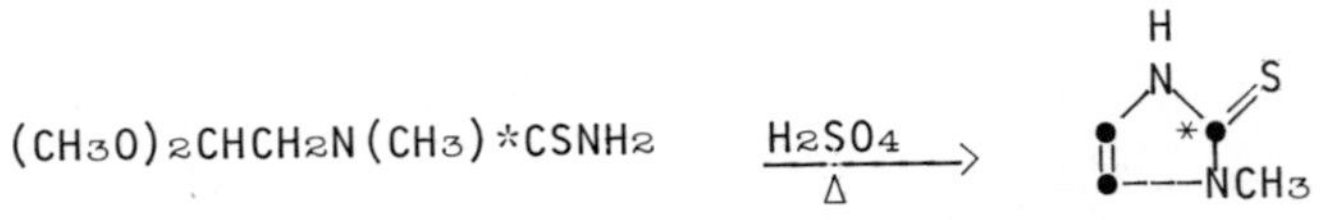
(CH3O)2CHCH2N(CH3)*CSNH2
H2SO4
Δ
H
N
S
NCH3

(86% overall)

Methimazole
[1,3-Dihydro-1-methyl-2H-imidazole-2-thione-2-^{14}C]

P. W. Lee, M. J. Gudzinowicz, and R. A. Neal, J. Label. Compound. Radiopharm., 14, 633 (1978).

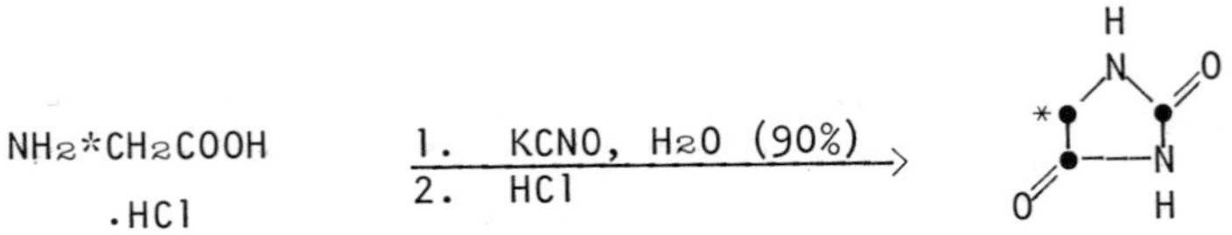
NH2*CH2COOH
·HCl
1. KCNO, H2O (90%)
2. HCl
H
N
O
N
H
O

Glycine-2-^{14}C hydrochloride

Hydantoin
[2,4-Imidazolidinedione-5-^{14}C]

V. Tolman, J. Hanuš, and K. Vereš, J. Label. Compounds, 4, 243 (1968).

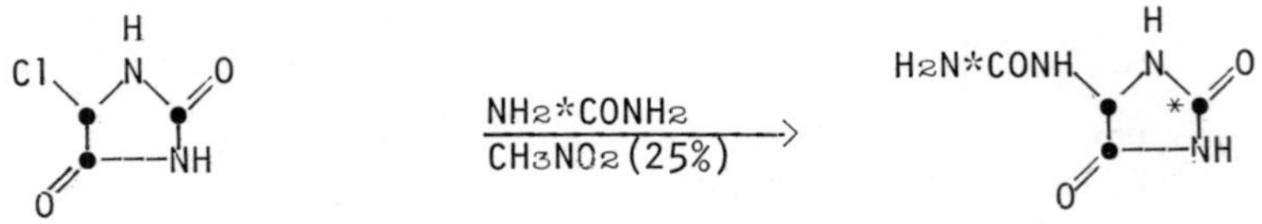
H
Cl
N
O
NH
O
NH2*CONH2
CH3NO2 (25%)
H2N*CONH
H
N
O
NH
O

5-Chlorohydantoin
(from parabanic acid)

Allantoin
[(2,5-Dioxo-4-imidazolidinyl-2-^{14}C)urea-^{14}C]

The label was found by degradation reactions to be equally distributed between positions 2 and 7. Involvement of the symmetrical glycouril derivative as an intermediate or in equilibrium with the product is proposed.

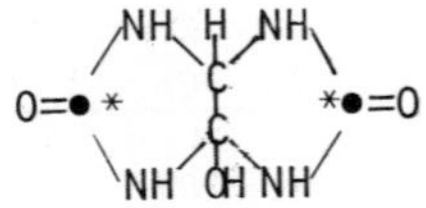
NH
H
NH
O=
=O
NH
OH
NH

J. Abblard and A. Meynaud, Bull. Soc. Chim. Fr., 942 (1971).

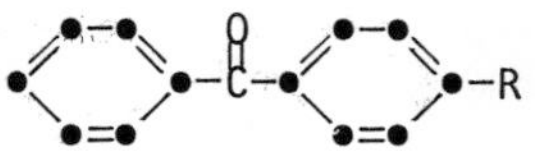

K*CN, $(NH_4)_2CO_3$ ⟶
DMSO, NaOH
Δ, pressure, 60 min

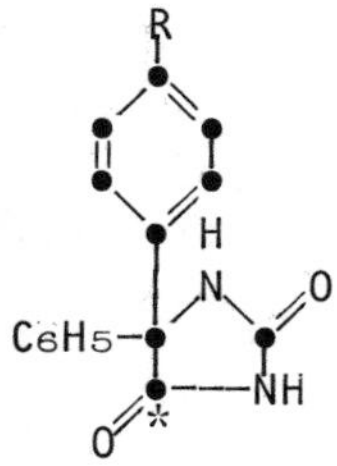

R=H; Diphenylhydantoin (59%)
[5,5-Diphenyl-2,4-imidazolidinedione-*4*-^{14}*C*]
R=OH; 5-(4-Hydroxyphenyl)-5-phenyl-2,4-imidazolidinedione-*4*-^{14}*C* (40%)

The synthesis is suitable for carbon-11 labeling; total time ∿70 min

S. Stavchansky and H. B. Kostenbauder, *J. Label. Compounds*, *10*, 469 (1974).

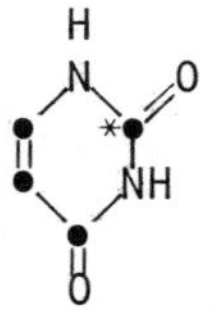

hν, H_2O_2 ⟶
2 hr

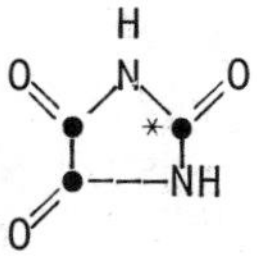

(41%)

Uracil
[2,4-(1H,3H)-pyrimidinedione-*2*-^{14}*C*]

Parabanic acid
[Imidazolidinetrione-*2*-^{14}*C*]

plus $H_2N*CO-NHCOCOOH$ (21%)

Oxaluric acid
[[(Aminocarbonyl-^{14}*C*-)amino]oxoacetic acid]

An 18% yield of urea was also obtained; the position of the label is assumed to remain at C-2.

H. Ochiai, *Agr. Biol. Chem.*, *Tokyo*, *35*, 622 (1971).

9-9 Six-Membered Rings

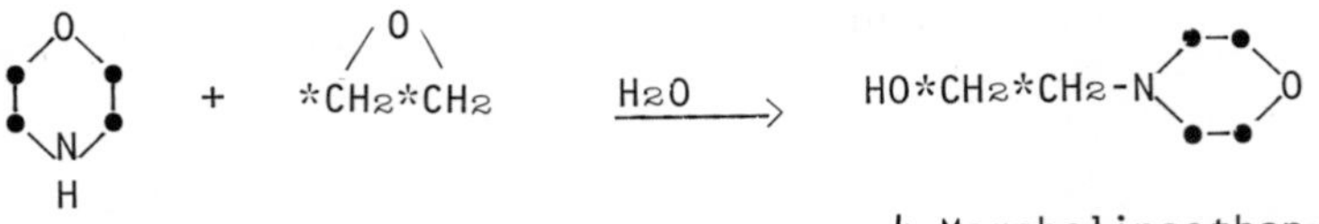
H2O
HO*CH2*CH2-N

(78%)

4-Morpholineethan-α,β-^{14}C-ol

C. Jacquot, J. Rapin, B. Lambrey, R. Baronnet, and L. Pichat, Eur. J. Med. Chem. - Chem. Ther., 13, 61 (1978).

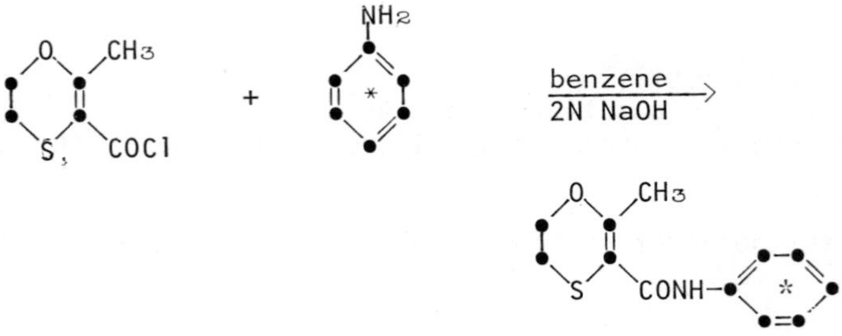
benzene
2N NaOH
CONH

(79%)

Carboxin
[5,6-Dihydro-2-methyl-N-(phenyl-U-^{14}C)-1,4-oxathiin-3-carboxamide]

Oxidation of carboxin-^{14}C with 30% hydrogen peroxide at 10-15°C gave carboxin-sulfoxide-(phenyl-U-^{14}C) (∿50% yield) and at 80°C gave carboxin-sulfone-(phenyl-U-^{14}C) (∿40% yield).

A. Unverricht, and H. R. Schütte, Z. Chem., 18, 21 (1978).

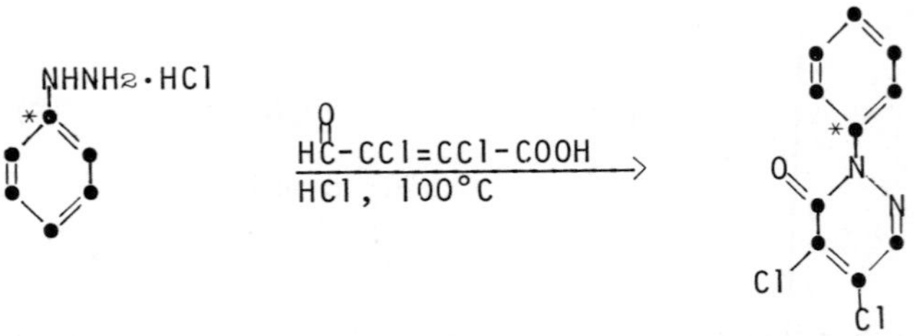
NHNH2·HCl
HC-CCl=CCl-COOH
HCl, 100°C

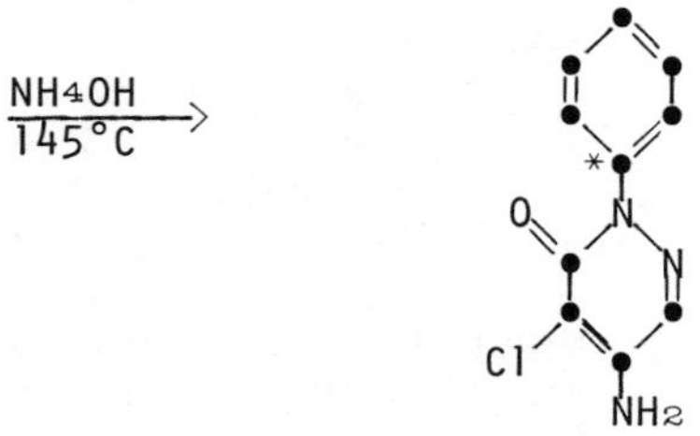

(73%)

4-Amino-5-chloro-1-(phenyl-1-^{14}C)-6-(1H)-pyridazinone

The analogue with phenyl-U-^{14}C was similarly prepared.

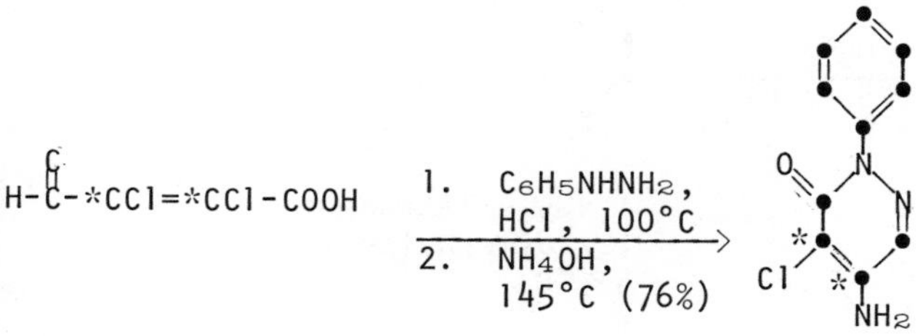

(18% for last two steps)

Mucochloric acid-2,3-^{14}C[(Z)-2,3-Dichloro-4-oxo-2-butenoic-2,3-$^{14}C_2$ acid]

4-Amino-5-chloro-1-phenyl-6(1H)-pyridazinone-4,5-^{14}C

The pyridazone-3,6-^{14}C derivative was similarly prepared from mucochloric-1,4-^{14}C acid.

T. F. Burger, J. Label. Compounds, 4, 262 (1968); A. Unverricht, G. Simon, and H. R. Schütte, Z. Chem., 16, 442 (1976).

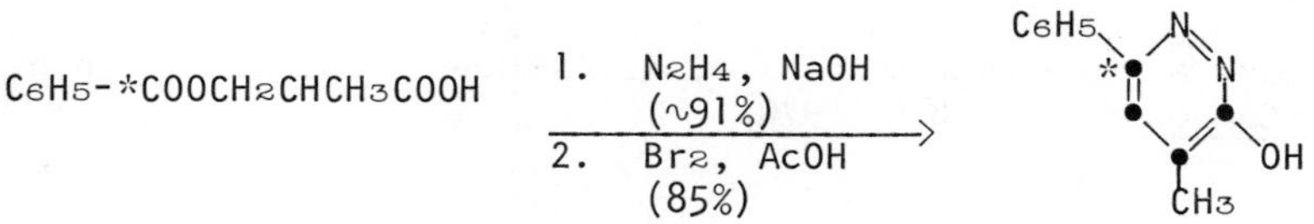

4-Methyl-6-phenyl-pyridazin-3-ol-6-^{14}C

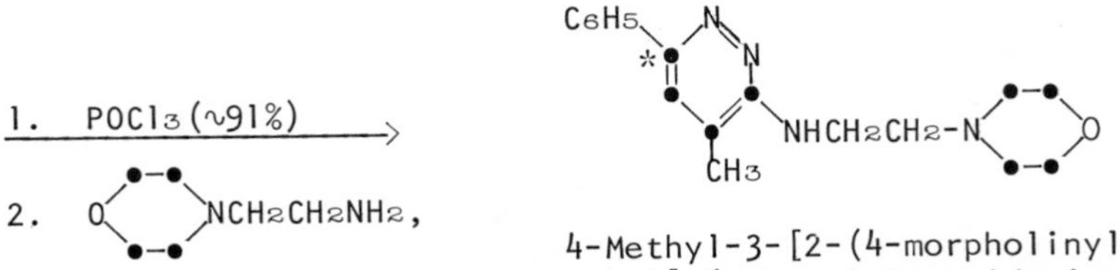

BuOH, Δ

(~38% yield; 16.7% from Ba*CO$_3$)

4-Methyl-3-[2-(4-morpholinyl)-ethyl]-6-phenyl-3-pyridazinamine-6-^{14}C

L. Pichat, J. P. Beaucourt, F. Krausz, and C. Moulineau, J. Label. Compound. Radiopharm., 12, 347 (1976).

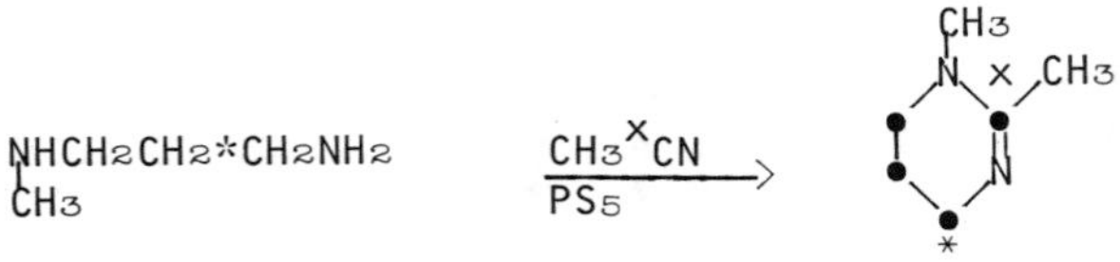

(69%)

1,4,5,6-Tetrahydro-1,2-dimethylpyrimidine-4-^{14}C

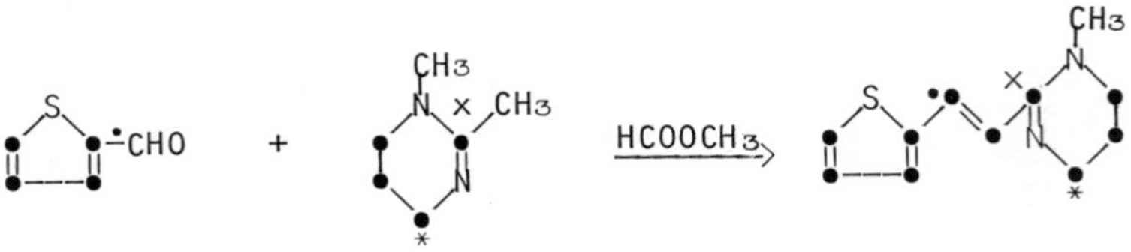

(40%)

Pyrantel
[(E)-1,4,5,6-Tetrahydro-1-methyl-2-[2-(2-thienyl)-vinyl]pyrimidine-^{14}C]

Three labeled syntheses are reported with the carbon label in three different positions (*,•,x); starting material (overall radiochemical yield): K*CN (19%); CH_3*CN (20%); $(CH_3)_2$N*CHO (67%).

S. K. Figdor, M. S. von Wittenau, J. K. Faulkner, and A. M. Monro, J. Label. Compounds, 6, 362 (1970).

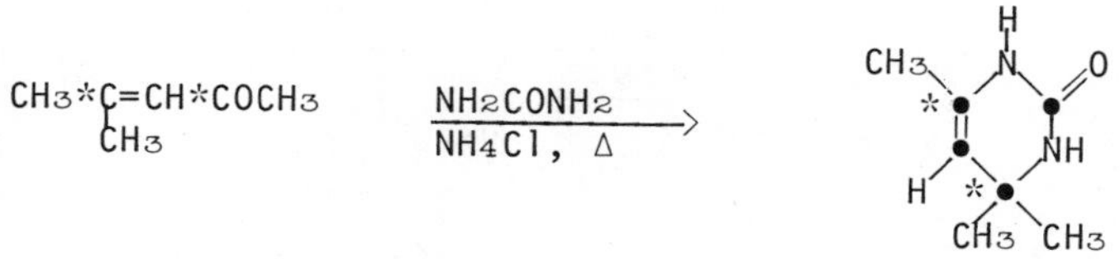
CH3*C=CH*COCH3
CH3
NH2CONH2
NH4Cl, Δ
H
CH3
N
O
*
NH
H
*
CH3 CH3

Mesityl oxide [3-Methyl-3-penten-1-one-2,4-^{14}C]

3,4-Dihydro-4,4,6-trimethyl-2-(1H)-pyrimidinone-4,6-^{14}C

H. H. Matt, G. D. Lichtenwalter, and G. H. Riesser, Aust. J. Chem., 23, 561 (1970).

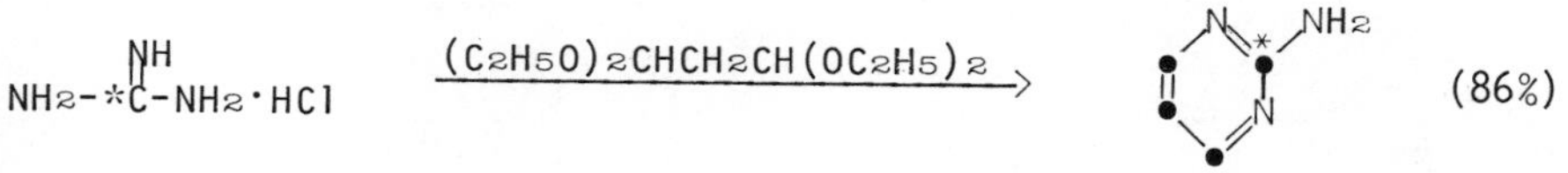
NH
NH2-*C-NH2·HCl
(C2H5O)2CHCH2CH(OC2H5)2
N
*
NH2
N
(86%)

2-Pyrimidinamine-2-^{14}C

Nguyen-Hoang-Nam, M. Herbert, Nguyen-Dat-Xuong, and L. Pichat, J. Label. Compounds, 7, 299 (1971); see also H. Hoellinger, Nguyen-Hoang-Nam, and L. Pichat, J. Label. Compounds, 9, 161 (1973).

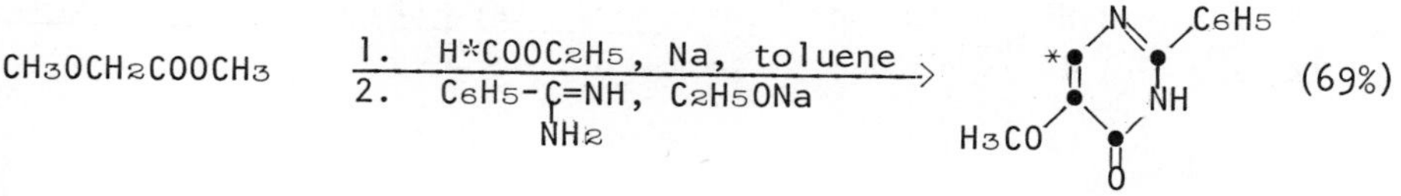
CH3OCH2COOCH3
1. H*COOC2H5, Na, toluene
2. C6H5-C=NH, C2H5ONa
NH2
N
C6H5
*
NH
H3CO
O
(69%)

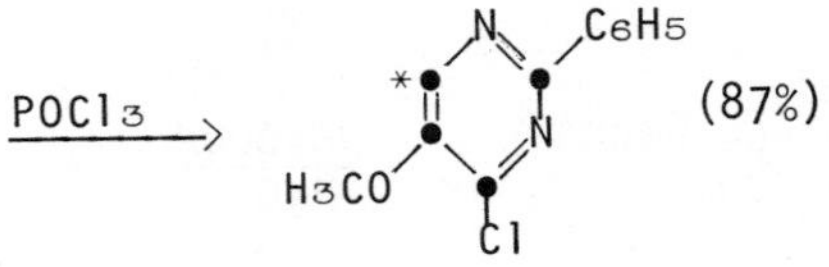

4-Chloro-5-methoxy-2-phenylpyrimidine-6-^{14}C

The above compound was used for mechanistic studies of ring opening reactions (KNH_2, NH_3). The position of the label was determined by degradation reactions, and a mechanism is proposed.

H. W. Van Meeteren and H. C. van der Plas, Rec. Trav. Chim., 90, 105 (1971).

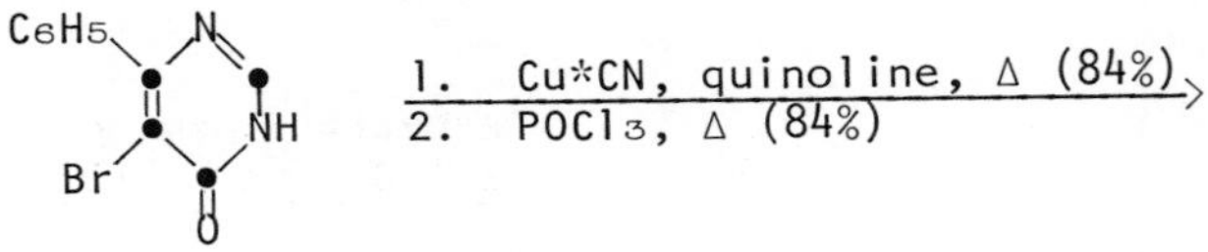

4-Chloro-6-phenylpyrimidine-4-carbonitrile-(cyano-^{14}C)

J. de Valk and H. C. van der Plas, Rec. Trav. Chim., J. Roy. Neth. Chem., 92, 471 (1973).

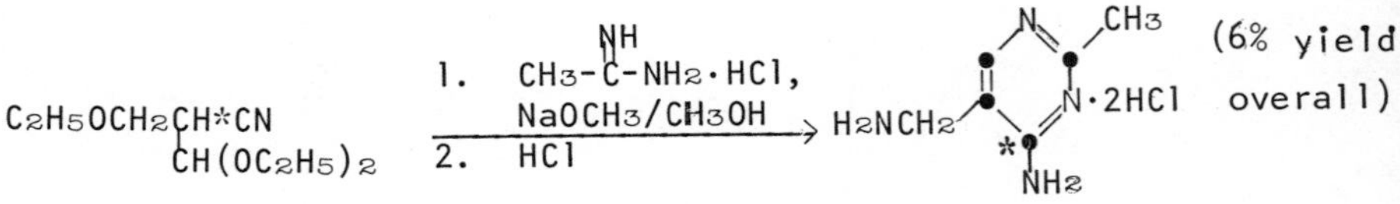

4-Amino-2-methylpyrimidine-5-methanamine-4-^{14}C dihydrochloride

$C_2H_5OCH_2CH_2CN$ —(1. $H{*}COOC_2H_5$, $NaOCH_3$, C_2H_5OH, C_6H_6; 2. steps as above)→

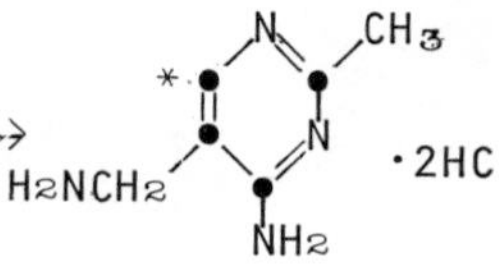

(16% overall)

4-Amino-2-methylpyrimidine-5-methanamine-6-^{14}C dihydrochloride

The positions of the label were determined by degradation reactions, and mechanisms are proposed.

H. Morimoto, N. Hayashi, T. Naka, and S. Kato, Chem. Ber., 106, 893 (1973).

$NH_2{-}{*}CS{-}NH_2$ —($(C_2H_5O)_2CHCOCH(C_2H_5)COOC_2H_5$; C_2H_5ONa, C_2H_5OH, Δ)→

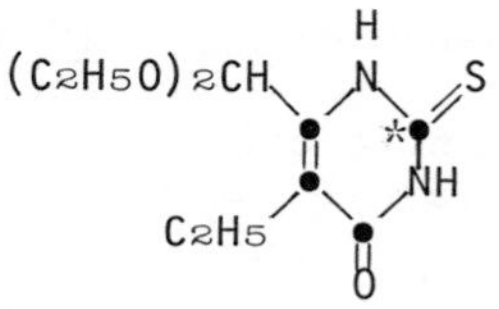

(94%)

6-Diethoxymethyl-5-ethyl-2-thiouracil-2-^{14}C

—(1. H_2O_2, NaOH; 2. H_2SO_4; 3. CrO_3, H_2SO_4)→

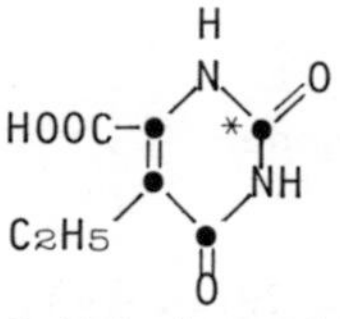

(52% from $NH_2{*}CSNH_2$)

5-Ethylorotic acid [1,2,3,6-Tetrahydro-2,6-dioxo-4-pyrimidinecarboxylic-2-^{14}C acid]

—(Cu, Δ; quinoline)→

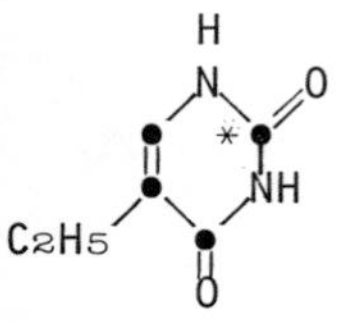

5-Ethyluracil [5-Ethyl-2,4(1H,3H)-pyrimidinedione-2-^{14}C]

—(P_2S_5; dioxane)→

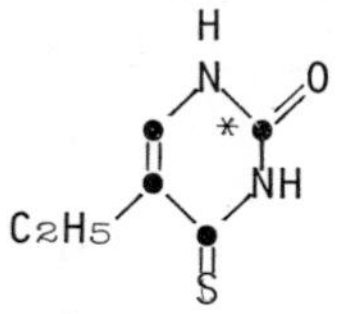

5-Ethyl-6-thiouracil [5-Ethyl-3,4-dihydro-4-thioxo-2(1H)-pyrimidinone-2-^{14}C]

—(NH_3; CH_3OH)→

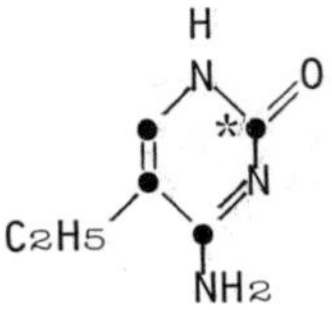

(65%; 22% from $NH_2{*}CSNH_2$)

5-Ethylcytosine
[4-Amino-5-ethyl-2
(1H)-pyrimidinone-2-^{14}C]

M. Skakun-Todorović and V. Jezdić, J. Label. Compounds, 9, 475 (1973).

$*CN\text{-}CH_2COOCH_3$ $\xrightarrow[NaOCH_3,\ \Delta]{[H_2NC(=NH)NH_2]_2 \cdot H_2CO_3}$

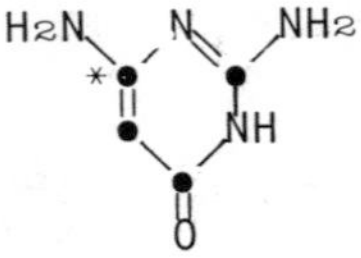

Cyanoacetic acid-
3-^{14}C methyl ester

1. nitration
2. reduction
3. H_2SO_4 →

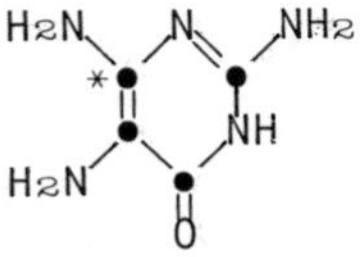

H_2SO_4 (42% from guanidine carbonate)

2,5,6-Triamino-4
(3H)-pyrimidinone-
6-^{14}C sulfate

G. B. Barlin and W. Pfleiderer, Chem. Ber., 104, 3069 (1971).

$H_2N{*}CH_2CH_2COOH$

1. KOCN, H_2O
2. 1N HCl, Δ (94%) →

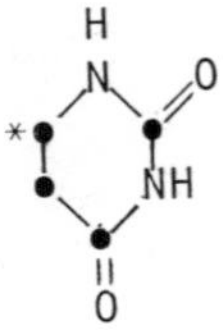

3-Aminopropanoic-
3-^{14}C acid

1. Br_2, AcOH (85%)
2. Δ (quant.) →

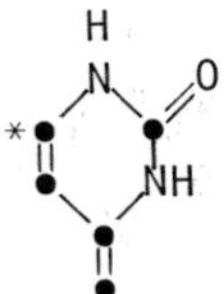

Uracil-6-^{14}C

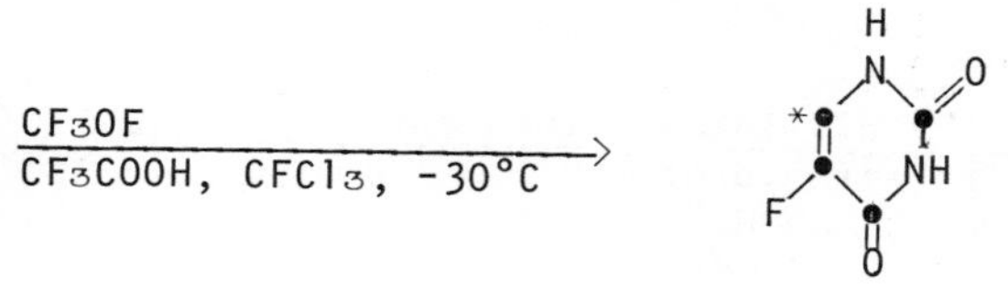
CF3OF
CF3COOH, CFCl3, -30°C
H
N
O
*
NH
F
O

(96% yield; 63% from K*CN)

5-Fluorouracil
[5-Fluoro-2,4(1H,3H)-pyrimidinedione-6-^{14}C]

C. W. Perry, W. Burger, G. J. Bader, and A. A. Liebman, J. Label. Compounds, 11, 583 (1975).

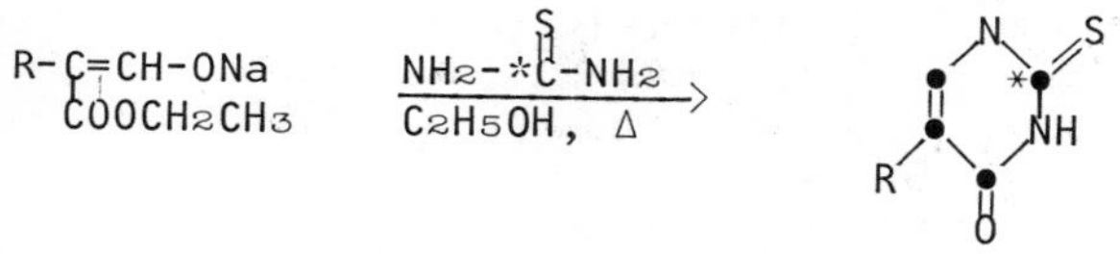
R-C=CH-ONa
COOCH2CH3
S
NH2-*C-NH2
C2H5OH, Δ
H
N
S
*
NH
R
O

R=H; 2-Thiouracil-2-^{14}C (94%)
R=CH_3; 2-Thiothymine-2-^{14}C (92%)

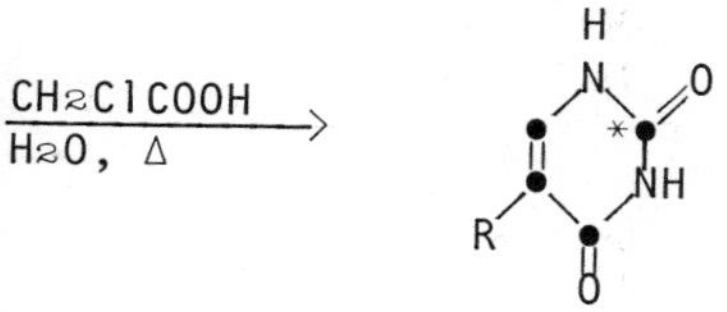
CH2ClCOOH
H2O, Δ
H
N
O
*
NH
R
O

Br_2 when R=H
H_2O, 0°C

R=H; Uracil-2-^{14}C (91% overall)
R=CH_3; Thymine-2-^{14}C (90% overall)

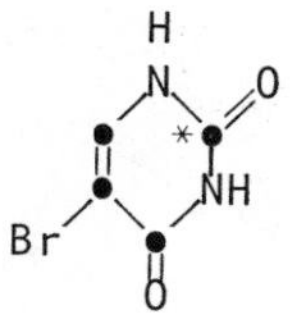
H
N
O
*
NH
Br
O

(95%)

5-Bromouracil
[5-Bromo-2,4(1H,3H)-pyrimidinedione-2-^{14}C]

V. Jezdić, N. Razumenić, M. Skakun, S. Albahari, and J. Odavić-Josić, J. Label. Compounds, 6, 88 (1970.

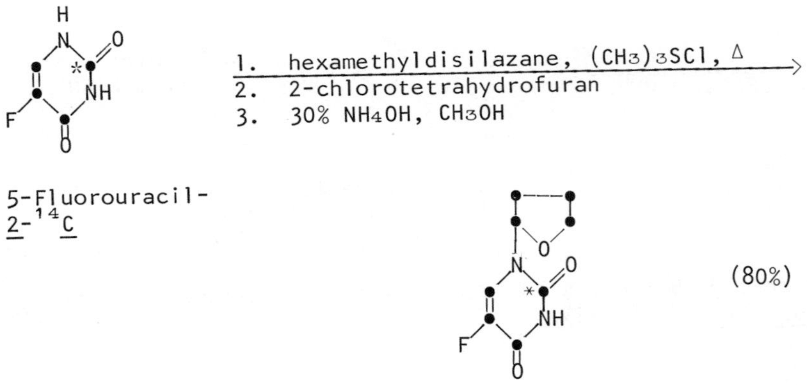
1. hexamethyldisilazane, $(CH_3)_3SCl$, Δ
2. 2-chlorotetrahydrofuran
3. 30% NH_4OH, CH_3OH
(80%)

5-Fluorouracil-2-^{14}C

Ftorafur
[5-Fluoro-1-(tetrahydro-2-furanyl)-2,4(1H,3H)-pyrimidinedione-2-^{14}C]

S. J. Manning, A. M. Cohen, and L. B. Townsend, J. Label. Compound. Radiopharm., 15, 723 (1978).

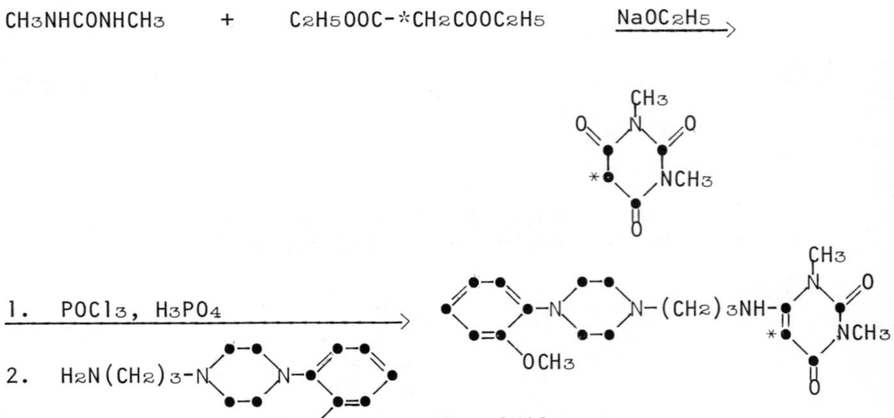
$CH_3NHCONHCH_3$ + C_2H_5OOC-*$CH_2COOC_2H_5$ $NaOC_2H_5$
1. $POCl_3$, H_3PO_4
2. $H_2N(CH_2)_3$-N
CH_3O
N-$(CH_2)_3$NH-
OCH_3
NCH_3

Urapidil
[6-[[3-(4-Methoxyphenyl-1-piperazinyl)propyl]amino]-1,3-dimethyl-2,4(1H,3H)-pyrimidinedione-5-^{14}C]

The piperazinyl-2,3-^{14}C derivative was also prepared.

G. Ludwig, H. Vergin, and K. Zech, Arzneim.-Forsch.-(Drug Res.), 27 (II), 2077 (1977).

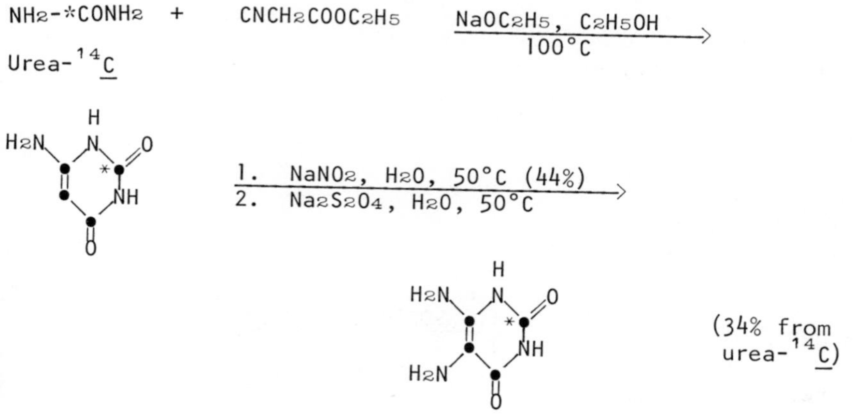
NH2-*CONH2 + CNCH2COOC2H5
Urea-14C
NaOC2H5, C2H5OH
100°C
1. NaNO2, H2O, 50°C (44%)
2. Na2S2O4, H2O, 50°C
(34% from urea-14C)

5,6-Diamino-2,4(1H,3H)-pyrimidinedione-2-^{14}C

G. Ayrey and M. A. Yeomans, J. Label. Compound. Radiopharm., 12, 323 (1976).

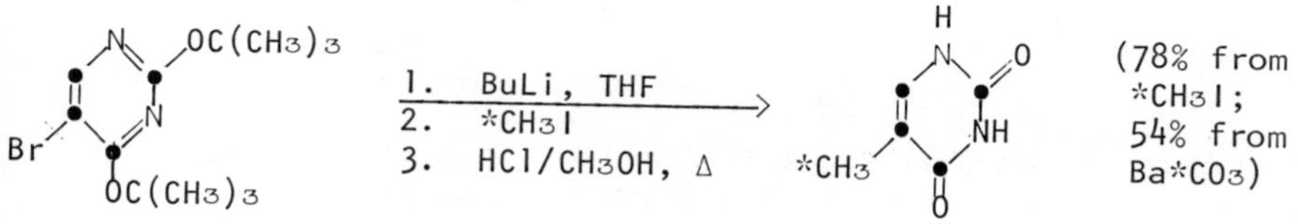
1. BuLi, THF
2. *CH3I
3. HCl/CH3OH, Δ
(78% from *CH3I; 54% from Ba*CO3)

Thymine
[5-(Methyl-^{14}C)-2,4-(1H,3H)-pyrimidinedione]

L. Pichat, J. Deschamps, B. Masse, and P. Dufay, Bull. Soc. Chim. Fr., 2110 (1971).

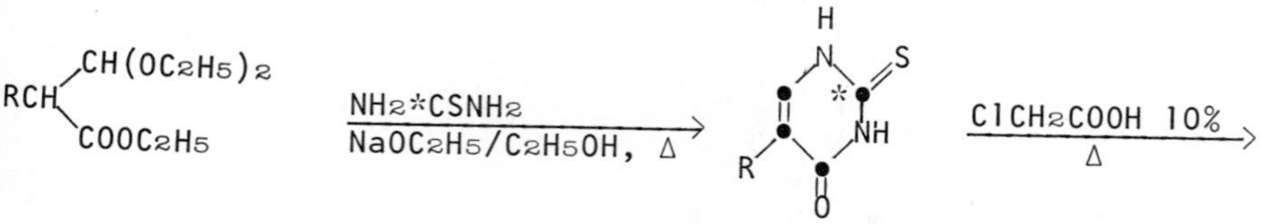
NH2*CSNH2
NaOC2H5/C2H5OH, Δ
ClCH2COOH 10%
Δ

2-Thio-5-alkyluracils-2-^{14}C

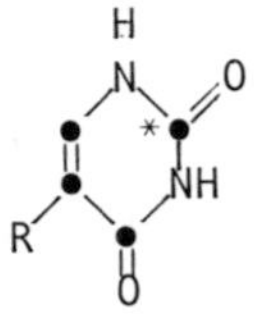

(36-66% from labeled thiourea)

5-Alkyluracils
[5-Alkyl-2,4(1H,3H)-pyrimidinedione-2-^{14}C]

$RCH_2{}^*COOH$ (obtained via thermal exchange of the potassium salt with $^*CO_2$)

1. $SOCl_2$
2. Br_2, EtOH
3. $HC(OC_2H_5)_3$, Zn

→ $R-CH(CH(OC_2H_5)_2)-{}^*COOC_2H_5$

1. NH_2CSNH_2
2. $ClCH_2COOH$, Δ

→

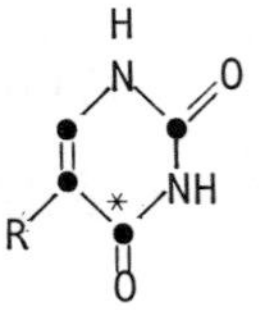

(24-35% from carboxylic acid)

5-Alkyluracil
[5-Alkyl-2,4(1H,3H)-pyrimidinedione-4-^{14}C]

β-Anomers of the 5-alkyluracil-2 and 4-^{14}C were prepared; R = a homologous series of hydrocarbons, $C_1 \longrightarrow C_{14}$.

A. Szabolcs, G. Kruppa, J. Sági, and L. Ötvös, J. Label. Compound. Radiopharm., 14, 713 (1978).

$NH_2-{}^*C(=S)-NH_2$ + $C_2H_5OCH=C(COOC_2H_5)_2$ $\xrightarrow[EtOH]{NaOC_2H_5}$

Thiourea-^{14}C

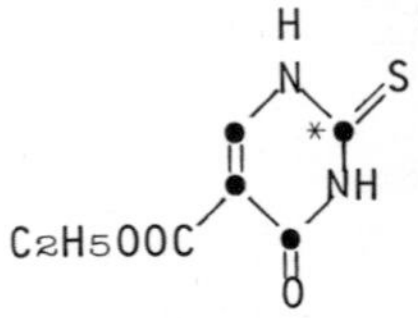

$\xrightarrow[H_2O,\ \Delta]{ClCH_2COOH}$

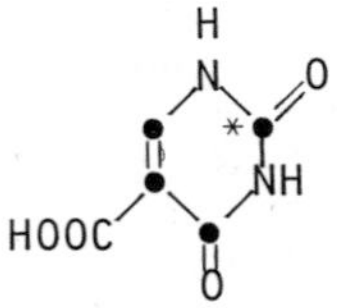

Uracil-5-carboxylic acid
[1,2,3,4-Tetrahydro-2,4-dioxo-5-pyrimidinecarboxylic-2-^{14}C acid]

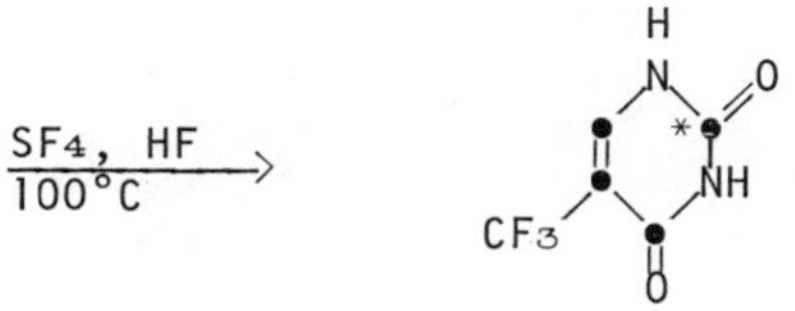

(25% from thiourea)

5-Trifluoromethyluracil
[5-(Trifluoromethyl)-2,4 (1H,3H)-pyrimidinedione-2-^{14}C]

A. J. Zambito and E. M. Chamberlin, J. Label. Compounds, 7, 495 (1971).

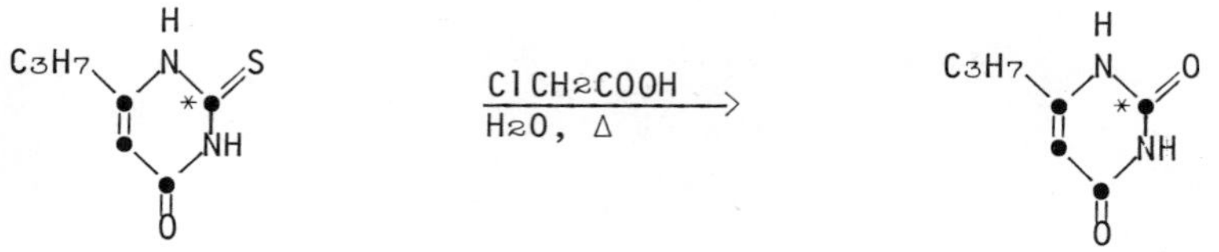

6-Propyl-2-thiouracil-2-^{14}C

6-Propyluracil
[6-Propyl-2,4(1H,3H)-pyrimidinedione-2-^{14}C]

H. Y. Aboul-Enein, J. Label. Compounds, 10, 515 (1974).

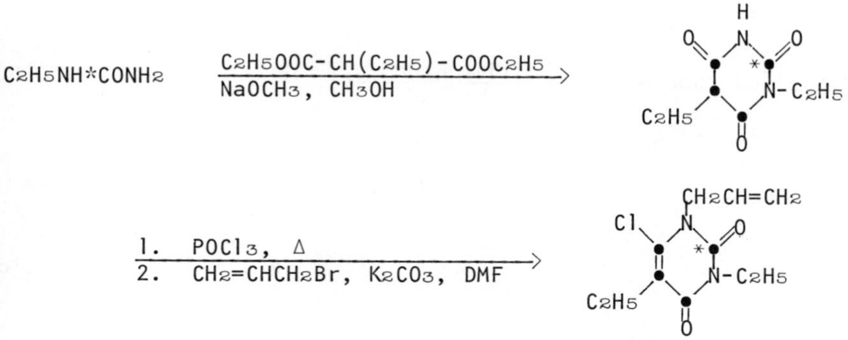

Aclu
[6-Chloro-3,5-diethyl-1-(2-propenyl)-2,4-(1H,3H)-pyrimidinedione-2-^{14}C]

R. Kaul, B. Hempel, and W. Schäfer, Arzneim.-Forsch.-(Drug Res.), 26, 489 (1976).

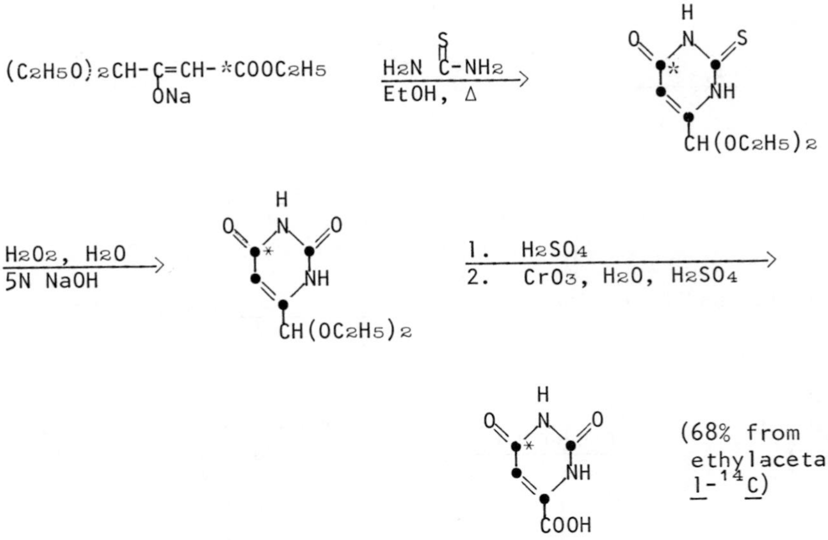
(C2H5O)2CH-C=CH-*COOC2H5
ONa
H2N C-NH2
S
EtOH, Δ
CH(OC2H5)2
H2O2, H2O
5N NaOH
1. H2SO4
2. CrO3, H2O, H2SO4
COOH

(68% from ethylacetate-1-^{14}C)

Orotic acid
[1,2,3,6-Tetrahydro-2,6-dioxo-4-pyrimidinecarboxylic-6-^{14}C acid]

V. Jezdić, N. Razumenić, M. Skakun, S. Albahari, and J. Odavić-Josić, J. Label. Compounds, 6, 88 (1970).

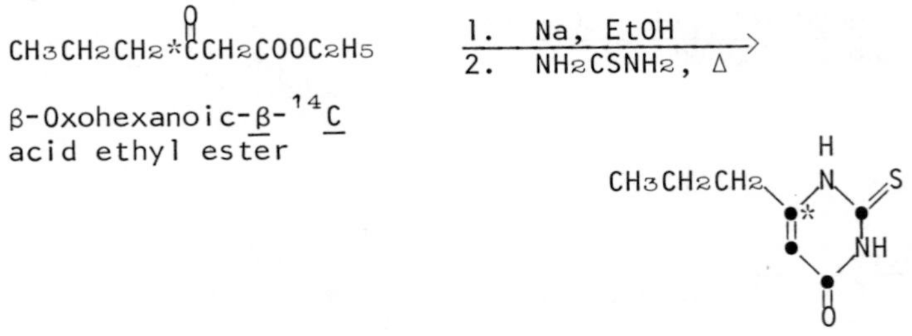
CH3CH2CH2*CCH2COOC2H5
1. Na, EtOH
2. NH2CSNH2, Δ
CH3CH2CH2

β-Oxohexanoic-β-^{14}C acid ethyl ester

(71%; 34% from butyric 1-^{14}C acid)

6-Propyl-2-thiouracil
[2,3-Dihydro-6-propyl-2-thioxo-4(1H)-pyrimidinone-6-^{14}C]

D. P. Thornhill and D. S. Sitar, J. Label. Compounds, 7, 145 (1971).

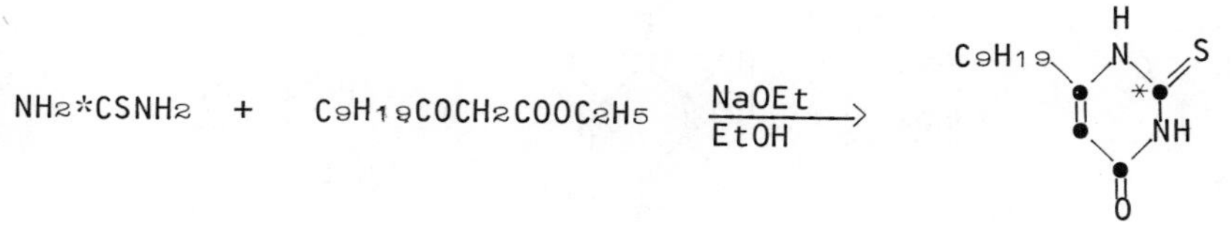
NH2*CSNH2
+
C9H19COCH2COOC2H5
NaOEt
EtOH
C9H19
H
N
S
NH
O

6-Nonyl-2-thiouracil
[2,3-Dihydro-6-nonyl-
2-thioxo-4(1H)-
pyrimidine-2-^{14}C]

E. Bäuerlein and R. Kiehl, Justus Liebigs Ann. Chem., 675 (1978).

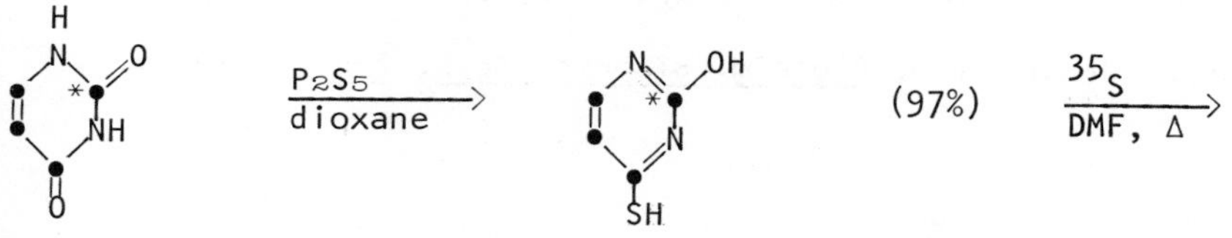
H
N
O
NH
O
P2S5
dioxane
N
OH
N
SH
(97%)
35S
DMF, Δ

Uracil
[2,4-(1H,3H)-
pyrimidinedione-
2-^{14}C]

4-Thiouracil
[4-Mercapto-2-
pyrimidinol-
2-^{14}C]

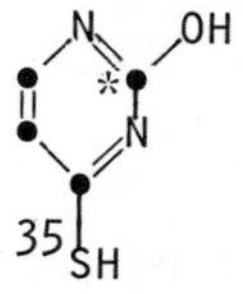
N
OH
N
35SH

4-Thiouracil
[4-(Mercapto-^{35}S)-2-
pyrimidinol-2-^{14}C]

J. Seda, L. I. Votruba, and R. Tykva, J. Label. Compounds, 10, 335 (1974).

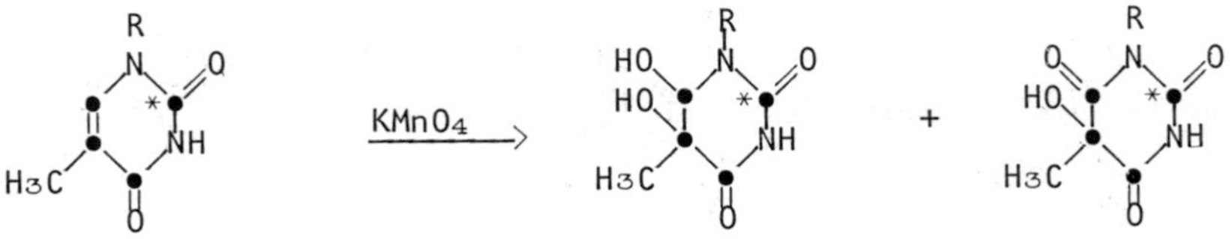

KMnO4
R
HO
HO
H3C
NH
O
R
HO
H3C
NH
O
+

Thymidine-2-^{14}C (R=2-deoxyribose)

1-(2-Deoxyribose)-dihydro-5,6-dihydroxy-5-methyl-2,4(1H,3H)-pyrimidinedione-2-^{14}C

1-(2-Deoxyribose)-5-hydroxy-5-methyl-2,4,6-pyrimidinetrione-2-^{14}C

At pH 8.6, thymidine glycol formation was preferred; at pH 4.3, barbituric acid predominated (separable by chromatography).

S. Lida and H. Hayatsu, Biochim. Biophys. Acta, 228, 1 (1971).

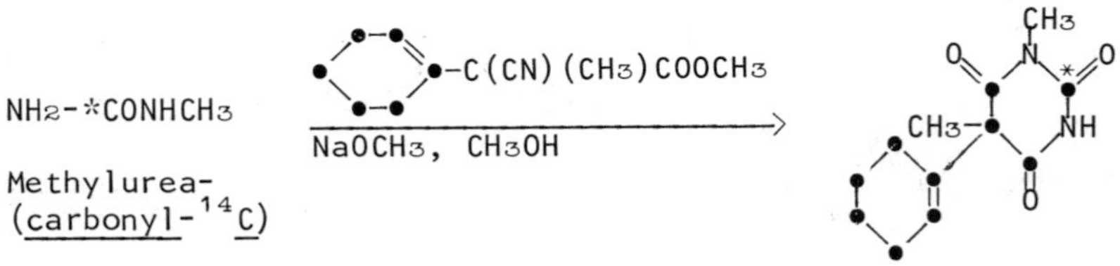

NH2-*CONHCH3
-C(CN)(CH3)COOCH3
NaOCH3, CH3OH
CH3
O
O
CH3
NH
O

Methylurea-(carbonyl-^{14}C)

(+) and (-) Acetate were used separately, giving (+)-hexobarbital-2-^{14}C (21% from KO*CN) and (-)-hexobarbital-2-^{14}C (32% from KO*CN).

Similarly:

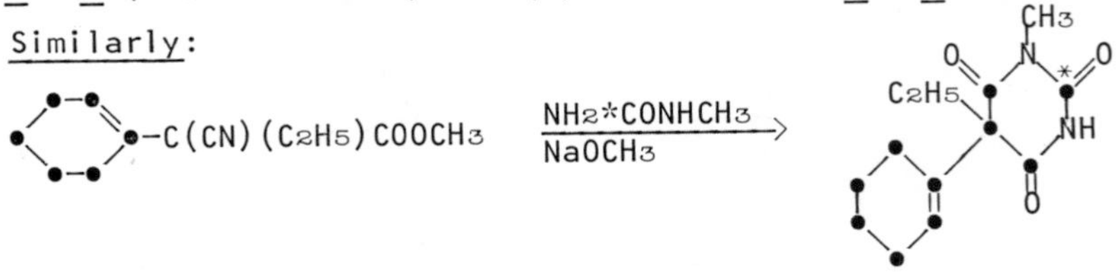

-C(CN)(C2H5)COOCH3
NH2*CONHCH3
NaOCH3
CH3
O
O
C2H5
NH
O

(+)-Methylcyclobarbital-2-^{14}C (42% from KO*CN)
(-)-Methylcyclobarbital-2-^{14}C (39% from KO*CN)
[5-(1-Cyclohexen-1-yl)-5-ethyl-2-hydroxy-1-methyl-2,4(1H,3H) pyrimidinedione-2-^{14}C]

J. Knabe, H. Junginger, D. Strauss, and H.-L. Schmidt, Arch. Pharm., 305, 277 (1972); Arch. Pharm., 306, 306 (1973).

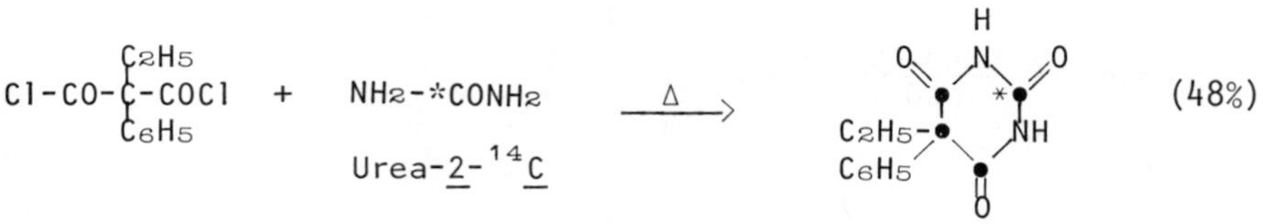

Phenobarbital
[5-Ethyl-5-phenyl-2,4,6(1H,3H,5H)-pyrimidinetrione-2-^{14}C]

H. A. Dugger and E. Oppenheimer, J. Label. Compounds, 10, 171 (1974).

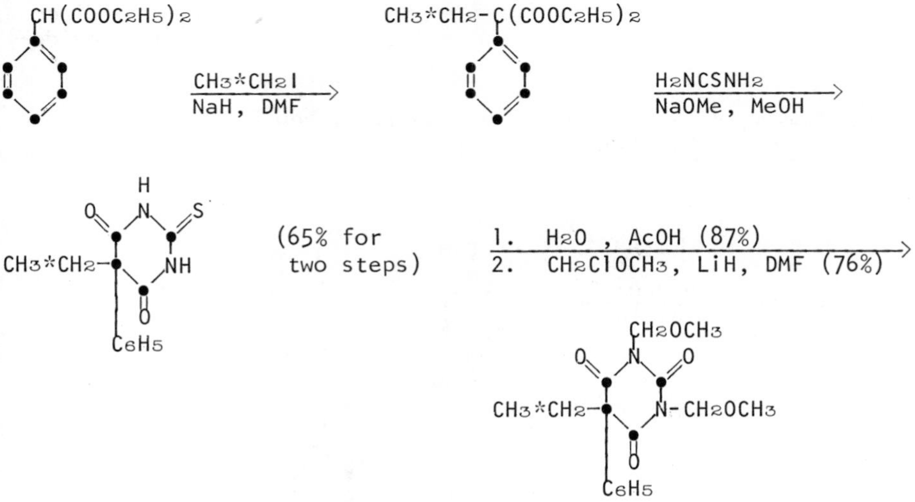

1,3-(Dimethoxymethyl)-5-(ethyl-1-^{14}C)-5-phenyl-2,4,6(1H,3H,5H)-pyrimidinetrione

Starting with phenobarbital-2-^{14}C, DMMP-2-^{14}C was prepared in 88% yield, and using chloromethyl ether-(methylene-^{14}C), DMMP-(dimethylene-^{14}C) was prepared in 30% yield.

T. S. T. Wang, J. Label. Compound. Radiopharm., 13, 575 (1977).

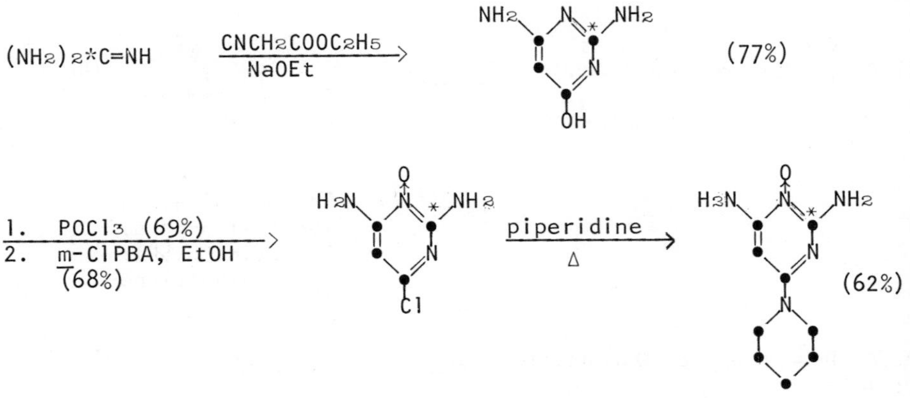

Minoxidil
[4-(1-Piperidinyl)-2,6-pyrimidinediamine 1-oxide-2-^{14}C]

R. C. Thomas, R. S. P. Hsi, H. Harpootlian, and R. W. Judy, J. Pharm. Sci., 64, 1360 (1975).

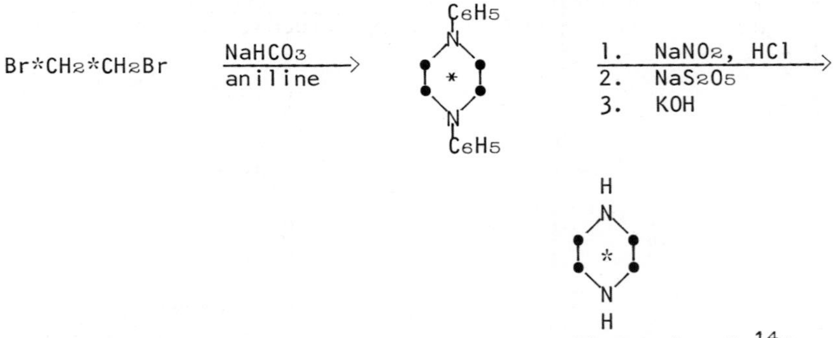

Piperazine-U-^{14}C

Y. I. Savin, A. S. Singin, G. K. Korolev, T. S. Safonova, V. G. Kurasova, and V. V. Kurchatova, Khim.-Farm. Zh., 10, 49 (1976).

$NH_2CH_2{*}COOH$ $\xrightarrow[\text{2. } NH_4OH]{\text{1. } HCl,\ CH_3OH}$ $NH_2CH_2{*}COOCH_3$ $\xrightarrow[\text{water}]{\text{ether}}$

Glycine-1-^{14}C

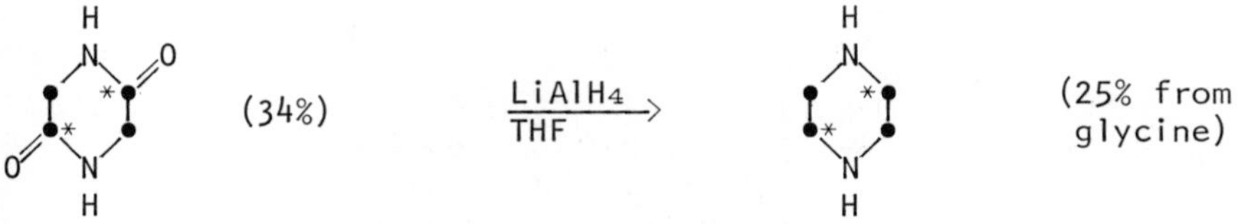

(34%)
LiAlH4
THF
(25% from glycine)

2,5-Piperazinedione-2,5-^{14}C

Piperazine-2,5-^{14}C

M. Herbert, F. Jimeno de Osso, and L. Pichat, J. Label. Compounds, 8, 45 (1972).

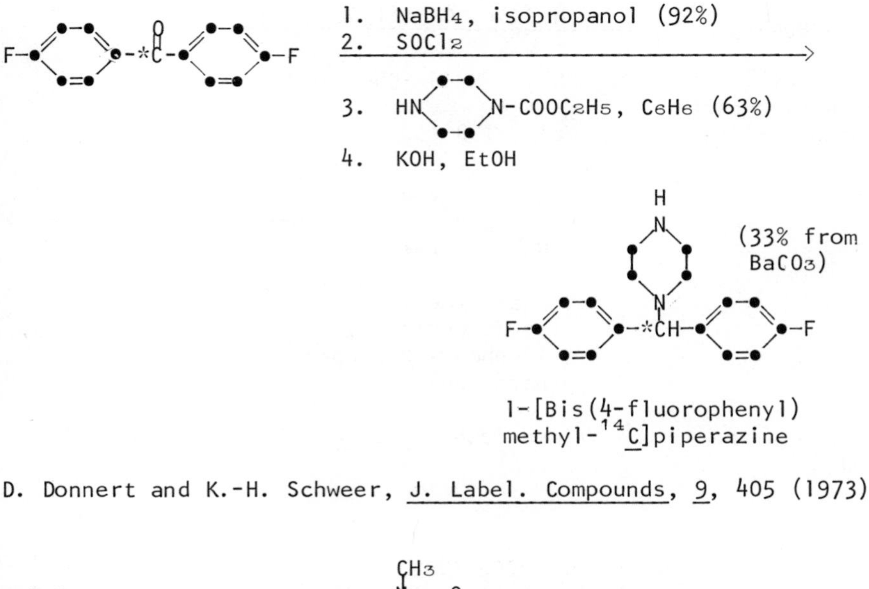

1. NaBH4, isopropanol (92%)
2. SOCl2
3. HN N-COOC2H5, C6H6 (63%)
4. KOH, EtOH
(33% from BaCO3)

1-[Bis(4-fluorophenyl)methyl-^{14}C]piperazine

D. Donnert and K.-H. Schweer, J. Label. Compounds, 9, 405 (1973).

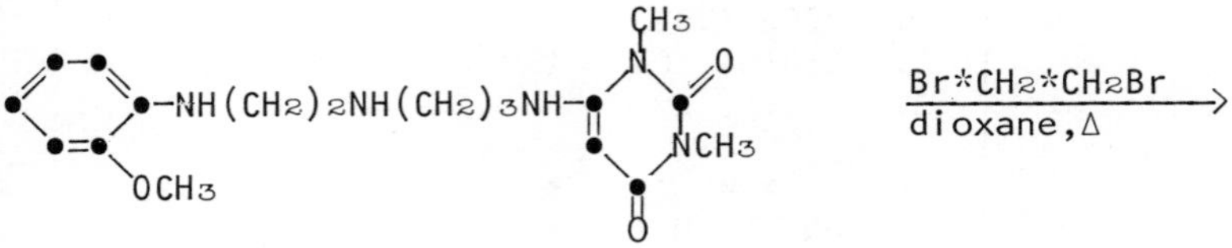

NH(CH2)2NH(CH2)3NH
OCH3
CH3
NCH3
Br*CH2*CH2Br
dioxane,Δ

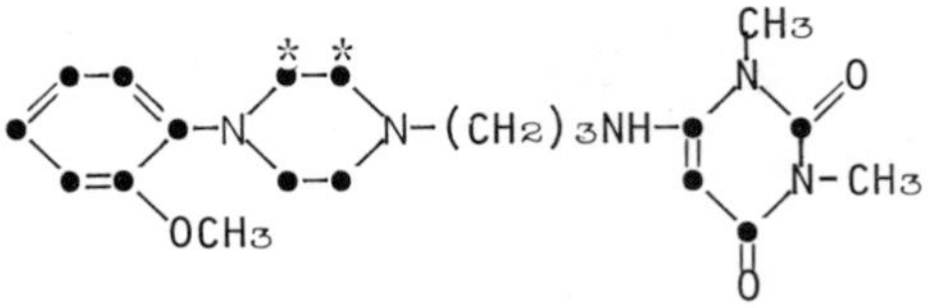

(57%)

Urapidil
[6-[[3-[4-(2-Methoxyphenyl)-1-piperazinyl-2,3-^{14}C]propyl]amino]-1,3-dimethyl-2,4(1H,3H)-pyrimidinedione]

The derivative with uracil-5-^{14}C was also prepared.

G. Ludwig, H. Vergin, and K. Zech, Arzneim.-Forsch.-(Drug Res.), 27 (II), 2077 (1977).

C_6H_5-*CHOH-C_6H_5

Benzhydrol
[α-Phenylbenzene-methanol-α-^{14}C]

1. CH_3COBr, C_6H_6 (90%) →

2. 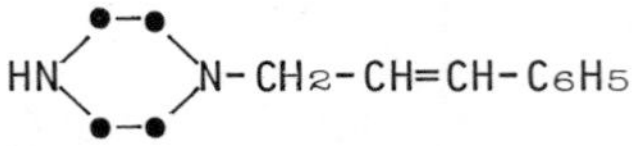

melt, 130-150°c

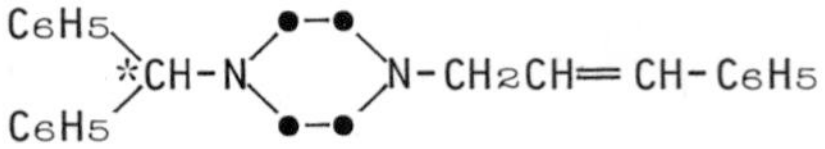

(75-85%)

Cinnarizine
[1-(Diphenylmethyl-^{14}C)-4-(3-phenyl-2-propenyl) piperazine]

W. Soudijn and I. van Wijngaarden. J. Label. Compounds, 4, 159 (1968).

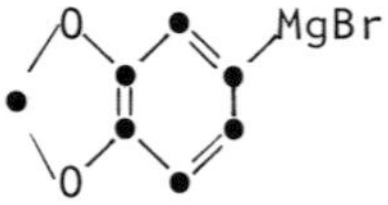

1. *CO_2 (80%)
2. $LiAlH_4$, Et_2O (80%)
3. $SOCl_2$, pyr (89%)
4. 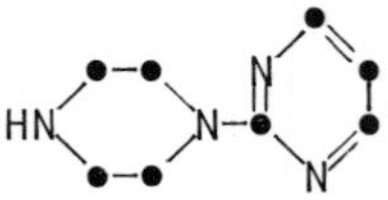, DMF, K_2CO_3, Δ (80%)
5. CH_3SO_3H, EtOH (70%)

→

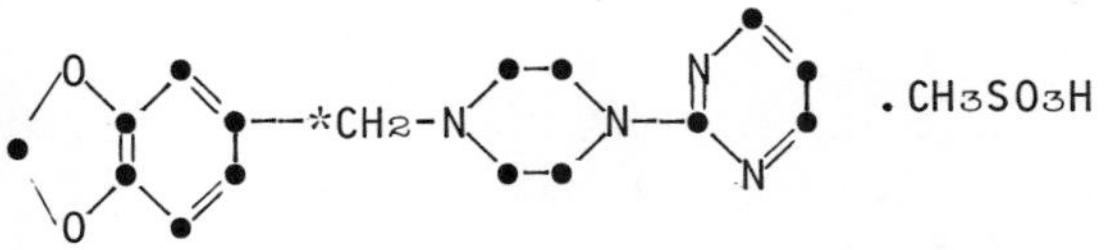

O
O
*CH2-N
N
N
N
N
.CH3SO3H

(32% overall yield)

2-[4-(1,3-Benzodioxol-5-ylmethyl-^{14}C)-1-piperazinyl]pyrimidine methanesulfonate

J. Lintermans, A. Benakis, M. Herbert, and L. Pichat, Helv. Chim. Acta, 54, 1713 (1971).

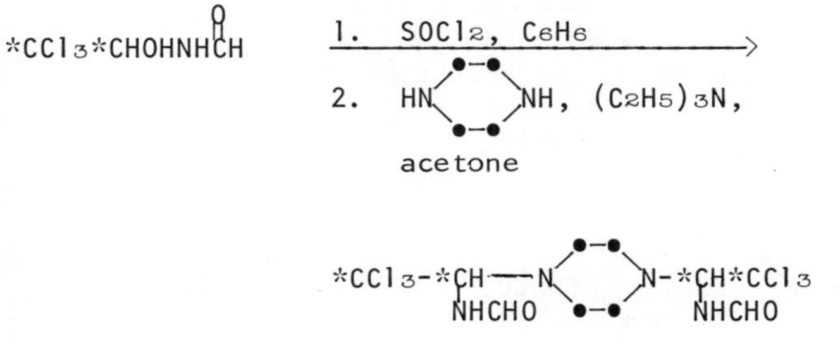

*CCl3*CHOHNHCH
O
1. SOCl2, C6H6
2. HN NH, (C2H5)3N,
acetone
*CCl3-*CH—N N-*CH*CCl3
NHCHO
NHCHO

(25% from paraldehyde-^{14}C)

Triforine
[N,N'-[1,4-Piperazinediylbis-2,2,2-trichloroethylidene-1,2-1',2'-^{14}C)bisformamide]

M. Stiasni and W. Ost, J. Label. Compounds, 9, 133 (1973).

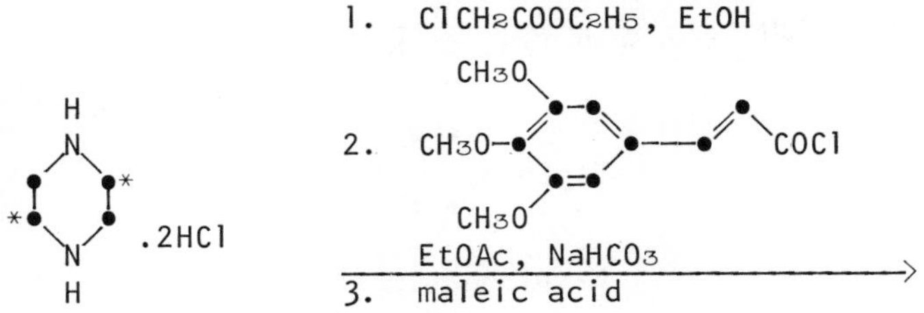

H
N
N
H
.2HCl
1. ClCH2COOC2H5, EtOH
CH3O
2. CH3O
COCl
CH3O
EtOAc, NaHCO3
3. maleic acid

Piperazine-2,5-^{14}C dihydrochloride

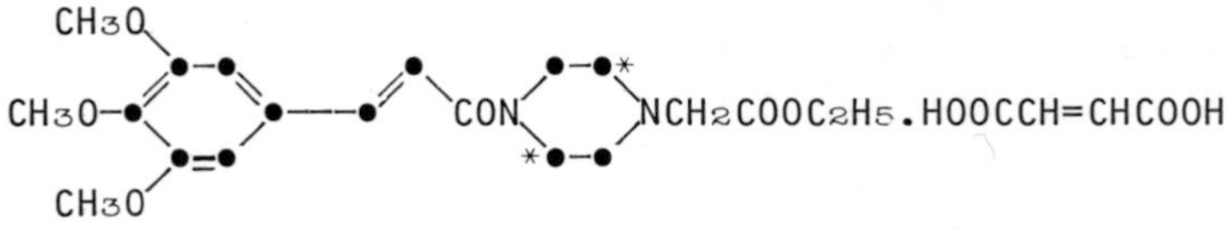

4-[3-(3,4,5-Trimethoxyphenyl)-1-oxo-2-propenyl]-1-piperazineacetic-2,5-^{14}C acid ethyl ester (E)-2-butenedioate salt

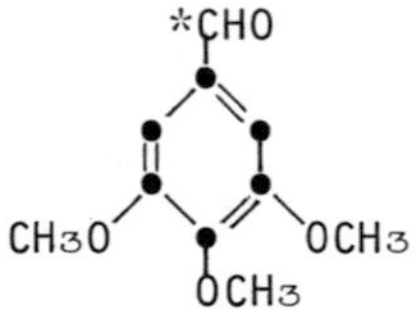

1. $HOOCCH_2COOH$, pyr, piperidine, Δ
2. $SOCl_2$

3. 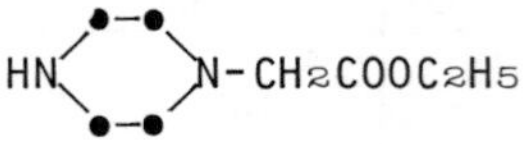

4. maleic acid

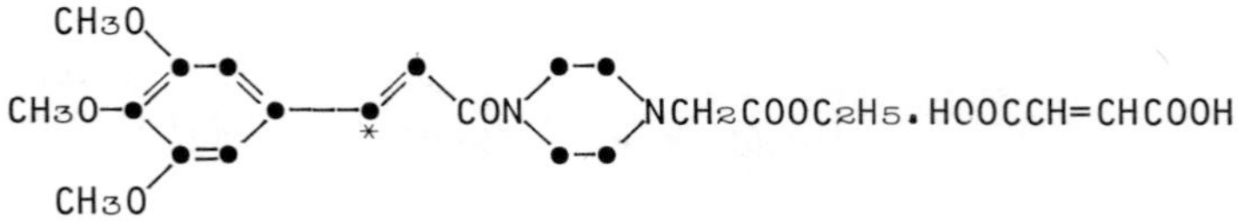

4-[3-(3,4,5-Trimethoxyphenyl)-1-oxo-2-propenyl-3-^{14}C]-1-piperazineacetic acid ethyl ester (E)-2-butenedioate salt

G. Hardy, I. P. Sword, and D. E. Hathway, J. Label. Compounds, 8, 221 (1972).

$C_6H_5-CH_2NH(CH_2)_2NHCH_2-C_6H_5$ —— $Br{*}CH_2{*}CH_2Br$ / $(C_2H_5)_3N$, dioxane ——>

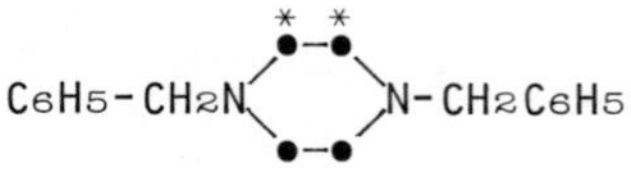 (34%)

1,4-(Diphenylmethyl) piperazine-2,3-[14]C

1. H_2, Pd/C, AcOH (90%)
2. $NaHCO_3/H_2O$
3. $BrCH_2CH_2COCl$, $NaHCO_3$, H_2O —> (69%)

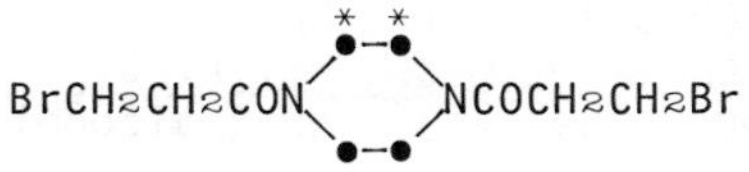

1,4-Bis(3-bromo-1-oxopropyl)-piperazine-2,3-^{14}C

A. Kagemoto, M. Kishi, Y. Minaki, and K. Nakamura, J. Label. Compounds, 9, 489 (1973).

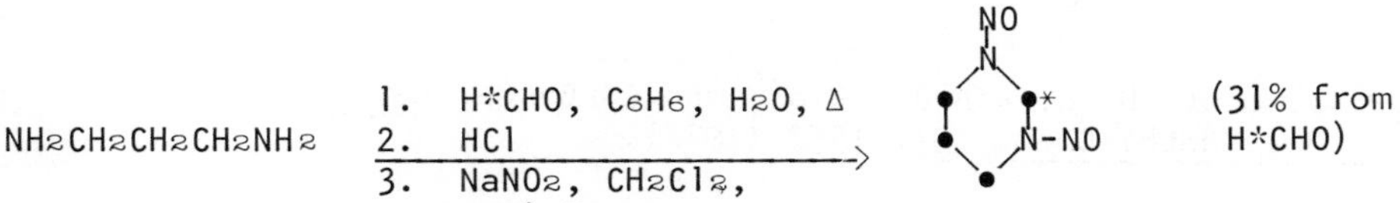

Hexahydro-1,3-dinitrosopyrimidine-2-^{14}C

H. Braun, B. Bertram, and M. Wiessler, J. Label. Compound. Radiopharm., 13, 375 (1977).

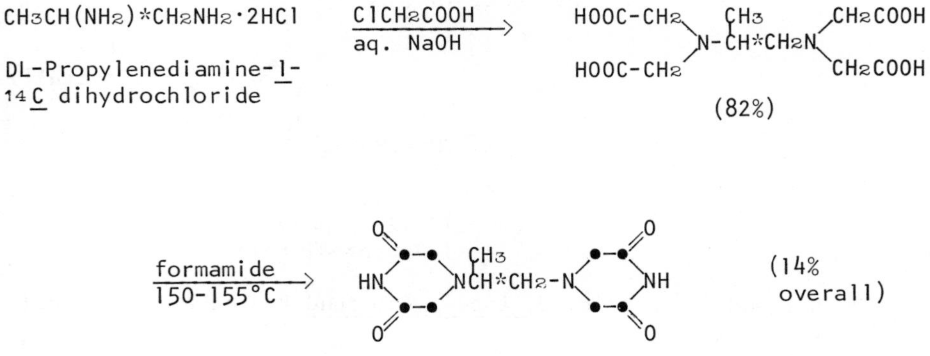

DL-Propylenediamine-1-^{14}C dihydrochloride

4,4'-(1-Methyl-1,2-ethanediyl-2-^{14}C)bis-2,6-piperazinedione

Use of chloroacetic-^{14}C acid gave the piperazinedione-2,6-^{14}C derivative in 25% overall yield.

Y. Lin, M. A. Leaffer, and M. Tanabe, J. Label. Compound. Radiopharm., 12, 591 (1976).

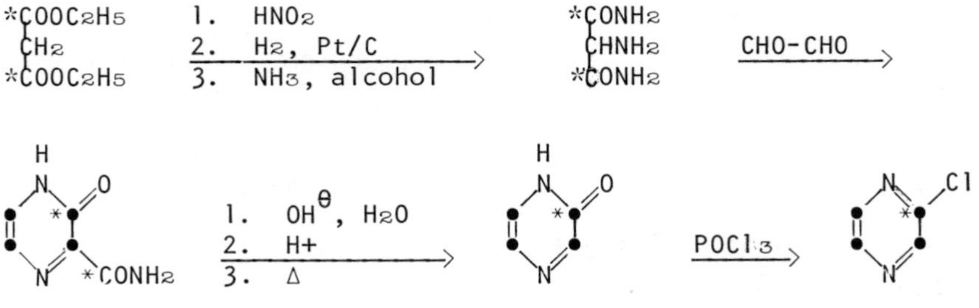
*COOC2H5
CH2
*COOC2H5
1. HNO2
2. H2, Pt/C
3. NH3, alcohol
*CONH2
CHNH2
*CONH2
CHO-CHO
H
N
O
*CONH2
1. OH⊖, H2O
2. H+
3. Δ
POCl3
Cl

2-Chloropyrazine-2-^{14}C

P. J. Lont, H. C. van der Plas, and E. Bosma, Rec. Trav. Chim., J. Roy. Neth. Chem., 91, 1352 (1972).

9-10 Bicyclic Compounds

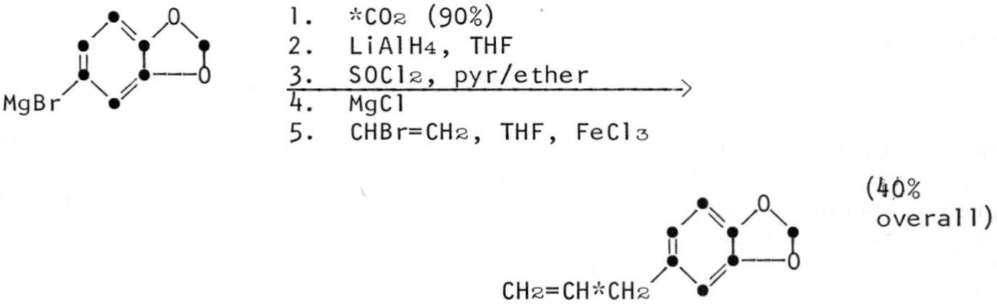
MgBr
O
1. *CO2 (90%)
2. LiAlH4, THF
3. SOCl2, pyr/ether
4. MgCl
5. CHBr=CH2, THF, FeCl3
(40% overall)
CH2=CH*CH2

Safrole
[5-(2-Propenyl-1-^{14}C)-1,3-benzodioxole]

L. Pichat and J. Tostain, J. Label. Compound. Radiopharm., 12, 621 (1976).

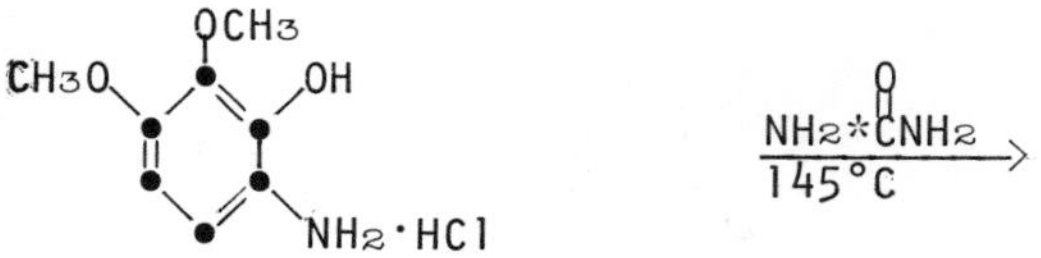
OCH3
CH3O
OH
NH2·HCl
O
NH2*CNH2
145°C
OCH3
CH3O
O
O
*
NH

6,7-Dimethoxy-2-benzoxazolone-2-^{14}C

J. A. Klun, C. L. Tipton, J. F. Robinson, D. L. Ostrem, and M. Beroza, J. Agr. Food Chem., 18, 663 (1970); E. E. Smissman, J. B. LaPidus, and S. D. Beck, J. Amer. Chem. Soc., 79, 4697 (1957).

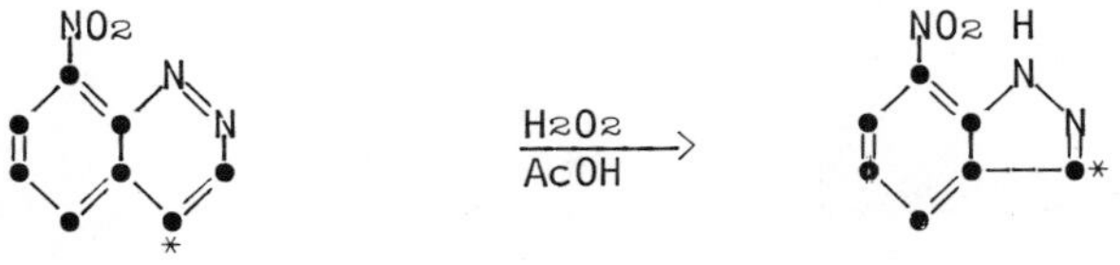
NO2
N
N
*
H2O2
AcOH
NO2 H
N
N
*

(33%)

8-Nitrocinnoline-4-^{14}C

7-Nitroindazole-3-^{14}C

The 4-nitroindazole-3-^{14}C product was also prepared (14% yield) from 5-nitrocinnoline-4-^{14}C. Products had about the same specific activity as the starting materials, indicating that ring contraction predominantly takes place through loss of the C-3 atom. Other products (oxides) were also isolated.

H. C. van der Plas, D. J. Buurman, and C. M. Vos, Rec. Trav. Chim.-J. Roy. Neth. Chem., 97, 50 (1978).

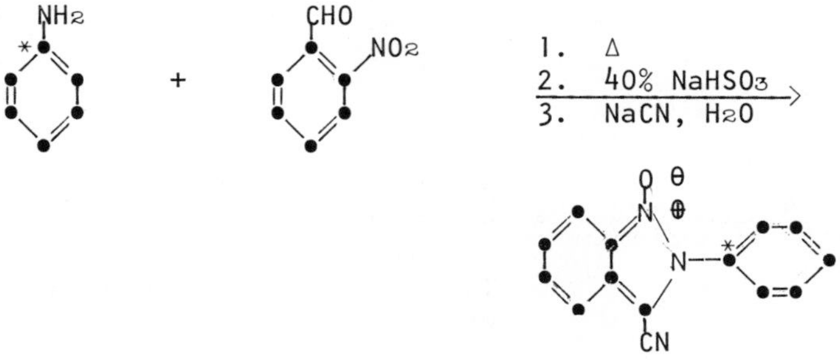
NH2
*
+
CHO
NO2
1. Δ
2. 40% NaHSO3
3. NaCN, H2O
O ⊖
N ⊕
N
*
CN

(70% overall)

2-(Phenyl-1-^{14}C)-2H-indazole-3-carbonitrile 1-oxide

L. C. Behr and E. C. Hendley, J. Org. Chem., 31, 2715 (1966).

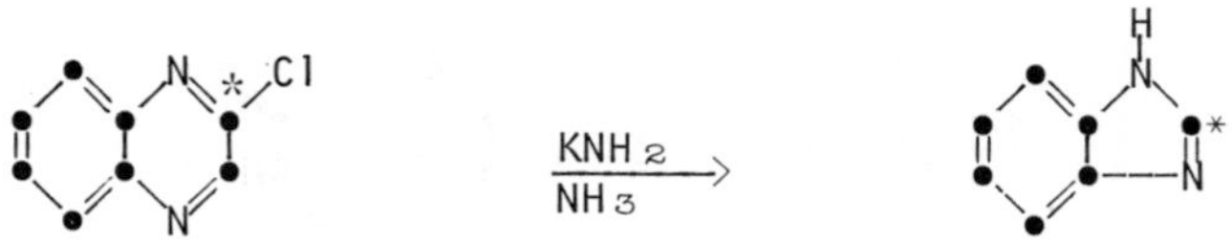

N
Cl
N
KNH2
NH3
H
N
N

(86% for unlabeled reaction)

2-Chloroquinoxaline-2-^{14}C 1H-Benzimidazole-2-^{14}C

The specific activity of the product was the same as that of the starting material; a mechanism is proposed.

P. J. Lont and H. C. vander Plas, Rec. Trav. Chim.-J. Roy. Neth. Chem., 91, 850 (1972).

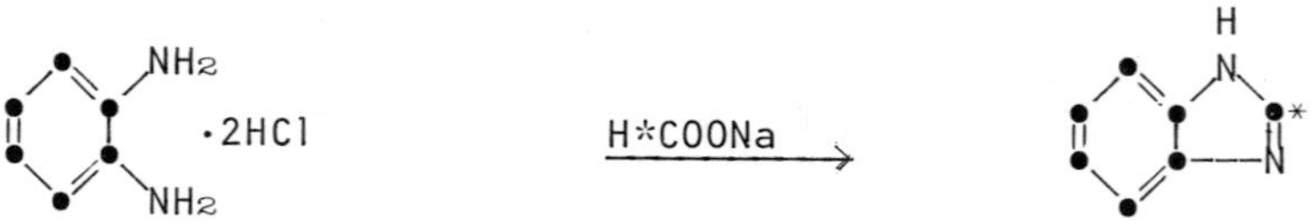

NH2
·2HCl
NH2
H*COONa
H
N
N

1H-Benzimidazole-2-^{14}C

Y. Y. Usaevich and L. I. Vekshina, Khim.-Farm. Zh., 11, 37 (1977).

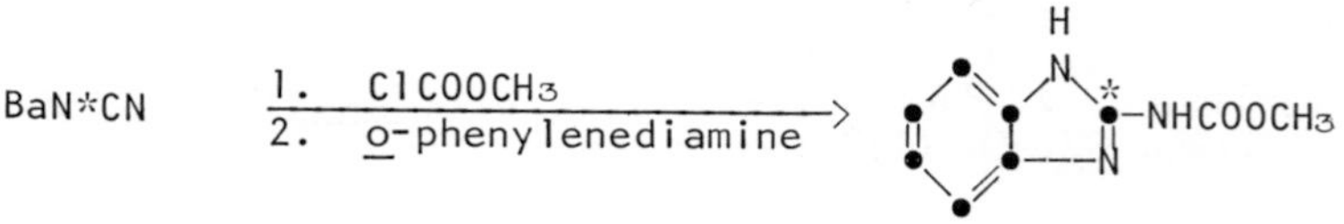

BaN*CN
1. ClCOOCH3
2. o-phenylenediamine
H
N
N
NHCOOCH3

1H-Benzimidazol-2-ylcarbamic acid-2-^{14}C methyl ester

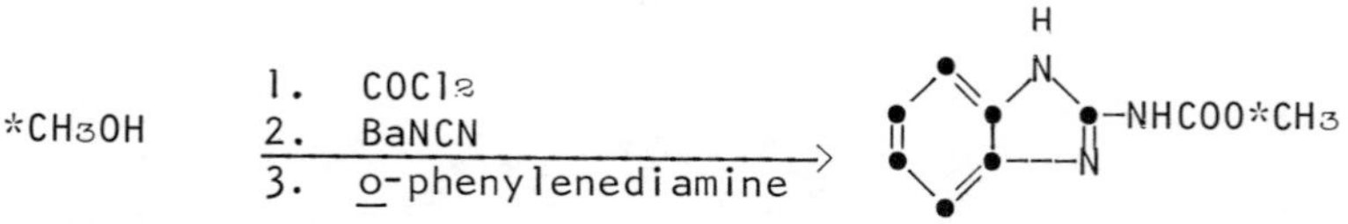

*CH3OH
1. COCl2
2. BaNCN
3. o-phenylenediamine
H
N
N
NHCOO*CH3

1H-Benzimidazol-2-ylcarbamic acid methyl-^{14}C ester

P. S. Khokhlov, G. D. Sokolova, N. M. Burmakin, and S. G. Shemchuzhin, Khim. Geterotsiklich Soedin, 1547 (1974).

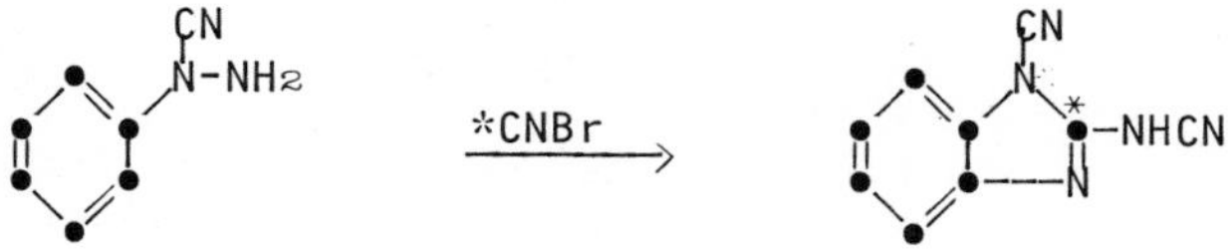
CN
N-NH2
*CNBr
CN
N
*
NHCN
N

1-Cyano-2-cyanoamino-benzimidazole-2-^{14}C

Both ^{14}C and ^{15}N derivatives were prepared to determine the mechanism of ring closing.

C. W. Bird and C. K. Wong, Tetrahedron Lett., 1251 (1974).

NH_2-*CS-NH_2 —— 1. $(CH_3O)_2SO_2$, H_2O 2. $ClCOOCH_3$, aq. NaOH ——> HN=*C(SCH_3)-$NHCOOCH_3$

—— 1. o-phenylenediamine 2. n-C_4H_9NCO, $CHCl_3$ ——>

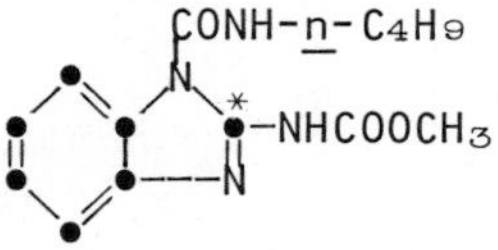
CONH-n-C4H9
N
*
NHCOOCH3
N

(86% from thiourea)

Benomyl
[[1-[(Butylamino)carbonyl]-1H-benzimidazol-2-yl-2-^{14}C] carbamic acid methyl ester]

J. A. Gardiner, J. J. Kirkland, K. L. Klopping, and H. Sherman, J. Agr. Food Chem., 22, 419 (1974).

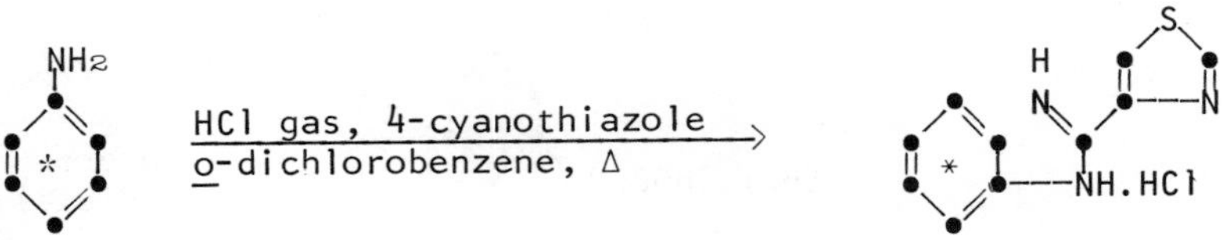
NH2
HCl gas, 4-cyanothiazole
o-dichlorobenzene, Δ
S
H
N
N
NH.HCl

—— 1. aq. $NaHCO_3$ 2. NaOCl ——>

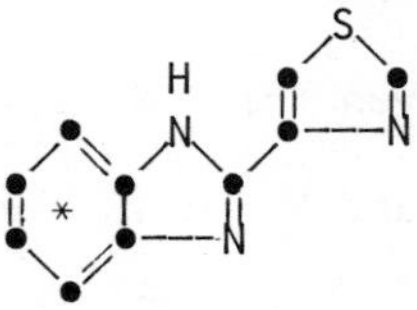
S
H
N
N
N

(94% from aniline-^{14}C)

1. HNO_3, H_2SO_4 (92%)
2. H_2, 10% Pd/C, CH_3OH
3. $(CH_3)_2CHOCOCl$

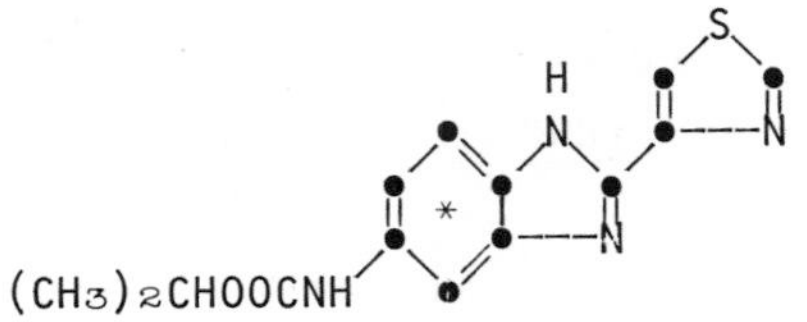

(66% from aniline-^{14}C)

Cambendazole
[[2-(4-Thiazolyl)-1H-benzimidazol-5-yl]carbamic acid 1-methylethyl ester-(ring-U-^{14}C)]

Using isopropyl chloroformate-(carbonyl-^{14}C) (generated from $*COCl_2$ and i-PrOH), cambendazole-(carbonyl-^{14}C) was prepared in 61% yield.

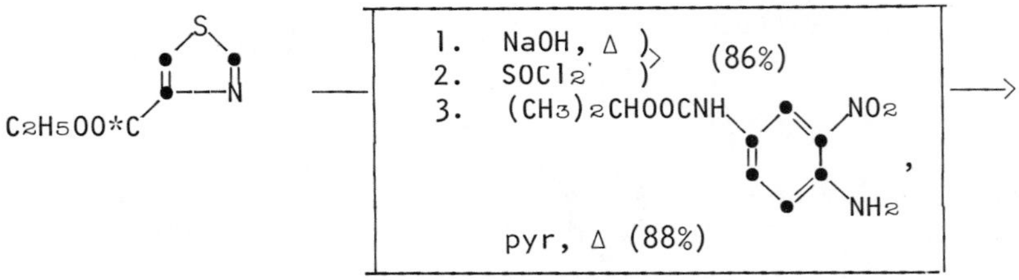
C2H5OO*C
1. NaOH, Δ
2. SOCl2
(86%)
3. (CH3)2CHOOCNH
NO2
NH2
pyr, Δ (88%)

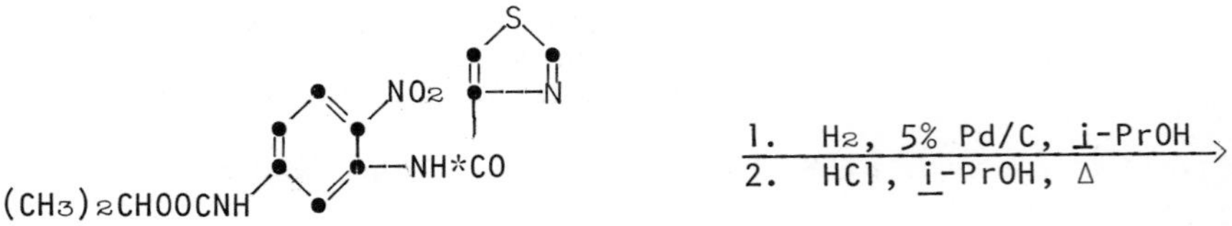
(CH3)2CHOOCNH
NO2
NH*CO
1. H2, 5% Pd/C, i-PrOH
2. HCl, i-PrOH, Δ

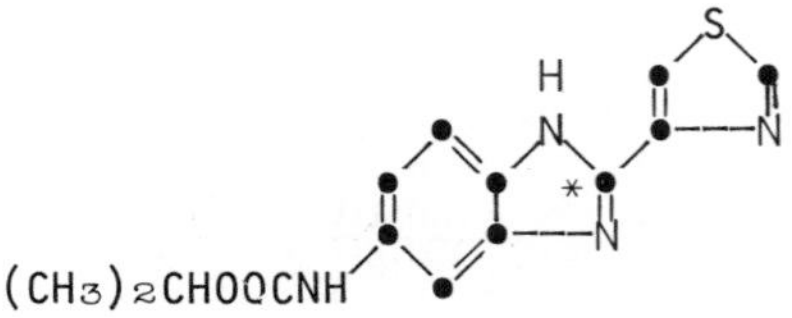

(65% from nitro-intermediate)

Cambendazole-(benzimidazol-2-^{14}C)

Yields for this sequence are given for ^{13}C-labeled reactions.

R. L. Ellsworth, H. E. Mertel, and W. J. A. VandenHeuvel, J. Agr. Food Chem., 24, 544 (1976).

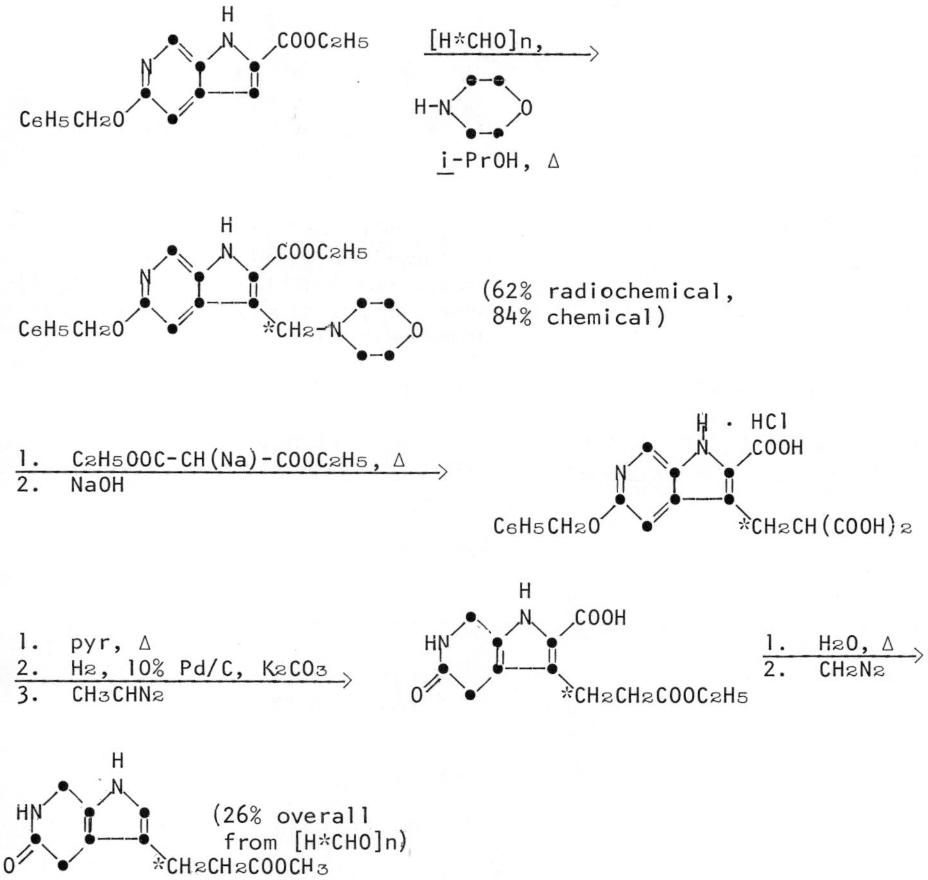
COOC2H5
C6H5CH2O
[H*CHO]n,
H-N O
i-PrOH, Δ
*CH2-N O
(62% radiochemical,
84% chemical)
1. C2H5OOC-CH(Na)-COOC2H5, Δ
2. NaOH
H · HCl
COOH
*CH2CH(COOH)2
1. pyr, Δ
2. H2, 10% Pd/C, K2CO3
3. CH3CHN2
HN
O
*CH2CH2COOC2H5
1. H2O, Δ
2. CH2N2
(26% overall
from [H*CHO]n)
*CH2CH2COOCH3

Porphobilinogen lactam
methyl ester

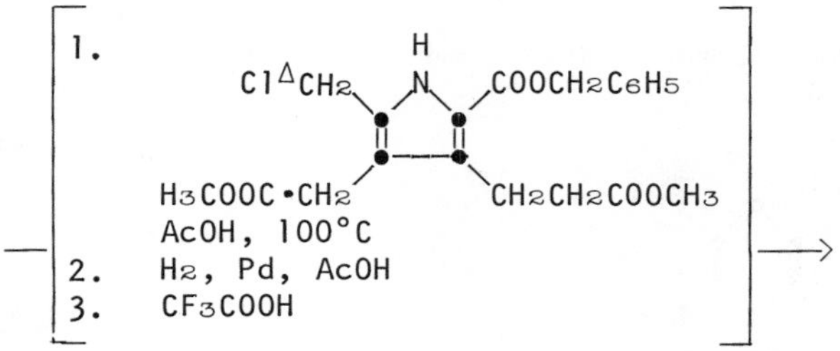
1.
ClΔCH2
COOCH2C6H5
H3COOC·CH2
CH2CH2COOCH3
AcOH, 100°C
2. H2, Pd, AcOH
3. CF3COOH

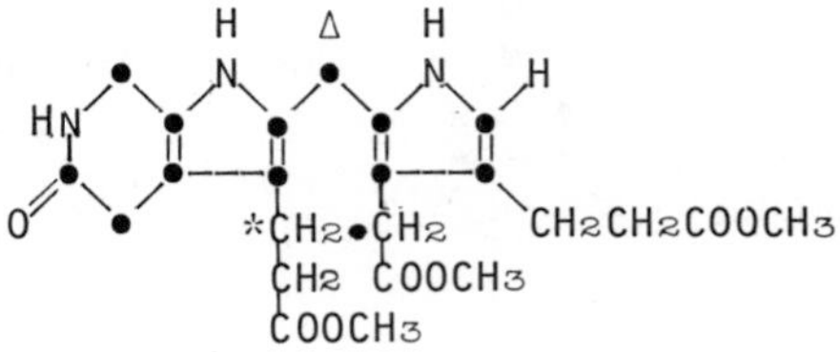

4,5,6,7-Tetrahydro-2-[[3-(2-methoxy-2-oxyethyl)-4-(3-methoxy-3-oxopropyl)-1H-pyrrol-2-yl]methyl]-5-oxo-1H-pyrrolo[2,3-c]pyridine-3-propanoic acid

Labeled separately at the three positions indicated (Δ,·,*).

A. R. Battersby, D. A. Evans, K. H. Gibson, E. McDonald, and L. Nixon, J. Chem. Soc., Perkin Trans. I, 1546 (1973).

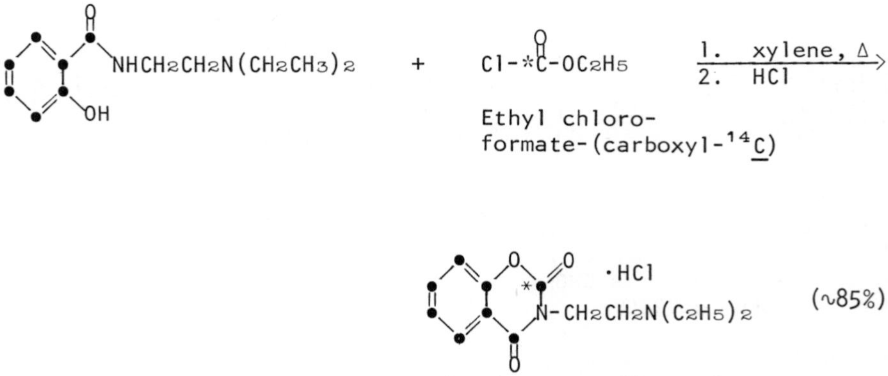

Ethyl chloroformate-(carboxyl-^{14}C)

3-(2-Diethylaminoethyl)-2H-1,3-benzoxazine-2,4(3H)-dione-2-^{14}C hydrochloride

B. M. Phillips, H. J. Havera, and T. L. Hammes, J. Pharm. Sci., 58, 1414 (1969).

$Br_2{*}CHCOCl$

(from malonic acid-2-^{14}C in three steps)

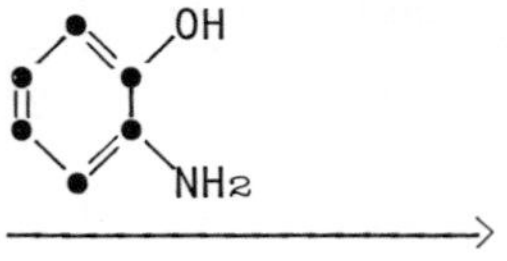

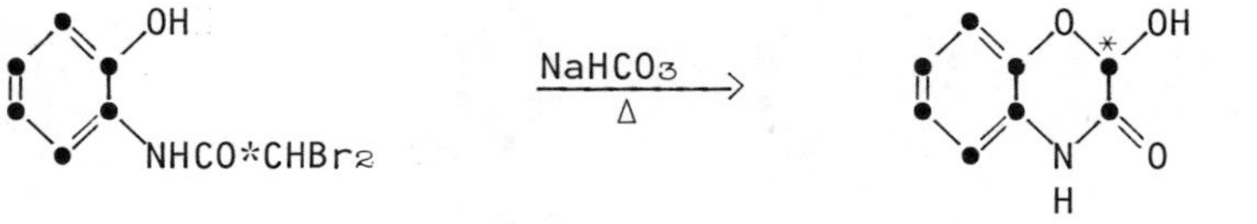
OH
NHCO*CHBr2
NaHCO3
Δ
O
OH
N
H
O

2-Hydroxy-2H-1,4-benzoxazin-3(4H)-one-2-^{14}C

The above compound was converted to 2,4-dihydroxy-2H-1,4-benzoxazin-3-one-2-^{14}C with enzymes from rye seedlings.

E. Honkanen, P. Karvonen, and A. I. Virtanen, Suomen Kemistilehti.B, 42, 445 (1969).

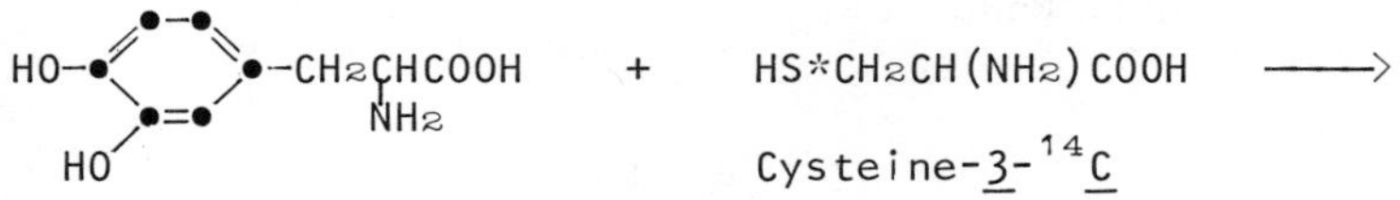
HO
HO
CH2CHCOOH
NH2
+
HS*CH2CH(NH2)COOH

Cysteine-3-^{14}C

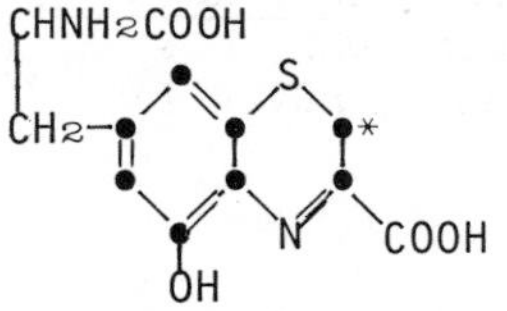
CHNH2COOH
CH2
S
N
COOH
OH

Dopaphalomelanin
[3-(3-Carboxy-5-hydroxy-2(H)-1,4-benzothiazin-7-yl)-L-alanine-2-^{14}C]

L. Minale, E. Fattorusso, S. De Stefano, and R. A. Nicolaus, Gazz. Chim. Ital., 100, 461 (1970).

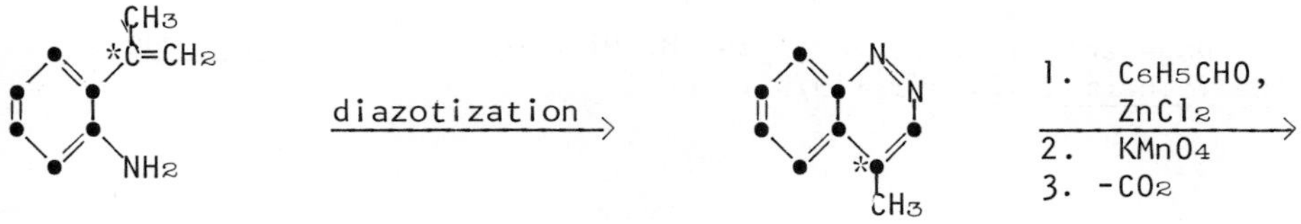
CH3
*C=CH2
NH2
diazotization
N
N
CH3
1. C6H5CHO, ZnCl2
2. KMnO4
3. -CO2

4-Methylcinnoline-4-^{14}C

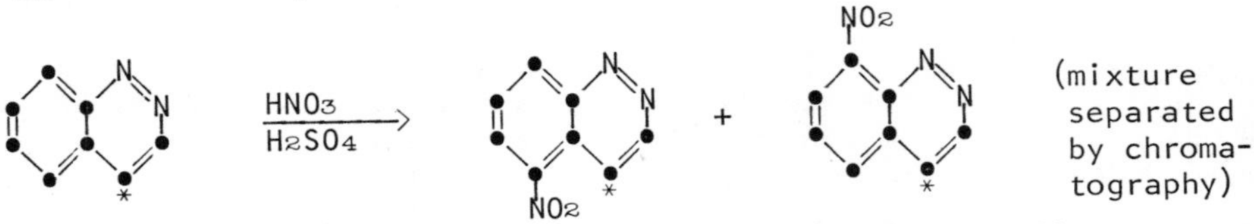
HNO3
H2SO4
NO2
NO2
(mixture separated by chromatography)

Cinnoline-4-^{14}C

5-Nitrocinnoline-4-^{14}C

8-Nitrocinnoline-4-^{14}C

H. C. vander Plas, D. J. Buurman, and C. M. Vos, Rec. Trav. Chim., J. Roy. Neth. Chem., 97, 50 (1978).

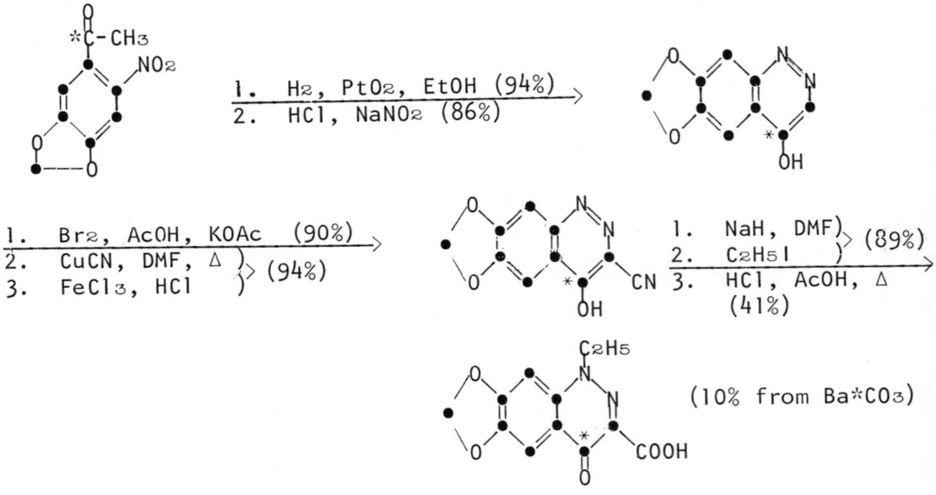
*C-CH3
NO2
1. H2, PtO2, EtOH (94%)
2. HCl, NaNO2 (86%)
OH
1. Br2, AcOH, KOAc (90%)
2. CuCN, DMF, Δ
3. FeCl3, HCl
(94%)
CN
OH
1. NaH, DMF
2. C2H5I
(89%)
3. HCl, AcOH, Δ
(41%)
C2H5
COOH
(10% from Ba*CO3)

Cinoxacin
[1-Ethyl-1,4-dihydro-4-oxo[1,3]dioxolo[4,5-g]cinnoline-3-carboxylic acid-4-^{14}C]

T. Nagasaki, Y. Katsuyama, and H. Minato, J. Label. Compound. Radiopharm., 12, 409 (1976).

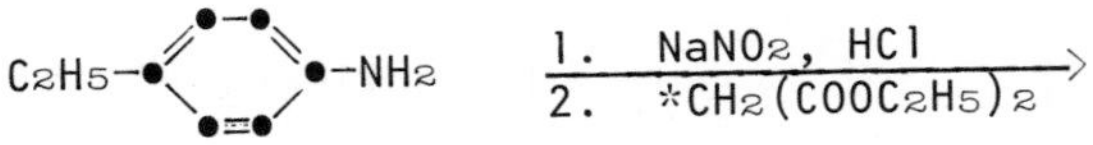
C2H5
NH2
1. NaNO2, HCl
2. *CH2(COOC2H5)2

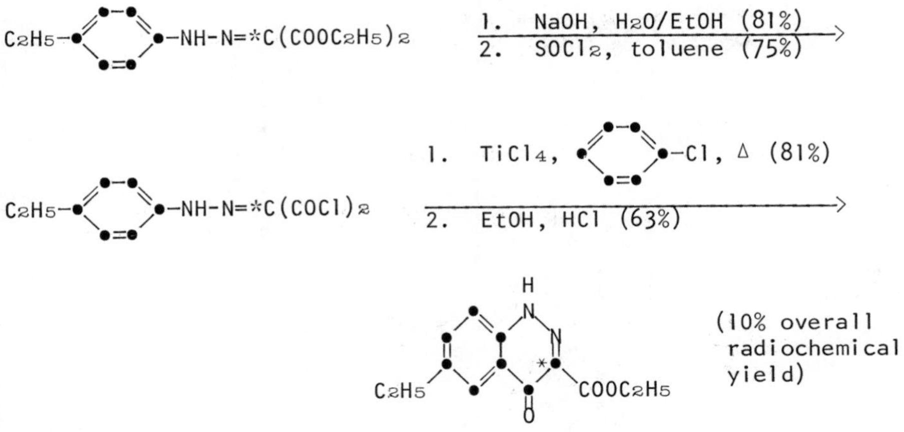
C2H5-
-NH-N=*C(COOC2H5)2
1. NaOH, H2O/EtOH (81%)
2. SOCl2, toluene (75%)
C2H5-
-NH-N=*C(COCl)2
1. TiCl4, -Cl, Δ (81%)
2. EtOH, HCl (63%)
H
N
N
*
C2H5
COOC2H5
O
(10% overall radiochemical yield)

Ethyl 6-ethyl-4-oxocinnol-3-yl-3-^{14}C carboxylate [ICI 75, 186]

S. W. Longworth, D. C. H. Bigg, D. F. White, and J. Burns, J. Label. Compounds, 10, 423 (1974).

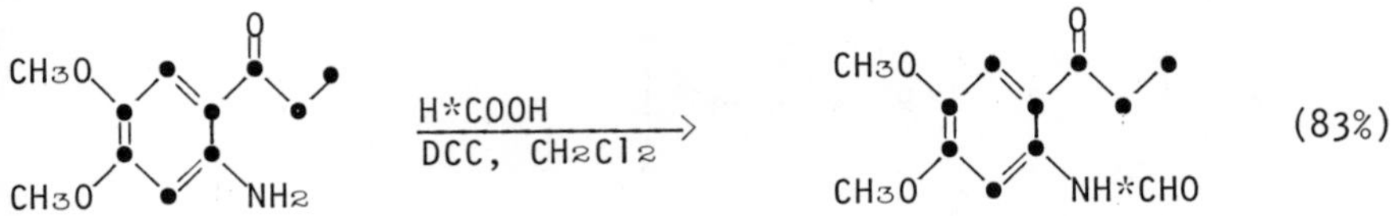
O
CH3O
CH3O
NH2
H*COOH
DCC, CH2Cl2
O
CH3O
CH3O
NH*CHO
(83%)

N-[4,5-Dimethoxy-2-(1-oxopropyl)phenyl] formamide-^{14}C

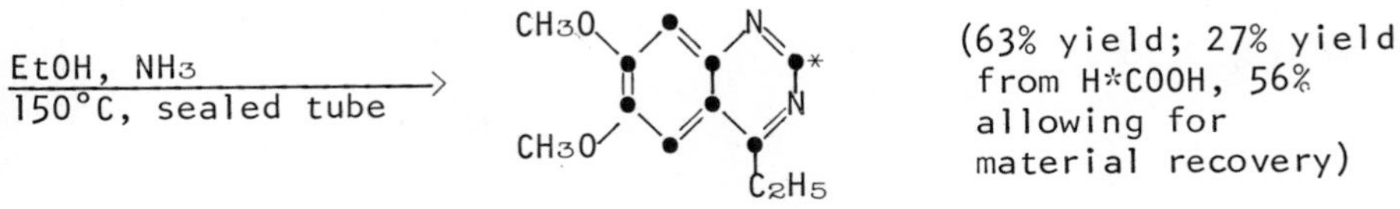
EtOH, NH3
150°C, sealed tube
CH3O
CH3O
N
*
N
C2H5
(63% yield; 27% yield from H*COOH, 56% allowing for material recovery)

6,7-Dimethoxy-4-ethylquinazoline-2-^{14}C

G. D. Madding, J. Org. Chem., 37, 1853 (1972).

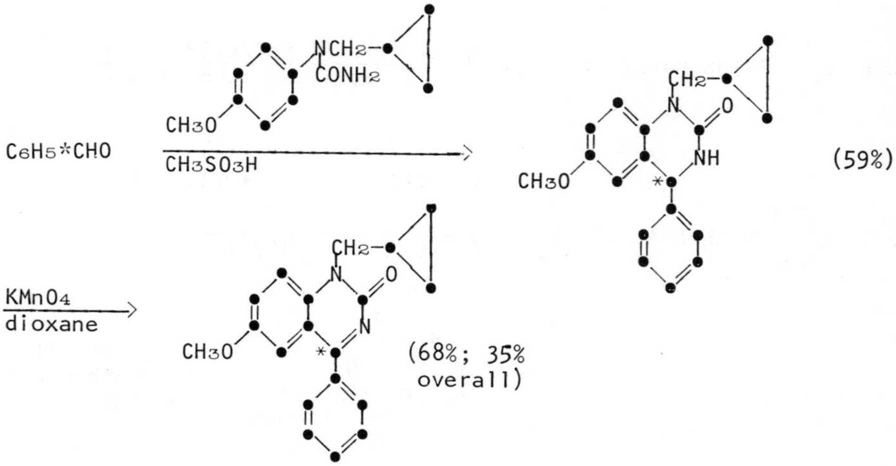
NCH2
CONH2
CH3O
C6H5*CHO
CH3SO3H
CH2
N
O
NH
CH3O
(59%)
KMnO4
dioxane
CH2
N
O
N
CH3O
(68%; 35% overall)

1-(Cyclopropylmethyl)-6-methoxy-4-phenyl-2(1H)-quinazolinone-4-[14]C

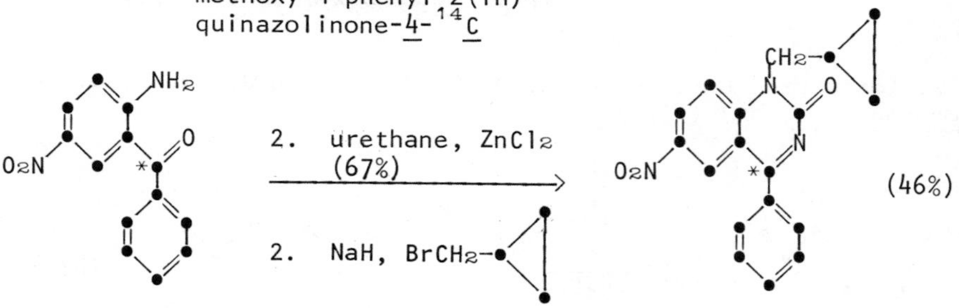
NH2
O
O2N
2. urethane, ZnCl2 (67%)
2. NaH, BrCH2
CH2
N
O
N
O2N
(46%)

(2-Amino-5-nitrophenyl)-phenylmethanone-[14]C

1-(Cyclopropylmethyl)-6-nitro-4-phenyl-2(1H)-quinazolinone-4-[14]C

plus

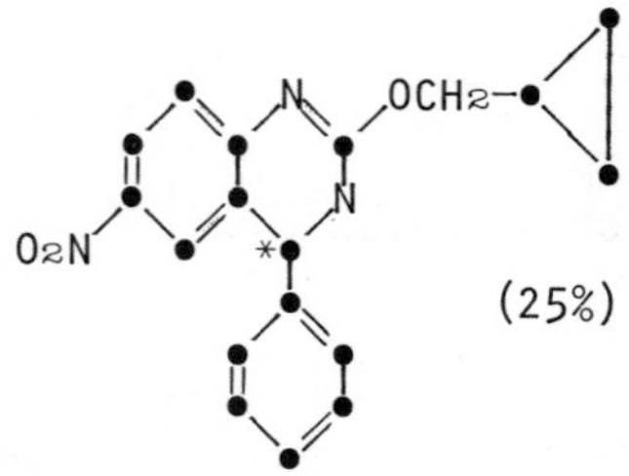
N
OCH2
N
O2N
(25%)

2-(Cyclopropylmethoxy)-6-nitro-4-phenyl-quinazoline-4-[14]C

A. Yoshitake, Y. Makari, K. Kawahara, and M. Endo, J. Label. Compounds, 9, 537 (1973).

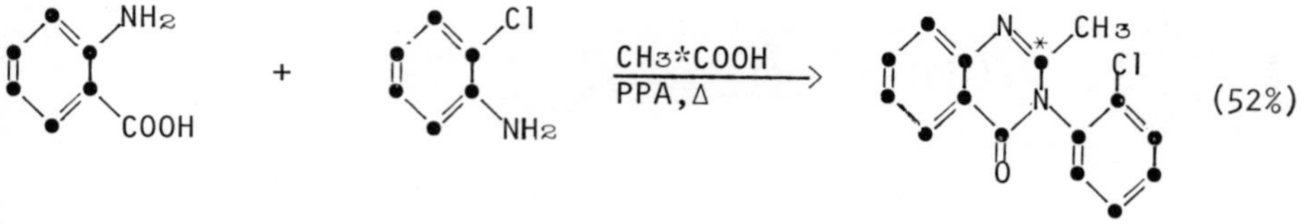
NH2
COOH
Cl
NH2
CH3*COOH
PPA,Δ
N
CH3
Cl
N
O
(52%)

3-(2-Chlorophenyl)-2-methyl-4(3H)-quinazoline-2-^{14}C

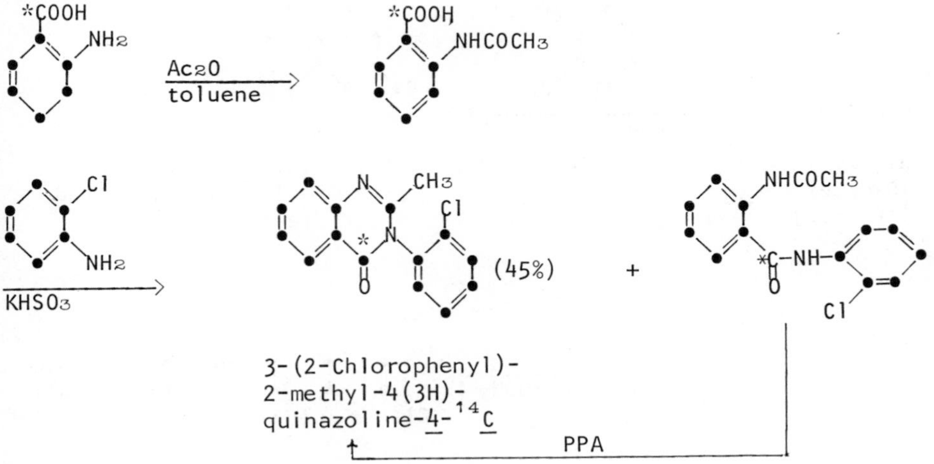
*COOH
NH2
Ac2O
toluene
*COOH
NHCOCH3
Cl
NH2
KHSO3
N
CH3
Cl
N
O
(45%)
+
NHCOCH3
*C—NH—
O
Cl
PPA

3-(2-Chlorophenyl)-2-methyl-4(3H)-quinazoline-4-^{14}C

E. J. Merrill, J. Label. Compounds, 5, 346 (1969).

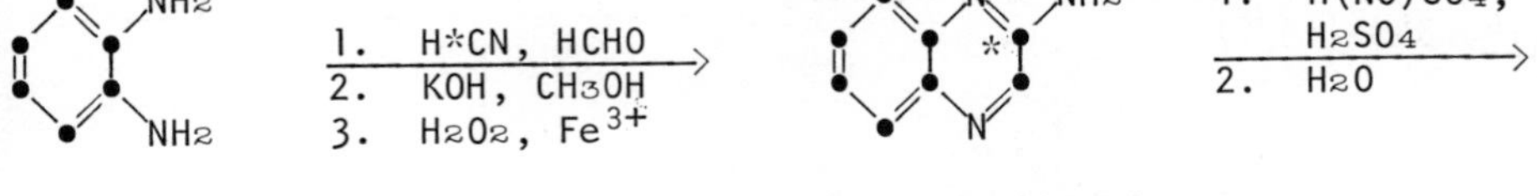
NH2
NH2
1. H*CN, HCHO
2. KOH, CH3OH
3. H2O2, Fe3+
N
NH2
N
1. H(NO)SO4, H2SO4
2. H2O

2-Quinoxalinamine-2-^{14}C

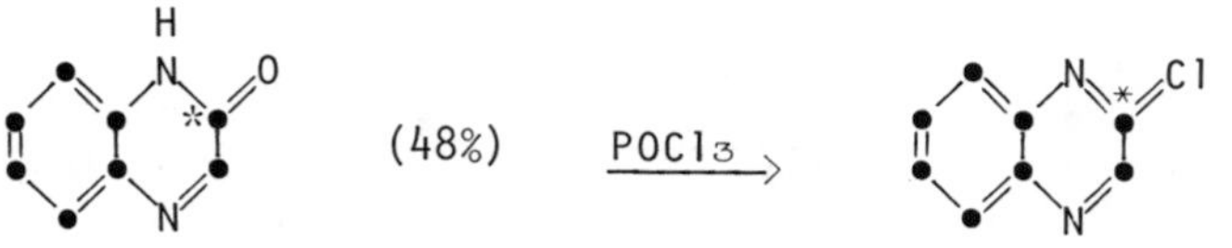
H
N
O
(48%)
POCl3
N
Cl
N

2-Chloroquinoxaline-2-^{14}C

P. J. Lont and H. D. van der Plas, Rec. Trav. Chim. - J. Roy. Neth. Chem., 91, 850 (1972).

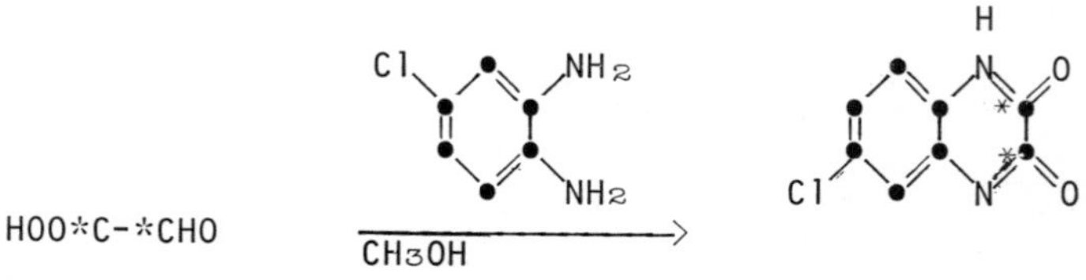
Cl
NH2
NH2
HOO*C-*CHO
CH3OH
H
N
O
Cl
N
O

Glyoxylic acid [Oxoacetic-1,2-^{14}C acid]	(mixture of 6-chloro and 7-chloro isomers separated by crystallization)

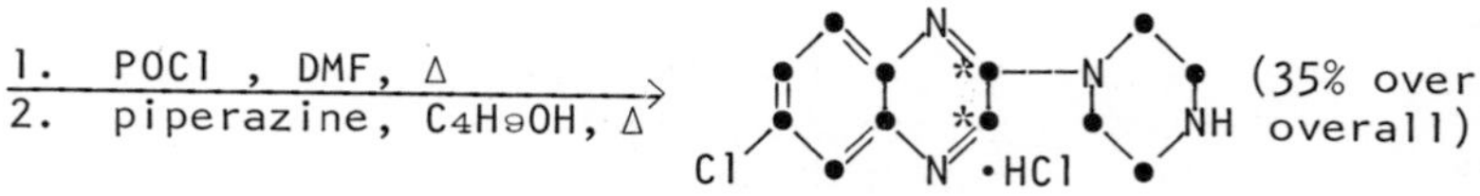
1. POCl , DMF, Δ
2. piperazine, C4H9OH, Δ
N
N
NH
Cl
N •HCl
(35% over overall)

6-Chloro-2-(1-piperazinyl)-quinoxaline-2,3-^{14}C hydrochloride

W. S. Saari and W. C. Lumma, Jr., J. Label. Compound. Radiopharm., 14, 349 (1978).

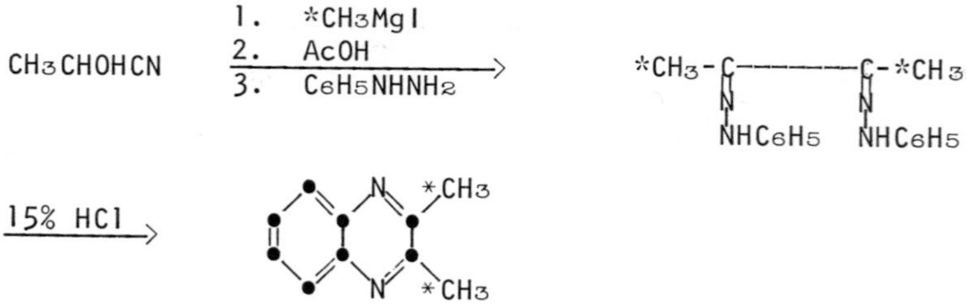
CH3CHOHCN
1. *CH3MgI
2. AcOH
3. C6H5NHNH2
*CH3-C
C-*CH3
N
N
NHC6H5
NHC6H5
15% HCl
N
*CH3
N
*CH3

1. H_2O_2, AcOH
2. Br_2, dioxane
3. AcOH, Et_3N
4. NaOH, CH_3OH

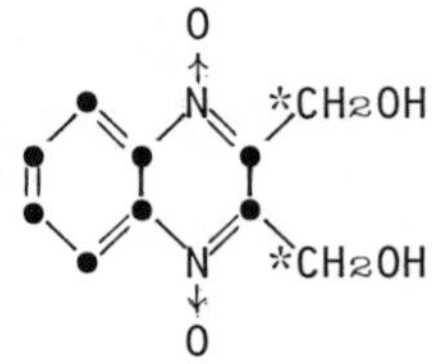
O
N
*CH2OH
N
*CH2OH
O

Dioxidine
[2,3-Quinoxaline
dimethan-α-^{14}C-ol
1,4-dioxide]

B. Z. Askinazi, S. M. Chiznik, and N. Y. Kozarinskaya, Khim.-Farm. Zh., 12, 21 (1978).

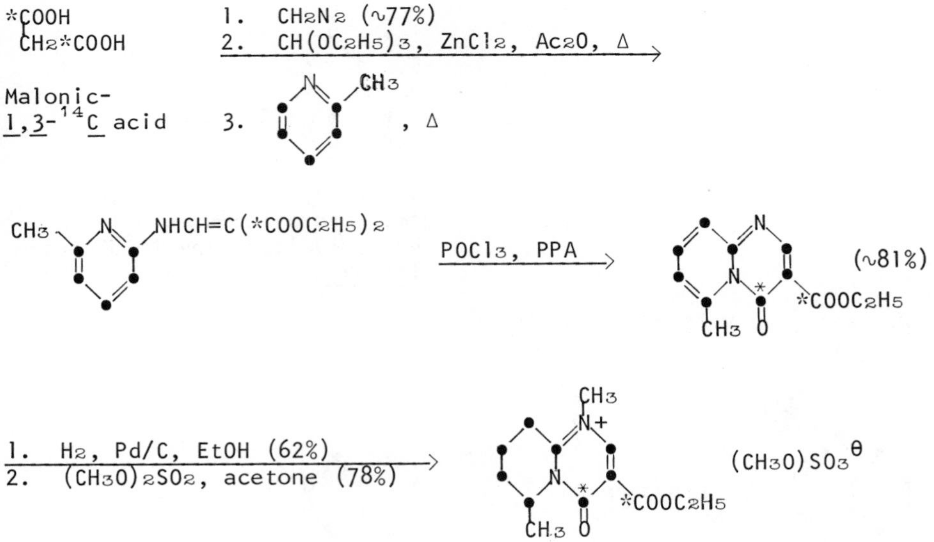
*COOH
CH2*COOH
Malonic-
1,3-14C acid
1. CH2N2 (~77%)
2. CH(OC2H5)3, ZnCl2, Ac2O, Δ
3. , Δ
CH3
N
CH3
NHCH=C(*COOC2H5)2
POCl3, PPA
(~81%)
*COOC2H5
CH3
O
1. H2, Pd/C, EtOH (62%)
2. (CH3O)2SO2, acetone (78%)
CH3
N+
(CH3O)SO3θ
*COOC2H5
CH3
O

Probon (Rimazolium)
[3-(Ethoxy(carbonyl-^{14}C)-6,7,
8,9-tetrahydro-1,6-dimethyl-
4-oxo-4H-pyrido[1,2a]pyrimidium-
(carboxyl-^{14}C)methylsulfate]

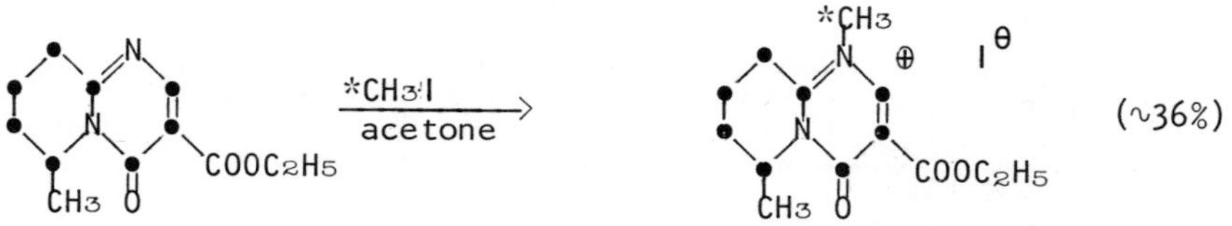

*CH3I
acetone
*CH3
COOC2H5
CH3 O
(~36%)

3-(Ethoxycarbonyl)-6,7,8,9-tetrahydro-1,6-dimethyl-4-oxo-4H-pyrido[1,2-a]pyrimidinium-(1-methyl-^{14}C) iodide

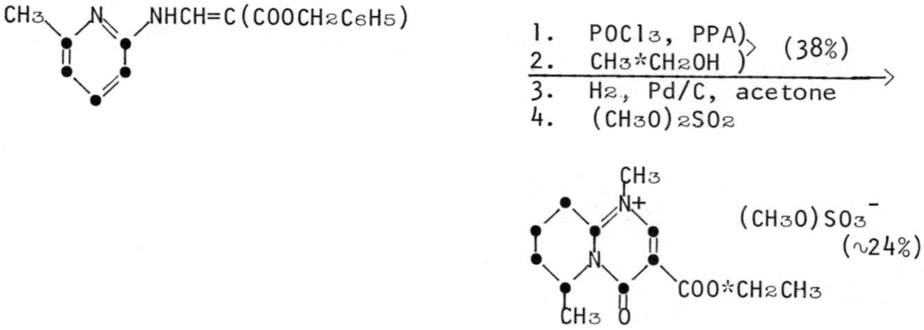

CH3
NHCH=C(COOCH2C6H5)
1. POCl3, PPA
2. CH3*CH2OH
(38%)
3. H2, Pd/C, acetone
4. (CH3O)2SO2
(CH3O)SO3-
(~24%)
COO*CH2CH3
CH3 O

3-(Ethoxycarbonyl)-6,7,8,9-tetrahydro-1,6-dimethyl-4-oxo-4H-pyrido[1,2-a]pyrimidinium-(ethoxy-1-^{14}C) methyl sulfate

D. Bánfi, J. Volford and Z. Mészáros, J. Label. Compounds, 11, 409 (1975).

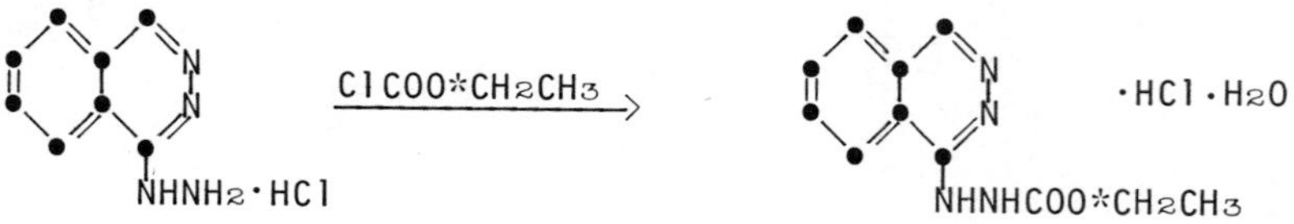

ClCOO*CH2CH3
NHNH2·HCl
·HCl·H2O
NHNHCOO*CH2CH3

Apiracohl
[2-(1-Phthalazinyl)hydrazinecarboxylic acid (ethyl-1-^{14}C) ester hydrochloride hydrate]

A. Isuii, T. Deguchi, and H. Takahira, J. Pharm. Soc. Jap., 93, 1383 (1973).

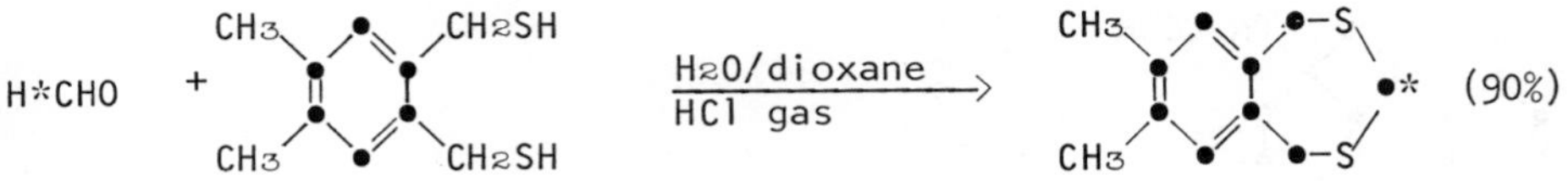
H*CHO
+
CH_3
CH_2SH
CH_3
CH_2SH
H_2O/dioxane
HCl gas
CH_3
S
•*
S
CH_3
(90%)

1,5-Dihydro-7,8-dimethyl-2,4-benzodithiepin-3-^{14}C

L. Pichat and J. P. Noel, J. Label. Compound. Radiopharm., 15, 753 (1978).

9-11 Tricyclic Compounds

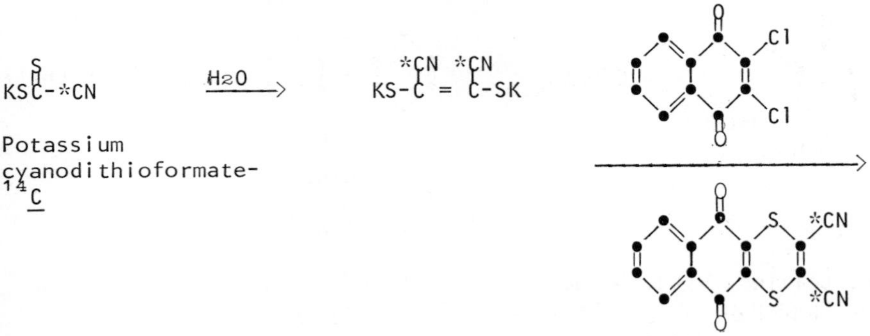
KSC(=S)-*CN
H_2O
*CN *CN
KS-C = C-SK
O
Cl
Cl
O
O
S
*CN
S
*CN
O

Potassium cyanodithioformate-^{14}C

Dithianone [5,10-Dihydro-5,10-dioxonaphtho[2,3b]-1,4-dithiin-2,3-dicarbonitrile-^{14}C]

Also prepared with both a ^{14}C and ^{35}S label.

J. Sěda, M. Faud, and R. Tykva, J. Label. Compound. Radiopharm., 14, 673 (1978).

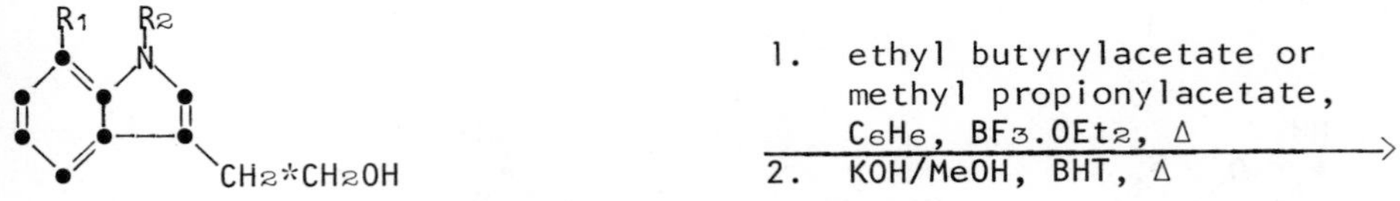
R_1
R_2
N
$CH_2{*}CH_2OH$
1. ethyl butyrylacetate or methyl propionylacetate, C_6H_6, $BF_3.OEt_2$, Δ
2. KOH/MeOH, BHT, Δ

$R_1=R_2=H$; Indole-3'-ethanol-1-^{14}C
$R_1=C_2H_5$, $R_2=H$; 7-Ethyl-1H-indole-3-ethanol-1'-^{14}C
$R_1=H$, $R_2=C_2H_5$; 1-Ethyl-1H-indole-3-ethanol-1'-^{14}C

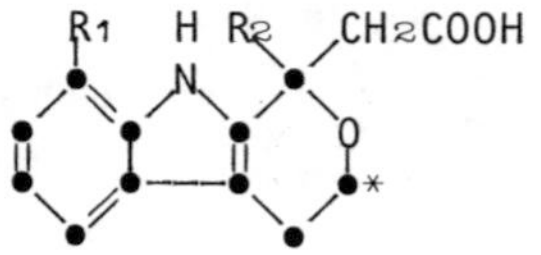

R_1=H,R_2=C_3H_7; Prodolic acid [1,3,4,9-Tetrahydro-1-propylpyrano [3,4b]indole-1-acetic acid-3-^{14}C] (26% overall)

R_1=R_2=C_2H_5; Etodolic acid [1,8-Diethyl-1,3,4,9-tetrahydropyrano [3,4b]indole-1-acetic acid-3-^{14}C] (26% overall)

E. S. Ferdinandi, D. R. Hicks, W. Verbestel, and P. Raman, J. Label. Compound. Radiopharm., 14, 411 (1978).

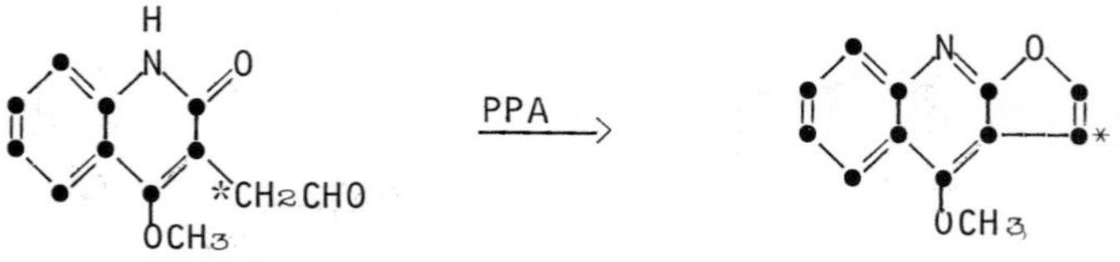

(43% overall)

Dictamnine
[4-Methoxyfuro[2,3b] quinoline-3-^{14}C]

J. F. Collins, W. J. Donnelly, M. F. Grundon, D. M. Harrison, and C. G. Spyropoulos, J. Chem. Soc., Chem. Commun., 1029 (1972).

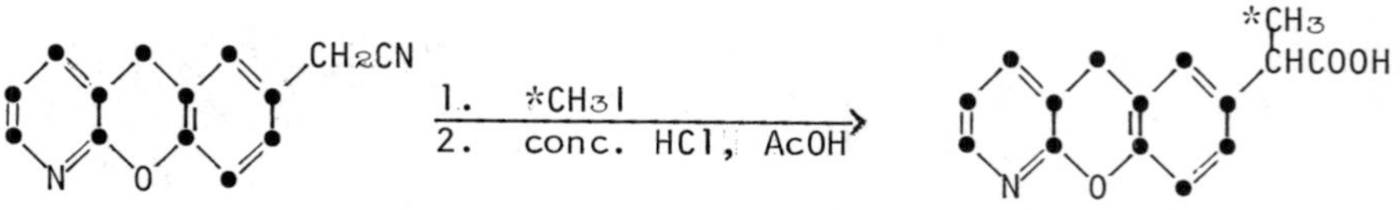

α-Methyl-^{14}C-5H[1]benzopyrano[2,3b]pyridinyl-7-acetic acid

Y. Kato, N. Arima, and H. Nishimine, J. Pharm. Soc. Jap., 96, 819 (1976)

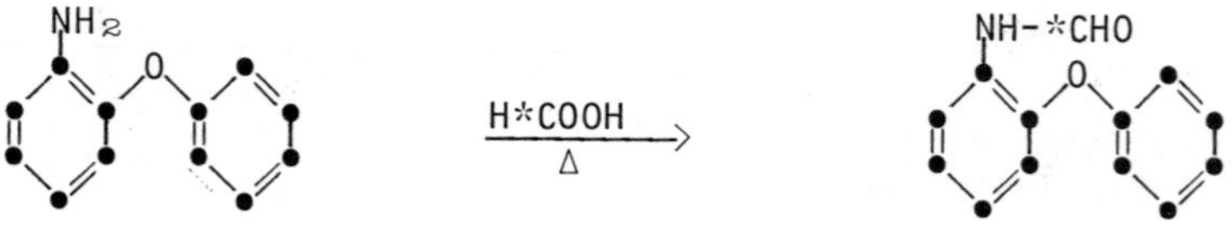

(90%)

PPA / $POCl_3$, →

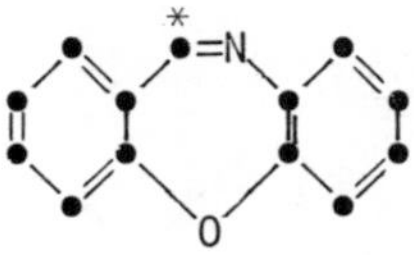
*
N
O

(79%)

Dibenz[b,f][1,4]
oxepine-11-^{14}C

H_2, Pd/C / EtOH →

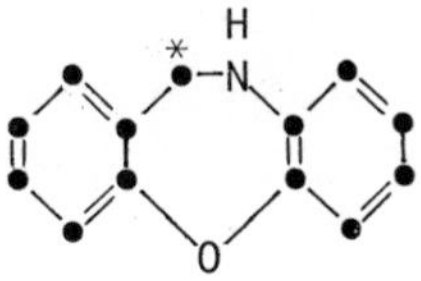
*
H
N
O

(79%)

10,11-Dihydrodibenz-
[b,f][1,4]oxepine-11-^{14}C

J. M. Harrison, T. D. Inch, and D. G. Upshall, J. Label. Compound. Radiopharm., 14, 375 (1978).

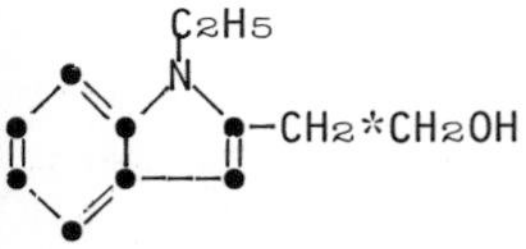
C2H5
N
-CH2*CH2OH

1. PBr_3
2. $Na_2S_2O_3$
3. (1-N,N-dimethylamino) butan-3-one, $BF_3 \cdot OEt_2$, toluene
4. HCl, Et_2O

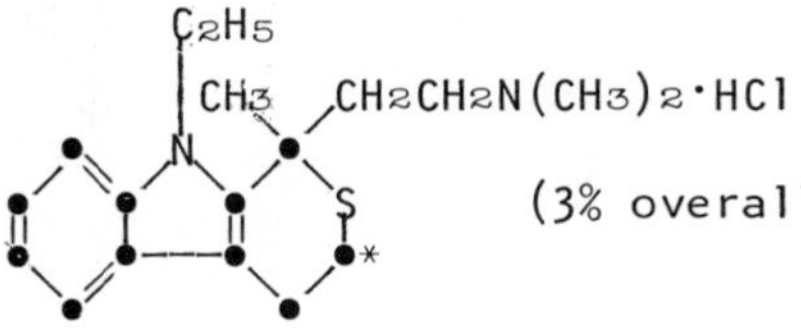
C2H5
CH3
CH2CH2N(CH3)2·HCl
N
S
*

(3% overall)

Tandamine
[9-Ethyl-1,3,4,9-tetrahydro-N,N,1-trimethylthiopyran[3,4-b]indole-1-ethanamine-3-^{14}C hydrochloride]

E. S. Ferdinandi, D. R. Hicks, W. Verbestel, and P. Raman, J. Label. Compound. Radiopharm., 14, 411 (1978).

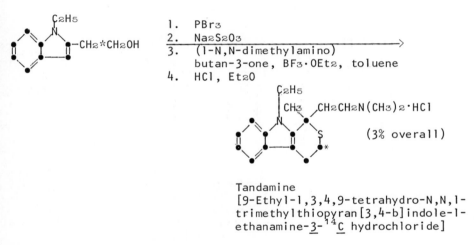

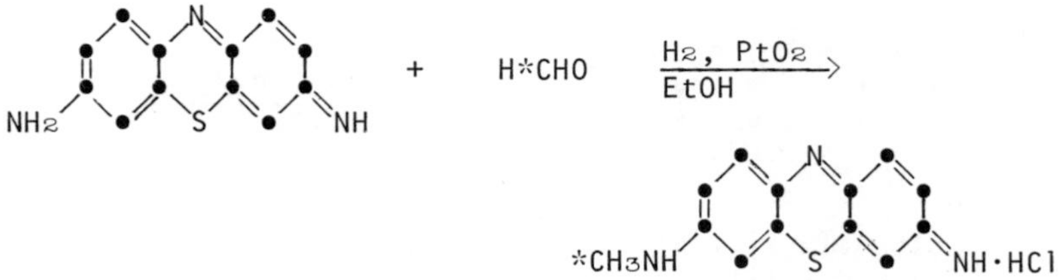
NH2
NH
N
S
+
H*CHO
H2, PtO2
EtOH
*CH3NH
NH·HCl

(29%)

N-Methylthionine hydrochloride
[3-Imino-3H-phenothiazin-7-(N-methylamine-^{14}C) hydrochloride]

R. R. Eng and L. A. Spitznagle, J. Label. Compounds, 11, 291 (1975).

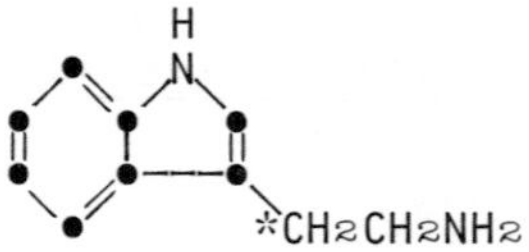
H
N
*CH2CH2NH2

Tryptamine
[1H-Indole-3-(ethanamine-1-^{14}C)

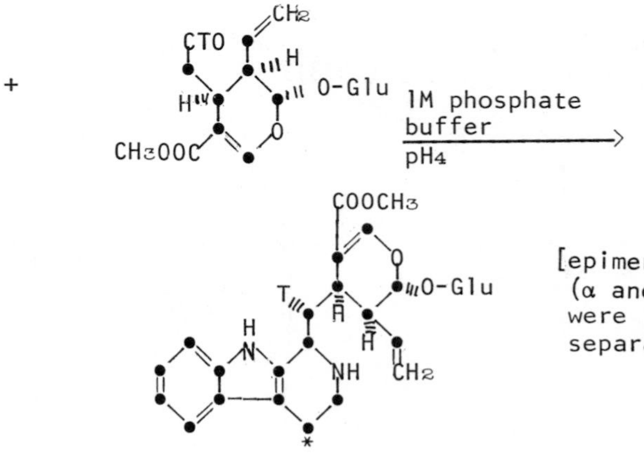
+
CTO
CH2
H
O-Glu
CH3OOC
O
1M phosphate buffer
pH4
COOCH3
T
H
NH
CH2

[epimers (α and β) were separated]

Strictosidine
[[2S-[2α,3β,3β(R*)]]-3-Ethenyl-2-(D-glucopyranosyloxy)-3,4-dihydro-4-[(2,3,4,9-tetrahydro-1H-pyrido-5-^{14}C-[3,4b]indol-1-yl)methyl-t]-2H-pyran-5-carboxylic acid methyl ester]

M. Rueffer, N. Nagakura, and M. H. Zenk, Tetrahedron Lett., 1593 (1978).

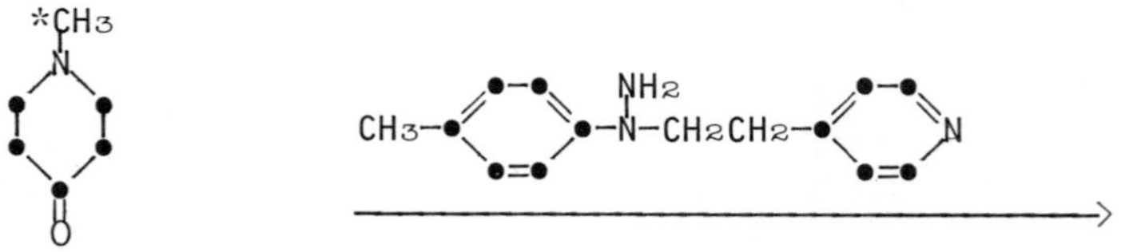
*CH3
N
O
CH3
NH2
N-CH2CH2
N

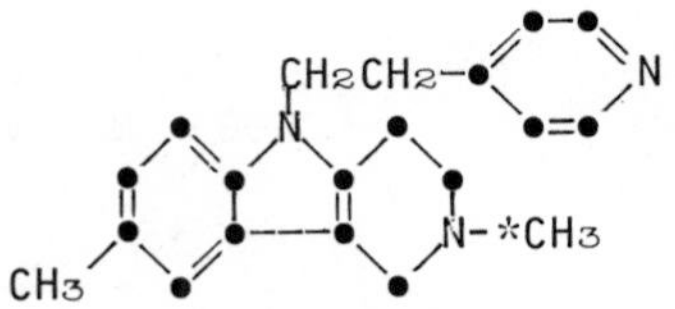
CH2CH2
N
N
N-*CH3
CH3

(60%)

9-(2-(4-Pyridyl)ethyl)-3,6-dimethyl-(3-methyl-^{14}C)-1,2,3,4-tetrahydro-γ-carboline

N. G. Tsyshkova and F. A. Trofimov, Khim.-Farm. Zh., 5, 14 (1971).

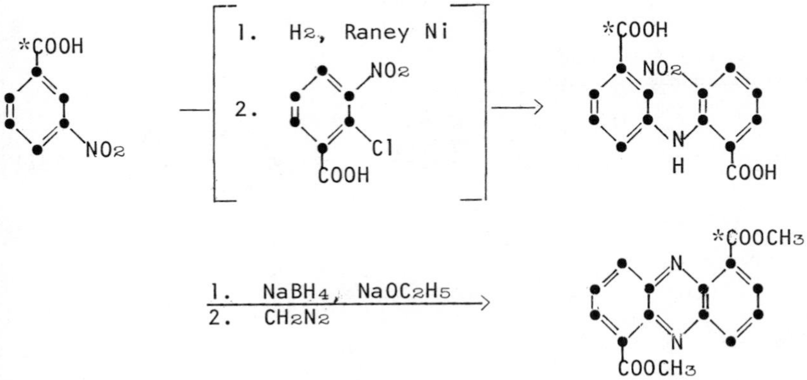
*COOH
NO2
1. H2, Raney Ni
2.
NO2
Cl
COOH
*COOH
NO2
N
H
COOH
1. NaBH4, NaOC2H5
2. CH2N2
*COOCH3
N
N
COOCH3

Dimethylphenazine-1,6-dicarboxylate-(monocarboxyl-^{14}C)

U. Hollstein, G. E. Krisov, and D. L. Mock, Tetrahedron Lett., 3267 (1976).

$C_2H_5OOC\text{-}CO{*}CH_2COOC_2H_5$

Ethyl oxaloacetate-3-^{14}C

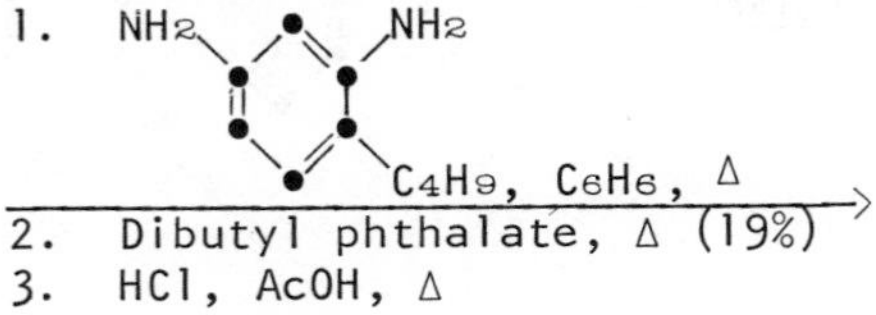
1. NH2
NH2
C4H9, C6H6, Δ
2. Dibutyl phthalate, Δ (19%)
3. HCl, AcOH, Δ

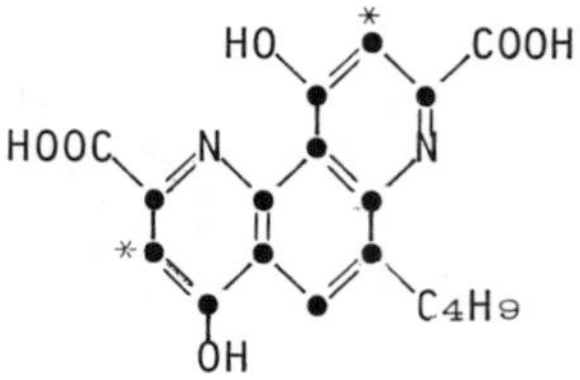

(80%; 12% overall)

5-Butyl-3,9-dicarboxy-1,7-dihydroxy-4,10-phenanthroline-2,8-^{14}C

D. C. H. Bigg, J. Label. Compound. Radiopharm., 12, 571 (1976).

9-12 Tetracyclic Compounds

(59%)

N-Methyl-N-phenyl-(formamide-^{14}C)

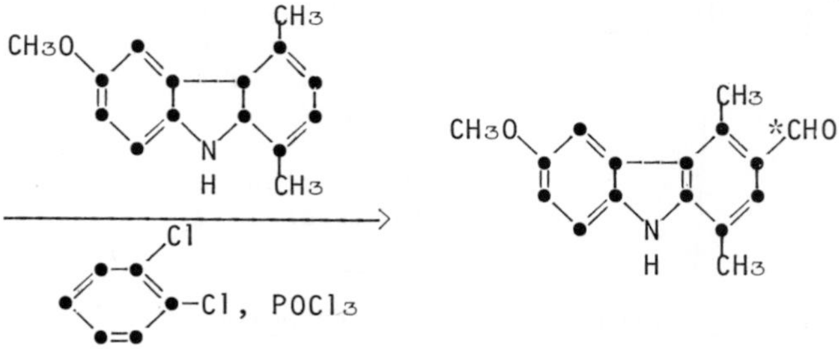

(73% crude)

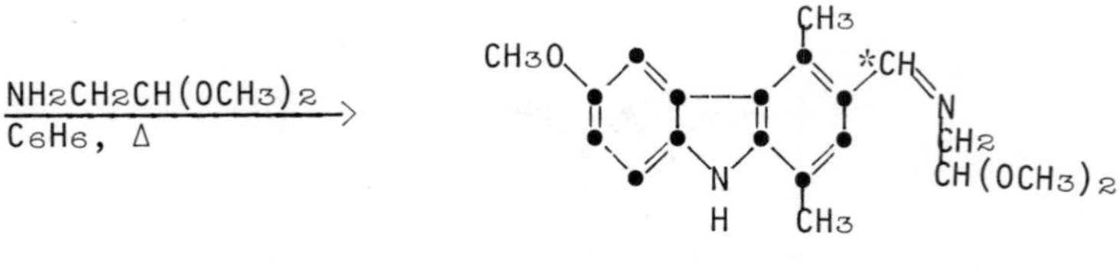

1. PPA (69%)
2. pyr.HCl (70%) →

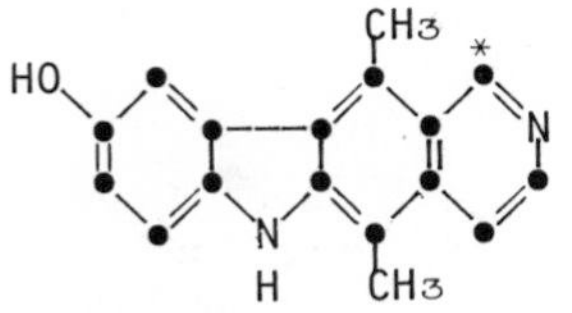
HO
CH3
N
H
CH3

(14% from $H{*}COONa$)

9-Hydroxyellipticcine
[5,11-Dimethyl-6H-pyrido
[4,3b]carbazol-9-ol-1-^{14}C]

Nguyen Van-Bac, M. Herbert, L. Pichat, M.-M. Janot, and Nguyen Dat-Xuong, J. Label. Compounds, 11, 241 (1975).

$CH_3{*}CH_2NHC_2H_5$

N-Ethylethanamine-1-^{14}C

(+)-lysergic acid-imidazole complex
DMF →

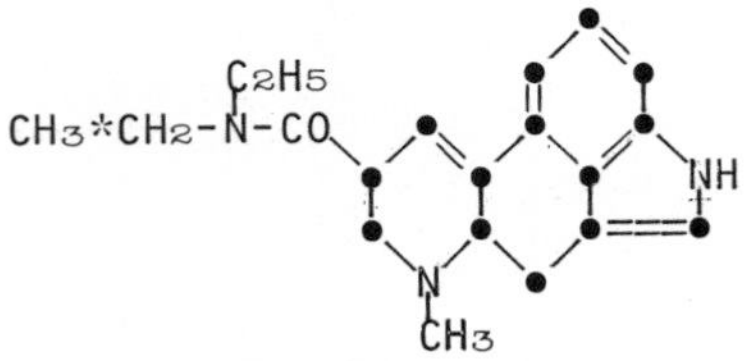
C2H5
CH3*CH2-N-CO
NH
N
CH3

(26%)

Lysergic acid diethylamide (LSD) [9,10-Didehydro-N,N-(diethyl-1-^{14}C)-6-methyl-ergoline-8β-carboxamide]

R. D. Barnes, J. Label. Compounds, 10, 207 (1974).

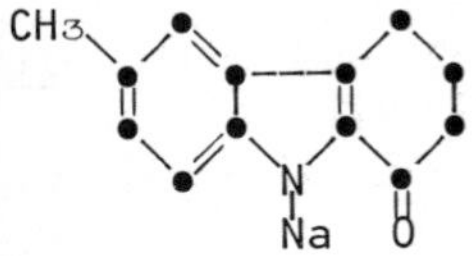
CH3
N
Na
O

$BrCH_2{*}COOC_2H_5$
DMF →

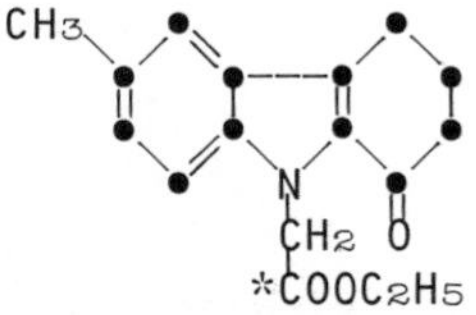
CH3
N
CH2
O
*COOC2H5

1. OH^{θ}
2. PCl_5, Et_2O
3. NH_3, Et_2O →

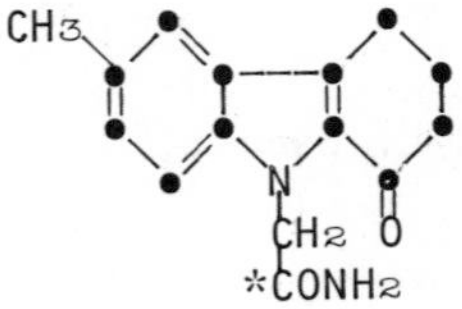
CH3
N
CH2
O
*CONH2

1. C_3H_7OH, Na
2. HCl, ether →

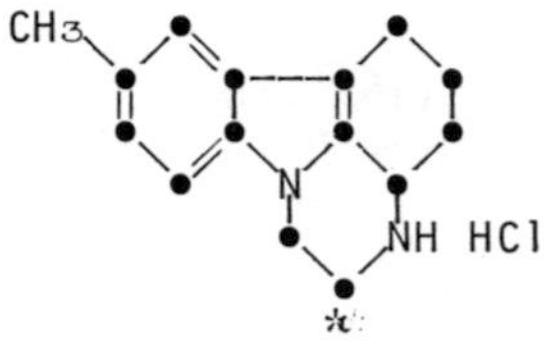
CH3
N
NH HCl
*

Pyrazidol
[2,3,3a,4,5,6-Hexahydro-8-methyl-1H-pyrazino[3,2,1jk]carbazole-2-^{14}C hydrochloride]

B. Z. Askinazi, M. I. Vlasova, and N. A. Kogan, Khim.-Farm.Zh., 10, 19 (1976).

9-13 Pentacyclic Compounds

N-Desmethyl vinblastine → 1. H*COOH (93%) 2. H_2SO_4, EtOH (77%)

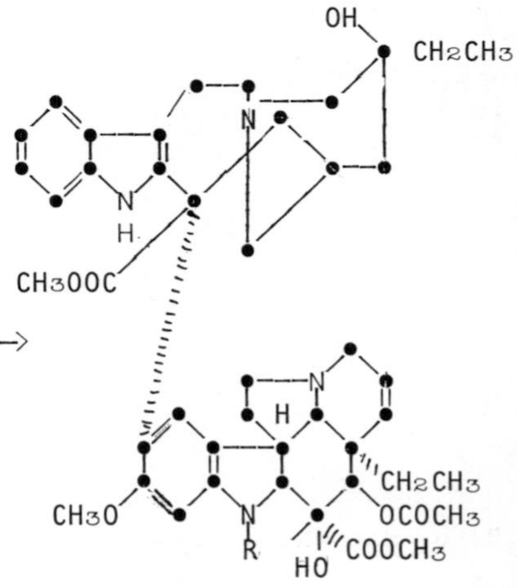
OH
CH2CH3
N
N
H
CH3OOC
N
H
CH2CH3
OCOCH3
CH3O
N
R
HO
COOCH3

R=H; 1-Desmethylvinleucoblastine
R=*CHO; Vincristine-(formyl-^{14}C)sulfate

(72% overall)

N-Desmethyl-N-formyl-^{14}C-leuosine sulfate was prepared in a similar manner in 58% yield.

G. Zólyomi, K. Jovánovics, and L. Dancsi, J. Label. Compound. Radiopharm., 13, 551 (1977).

Compounds with Three Heteroatoms

9-14 Five-Membered Rings

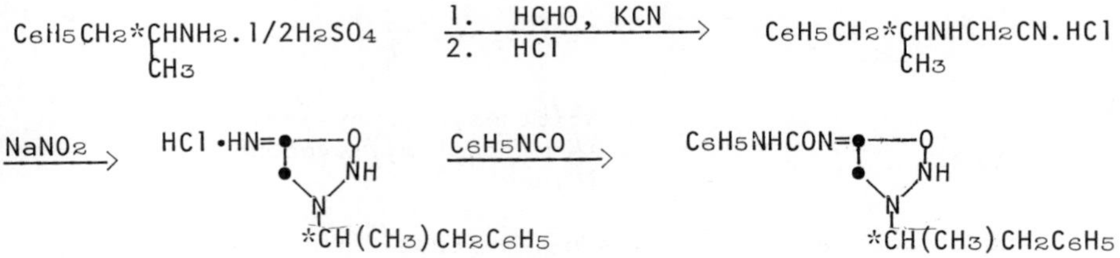
C6H5CH2*CHNH2.1/2H2SO4
CH3
1. HCHO, KCN
2. HCl
C6H5CH2*CHNHCH2CN.HCl
CH3
NaNO2
HCl·HN=
O
NH
N
*CH(CH3)CH2C6H5
C6H5NCO
C6H5NHCON=
O
NH
N
*CH(CH3)CH2C6H5

Sydnophen
[3-(1-Methyl-2-phenylethyl-1-^{14}C)sydnone imine hydrochloride]

Sydnocarb
[3-(1-Methyl-2-phenylethyl-1-^{14}C)-N-[(phenylaminocarbonyl] syndone imine]

Labeled KCN was also used with unlabeled starting material.

A. D. Bulat, L. E. Kholodov, Y. Y. Usaevich, and L. N. Kivokurtseva, Khim.-Farm. Zh. 9, 9 (1975).

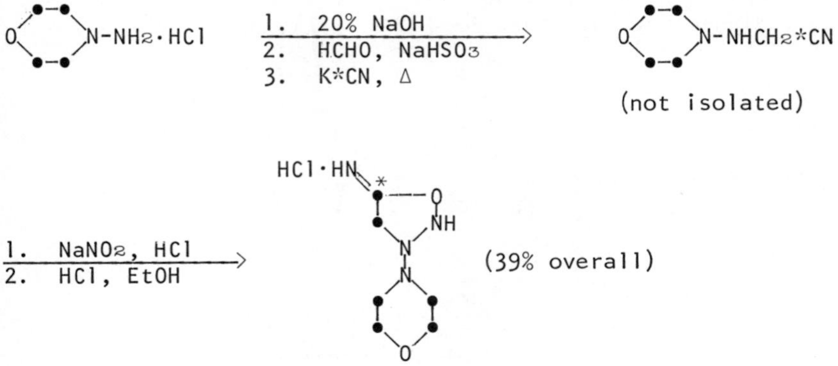
O
N-NH2·HCl
1. 20% NaOH
2. HCHO, NaHSO3
3. K*CN, Δ
O
N-NHCH2*CN
(not isolated)
HCl·HN
*
O
NH
N
N
O
1. NaNO2, HCl
2. HCl, EtOH
(39% overall)

3-(4-Morpholinyl) syndone imine-5-^{14}C hydrochloride

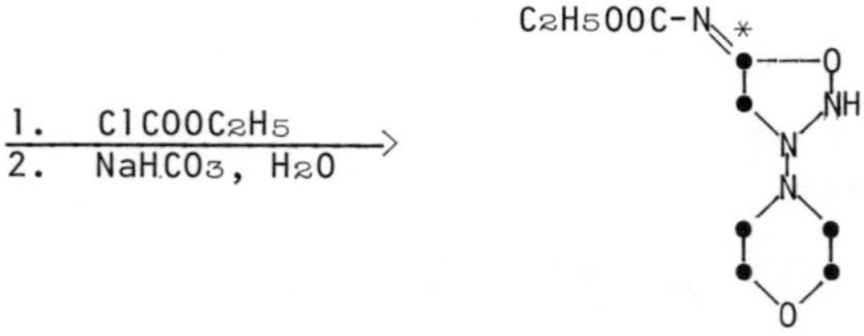

1. ClCOOC2H5
2. NaHCO3, H2O
C2H5OOC-N
NH
N
N
O

(23% from K*CN)

N-(Ethoxycarbonyl)-3-(4-morpholinyl)syndone imine-_5_-^{14}_C_

K. Masuda, T. Toga, and N. Hayashi, _J. Label. Compounds_, _11_, 301 (1975).

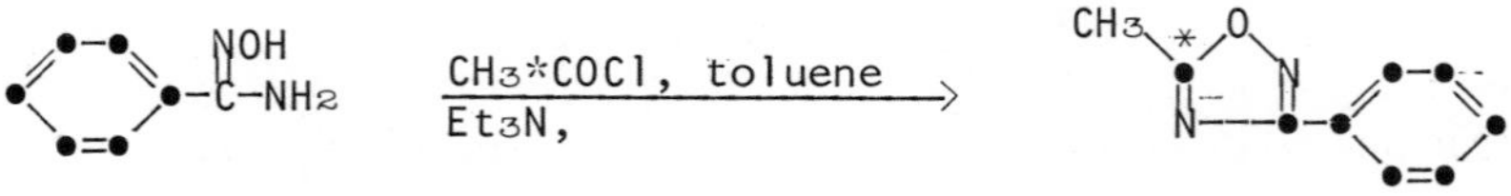

NOH
C-NH2
CH3*COCl, toluene
Et3N,
CH3
O
N
N

(65%)

5-Methyl-3-phenyl-1,2,4-oxadiazole-_5_-^{14}_C_ (PMO)

P. D. Schickedantz, M. A. Skladanowski, J. Zaletel, R. S. Marmor, and H. J. Minnemeyer, _J. Agr. Food Chem._, _24_, 876 (1976).

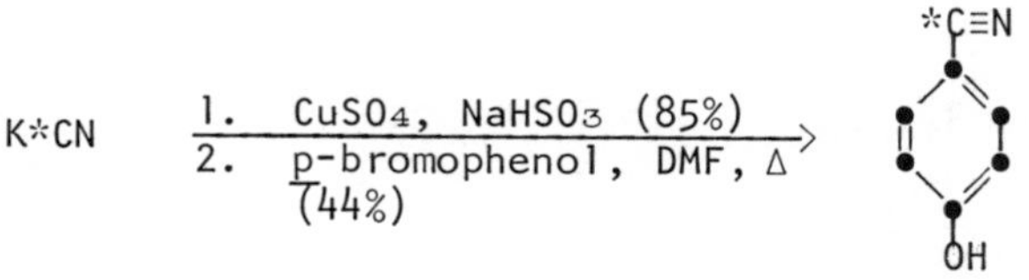

K*CN
1. CuSO4, NaHSO3 (85%)
2. p-bromophenol, DMF, Δ (44%)
*C≡N
OH

p-Hydroxybenzonitrile-(nitrile-^{14}C)

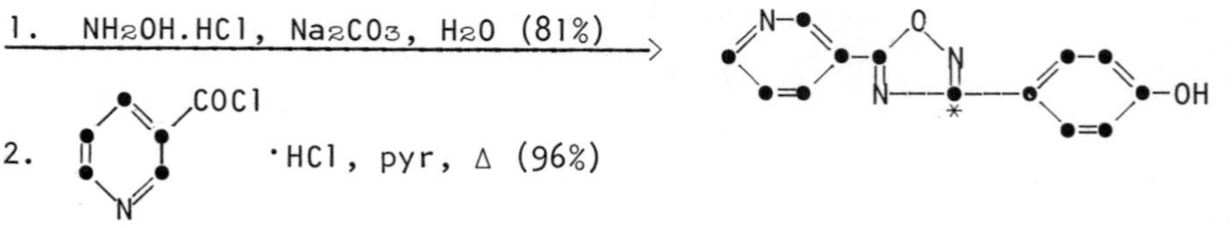

1. NH2OH.HCl, Na2CO3, H2O (81%)
2.
COCl
N
·HCl, pyr, Δ (96%)
N
O
N
N
OH

$BrC(CH_3)_2COOC_2H_5$ → DMF, Δ

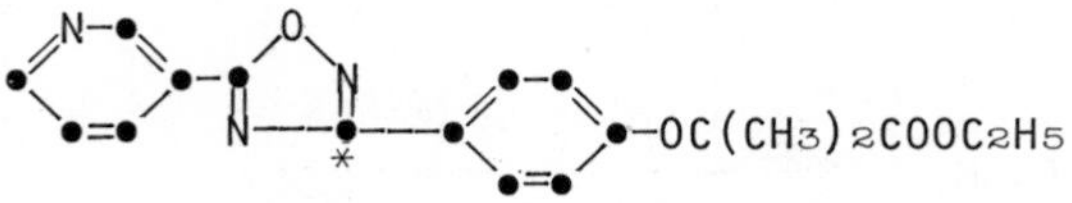

2,2-Dimethyl-4-[[5-(3-pyridinyl)-3-1,2,4-oxadiazol-3-yl-3-^{14}C]oxy]acetic acid ethyl ester

N. Hayashi, T. Toga, and A. Miyake, J. Label. Compound. Radiopharm., 14, 185 (1978).

9-15 Six-Membered Rings

$C_6H_5CH_2NH_2$ → 1. Na_2CO_3, CS_2; 2. CH_2O, H_2O; 3. $NH_2{*}CH_2COOH$

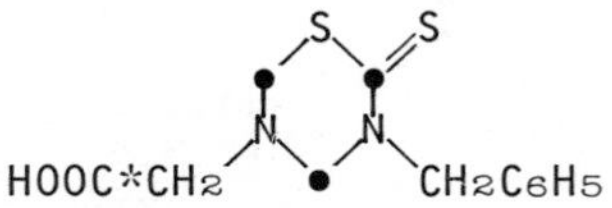

Dihydro-5-(phenylmethyl)-6-thioxo-2H-1,3,5-thiadiazine-3(4H)-acetic-2-^{14}C acid

J. Augustin, J. Bernat, L. Drobnica, and P. Kristian, Chem. Zvesti, 25, 304 (1971); Chem. Zvesti, 20, 687 (1966).

NC-N=C$(NH_2)_2$ +

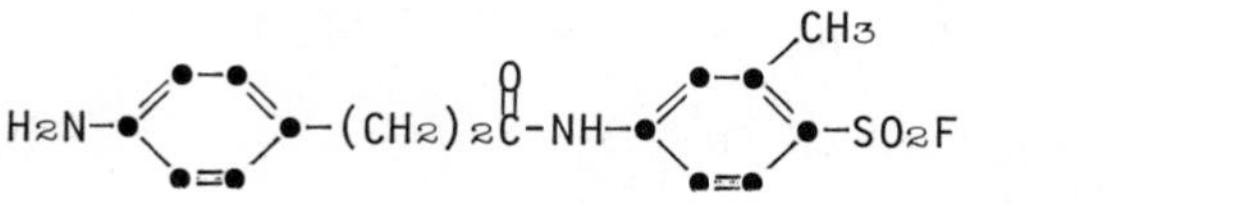

Dicyanodiamide-^{14}C-
(cyanoguanidine-^{14}C)
(position of label
not specified)

→ acetone, $(C_2H_5)_3SO_3H$

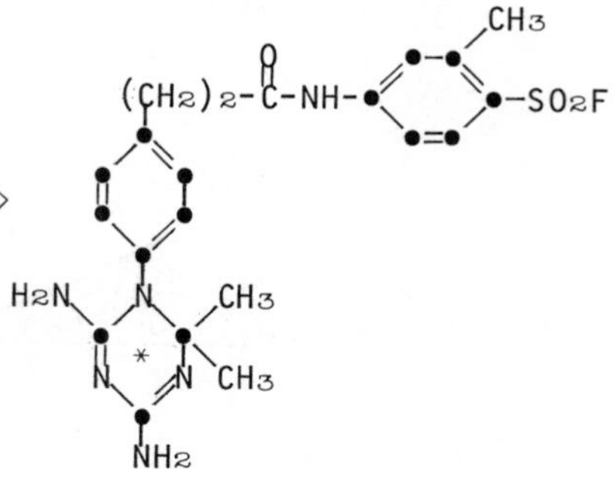

4-[4-(4,6-Diamino-1,2-dihydro-2,2-dimethyl-1,3,5-triazin-1-yl-U-^{14}C]-N-[4-(fluorosulfonyl)-3-methylphenyl]benzenepropanamide

A. J. Ryan, N. M. J. Vermeulen, and B. R. Baker, J. Med. Chem., 13, 1140 (1970).

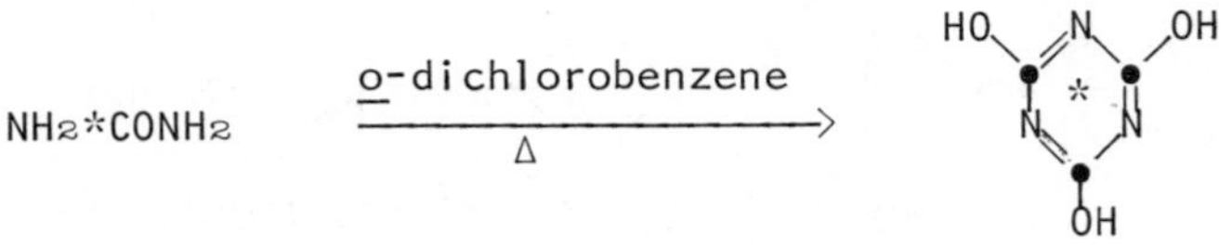
NH2*CONH2
o-dichlorobenzene
Δ
HO
N
OH
*
N
N
OH

(46%)

Cyanuric acid
[1,3,5-Triazine-2,4,6-triol-U-^{14}C]

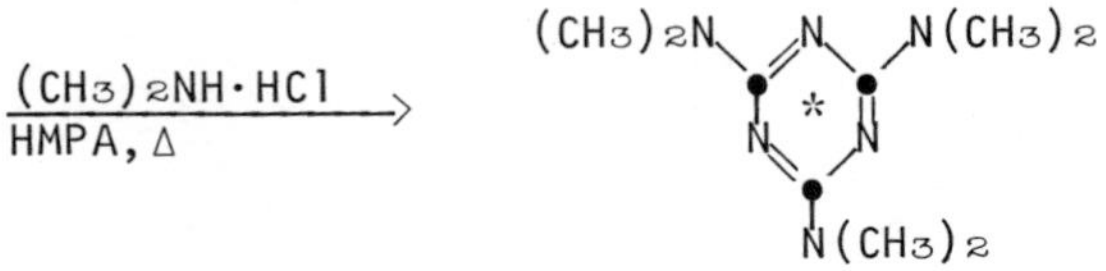
(CH3)2NH·HCl
HMPA, Δ
(CH3)2N
N
N(CH3)2
*
N
N
N(CH3)2

(40%; 18% from urea)

Hexamethylmelamine (Noyau)
[N,N,N',N',N'',N''-Hexamethyl-1,3,5-triazine-2,4,6-triamine-(ring-^{14}C)]

Nguyen-Hoang-Nam, E. Hoellinger, and L. Pichat, J. Label. Compound. Radiopharm., 12, 517 (1976).

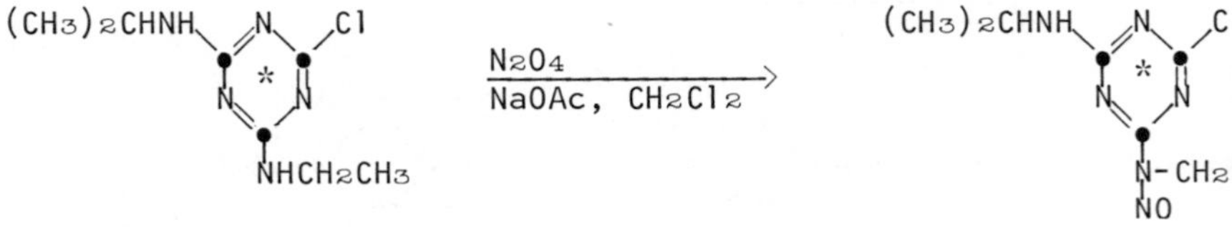
(CH3)2CHNH
N
Cl
*
N
N
NHCH2CH3
N2O4
NaOAc, CH2Cl2
(CH3)2CHNH
N
Cl
*
N
N
N-CH2CH3
NO

(49%)

N-Nitrosoatrazine
[2-Chloro-4-(N-nitroso-N-ethylamino)-6-(isopropylamino)-s-triazine-(ring-^{14}C)]

P. C. Kearney, J. E. Oliver, C. S. Helling, A. R. Isensee, and A. Konston, J. Agr. Food Chem., 25, 1177 (1977).

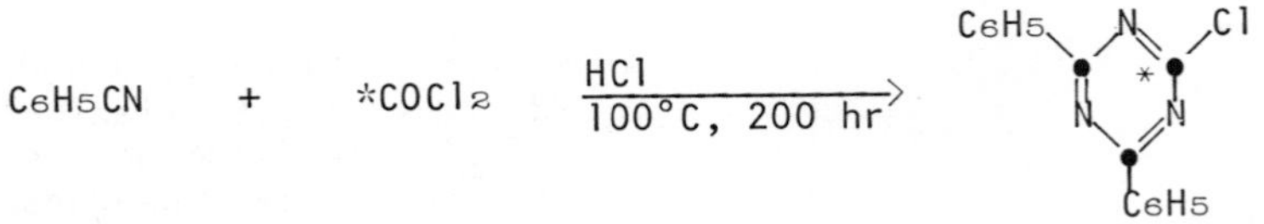
C6H5CN
+
*COCl2
HCl
100°C, 200 hr
C6H5
N
Cl
*
N
N
C6H5

(83%)

2-Chloro-4,6-diphenyl-1,3,5-triazine-2-^{14}C

Radioactivity was found only in the triazine, and it is assumed that the chlorine-bearing carbon in the triazine is labeled.

S. Yanagida, H. Hayama, M. Yokoe, and S. Komori, J. Org. Chem., 34, 4125 (1969)/

$H_2N^*C(=NH)NH^*CN$ (39% from KCN) $\xrightarrow[\text{methylcellosolve, } \Delta]{NCN(CH_2CH=CH_2)_2}$

Cyanoguanidine-^{14}C

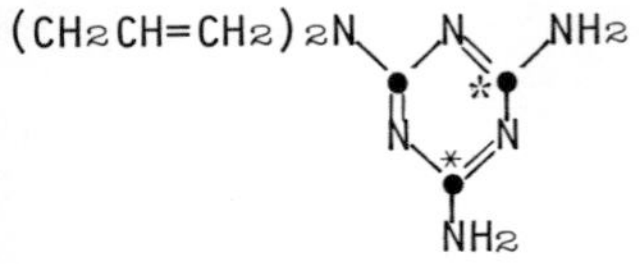

(CH2CH=CH2)2N
N
NH2
N
N
NH2

(67%; 26% overall) $\xrightarrow[\text{EtOH}]{m\text{-Cl-PBA}}$

N^6,N^6-Di-1-propenyl-1,3,5-triazine-2,4,6-triamine-2,4-^{14}C

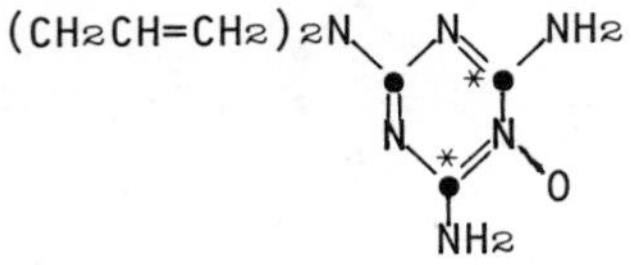

(CH2CH=CH2)2N
N
NH2
N
N
O
NH2

(37%)

N^6,N^6-Di-1-propenyl-1,3,5-triazine-2,4,6-triamine-2,4-^{14}C 3-oxide

R. C. Thomas, J. Label. Compound. Radiopharm., 14, 807 (1978).

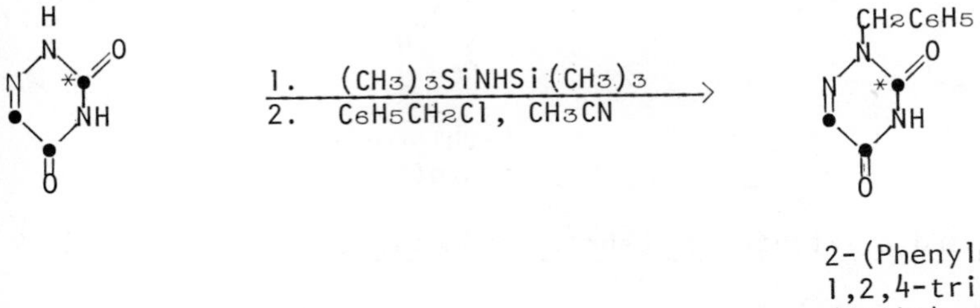

H
N
O
N
NH
O
1. (CH3)3SiNHSi(CH3)3
2. C6H5CH2Cl, CH3CN
CH2C6H5
N
O
N
NH
O

2-(Phenylmethyl)-1,2,4-triazine-3,5(2H,4H)-dione-3-^{14}C

2-[Phenyl(methyl-$^{14}\underline{C}$)]-1,2,4-triazine-3,5(2H,4H)-dione-$\underline{3}$-$^{14}\underline{C}$ was similarly prepared from $C_6H_5{*}CH_2Cl$ and unlabeled 6-azauracil.

B. L. Mylari, M. W. Miller, H. L. Howes, Jr., S. K. Figdor, J. E. Lynch, and R. C. Koth, J. Med. Chem., 20, 475 (1977).

9-16 Bicyclic Compounds

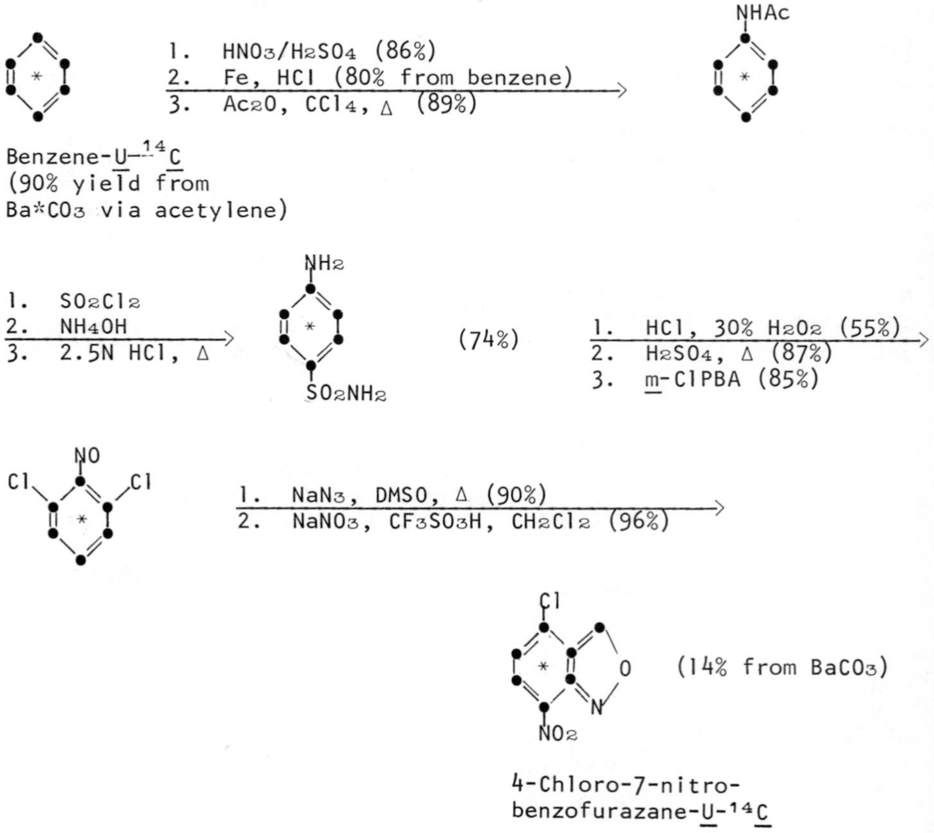
NHAc
1. HNO3/H2SO4 (86%)
2. Fe, HCl (80% from benzene)
3. Ac2O, CCl4, Δ (89%)
Benzene-U-14C
(90% yield from
Ba*CO3 via acetylene)
NH2
1. SO2Cl2
2. NH4OH
3. 2.5N HCl, Δ
SO2NH2
(74%)
1. HCl, 30% H2O2 (55%)
2. H2SO4, Δ (87%)
3. m-ClPBA (85%)
NO
Cl
Cl
1. NaN3, DMSO, Δ (90%)
2. NaNO3, CF3SO3H, CH2Cl2 (96%)
Cl
O
N
NO2
(14% from BaCO3)
4-Chloro-7-nitro-
benzofurazane-U-14C

J.-P. Noel and L. Pichat, J. Label. Compound. Radiopharm., 13, 87 (1977).

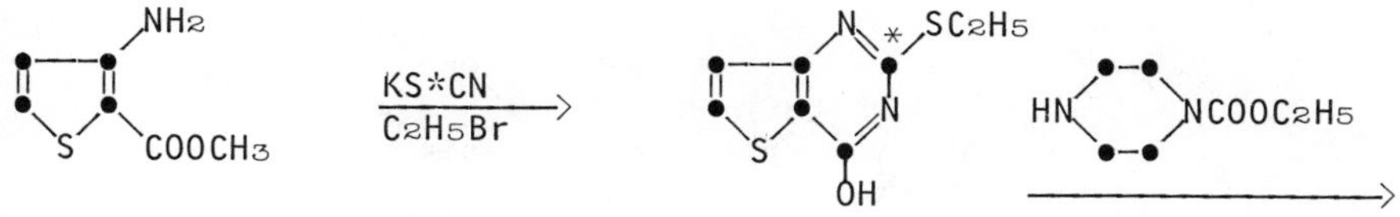
KS*CN
C2H5Br
NH2
COOCH3
SC2H5
OH
HN
NCOOC2H5

(*C is a mixture of ^{13}C and ^{14}C for the simultaneous labeling of the same position for drug metabolism studies.)

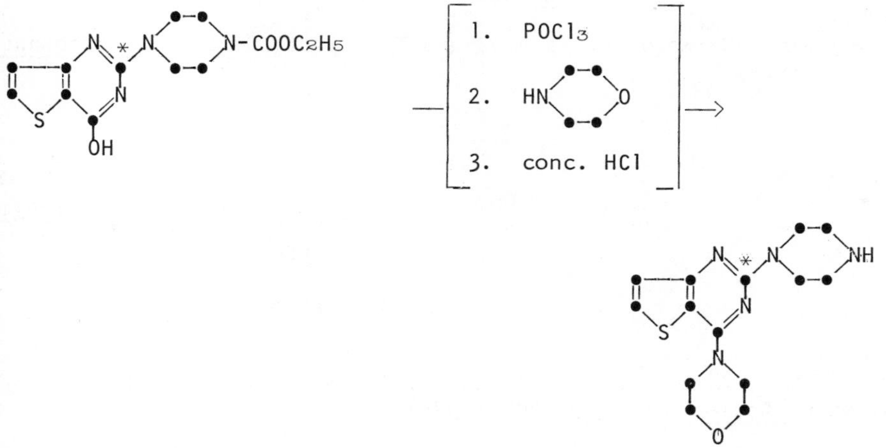
N-COOC2H5
OH
1. POCl3
2. HN O
3. conc. HCl
NH

4-Morpholino-2-piperazinothieno[3,2d]pyrimidine-2-^{14}C (V-K 774)

A. Zimmer, A. Prox, H. Pelzer, and R. Hankwitz, Biochem. Pharmacol., 22, 2213 (1973).

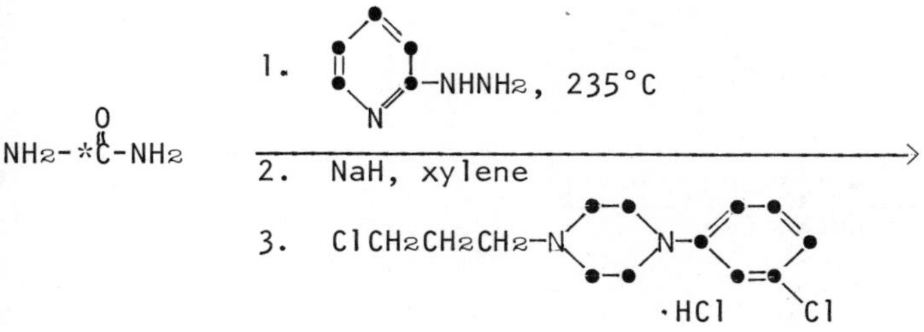
NH2-*C-NH2
1. -NHNH2, 235°C
2. NaH, xylene
3. ClCH2CH2CH2-N N-
·HCl
Cl

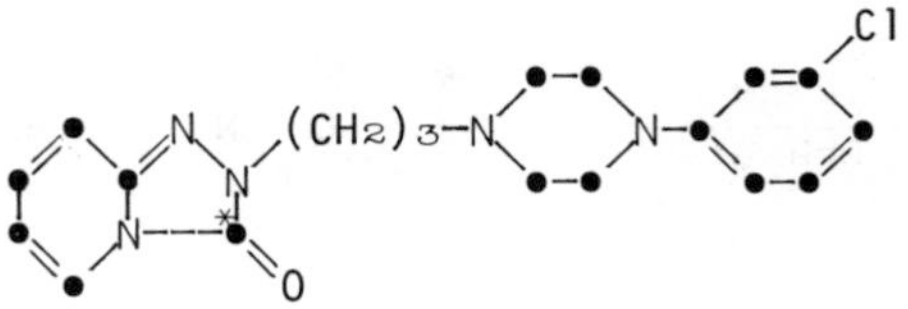
Cl
N
(CH2)3-N
N
N
N
O

(37% from urea)

Trazodone
[2-[3-[4-(3-Chlorophenyl)-1-piperazinyl]-propyl]1,2,4-triazolo[4,3-a]pyridin-3(2H)-one-3-^{14}C hydrochloride]

K. Sugiyama, S. Kono, C. Yamato, and T. Fujita, J. Label. Compounds, 9, 723 (1973).

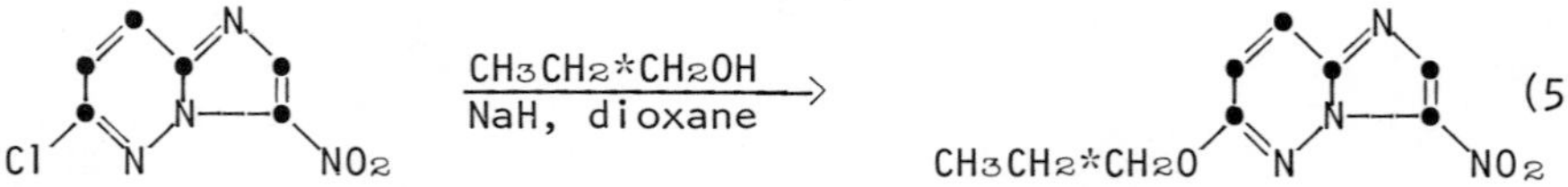
Cl
N
N
N
NO2
CH3CH2*CH2OH
NaH, dioxane
CH3CH2*CH2O
N
N
N
NO2

(58%)

3-Nitro-6-(propoxy-1-^{14}C) imidazo[1,2b]pyridazine

P. F. Fabio, A. E. Lanzilotti, and S. A. Lang, Jr., J. Label. Compound. Radiopharm., 15, 407 (1978).

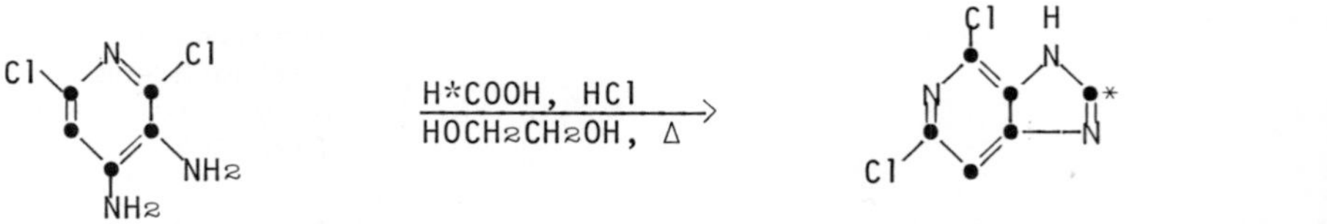
Cl
N
Cl
NH2
NH2
H*COOH, HCl
HOCH2CH2OH, Δ
Cl
H
N
N
N
Cl

4,6-Dichloro-3H-imidazo [4,5c]pyridine-2-^{14}C

J. A. Montgomery and H. J. Thomas, J. Label. Compound. Radiopharm., 15, 539 (1978).

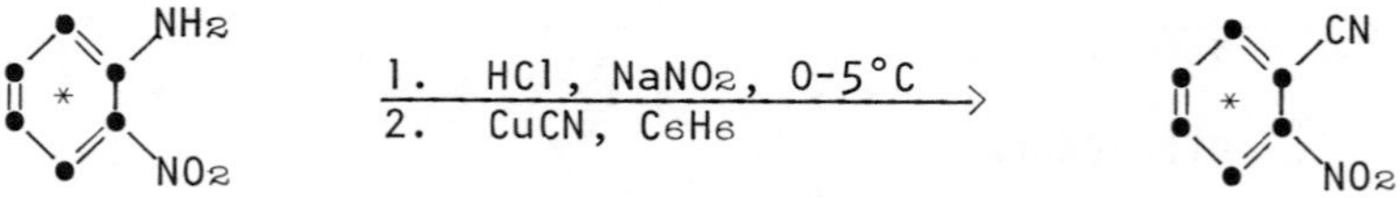
NH2
NO2
1. HCl, NaNO2, 0-5°C
2. CuCN, C6H6
CN
NO2

o-Nitroaniline-U-^{14}C

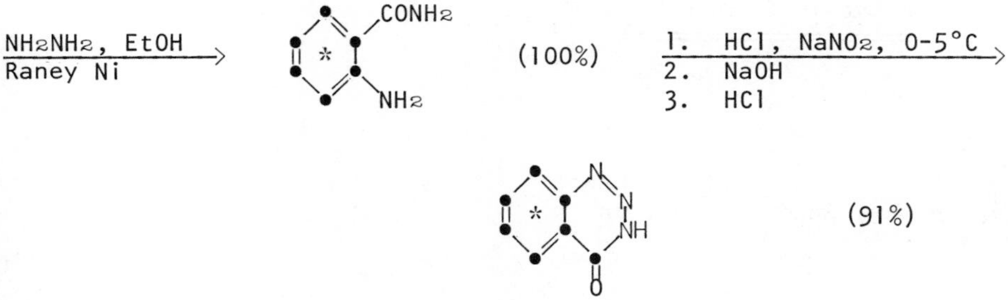
NH2NH2, EtOH
Raney Ni
CONH2
NH2
(100%)
1. HCl, NaNO2, 0-5°C
2. NaOH
3. HCl
N
N
NH
O
(91%)

1,2,3-Benzotriazin-4(3H)-one-(ring-^{14}C)

E. R. White, K. M. Al-Adil, W. L. Winterlin, and W. W. Kilgore, J. Agr. Food Chem., 20, 1184 (1972).

Compounds With Four Heteroatoms

9-17 Five-Membered Rings

H2N-*CN + HN3
H
N
NH2
N
N
N

1H-Tetrazol-5-amine-5-^{14}C

S. Kammula and P. B. Shevlin, J. Amer. Chem. Soc., 96, 7830 (1974); see also N. H. Nam, N. D. Xuong, M. Herbert, and L. Pichat, J. Label. Compounds, 2, 57 (1966).

9-18 Bicyclic Compounds

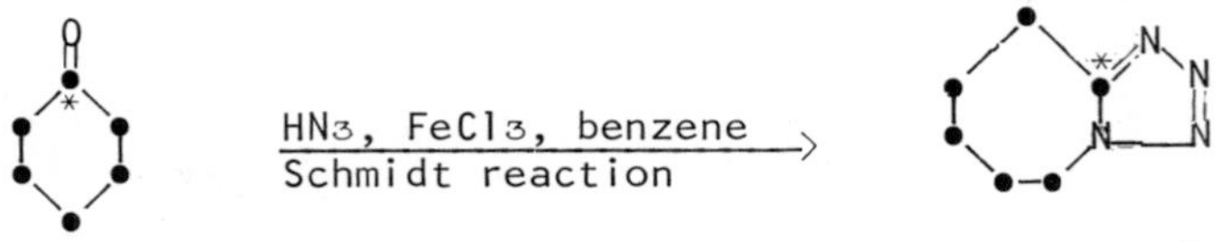
HN3, FeCl3, benzene
Schmidt reaction

Tetrazolo[1,5a]azepine-<u>9a</u>-^{14}<u>C</u>

J. F. Stiver, J. B. Data and J. E. Christian, <u>J. Label. Compounds</u>, <u>6</u>, 40 (1970).

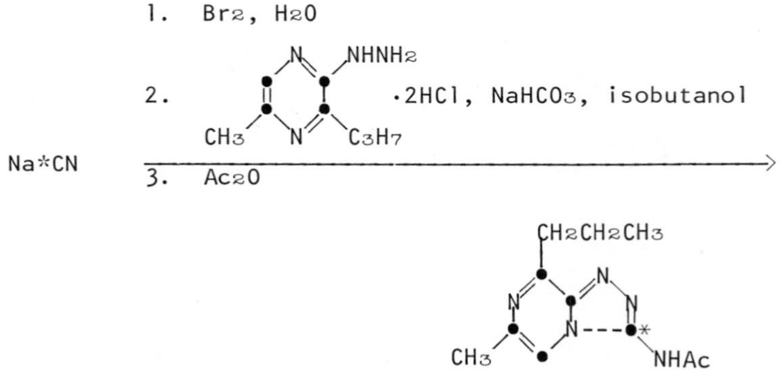
1. Br2, H2O
2. ·2HCl, NaHCO3, isobutanol
CH3
C3H7
Na*CN
3. Ac2O
CH2CH2CH3
NHAc
CH3

(26%)

N-(6-Methyl-8-propyl-1,2,4-triazolo[4,3a]pyrazin-3-yl-<u>3</u>-^{14}<u>C</u>) acetamide

D. F. White and J. Burns, <u>J. Label. Compounds</u>, <u>11</u>, 171 (1975).

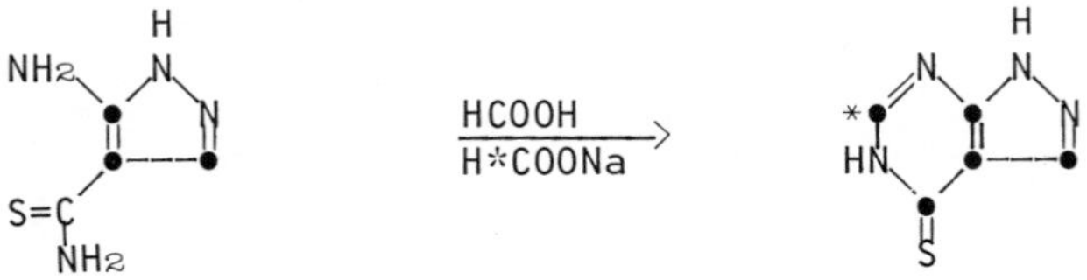
HCOOH
H*COONa

1,5-Dihydro-4H-pyrazolo [3,4d]pyrimidine-4-thione-<u>6</u>-^{14}<u>C</u>

R. Bovara, R. Largaiolli, and G. Meroni, <u>J. Label. Compounds</u>, <u>7</u>, 357 (1971).

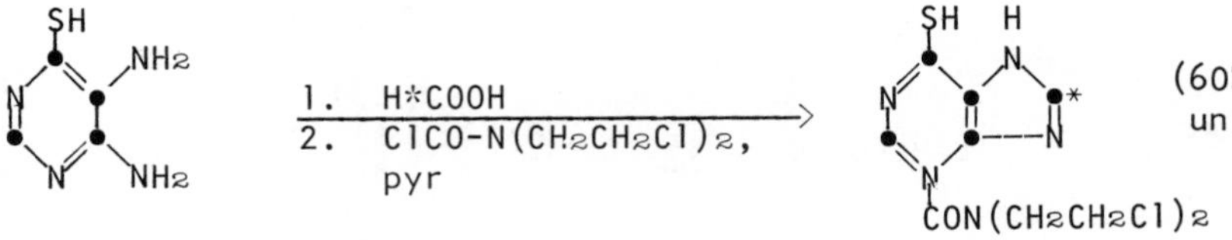
SH
NH2
NH2
1. H*COOH
2. ClCO-N(CH2CH2Cl)2,
pyr
SH H
CON(CH2CH2Cl)2

(60% for unlabeled)

3-[Bis(2-chloroethyl)-carbamoyl]-3,6-dihydropurin-6-thione-8-^{14}C

W. Schulze, G. Letsch, and D. Tresselt, Pharmazie, 30, 498 (1975).

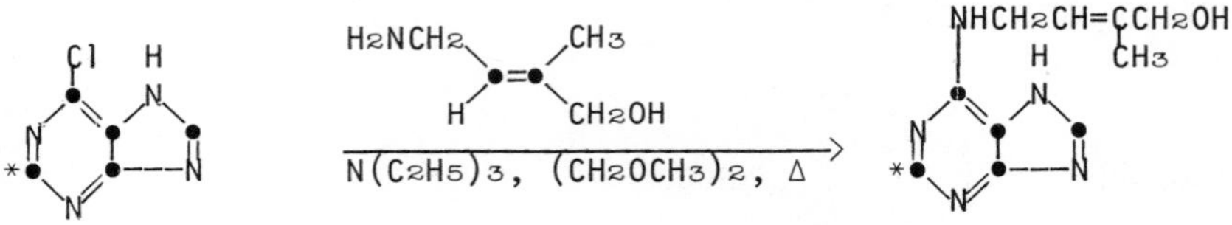
Cl H
H2NCH2
CH3
H
CH2OH
N(C2H5)3, (CH2OCH3)2, Δ
NHCH2CH=CCH2OH
H CH3

(60%)

6-Chloro-1H-purine-2-^{14}C

Zeatin [(E)-2-Methyl-4-(1H-purin-6-ylamino)-2-buten-1-ol-2-^{14}C]

D. S. Letham and H. Young, Phytochemistry, 10, 2077 (1971).

$(CH_3)_2C{=}CH^{*}CH_2NH_2 \cdot HCl$ —6-chloropurine / $(C_2H_5)_3N$, C_4H_9OH→

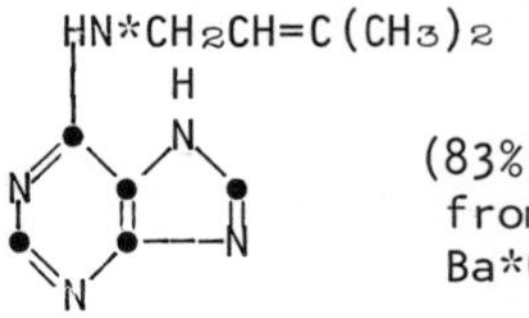
HN*CH2CH=C(CH3)2
H

(83%; 14% from Ba*CO$_3$)

N-(3-Methyl-2-butenyl-1-^{14}C)1H-purin-6-amine

Nguyen-Van-Bac, M. Herbert, Nguyen-Hoang-Nam, L. Pichat, and Nguyen-Dat-Xuong, J. Label. Compounds, 7, 319 (1971).

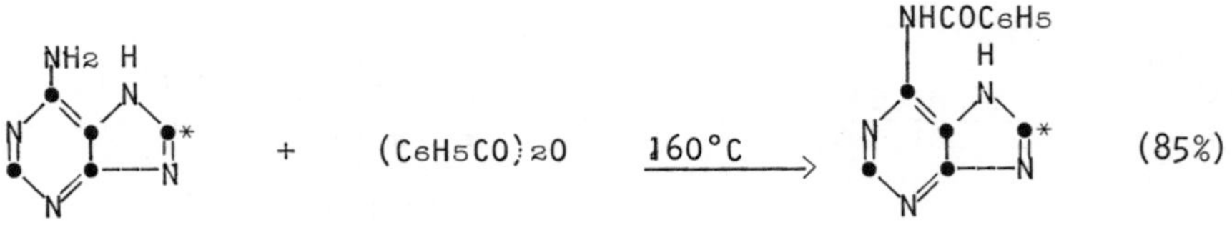

NH2 H
+
(C6H5CO)2O
160°C
NHCOC6H5
H
(85%)

Adenine
[1H-Purin-6-amine-8-^{14}C]

N^6-Benzoyladenine-8-^{14}C
[6-N-Benzoyladenine-8-^{14}C]

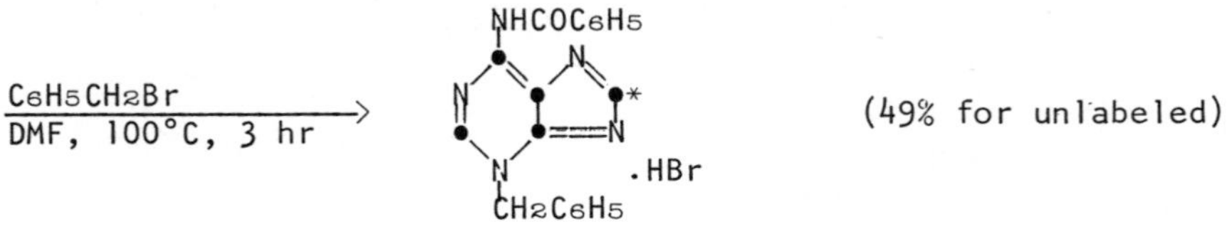

C6H5CH2Br
DMF, 100°C, 3 hr
NHCOC6H5
·HBr
CH2C6H5
(49% for unlabeled)

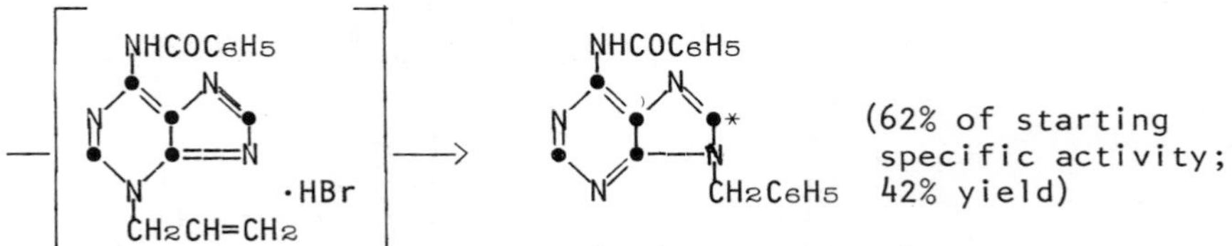

NHCOC6H5
·HBr
CH2CH=CH2
DMF, Δ
NHCOC6H5
CH2C6H5
(62% of starting specific activity; 42% yield)

N-[9-(Phenylmethyl)-9H-purin-6-yl-8-^{14}C]-benzamide

plus

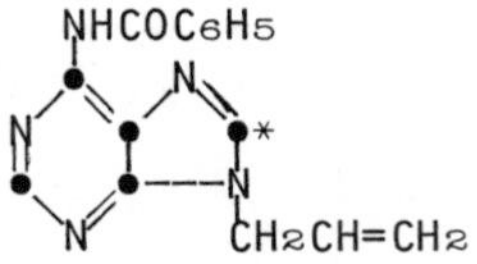

NHCOC6H5
CH2CH=CH2

N-[9-(3-propenyl)-9H-purin-6-yl-8-^{14}C] benzamide

Labeling results suggest that benzyl and allyl migration are intermolecular.

B. Shimizu and M. Miyaki, Chem. Pharm. Bull., Tokyo, 18, 570 (1970).

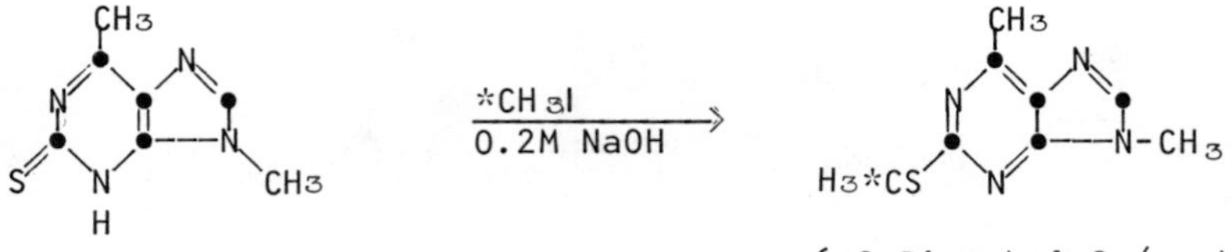

(85%)

6,9-Dimethyl-2-(methyl-^{14}C-thio)purine

D. J. Brown, R. L. Jones, A. M. Angyal and G. W. Grigg, J. Chem. Soc., Perkin Trans. I, 1819 (1972).

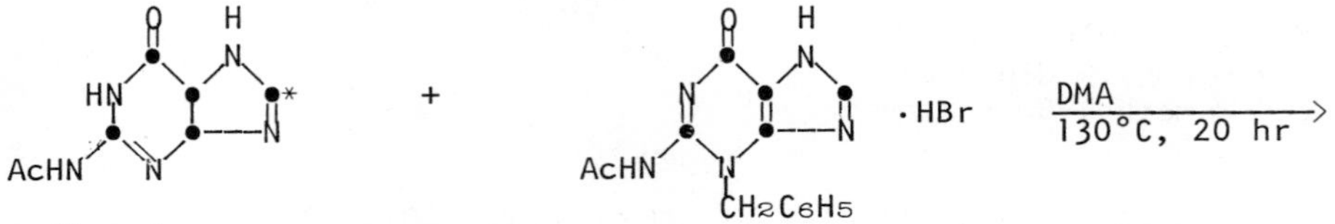

N-(4,5,6,7-Tetrahydro-6-oxo-1H-purin-8-^{14}C-2-yl)acetamide

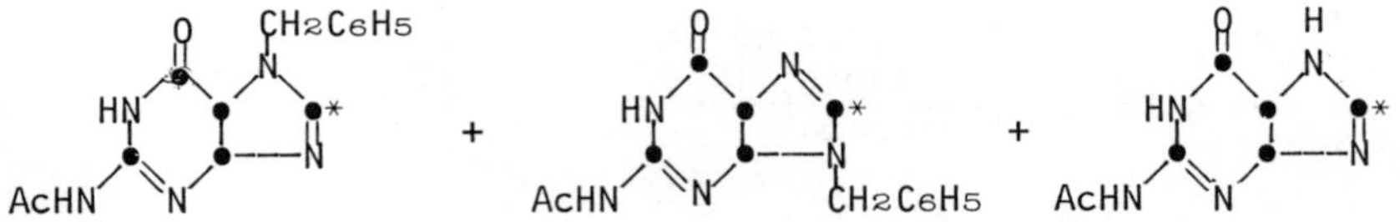

N-[4,5,6,7-Dihydro-6-oxo-7-(phenylmethyl)-1H-purin-2-yl-8-^{14}C] acetamide (28% recovery with specific activity 53% of starting material

N-[4,5,6,9-Tetrahydro 6-oxo-9-(phenylmethyl)-1H-purin-2-yl-8-^{14}C] acetamide (59% recovery with specific activity 46% of starting material)

N-[4,5,6,7-Tetrahydro-6-oxo-1H-purin-2-yl-8-^{14}C]acetamide (30% recovery with specific activity 56% of starting material)

Results suggested benzyl migration to be intermolecular.

M. Miyaki and B. Shimizu, Chem. Pharm. Bull., Tokyo, 18, 1446 (1970).

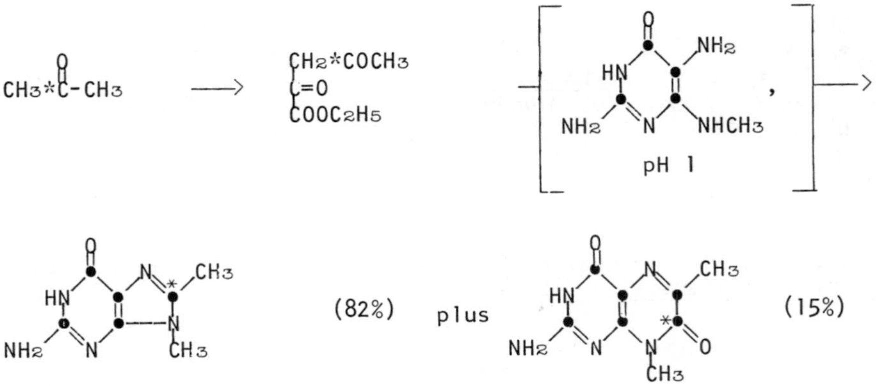
CH3*C-CH3
CH2*COCH3
C=O
COOC2H5
NH2
HN
NH2
N
NHCH3
pH 1
CH3
HN
NH2
N
N
CH3
(82%)
plus
CH3
HN
NH2
N
N
O
CH3
(15%)

8,9-Dimethylguanine
[2-Amino-1,9-dihydro-8,9-dimethyl-6H-purin-6-one-8-^{14}C]

G. B. Barlin and W. Pfleiderer, Chem. Ber., 102, 4032 (1969).

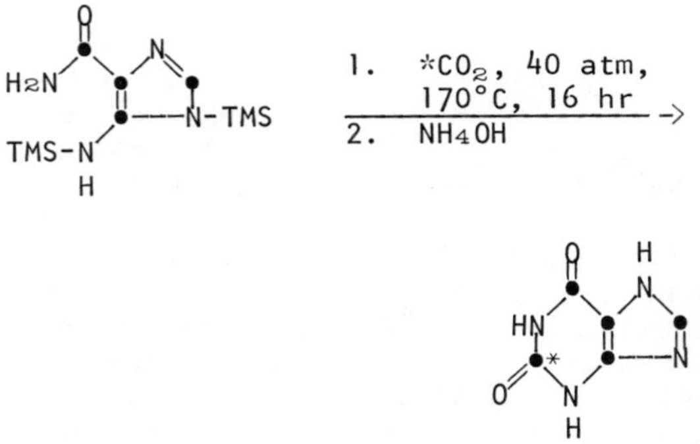
H2N
N-TMS
TMS-N
H
1. *CO2, 40 atm, 170°C, 16 hr
2. NH4OH
H
HN
N
O
N
H

(65% of *CO_2 recovered, 80% yield based on *CO_2 consumed)

Xanthine
[3,7-Dihydro-1H-purine-2,6-dione-2-^{14}C]

L. Pichat, B. Masse, and P. Dufay, C. R. Acad. Sc., Paris, Ser. C., 269, 1408 (1969).

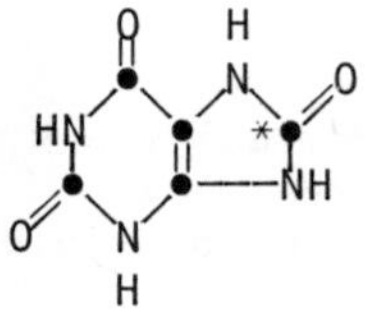

$(CH_3)_3N \cdot HCOOH$ →

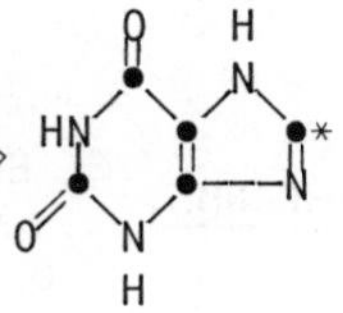

(label presumably at position 8)

Uric acid
[7,9-Dihydro-1H-purine-2,6,8(3H)-trione-8-^{14}C]

Xanthine-8-^{14}C

S. Takayama, F. Ashizawa, J. Suzuki, and M. Sekiya, Chem. Pharm. Bull. (Tokyo), 22, 1200 (1974).

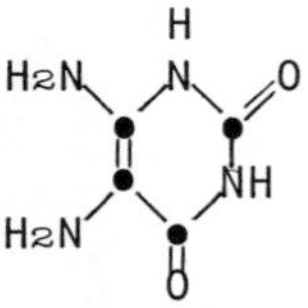

H*COOH
H_2O, Δ
→

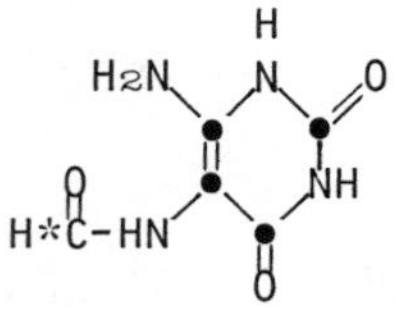

4-Amino-5-(formamido-^{14}C)uracil

1. $(CH_3O)_2SO_2$, 6M NaOH, pH 8.5-9, 25-35°C
2. 6M NaOH, 100°C
→

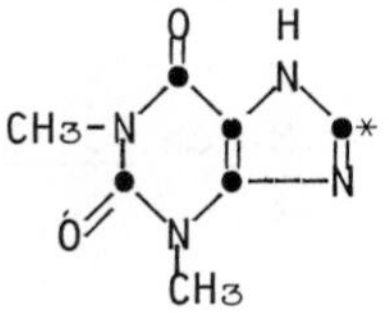

(61% chemical yield; 20% radiochemical yield)

Theophylline
[3,7-Dihydro-1,3-dimethyl-1H-purine-2,6-dione-8-^{14}C]

$(MeO)_2SO_2$
6M NaOH, 80°C
→

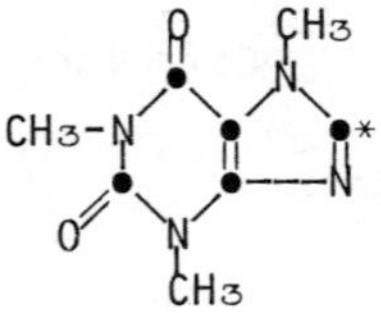

(95%)

Caffeine
[3,7-Dihydro-1,3,7-trimethyl-1H-purine-2,6-dione-8-^{14}C]

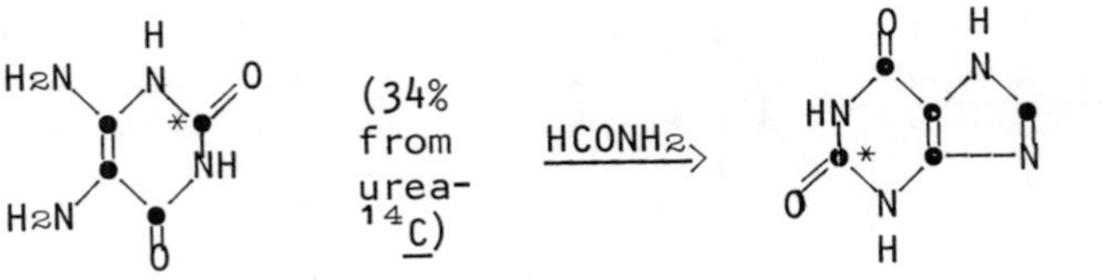
H
H_2N
O
NH
H_2N
O
(34%
from
urea-
^{14}C)
$HCONH_2$
O
H
HN
N
N
O
N
H

(36% chemical yield from urea; 32% radiochemical yield from urea)

Xanthine-2-^{14}C

Reaction of xanthine-2-^{14}C with methyl sulfate in 2% aq. NaOH/MeOH gave a reaction mixture having the approximate composition of: xanthine-2-^{14}C (26%) 3-methylxanthine-2-^{14}C (2%); theobromine-2-^{14}C (8%); theophylline-2-^{14}C (2%); caffeine-2-^{14}C (60%). All products were separable in pure form by chromatography. Pure caffeine-2-^{14}C was isolated in 45% yield.

G. Ayrey and M. A. Yeomans, J. Label. Compound. Radiopharm., 12, 323 (1976).

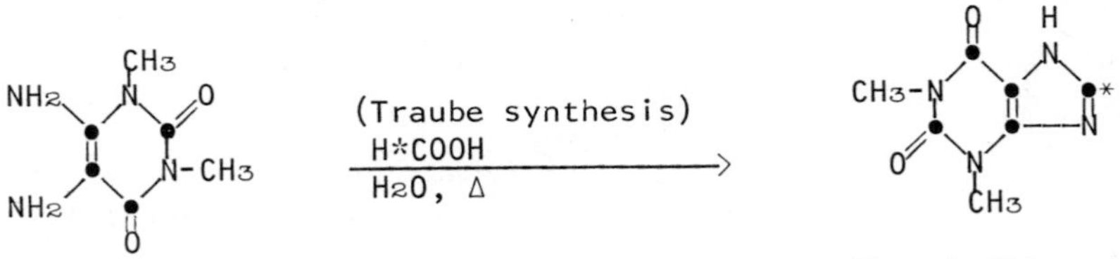
CH_3
NH_2
O
N-CH_3
NH_2
O
(Traube synthesis)
H*COOH
H_2O, Δ
O
H
CH_3-N
N
O
N
CH_3

Theophylline-8-^{14}C

S. M. Lohmann and R. P. Miech, J. Label. Compounds, 11, 515 (1975).

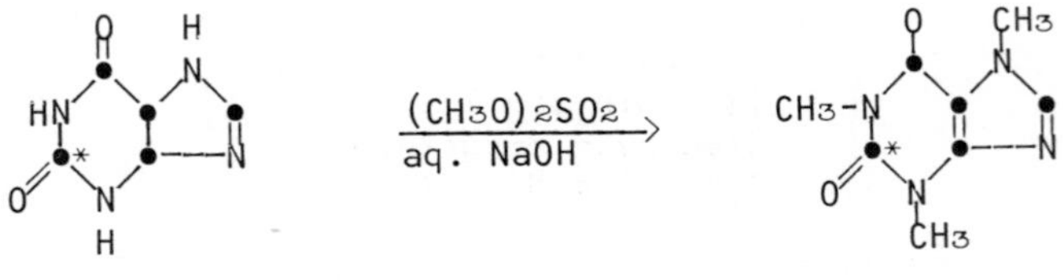
O
H
HN
N
O
N
H
$(CH_3O)_2SO_2$
aq. NaOH
O
CH_3
CH_3-N
N
O
N
CH_3

(73% yield)

Xanthine-2-^{14}C

Caffeine-2-^{14}C

E. Heftmann, J. Label. Compounds, 7, 463 (1971).

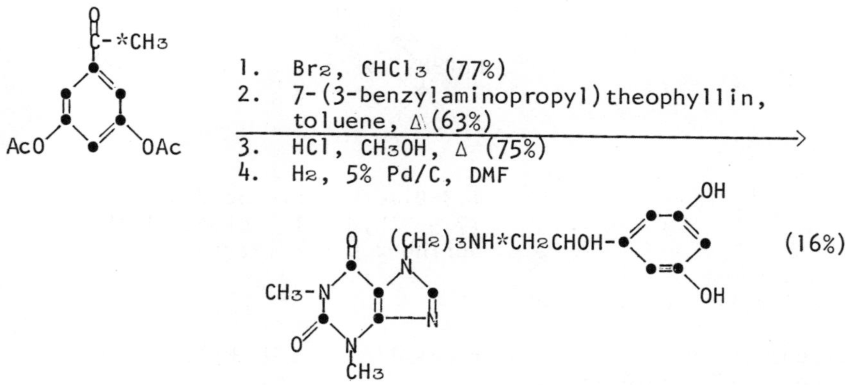
C-*CH3
AcO
OAc
1. Br2, CHCl3 (77%)
2. 7-(3-benzylaminopropyl)theophyllin, toluene, Δ (63%)
3. HCl, CH3OH, Δ (75%)
4. H2, 5% Pd/C, DMF
(CH2)3NH*CH2CHOH-
OH
OH
CH3-N
CH3
(16%)

Reproterol
[7-[3-[[2-(3,5-Dihydroxyphenyl-2-hydroxyethyl)amino]-1-^{14}C]-propyl]-3,7-dihydro-1,3-dimethyl-1H-purine-2,6-dione hydrochloride]

A. Saus, K. H. Klingler, and E. Bickel, Arzneim.-Forsch.-(Drug. Res.), 27, 35 (1977).

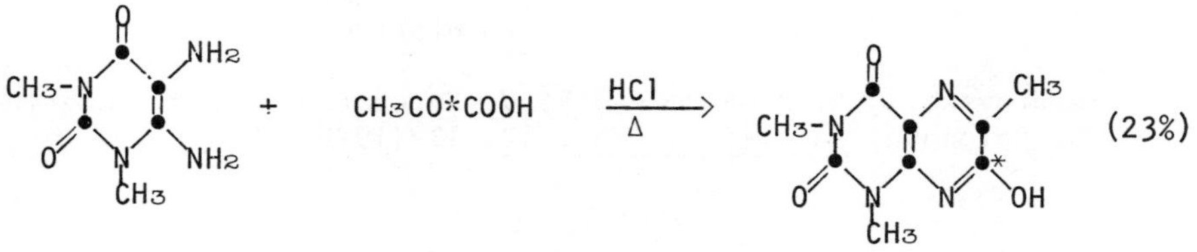
CH3-N
NH2
NH2
CH3
+
CH3CO*COOH
HCl
Δ
CH3
OH
(23%)

7-Hydroxy-1,3,6-trimethyllumazine-7-[14]C

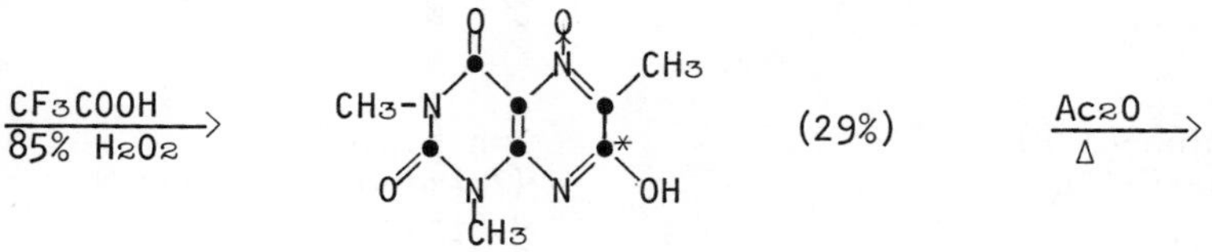
CF3COOH
85% H2O2
CH3-N
CH3
OH
(29%)
Ac2O
Δ

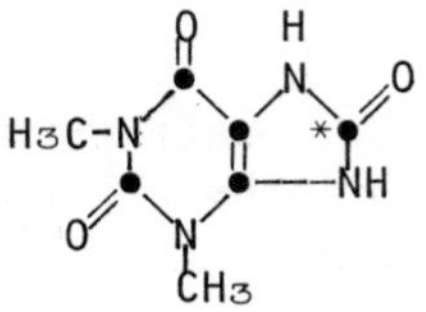

(35%)

1,3-Dimethyluric acid
[7,9-Dihydro-1,3-dimethyl-1H-purine-2,6,8(3H)-trione-6-^{14}C]

A mechanism is proposed.

W. Hutzenlaub, H. Yamamoto, G. B. Barlin, and W. Pfleiderer, Chem. Ber., 106, 3203 (1973).

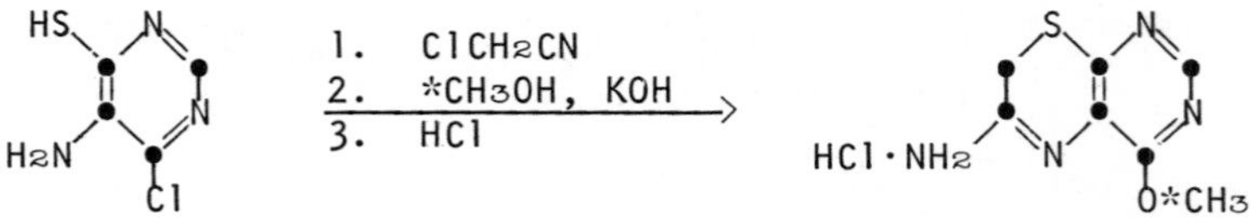

Tomizine
[4-Methoxy-^{14}C-7H-pyrimido [4,5b][1,4]thiazin-6-amine hydrochloride]

V. A. Yardrovskaya, G. K. Korolev, V. V. Kurchatova, M. P. Nemeryuk, and T. S. Safonova, Khim.-Farm. Zh., 12, 12 (1978).

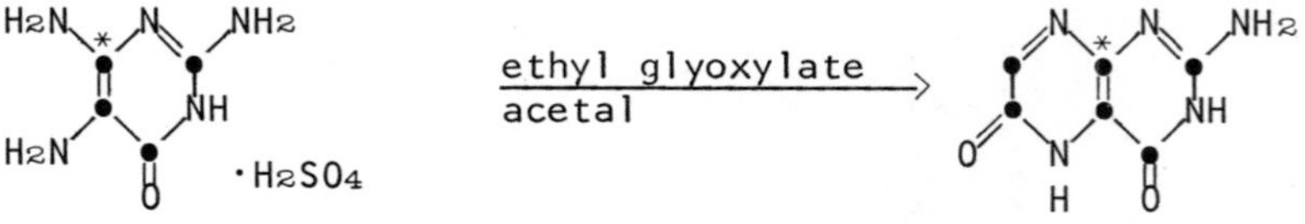

(56%)

2,5,6-Triamino-4(3H)-pyrimidinone-6-^{14}C sulfate

Xanthopterin
(2-Amino-1,5-dihydro-4,6-pteridinedione-8a-^{14}C)

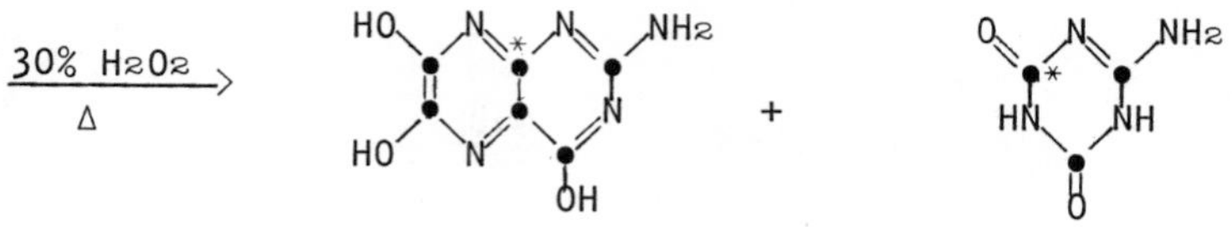
30% H_2O_2
Δ

(∿10%)

Leucopterin
[2-Amino-5,8-dihydro-4,6,7(1H)-pteridinetrione]
(label presumed to be at position 8a)

Melanurenic acid
[6-Amino-1,3,5-triazine-2,4(1H,3H)-dione-2-^{14}C]

A mechanism is proposed.

G. B. Barlin and W. Pfleiderer, Chem. Ber., 104, 3069 (1971).

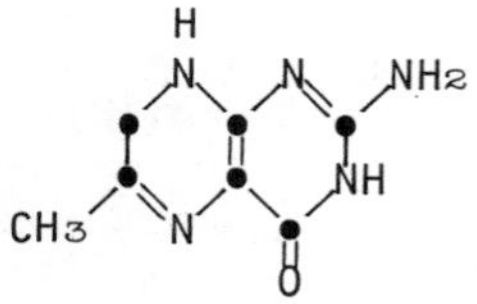

1. K*CN (5.5%)
2. acetylation
3. reduction } (17%)
4. deacetylation

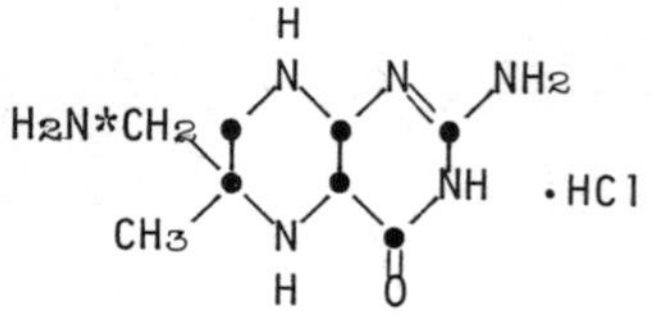

O_2, pH 6.8 →

2-Amino-6-(aminomethyl-^{14}C)-4a,5,6,7,8,8a-hexahydro-6-methyl-4(3H)-pteridinone hydrochloride

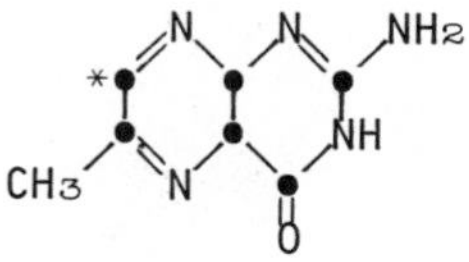

(45% chemical yield; 11.5% radiochemical yield)

2-Amino-6-methyl-4(3H)-pteridinone-7-^{14}C

Two pathways to the product are proposed.

M. Viscontini and M. Argentini, Helv. Chim. Acta, 54, 2287 (1971).

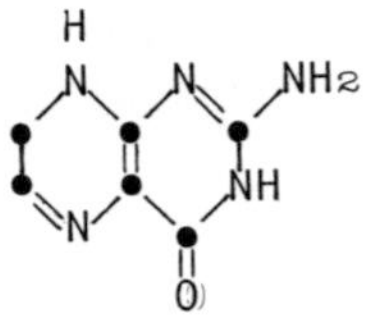
H
N
N
NH2
NH
N
O

+ *$CH_3COCHOHCOOH$ —NaOH, pH 11.5→

2-Hydroxy-3-oxobutanoic-4-^{14}C acid

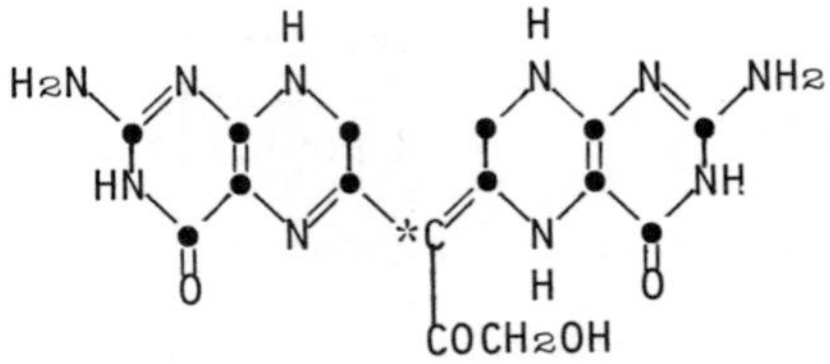
H
H
H2N
N
N
N
N
NH2
HN
NH
N
*C
N
O
H
O
COCH2OH

Droso- and isodrosopterin [2-Amino-6-[1-(2-amino-1,4,7,8-tetrahydro-4-oxo-6-pteridinyl)-3-hydroxy-2-oxopropylidene-1-^{14}C]-5,6,7,8-tetrahydro-4(1H)-pteridinone]

The mixture was oxidized with H_2O_2/1N NaOH to pterin-6-carboxylic-^{14}C acid.

H. Schlobach and W. Pfleiderer, Helv. Chim. Acta, 55, 2533 (1973); see also K. Sugiura and M. Goto, Tetrahedron Lett., 1187 (1973).

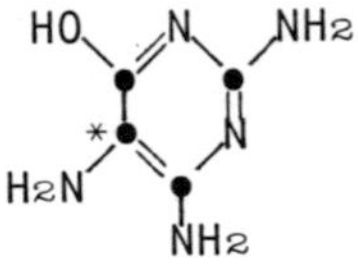
HO
N
NH2
*
N
H2N
NH2

(3% from Na*CN) —$CHO\text{-}COOC_2H_5$→

2,4,5-Triamino-6-pyrimidinol-5-^{14}C

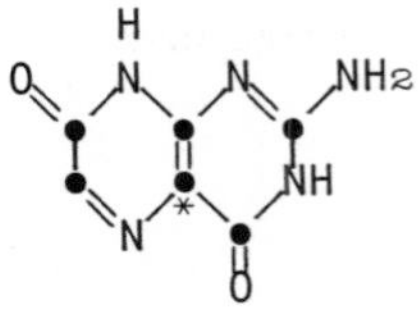
H
O
N
N
NH2
NH
N
*
O

Isoxanthopterin (2-Amino-4,7(1H,8H)-pteridinedione-4a-^{14}C)

Isoxanthopterin-7-^{14}C was prepared in a similar manner using ethyl glyoxylate-(carboxyl-^{14}C).

E. Shaw, C. M. Baugh, and C. L. Krumdieck, J. Biol. Chem., 241, 379 (1966); E. L. Bennett, J. Amer. Chem. Soc., 74, 2420 (1952).

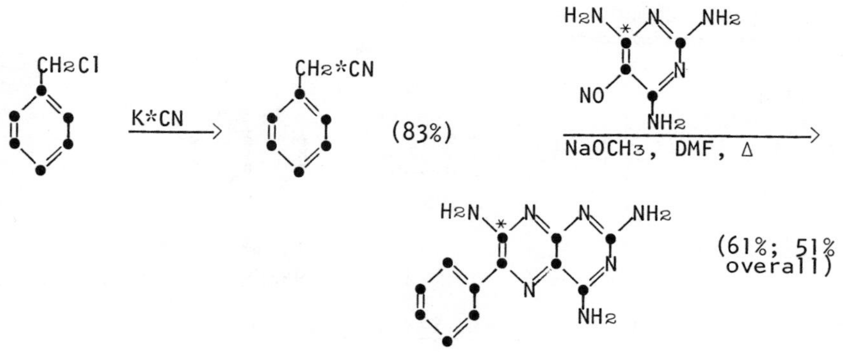

6-Phenylpteridine-2,4,7-triamine-7-^{14}C

D. Blackburn and G. Burghard, J. Label. Compounds, 2, 62 (1966).

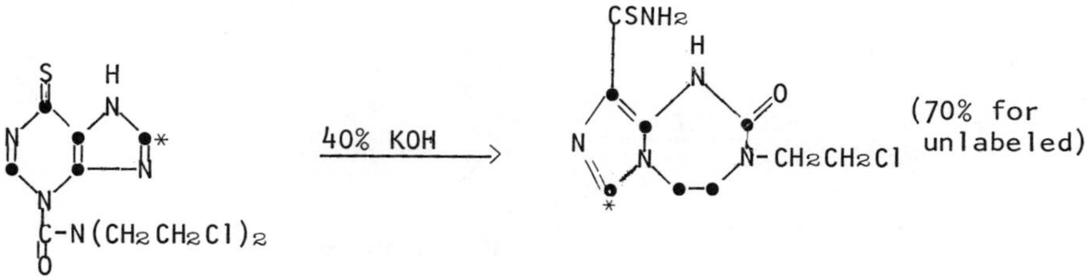

3-[Bis(2-chloroethyl)carbamoyl]-3,6-dihydropurin-6-9(H)-thione-8-^{14}C

3-(2-Chloroethyl)-2,3,4,5-tetrahydro-2-oxo-1H-imidazo-[1,5a][1,3,5]triazepine-7-^{14}C-9-carbothioamide

W. Schulze, G. Letsch, and D. Tresselt, Pharmazie, 30, 498 (1975).

9-19 Tricyclic Compounds

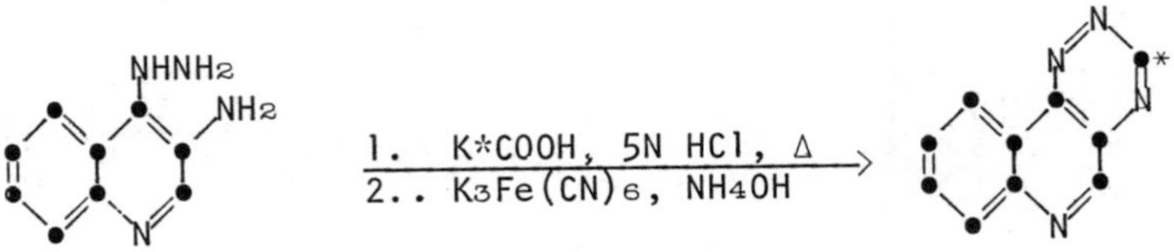

NHNH2
NH2
1. K*COOH, 5N HCl, Δ
2.. K3Fe(CN)6, NH4OH
N

(67%)

1,2,4-Triazino[5,6c] quinoline-3-^{14}C

C. Zólyomo and E. Berényi, Chem. Ber., 109, 2338 (1976).

Compounds With Five Heteroatoms

9-20 Polycyclic Compounds

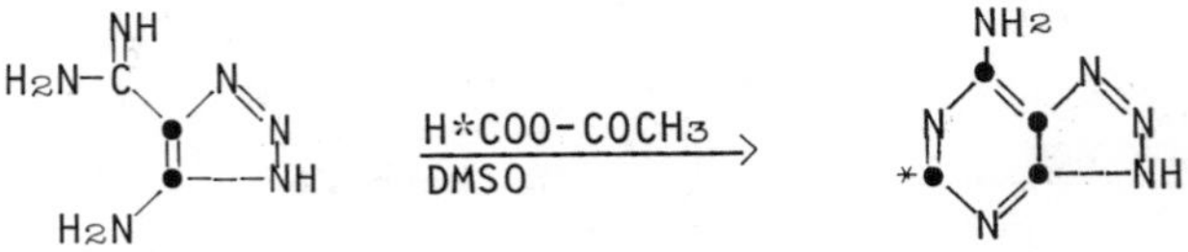

NH
H2N-C
H2N
NH
H*COO-COCH3
DMSO
NH2

(77%)

8-Azadenine
[1H-1,2,3-Triazolo [4,5d]pyrimido-7-amine-5-^{14}C]

J. A. Montgomery and H. J. Thomas, J. Label. Compound. Radiopharm., 15, 727 (1978).

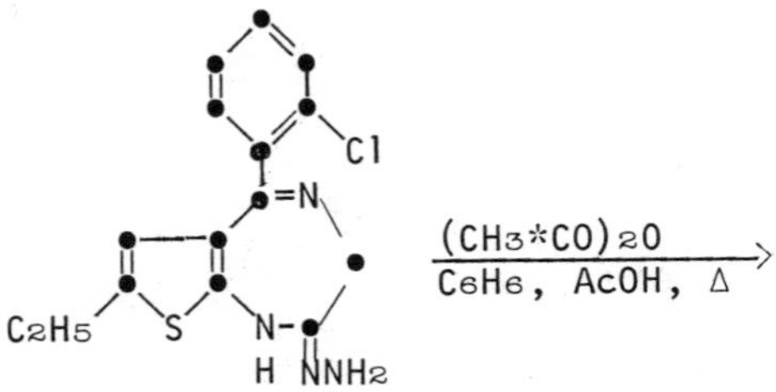

Cl
C2H5
S
H NNH2
(CH3*CO)2O
C6H6, AcOH, Δ

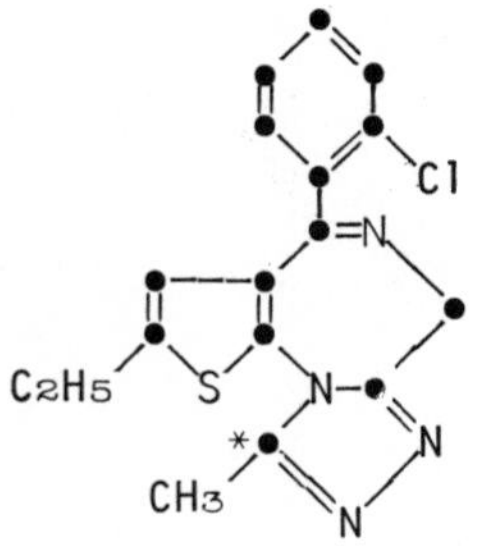

(∿40%)

4-(2-Chlorophenyl)-2-ethyl-9-methyl-6H-thieno[3,2f][1,2,4]triazolo[4,3a][1,4]diazepine-9-^{14}C

Y. Kato and H. Nishimine, Arzneim.-Forsch.-(Drug Res.), 28, (II) 1170 (1978).

10

Carbohydrates

10-1 Pentoses

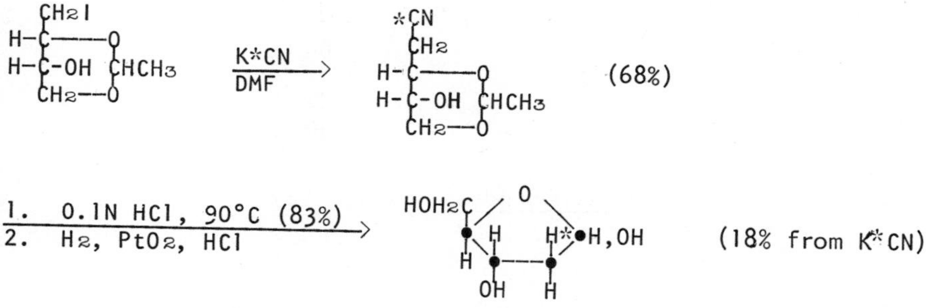

2-Deoxy-D-ribose-1-^{14}C

R. J. Bayly and J.C. Turner, J.Chem. Soc. (C), 704 (1966); for a similar procedure, see V. Soukupová and K. Vereš, J. Label. Compounds, 7, 213 (1971).

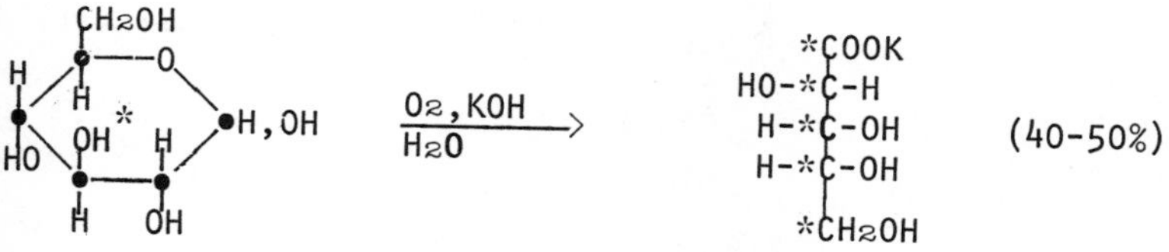

D-Glucose-U-^{14}C

D-Arabinonic acid monopotassium salt-U-^{14}C

J. C. Turner, J. Label. Compounds, 3, 217 (1967).

10-2 Glucose Derivatives

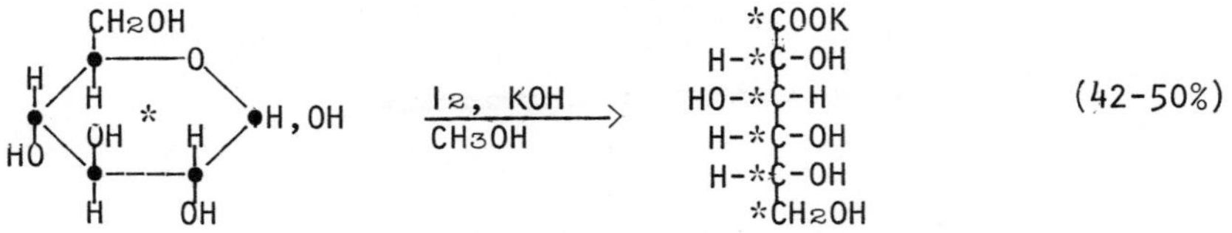
I2, KOH
CH3OH
(42-50%)

D-Glucose-U-^{14}C

D-Gluconic acid monopotassium salt-U-^{14}C

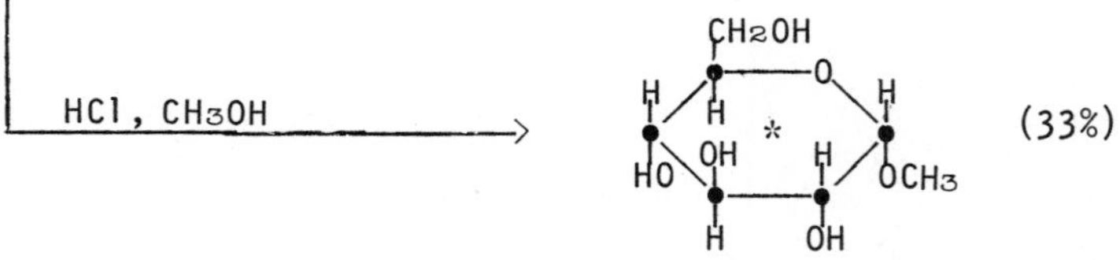
HCl, CH3OH
(33%)

Methyl-α-D-glucopyranoside-U-^{14}C

J. C. Turner, J. Label. Compounds, 3, 217 (1967).

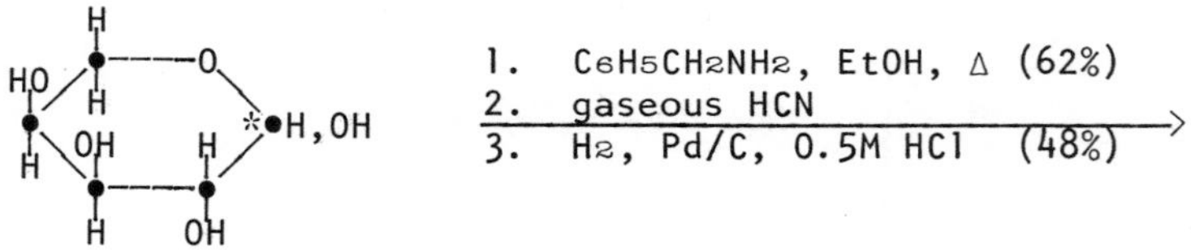
1. C6H5CH2NH2, EtOH, Δ (62%)
2. gaseous HCN
3. H2, Pd/C, 0.5M HCl (48%)

L-Arabinose-1-^{14}C

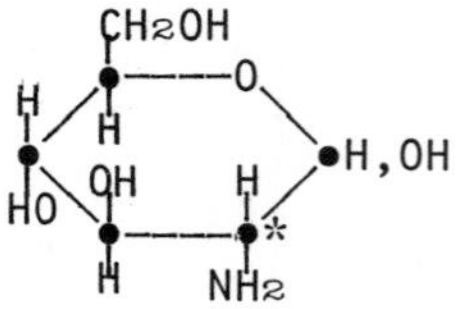

(30% overall)

2-Amino-2-deoxy-D-glucose-2-^{14}C hydrochloride

U. Hornemann, Carbohyd. Res., 28, 171 (1973).

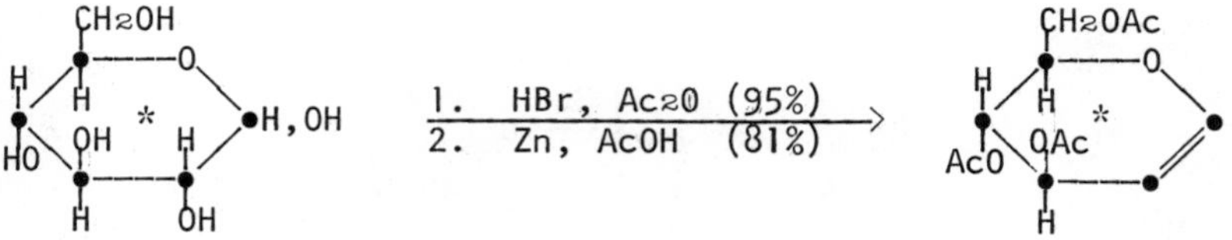

D-Glucose-U-^{14}C

1,2-Dideoxy-D-gluco-hex-1-enopyranose triacetate-U-^{14}C (3,4,6-tri-O-acetylglucal)

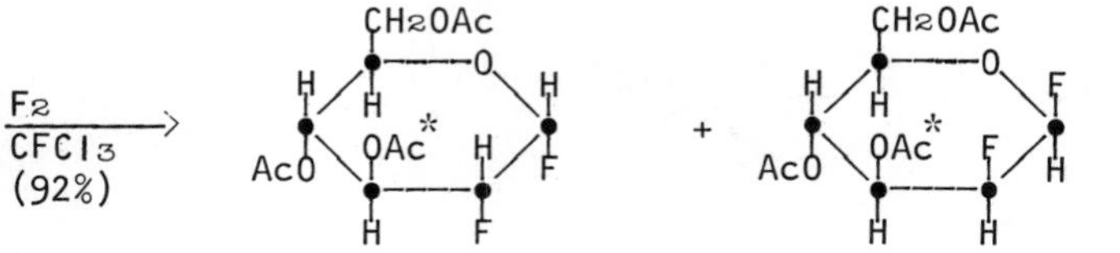

(92% yield total; separated in the ratio of 2:5, respectively)

2-Deoxy-2-fluoro-α-D glucopyranosyl fluoride triacetate-U-^{14}C

2-Deoxy-2-fluoro-β-D-mannopyranosyl fluoride triacetate-U-^{14}C

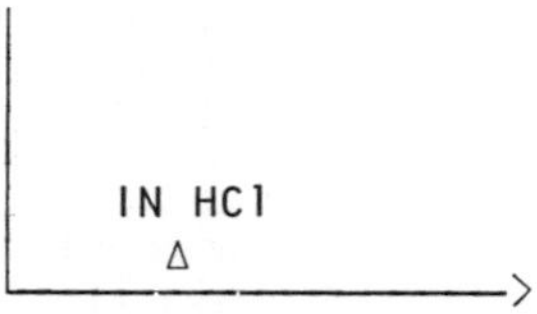

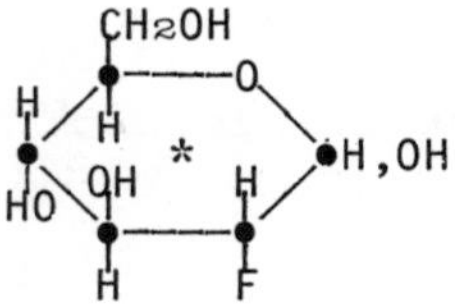

(79%)

2-Deoxy-2-fluoro-D-glucose-U-^{14}C

T. Ido, C.-N. Wan, V. Casella, J.S. Fowler, A. P. Wolf, M. Reivich, and D. E. Kuhl, J. Label. Compound. Radiopharm., 14, 175 (1978).

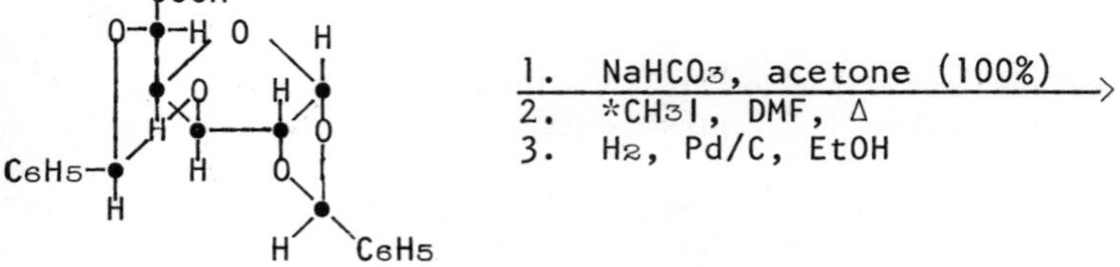

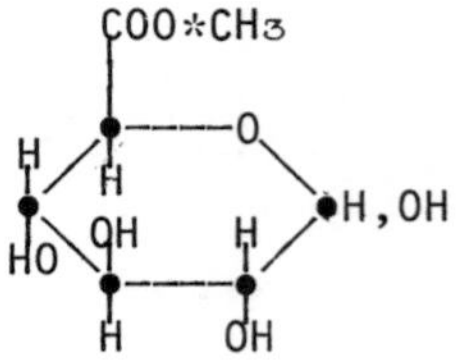

(95%)

D-Glucuronic acid (methyl-^{14}C) ester

R. H. Shah, Carbohyd. Res., 12, 42 (1970).

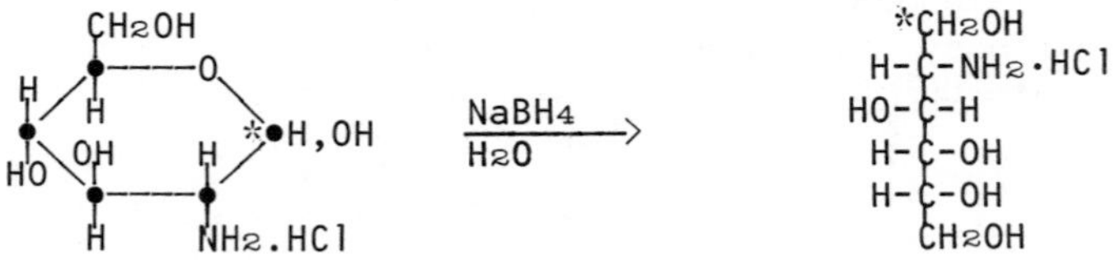

(95%)

2-Amino-2-deoxy-D-glucose-1-^{14}C

2-Amino-2-deoxy-D-glucitol-1-^{14}C hydrochloride

M. A. E. Sallam, Carbohyd. Res., 59, 612 (1977).

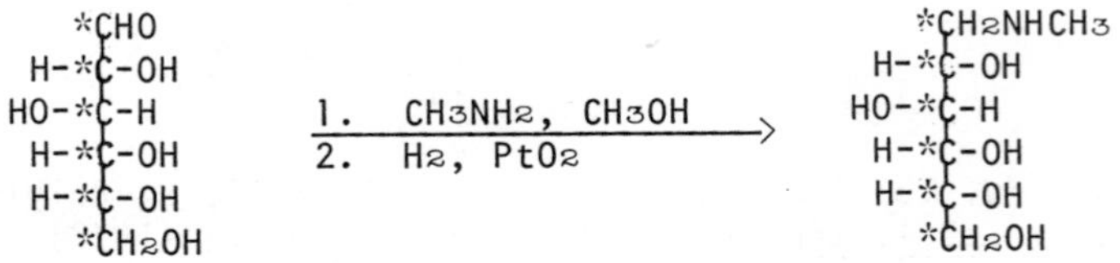

(81-86%)

D-Glucose-U-^{14}C

1-Deoxy-1-(methylamino)-D-glucitol-U-^{14}C

N-Methylglucamine-(methylamine-^{14}C) was prepared in 80-83% yield (based on glucose) using 1.5 equivalents of $^*CH_3NH_2$

J F. Heeg, G. S. Born, W. V. Kessler, S. M. Shaw, J. E. Christian, and W. E. Lang, Can. J. Pharm. Sci., 10, 75 (1975).

10-3 Ascorbic Acid Derivatives

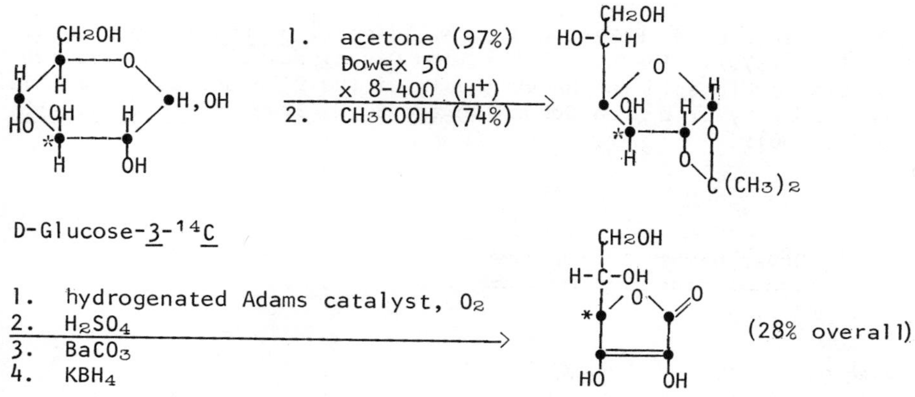
1. acetone (97%)
Dowex 50
x 8-400 (H+)
2. CH_3COOH (74%)
1. hydrogenated Adams catalyst, O_2
2. H_2SO_4
3. $BaCO_3$
4. KBH_4
(28% overall)

D-Glucose-3-^{14}C

L-Ascorbic acid-4-^{14}C

Similarly, from D-glucose-1-^{14}C and -U-^{14}C, L-ascorbic acid-6-^{14}C and -U-^{14}C were prepared, respectively.

M. Williams and F. A. Loewus, Carbohyd. Res., 63, 149 (1978).

D-Glucose-1-^{14}C $\xrightarrow[NH_4OH]{NaBH_4}$ D-Sorbitol-1-^{14}C $\xrightarrow{\textit{A. suboxydans}}$

L-Sorbose-6-^{14}C $\xrightarrow[H_2SO_4]{\text{acetone}}$ D-iisopropylidene-L-sorbose-6-^{14}C $\xrightarrow[KOH]{KMnO_4}$

Potassium diisopropylidene-2-keto-L-gulonate-6-^{14}C $\xrightarrow[\text{IR-120-H}^+]{\text{Amberlite}}$ Isopropylidene-2-keto-L-gulonate-6-^{14}C

$\xrightarrow{CF_3COOH}$ L-Ascorbic acid-6-^{14}C (10%)

In the same manner:

D-Glucose-2-^{14}C ——→ L-Ascorbic acid-5-^{14}C

D. B. Karr, E. M. Baker, and B. M. Tolbert, J. Label. Compounds, 6, 155 (1970). The use of the mono-O-cyclohexylidene derivative of L-ascorbic acid in the synthesis of the C-1 labeled vitamin is described by S. L. von Schuching and G. H. Frye, Biochem. J., 98, 652 (1966).

10-4 Other Hexose Derivatives

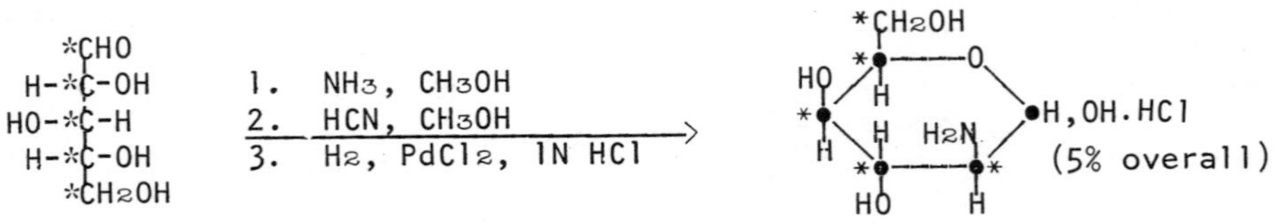

*CHO
H-*C-OH
HO-*C-H
H-*C-OH
*CH2OH
1. NH3, CH3OH
2. HCN, CH3OH
3. H2, PdCl2, 1N HCl
*CH2OH
HO
H
H2N
H,OH.HCl
(5% overall)

D-Xylose-U-^{14}C

2-Amino-2-deoxy-α-D-idose 2,3,4,5,6-^{14}C hydrochloride

K. K. De and J. S. Rodia, J. Carbohyd., Nucl., Nucl., 3, 359 (1976).

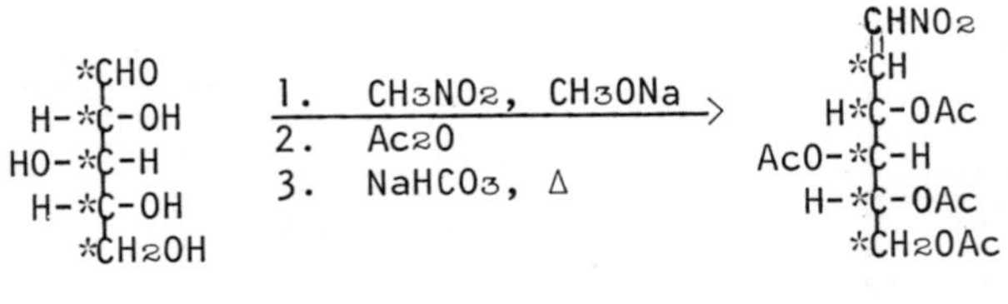

*CHO
H-*C-OH
HO-*C-H
H-*C-OH
*CH2OH
1. CH3NO2, CH3ONa
2. Ac2O
3. NaHCO3, Δ
CHNO2
*CH
H*C-OAc
AcO-*C-H
H-*C-OAc
*CH2OAc

D-Xylose-U-^{14}C

1,2-Dideoxy-1-nitro-D-xylohex-1-enitol 3,4,5,6-tetraacetate-2,3,4,5,6-^{14}C

1. NH_3, CH_3OH
2. $Ba(OH)_2$, H_2SO_4, H_2O
3. HCl

→

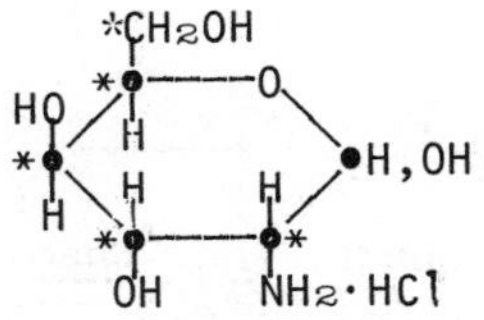

(9% overall)

2-Amino-2-deoxy-β-D-gulose hydrochloride-2,3,4,5,6-^{14}C

J. S. Rodia and K. K. De, J. Carbohyd., Nucl., Nucl., 3, 351 (1976).

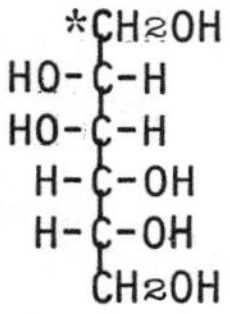

D-Mannitol-1-^{14}C

PPA →

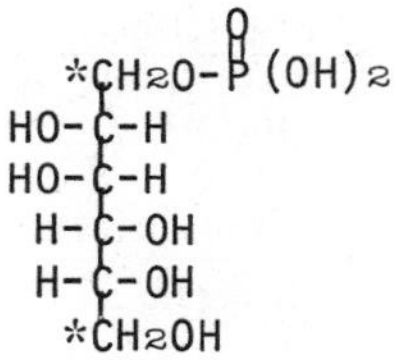

D-Mannitol-1,6-^{14}C-1-(dihydrogen phosphate)

E. T. McGuinness and J. L. Beebe, J. Label. Compounds, 3, 419 (1967).

Diethylidene-L-xylo (acid chloride) —diazomethane-^{14}C→

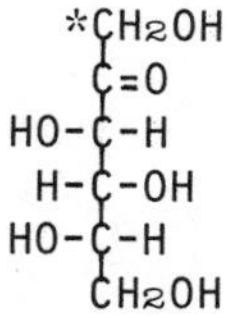

(80%)

D-Sorbose-1-^{14}C

D-Threose + Nitroethanol 2-^{14}C → Sorbose-2-^{14}C + Tagatose-2-^{14}C

D-Glucose-3,4-^{14}C —1. Raney Ni; 2. *A. Suboxydans*→ L-Sorbose-3,4-^{14}C (78%)

Similarly:

D-Glucose-2-^{14}C ⟶ L-Sorbose-5-^{14}C

K. Heynes and R. Hauber, Ann. Chem., 733, 159 (1970).

10-5 Heptoses and Nonoses

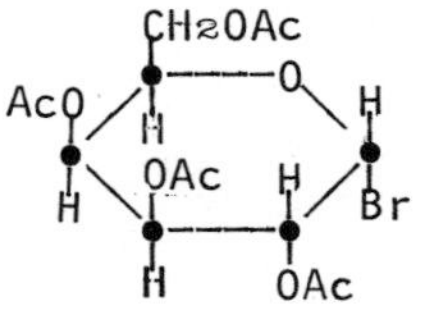

Tetra-O-acetyl-α-D galactesyl bromide

1. H*CN, HgO, CH_3NO_2
2. 25% NaOH, Δ
3. CH_3OH, Δ

⟶

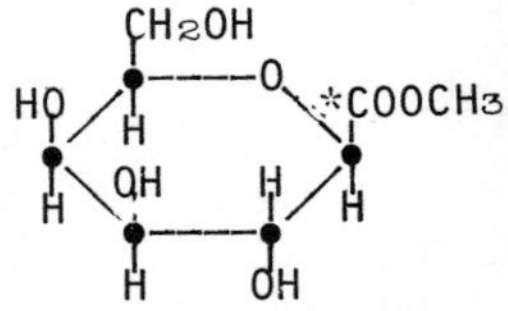

2,6-Anhydro-D-glycero-L-manno-heptonic acid 1-^{14}C methyl ester

1. C_6H_5CHO, $ZnCl_2$
2. $LiAlH_4$, THF, Δ
3. TsCl, pyr
4. 50% AcOH, 95°C

⟶

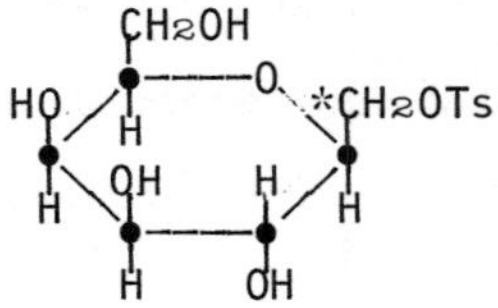

2,6-Anhydro-1-O-tosyl-D-glycero-L-manno-heptitol-1-^{14}C

1. Ac_2O, pyr
2. NaI, Ac_2O, Δ
3. AgF, pyr
4. $NaOCH_3$, CH_3OH

⟶

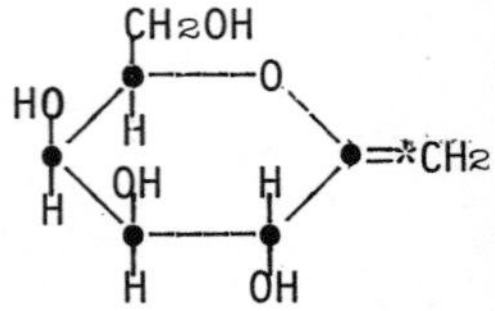

2,6-Anhydro-1-deoxy-D-galacto-hept-1-enitol-1-^{14}C

M. Brockhaus and J. Lehmann, Carbohyd. Res., 53, 21 (1977).

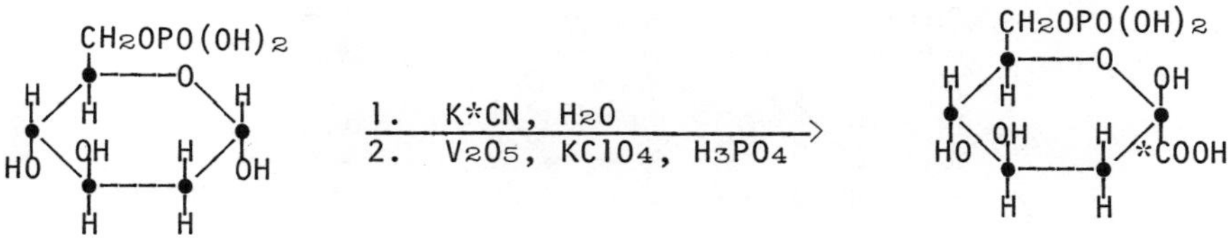
1. K*CN, H₂O
2. V₂O₅, KClO₄, H₃PO₄

3-Deoxy-7-(dihydrogen phosphate)-D-arabinoheptulosonic 1-^{14}C acid

F. Trigalo and L. Szabo, J. Chem. Soc., Perkin Trans. 1, 600 (1975).

$HOCH_2{*}COOH$ — 1. $COCl_2$, 0°C, dioxane; 2. neuraminic acid-β-methylglycoside, H_2O, $NaHCO_3$, dioxane; 3. 0.025N HCl, Dowex 50 →

Hydroxyacetic-1-^{14}C acid

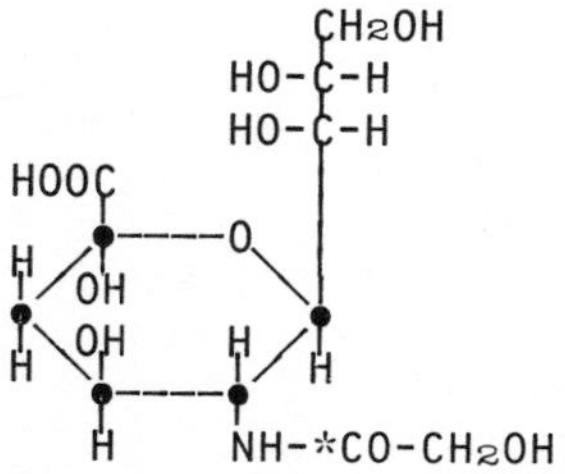

(46% overall)

N-(Glycoloyl) neuraminic acid [5-(Hydroxyacetyl-1-^{14}C-amino)-3,5-dideoxy-D-glycero-D-galacto-nonulosonic acid]

R. Schauer, F. Wirtz-Peitz, and H. Faillard, Hoppe-Seyler's Z. Physiol. Chem., 351, 359 (1970).

10-6 Polysaccharides

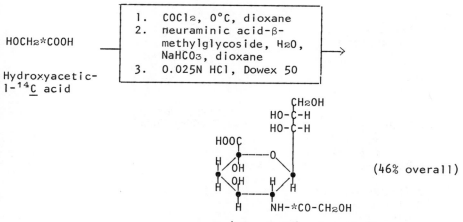

Chitosan —— Amberlite IRA-400 (carbonate), $({*}CH_3CO)_2O$, H_2O/CH_3OH →

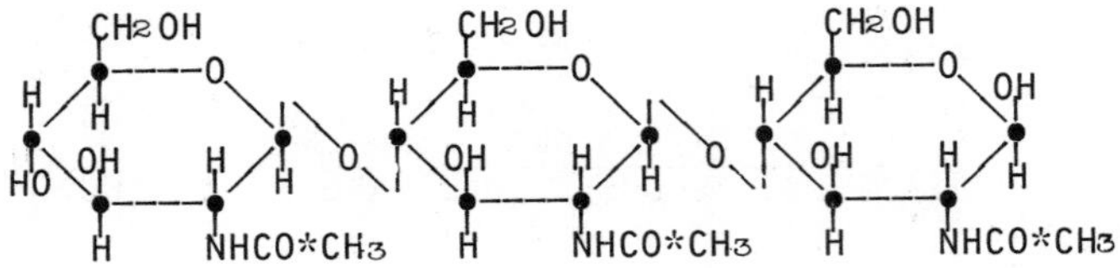

N,N',N''-(Triacetyl-2-^{14}C) chitotriose
[O-2-(Acetylamino)-2-deoxy-β-D-glucopyranosyl-(1→4)-O-2-(acetylamino)-2-deoxy-β-D-glucopyranosyl-(1→4)-2-acetylamino)-2-deoxy-D-glucose triacetyl-2-^{14}C]

L. E. H. Smith, L. H. Mohr, and M. A. Raftery, J. Amer. Chem. Soc., 95, 7497 (1973).

10-7 Nucleosides

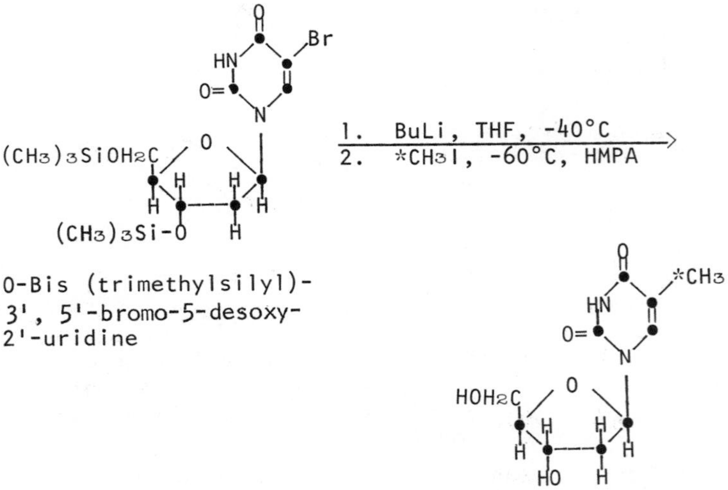

O-Bis (trimethylsilyl)-3', 5'-bromo-5-desoxy-2'-uridine

Thymidine
[1-(2-Deoxy-β-D-ribofuranosyl)-5-(methyl-^{14}C)-uracil]
(63-69% from $*CH_3I$;
41-50% from $Ba*CO_3$;
12% isothymidine also isolated).

L. Pichat, B. Massé, J. Deschamps, and P. Dufay, Bull. Soc. Chim. Fr., 2102 (1971).

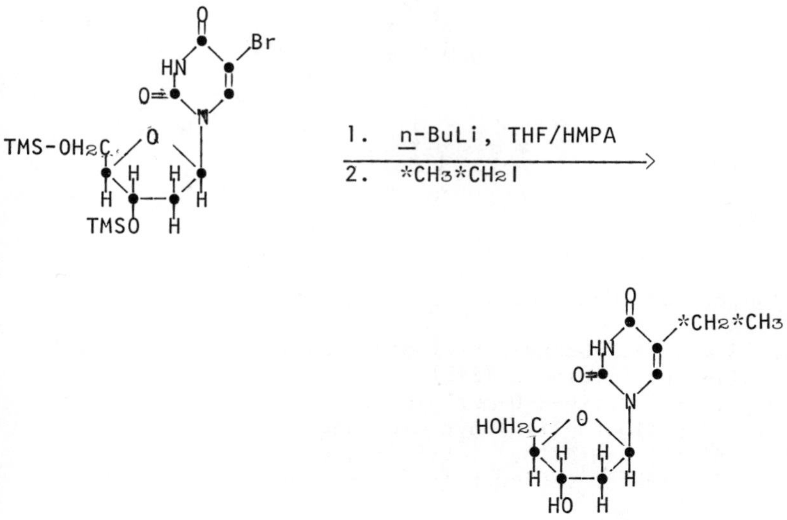

TMS-OH2C
TMSO
Br
1. n-BuLi, THF/HMPA
2. *CH3*CH2I
HOH2C
HO
*CH2*CH3

(8%)

1-(2-Deoxy-β-D-ribofuranosyl)-5-(ethyl-^{14}C)-uracil

L. Pichat, J. Godbillon, and M. Herbert, Bull. Soc. Chim. Fr., Part 2, 2712, 2715 (1973).

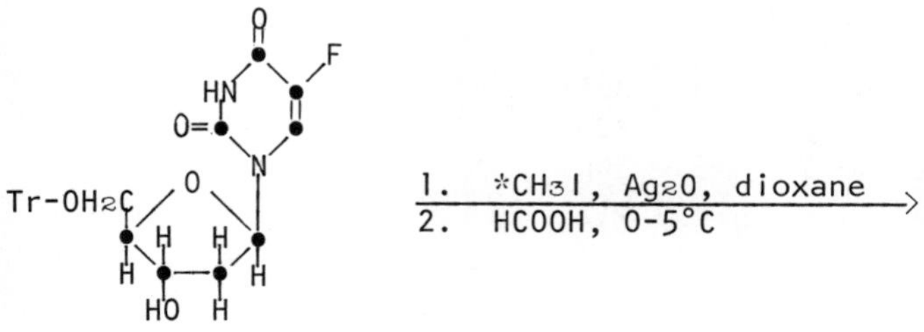

Tr-OH2C
HO
F
1. *CH3I, Ag2O, dioxane
2. HCOOH, 0-5°C

5'-O-Trityl-5-fluro-2'deoxyuridine

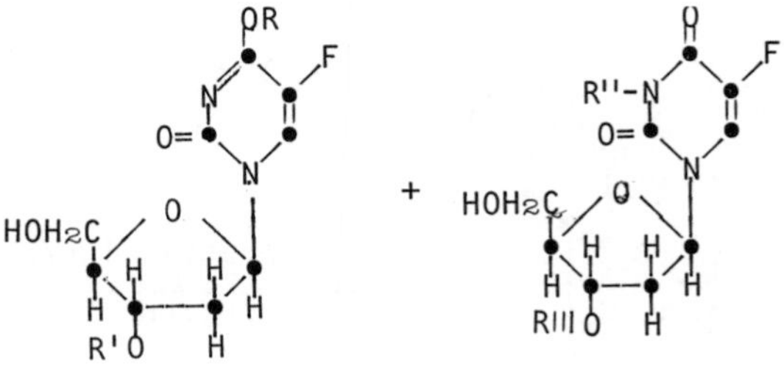
OR
F
N
O=
N
HOH$_2$C
O
H
R'O
+
O
R''-N
HOH$_2$C
R'''O

(1+2) (3+4)

The reaction mixture contained:

1. R=*CH_3, R'=H; 1-(2-Deoxy-β-D-ribofuranosyl)-4-methoxy-^{14}C-5-fluoro-2(1H)-pyrimidinone (21%)
2. R=R'=*CH_3; 1-(2-Deoxy-3-O-methyl-^{14}C-β-D-ribofuranosyl)-4-methoxy-^{14}C-5-fluoro-2(1H)-pyrimidinone (13%)
3. R''=*CH_3, R'''=H; 3-N-Methyl-^{14}C-5-fluoro-2'-deoxyuridine
4. R''=R'''=*CH_3; 3-N,3'-O-Dimethyl-^{14}C-5-fluoro-2'-deoxyuridine

All derivatives were separable by preparative TLC.

T. A. Khwaja and C. Heidelberger, J. Med. Chem., 13, 64 (1970).

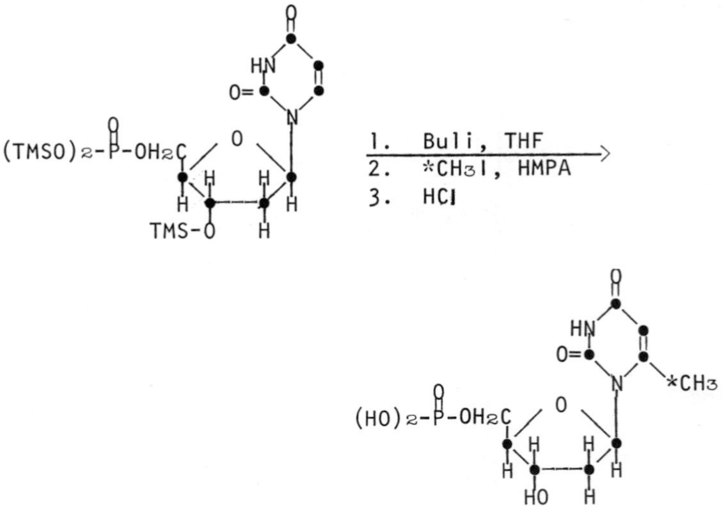
(TMSO)$_2$-P-OH$_2$C
TMS-O
1. BuLi, THF
2. *CH_3I, HMPA
3. HCl
(HO)$_2$-P-OH$_2$C
*CH_3
HO

(24% from *CH_3I)

(6-Methyl-^{14}C) deoxyuridine-5'-monophosphate

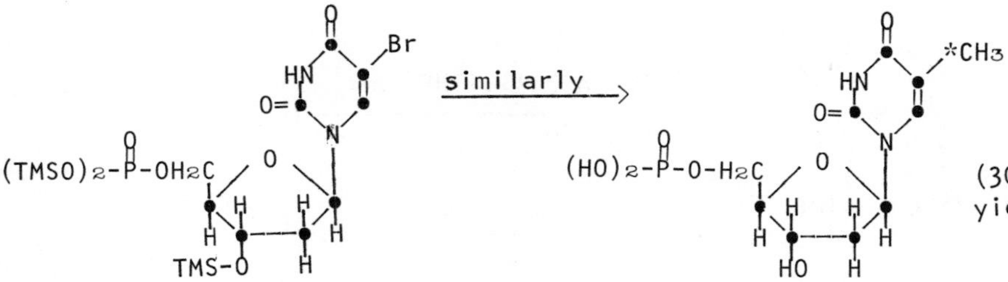
similarly

(30% yield)

Thymidine-5'-monophosphate-(5-methyl-^{14}C)

L. Pichat, J. Godbillon, and M. Herbert, J. Label. Compounds, 9, 607 (1973).

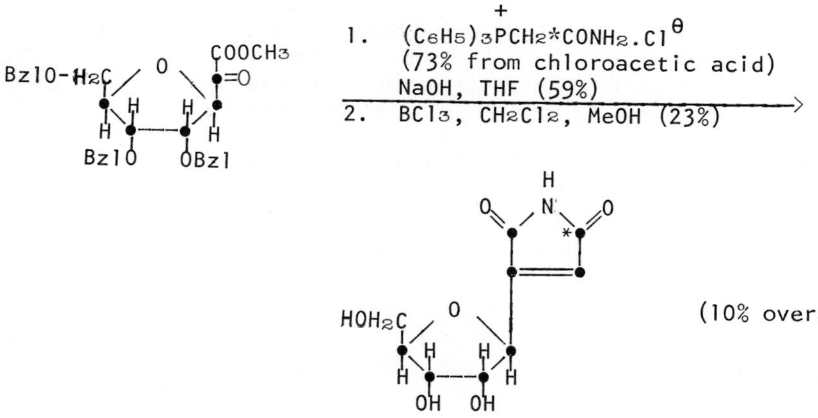
1. $(C_6H_5)_3\overset{+}{P}CH_2{*}CONH_2.Cl^{\ominus}$
(73% from chloroacetic acid)
NaOH, THF (59%)
2. BCl_3, CH_2Cl_2, MeOH (23%)

(10% overall)

Showdomycin [3-(β-D-Ribofuranosyl)-3-pyrroline-2,5-dione-5-^{14}C]

H. Minato, Y. Katsuyama, T. Nagasaki, J. Irisawa, and K. Igarashi, J. Label. Compound. Radiopharm., 14, 455 (1978).

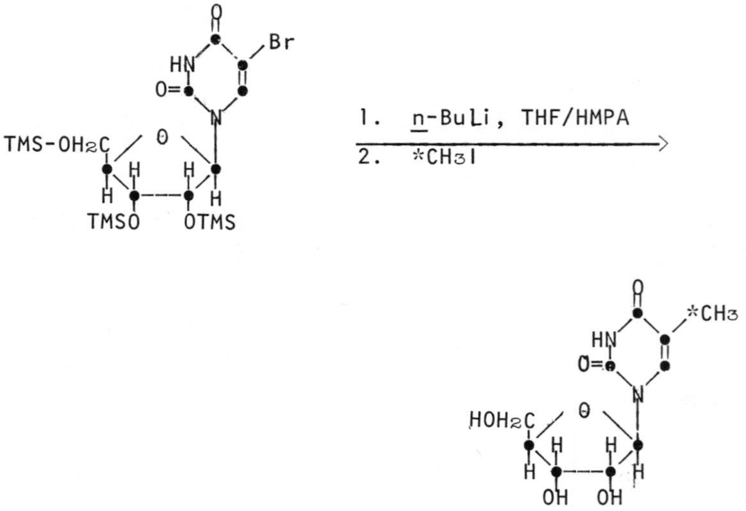

1. n-BuLi, THF/HMPA
2. *CH3I

(38%)

5-Methyl-^{14}C uridine (~2% of 6-methyl-^{14}C uridine separated by chromatography)

L. Pichat, J. Godbillon, and M. Herbert, Bull. Soc. Chim. Fr., Part 2, 2712, 2715 (1973).

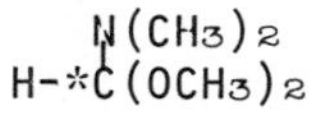

Dimethylformamide dimethyl acetal-5-^{14}C

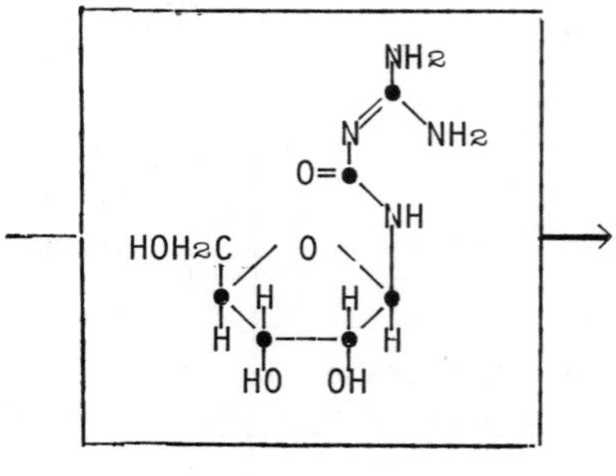

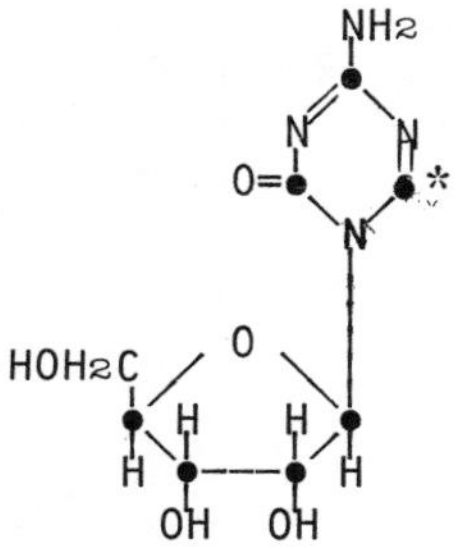
NH2
N
N
O=
*
N
O
HOH2C
H
H
H
H
OH OH

(51%)

5-Azacytidine-6-^{14}C

K. K. Chan, J. A. Staroscik, and W. Sadée, J. Med. Chem., 20, 598 (1977).

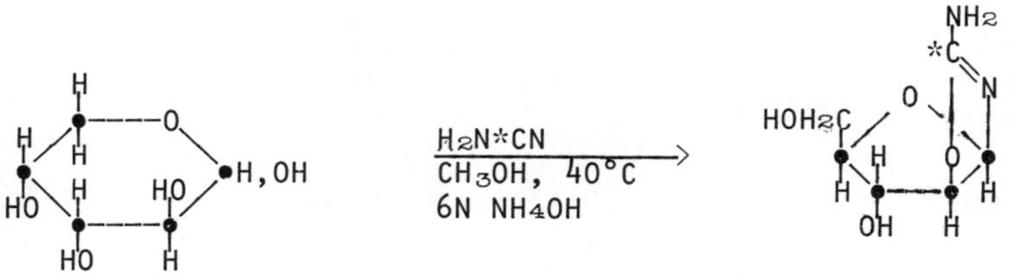
H2N*CN
CH3OH, 40°C
6N NH4OH
H,OH
HOH2C
NH2
*C
N
O

(48%)

D-Arabinose

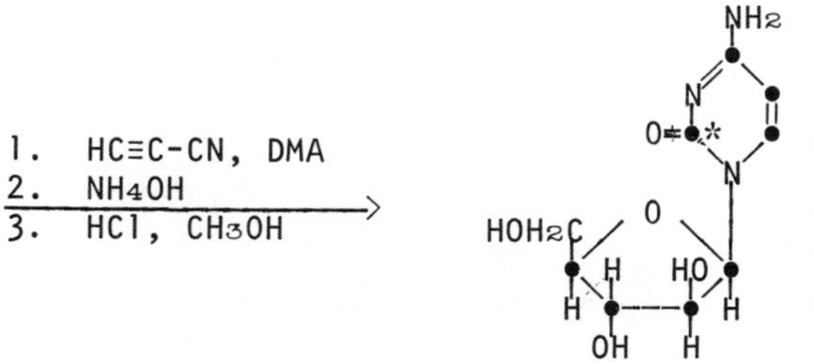
1. HC≡C-CN, DMA
2. NH4OH
3. HCl, CH3OH
NH2
N
O=
*
N
O
HOH2C
HO
OH

(43%)

Cytarabine
[4-Amino-1β-D-arabinofuranosyl-2(1H)-pyrimidinone-2-^{14}C]

R. S. P. Hsi, J. Label. Compounds, 8, 407 (1972).

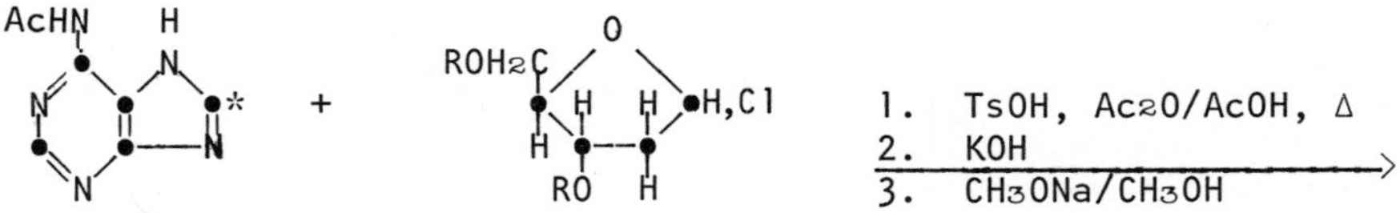
AcHN
H
N
N
N
N
*
+
ROH$_2$C
O
H
H
H,Cl
H
RO
H
1. TsOH, Ac_2O/AcOH, Δ
2. KOH
3. CH_3ONa/CH_3OH

N_6-Acetyl adenine-8-^{14}C

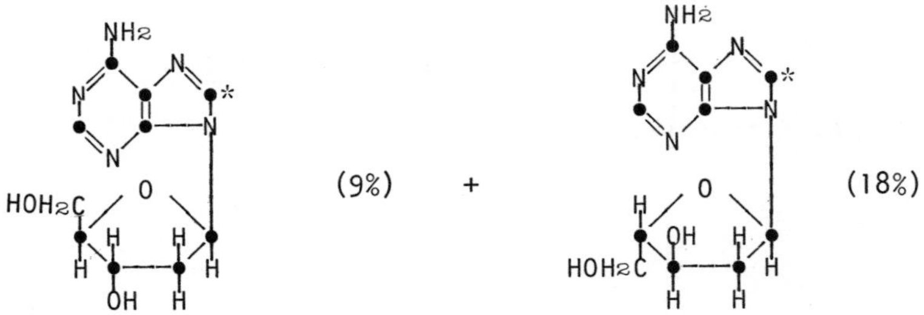
NH$_2$
N
N
N
N
*
HOH$_2$C
O
H
H
H
H
OH
H
(9%)
+
NH$_2$
N
N
N
N
*
H
O
OH
H
HOH$_2$C
H
H
H
(18%)

β-2'-Desoxyadenosine-8-^{14}C

α-2'-Desoxyadenosine-8-^{14}C

L. Pichat, P. Dufay, and Y. Lamorre, Bull. Soc. Chim. Fr., 177 (1966).

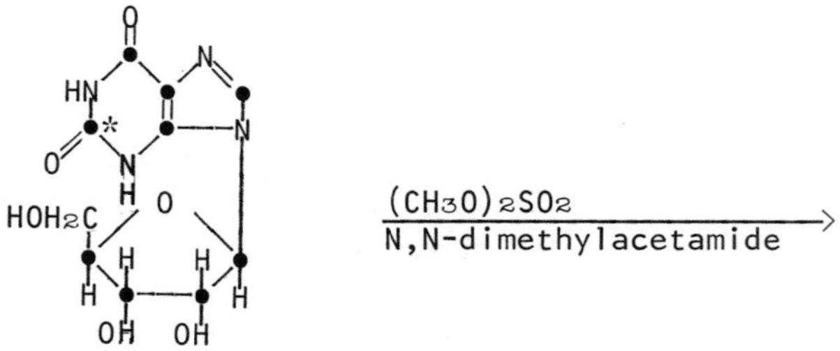
O
HN
N
*
O
N
H
N
HOH$_2$C
O
H
H
H
H
OH
OH
$(CH_3O)_2SO_2$
N,N-dimethylacetamide

Xanthosine-2-^{14}C

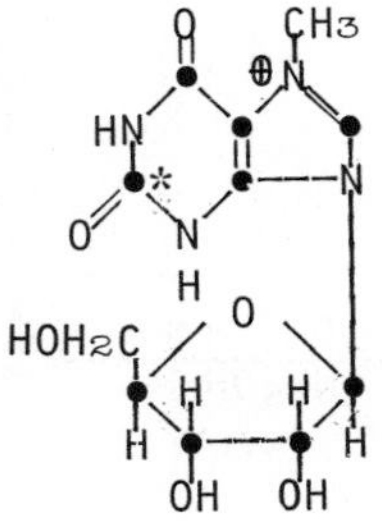
(MeO)SO_3^{θ}
(69% crude)

7-Methylxanthosine-
2-^{14}C methyl sulfate salt

T. W. Baumann, E. Dupont-Looser, and H. Wanner, Phytochemistry, 17, 2075 (1978).

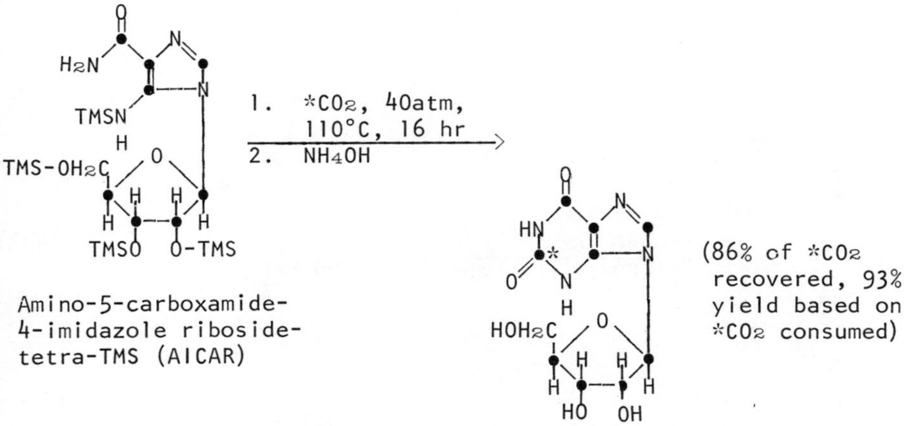
1. $*CO_2$, 40atm, 110°C, 16 hr
2. NH_4OH
(86% of $*CO_2$ recovered, 93% yield based on $*CO_2$ consumed)

Amino-5-carboxamide-4-imidazole riboside-tetra-TMS (AICAR)

Xanthosine-2-[14]C

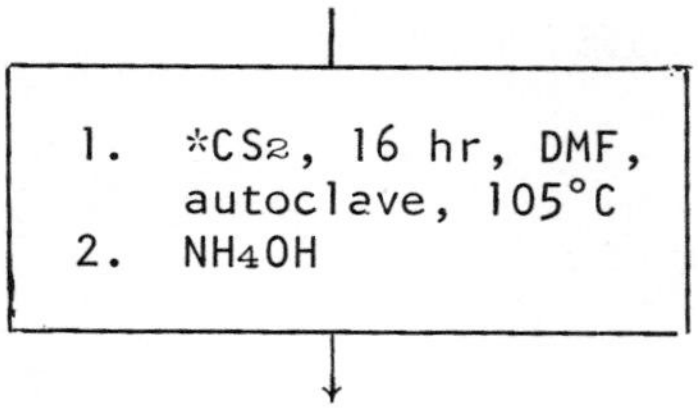
1. $*CS_2$, 16 hr, DMF, autoclave, 105°C
2. NH_4OH

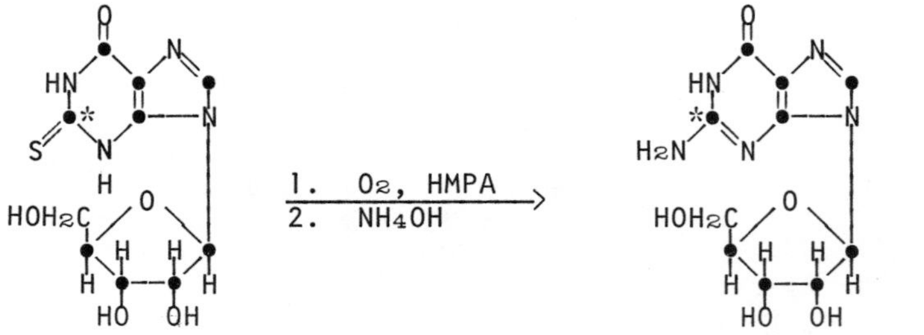
1. O_2, HMPA
2. NH_4OH

(50% of $*CS_2$ recovered, 30% yield based on $*CS_2$ consumed)

2-Thioxanthosine-2-^{14}C → Guanosine-2-^{14}C

L. Pichat, B. Masse, and P. Dufay, C. R. Acad. Sc., Paris, Ser. C., 269, 1408 (1969).

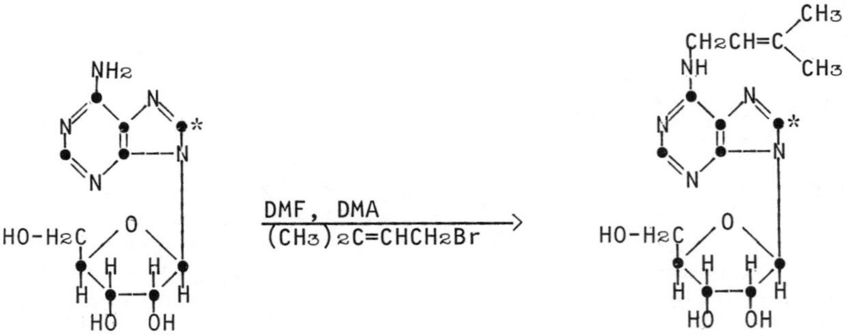
DMF, DMA
$(CH_3)_2C{=}CHCH_2Br$

(43%)

Adenosine-8-^{14}C → N^6-Δ^2-Isopentyladenosine-8-^{14}C

M. H. Fleysher, J. Label. Compounds, 8, 455 (1972).

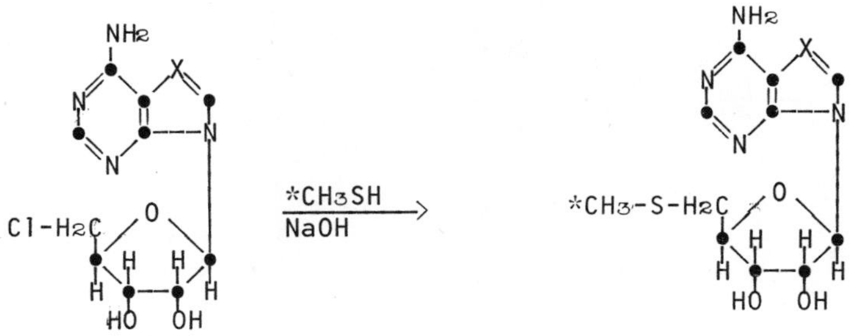
NH2
X
N
O
Cl-H2C
H
HO
OH
*CH3SH
NaOH
*CH3-S-H2C

X=N; 5'-(Methyl-^{14}C-thio)-5'-deoxyadenosine (9%)
X=CH; 5'-(Methyl-^{14}C-thio)-5'-deoxytubercidin (4%)

J. K. Coward, N. C. Motola, and J. D. Moyer, J. Med. Chem., 20, 500 (1977).

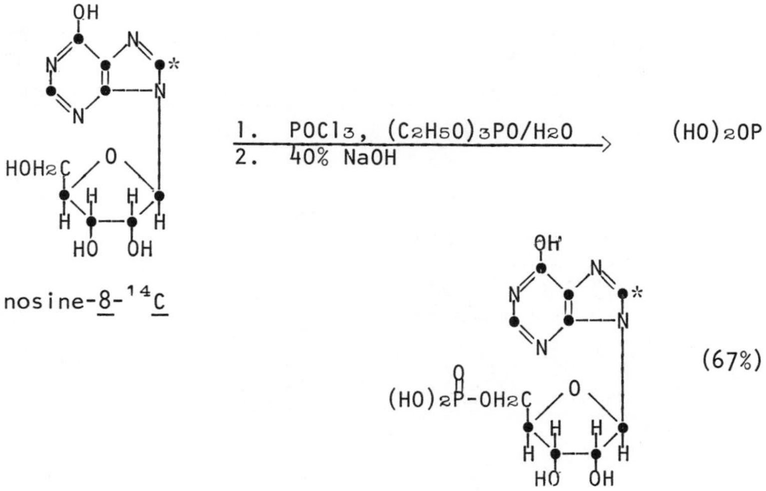
OH
N
O
HOH2C
H
HO
OH
1. POCl3, (C2H5O)3PO/H2O
2. 40% NaOH
(HO)2OP
(HO)2P-OH2C
(67%)

Inosine-8-^{14}C

Inosine-5'-phosphate-8-^{14}C
[5'-Inosinic acid-8-^{14}C
disodium salt]

S. Sakata and S. Ikegami, J. Label. Compound. Radiopharm., 14, 293 (1978).

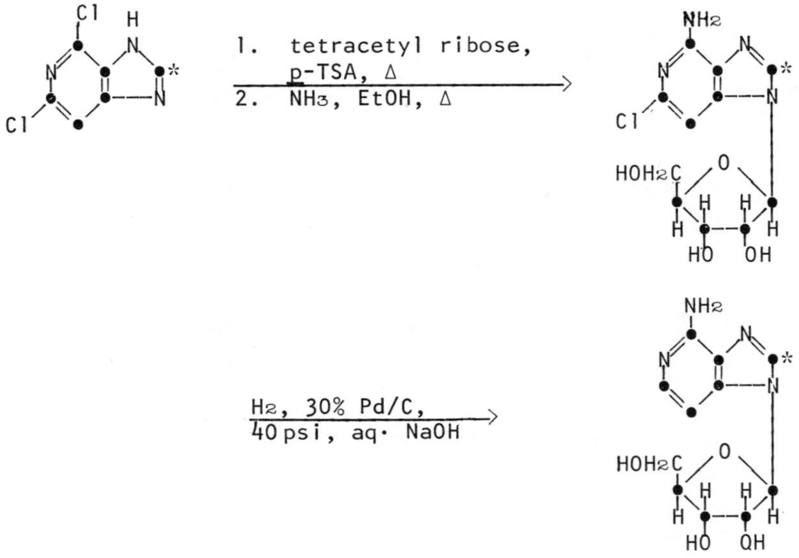
Cl
H
N
*
Cl
1. tetracetyl ribose, p-TSA, Δ
2. NH3, EtOH, Δ
NH2
HOH2C
O
H
HO
OH
H2, 30% Pd/C, 40 psi, aq· NaOH

3-Deazadenosine-8-^{14}C

J. A. Montgomery and H. J. Thomas, J. Label. Compound. Radiopharm., 15, 539 (1978).

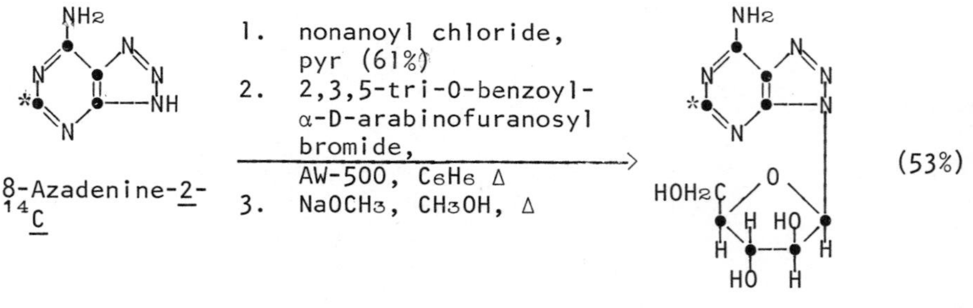
NH2
N
NH
*
8-Azadenine-2-^{14}C
1. nonanoyl chloride, pyr (61%)
2. 2,3,5-tri-O-benzoyl-α-D-arabinofuranosyl bromide, AW-500, C6H6 Δ
3. NaOCH3, CH3OH, Δ
HOH2C
O
H
HO
(53%)

9-α-D-Arabinofuranosyl-8-azaadenine-2-^{14}C

J. A. Montgomery and H. J. Thomas, J. Label. Compound. Radiopharm., 15, 727 (1978).

10-8 Carbocyclic Polyols

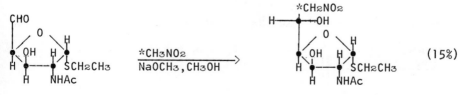

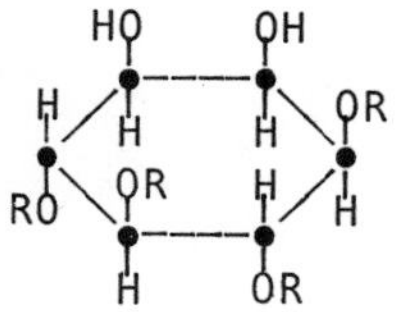

R=$CH_2C_6H_5$

1. KOH, $^*CH_3I$, C_6H_6, Δ
2. H_2, Pd/C, $PdCl_2$, CH_3COOH

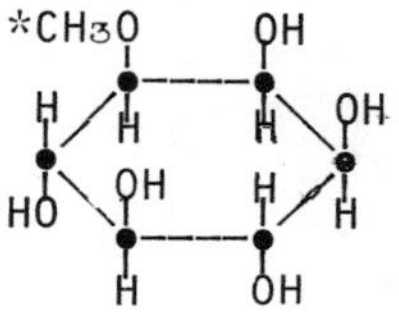

(∼8% from $^*CH_3I$)

1-O-(Methyl-^{14}C)-D-myo-inositol

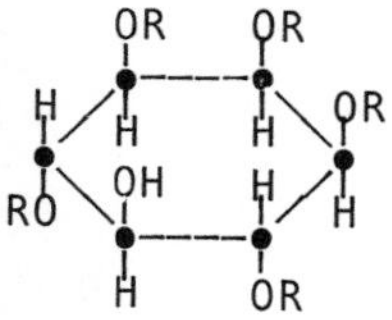

R=$CH_2C_6H_5$

1. KOH, $^*CH_3I$, C_6H_6, Δ
2. H_2,Pd/C, $PdCl_2$, CH_3COOH

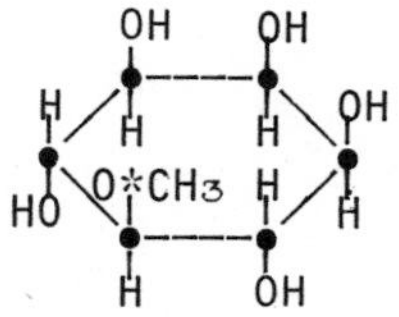

(59% from $^*CH_3I$)

5-O-(Methyl-^{14}C)-D-myo-inositol

R. H. Shah and F. Loewus, J. Label. Compounds, 6, 333 (1970).

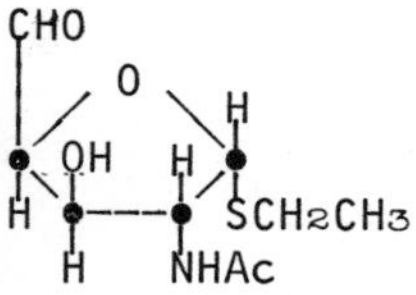

$^*CH_3NO_2$
$NaOCH_3$, CH_3OH

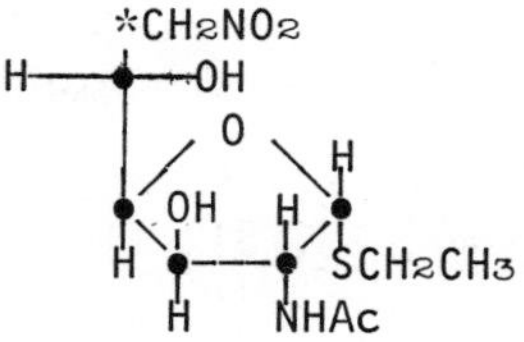

(15%)

Ethyl-2-acetamido-2,6-dideoxy-6-nitro-1-thio-β-L-idofuranoside-6-^{14}C

1. $HgCl_2$, H_2O
2. AgOAc

→

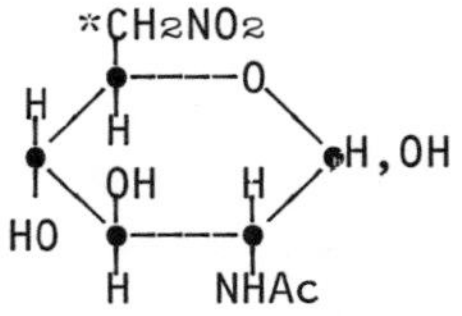

2-(Acetylamino)-2,6-dideoxy-6-nitro-D-glucose-6-^{14}C

(34%)

1. silica gel
2. H_2, Pt, HCl
3. Ac_2O, pyr

→

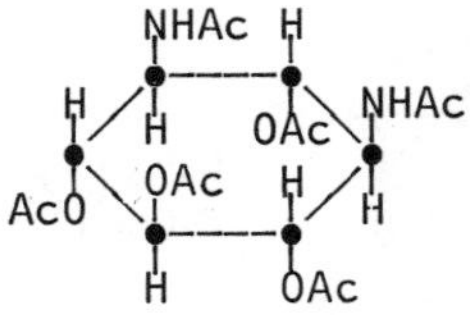

N,N'-Diacetyl-D-Streptamine-2,4,5,6-tetraacetate 1-^{14}C

(9%) +

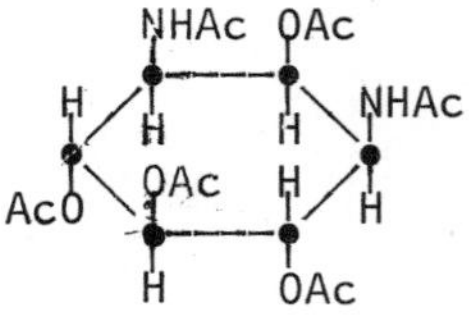

1,3-Bis (acetylamino)-1,3-dideoxy-myoinositol-2,4,5,6-tetraacetate-1-^{14}C

(34% separable by crystalization)

HCl, Δ

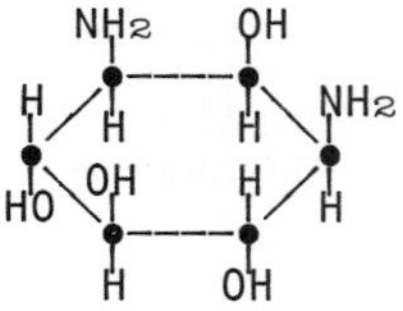

1,3-Diamino-1,3-dideoxy-myo-inositol-1-^{14}C

(88%)

Neosamine-6-^{14}C dihydrochloride was similarly prepared in 56% yield.

S. Ogawa, K. L. Rinehart Jr., G. Kimura, and R. P. Johnson, J. Org. Chem., 39, 812 (1974).

11

Terpenes

Monoterpenes

11-1 Acyclic

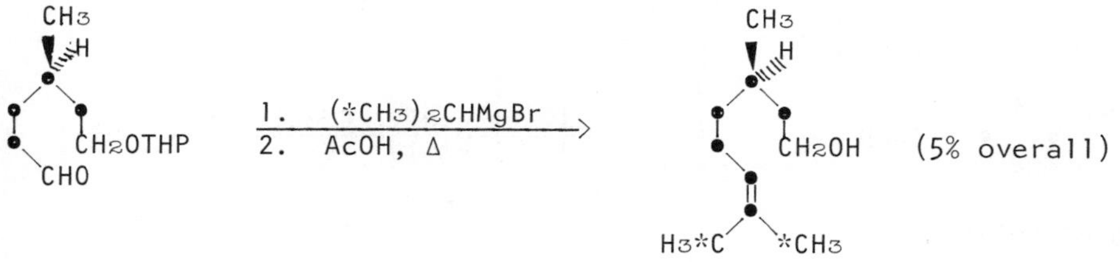

(from ozonolysis of citronellol-OTHP)

β-Citronellol
[3-Methyl-(7-methyl-^{14}C)-6-octen-1-ol-8-^{14}C]

The product was used to study the cyclization of citronellol with $HFSO_3$ at -78°C to 2,2,5-trimethyl- and 2-ethyl-2,5-dimethyloxacycloheptane (40%; 1:1). The former product resulted from loss of a methyl group at C-7 (one-half specific activity).

D. V. Banthorpe and P. A. Boullier, J. Chem. Soc., Perkin Trans. I, 114 (1977).

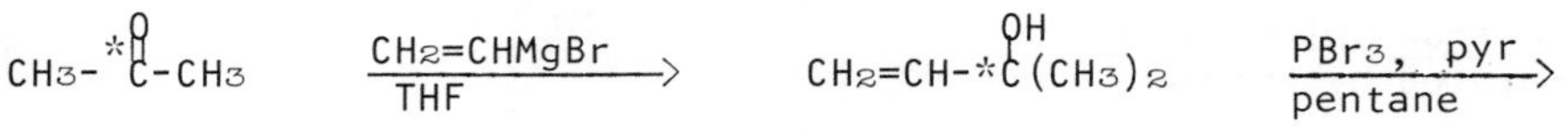

2-Propanone-2-^{14}C

2-Methyl-3-buten-2-ol-2-^{14}C

$BrCH_2CH{=}^{*}C(CH_3)_2$ —(1. $CH_3COCH_2COOC_2H_5$, Na, EtOH; 2. aq. KOH)→ $CH_3\overset{O}{\overset{\|}{C}}{-}CH_2{-}CH_2CH{=}^{*}C(CH_3)_2$

1-Bromo-3-methyl-2-butene-3-^{14}C

6-Methyl-5-hepten-2-one-6-^{14}C

—($(C_2H_5)_3PCH_2COOC_2H_5$, NaH, DME)→ $C_2H_5O{-}\overset{O}{\overset{\|}{C}}CH{=}\overset{CH_3}{\overset{|}{C}}CH_2CH_2CH{=}^{*}C(CH_3)_2$ —($LiAlH_4$, ether)→

(cis:trans ratio, 1:4)

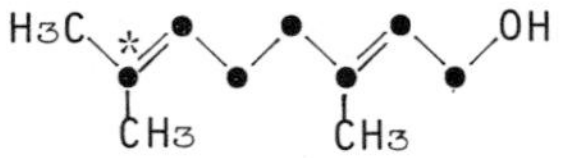
H3C
OH
CH3
CH3

(46%)

Geraniol
[(E)-3,7-Dimethyl-2,6-octadien-l-ol-7-^{14}C]

H. D. Durst and E. Leete, J. Label. Compounds, 7, 52 (1971).

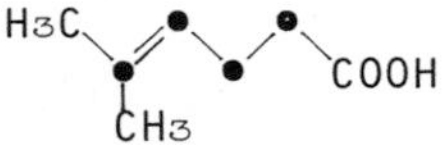
H3C
COOH
CH3

—(1. 1 equiv. CH_3Li, ether; 2. 1 equiv. $^{*}CH_3Li$, ether)→

5-Methyl-4-hexenoic acid

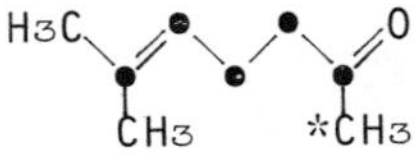
H3C
O
CH3
*CH3

(~70% crude) —($(C_2H_5O)_2POCH_2COOC_2H_5$, NaH, DME)→

6-Methyl-5-hepten-2-one-1-^{14}C

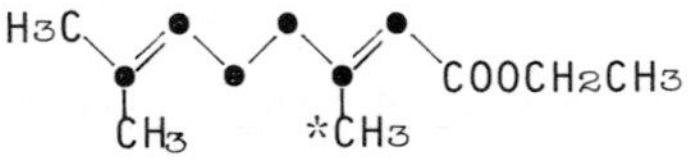
H3C
COOCH2CH3
CH3
*CH3

—($LiAlH_4$, Et_2O)→

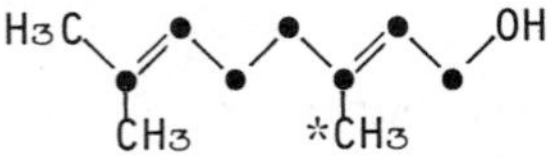
H3C
OH
CH3
*CH3

(64%)

3,7-Dimethyl-2,6-octadienoic acid ethyl ester-(3-methyl-^{14}C)

(55% trans plus 13% cis; separated by chromatography)

Geraniol
[(E)-3,7-Dimethyl-2,6-octadien-1-ol-(3-methyl-^{14}C)]

S. J. Rajan and J. Wemple, J. Label. Compounds, 11, 467 (1975).

11-2 Monocyclic

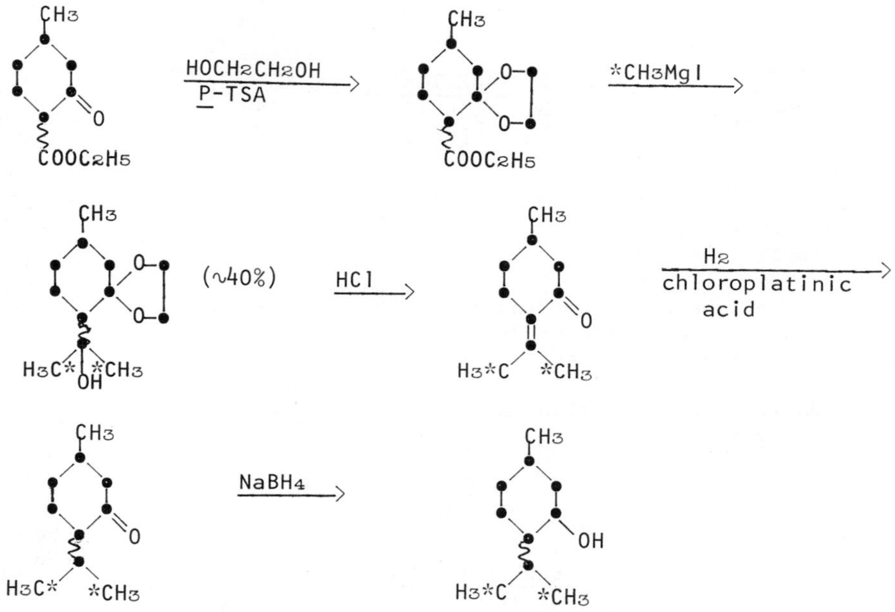
HOCH2CH2OH
P-TSA
*CH3MgI
(~40%)
HCl
H2
chloroplatinic acid
NaBH4

DL-Menthol
[5-Methyl-2-(1-methyl-^{14}C)-ethyl-2-^{14}C)cyclohexanol]

J. F. DeBardeleben, R. W. Jenkins, W. C. Bailey, and T. S. Osdene, J. Label. Compounds, 5, 261 (1969).

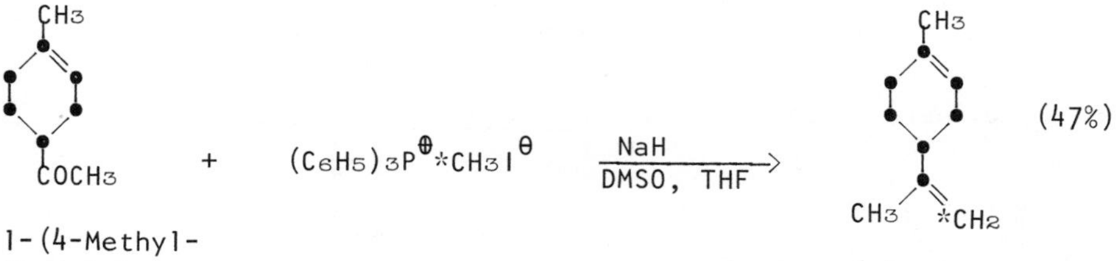
(C6H5)3P⊕*CH3I⊖
NaH
DMSO, THF
(47%)

1-(4-Methyl-3-cyclohexen-1-yl)ethanone

(+)-Limonene
[1-Methyl-4-(1-methylethenyl-1-^{14}C)-cyclohexene]

K. Noda, T. Matsuda, and Y. Ishikura, J. Label. Compounds, 10, 309 (1974).

11-3 Bicyclic

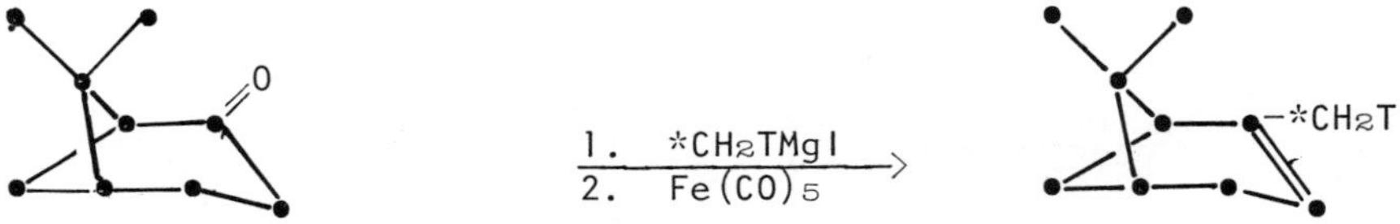
O
1. *CH2TMgI
2. Fe(CO)5
–*CH2T

Nopinone (from ozonolysis of β-pinene) [6,6-Dimethyl-bicyclo [3.1.1]heptan-2-one]

α-Pinene [2-Methyl-^{14}C,t-6,6-dimethyl-bicyclo-[3.1.1]hept-2-ene]

Labeled α-pinene was pyrolyzed to a mixture of allo-ocimenes which were used in mechanistic studies of thermal rearrangements of tricarbonyliron complexes.

D. V. Banthorpe, H. Fritton, and J. Lewis, J. Chem. Soc., Perkin Trans. I, 2051 (1973).

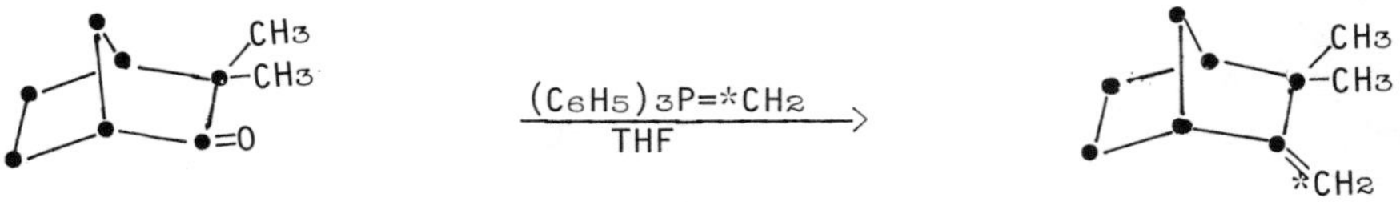
CH3
CH3
=O
(C6H5)3P=*CH2
THF
CH3
CH3
*CH2

3,3-Dimethyl-bicyclo [2.2.1]heptan-2-one

Camphene [2,2-Dimethyl-3-(methylene-^{14}C)-bicyclo[2.2.1] heptane]

$\xrightarrow[CCl_4]{Cl_2,\ h\nu}$ Toxaphene-^{14}C (68% overall)

J. E. Oliver, J. Label. Compound.Radiopharm., 13, 349 (1977).

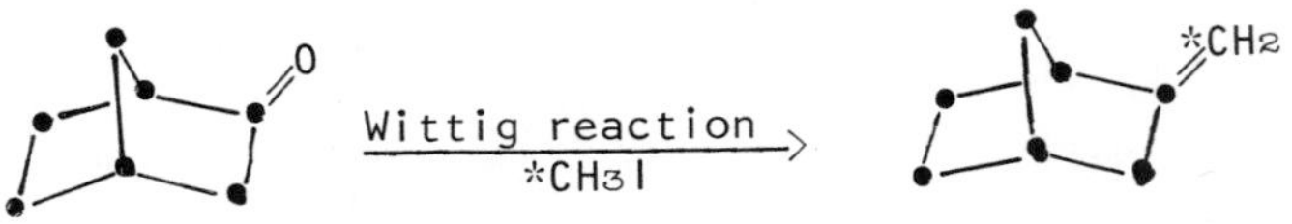
O
Wittig reaction
*CH3I
*CH2

(55%)

Norcamphor [Bicyclo[2.2.1] heptan-2-one]

Norcamphene [2-Methylene-^{14}C-bicyclo[2.2.1]-heptane]

$\xrightarrow[250°C]{H_3PO_4/SiO_2}$ 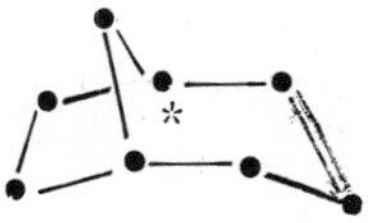 + 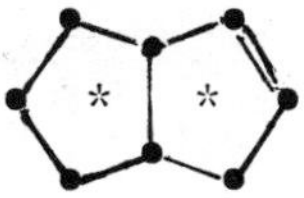

Bicyclo[3.2.1]oct-2-ene (label distributed throughout except at position 8)

Bicyclo[3.3.0]oct-2-ene (label distributed throughout)

Various mechanisms are proposed.

M. Evrard-Heude, F. Petit, and M. Blanchard, Bull. Soc. Chim. Fr., 2545 (1971).

$*CH_2(COOCH_3)_2$ + $ClCH_2$-CH=CH-CH_2Cl $\xrightarrow{EtOH}$ 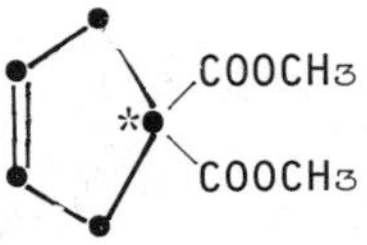
COOCH3
COOCH3

Dimethyl-malonate-2-^{14}C

(cis)

3-Cyclopentene-1,1-dicarboxylic-1-^{14}C acid dimethyl ester

1. KOH, EtOH
2. Δ
3. $SOCl_2$
4. CH_2N_2
5. AgO, CH_3OH

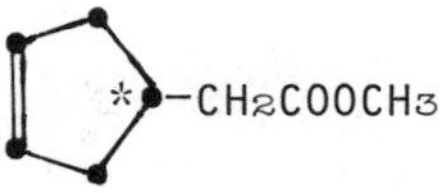
-CH2COOCH3

3-Cyclopentene-1-acetic-1-^{14}C acid methyl ester

1. $LiAlH_4$, Et_2O
2. TsCl, pyr

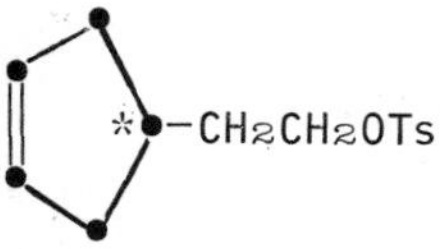
-CH2CH2OTs

(~17% from malonate) $\xrightarrow[AcOH,\ Ac_2O]{NH_2CONH_2}$ 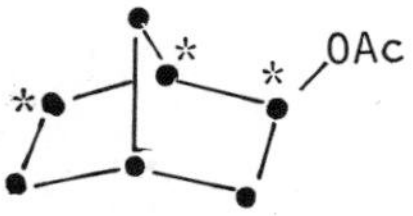
OAc

3-Cyclopenten-1-ethanol-1-^{14}C 4-methylbenzenesulfonate

Exo-bicyclo[2.2.1]-heptan-2-ol-1,2,6-^{14}C -2-acetate

A mechanism is discussed.

C. J. Collins and C. E. Harding, Ann. Chem., 745, 124 (1971).

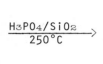

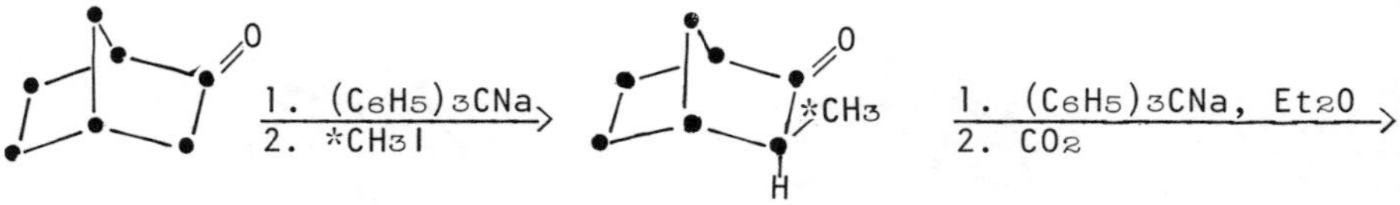
1. (C6H5)3CNa
2. *CH3I
*CH3
H
1. (C6H5)3CNa, Et2O
2. CO2

Norcamphor
[Bicyclo[2.2.1]
heptan-2-one]

Exo-3-methyl-^{14}C-
bicyclo-[2.2.1]-
heptan-2-one

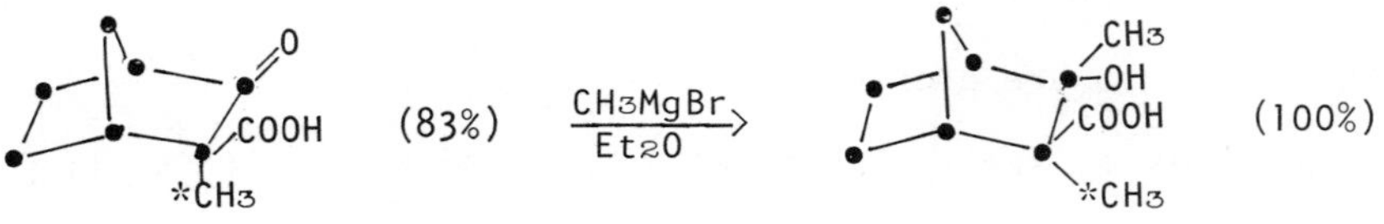
COOH
*CH3
(83%)
CH3MgBr
Et2O
CH3
OH
COOH
*CH3
(100%)

2,3-Dimethyl-2-hydroxy-
bicyclo[2.2.1]heptane-
3-carboxylic acid-(3-
methyl-^{14}C)

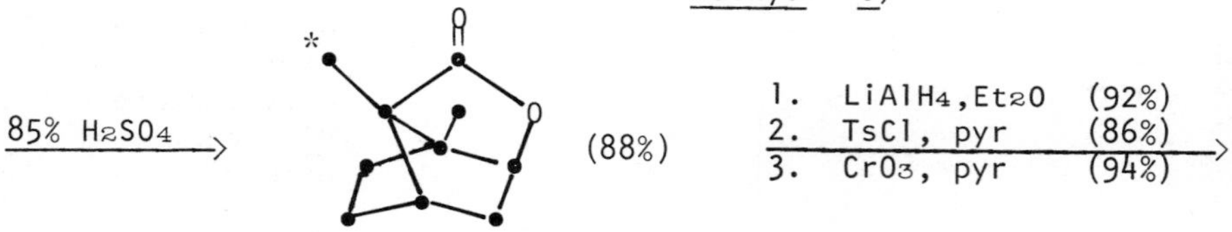
85% H2SO4
*
O
O
(88%)
1. LiAlH4,Et2O (92%)
2. TsCl, pyr (86%)
3. CrO3, pyr (94%)

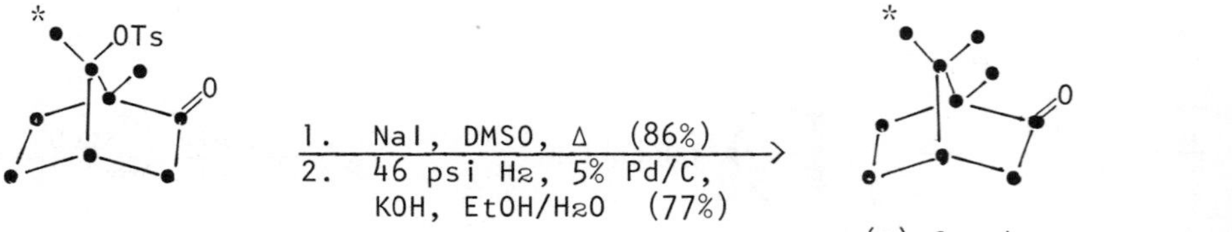
*
OTs
O
1. NaI, DMSO, Δ (86%)
2. 46 psi H2, 5% Pd/C,
KOH, EtOH/H2O (77%)
*
O

(+)-Camphor
[1.7.7-Trimethyl-
bicyclo[2.2.1]heptan-
2-one-9-^{14}C]

Similarly:

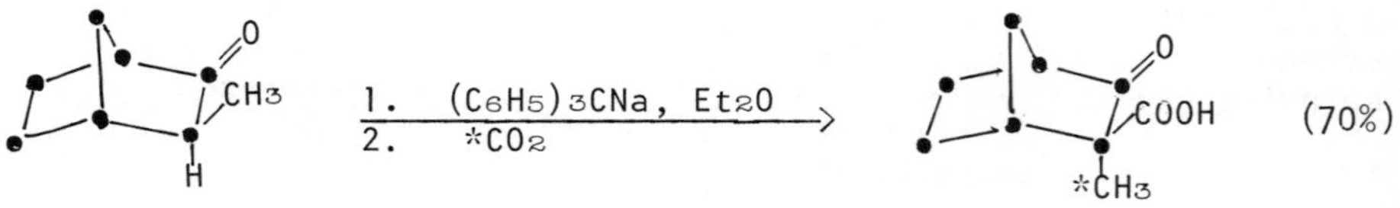
O
CH3
H
1. (C6H5)3CNa, Et2O
2. *CO2
O
COOH
*CH3
(70%)

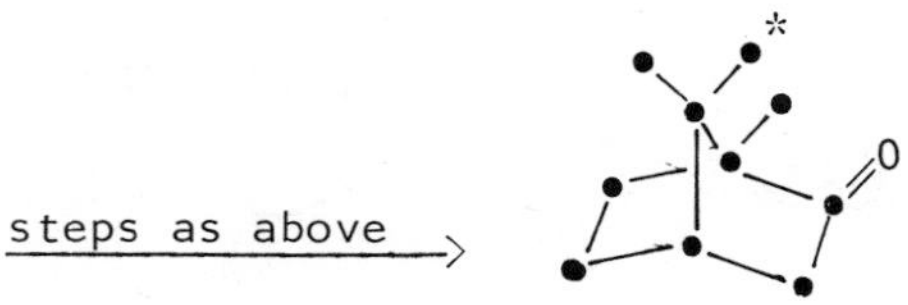
steps as above
O
*

(+)-Camphor
[1.7.7-Trimethylbicyclo-
[2.2.1]heptan-2-one-8-^{14}C]

The use of labeled methyl Grignard would yield (+)-camphor-10-^{14}C.

O. R. Rodig and R. J. Sysko, J. Org. Chem., 36, 2324 (1971).

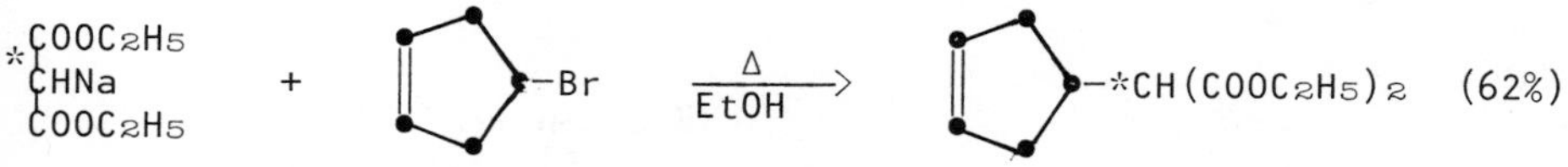
*$COOC_2H_5$
CHNa
$COOC_2H_5$
+
Br
Δ
EtOH
*$CH(COOC_2H_5)_2$
(62%)

4-Bromo-
cyclopentene

3-Cyclopentene-2-
propanedioic-β-^{14}C
acid diethyl ester

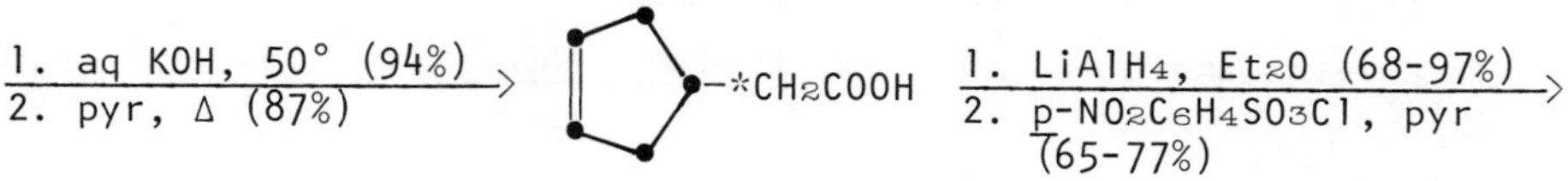
1. aq KOH, 50° (94%)
2. pyr, Δ (87%)
*CH_2COOH
1. $LiAlH_4$, Et_2O (68-97%)
2. p-$NO_2C_6H_4SO_3Cl$, pyr
(65-77%)

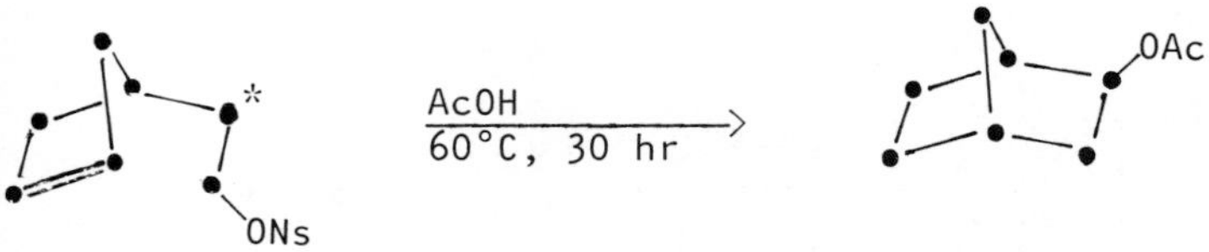
*
ONs
AcOH
60°C, 30 hr
OAc

3-Cyclopenten-1-ethanol-β-^{14}C
4-nitrobenzenesulfonate

Yields are given for unlabeled reactions. ^{14}C distribution was determined by degradation studies: C-2,3 (38%); C-1,4 (1%); C-7 (25%); C-5,6 (36%).

C. C. Lee and L. K. M. Lam, J. Amer. Chem. Soc., 88, 2834 (1966).

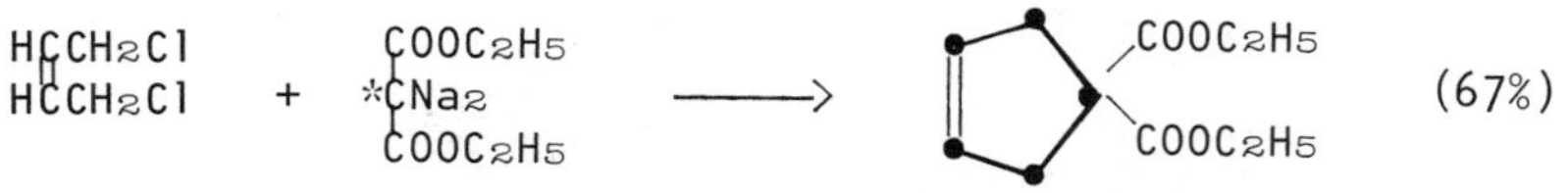

(Z)-1,4-Dichloro-2-butene

3-Cyclopentene-1,1-dicarboxylic-1-^{14}C acid diethyl ester

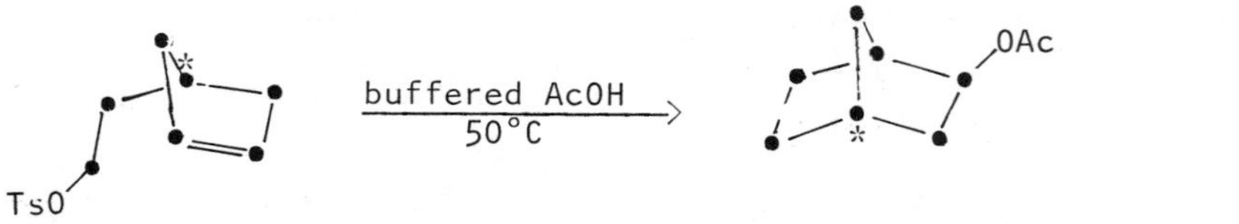

3-Cyclopenten-1-ethanol-1-^{14}C 4-methylbenzenesulfonate

2-exo-norbornyl acetate [Exo-Bicyclo[2.2.1]-heptan-2-ol acetate-^{14}C]

The ^{14}C distribution was determined by degradation reactions: C-1 (0.52%); C-2 (0.33%); the remainder was presumed to be at C-4. Yields are for unlabeled reactions.

C. J. Collins and C. E. Harding, J. Amer. Chem. Soc., 91, 7194 (1969).

Sesquiterpenes

11-4 Acyclic

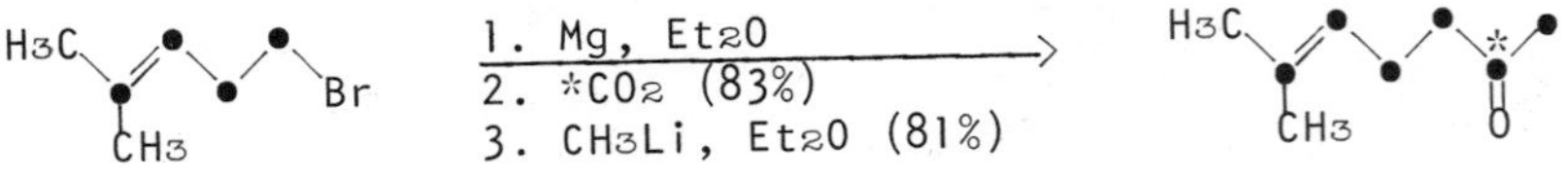

5-Bromo-2-methyl-2-pentene

6-Methyl-5-hepten-2-one-2-^{14}C

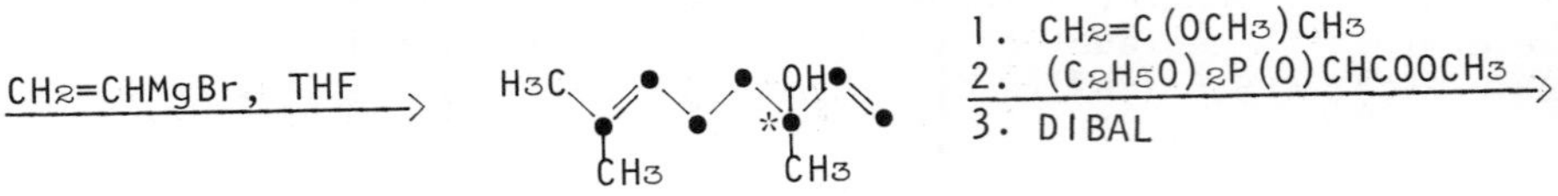

Linalool [3,7-Dimethyl-1,6-octadien-3-ol-3-^{14}C]

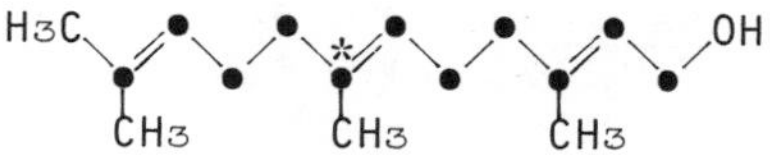

(44% overall yield; mixture of E,E (40%), 2E,6Z (34%), 2Z,6E (11%), and Z,Z (10%) isomers)

Farnesol
[3,7,11-Trimethyl-2,6,10-dodecatrien-1-ol-7-^{14}C]

Similarly:

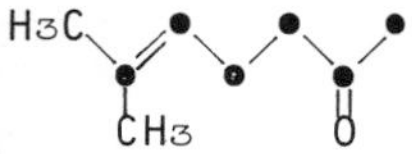

6-Methyl-5-hepten-2-one

1. H*C≡*CLi (58%)
2. Lindlar (96%)
→

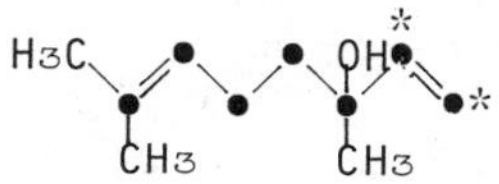

Linalool
[3,7-Dimethyl-1,6-octadien-3-ol-1,2-^{14}C]

steps as above →

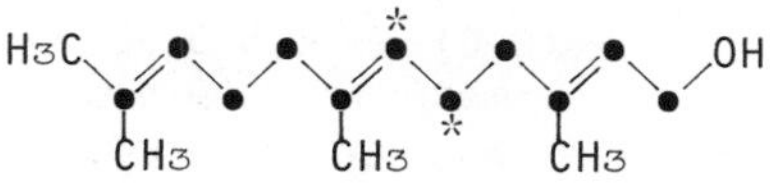

(42% overall yield; similar mixture of isomers as above)

Farnesol
[3,7,11-Trimethyl-2,6,10-dodecatrien-1-ol-5,6-^{14}C]

M. G. Peter, H.-R. Waespe, W.-D. Woggen, and H. Schmid, Helv. Chim. Acta, 60, 1262 (1977).

$Br^*CH_2COOCH_3$ —(1. $P(OC_2H_5)_3$; 2. NaH)→ $(C_2H_5O)_2\overset{O^{\ominus}}{P}{=}^*CHCOOCH_3$ $Na^{\oplus}$

Bromoacetic-2-^{14}C acid methyl ester

(Diethoxyphosphoranylidene)-acetic-2-^{14}C acid methyl ester

1. geranylacetone
2. $LiAlH_4$
→

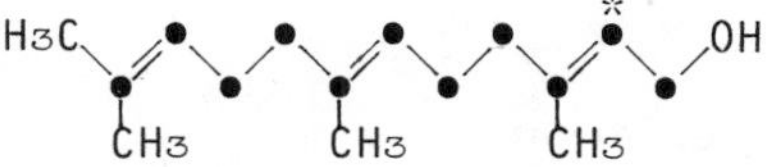

(40% from methyl bromoacetate)

Farnesol
[E,E,E-3,7,11-Trimethyl-2,6,10-dodecatrien-1-ol-2-^{14}C]

I. Oguni and I. Uritani, Agr. Biol. Chem. (Tokyo), 33, 1654 (1969).

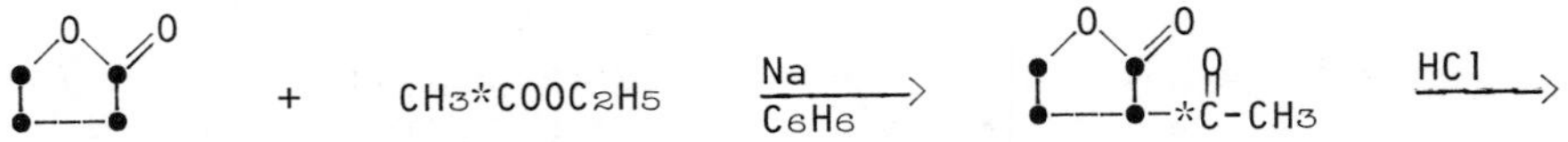

Dihydro-2(3H)-furanone

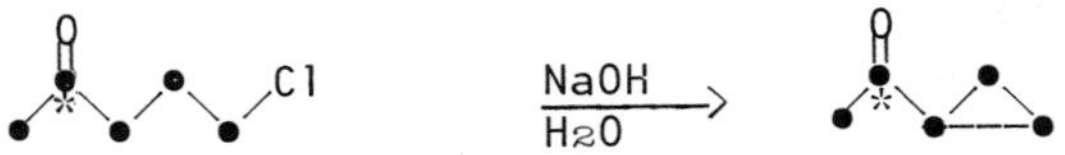

(63% from Ba*CO_3)

5-Chloro-2-pentanone-2-^{14}C

1-(Cyclopropyl)ethanone-1-^{14}C

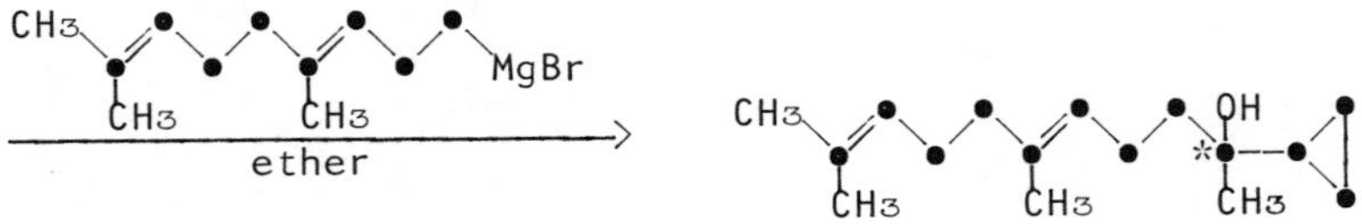

(E,E)-α-(4,8-Dimethyl-3,7-nonadienyl)-α-methylcyclopropanemethanol-α-^{14}C

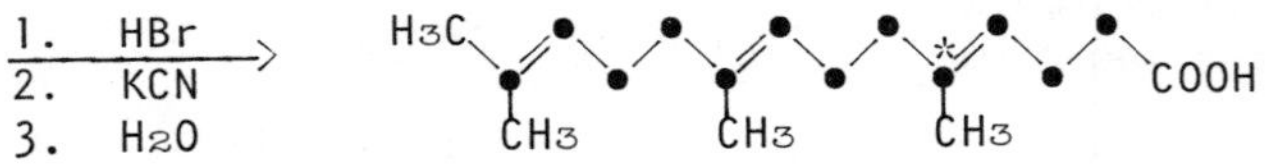

(48% from ketone; 30% from Ba*CO_3)

5,9,13-Trimethyl-4,8,12-tetradecatrienoic-5-^{14}C acid

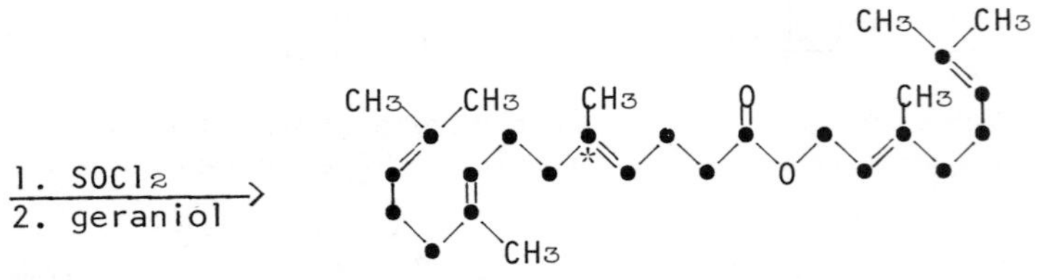

(37% from ketone, 23% from Ba*CO_3)

Gefarnate [5,9,13-Trimethyl-4,8,12-tetradecatrienoic acid-5-^{14}C 3,7-dimethyl-2,6-octadienyl ester]

M. Hazue, K. Miyake, and M. Endo, J. Label. Compounds, 5, 220 (1969).

11-5 Monocyclic

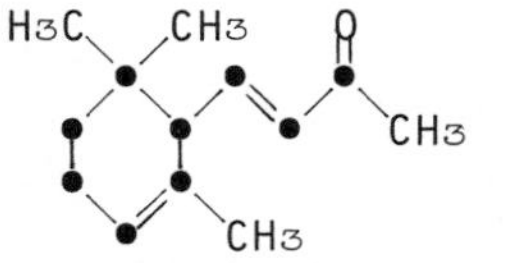

(E)-4-(2,6,6-Trimethyl-2-cyclohexen-1-yl)-3-buten-2-one

$\xrightarrow[\text{Zn, } C_6H_6\text{, } \Delta]{\text{Br*}CH_2COOC_2H_5}$

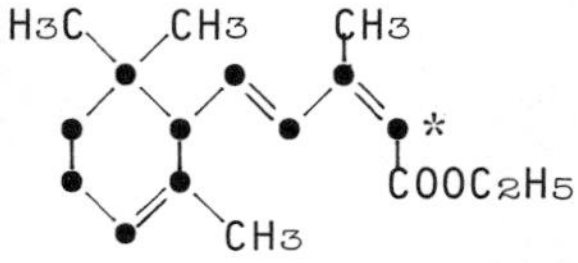

(Z,E)-3-Methyl-5-(2,6,6-trimethyl-2-cyclohexen-1-yl)-2,4-pentadienoic-2-^{14}C acid ethyl ester

+

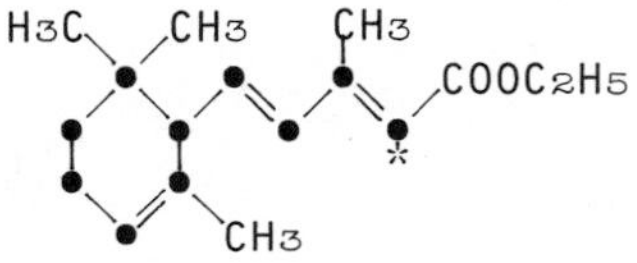

(E,E)-3-Methyl-5-(2,6,6-trimethyl-2-cyclohexen-1-yl)-2,4-pentadienoic-2-^{14}C acid ethyl ester

(separable by chromatography)

↓ KOH/EtOH

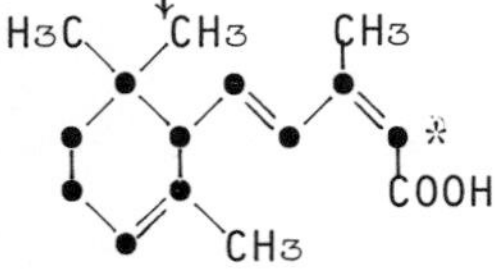

(Z,E)-3-Methyl-5-(2,6,6-trimethyl-2-cyclohexen-1-yl)-2,4-pentadienoic-2-^{14}C acid

↓ KOH/EtOH

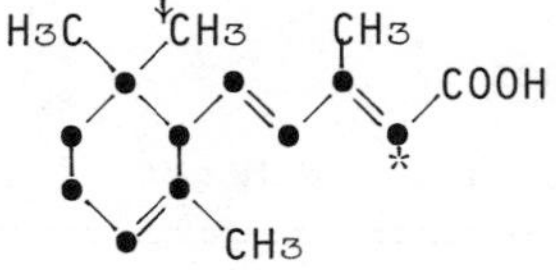

(E,E)-3-Methyl-5-(2,6,6-trimethyl-2-cyclohexen-1-yl)-2,4-pentadienoic-2-^{14}C acid

The cis, trans and trans, trans isomers were obtained in a ratio of 1:2, respectively.

H. Lehmann, D. Gross, and H. R. Schütte, Z. Chem., 12, 416 (1972).

Br*CH_2COOH $\xrightarrow[\text{2. } (C_6H_5)_3P\text{, } C_6H_6]{\text{1. } CH_2N_2}$ $(C_6H_5)_3P$=*$CHCOOCH_3$
3. NaOH

Bromoacetic-2-^{14}C acid

(Triphenylphosphoranylidene)-acetic-α-^{14}C acid methyl ester

1. 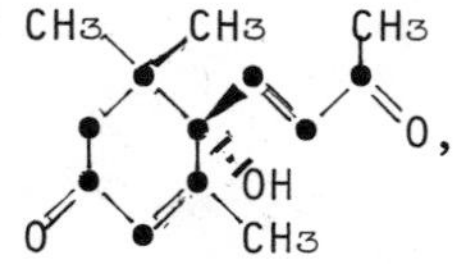

toluene, Δ

2. $NaOCH_3$, CH_3OH →

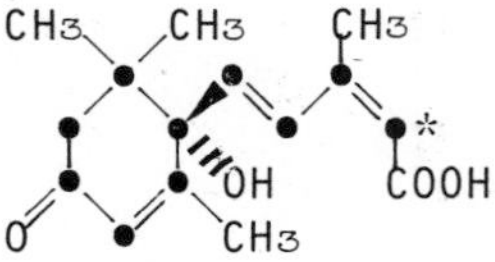

Abscisic acid
[[R-(Z,E)]-5-(1-Hydroxy-2,6,6-trimethyl-4-oxo-2-cyclohexen-1-yl)-3-methyl-2,4-pentadienoic-2-^{14}C acid]

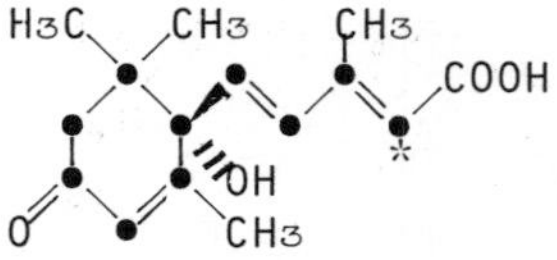

(trans-Δ^2)-Abscisic acid
[[S-(E,E)]-5-(1-Hydroxy-2,6,6-trimethyl-4-oxo-2-cyclohexen-1-yl)-3-methyl-2,4-pentadienoic-2-^{14}C acid]

A mixture of chromatographically separable isomers was obtained in 20% yield.

J.-C. Bonnafous and M. Mousseron-Canet, Bull. Soc. Chim. Fr., 4551 (1971).

Diterpenes

11-6 Acyclic and Monocyclic

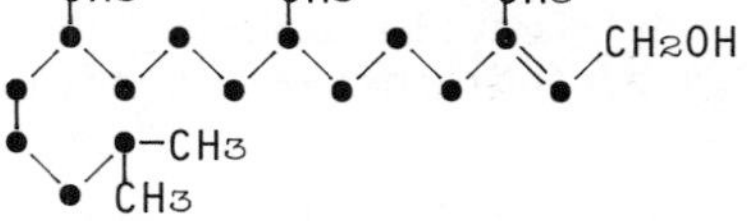

1. H_2, PtO_2
2. MsCl
3. $LiAlH_4$ →

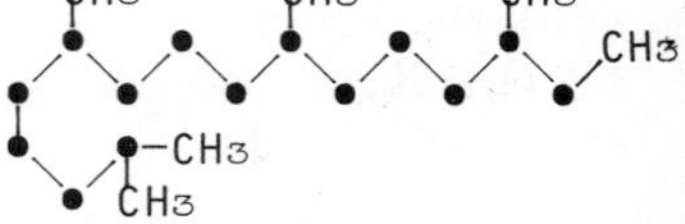

Phytol
[(E)-3,7,11,15-Tetramethyl-2-hexadecen-1-ol-U-^{14}C]

Phytane
[2,6,10,14-Tetramethylhexadecane-U-^{14}C]

P. W. Albro and R. O. Thomas, Biochem. Biophys. Acta, 372, 1 (1974).

$BrCH_2COOCH_3$ (with * on the CH_2 carbon: Br*CH_2COOCH_3) —[$(C_2H_5O)_3P$, Δ]→ $(C_2H_5O)_2P(=O)$*CH_2COOCH_3 (93%)

Bromacetic-2-^{14}C acid methyl ester → (Diethoxyphosphinyl)acetic-2-^{14}C acid methyl ester

1. NaH, DME
2. (E,E)-farnesylacetone (74% crude)
3. $LiAlH_4$ (78%)

→ $(CH_3)_2C{=}CHCH_2(CH_2C(CH_3){=}CHCH_2)_2CH_2C(CH_3){=}$*$CHCH_2OH$

3,7,11,15-Tetramethyl-2,6,10,14-heptadecatetraen-1-ol-2-[14]C

W. M. Walter, Jr., J. Label. Compounds, 3, 54 (1967).

Br*CH_2COOH —[1. CH_2N_2; 2. $P(OCH_3)_3$]→ $(CH_3O)_2PO$*CH_2COOCH_3 (81%)

Bromoacetic-2-2-^{14}C acid → (Dimethoxyphosphinyl)-acetic-2-^{14}C acid methyl ester

1. NaH, THF/HMPA
2. β-ionone

→

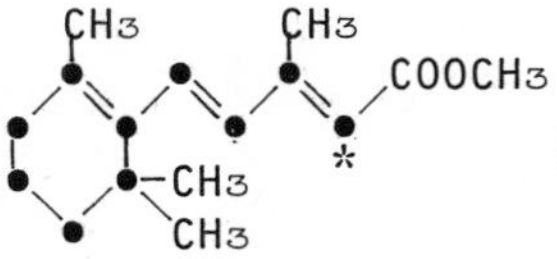

CH3
CH3
COOCH3
CH3
CH3
*

(70%)

trans-Methyl-β-ionylidene acetate
[(E,E)-3-Methyl-5-(2,6,6-trimethyl-1-cyclohexen-1-yl)-2,4-pentadienoic-2-^{14}C acid methyl ester]

1. $LiAlH_4$, Et_2O, -50°C (94%)
2. MnO_2, CH_3OH (97%)
3. NaOH, CH_3COCH_3 (54%)

→

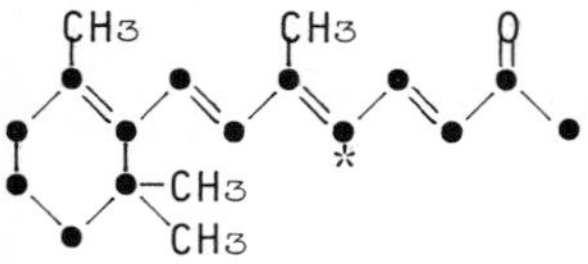

CH3
CH3
O
CH3
CH3
*

trans-C_{18}-Ketone
[(E,E,E)-6-Methyl-8-(2,6,6-trimethyl-1-cyclohexen-1-yl)-3,5,7-octatrien-2-one-5-^{14}C]

—[NaH, $(CH_3O)_2POCH_2COOCH_3$, THF/HMPA]→

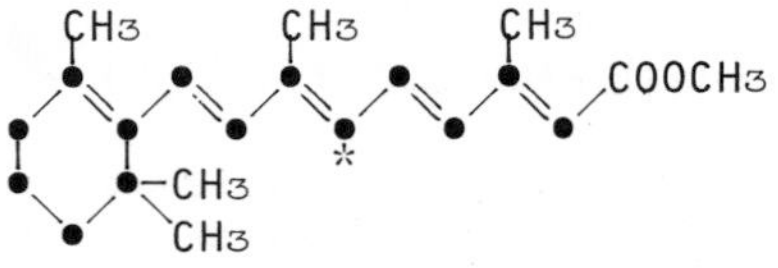
CH3
CH3
CH3
COOCH3
*
CH3
CH3

(73%)

LiAlH
Et2O, -60°C

Retinoic acid methyl ester
[3,7-Dimethyl-9-(2,6,6-trimethyl-1-cyclohexen-1-yl)-2,4,6,8-nonatetraenoic acid-6-^{14}C methyl ester]

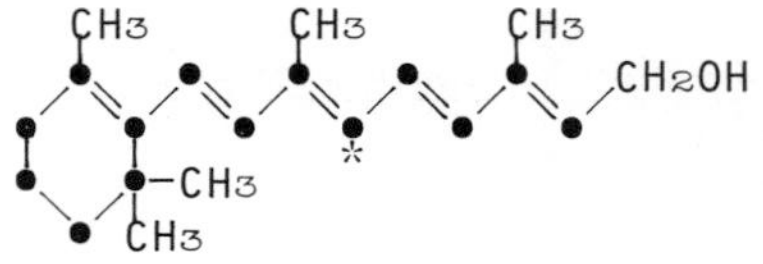
CH3
CH3
CH3
CH2OH
*
CH3
CH3

(100%; 20% overall from bromo acetic acid)

trans-Retinol
[3,7-Dimethyl-9-(2,6,6-trimethyl-1-cyclohexen-1-yl)-2,4,6,8-nonatetraenol-6-^{14}C]

J. D. Bu'Lock, S. A. Quarrie, and D. A. Taylor, J. Label. Compounds, 9, 311 (1973).

11-7 Polycyclic

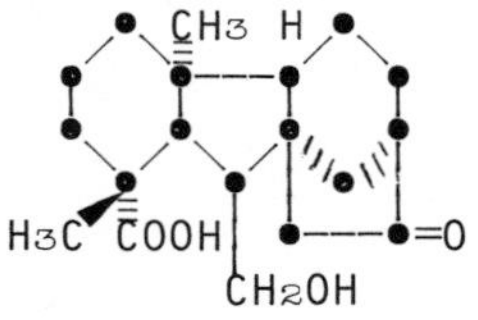
CH3 H
H3C COOH
=O
CH2OH

$(C_6H_5)_3P{=}{*}CH_2$

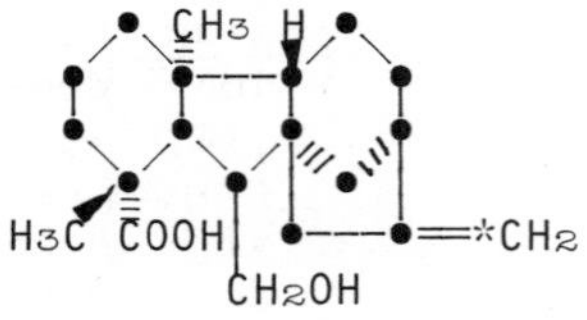
CH3 H
H3C COOH
=*CH2
CH2OH

(1α,4aα,4bβ,10β)-10-(Hydroxymethyl)-1,4a-dimethyl-8-oxo-gibbane-1-carboxylic acid

(1α,4aα,4bβ,10β)-10-(Hydroxymethyl)-1,4a-dimethyl-8-(methylene-^{14}C) gibbane-1-carboxylic acid

This substrate was converted to gibberellic acid-^{14}C (in 29% yield) under microbiological conditions.

J. R. Hanson and J. Hawker, Phytochemistry, 12, 1073 (1973); Tetrahedron Lett., 4299 (1972).

(1α,2β,4aα,4bβ,10β)-2,4a,7-Trihydroxy-1-methyl-8-methylenegibb-3-ene-1,10-dicarboxylic acid 1,4a-lactone anhydride

$\xrightarrow[CH_3OLi,\ CH_3OH]{NH_2{*}CH_2COOH}$

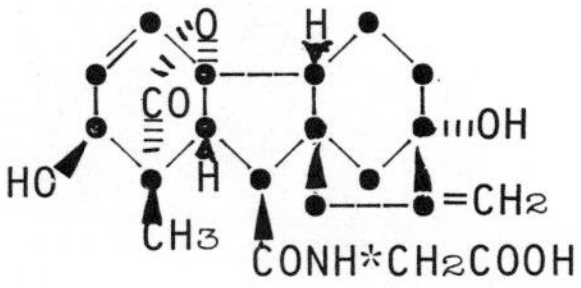
O
H
CO
OH
HO
H
=CH2
CH3
CONH*CH2COOH

(28%)

(1α,2β,4aα,4bβ,10β)-10-[[Carboxy-methyl-^{14}C amino]carbonyl]-2,4a,7-trihydroxy-1-methyl-8-methylene-gibbene-1-carboxylic acid-δ-lactone

M. Lischewski and G. Adam, Z. Chem., 16, 357 (1976).

Triterpenes

$(^*CH_3)_2CHI$ $\xrightarrow[2.\ C_6H_5Li]{1.\ (C_6H_5)_2S,\ AgBF_4}$ $(C_6H_5)_2S{=}C(^*CH_3)_2$

1,1'-[(1-Methyl-ethylidene)thio]-bisbenzene

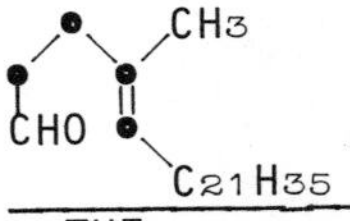
CH3
CHO
C21H35

$\xrightarrow{THF}$

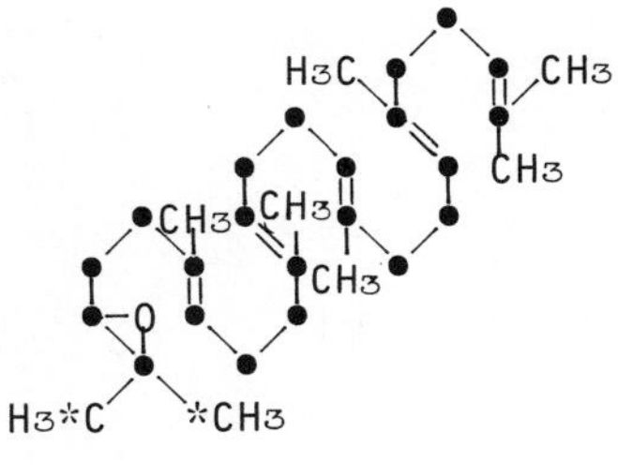
H3C
CH3
CH3
CH3
CH3
CH3
O
H3*C
*CH3

2,3-Epoxysqualene-(1,2-methyl-^{14}C)

J. Bascoul, D. Nikolaidis, A. Crastes de Paulet, and L. Pichat, Bull. Soc. Chim. Fr., Part 2, 2318 (1973).

12

Steroids

12-1 Androgens

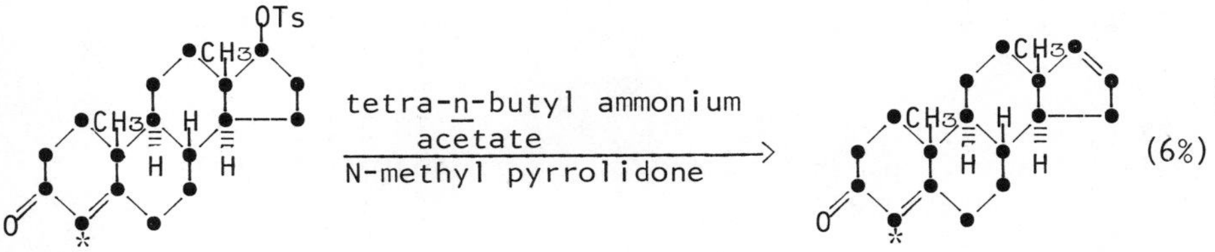

OTs
CH3
CH3
H
H
H
O
*
tetra-n-butyl ammonium acetate
N-methyl pyrrolidone
(6%)

Testosterone tosylate
[(17β)-17-[[(4-Methylphenyl)-sulfonyl]oxy]adrost-4-en-3-one-4-^{14}C]

Androsta-4,16-dien-3-one-4-^{14}C

M. Wilkinson, M. M. Coombs, and D. B. Gower, J. Label. Compounds, 6, 386 (1970).

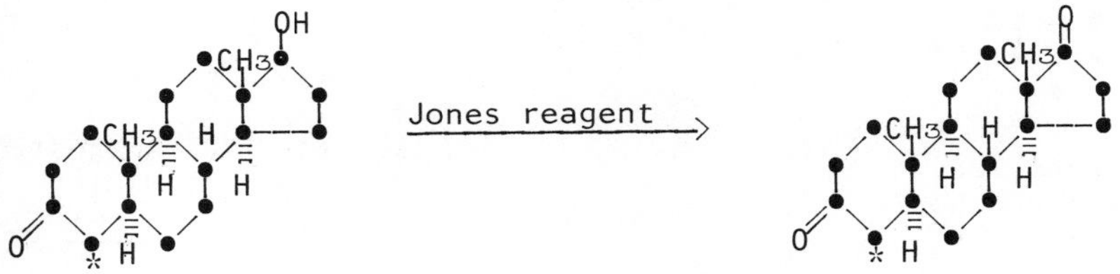

OH
CH3
CH3
H
H
H
O
*
H
Jones reagent

(5α,17β)-17-Hydroxy-androstan-3-one-4-^{14}C

(5α)-Androstane-3,17-dione-4-^{14}C

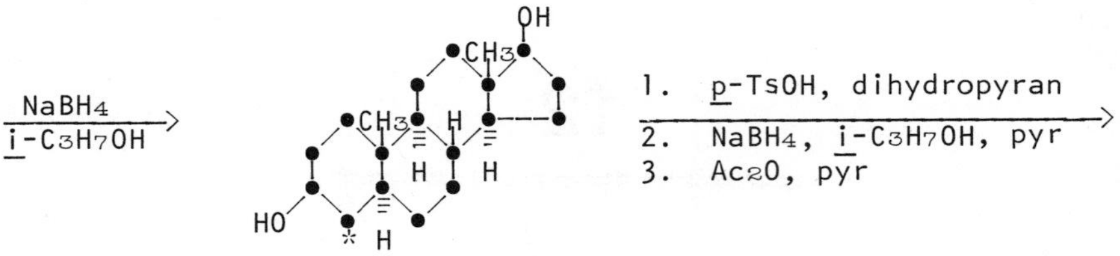
NaBH4
i-C3H7OH
OH
CH3
CH3
H
H
H
HO
H
1. p-TsOH, dihydropyran
2. NaBH4, i-C3H7OH, pyr
3. Ac2O, pyr

(3β,5α,17β)-Androstane-3,17-diol-4-[14]C

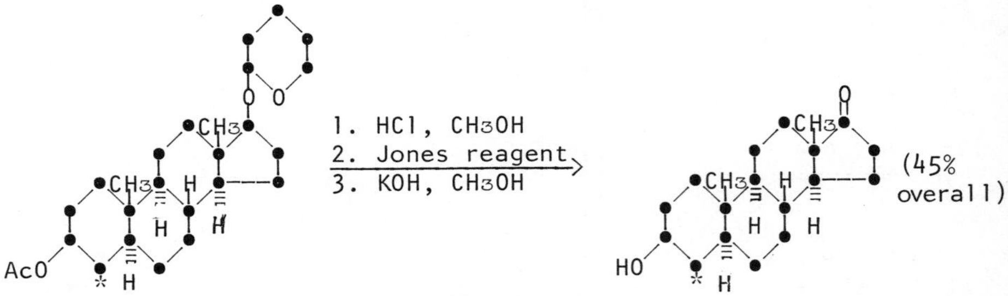
O
O
CH3
CH3
H
H
H
AcO
H
1. HCl, CH3OH
2. Jones reagent
3. KOH, CH3OH
O
CH3
CH3
H
H
H
(45% overall)
HO
H

(3β,5α,17β)-17-[(Tetrahydro-2H-pyran-2-yl)oxy]androstan-3-ol acetate-4-[14]C

(3β,5α)-3-Hydroxy-androstan-17-one-4-[14]C

L. Milewich and H. U. Schweikert, J. Label. Compound. Radiopharm., 14, 427 (1978).

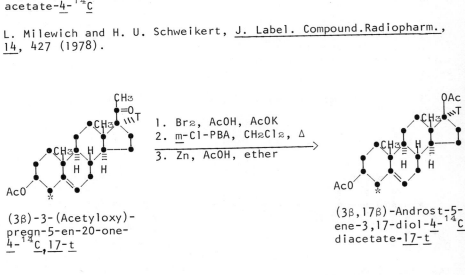

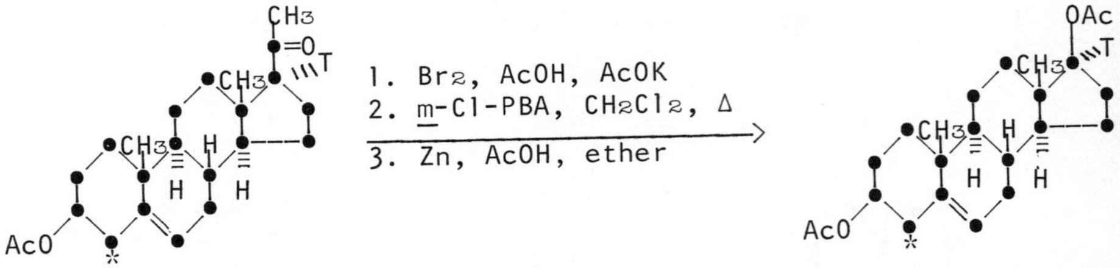
CH3
=O
T
CH3
CH3
H
H
H
AcO
1. Br2, AcOH, AcOK
2. m-Cl-PBA, CH2Cl2, Δ
3. Zn, AcOH, ether
OAc
T
CH3
CH3
H
H
H
AcO

(3β)-3-(Acetyloxy)-pregn-5-en-20-one-4-^{14}C, 17-t

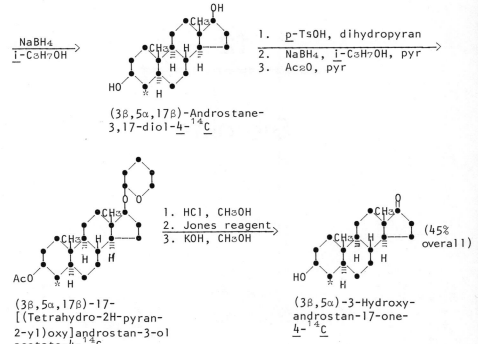

(3β,17β)-Androst-5-ene-3,17-diol-4-^{14}C diacetate-17-t

1. CH_3ONa, CH_3OH, Et_2O
2. Br_2, AcOH, AcOK
3. Jones reagent
4. Zn, AcOH, ether

→

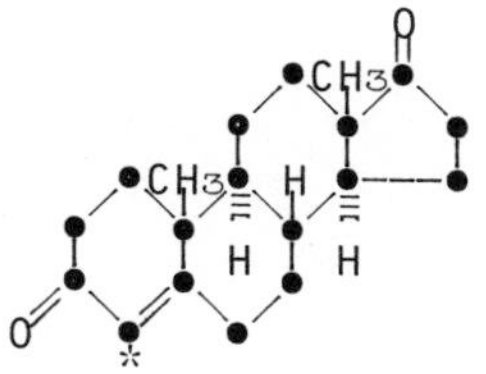

Androst-4-ene-3,17-dione-4-^{14}C

L. Milewich and L. R. Axelrod, J. Label. Compounds, 7, 101 (1971).

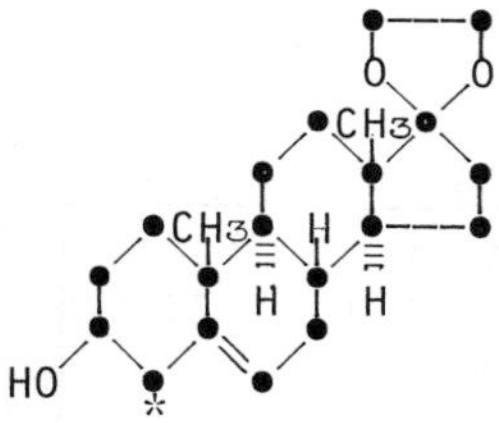

(3β)-3-Hydroxyandrost-5-en-17-one-4-^{14}C cyclic-1,2-ethanediyl acetal

1. m-ClPBA, $CHCl_3$ (quant.)
2. $LiAlH_4$, THF, Δ (90%)

→

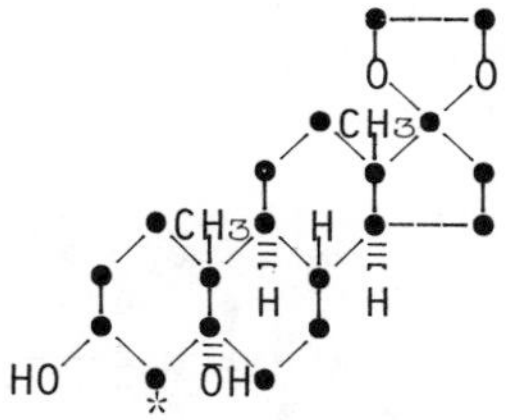

(3β,5α)-3,5-Dihydroxyandrostan-17-one-4-^{14}C cyclic-1,2-ethanediyl acetal

1. CH_3SO_2Cl, pyr
2. $C_6H_5N(C_2H_5)_2$, CH_3COCl, $CHCl_3$, Δ

→

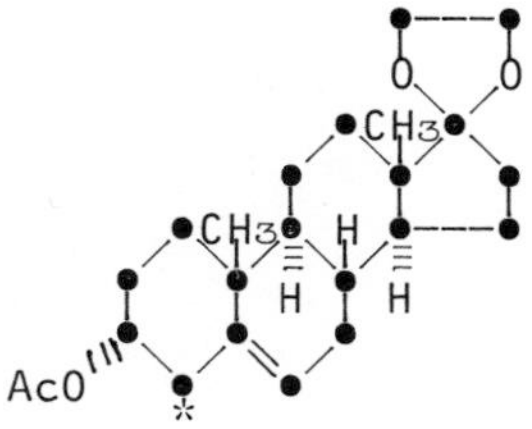

(3α)-3-(Acetyloxy)androst-5-en-17-one-4-^{14}C cyclic-1,2-ethanediyl acetal

1. CrO_3, pyr, $CHCl_3$ (~60%)
2. Li, NH_3, Et_2O (~35%)
3. H_2NOCH_2COOH } (~90%)
4. conc. HCl, EtOH }

→

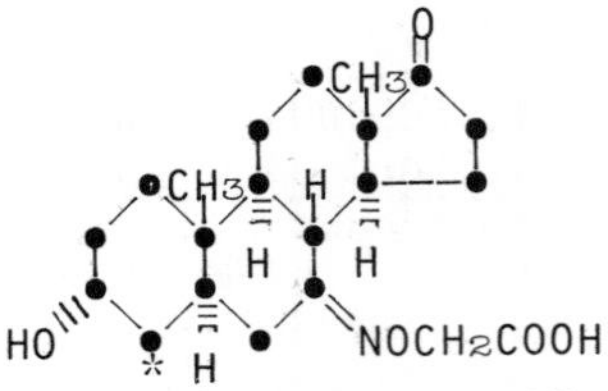

[[[(3α,5α)-3-Hydroxy-17-oxoandrostan-7-ylidene]amino]oxy]acetic-4-^{14}C acid

The labeled compound was to be used as a conjugate in radioimmuno-assay studies.

R. S. Rosenfeld, J. Kream, I. Paul, and L. Hellman, Steroids, 25, 153 (1975).

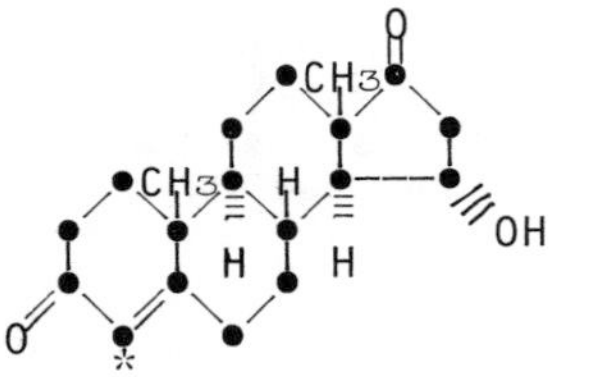

(15α)-15-Hydroxyandrost-4-ene-3,17-dione-4-^{14}C

→

1. AcCl, Ac_2O, Δ
2. $HOCH_2CH_2OH$, C_6H_6, p-TSA, Δ
3. $NaBH_4$, EtOH
4. $LiAlH_4$, Et_2O
5. p-TSA, acetone/H_2O, Δ

→

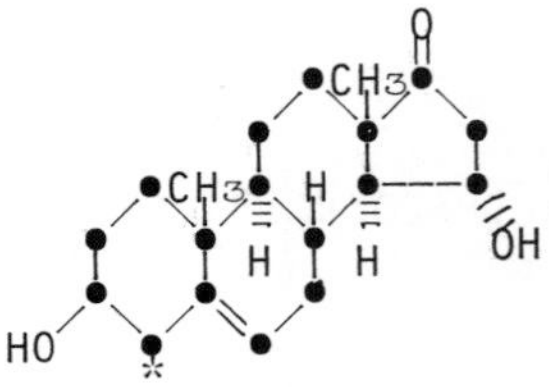

(8% overall)

(3β,15α)-3,15-Dihydroxyandrost-5-en-17-one-4-^{14}C

B. R. Bhavnani and F. Z. Stanczyk, Steroids, 20, 129 (1972).

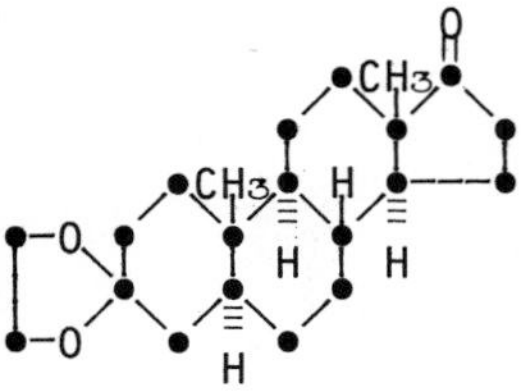

(5α)-Androstane-3,17-dione cyclic-3-(1,2-ethanediyl acetal)

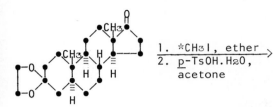

1. $^*CH_3I$, ether
2. p-TsOH.H_2O, acetone
→

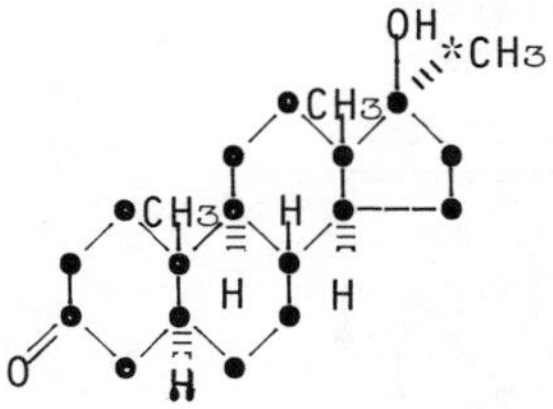

(5α,17β)-17-Hydroxy-17-methylandrostan-3-one-(17-methyl-^{14}C)

1. 35% HCl, $CH_3OH/H_2O/C_6H_6$, t-butyl nitrite
2. $NH_2OH.HCl$, pyr, CH_3OH
→

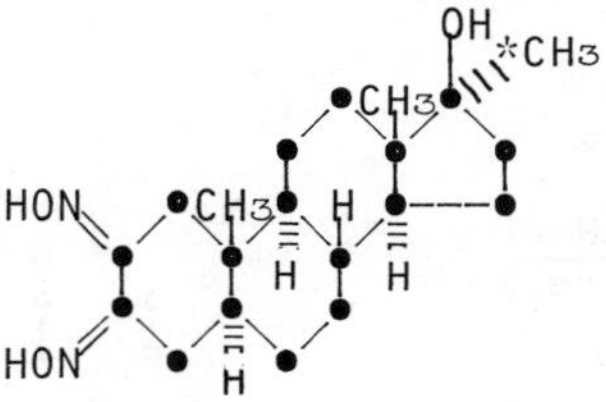

(5α,17β)-17-Hydroxy-17-methylandrostane-2,3-dione dioxime-(17-methyl-^{14}C)

KOH / ethylene glycol
→

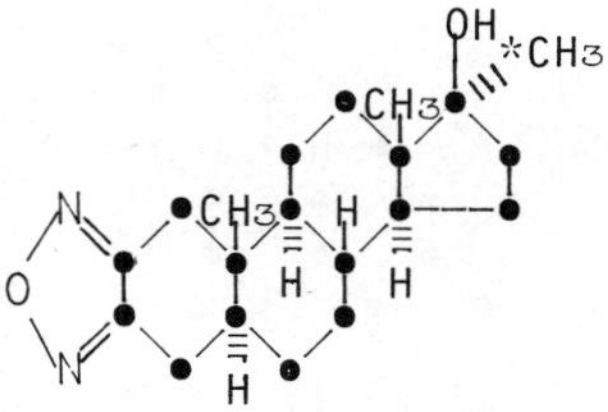

(21% from $^*CH_3I$)

(5α,17β)-17-Methylandrostano[2,3-C][1,2,5]-oxadiazol-17-ol-(17-methyl-^{14}C)

T. Takegoshi, Chem. Pharm. Bull. (Tokyo), 20, 1260 (1972).

12-2 Estrogens

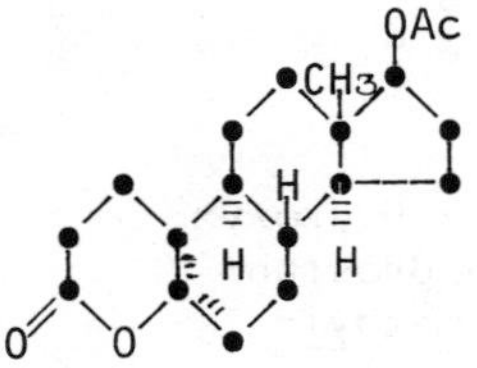

$\xrightarrow{*CH_3MgI}$

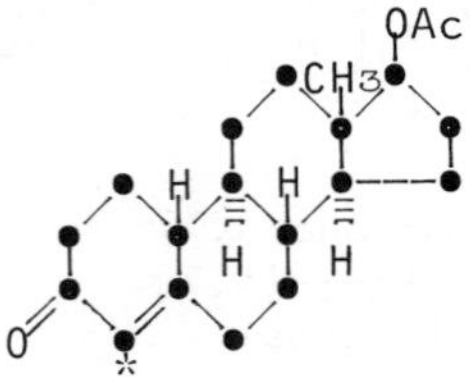

(17β)-17-(Acetyloxy)-4-oxaestr-5(10)-en-3-one (mixture of isomers)

(17β)-17-(Acetyloxy)estr-4-en-3-one-4-^{14}C

1. KOH, CH_3OH
2. Jones reagent

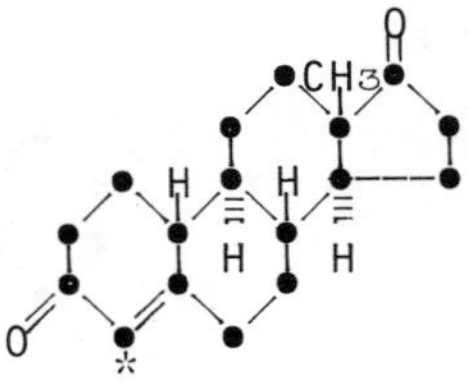

Estr-4-ene-3,17-dione-4-^{14}C

1. HC≡CH
2. $CH_3(CH_2)_5COOH$

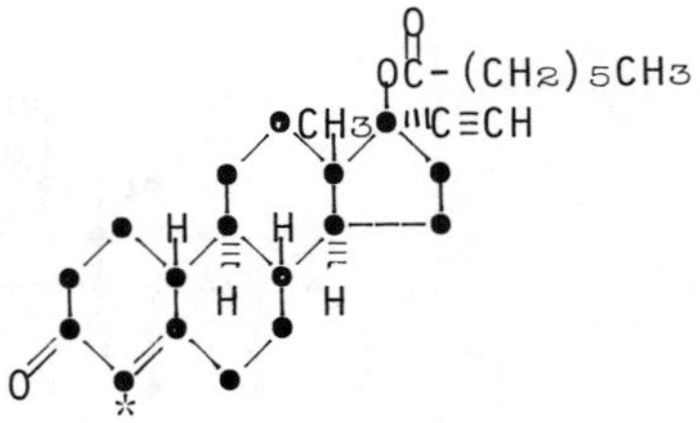

(6% from Ba*CO_3)

(17β)-17-Ethynyl-17-(1-oxoheptyloxy)estr-4-en-3-one-4-^{14}C

$CH_3(CH_2)_5MgCl \xrightarrow{*CO_2} CH_3(CH_2)_5{*}COOH$

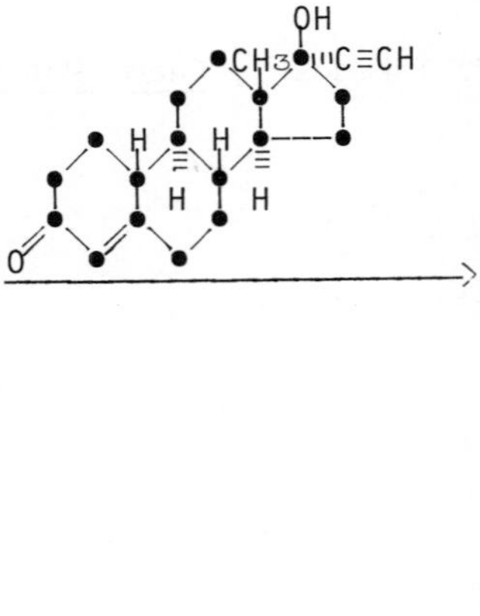

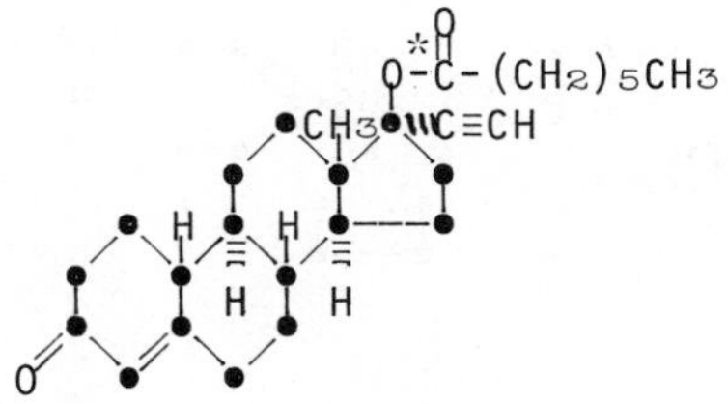

(35% from Ba*CO_3)

(17β)-17-Ethynyl-17-(1-oxoheptyloxy-1-^{14}C)-estr-4-en-3-one

P. E. Schulze, J. Label. Compounds, 5, 312 (1969).

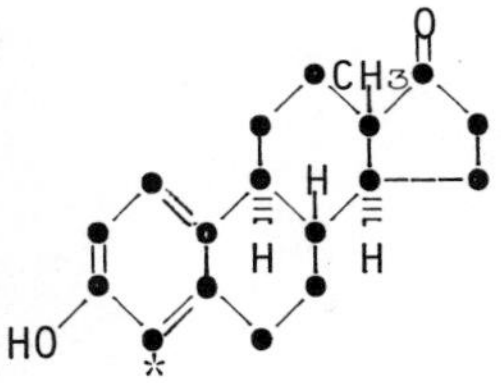

3-Hydroxyestra-1,3,5(10)-trien-17-one-4-^{14}C

HC≡CLi, ethylenediamine / DMSO →

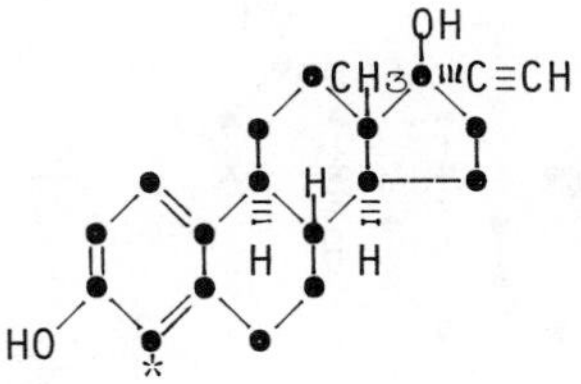

(45%)

(17β)-17-Ethynylestra-1,3,5-(10)-triene-3,17-diol-4-^{14}C

G. Cooley and I. A. Harris, J. Label. Compounds, 5, 8 (1969).

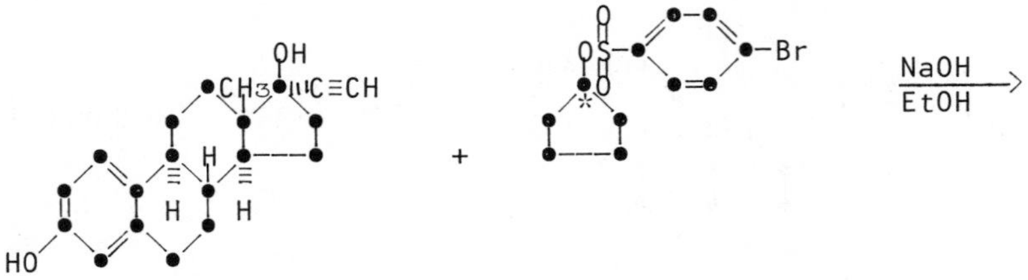
OH
CH3
C≡CH
H
H
H
HO
+
O
OS
O
Br
NaOH
EtOH

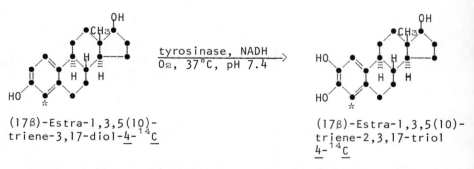

(17β)-17-Ethynylestra-1,3,5(10)-triene-3,17-diol

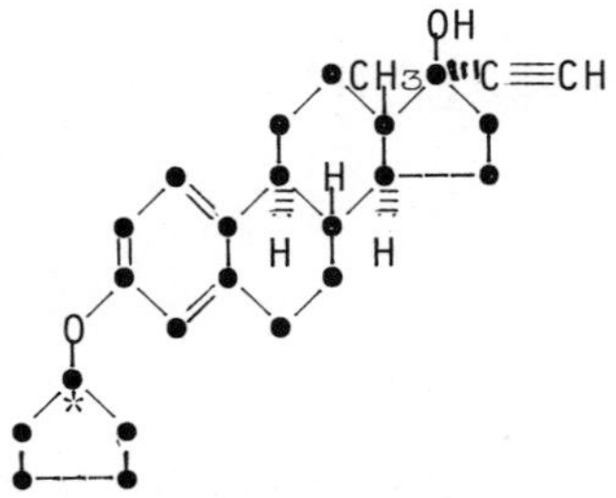
OH
CH3
C≡CH
H
H
H
O

(~10% from cyclopentanol-^{14}C; ~3% from Ba*CO_3)

(17β)-3-(Cyclopentyloxy-1-^{14}C)-17-ethynylestra-1,3,5-(10)-trien-17-ol

E. J. Merrill and G. G. Vernice, J. Label. Compounds, 6, 266 (1970)

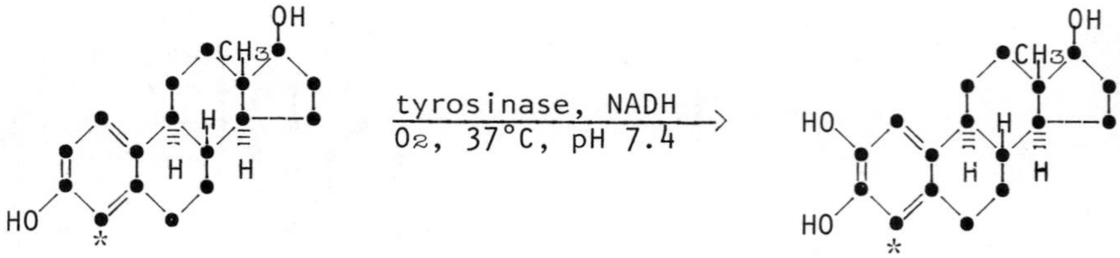
OH
CH3
H
H
H
HO
tyrosinase, NADH
O2, 37°C, pH 7.4
HO
HO

(17β)-Estra-1,3,5(10)-triene-3,17-diol-4-^{14}C

(17β)-Estra-1,3,5(10)-triene-2,3,17-triol 4-^{14}C

P. H. Jellinck and B. J. Brown, Steroids, 17, 133 (1971).

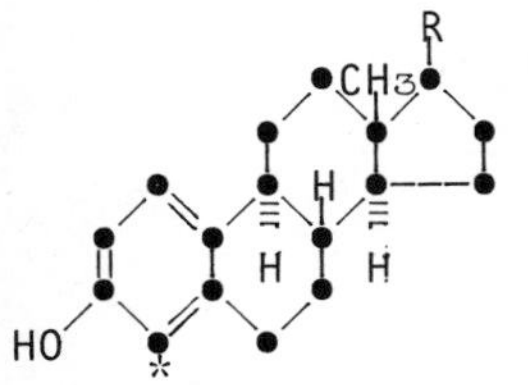

1. $(KSO_3)_2NO$, acetone/10% AcOH
2. KI, acetone

R=O; 3-Hydroxyestra-1,3,5(10)-trien-17-one-4-^{14}C

R= OH / H; (17β)-Estra-1,3,5(10)-triene-3,17-diol-4-^{14}C

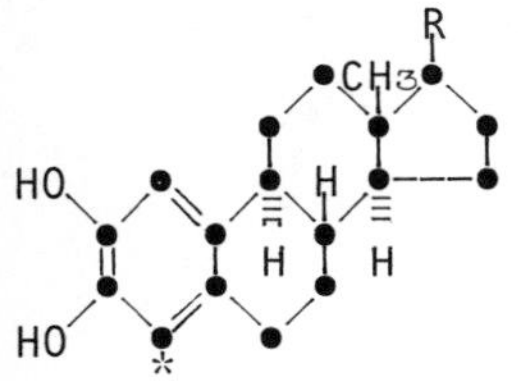

+

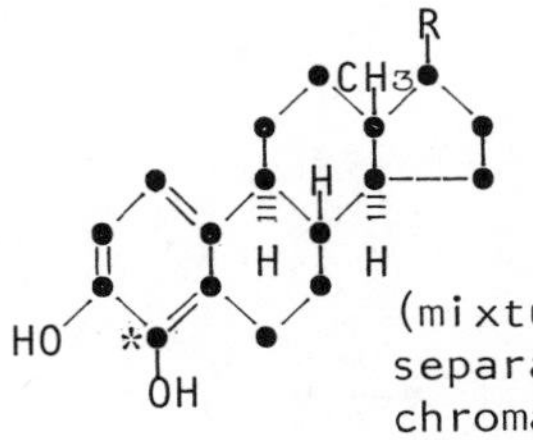

(mixture separable by chromatography)

R=O; 2,3-Dihydroxyestra-1,3,5(10)-trien-17-one-4-^{14}C (15%)

R= OH / H; (17β)-Estra-1,3,5(10)-triene-2,3,17-triol-4-^{14}C (23%)

R=O; 3,4-Dihydroxyestra-1,3,5(10)-trien-17-one-4-^{14}C (7%)

R= OH / H; (17β)-Estra-1,3,5-(10)-triene-3,4,17-triol-4-^{14}C (11%)

H. P. Gelbke, O. Haupt, and R. Knuppen, Steroids, 21, 205 (1973).

$CH_3CH_2OOC^*CH_2^*CH_2COOCH_2CH_3$ +

Butanedioic acid diethyl ester-2,3-^{14}C

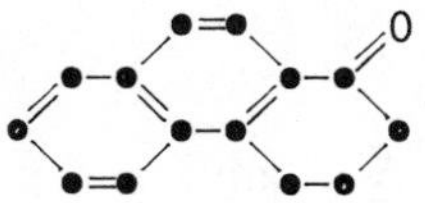

3,4-Dihydro-1(2H)-phenanthrenone

K / t-butanol →

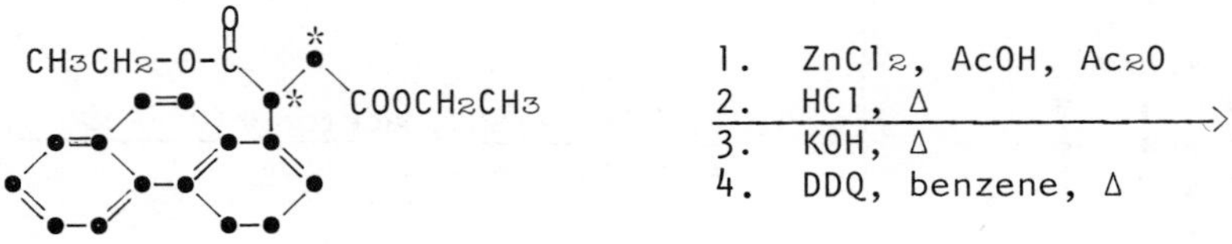
CH3CH2-O-C
COOCH2CH3
1. ZnCl2, AcOH, Ac2O
2. HCl, Δ
3. KOH, Δ
4. DDQ, benzene, Δ

3,4-Dihydrophenanthrene-1-(2-butanedioic-2,3-^{14}C)-acid diethyl ester

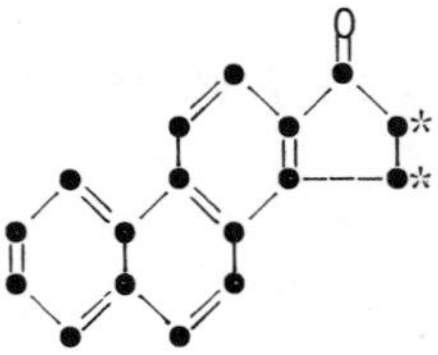

(33% overall chemical yield)

15,16-Dihydro-17H-cyclopenta[a]phenanthren-17-one-15,16-^{14}C

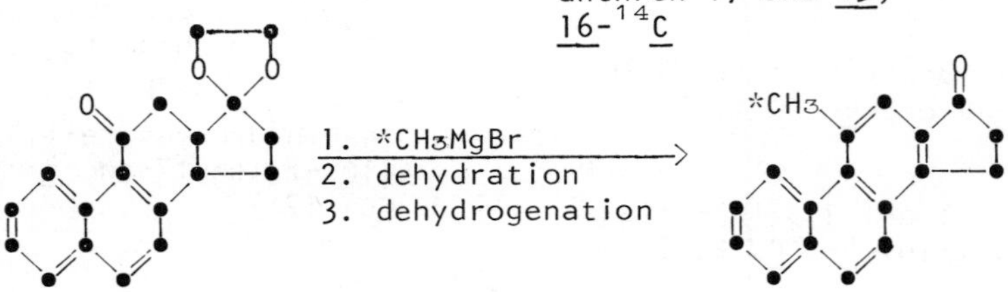
1. *CH3MgBr
2. dehydration
3. dehydrogenation
*CH3

(55% overall)

15,16-Dihydro-11-methyl-^{14}C-17H-cyclopenta[a]phenanthren-17-one

M. M. Coombs, S. B. Jaitly, and F. E. H. Crawley, J. Chem. Soc. (C), 1266 (1970).

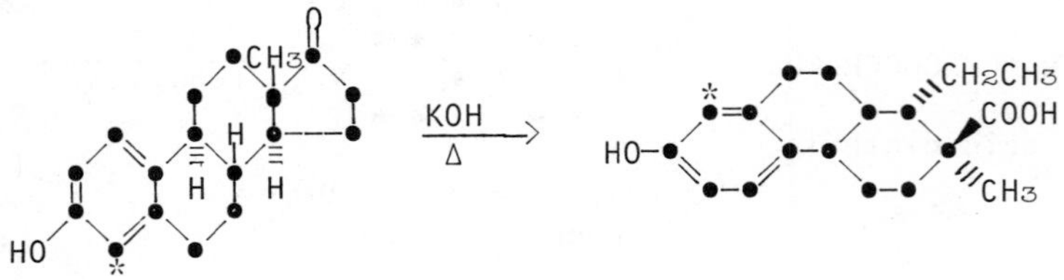
CH3
HO
KOH
Δ
HO
CH2CH3
COOH
CH3

3-Hydroxyestra-1,3,5(10)-trien-17-one-4-^{14}C

1-Ethyl-1,2,3,4,4a,9,10,10a-Octahydro-7-hydroxy-2-methyl-2-phenanthrene-carboxylic-8-^{14}C acid

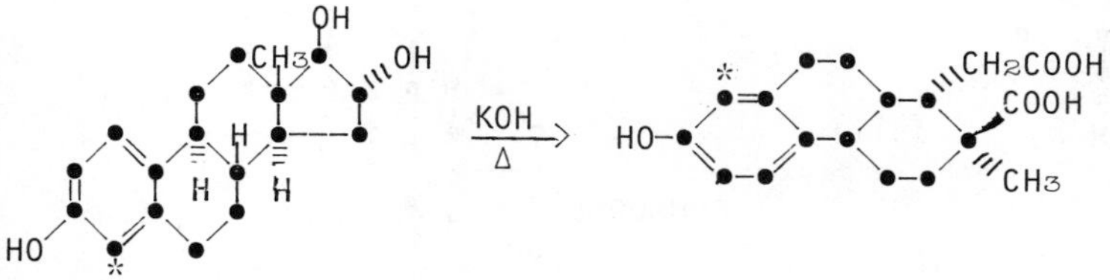
KOH
Δ

(yields: 0.1-2.0%)

Estra-1,3,5(10)-triene-3,16,17-triol-4-^{14}C

2-Carboxy-1,2,3,4,4a,9,10,10a-octahydro-7-hyroxy-2-methyl-1-phenanthreneacetic-8-^{14}C acid

N. Kundu and Y. Osawa, J. Label. Compounds, 10, 31 (1974).

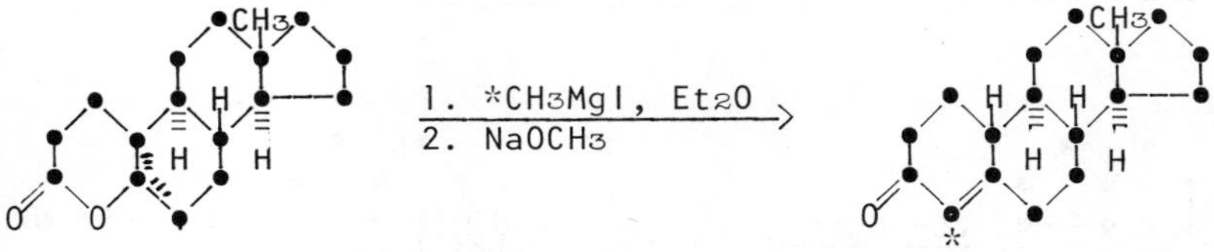
1. *CH_3MgI, Et_2O
2. $NaOCH_3$

(∿30%)

4-Oxaestr-5[and 5(10)]-en-3-one
(from ozonolysis of estr-4-en-3-one)

Estr-4-en-3-one-4-^{14}C

H_2, Pd/C
EtOAc →

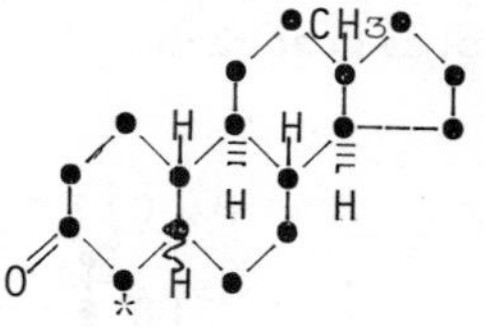

(quant.)

oxidation →

Estran-3-one-4-^{14}C
(mixture of 5α and 5β)

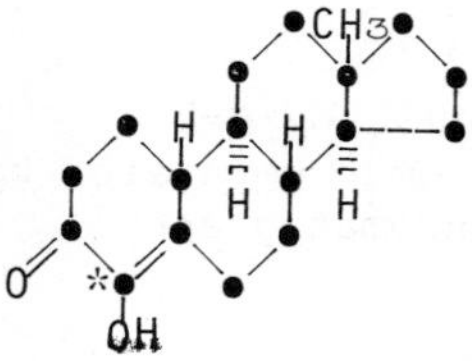

(∿39% yield plus ∿8% of the 2,3-dione isomer)

1. $Ba(OH)_2$ methyl-cellosolve, Δ
2. CH_2N_2 →

4-Hydroxyestr-4-en-3-one-4-^{14}C

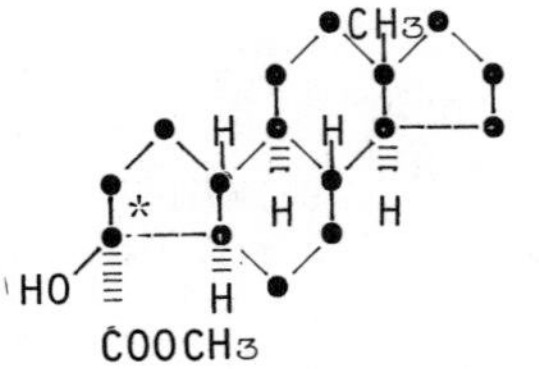

(41%) +

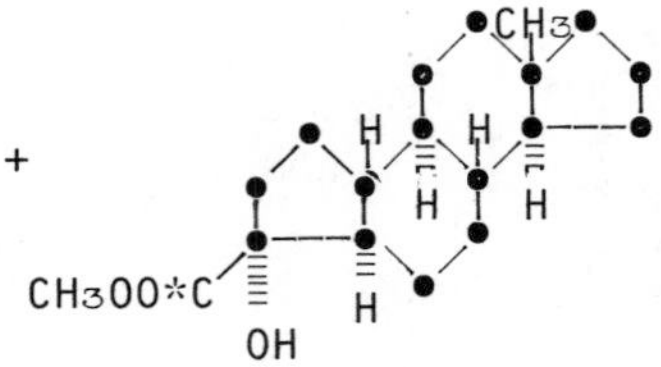

(13%)

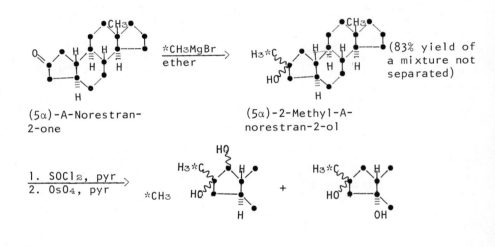

(3α,5α)-3-Hydroxy-A-norestrane-3-carboxylic-acid methyl ester-3-^{14}C

(3α,5β)-3-Hydroxy-A-norestrane-3-carboxylic-^{14}C acid methyl ester

The position of the carboxyl label was determined by degradation reactions; the position of the ring label was assumed. A mechanism is proposed.

J. Alais and J. Levisalles, Bull. Soc. Chim. Fr., 3731 (1971).

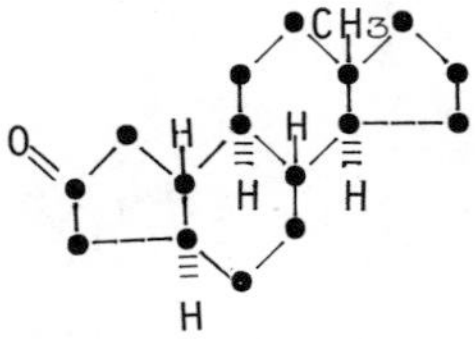

$*CH_3MgBr$ → ether

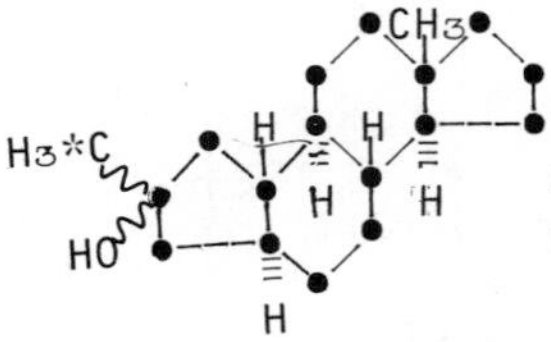

(83% yield of a mixture not separated)

(5α)-A-Norestran-2-one

(5α)-2-Methyl-A-norestran-2-ol

1. $SOCl_2$, pyr →
2. OsO_4, pyr

$*CH_3$

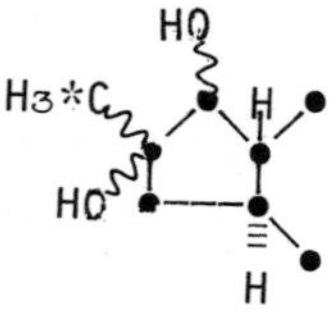

+

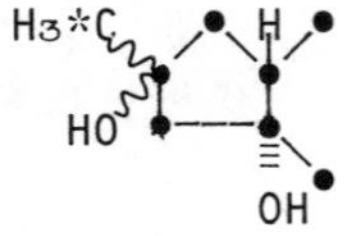

1. H_5IO_6, EtOH
2. 5% $NaOCH_3$ →
3. H_2, 5% Pd/C, EtOAc

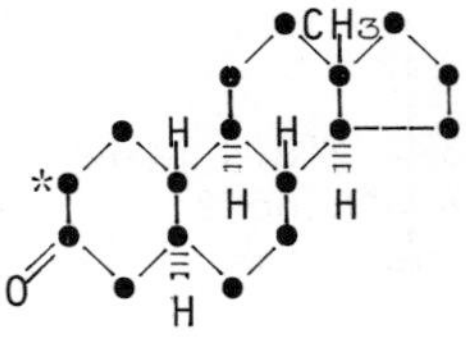

(∿14% of 2-keto isomer separated by chromatography)

(5α)-Estran-3-one-2-^{14}C

oxidation →

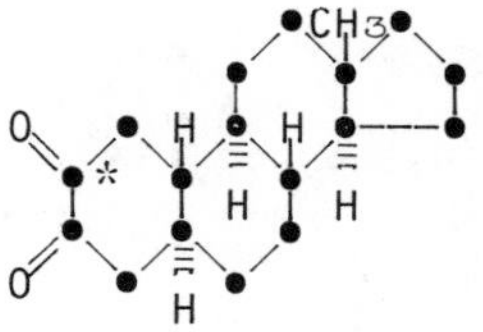
O
O
H
H
H
H
H
CH3

(38%)

1. $Ba(OH)_2$, methyl-cellosolve, Δ
2. CH_2N_2 →

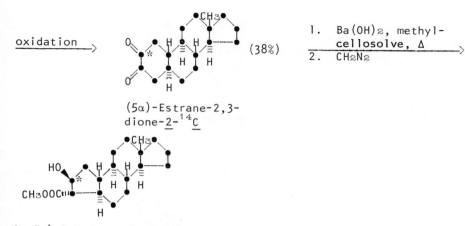

(5α)-Estrane-2,3-dione-2-[14]C

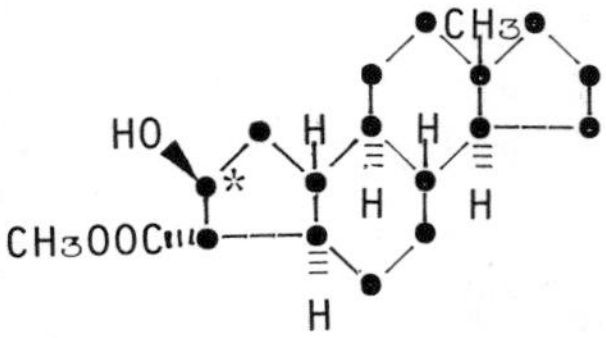
HO
CH3OOC
H
H
H
H
H
CH3

2α,5α)-2-Hydroxy-A-norestrane--carboxylic-2-^{14}C acid methyl ester

plus

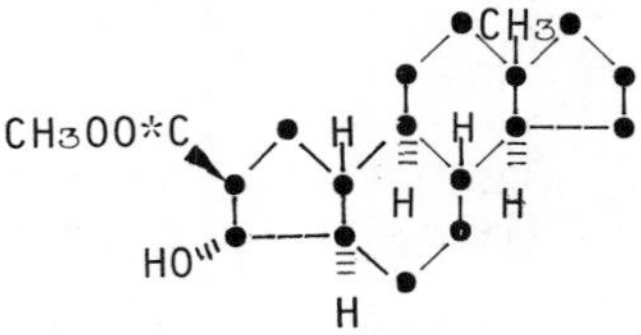
CH3OO*C
HO
H
H
H
H
H
CH3

(a 70% yield of a mixture of isomers in the ratio of 1:1 was obtained; the mixture was separable by chromotography)

(2β,5α)-2-Hydroxy-A-norestrane-2-carboxylic-^{14}C acid methyl ester

Decarboxylation reactions showed that 79% of the activity was in the carboxyl group of the β-isomer and only 17% of the activity was in the carboxyl group of the α-isomer (the remainder was assumed to be at position 2 in the ring). A mechanism is proposed.

J. Alais, P. Bourguignon, and J. Levisalles, Bull. Soc. Chim. Fr., 3737 (1971).

$Br^*CH_2{}^*CH_2OH$ —— 1. KCN, $EtOH/H_2O$, Δ (60%); 2. $N(C_2H_5)_3$, $Cl\text{-}PO(C_6H_5)_2$ (50%); 3. Δ → $^*CH_2={}^*CHCN$

2-Bromoethanol-1,2-[14]C

Acrylonitrile [2-Propenenitrile-1,2-^{14}C] (not isolated)

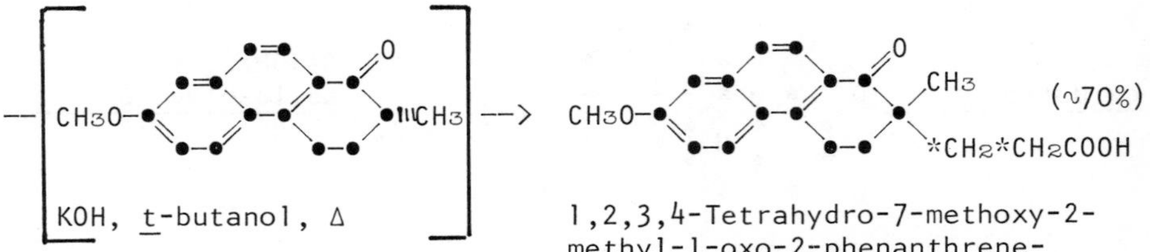
CH3O
O
CH3
KOH, t-butanol, Δ
CH3
(~70%)
*CH2*CH2COOH

1,2,3,4-Tetrahydro-7-methoxy-2-methyl-1-oxo-2-phenanthrene-propanoic α,β-^{14}C acid

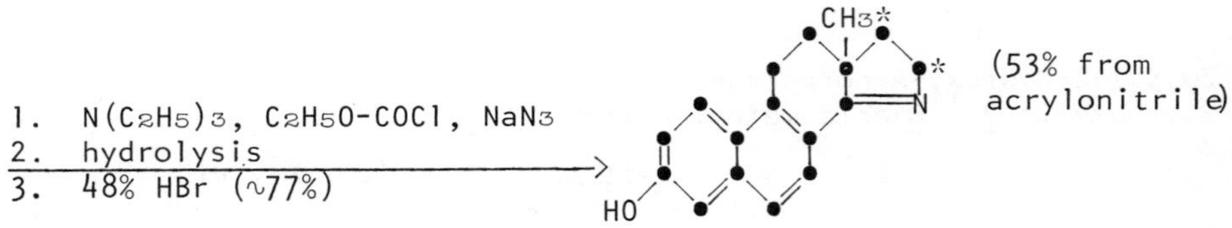
1. N(C2H5)3, C2H5O-COCl, NaN3
2. hydrolysis
3. 48% HBr (~77%)
CH3*
N
HO
(53% from acrylonitrile)

2,10,11,11a-Tetrahydro-11a-methyl-1H-napth[1,2g]indol-7-ol-1,2-^{14}C

K. D. Berlin, J. G. Morgan, N. N. Durham, and R. W. Chestnut, Steroids, 18, 577 (1971).

12-3 Progestogens

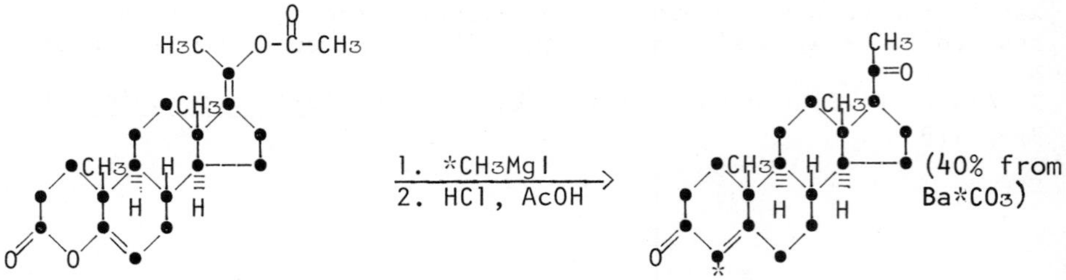
H3C
O-C-CH3
CH3
H
H
O
1. *CH3MgI
2. HCl, AcOH
CH3
=O
(40% from Ba*CO3)

20-(Acetyloxy)-4-oxapregna-5,17(20)-dien-3-one

Pregn-4-ene-3,20-dione-4-^{14}C

[plus 6% of (8α)-pregn-4-ene-3,20-dione-4-^{14}C and 2% of 3,5,20-trioxo-4,5-seco-A-pregnane-4-^{14}C]

H. Hoellinger, Nguyen-Hoang-Nam, and L. Pichat, J. Label. Compounds, 10, 617 (1974).

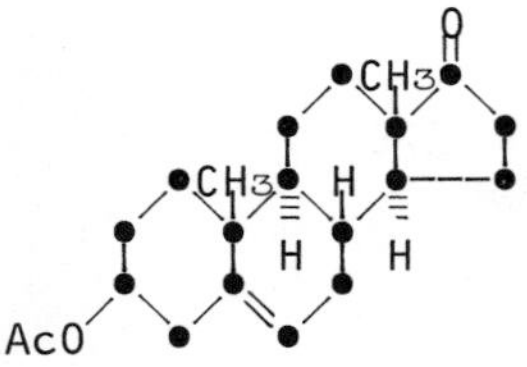
O
CH3
CH3
H
H
H
AcO

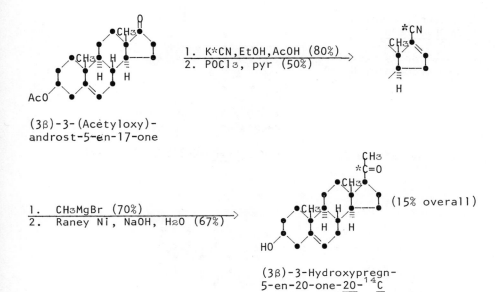

(3β)-3-(Acetyloxy)-androst-5-en-17-one

1. K*CN, EtOH, AcOH (80%)
2. $POCl_3$, pyr (50%)

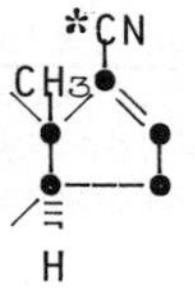
*CN
CH3
H

1. CH_3MgBr (70%)
2. Raney Ni, NaOH, H_2O (67%)

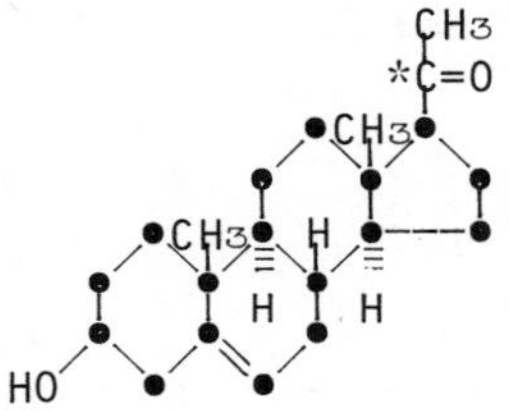
CH3
*C=O
CH3
CH3
H
H
H
HO

(15% overall)

(3β)-3-Hydroxypregn-5-en-20-one-<u>20</u>-^{14}<u>C</u>

A. M. Porto and E. G. Gros, <u>J. Label. Compounds</u>, <u>4</u>, 276 (1968).

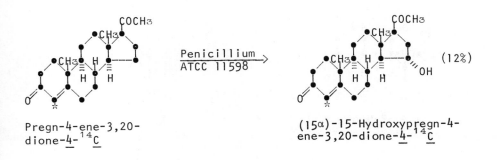

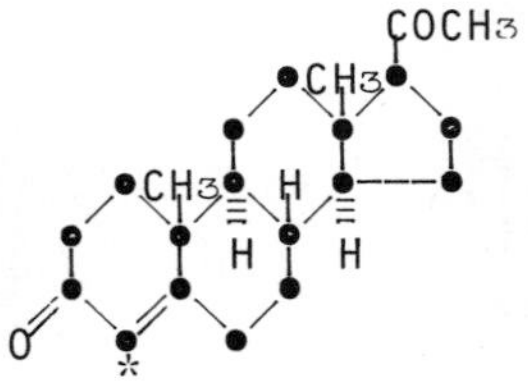
COCH3
CH3
CH3
H
H
H
O
*

Pregn-4-ene-3,20-dione-<u>4</u>-^{14}<u>C</u>

Penicillium ATCC 11598

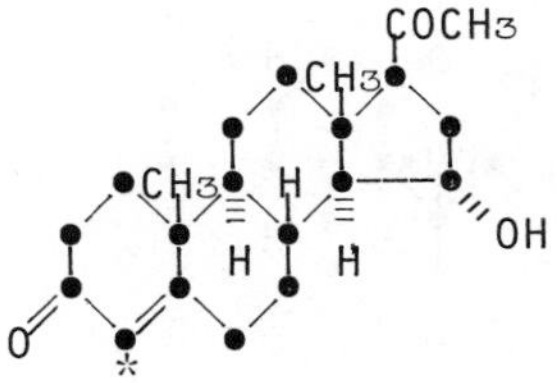
COCH3
CH3
CH3
H
H
H
OH
O
*

(12%)

(15α)-15-Hydroxypregn-4-ene-3,20-dione-<u>4</u>-^{14}<u>C</u>

1. CH_3COCl, Ac_2O, Δ
2. $NaBH_4$, EtOH
3. $LiAlH_4$, Et_2O
4. 20β-hydroxy steroid dehydrogenase, β-NAD^+

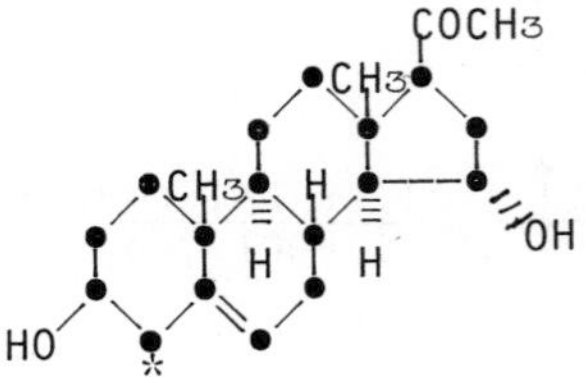

(25%)

(3β,15α)-3,15-Dihydroxypregn-5-ene-20-one-4-[14]C

B. R. Bhavnani and F. Z. Stanczyk, Steroids, 20, 129 (1972).

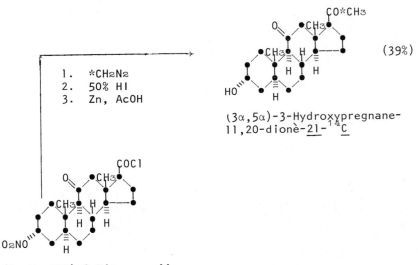

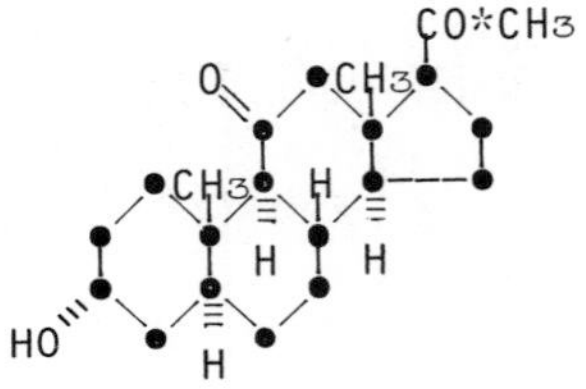

(39%)

(3α,5α)-3-Hydroxypregnane-11,20-dionè-21-[14]C

1. $*CH_2N_2$
2. 50% HI
3. Zn, AcOH

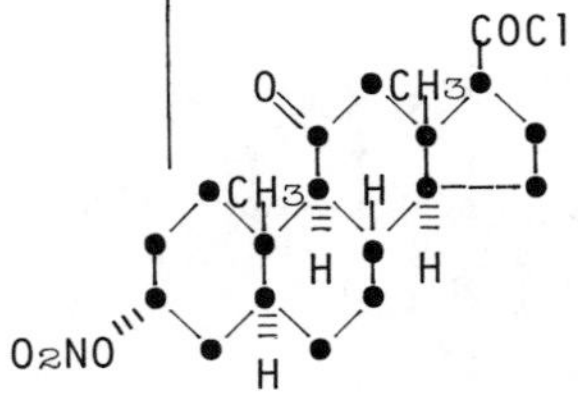

(3α,5α,17β)-3-Nitrooxy-11-oxoandrostane-17-carbonyl chloride

1. $*CH_2N_2$
2. conc. HCl, CH_2Cl_2
3. Zn, AcOH

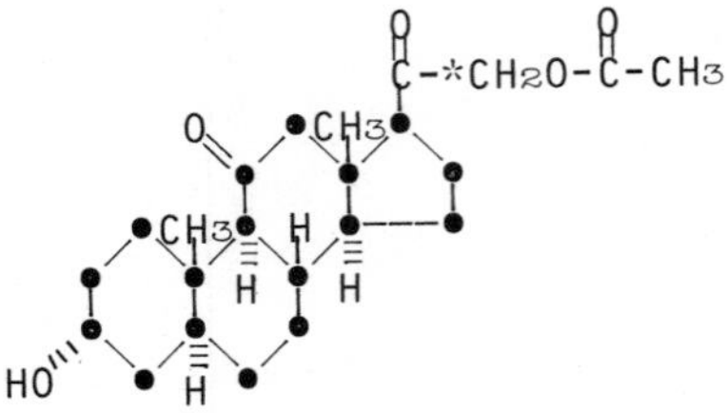

(43%)

(3α,5α)-21-(Acetyloxy)-3-hydroxypregnane-11,20-dione-21-[14]C

B. E. Ayres, C. E. Newall, and G. H. Phillips, Steroids, 26, 219 (1975).

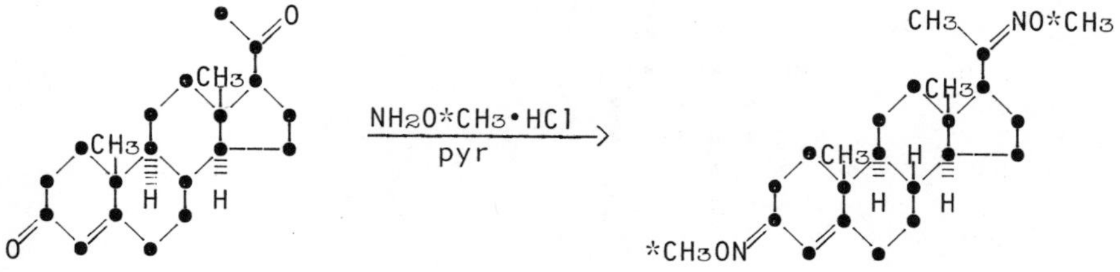
O
CH3
CH3
H
H
O
NH2O*CH3•HCl
pyr
CH3
NO*CH3
CH3
CH3
H
H
H
*CH3ON

Pregn-4-ene-3,20-dione

O,O'-(Dimethyl-^{14}C)-pregn-4-ene-3,20-dione dioxime

The procedure is also useful for 11-, 16-, 17-, and 20-ketosteroids.

F. Dray and I. Weliky, Anal. Biochem., 34, 387 (1970).

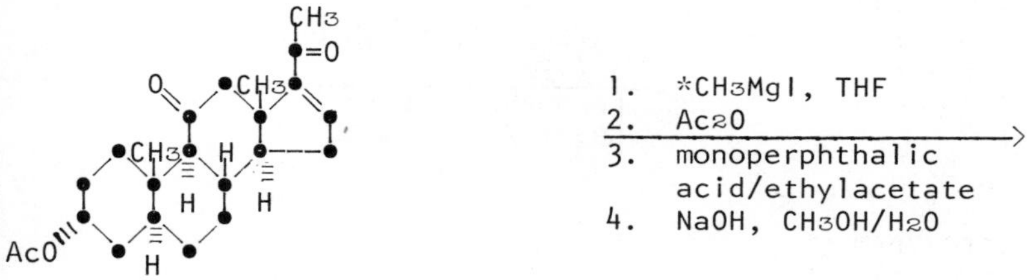
CH3
=O
O
CH3
CH3
H
H
H
H
AcO
1. *CH3MgI, THF
2. Ac2O
3. monoperphthalic acid/ethylacetate
4. NaOH, CH3OH/H2O

(3α,5α)-3-(Acetyloxy)pregn-16-ene-11,20-dione

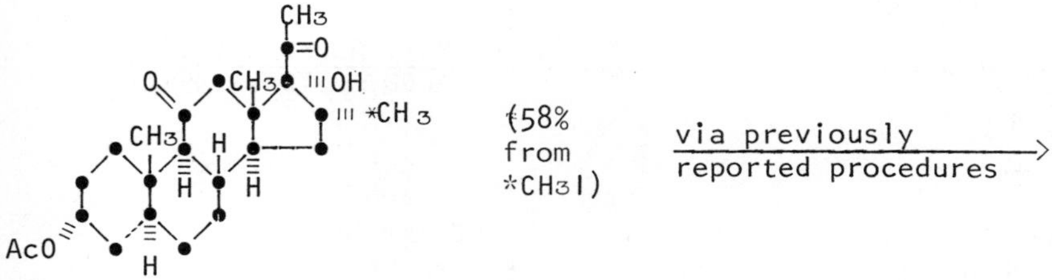
CH3
=O
O
CH3
OH
*CH3
CH3
H
H
H
AcO
H
(58% from *CH3I)
via previously reported procedures

(3α,5α,16α)-3,17-Dihydroxy-16-methyl-^{14}C-pregnane-11,20-dione

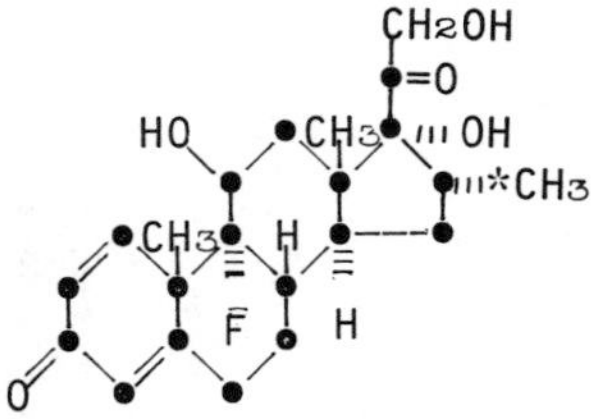

Dexamethasone
[(9α,11β,17α,16α)-9-Fluoro-11,17,21-trihydroxy-16-methyl-^{14}C-pregna-1,4-diene-3,20-dione]

H. E. Mertel, A. M. Gerber, and H. T. Meriwether, J. Label. Compounds, 6, 250 (1970).

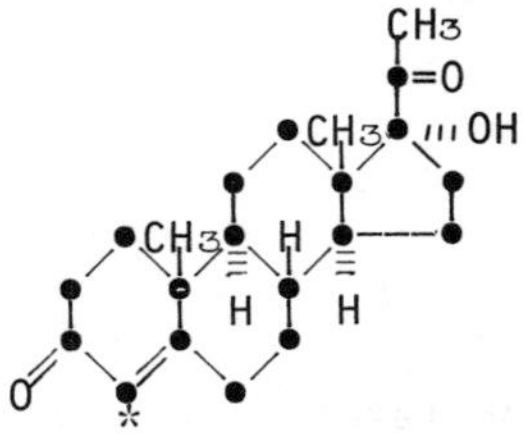

(17α)-17-Hydroxypregn-4-ene-3,20-dione-4-^{14}C

1. chloranil, t-C_4H_9OH, Δ (~50%)
2. perphthalic acid, CH_2Cl_2/Et_2O (~73%)

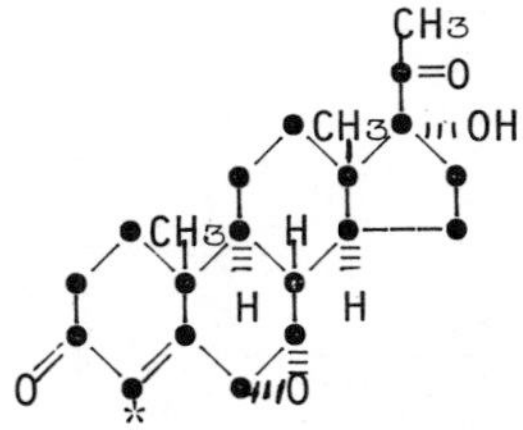

6,7-Epoxy-17-Hydroxypregn-4-ene-3,20-dione-4-^{14}C

1. conc. HCl, AcOH, Δ (~52%)
2. Ac_2O, AcOH, p-TSA (~54%)

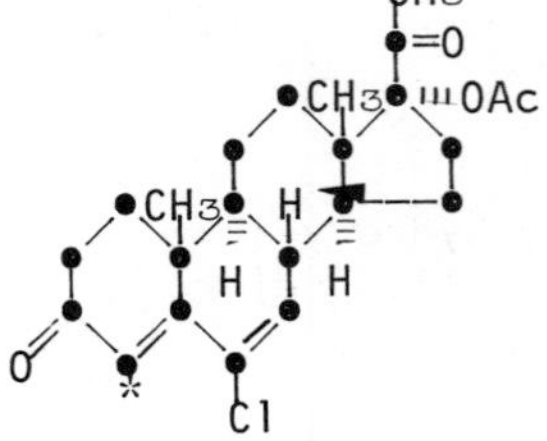

(13% overall)

Chlormadinone acetate
[17-acetyloxy-6-chloro-pregna-4,6-diene-3,20-diene-3,20-dione-4-^{14}C]

K. H. Palmer, R. W. Handy, and M. E. Wall, J. Label. Compounds, 7, 16 (1971).

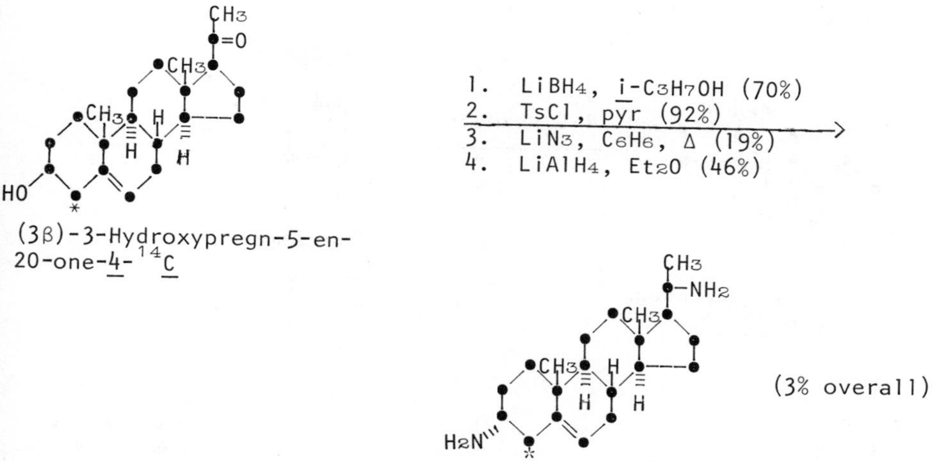

1. LiBH4, i-C3H7OH (70%)
2. TsCl, pyr (92%)
3. LiN3, C6H6, Δ (19%)
4. LiAlH4, Et2O (46%)
(3% overall)

(3β)-3-Hydroxypregn-5-en-20-one-4-^{14}C

(3α,20S)-Pregn-5-ene-3,20-diamine-4-^{14}C

H. Hoellinger, Nguyen-Hoang Nam, and L. Pichat, Bull. Soc. Chim. Fr., 237 (1975).

12-4 Bile Acids

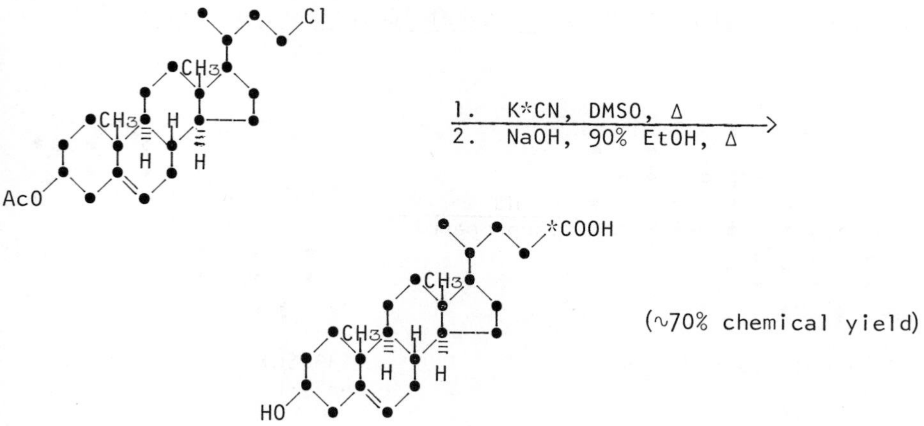

1. K*CN, DMSO, Δ
2. NaOH, 90% EtOH, Δ
(~70% chemical yield)

(3β)-3-Hydroxychol-5-en-24-oic-^{14}C acid

G. Burton and E. G. Gros, J. Label. Compound. Radiopharm., 13, 627 (1977).

12-5 Cholestanes

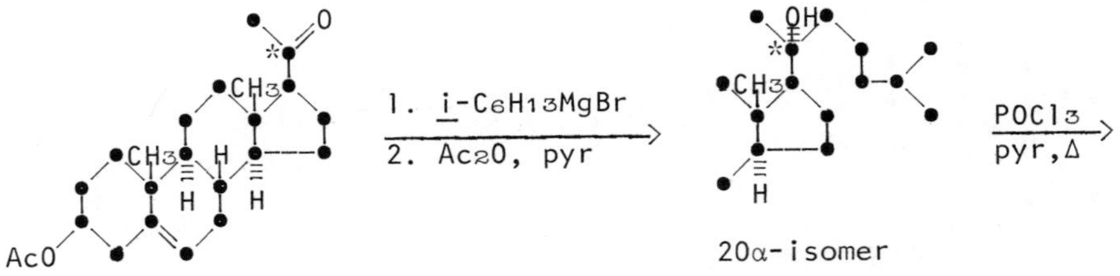
O
CH3
CH3
H
H
H
AcO
1. i-C6H13MgBr
2. Ac2O, pyr
OH
CH3
H
20α-isomer
POCl3
pyr, Δ

(3β)-3-(Acetyloxy)pregn-5-en-20-one-20-^{14}C

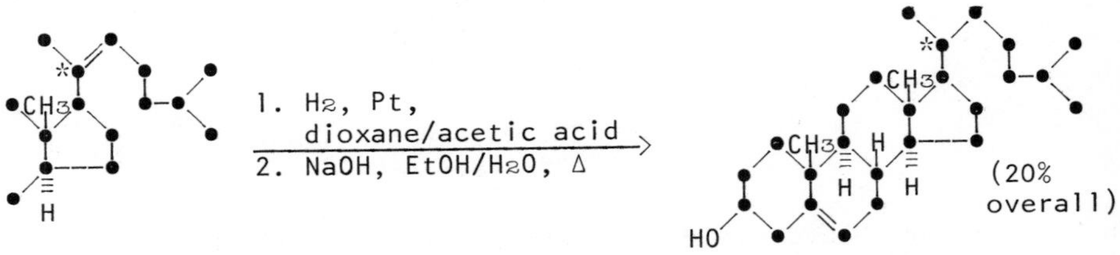
CH3
H
1. H2, Pt, dioxane/acetic acid
2. NaOH, EtOH/H2O, Δ
CH3
CH3
H
H
H
HO
(20% overall)

(3β)-Cholest-5-en-3-ol-20-^{14}C

A. M. Porto and E. G. Gros, J. Label. Compounds, 6, 369 (1970).

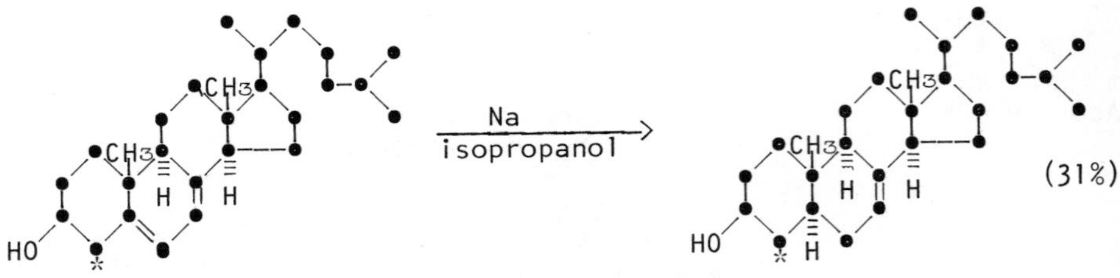
CH3
CH3
H
H
HO
Na
isopropanol
CH3
CH3
H
H
HO
H
(31%)

(3β)-Cholesta-5,7-dien-3-ol-4-^{14}C

(3β,5α)-Cholest-7-en-3-ol-4-^{14}C

D. Dvornik, M. Kraml, and J. F. Bagli, Biochemistry, 5, 1060 (1966).

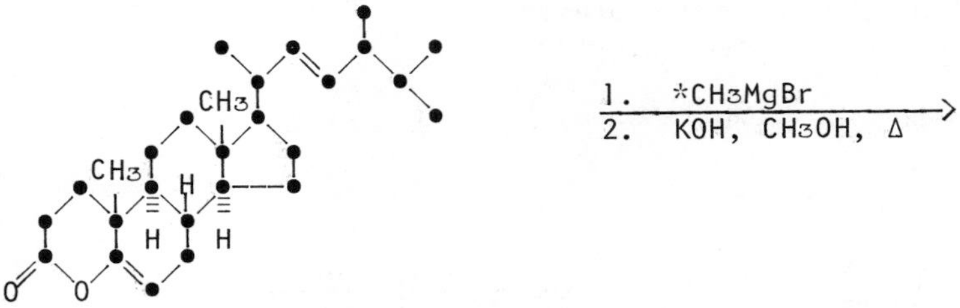
1. *CH3MgBr
2. KOH, CH3OH, Δ

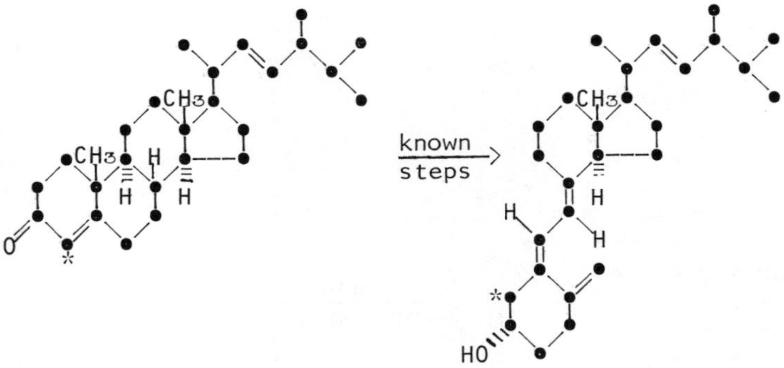
known steps

Ergocalciferol
[(3β,5Z,7E,22E)-9,10-Secoergosta-5,7,10(19),22-tetraen-3-ol-4-^{14}C]

B. Pelc and E. Kodicek, J. Chem. Soc., Perkin Trans. I, 2980 (1972).

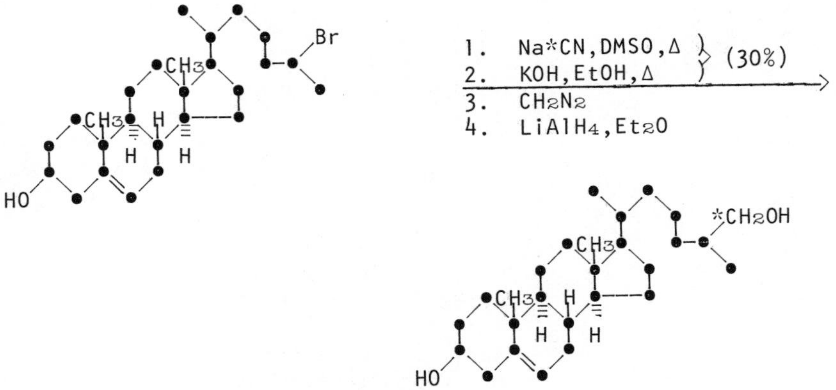
1. Na*CN,DMSO,Δ
2. KOH,EtOH,Δ
(30%)
3. CH2N2
4. LiAlH4,Et2O
*CH2OH

(dl)-Cholest-5-ene-3β,26-diol-26-^{14}C

The preparation of 7α-hydroxycholesterol-26-^{14}C and 7-dehydrocholesterol-26-^{14}C are also reported.

P. D. G. Dean and M. W. Whitehouse, Biochem. J., 98, 410 (1966).

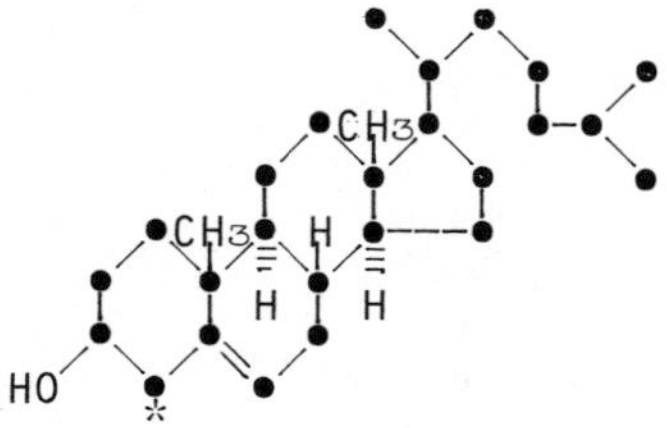

(3β)-Cholest-5-en-3-ol-4-^{14}C

1. benzoylation
2. NBS, ligroine, Δ

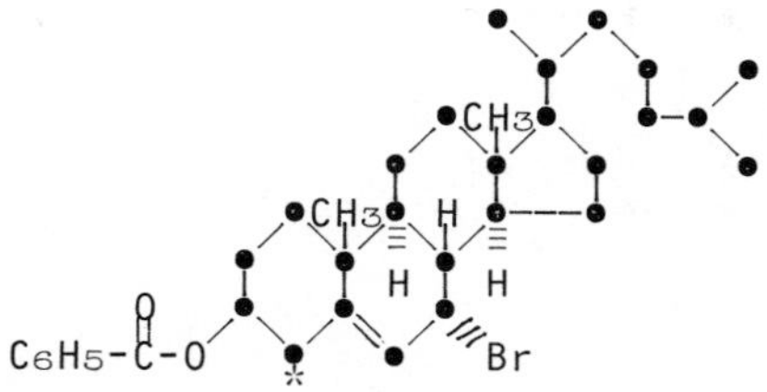

(3β,7α)-7-Bromocholest-5-en-3-ol-4-^{14}C phenylmethyl ester

1. HCOONa, HCOOH, Et_2O
2. hydrolysis

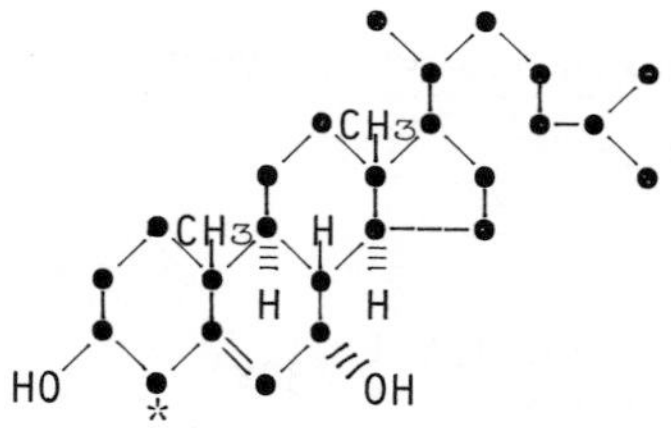

(∿16% overall)

(3β,7α)-Cholest-5-ene-3,7-diol-4-^{14}C

$(C_{17}H_{35}CO)_2O$ / C_6H_6

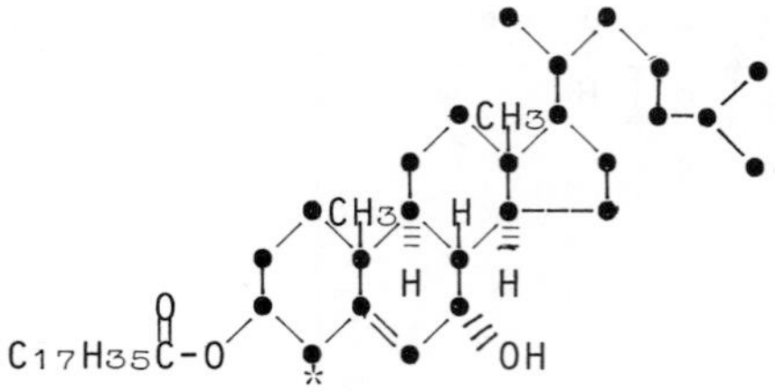

(∿20%)

(3β,7α)-Cholest-5-ene-3,7-diol-4-^{14}C-3-octadecanoate

M. Ogura and K. Yamasaki, J. Biochem., Tokyo, 67, 643 (1970).

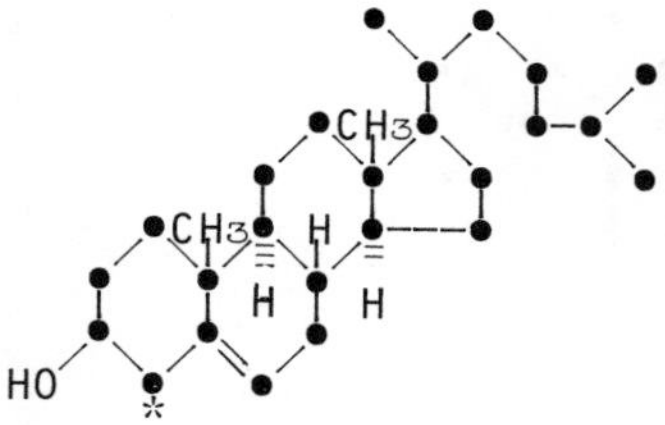

(3β)-Cholest-5-en-3-ol-4-^{14}C

1. benzoquinone
2. monoperphthalic acid
3. $LiAlH_4$
4. MnO_2

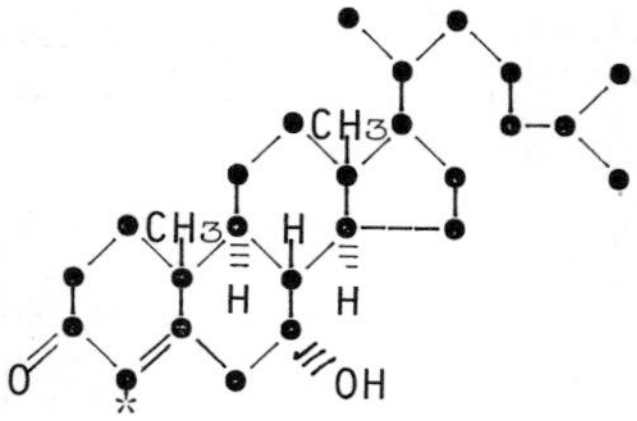

(7α)-7-Hydroxycholest-4-en-3-one-4-^{14}C

$NaBH_4$
70% CH_3OH

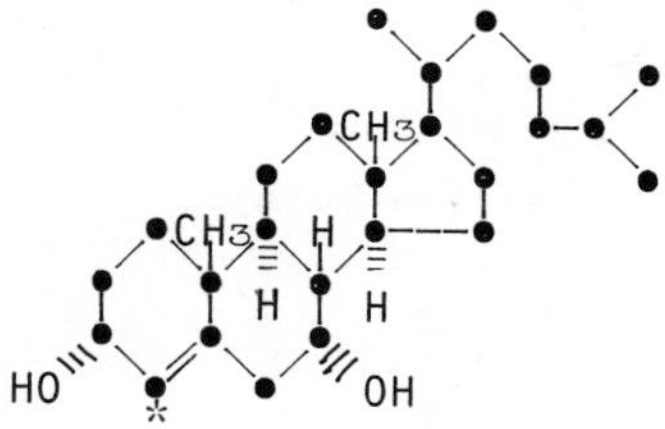

(3α,7α)-Cholest-4-ene-3,7-diol-4-^{14}C

isovaleric acid
electrolytic coupling

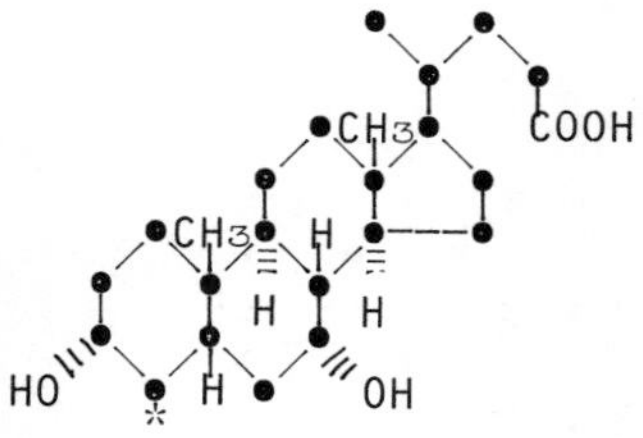

(3α,5β,7α)-3,7-Dihydroxycholan-24-oic-4-^{14}C acid

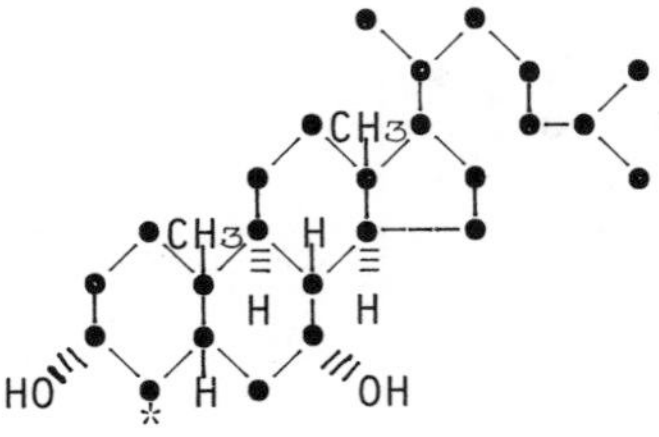

(3α,5β,7α)-Cholestane-3,7-diol-4-^{14}C

I. Björkhem., Acta Chem. Scand., 21, 2661 (1967); Eur. J. Biochem., 51, 137 (1975); H. R. B. Hutton and G. S. Boyd, Biochim. Biophys. Acta, 116, 336 (1966).

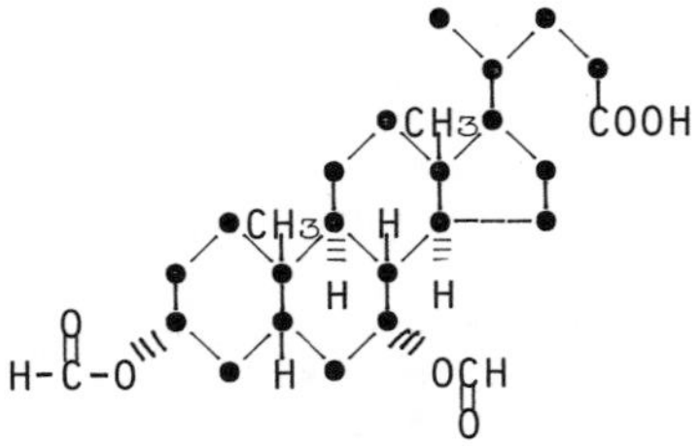

(3α,5β,7α)-3,7-Bis(formyloxy)-chenodeoxycholic acid

1. $SOCl_2$
2. *CH_2N_2, Et_2O/C_6H_6 (72%)
3. $C_6H_5CH_2OH$, collidine, Δ } (63%)
4. 10% KOH/CH_3OH }

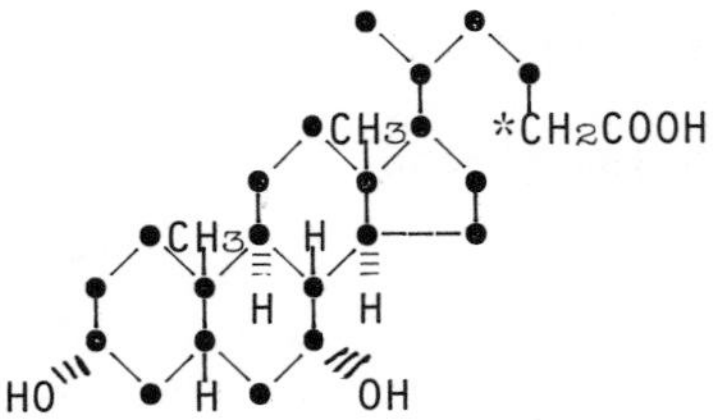

(3α,5β,7α)-3,7-Dihydroxycholane-24-carboxylic-24-^{14}C acid

1. HCl, CH_3OH/benzene (87%)
2. CH_3MgI, Et_2O (64%)

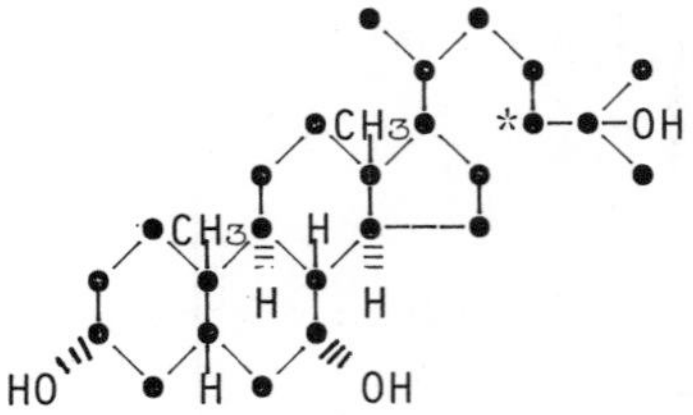

(3α,5β,7α)-Cholestane-3,7,25-triol-24-^{14}C

B. I. Cohen, G. S. Tint, T. Kuramoto, and E. H. Mosbach, Steroids, 25, 365 (1975).

H*C ≡ *CH

Acetylene-^{14}C

1. Na, DMSO
2. CH_3COCH_3
3. 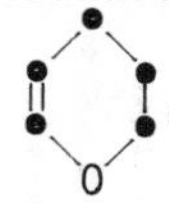, p-TSA

→

OTHP
H*C ≡ *C-C$(CH_3)_2$

2-Methyl-3-butyn-2-ol-3,4-^{14}C tetrahydropyranyl ether

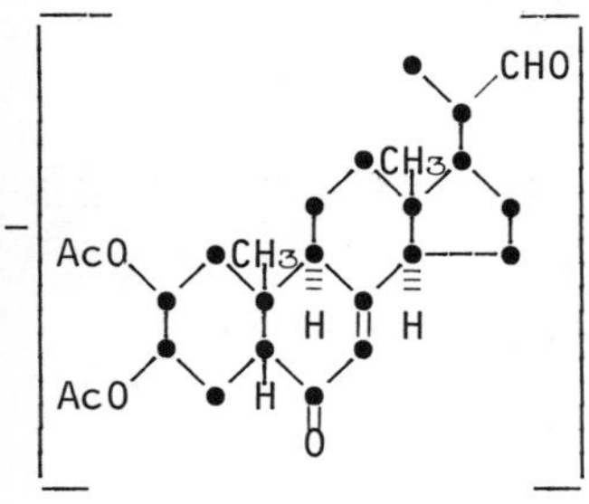

CHO
CH3
AcO
CH3
H
H
AcO
H
O

→

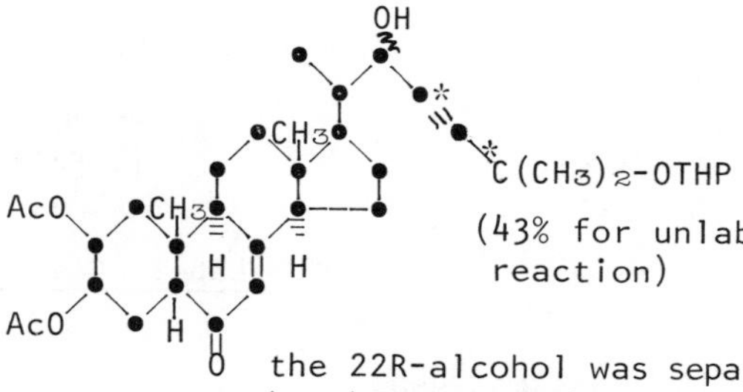

OH
CH3
AcO
CH3
H
H
AcO
H
O

C$(CH_3)_2$-OTHP

(43% for unlabeled reaction)

the 22R-alcohol was separated by chromatography

1. H_2, 5% Pd/C, EtOAc, $N(C_2H_5)_3$
2. SeO_2, dioxane
3. HCl, CH_3OH
4. aq. K_2CO_3, CH_3OH, Δ

→

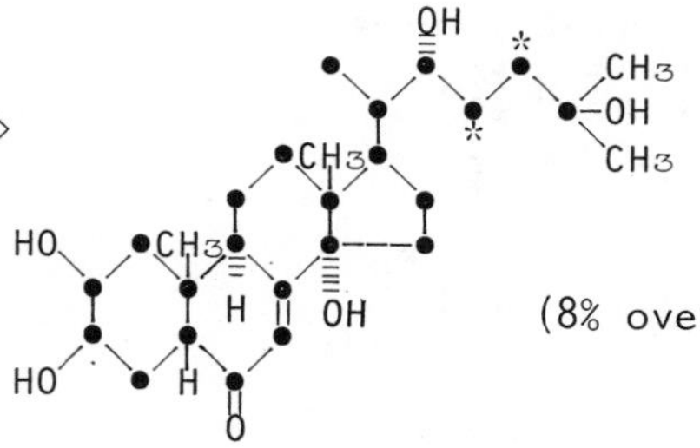

OH
CH3
OH
CH3
CH3
HO
CH3
H
OH
HO
H
O

(8% overall)

Ecdysene
[(2β,3β,5β,22R)-2,3,14,22,25-Pentahydroxycholest-7-en-6-one-23,24-^{14}C]

W. B. Smith and G. P. Newsoroff, Steroids, 22, 819 (1973).

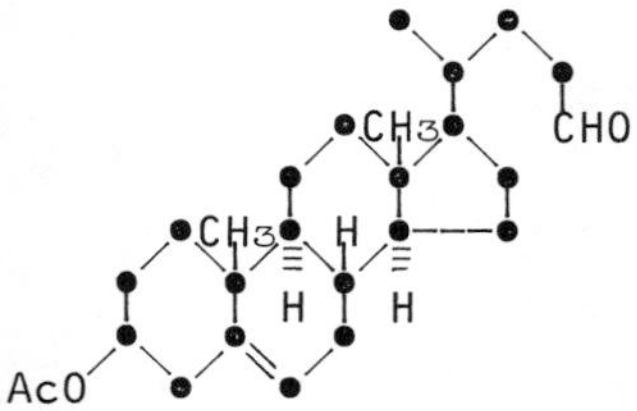

CH3
CHO
CH3
H
H
H
AcO

(3β)-(Acetyloxy)chol-5-en-24-al

1. $(C_6H_5)_3P$=*C$(CH_3)_2$, DMSO
2. KOH, CH_3OH

→

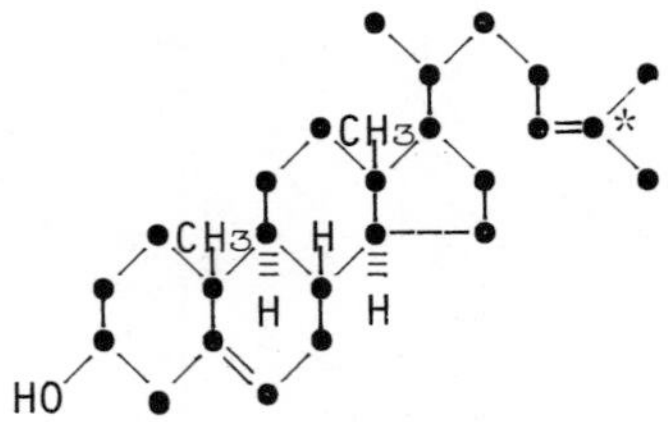
CH3
CH3
H
H
H
HO
*

(∿4%)

Desmosterol
[(3β)-Cholesta-5,24-dien-3-ol-25-^{14}C]

B. Danieli and G. Russo, J. Label. Compounds, 1, 275 (1965).

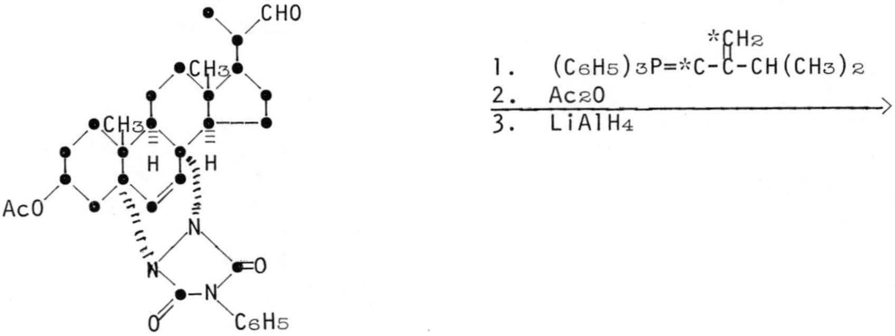
CHO
CH3
CH3
H
H
AcO
N
N
N
O
O
C6H5
*CH2
1. (C6H5)3P=*C-C-CH(CH3)2
2. Ac2O
3. LiAlH4

(Derived by ozonolysis of the triazoline adduct of ergosterol.)

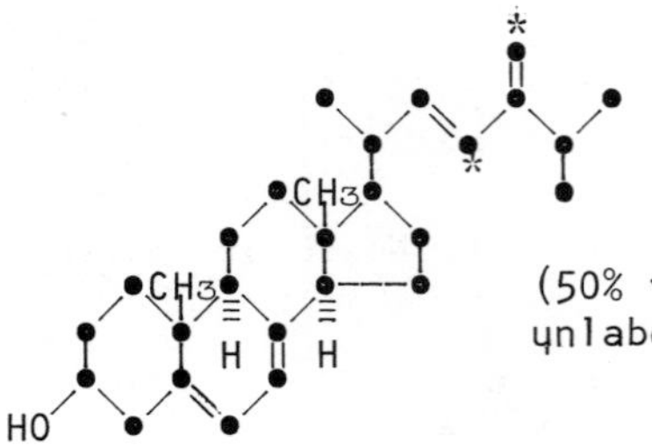
*
*
CH3
CH3
H
H
HO

(50% yield on unlabeled reaction)

(3β,22E)-Ergosta-5,7,22,24(28)-tetraen-3-ol-23,28-^{14}C

D. H. R. Barton, T. Shiori, and D. A. Widdowson, J. Chem. Soc., Chem.Commun., 939 (1970).

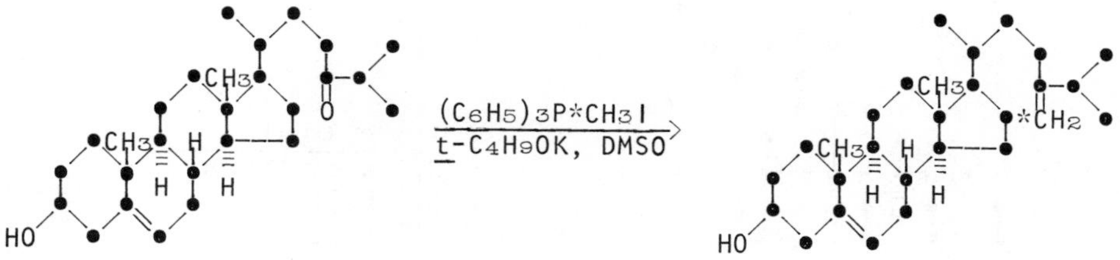
$(C_6H_5)_3P{*}CH_3I$
t-C_4H_9OK, DMSO

(From 3β-hydroxychol-5-enic acid in 7 steps)

(3β)-Ergosta-5,24(28)-dien-3-ol-28-^{14}C

J. Bottin and M. Fétizon, J. Label. Compounds, 7, 305 (1971).

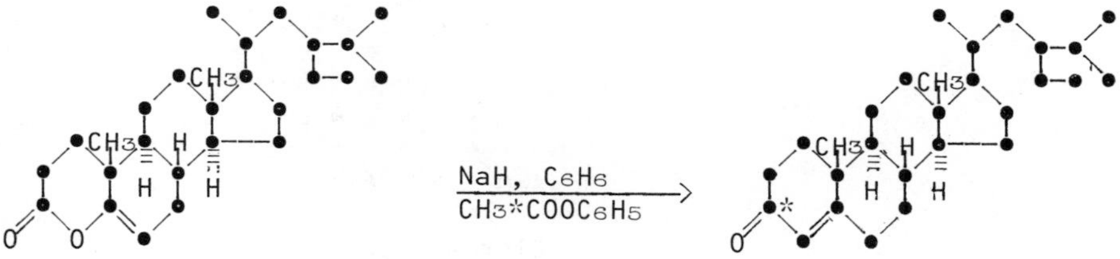
NaH, C_6H_6
$CH_3{*}COOC_6H_5$

4-Oxa-stigmast-5-en-3-one- (from oxidation of β-sitosterol)

Stigmast-4-en-3-one-3-^{14}C

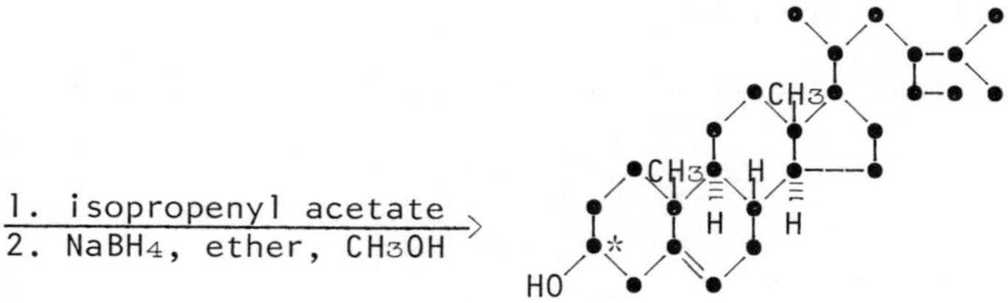
1. isopropenyl acetate
2. $NaBH_4$, ether, CH_3OH

(73%; 10% from phenyl acetate-1-^{14}C)

(3β)-Stigmast-5-en-3-ol-3-^{14}C

A competing mechanism giving unlabeled product was proposed to account for an 18% loss in specific activity.

P. Ph. H. L. Otto, A. C. Besemer, and W. H. J. M. Wientjens, J. Label. Compounds, 6, 111 (1970).

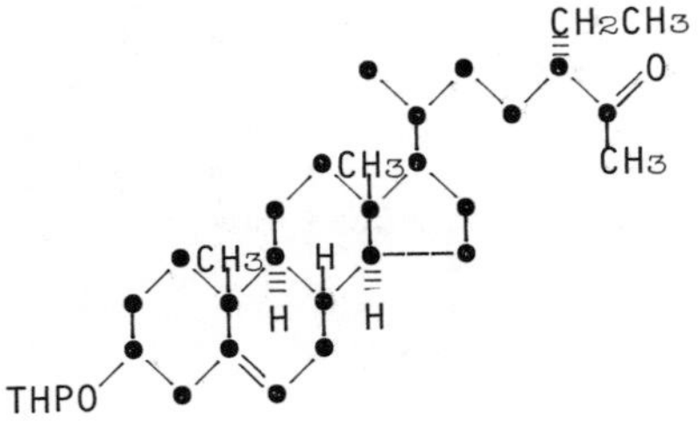

1. *CH_3MgI
2. acetylation
3. $POCl_3$

(3β,24S)-3-[(Tetrahydro-2H-pyran-2-yl)oxy]stigmast-5-en-25-one (from osmium tetroxide/sodium periodate oxidation of clerosterol)

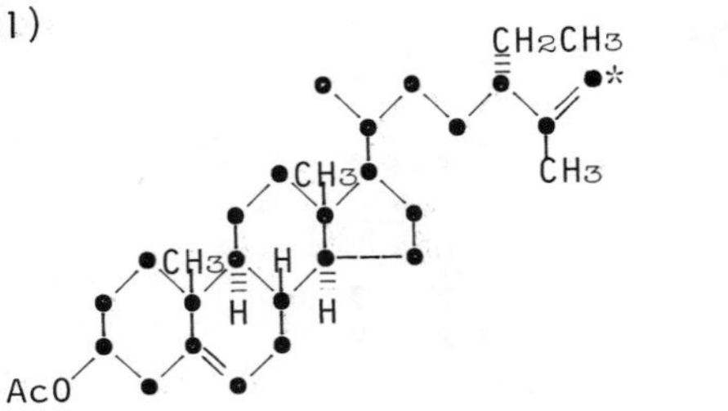

Clerosterol
[(3β,24S)-Stigmasta-5,25-dien-3-ol-<u>26</u>-^{14}<u>C</u> acetate]

A mixture of the $\Delta^{24(25)}$ isomer (30%) and the $\Delta^{25(26)}$ isomer was obtained, separable by $AgNO_3$/TLC.

C. Largeau, L. J. Goad, and T. W. Goodwin, Phytochemistry, 16, 1925 (1977).

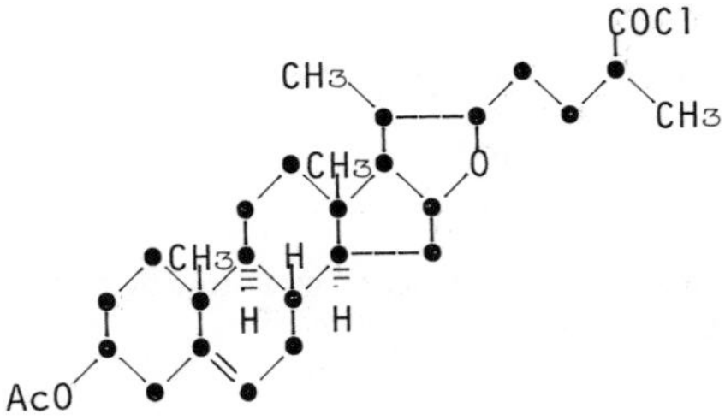

1. *CH_2N_2, ether
2. C_6H_5OH
N,N-dimethylaniline

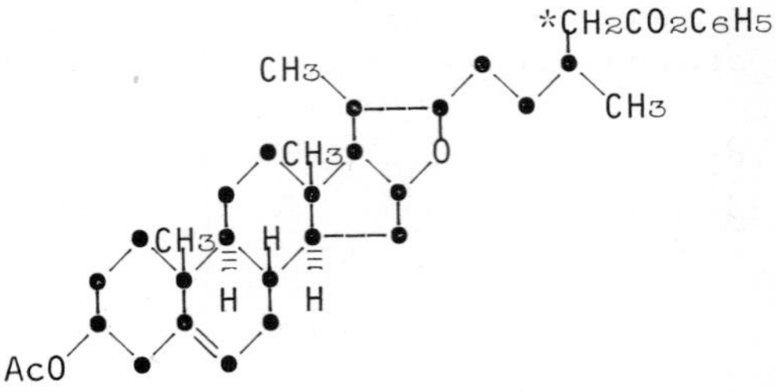

1. NaOH, 80% CH_3OH
2. Ac_2O, pyr
3. $(COCl)_2$, C_6H_6
4. m-ClPBA, pyr, C_6H_6

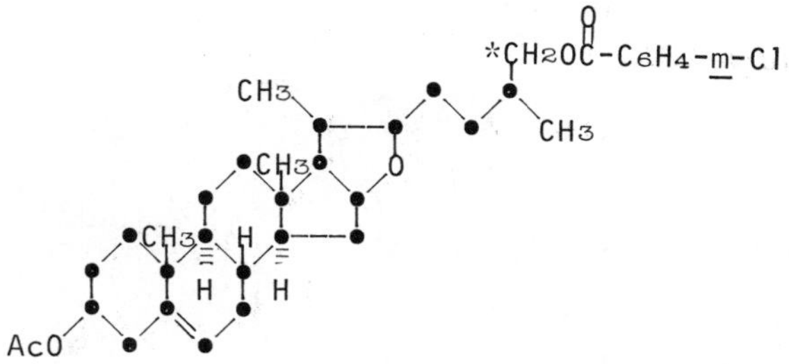
*CH2OC-C6H4-m-Cl
O
CH3
CH3
O
CH3
CH3
H
H
H
AcO

1. KOH, CH_3OH, H_2O, C_6H_6
2. Ac_2O, pyr

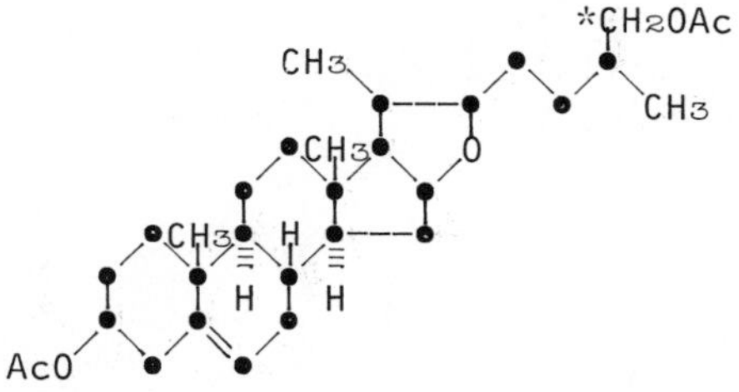
*CH2OAc
CH3
CH3
O
CH3
CH3
H
H
H
AcO

1. Br_2, AcOH
2. CrO_3, 80% AcOH
3. Zn, NaOAc/AcOH
4. $KHCO_3$, CH_3OH, Δ

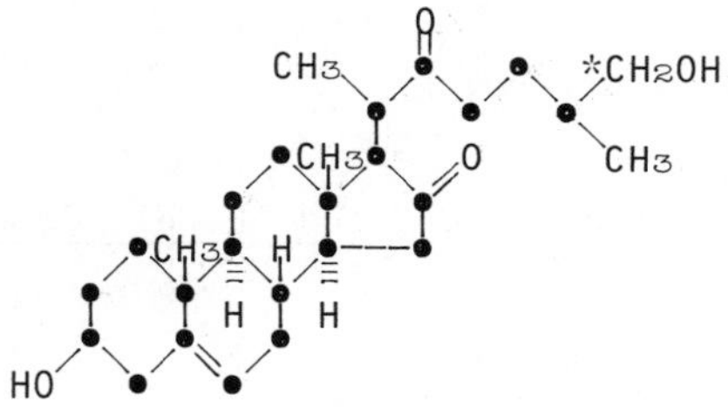
O
CH3
*CH2OH
CH3
O
CH3
CH3
H
H
H
HO

Kryptogenin
[(3β,25R)-3,26-Dihydroxycholest-5-en-16,22-dione-26-^{14}C]

$BH_3 \cdot N(CH_3)_3$
AcOH

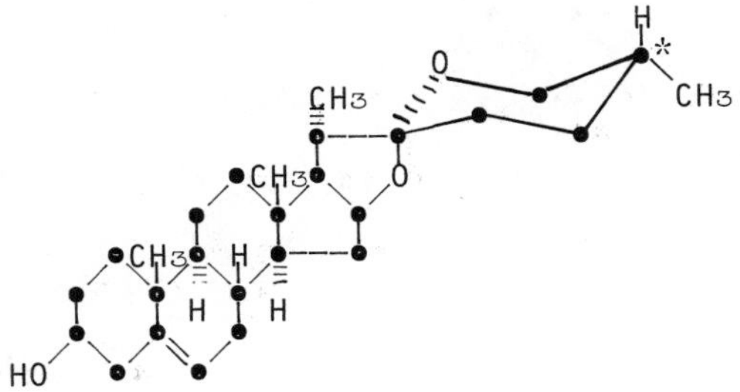
H
*
O
CH3
CH3
O
CH3
CH3
H
H
H
HO

Diosgenin
[(3β,25R)-Spirost-5-en-3-ol-25-^{14}C]

R. D. Bennett, H. H. Sauer, and E. Heftmann, J. Label. Compounds, 5, 160 (1969).

12-6 Lanostanes

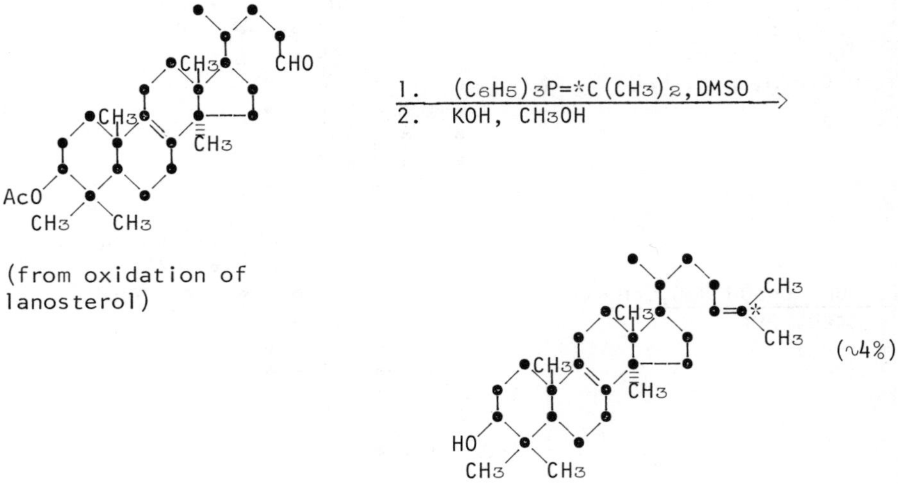
CHO
AcO
1. $(C_6H_5)_3P{=}{*}C(CH_3)_2$, DMSO
2. KOH, CH_3OH
(from oxidation of lanosterol)
HO
(∿4%)

Lanosterol
[(3β)-Lanosta-8,24-dien-3-ol-25-^{14}C]

B. Danieli and G. Russo, J. Label. Compounds, 1, 275 (1965).

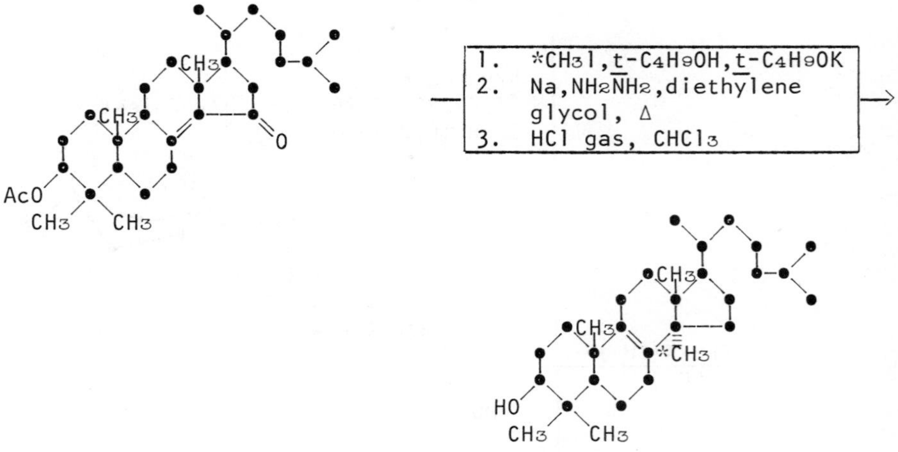
AcO
O
1. $*CH_3I$, t-C_4H_9OH, t-C_4H_9OK
2. Na, NH_2NH_2, diethylene glycol, Δ
3. HCl gas, $CHCl_3$
HO
$*CH_3$

(3β)-Lanost-8-en-3-ol-32-^{14}C

K. A. Mitropoulos, G. F. Gibbons, and B. E. A. Reeves, Steroids, 27, 821 (1976).

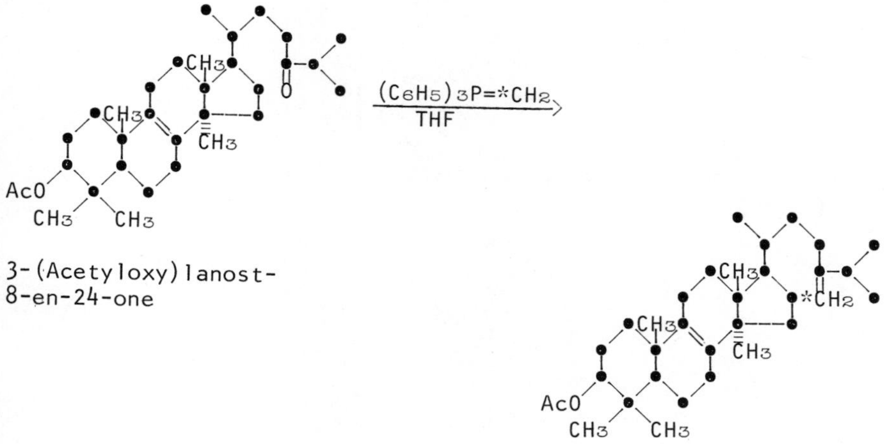
AcO
CH3
CH3
CH3
CH3
CH3
O
(C6H5)3P=*CH2
THF
*CH2

3-(Acetyloxy)lanost-8-en-24-one

(24-Methylene-^{14}C)lanost-8-en-3-ol acetate

D. H. R. Barton, D. M. Harrison, G. P. Moss, and D. A. Widdowson, J. Chem. Soc. (C) Org., 775 (1970).

13

Miscellaneous Compound Classes

13-1 Benzodiazepines

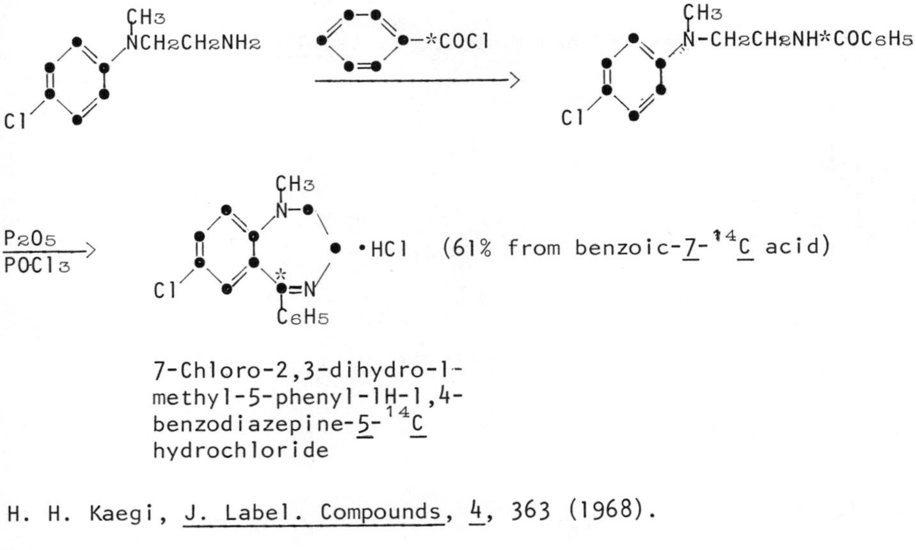

CH3
NCH2CH2NH2
Cl
*COCl
CH3
N-CH2CH2NH*COC6H5
Cl
P2O5
POCl3
CH3
N
•HCl
Cl
N
C6H5
(61% from benzoic-7-14C acid)

7-Chloro-2,3-dihydro-1-methyl-5-phenyl-1$\underline{H}$-1,4-benzodiazepine-$\underline{5}$-$^{14}\underline{C}$ hydrochloride

H. H. Kaegi, J. Label. Compounds, 4, 363 (1968).

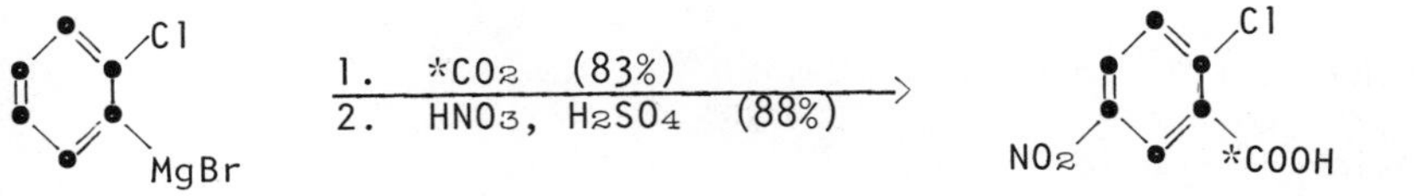

Cl
MgBr
1. *CO2 (83%)
2. HNO3, H2SO4 (88%)
Cl
NO2
*COOH

2-Chloro-5-nitrobenzoic-$\underline{7}$-$^{14}\underline{C}$ acid

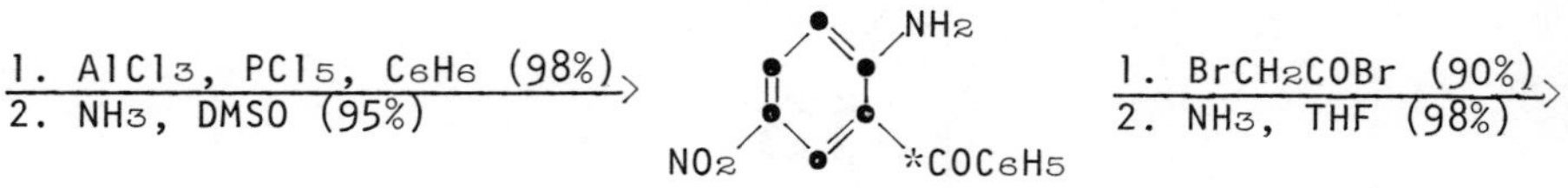
1. AlCl3, PCl5, C6H6 (98%)
2. NH3, DMSO (95%)
NH2
NO2
*COC6H5
1. BrCH2COBr (90%)
2. NH3, THF (98%)

(2-Amino-5-nitrophenyl)-phenylmethanone-^{14}C

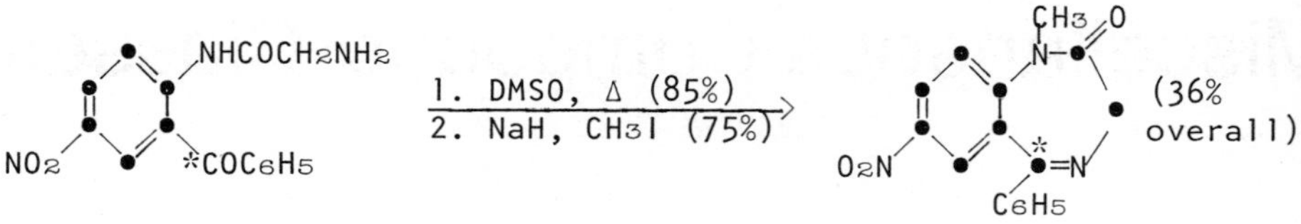
NHCOCH2NH2
NO2
*COC6H5
1. DMSO, Δ (85%)
2. NaH, CH3I (75%)
CH3
O
N
O2N
*
N
C6H5
(36% overall)

2-Amino-N-[(2-benzoyl-^{14}C)-4-nitrophenyl] acetamide

Nimetazepam [1,3-Dihydro-1-methyl-7-nitro-5-phenyl-2H-1,4-benzodiazepin-2-one-5-^{14}C]

A. Yoshitake, Y. Makari, and M. Endo, J. Label. Compounds, 8, 615 (1972).

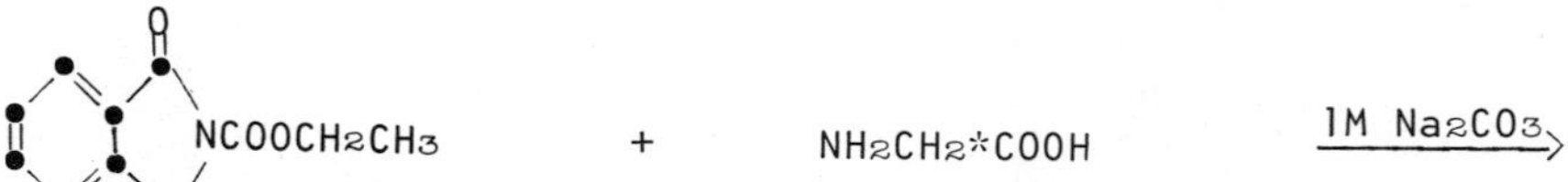
O
NCOOCH2CH3
O
+
NH2CH2*COOH
1M Na2CO3

Glycine-1-^{14}C

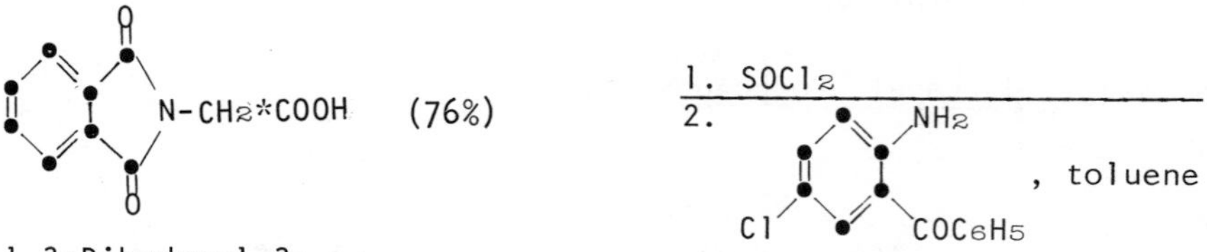
O
N-CH2*COOH
O
(76%)
1. SOCl2
2.
NH2
Cl
COC6H5
, toluene

1,3-Dihydro-1,3-dioxo-2H-isoindole-2-acetic-1-^{14}C acid

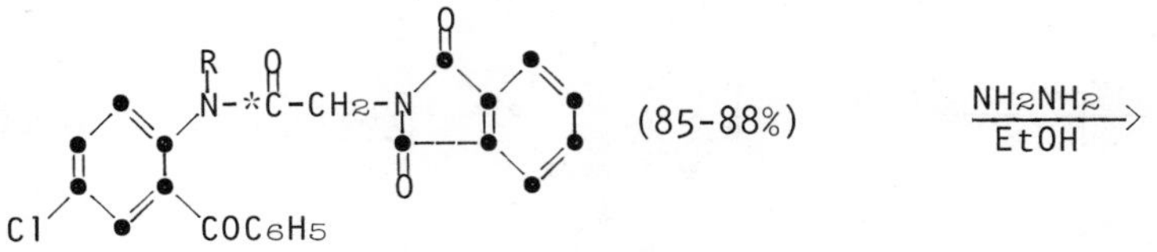

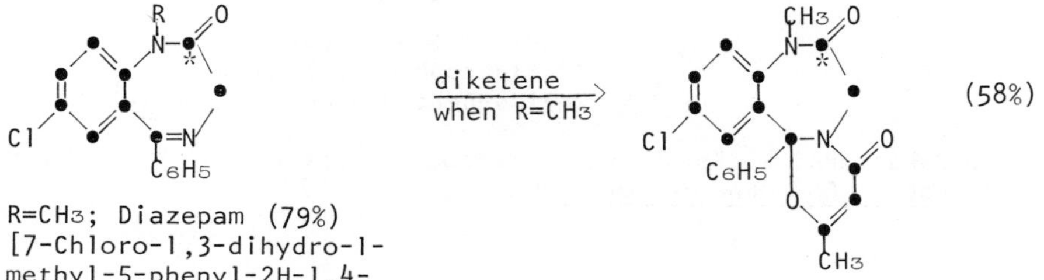

R=CH_3; Diazepam (79%)
[7-Chloro-1,3-dihydro-1-methyl-5-phenyl-2H-1,4-benzodiazepin-2-one-2-^{14}C]

R=H; Demethyldiazepam (36%)
[7-Chloro-1,3-dihydro-5-phenyl-2H-1,4-benzodiazepin-2-one-^{14}C]

Ketazolam
[11-Chloro-8-12b-dihydro-2,8-dimethyl-12b-phenyl-4H[1,3]-oxazino[3,2d][1,4]benzodiazepine-4,7(6H)-dione-7-^{14}C]

R. S. P. Hsi, J. Label. Compounds, 10, 389 (1974).

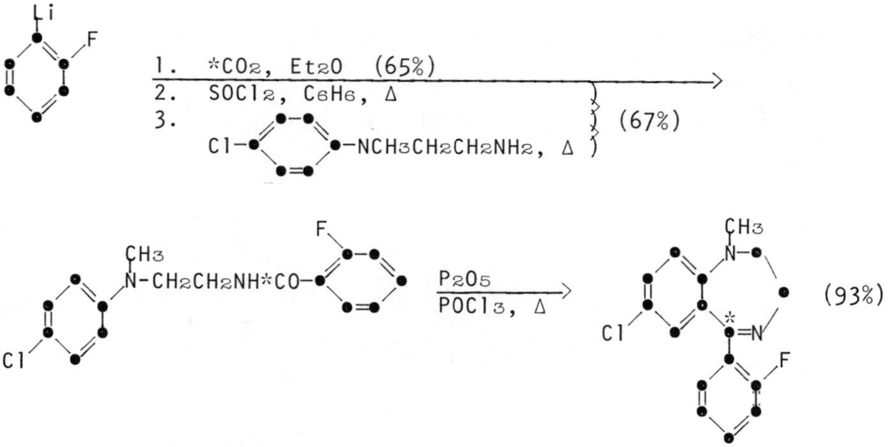

7-Chloro-1,3-dihydro-5-(2-fluorophenyl)-2H-1,4-benzodiazepine-5-^{14}C

NBS, THF / aq. $NaHCO_3$ →

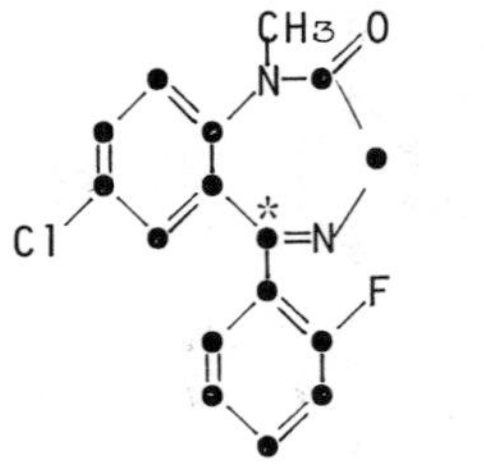

CH_3
O
N
*
N
Cl
F

(59%; 24% from Ba*CO_3)

7-Chloro-1,3-dihydro-5-(2-fluorophenyl)-1-methyl-2H-1,4-benzodiazepin-2-one-5-^{14}C

I. Nakatsuka, K. Kawahara, T. Kamada, F. Shono, and A. Yoskitake, J. Label. Compound. Radiopharm., 13, 453 (1977).

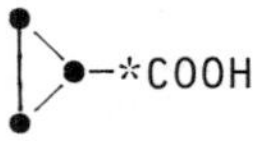

*COOH

Cyclopropane-carboxylic-^{14}C acid

1. $SOCl_2$, C_6H_6
2.

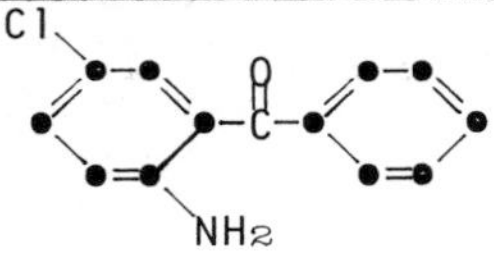

Cl
O
C
NH_2

→

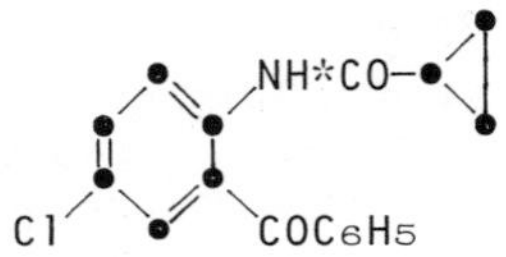

NH*CO
Cl
COC_6H_5

N-(2-benzoyl-4-chlorophenyl)-cyclopropanecarboxamide-^{14}C

1. $LiAlH_4$ (45% overall)
2.

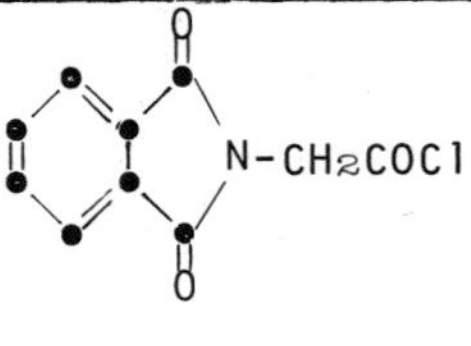

O
N-CH_2COCl
O

(62%) →

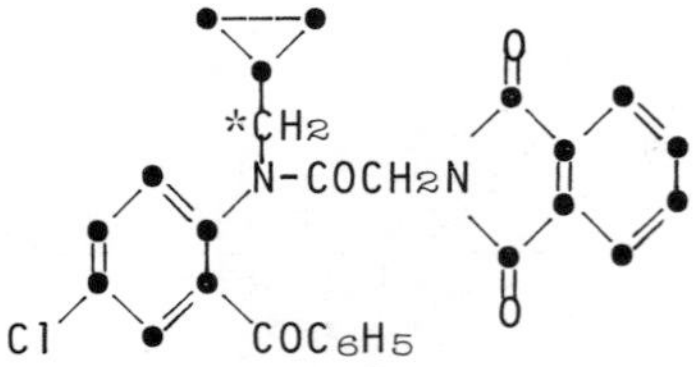

*CH_2
N-$COCH_2N$
O
O
Cl
COC_6H_5

1. CrO_3 (quant.)
2. $NH_2NH_2.H_2O$ (69%) →

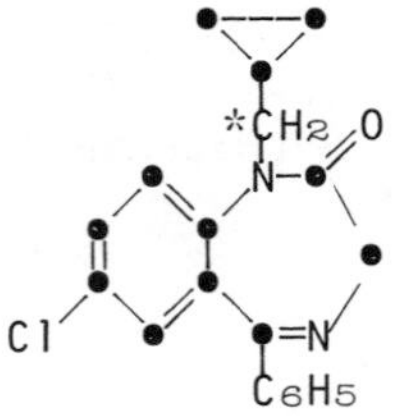

*CH_2
O
N
N
Cl
C_6H_5

(9% from K*CN)

7-Chloro-1-cyclopropyl-(methyl-^{14}C)-1,3-dihydro-5-phenyl-2H-1,4-benzodiazepin-2-one

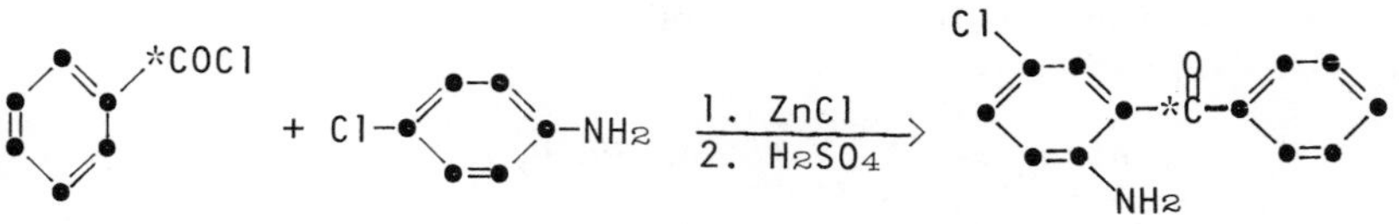
*COCl
+ Cl-
-NH2
1. ZnCl
2. H2SO4
Cl
*C
NH2

(44%)

Benzoyl-^{14}C chloride

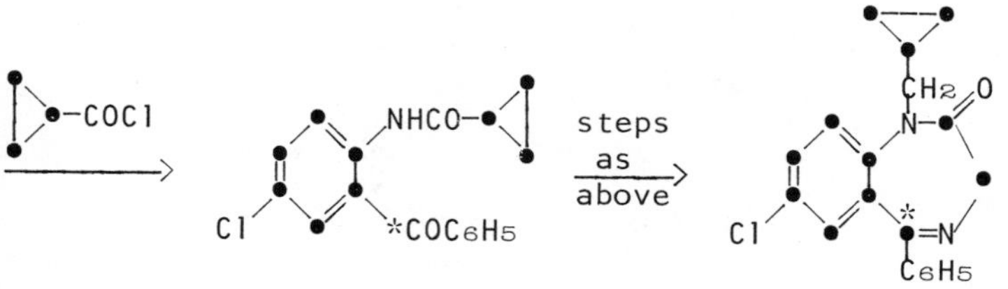
-COCl
NHCO-
Cl
*COC6H5
steps as above
CH2
O
N-
Cl
*
=N
C6H5

(12% from benzoic acid)

7-Chloro-1-(cyclopropylmethyl)-1,3-dihydro-5-phenyl-2H-1,4-benzodiazepin-2-one-5-^{14}C

E. J. Merrill and G. G. Vernice, J. Label. Compounds, 7, 89 (1971); for improved procedures, see also H. Ishihama, S. Kabuto, and T. Tamaki, Radioisotopes, 27, 9 (1978).

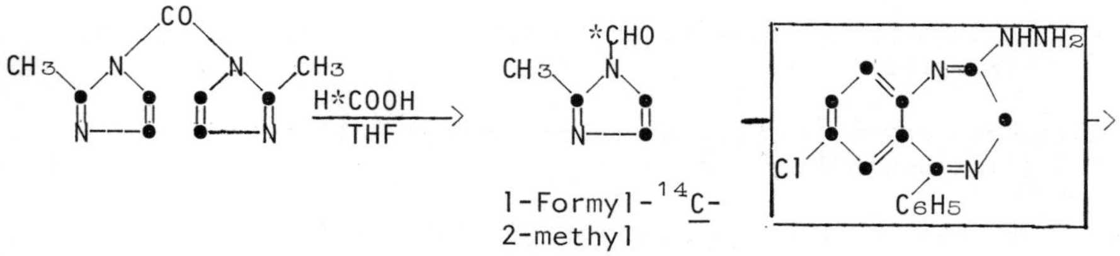
CO
CH3
N
N
CH3
H*COOH
THF
*CHO
CH3
N
NHNH2
N=
Cl
=N
C6H5

1-Formyl-^{14}C-2-methyl imidazole

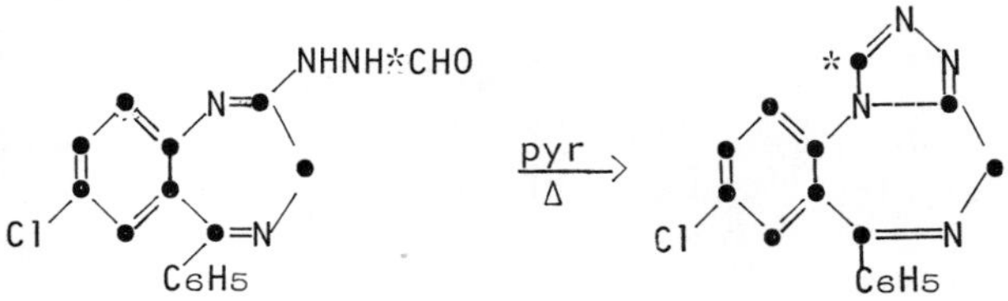
NHNH*CHO
N=
Cl
=N
C6H5
pyr
Δ
N
*
N
Cl
N
C6H5

(58% overall radiochemical yield)

8-Chloro-6-phenyl-4H-[1,2,4]triazolo-[4,3a]-[1,4]benzodiazepine-1-^{14}C

The use of the formylimidazole reagent eliminates the need for excess formic acid-$^{14}\underline{C}$.

N. Hayashi, K. Shinozaki, S. Kato, K. Meguro, and Y. Kuwada, J. Label. Compounds, 10, 73 (1974).

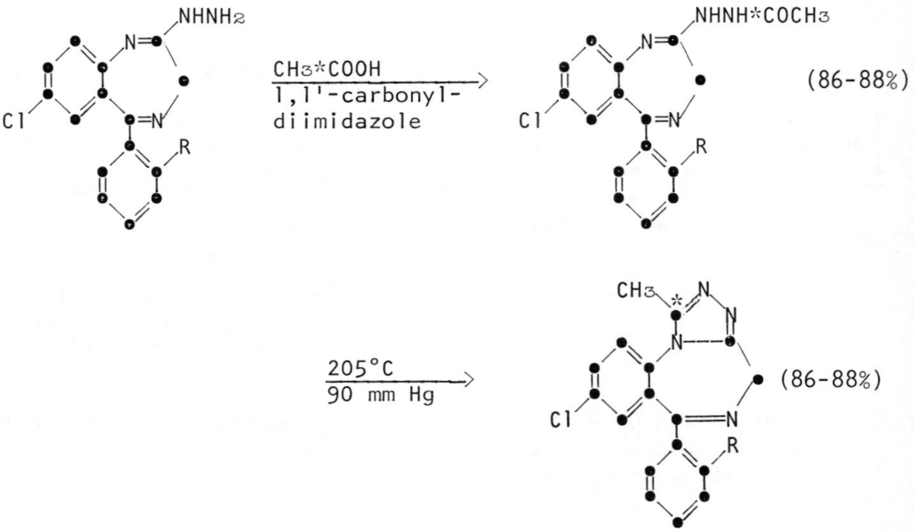
NHNH2
Cl
R
CH3*COOH
1,1'-carbonyl-
diimidazole
NHNH*COCH3
(86-88%)
205°C
90 mm Hg
CH3
(86-88%)

R=H; 8-Chloro-1-methyl-6-phenyl-4H[1,2,4]triazolo[4,3a][1,4]-benzodiazepine-$\underline{1}$-$^{14}\underline{C}$

R=Cl; 8-Chloro-6-(2-chlorophenyl)-1-methyl-4H[1,2,4]triazolo-[4,3a][1,4]benzodiazepine-$\underline{1}$-$^{14}\underline{C}$

R. S. P. Hsi, J. Label. Compounds, 9, 435 (1973).

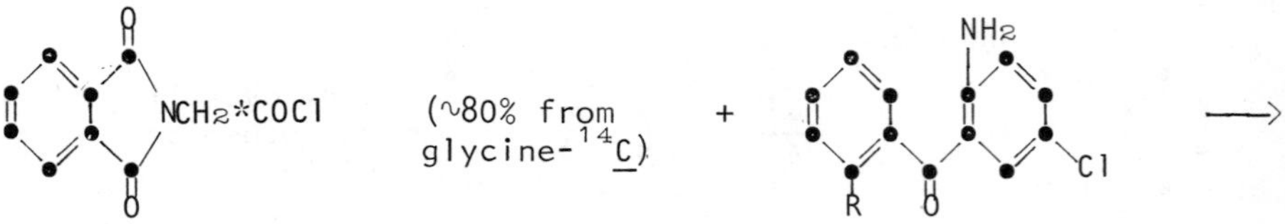
NCH2*COCl
(~80% from
glycine-14C)
+
NH2
Cl
R

R=H or Cl

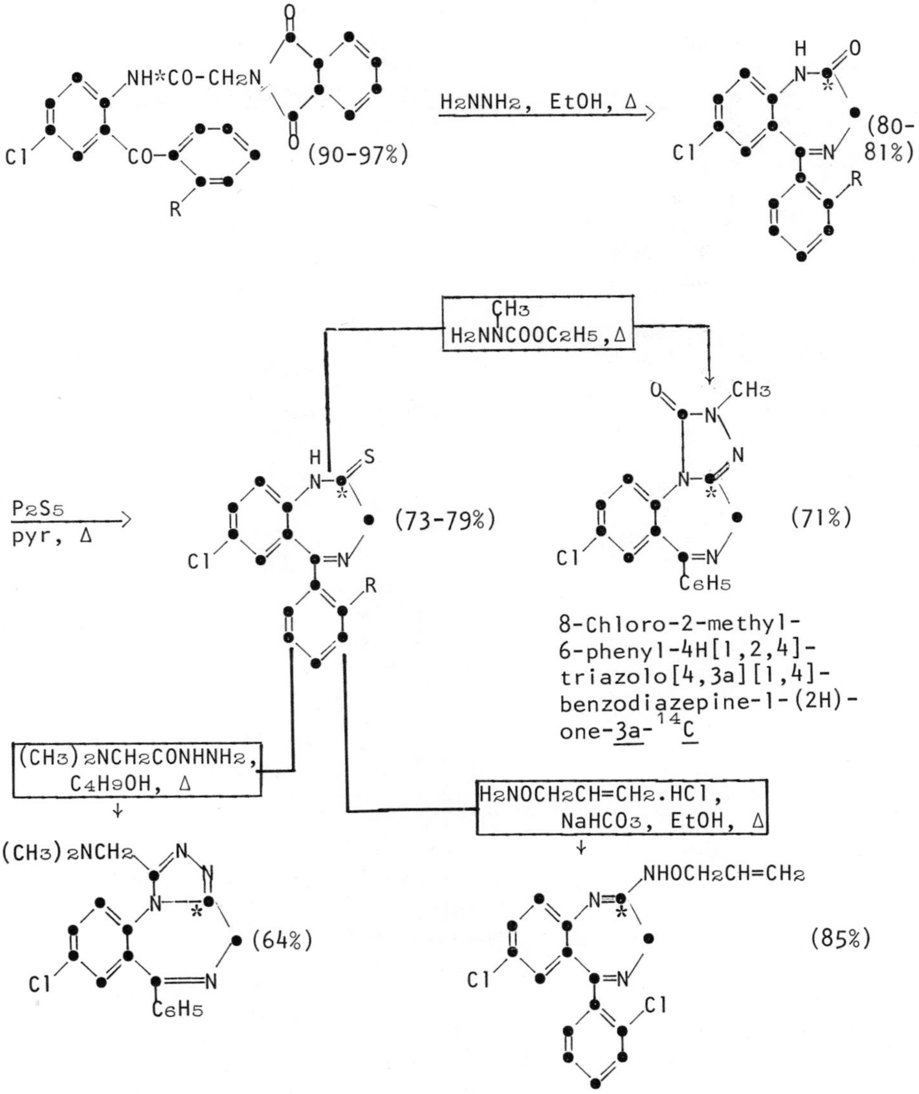
NH*CO-CH2N
Cl
CO
R
(90-97%)
H2NNH2, EtOH, Δ
(80-81%)
CH3
H2NNCOOC2H5, Δ
P2S5
pyr, Δ
(73-79%)
(71%)
C6H5
(CH3)2NCH2CONHNH2,
C4H9OH, Δ
H2NOCH2CH=CH2.HCl,
NaHCO3, EtOH, Δ
(CH3)2NCH2
(64%)
NHOCH2CH=CH2
(85%)

8-Chloro-2-methyl-6-phenyl-4H[1,2,4]-triazolo[4,3a][1,4]-benzodiazepine-1-(2H)-one-3a-^{14}C

8-Chloro-N,N-dimethyl-6-phenyl-4H-[1,2,4]triazolo[4,3a][1,4]-benzodiazepine-1-methanamine-3a-^{14}C

7-Chloro-5-(2-chlorophenyl)-N-(2-propenyloxy)-3H-1,4-benzodiazepin-2-amine-2-^{14}C

R. S. P. Hsi and T. D. Johnson, J. Label. Compound. Radiopharm., 12, 613 (1976).

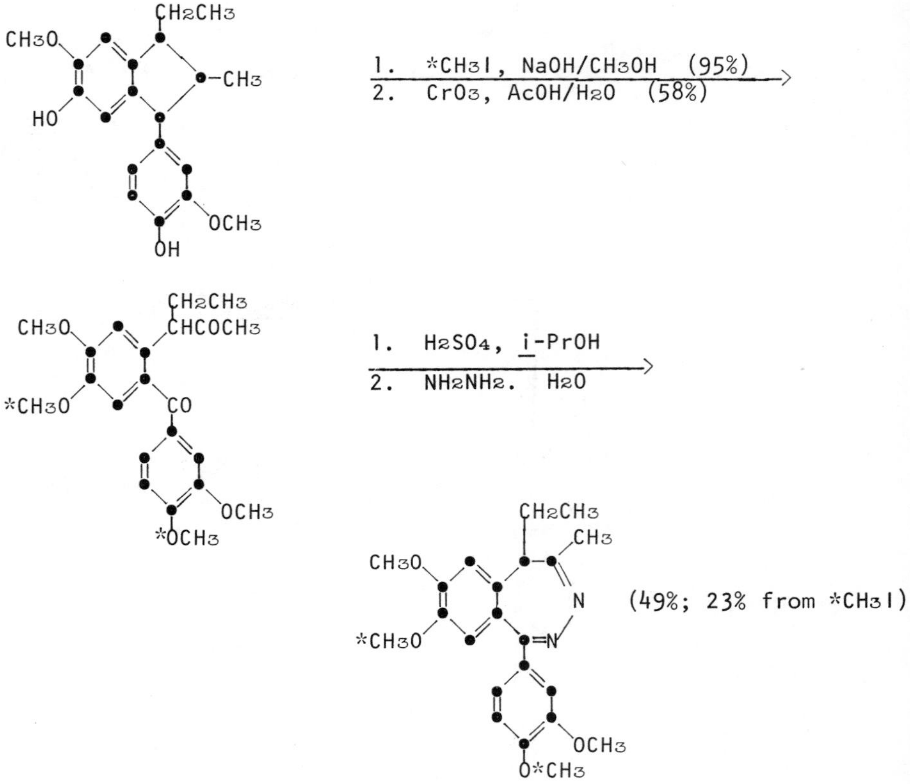
1. *CH3I, NaOH/CH3OH (95%)
2. CrO3, AcOH/H2O (58%)
1. H2SO4, i-PrOH
2. NH2NH2. H2O
(49%; 23% from *CH3I)

5-Ethyl-1-[3,4-dimethoxyphenyl-(4-methoxy-^{14}C)]-7,8-dimethoxy-(8-methoxy-^{14}C-)-4-methyl-5H-2,3-benzodiazepine

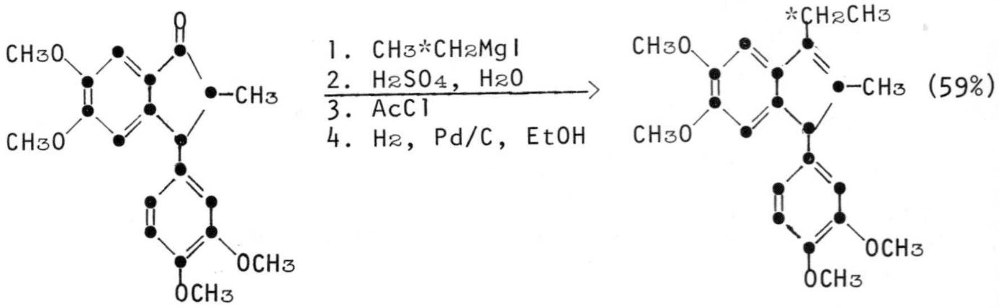
1. CH3*CH2MgI
2. H2SO4, H2O
3. AcCl
4. H2, Pd/C, EtOH
(59%)

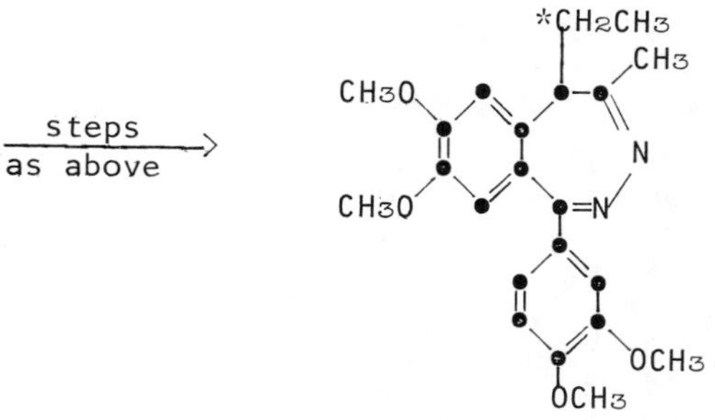
steps
as above
*CH2CH3
CH3
CH3O
N
CH3O
N
OCH3
OCH3

(10% from $CH_2{*}CH_3I$)

5-(Ethyl-1-^{14}C)-1-[3,4-dimethoxyphenyl]-7,8-dimethoxy-4-methyl-5H-2,3-benzodiazepine

G. Zolyomi, D. Banfi, T. Lang, and J. Körösi, Chem. Ber., 107, 3904 (1974).

13-2 Natural Products

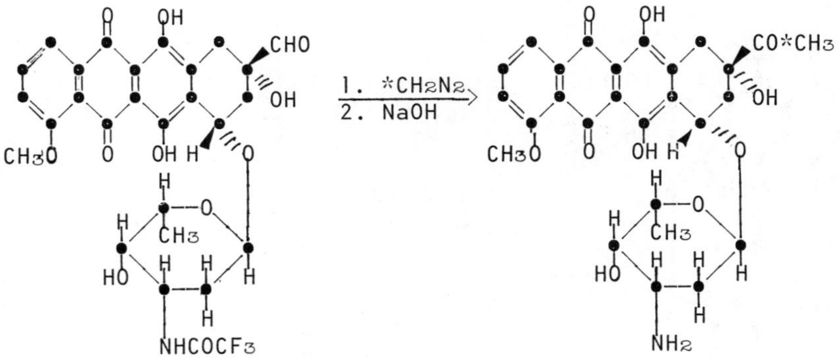
O
OH
CHO
OH
CH3O
O
OH
H
O
H
O
H
CH3
HO
H
H
H
H
NHCOCF3
1. *CH2N2
2. NaOH
O
OH
CO*CH3
OH
CH3O
O
OH
H
O
H
O
H
CH3
HO
H
H
H
H
NH2

(15%)

(from 13-dihydrodoxorubcin in two steps)

Daunorubicin
[(8S-cis)-(8-Acetyl-2-^{14}C)-10-[(3-amino-2,3,6-trideoxy-α-L-lyxo-hexopyranosyl)oxy]-7,8,9,10-tetrahydro-6,8,11-trihydroxy-1-methoxy-5,12-naphthacenedione]

via 14-bromo-derivative →

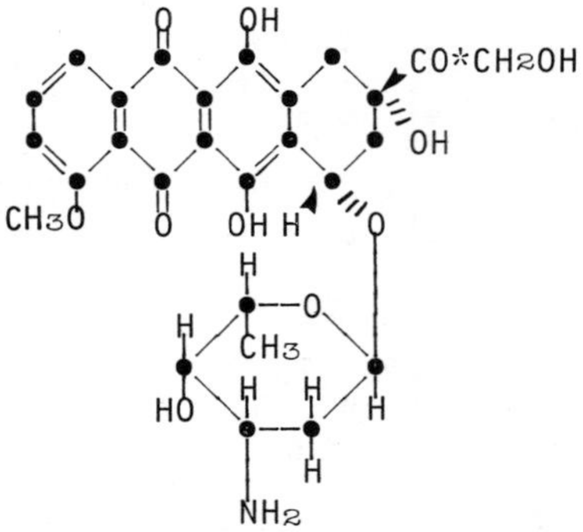

(60%)

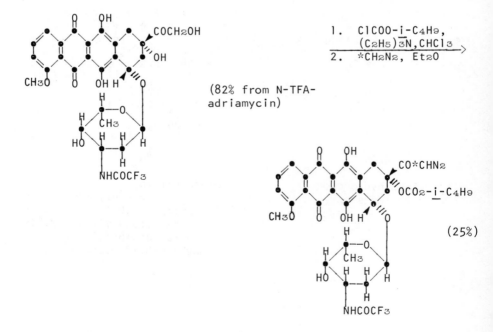

Doxorubicin
[(8S-cis)-10-[(3-Amino-2,3,6-trideoxy-α-L-lyxo-hexopyranosyl)oxy]-7,8,9,10-tetrahydro-6,8,11-trihydroxy-8-(hydroxyacetyl-2-^{14}C)-1-methoxy-5,12-naphthacene dione; 14-hydroxydaunomycin; or adriamycin]

S. Penco, G. Vicario, F. Angelucci, and F. Arcamone, J. Antibiot. (Tokyo), 30, 773 (1977).

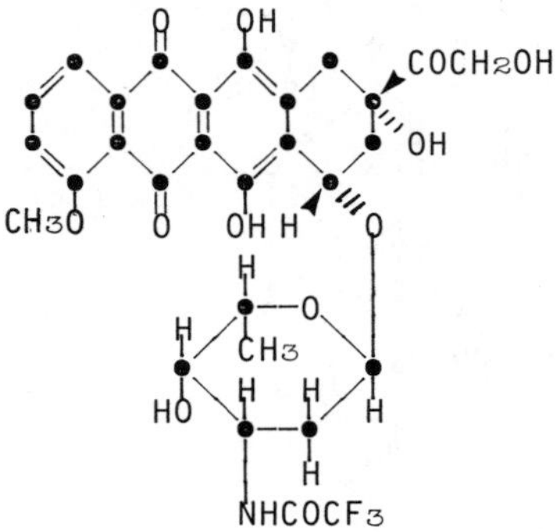

(82% from N-TFA-adriamycin)

1. ClCOO-i-C_4H_9, $(C_2H_5)_3N$, $CHCl_3$
2. $^{*}CH_2N_2$, Et_2O
→

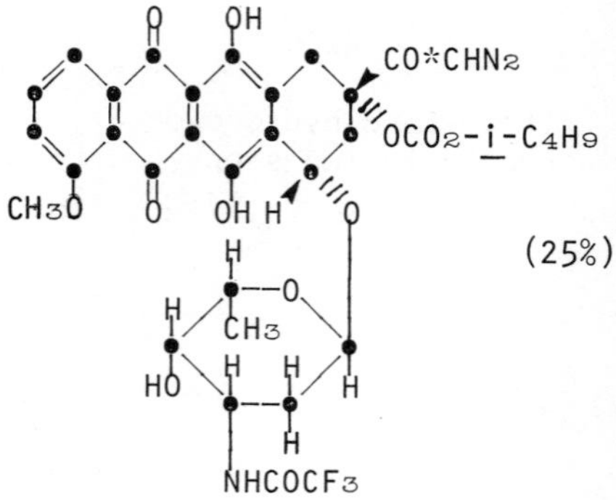

(25%)

1. HBr, CH_2Cl_2 (95%)
2. 5% K_2CO_3 (80%)
3. p-anisyldiphenylmethyl chloride, pyr, Δ (56%)
4. 0.1N NaOH
5. 80% AcOH } (45%)
6. HCl/CH_3OH }

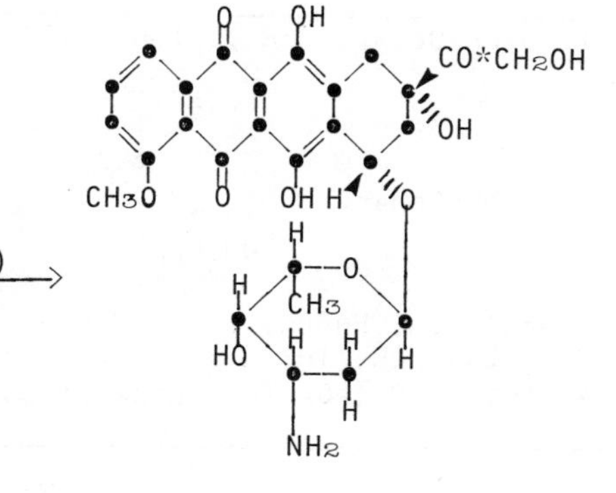
CO*CH2OH
OH
CH3O
OH
NH2
CH3
HO

Doxorubicin-(hydroxy-acetyl-2-^{14}C)

B. R. Vishnuvajjala, T. Kataoka, F. D. Cazer, D. T. Witiak, and L. Malspeis, J. Label. Compound. Radiopharm., 14, 77 (1978).

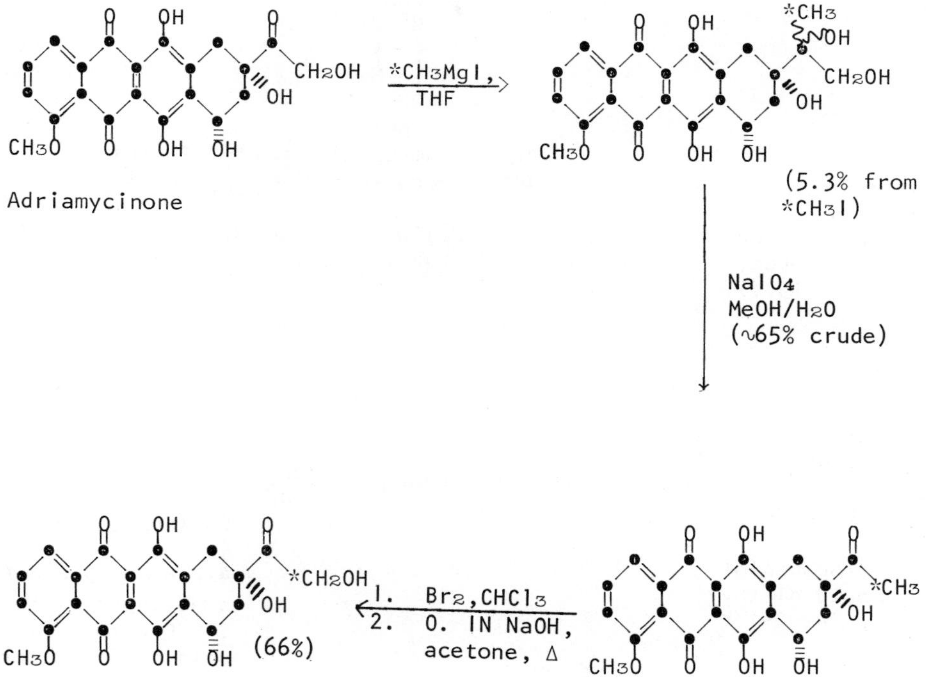
*CH3MgI,
THF
CH2OH
*CH3
CH3O
(5.3% from
*CH3I)
NaIO4
MeOH/H2O
(~65% crude)
1. Br2, CHCl3
2. 0.1N NaOH,
acetone, Δ
*CH2OH
(66%)

Adriamycinone

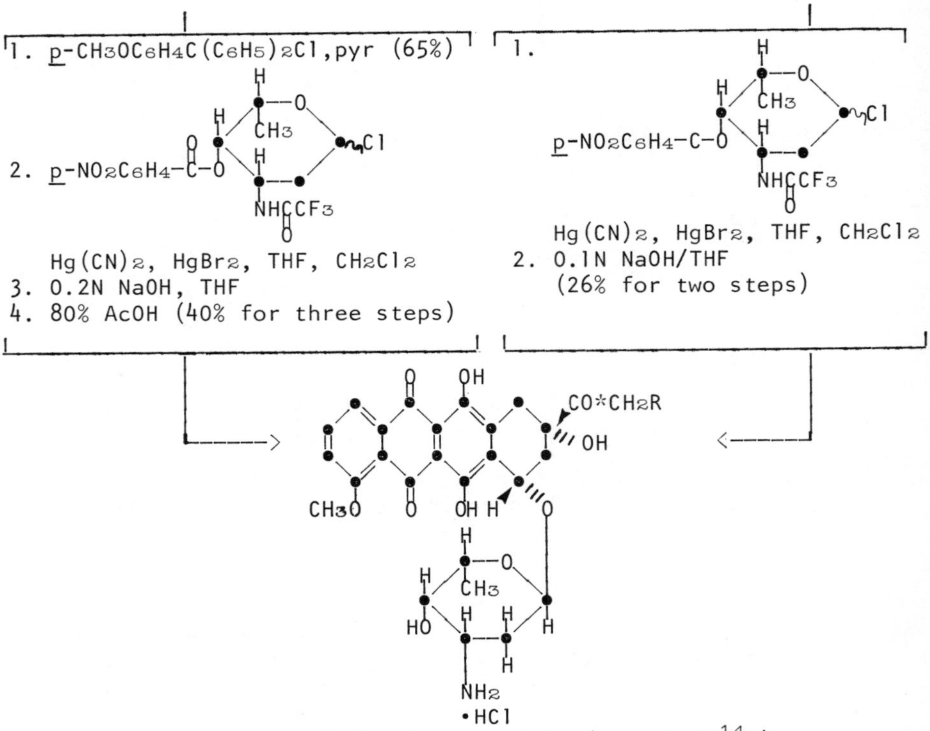
1. p-CH3OC6H4C(C6H5)2Cl,pyr (65%)
2. p-NO2C6H4-C-O
NHCCF3
Cl
Hg(CN)2, HgBr2, THF, CH2Cl2
3. 0.2N NaOH, THF
4. 80% AcOH (40% for three steps)
1.
p-NO2C6H4-C-O
NHCCF3
Cl
Hg(CN)2, HgBr2, THF, CH2Cl2
2. 0.1N NaOH/THF
(26% for two steps)
CO*CH2R
OH
CH3O
HO
NH2
•HCl

R=H; Daunorubicin-(acetyl-2-^{14}C)
R-OH; Doxorubicin-(hydroxyacetyl-2-^{14}C)

C. R. Chen, M. T. Fong, A. N. Fujiwara, D. W. Henry, M. A. Leaffer, W. W. Lee, and T. H. Smith, J. Label. Compound.Radiopharm., 14, 111 (1978).

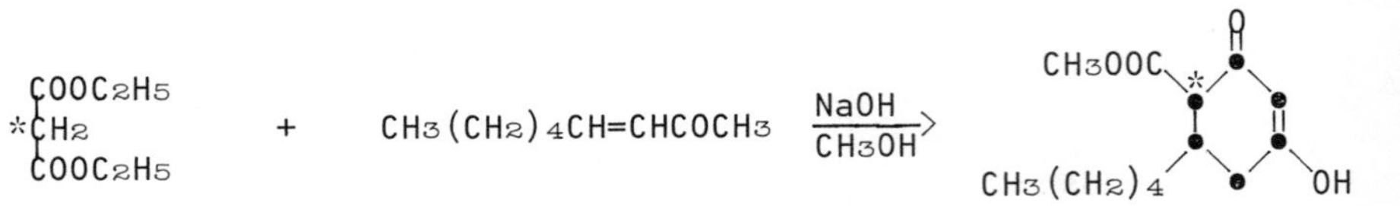
COOC2H5
*CH2
COOC2H5
+
CH3(CH2)4CH=CHCOCH3
NaOH
CH3OH
CH3OOC
CH3(CH2)4
OH

Propanedioic acid diethyl ester-2-^{14}C	3-Nonen-2-one	4-Hydroxy-2-oxo-6-pentyl-3-cyclohexene-1-^{14}C carboxylic acid methyl ester

1. aq. NaOH, 90°C
2. conc. HCl, 90°C
3. $Hg(OAc)_2$, AcOH, Δ
→

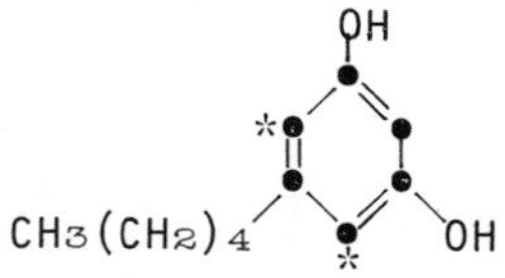
OH
$CH_3(CH_2)_4$
OH

(48% from diethyl malonate)

Olivetol
[5-Pentyl-1,3-benzenediol-4,6-^{14}C]

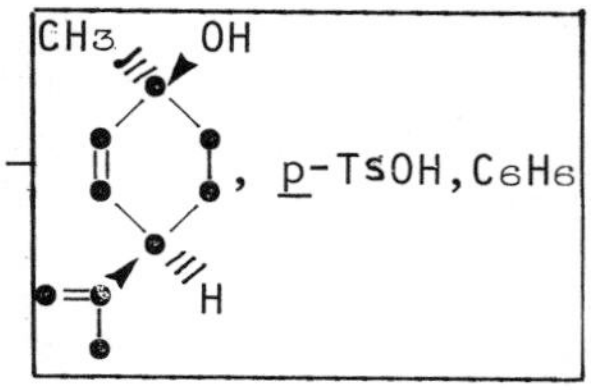
CH_3
OH
H
, p-TsOH, C_6H_6

→

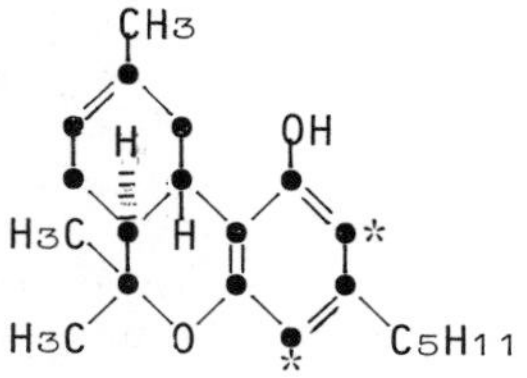
CH_3
H
OH
H_3C
H
H_3C
O
C_5H_{11}

(35% from olivetol)

(-)-Δ^8-6a,10a-trans-
Tetrahydrocannabinol-
2,4-^{14}C
[6aR-trans-6a,7,10,10a-Tetrahydro-6,6,9-trimethyl-3-pentyl-6H-dibenzo[b,d]pyran-1-ol-2,4-^{14}C]

1. HCl, $ZnCl_2$, CH_2Cl
2. t-$C_5H_{11}OH$,
   t-C_5H_{11}-OK
→

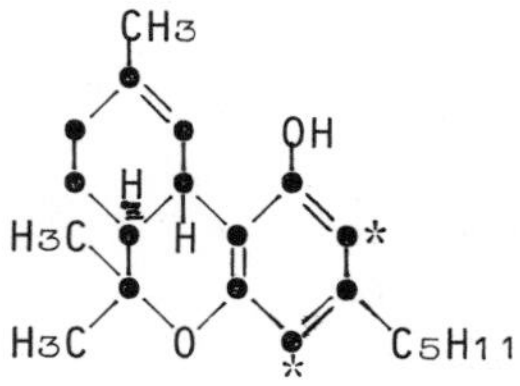
CH_3
OH
H
H_3C
H
H_3C
O
C_5H_{11}

(20% from olivetol; 55% yield of both isomers from olivetol)

(-)-Δ^9-6a,10a-trans-
Tetrahydrocannabinol-
2,4-^{14}C
[(6aR-trans)-6a,7,8,10a-Tetrahydro-6,6,9-trimethyl-3-pentyl-6H-dibenzo[b,d]pyran-1-ol-2,4-^{14}C]

A. A. Liebman, D. H. Malarek, A. M. Dorsky, and H. H. Kaegi, J. Label. Compounds, 7, 241 (1971).

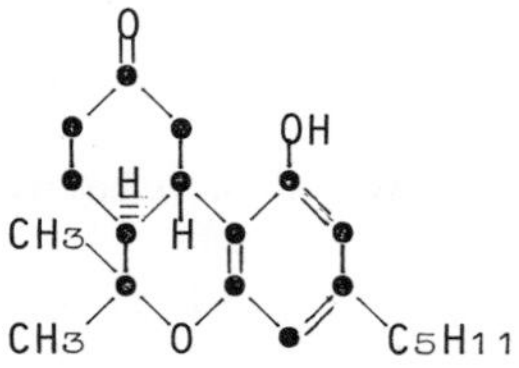

1. Ac_2O, pyr, Δ
2. $^*CH_3MgBr$, ether
3. p-TSA, C_6H_6

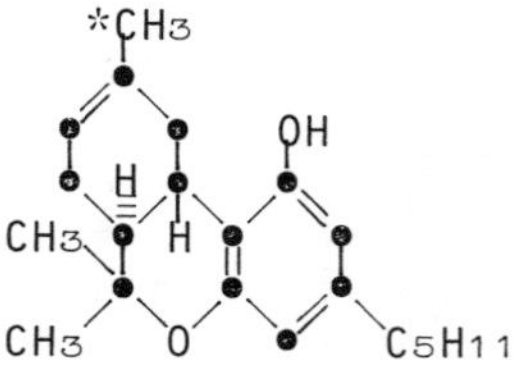

(~1% from $^*CH_3I$; 44% from ketone)

(+)-Δ^8-Tetrahydrocannabinol
[(6aR-trans)-6a,7,10,10a-Tetrahydro-6,6-dimethyl-9-(methyl-^{14}C)-3-pentyl-6H-dibenzo[b,c]pyran-1-ol]

$CH_3{}^*COCH_2COOC_2H_5$ + $CH_3(CH_2)_4CH{=}CHCOOCH_3$ $\xrightarrow[C_2H_5OH]{NaOC_2H_5}$

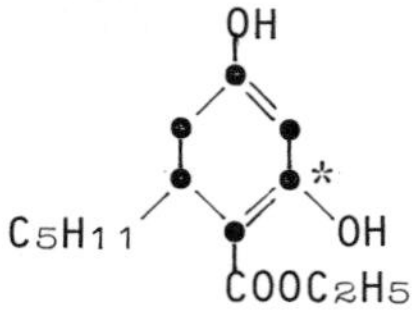

1. Br_2, AcOH
2. H_2, 10% Pd/C, C_2H_5OH, $(C_2H_5)_3N$
3. 5N NaOH, Δ
4. HCl, Δ

2,4-Dihydroxy-6-pentyl-1,3-cyclohexadiene-1-carboxylic acid ethyl ester-2-^{14}C

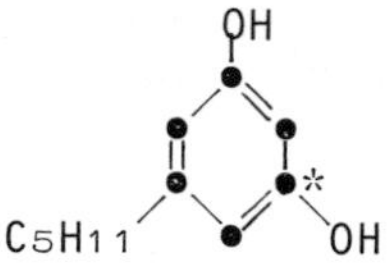

Olivetol
[5-Pentyl-1,3-benzenediol-3-^{14}C]

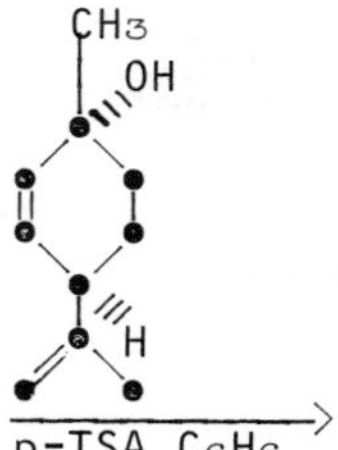

p-TSA, C_6H_6

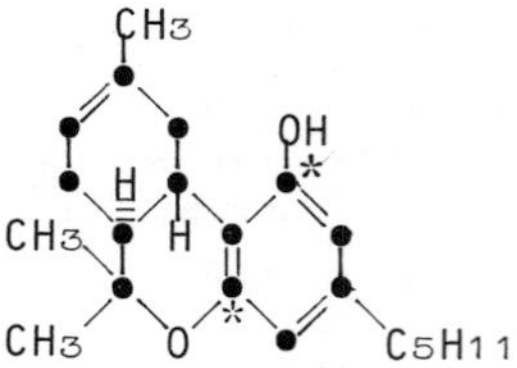

(~6% from ethyl acetoacetate)

(-)-Δ^8-Tetrahydrocannabinol
[(6aR-trans-6a,7,10a-Tetrahydro-6,6,9-trimethyl-3-pentyl-6H-dibenzo[b,d]pyran-1-ol-1,4a-^{14}C]

J. L. G. Nilsson, I. M. Nilsson, and S. Agurell, Acta Chem. Scand., 23, 2209 (1969).

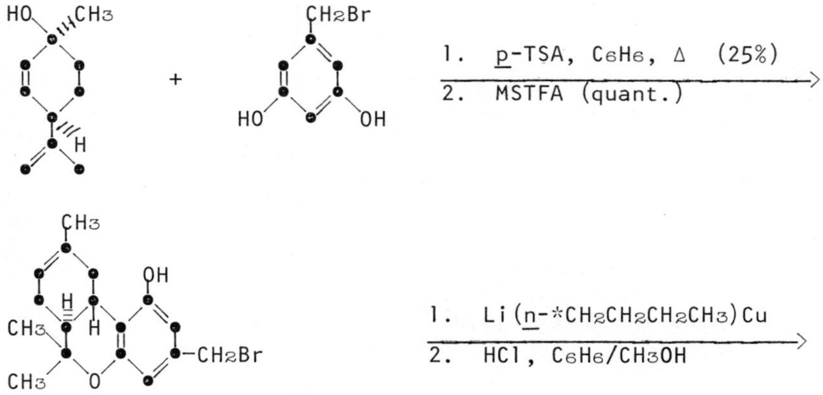
HO
CH3
H
CH2Br
HO
OH
1. p-TSA, C6H6, Δ (25%)
2. MSTFA (quant.)
CH3
OH
CH3
H
H
CH2Br
CH3
O
1. Li(n-*CH2CH2CH2CH3)Cu
2. HCl, C6H6/CH3OH

(6aR-trans)-3-(Bromomethyl)-6a,7,10,10a-tetrahydro-6,9,9-trimethyl-6H-dibenzo[b,d]pyran-1-ol

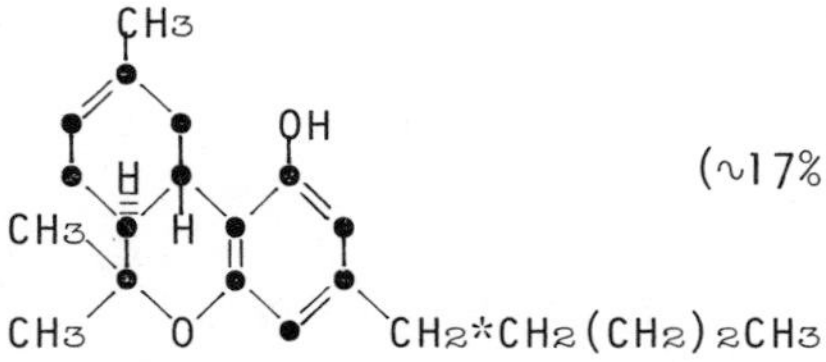
CH3
OH
H
CH3
H
CH3
O
CH2*CH2(CH2)2CH3

(~17%)

(-)-Δ^8-6a,10a-trans-Tetrahydrocannabinol [(6aR-trans)-6,6a,10,10a-Tetrahydro-6,6,9-trimethyl-3-(pentyl-2-^{14}C)-6H-dibenzo[b,d]pyran-1-ol]

W. Gau, D. Bieniek, and F. Korte, Tetrahedron Lett., 2507 (1972).

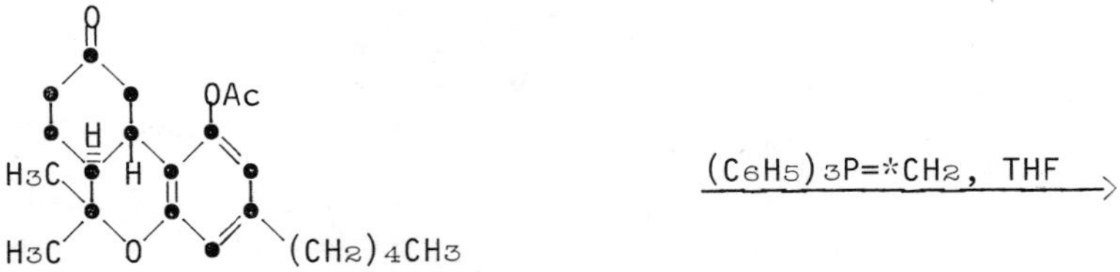
O
OAc
H
H3C
H
H3C
O
(CH2)4CH3
(C6H5)3P=*CH2, THF

(6aR-trans)-1-(Acetyloxy)-6,6a,7,8,10,10a-Hexahydro-6,6-dimethyl-3-pentyl-9H-dibenzo[b,d]pyran-9-one

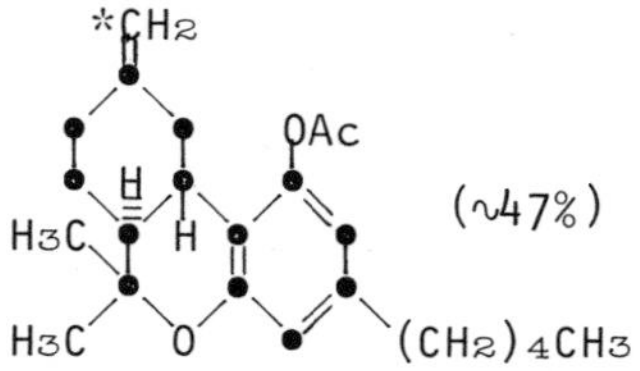

(~47%)

1. $ZnCl_2$, CH_2Cl_2
   HCl gas, 0-5°
2. potassium triethylcarbonolate, benzene, Δ

$\Delta^{9(11)}$-THC-11-^{14}C
[(6aR-trans)-6a,7,8,9,10,10a-Hexahydro-6,6-dimethyl-9-(methylene-^{14}C)-3-pentyl-6H-dibenzo[b,d]pyran-1-ol acetate]

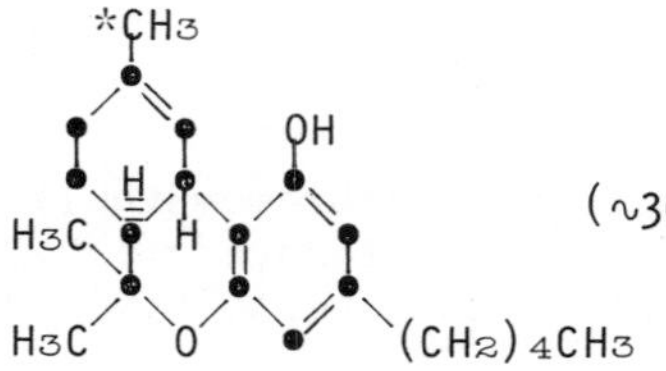

(~30%)

Δ^{9}-THC-11-^{14}C
[(6aR-trans)-6a,7,8,10a-Tetrahydro-6,6-dimethyl-9-(methyl-^{14}C)-3-pentyl-6H-dibenzo[b,d] pyran-1-ol]

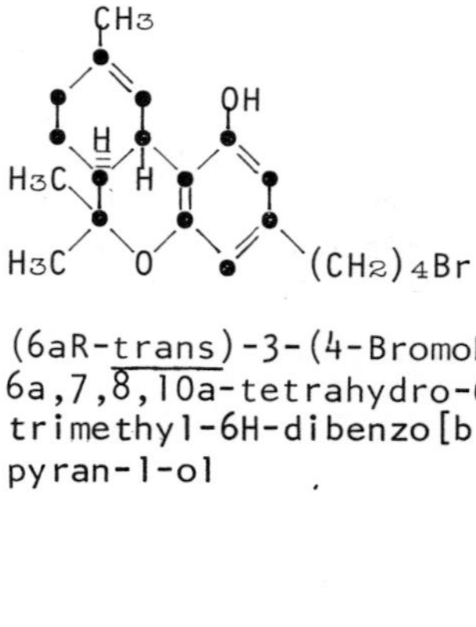

(6aR-trans)-3-(4-Bromobutyl)-6a,7,8,10a-tetrahydro-6,6,9-trimethyl-6H-dibenzo[b,d]-pyran-1-ol

1. Na*CN, DMSO, (97%)
2. KOH, EtOH/H_2O, (83%)

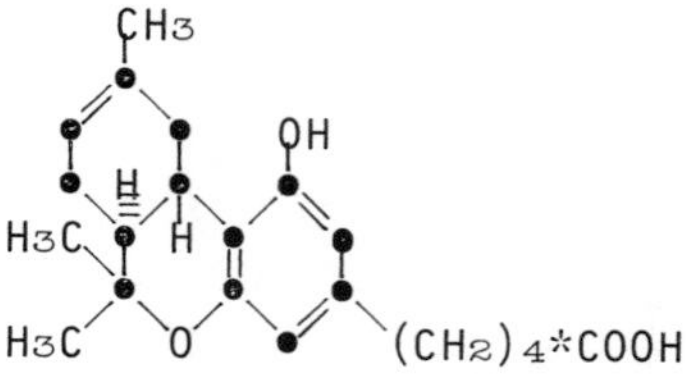

Δ^{8}-THC-5'-carboxylic-^{14}C acid
[(6aR-trans)-6a,7,10,10a-Tetrahydro-1-hydroxy-6,6,9-trimethyl-6H-dibenzo[b,d]pyran-3-pentanoic-1-^{14}C acid]

C. G. Pitt, D. T. Hobbs, H. Schran, C. E. Twine, Jr., and D. L. Williams, J. Label. Compounds, 11, 551 (1975).

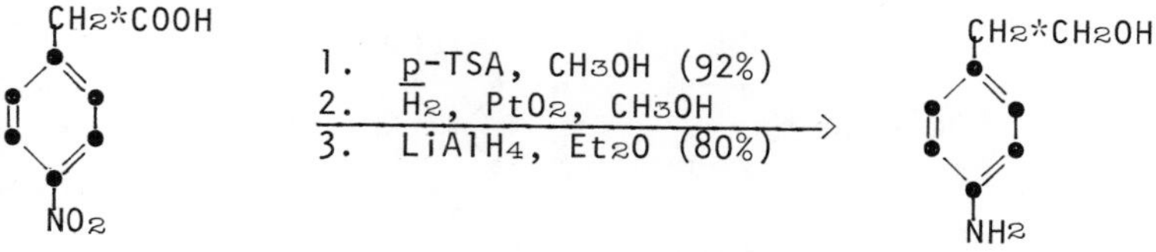
CH2*COOH
1. p-TSA, CH3OH (92%)
2. H2, PtO2, CH3OH
3. LiAlH4, Et2O (80%)
NO2
CH2*CH2OH
NH2

4-Nitrobenzene-acetic-^{14}C acid

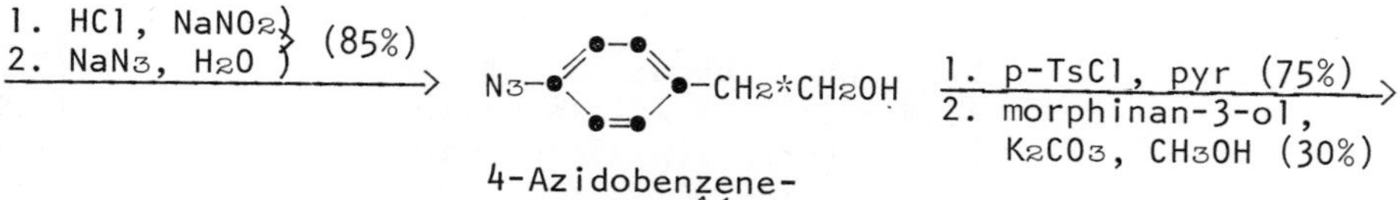
1. HCl, NaNO2
2. NaN3, H2O
(85%)
N3
CH2*CH2OH
1. p-TsCl, pyr (75%)
2. morphinan-3-ol,
K2CO3, CH3OH (30%)

4-Azidobenzene-ethanol-α-^{14}C

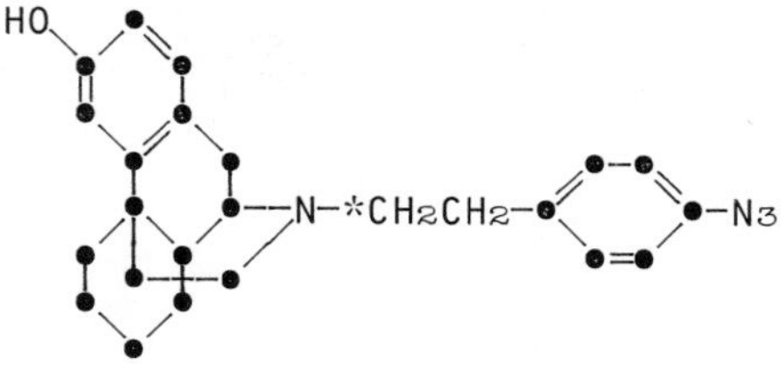
HO
N-*CH2CH2
N3

17-[2-(4-Azidophenyl)ethyl-1-^{14}C] morphinan-3-ol

J. I. DeGraw and J. S. Engstrom, J. Label. Compounds, 11, 233 (1975).

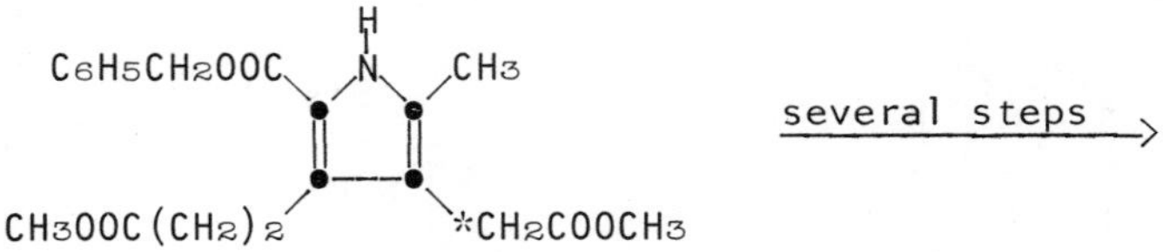
H
N
C6H5CH2OOC
CH3
CH3OOC(CH2)2
*CH2COOCH3
several steps

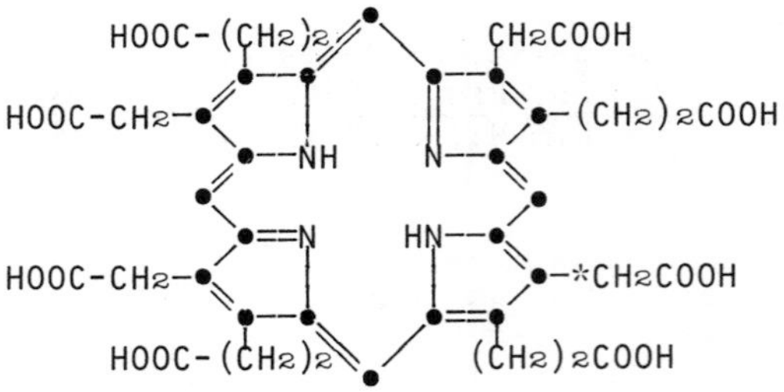
HOOC-(CH2)2
CH2COOH
HOOC-CH2
(CH2)2COOH
NH
N
N
HN
HOOC-CH2
*CH2COOH
HOOC-(CH2)2
(CH2)2COOH

(for incorporation experiments)

Uroporphyrinogen-^{14}C-III
[3,8,13,17-Tetrakis(carboxymethyl)-5,10,15,20,22,24-hexahydro-21H,23H-prophine-2,7,12,18 tetrapropanoic acid-^{14}C]

A. R. Battersby, M. Ihara, E. McDonald, F. Satoh, and D. C. Williams, J. Chem. Soc., Chem. Commun., 436 (1975).

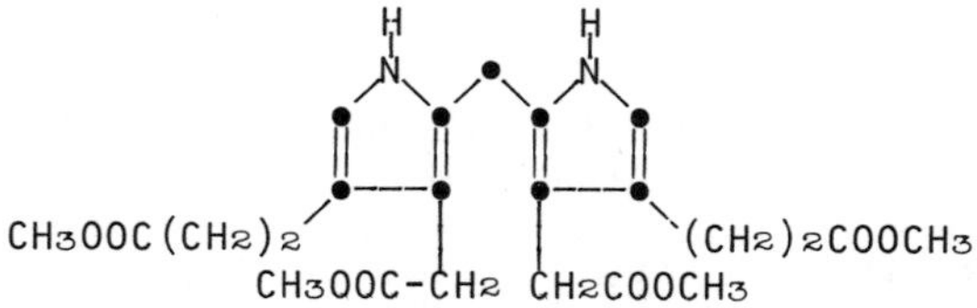
H
N
H
N
CH3OOC(CH2)2
(CH2)2COOCH3
CH3OOC-CH2
CH2COOCH3

$(CH_3)_2N^{14}CHO$
$POCl_3$, CH_2Cl_2 →

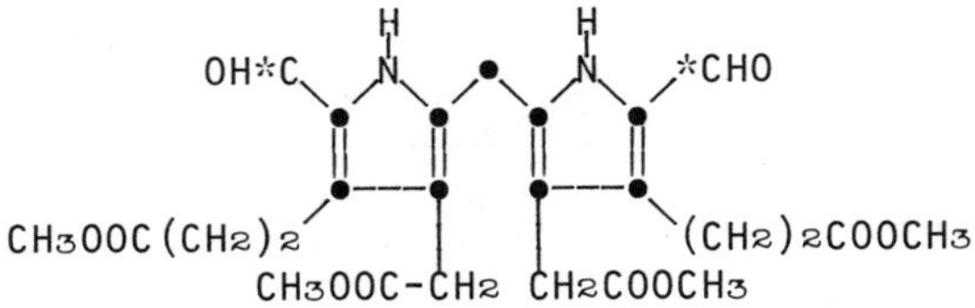
H
N
H
N
OH*C
*CHO
CH3OOC(CH2)2
(CH2)2COOCH3
CH3OOC-CH2
CH2COOCH3

(93% chemical yield; 17% radiochemical yield)

Dipyrrylmethane-(dicarboxaldehyde-^{14}C)

1.
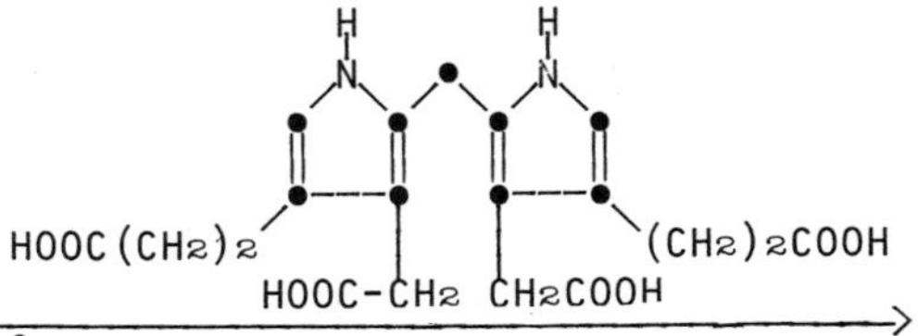
H
N
H
N
HOOC(CH2)2
(CH2)2COOH
HOOC-CH2
CH2COOH

2. O_2
3. CH_3OH, HCl

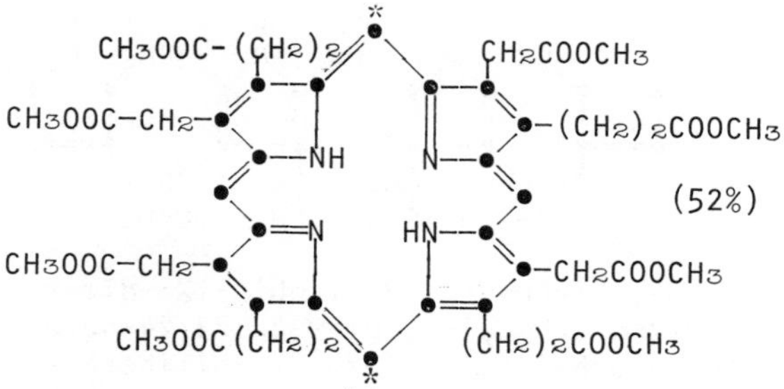
CH3OOC-(CH2)2
CH2COOCH3
CH3OOC-CH2
-(CH2)2COOCH3
NH
N
(52%)
N
HN
CH3OOC-CH2
-CH2COOCH3
CH3OOC(CH2)2
(CH2)2COOCH3

Uroporphyrin-(α,γ-^{14}C)-III-octa-methylester

B. Franck, D. Gantz, and F. Hüper, Angew. Chem., 84, 432 (1972).

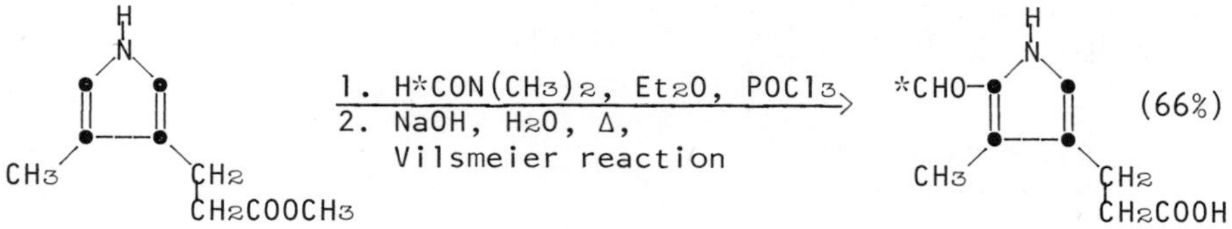
1. H*CON(CH3)2, Et2O, POCl3
2. NaOH, H2O, Δ,
Vilsmeier reaction
CH3
CH2
CH2COOCH3
*CHO
(66%)
CH3
CH2
CH2COOH

5-Formyl-^{14}C-4-methyl-1H-pyrrole-3-propanoic acid

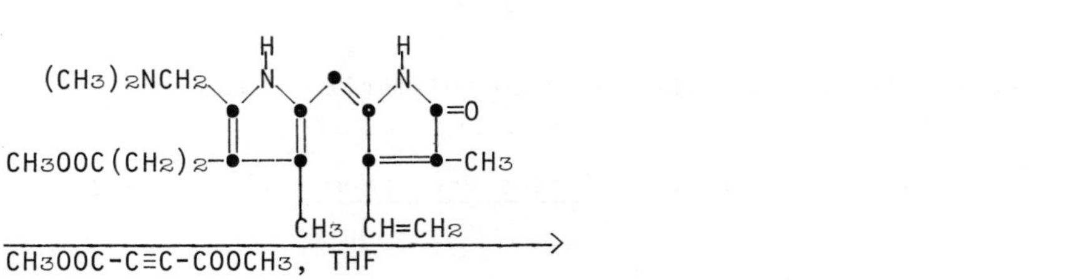
1.
KOH,H2O
(36%)
H3C
(CH2)2N(CH3)3I
2. CH2N2
CH3OOC(CH2)2
-CH=CH2
H3C
CH3
(CH3)2NCH2
=O
CH3OOC(CH2)2
-CH3
CH3
CH=CH2
CH3OOC-C≡C-COOCH3, THF

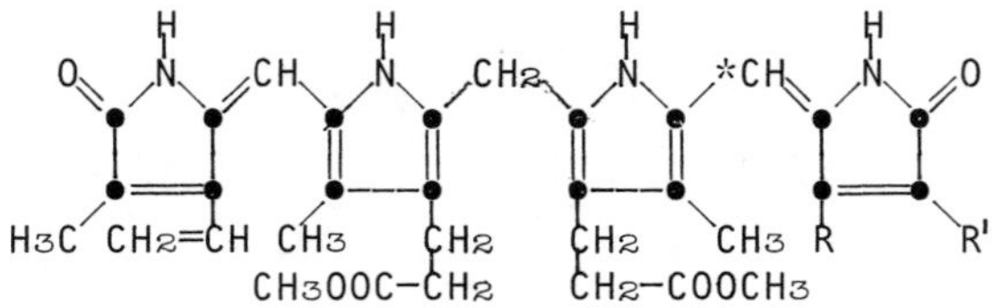

(80% crude yield; 60% yield of crystals)

R=CH_3, R'=CH=CH_2; Bilirubin-IXα-dimethylester [2,17-diethenyl-1,10,19,22,23,24-hexahydro-3,7,13,18-tetramethyl-1,19-dioxo-21H-biline-8,12-dipropanoic acid dimethyl ester]

R=CH=CH_2, R'=CH_3, Bilirubin-XIIIα-dimethylester [3,17-diethenyl-1,10,19,22,23,24-hexahydro-2,17,13,18-tetramethyl-1,19-dioxo-3,17-diethenyl-8,12-dipropanoic acid]

Ratio of IXα:XIIIα, 3:1. Yields are for unlabeled reactions.

H. Plieninger, F. El-Barkawi, K. Ehl, R. Hokler, and A. F. McDonagh, Ann. Chem., 758, 195 (1972).

13-3 Onium Compounds

$(*CH_3CH_2)_2O$ (66%) $\xrightarrow[\text{epichlorohydrin}]{BF_3 \cdot O(CH_2CH_3)_2}$

Diethylether-2,2'-^{14}C

$(*CH_3CH_2)_3O^{\oplus}BF_4^{\ominus}$ (81% from $BF_3 \cdot O(CH_2CH_3)_2$

Triethyloxonium-tetrafluoroborate-2,2'2''-^{14}C

The labeled reagent was then used to polymerize glucopyranose derivatives.

F. Micheel and O.-E. Brodde, Liebigs Ann. Chem., 1107 (1975).

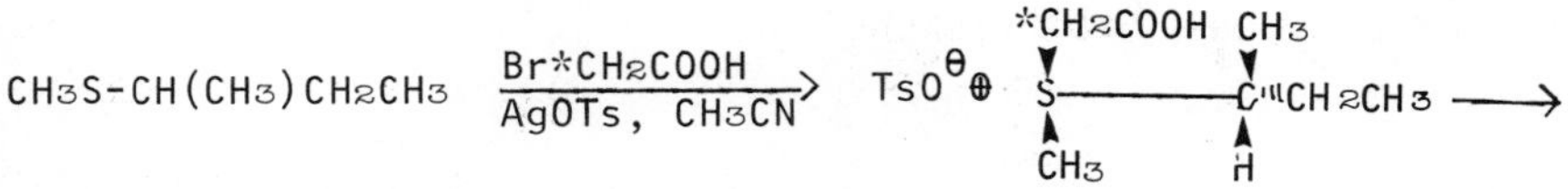

$$CH_3S-CH(CH_3)CH_2CH_3 \xrightarrow[\text{AgOTs, CH}_3\text{CN}]{\text{Br}^*\text{CH}_2\text{COOH}}$$

$$TsO^{\ominus} \oplus \overset{\displaystyle ^*CH_2COOH}{\underset{CH_3}{S}}\!\!-\!\!\overset{\displaystyle CH_3}{\underset{H}{C^{'''}CH_2CH_3}} \longrightarrow$$

(RcSs)-(ScRs)salt
(separated by fractional
crystallization

$$TsO^{\ominus} \oplus \overset{\displaystyle ^*CH_3}{\underset{CH_3}{S}}\!\!-\!\!\overset{\displaystyle CH_3}{\underset{H}{C^{'''}CH_2CH_3}}$$

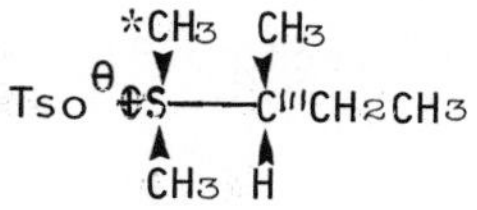

(RcRs)-(ScSs)-2-Methyl-
propyl)dimethyl-^{14}C-sulfonium
4-methylphenyl sulfonate salt

The product was used to study the methyl group transfer to p-thiocresolate.

G. Grue-Sorensen, A. Kjaer, and E. Wieczorkowska, J. Chem. Soc., Chem. Commun., 355 (1977).

$$HOCH_2CH_2N(CH_3)_2 \xrightarrow{^*CH_3I} [HOCH_2CH_2N(^*CH_3)_3]^{\oplus}I^{\ominus} \xrightarrow[\begin{array}{l}3. \text{ SOCl}_2\end{array}]{\begin{array}{l}1. \text{ Ag}_2\text{O, H}_2\text{O}\\2. \text{ HCl}\end{array}}$$

$$[ClCH_2CH_2N(^*CH_3)_3]^{\oplus}Cl^{\ominus} \quad (94\%)$$

2-Chloro-N,N,N-trimethyl-^{14}C
ethanaminium chloride

$$\overset{^*CH_2-^*CH_2}{\underset{O}{\diagdown\diagup}} \xrightarrow{HCl} HOCH_2^*CH_2Cl \xrightarrow[2. \text{ SOCl}_2]{1. \quad N(CH_3)_3}$$

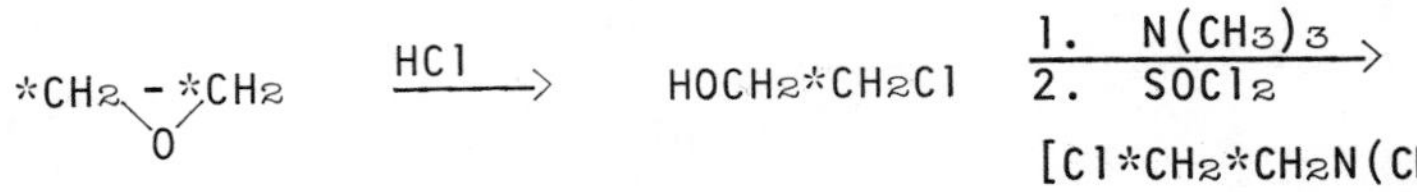

$$[Cl^*CH_2^*CH_2N(CH_3)_3]^{\oplus}Cl^{\ominus} \quad (93\%)$$

2-Chloro-N,N,N-trimethyl-
(ethanaminium-1,2-^{14}C)
chloride

Ch. Chwala, J. Label. Compounds, 4, 10 (1968).

$$CH_3CH_2{*}CH_2Br \quad + \quad (C_4H_9)_2NCH_2C_6H_5 \quad \xrightarrow[80°C]{CH_3NO_2}$$

$$(CH_3CH_2{*}CH_2)\overset{CH_2C_6H_5}{\underset{\oplus}{N}}(C_4H_9)_2 \cdot Br^{\ominus} \quad (56\%)$$

N,N-Dibutyl-N-(propyl-1-^{14}C)-benzenemethanaminium bromide

H. Elias, K. Lötzsch, and K. Weimer, Chem. Ber., 104, 683 (1971).

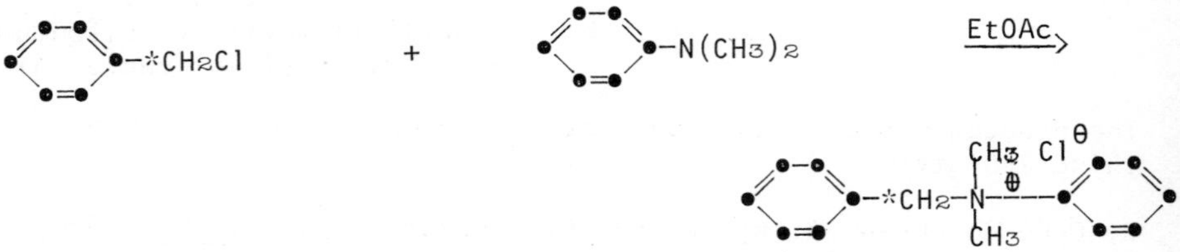

*CH2Cl
+
N(CH3)2
EtOAc
CH3 Cl
*CH2
N
CH3

N,N,-Dimethyl-N-phenyl-benzene-(methanaminium-^{14}C) chloride

T. Otsu, T. Sato, and M. Ko, J. Polym. Sci. Pt. A-1, 7, 3329 (1969).

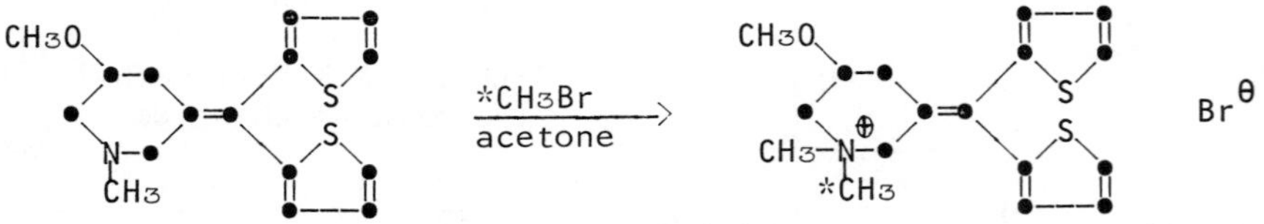

CH3O
S
S
N
CH3
*CH3Br
acetone
CH3O
S
S
CH3
N
*CH3
Br

3-(Di-2-thienylmethylene)-5-methoxy-1,1'-(dimethyl-^{14}C)-piperidinium bromide

T. Meshi, S. Nakamura, and T. Kanno, Chem. Pharm. Bull., 21, 1709 (1973).

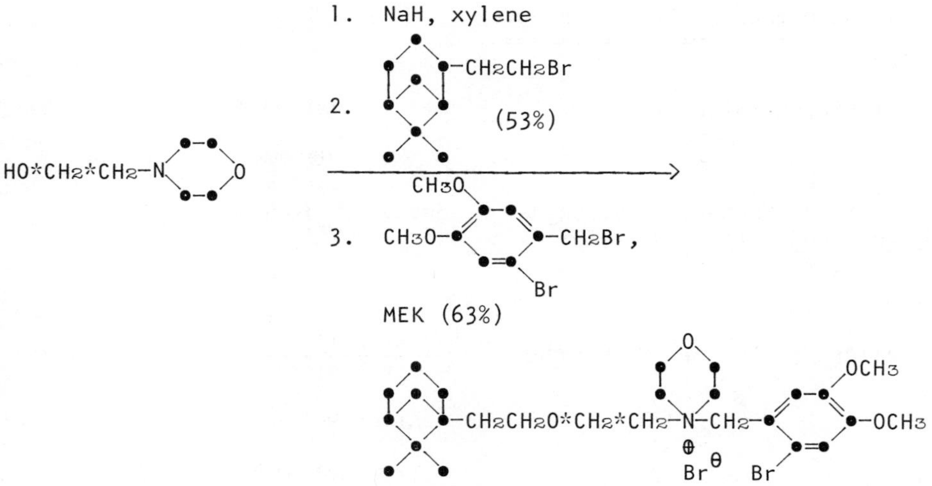
1. NaH, xylene
2. (53%)
3. MEK (63%)

Pinaverium bromide
[4-[(2-Bromo-4,5-dimethoxyphenyl)-methyl]-4-[2-[2-(6,6-dimethylbicyclo-[3.1.1]hept-2-yl)ethoxy]ethyl-1,2-^{14}C-morpholinium bromide]

C. Jacquot, J. Rapin, B. Lambrey, R. Baronnet, and L. Pichat, Eur. J. Med. Chem., Chem. Ther., 13, 61 (1978).

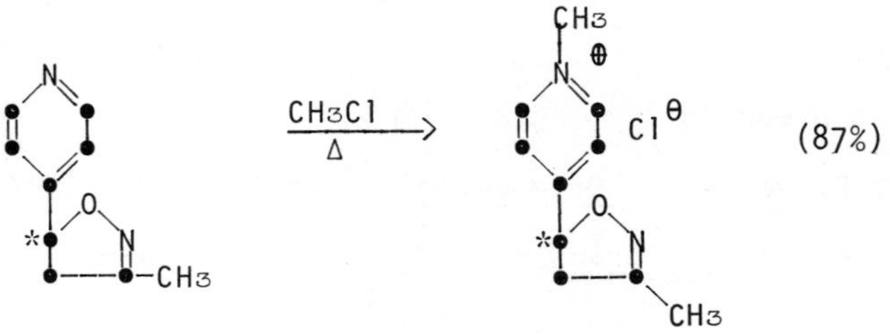
(87%)

4-(4,5-Dihydro-3-methyl-5-isoxazolyl-5-^{14}C)-1-methylpyridinium chloride

V. J. Bauer and A. E. Lanzilotti, J. Label. Compounds, 5, 87 (1969).

13-4 Organometallic Compounds

$Cl(CH_3)_2Si\text{-}Si(CH_3)_2Cl \xrightarrow[\text{ether}]{*CH_3MgI} (*CH_3)_3SiSi(*CH_3)_3$ (37%)

Hexamethyldisilane-^{14}C

M. Y. Al-Shaker, A. V. Chadwick, and J. W. Forrest, J. Label. Compounds, 11, 249 (1975).

$Al(OCH_2CH_3)_3$ + $*CH_2{=}*CH_2$ $\xrightarrow[\text{acetylacetonate}]{\text{nickel}}$

$Al(O*CH_2*CH_3)_3$ (~80% exchange)

Triethyl aluminum-^{14}C

G. Ayrey and R. J. Mazza, J. Label. Compounds, 8, 677 (1972).

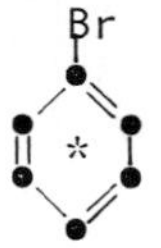

1. Mg, Et_2O
2. lead chloride
→ $Pb(*C_6H_5)_4$

Tetraphenyllead-U-^{14}C

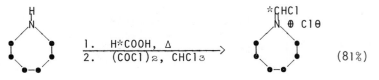

Bromobenzene-U-^{14}C

$Pb_2(*C_6H_5)_6$ was also prepared

V. G. K. Das and P. R. Wells, J. Organometal. Chem., 23, 143 (1970).

13-5 Penicillins and Cephalosporins

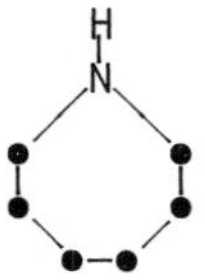

1. H*COOH, Δ
2. $(COCl)_2$, $CHCl_3$
→

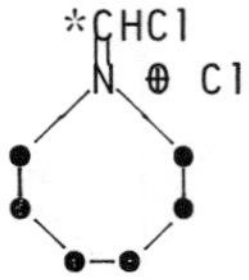
*CHCl
N ⊕ Cl⊖

(81%)

1-(Chloromethyl-^{14}C)-hexahydro-1H-azepine chloride

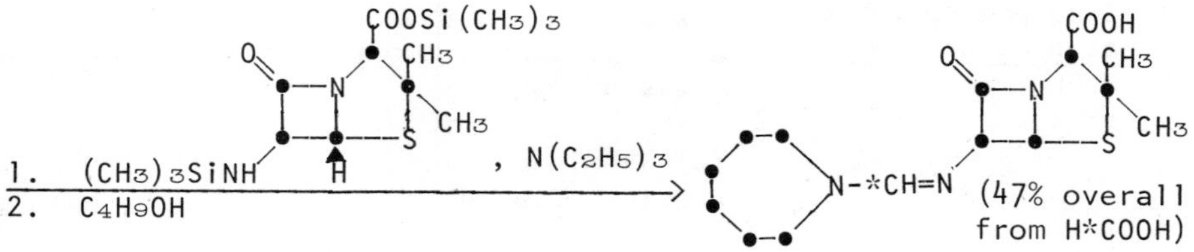
COOSi(CH3)3
CH3
CH3
1. (CH3)3SiNH
2. C4H9OH
, N(C2H5)3
COOH
CH3
CH3
N-*CH=N
(47% overall
from H*COOH)

Mecillinam, Amdinocillin
[[2S-(2α,5α,6β)]-6[[(Hexahydro-1H-azepin-1-yl)methylene-^{14}C]amino]-3,3-dimethyl-7-oxo-4-thia-1-azabicyclo-[3.2.0]heptane-2-carboxylic acid]

J. Zupanska, K. Szymoniak, I. Busko-Oszczapowicz, and J. Cieslak, J. Label. Compounds, 10, 431 (1974).

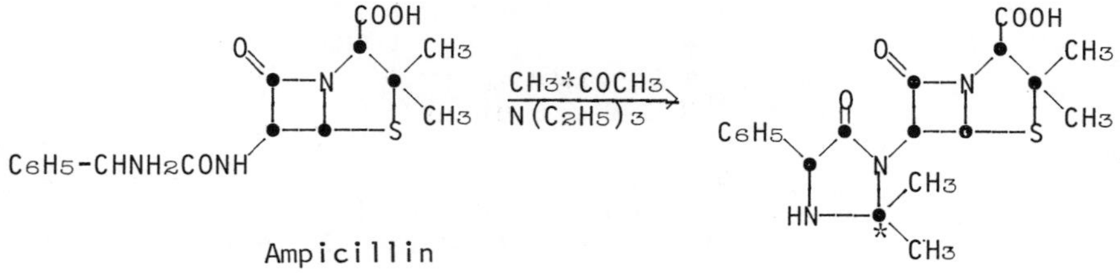
COOH
CH3
CH3
C6H5-CHNH2CONH
CH3*COCH3
N(C2H5)3
COOH
CH3
CH3
C6H5
HN
CH3
CH3

Ampicillin

Hetacillin
[[2S-(2α,5α,6β]-6-(2,2-Dimethyl-5-oxo-4-phenyl-1-imidazolidinyl-2-^{14}C)-3,3-dimethyl-7-oxo-4-thia-1-azabicyclo[3.2.0]heptane-2-carboxylic acid]

G. N. Levy, J. V. Ioia, and E. J. Kuchinskas, J. Pharm. Sci., 63, 1197 (1974).

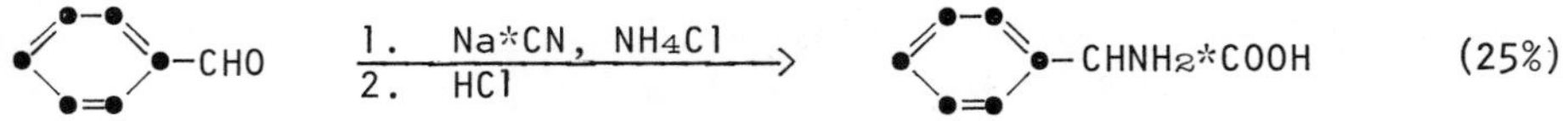
-CHO
1. Na*CN, NH4Cl
2. HCl
-CHNH2*COOH
(25%)

DL-Phenylalanine
[α-Aminobenzeneacetic-^{14}C acid]

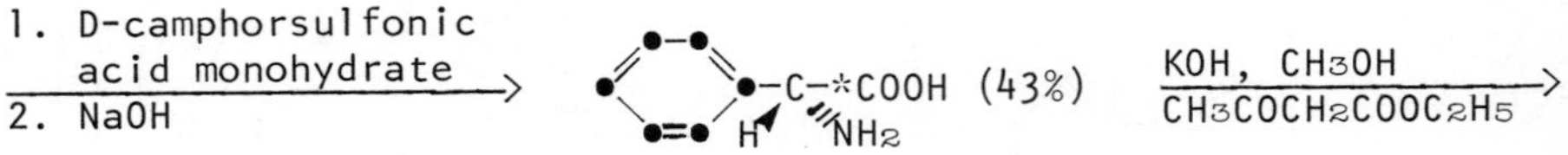
1. D-camphorsulfonic acid monohydrate
2. NaOH
C-*COOH (43%)
H NH2
KOH, CH3OH
CH3COCH2COOC2H5

(R)-α-Aminobenzene-acetic-$^{14}\underline{C}$ acid

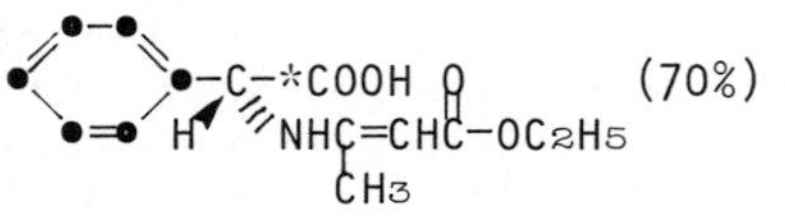
C-*COOH
H NHC=CHC-OC2H5
CH3
(70%)

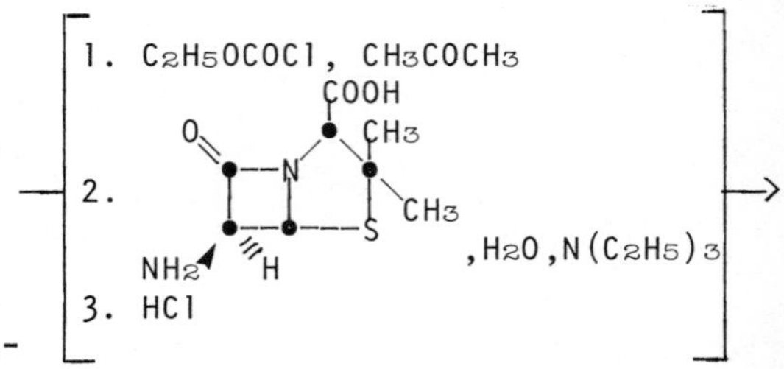
1. C2H5OCOCl, CH3COCH3
COOH
O
CH3
N
2.
CH3
S
NH2 H
,H2O,N(C2H5)3
3. HCl

(R)-α-[(3-Ethoxy-1-methyl-3-oxo-1-propenyl)amino]benzene-acetic-$^{14}\underline{C}$ acid

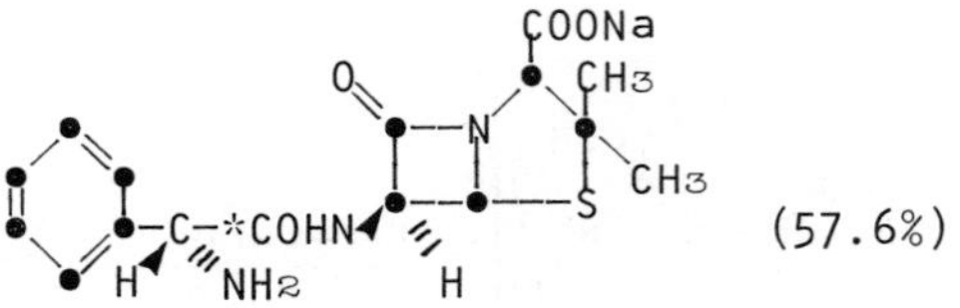
COONa
O
CH3
N
CH3
C-*COHN
S
H NH2 H
(57.6%)

[2S-(2α,5α,6β(R*)]-6-[(Aminophenylacetyl-1-$^{14}\underline{C}$) amino]-3,3-dimethyl-7-oxo-4-thia-1-azabicyclo[3.2.0]heptane-2-carboxylic acid sodium salt

U. Valcavi, J. Label. Compounds, 8, 687 (1972).

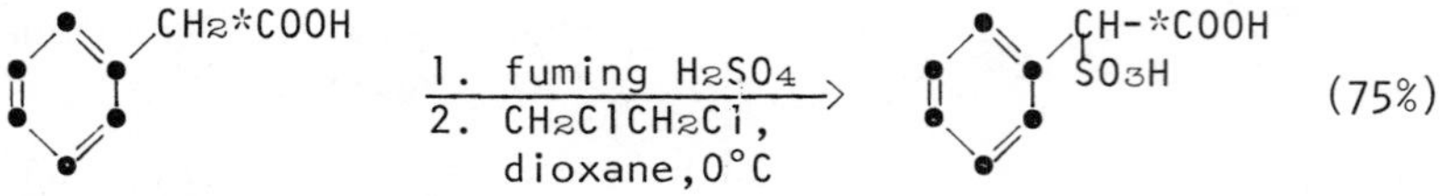
CH2*COOH
1. fuming H2SO4
2. CH2ClCH2Cl, dioxane,0°C
CH-*COOH
SO3H
(75%)

Benzeneacetic-$^{14}\underline{C}$ acid

α-Sulfobenzeneacetic-$\underline{1}$-$^{14}\underline{C}$ acid

1. $SOCl_2$, Et_2O, DMF
2. 6-aminopenicillanic acid, NaOH, $NaHCO_3$, ether } (54%) →
3. fractional crystallization

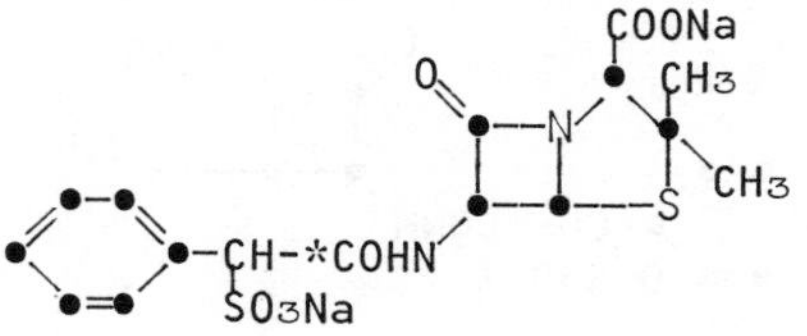

(9% overall yield)

Sulbenicillin[sulfocillin]
[[2S-(2α,5α,6β)]-3,3-dimethyl-7-oxo-6-[(phenylsulfoacetyl-^{14}C)amino]-4-thia-1-azabicyclo[3.2.0]heptane-2-carboxylic acid disodium salt]

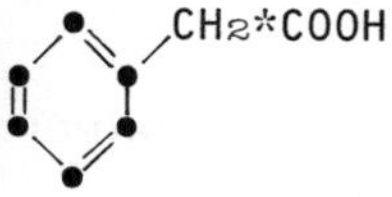

1. fuming H_2SO_4
2. $SOCl_2$, ether, DMF } (63%) →
3. $t\text{-}C_4H_9OH$, pyr, $ClCH_2CH_2Cl$
4. $HOCH_2C(CH_2T)TCH_3$, pyr

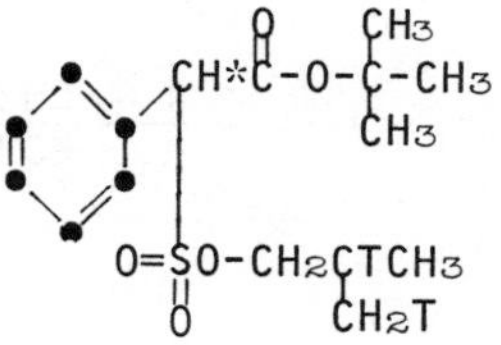

(36%)

α-[(2-Methylpropoxy-2,3-t)sulfonyl]-benzeneacetic-^{14}C acid-1,1-dimethylethyl ester

conc. H_2SO_4 / CH_2ClCH_2Cl →

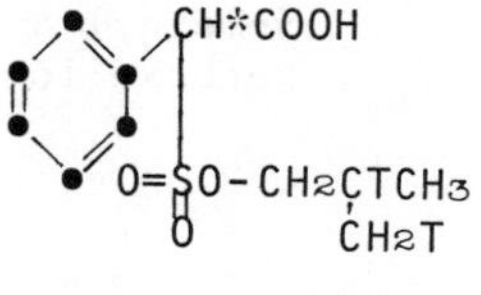

(19% from benzeneacetic-^{14}C acid; 37% from 2-methyl-1-propanol-2,3-t)

α-[(3-Methylpropoxy-2,3-t)sulfonyl]-benzeneacetic-^{14}C acid

1. $SOCl_2$, ether, DMF
2. 6-APA-$SiMe_3$, CH_2Cl_2
3. (i-Pro)$_2$O, HCl

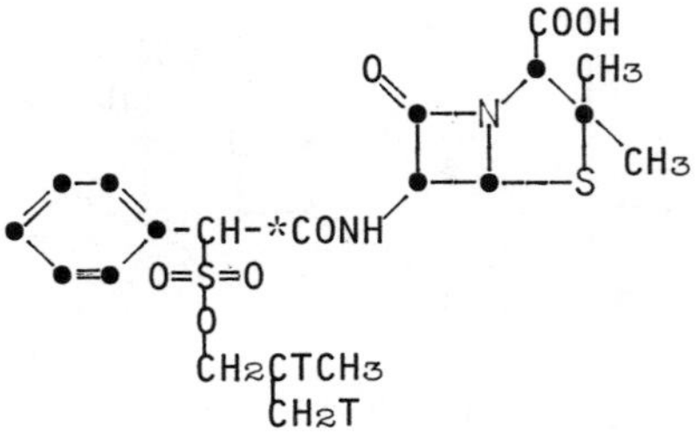

(17% from phenylacetic-1-^{14}C; 34% from isobutanol-2,3-t)

[(2S)-(2α,5α,6β)]-3,3,Dimethyl-6-[[[(2-methylpropoxy-2,3-t)sulfonyl]phenylacetyl-^{14}C]amino]-7-oxo-4-thia-1-azabicyclo[3.2.0]heptane-2-carboxylic acid

N. Hayashi, S. Kato, T. Toga, K. Nishijima, T. Hanaoka, H. Akimoto, and K. Sugimoto, J. Label. Compounds, 11, 375 (1975).

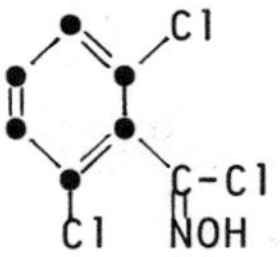

1. $CH_3{}^*COCH_2COOC_2H_5$, NaH, DMF
2. KOH/aq. EtOH, Δ

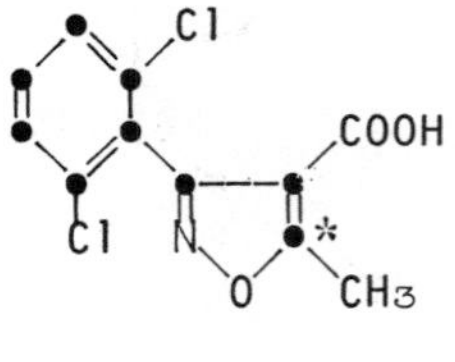

(30%)

3-(2,6-Dichlorophenyl)-5-methyl-4-isoxazolecarboxylic-5-^{14}C-acid

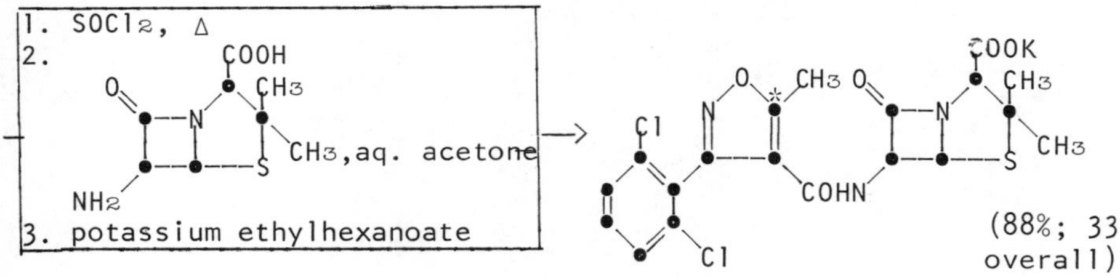
1. SOCl2, Δ
2.
COOH
CH3
CH3, aq. acetone
NH2
3. potassium ethylhexanoate
Cl
Cl
CH3
COHN
COOK
CH3
CH3

(88%; 33% overall)

Dicloxacillin
[[2S-(2α,5α,6β)]-6-[[[3-(2,6-Dichlorophenyl)-5-methyl-4-(isoxazolyl-5-^{14}C)]carbonyl]-amino]-3,3-dimethyl-7-oxo-4-thia-1-azabicyclo[3.2.0]heptane-2-carboxylic acid monopotassium salt]

E. S. Ferdinandi, J. Label. Compound.Radiopharm., 14, 751 (1978).

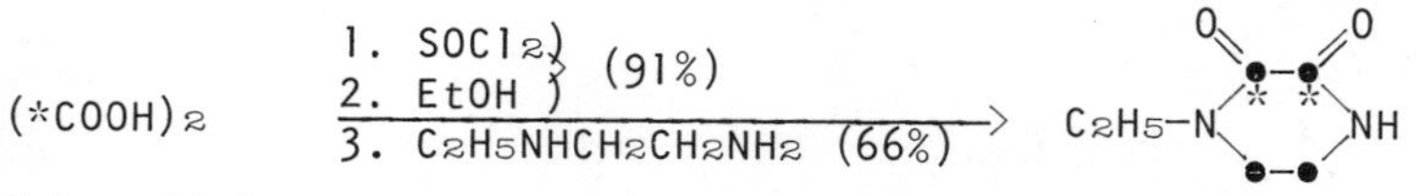
(*COOH)2
1. SOCl2
2. EtOH
(91%)
3. C2H5NHCH2CH2NH2 (66%)
C2H5–N
NH

Ethanedioic-1,2-^{14}C acid

1-Ethyl-2,3-piperazine-dione-2,3-^{14}C

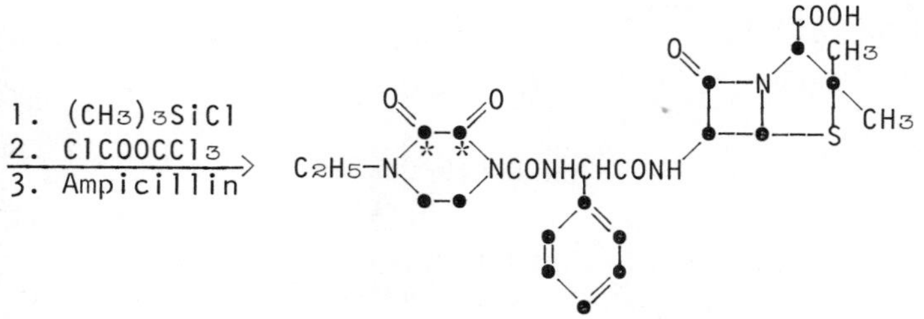
1. (CH3)3SiCl
2. ClCOOCCl3
3. Ampicillin
C2H5–N
NCONHCHCONH
COOH
CH3
CH3

(45%)

Piperacillin
[[2S-(2α,5α,6β)]-6-[[[[(4-Ethyl-2,3-dioxo-1-piperazinyl-2,3-^{14}C)carbonyl]amino]phenylacetyl]-amino]-3,3-dimethyl-7-oxo-4-thia-1-azabicyclo-[3.2.0]heptane-2-carboxylic acid]

I. Saikawa, A. Takai, Y. Nakashima, C. Yoshida, T. Yasuda, E. Shimizu, H. Sakai, H. Taki, M. Tai, and Y. Takashita, J. Pharm. Soc. Jap., 97, 1071 (1977).

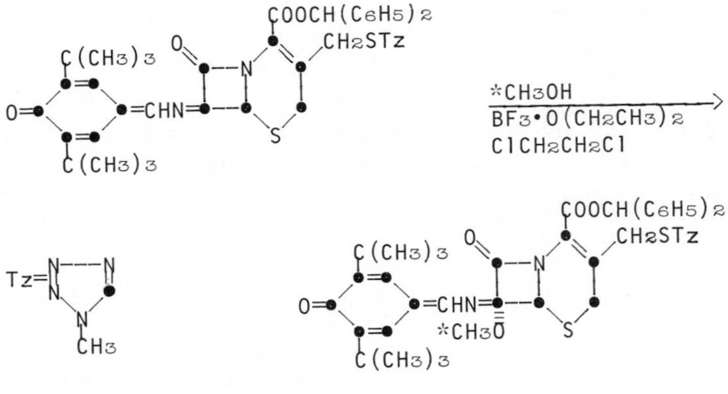
COOCH(C6H5)2
CH2STz
C(CH3)3
O=
=CHN=
N
S
*CH3OH
BF3·O(CH2CH3)2
ClCH2CH2Cl
Tz=
N
CH3
*CH3O

1. Girard T, $CH_3OH/THF/H_2O$ (73%)
2. CH_2CNSCH_2COOH, $C_6H_5N(C_2H_5)_2$, $ClCH_2CH_2Cl$
3. CF_3COOH, $C_6H_5OCH_3$
4. 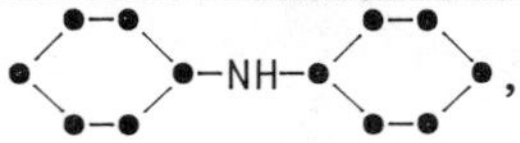
NH
   ,
   CH_2Cl_2/EtOH
   (43%, three steps)
5. sodium 2-ethylhexanoate, AcOEt/i-C_3H_7OH (90%)

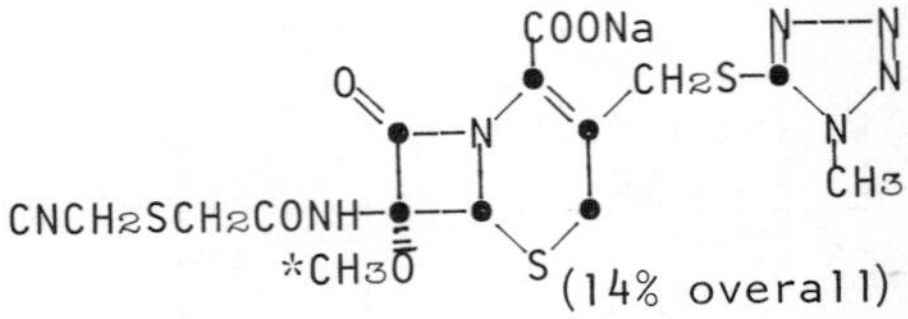
COONa
CH2S
N
CH3
CNCH2SCH2CONH
*CH3O
S

(14% overall)

Cetmetazole
[7-[[[(Cyanomethyl)thio]acetyl]amino]-7-methoxy-^{14}C-3-[[(1-methyl-1H-tetrazol-5-yl)thio]-methyl]-8-oxo-5-thia-1-azabicyclo-[4.2.0]oct-2-ene-2-carboxylic acid monosodium salt]

H. Nakao, K. Fujimoto, and H. Yanagisaw, J. Label. Compound. Radiopharm., 15, 381 (1978).

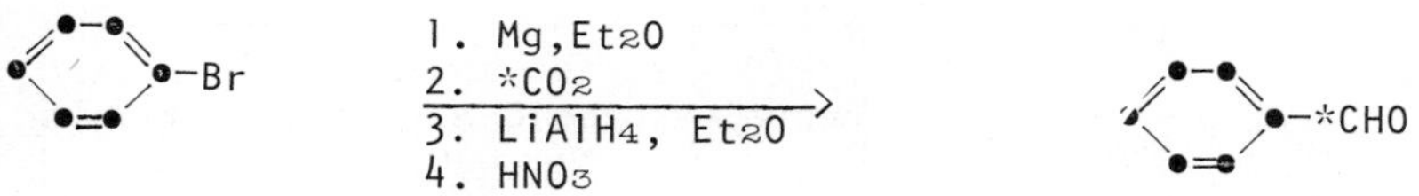
Br
1. Mg, Et_2O
2. $*CO_2$
3. $LiAlH_4$, Et_2O
4. HNO_3
*CHO

Benzaldehyde-7-^{14}C

1. aq. $NaHSO_3$
2. NaCN
3. conc. HCl
4. alc. morphine resolution
*CHCOOH
OH

D-(-)-Mandelic-β-^{14}C acid
[50% yield of (±) mixture from $BaCO_3$; D-isomer resolved in 57% yield]

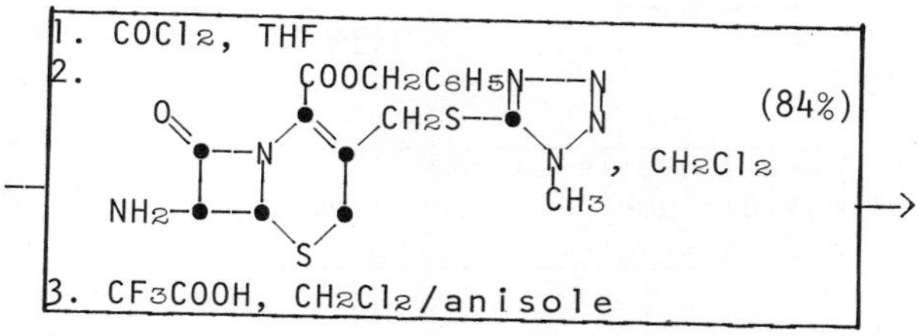
1. $COCl_2$, THF
2.
O
$COOCH_2C_6H_5$
N
N
N
CH_2S
N
N
NH_2
S
CH_3
, CH_2Cl_2
(84%)
3. CF_3COOH, CH_2Cl_2/anisole

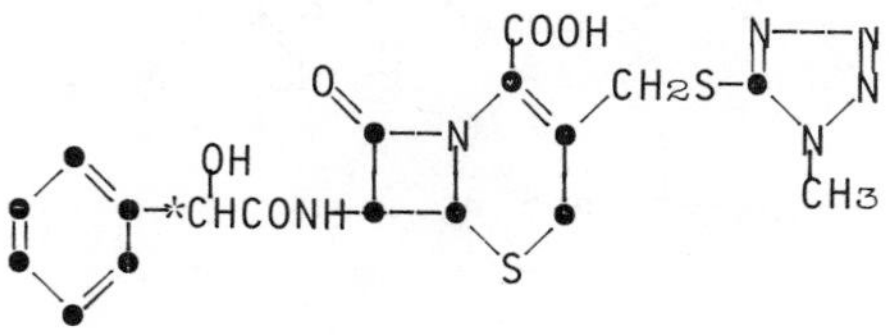
COOH
O
N
CH_2S
N
N
N
N
OH
*CHCONH
S
CH_3

(11% overall)

Cefamandole
[[6R-[6α,7β(R*)]]-7-[(Hydroxyphenylacetyl-2-^{14}C-amino]-3-[[(1-methyl-1H-tetrazol-5-yl)thio]methyl]-8-oxo-5-thia-1-azabicyclo[4.2.0]oct-2-ene-2-carboxylic acid]

H. Minato, T. Nagasaki, Y. Katsuyama, M. Hamada, and R. Kiritani, J. Label. Compound. Radiopharm., 14, 461 (1978).

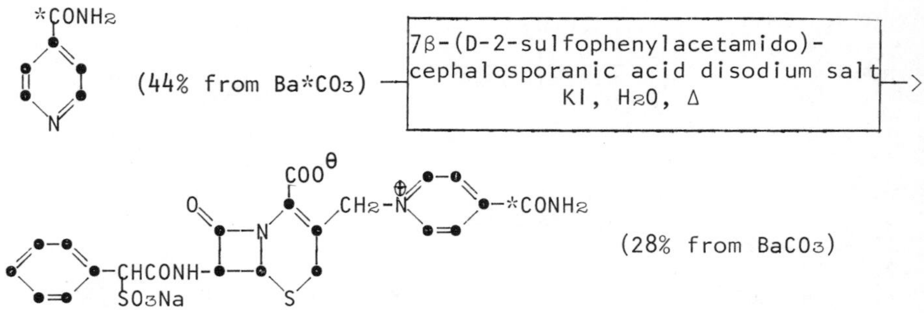
*CONH2
(44% from Ba*CO3)
7β-(D-2-sulfophenylacetamido)-
cephalosporanic acid disodium salt
KI, H2O, Δ
COO
O
CH2-N
-*CONH2
N
-CHCONH-
SO3Na
S
(28% from BaCO3)

Cefsoludin
[[6R-[6α,7β(R*)]]-4-(Aminocarbonyl-¹⁴C)-1-[(phenylsulfonylacetyl)amino]-8-oxo-5-thia-1-azabicyclo[4.2.0]oct-2-ene-3-yl-methyl-carboxylic pyridinium hydroxide monosodium salt]

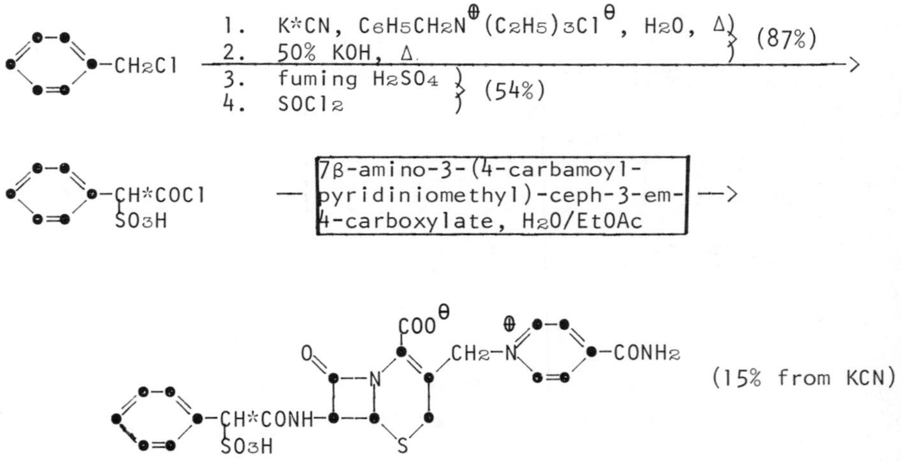
-CH2Cl
1. K*CN, C6H5CH2N(C2H5)3Cl, H2O, Δ
2. 50% KOH, Δ
(87%)
3. fuming H2SO4
4. SOCl2
(54%)
-CH*COCl
SO3H
7β-amino-3-(4-carbamoyl-
pyridiniomethyl)-ceph-3-em-
4-carboxylate, H2O/EtOAc
COO
O
CH2-N
-CONH2
N
-CH*CONH-
SO3H
S
(15% from KCN)

[6R-[6α,7β(R*)]]-4-(Aminocarbonyl)-1-[(phenylsulfonyl(acetyl-¹⁴C))amino]-8-oxo-5-thia-1-azabicyclo[4.2.0]oct-2-ene-3-yl-methyl-2-carboxylic pyridinium salt

N. Hayashi, T. Toga, N. Tada, and T. Azuma, J. Label. Compound. Radiopharm., 15, 489 (1978).

13-6 Polymers

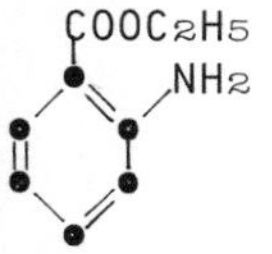
COOC2H5
NH2

2-Aminobenzoic acid ethyl ester

1. HCl, $NaNO_2$
2. Cu*CN

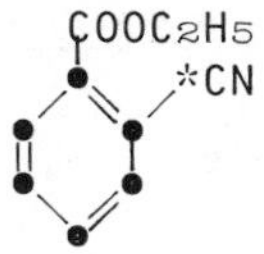
COOC2H5
*CN

2-Cyanobenzoic acid ethyl ester-(cyano-^{14}C)

1. NaOH, CH_3OH/H_2O
2. Ac_2O

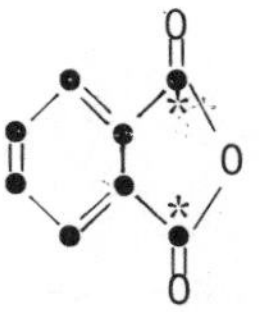
O
*
O
*
O

1,3-Isobenzofurandione-1-^{14}C (90%)

polyvinyl alcohol
CH_3COOH, Δ

Polyvinyl acetate phthalate-^{14}C (PVAP) (83%)

J. F. Stiver, J. B. Data, and J. E. Christian, J. Label. Compounds, 6, 150 (1970).

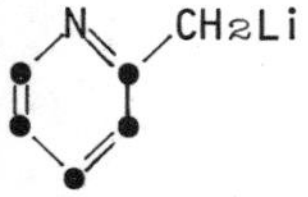
N
CH2Li

(2-Pyridinyl)-methyllithium

1. $^{*}CO_2$
2. EtOH, HCl

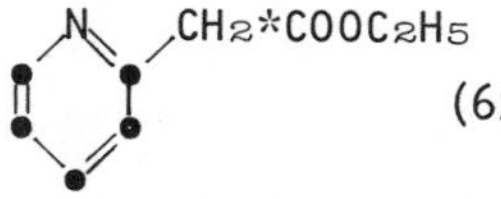
N
CH2*COOC2H5

2-Pyridine acetic-1-^{14}C acid ethyl ester (62%)

1. $LiAlH_4$, Et_2O (82%)
2. KOH, hydroquinone (93%)

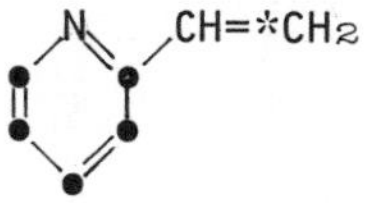
N
CH=*CH2

1. 2,2'-azodiiso-butyronitrile
2. H_2O_2

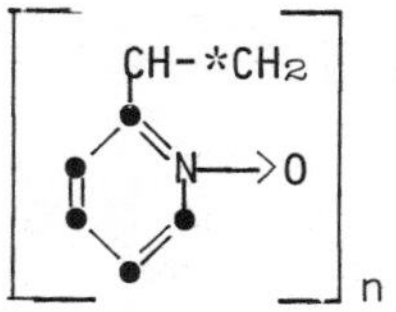
CH-*CH2
N→O
n

Polyvinylpyridine-N-oxide-[vinyl-2-^{14}C]

W. Maul, J. Label. Compounds, 4, 350 (1968).

$^{*}CH_2 = {}^{*}CHCOONa$ → (1. C_6H_5COCl (94%); 2. sulfadiazine, $NaHCO_3$ (43%); 3. AIBN, 60°C (67%))

2-Propenoic-2,3-^{14}C acid sodium salt

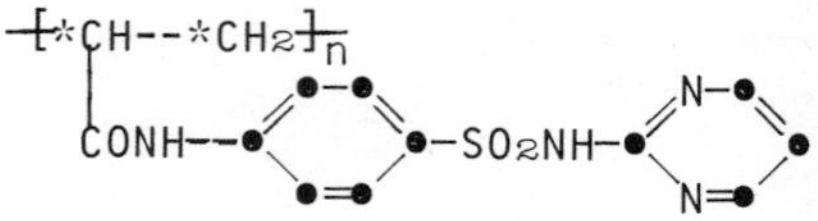
*CH--*CH2
n
CONH
SO2NH
N
N

Poly[sulfadiazine-(acrylamide-1,2-^{14}C)]

G. Abel, T. A. Conners, V. Hofmann, and H. Ringsdorf, Makromol. Chem., 177, 2669 (1976).

$H(O\text{-}CH(CH_3)\text{-}CH_2)_n\text{-}OCH_2\text{-}CH{=}CH_2$ → ($^{*}CH_3OH$, $Hg(OAc)_2$)

$H(O\text{-}CHCH_3\text{-}CH_2)_n\text{-}OCH_2\text{-}CH(O^{*}CH_3)\text{-}CH_2HgOAc$

Copolymer of propylene oxide and unsaturated epoxide.

D. R. Campbell, J. Appl. Polym. Sci., 14, 847 (1970).

13-7 Prostaglandins

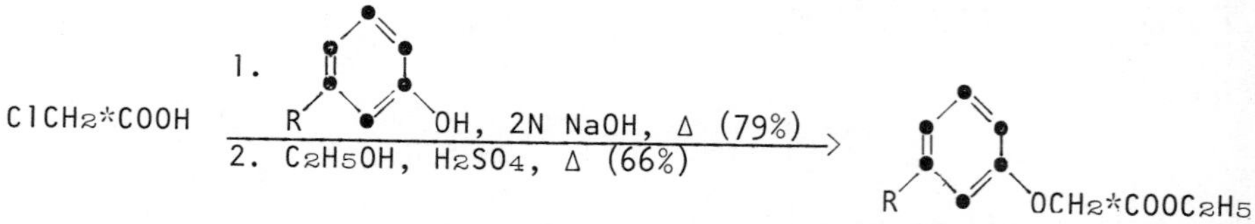
ClCH2*COOH
1.
R
OH, 2N NaOH, Δ (79%)
2. C2H5OH, H2SO4, Δ (66%)
R
OCH2*COOC2H5

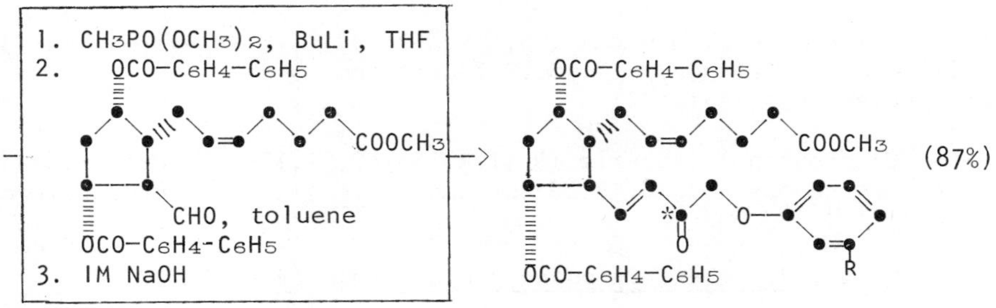
1. $CH_3PO(OCH_3)_2$, BuLi, THF
2. $OCO-C_6H_4-C_6H_5$
COOCH3
CHO, toluene
$OCO-C_6H_4-C_6H_5$
3. 1M NaOH
$OCO-C_6H_4-C_6H_5$
COOCH3
O
R
$OCO-C_6H_4-C_6H_5$
(87%)

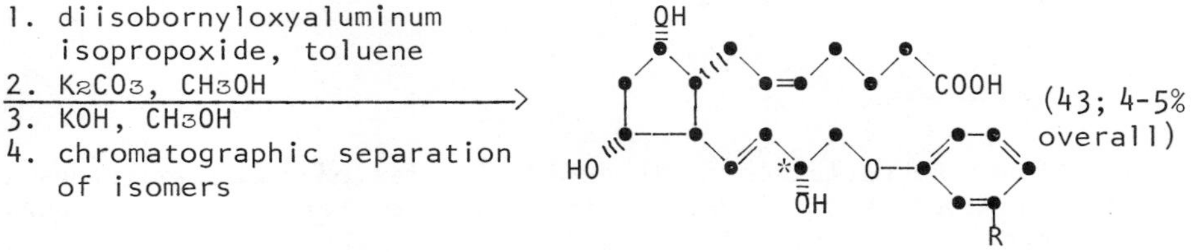
1. diisobornyloxyaluminum isopropoxide, toluene
2. K_2CO_3, CH_3OH
3. KOH, CH_3OH
4. chromatographic separation of isomers
OH
COOH
HO
O
OH
R
(43; 4-5% overall)

R=CF_3; Fluprostenol [racemic (9S,11R,15R)-9,11,15-Trihydroxy-16-(3-trifluormethylphenoxy)-17,18,19,20-tetranor-5-cis-, 13-trans-prostadienoic acid-15-^{14}C]

R=Cl; Cloprostenol [racemic (9S,11R,15R)-9,11,15-Trihydroxy-16-(3-chlorophenoxy)-17,18,19,20-tetranor-5-cis,13-trans-prostadienoic acid-15-^{14}C]

K*CN —(1. $Br(CH_2)_4Br$, CH_3OH, Δ; 2. 48% HBr, AcOH; 3. $(C_6H_5)_3P$, toluene, Δ)→ $(C_6H_5)_3\overset{\oplus}{P}(CH_2)_4{}^*COOH\ Br^{\ominus}$ (81%)

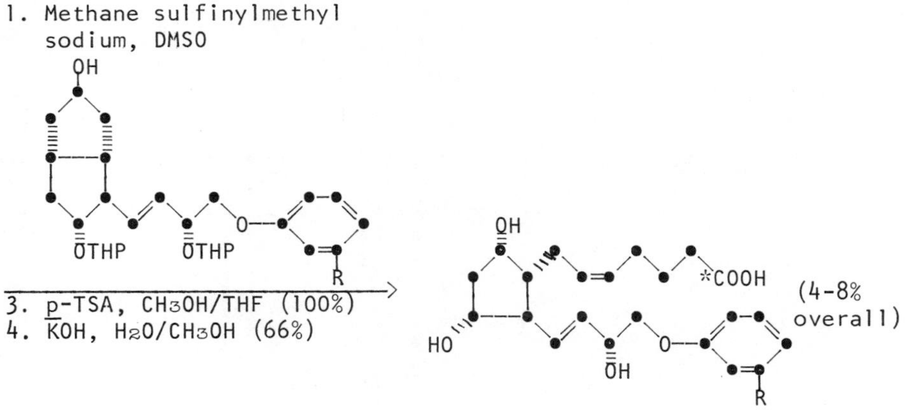
1. Methane sulfinylmethyl sodium, DMSO
OH
OTHP
OTHP
R
3. p-TSA, CH_3OH/THF (100%)
4. KOH, H_2O/CH_3OH (66%)
OH
*COOH
HO
O
OH
R
(4-8% overall)

R=CF_3; Fluprostenol [racemic (9S,11R,15R)-9,11,15-Trihydroxy-16-(3-trifluoromethylphenoxy)-17,18,19,20-tetranor-5-cis,13-trans-prostadienoic acid-1-^{14}C]

R-Cl; Cloprostenol [racemic (9S,11R,15R)-9,11,15-Trihydroxy-16-(3-chlorophenoxy)-17,18,19,20-tetranor-5-cis,13-trans-prostadienoic acid-1-^{14}C]

D. F. White, J. Label. Compound.Radiopharm., 13, 23 (1977).

13-8 Proteins

Additional Abbreviations: IUPAC-IUB Commission recommendations are used in most cases: AcOH, acetic acid; Boc, tert-butyloxycarbonyl; Bzl, benzyl; DDC, dicyclohexylcarbodiimide; DME, dimethoxyethane; DMF, dimethylformamide; HONB, N-hydroxy-5-norborene-2,3-dicarboximide; PCP, pentachlorophenol; tBu, tert-butyl; TEPP, tetraethylpyrophosphite; TFA, trifluoroacetic acid.

[Proline-U-^{14}C] ethylester•HCl + Z-Valine-p-nitrophenylester

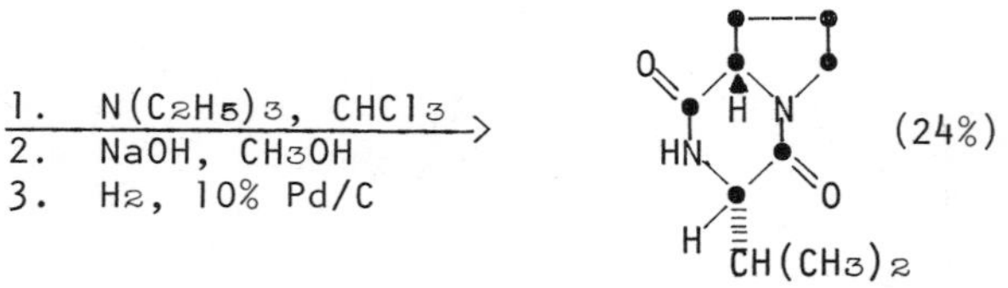

1. N(C_2H_5)$_3$, $CHCl_3$
2. NaOH, CH_3OH
3. H_2, 10% Pd/C
O
H
N
HN
O
H
CH(CH_3)$_2$
(24%)

Valyl-[proline-U-^{14}C]lactam

Similarly:

[Proline-U-^{14}C]-ethylester•HCl + Z-Leucine-p-nitrophenylester ⟶

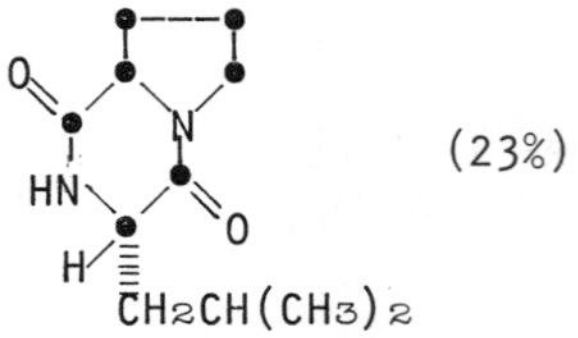

O
N
HN
O
H
$CH_2CH(CH_3)_2$
(23%)

Leucyl-[proline-U-^{14}C]lactam

In the same manner, [leucyl-*U*-^{14}*C*]-prolinlactam was prepared in 38% yield and [phenylalanyl-*U*-^{14}*C*]-prolinlactam in 17% yield.

The following linear peptides were prepared in the indicated yield:

[Prolyl-*U*-^{14}*C*]-alanine (38%)

[Prolyl-*U*-^{14}*C*]-glycine (32%)

[Valyl-^{15}N]-[leucine-*U*-^{14}*C*] (12%)

Valylleucyl-[proline-*U*-^{14}*C*]

S. Johne and D. Gröger, *Pharmazie*, *29*, 181 (1974).

BOC-glycine-*1*-^{14}*C* —(1. pH 4.5, CH_2Cl_2, N-ethylbenzisoxazolium fluoroborate; 2. methyl D-phenylalaninate; 3. NaOH, H_2O)→ BOC-glycyl-*1*-^{14}C-D-phenylalanine (not isolated)

—(1. L-isomer; 2. steps as above, ethyl glycinate)→ BOC-glycyl-*1*-^{14}*C*-DL-phenylalanylglycine

D. S. Kemp, S. W. Wang, G. Busby III, and G. Hugel, *J. Amer. Chem. Soc.*, *92*, 1043 (1970).

pGlu-PCPE + histidine-*U*-^{14}*C* —(NaOH / DMF)→ pGlu-*His Pyroglutamylhistidine

—($Pro-NH_2 \cdot HCl$ / N-hydroxysuccinimide, DCC)→ pGlu-*His-Pro-NH_2 (37% from histidine)

TRH (Thyrotropin-releasing hormone)
[Pyroglutamylhistidyl-*U*-^{14}*C*-prolineamide]

G. Flouret, A. Alter, and R. Genrich, *J. Label. Compounds*, *8*, 53 (1972).

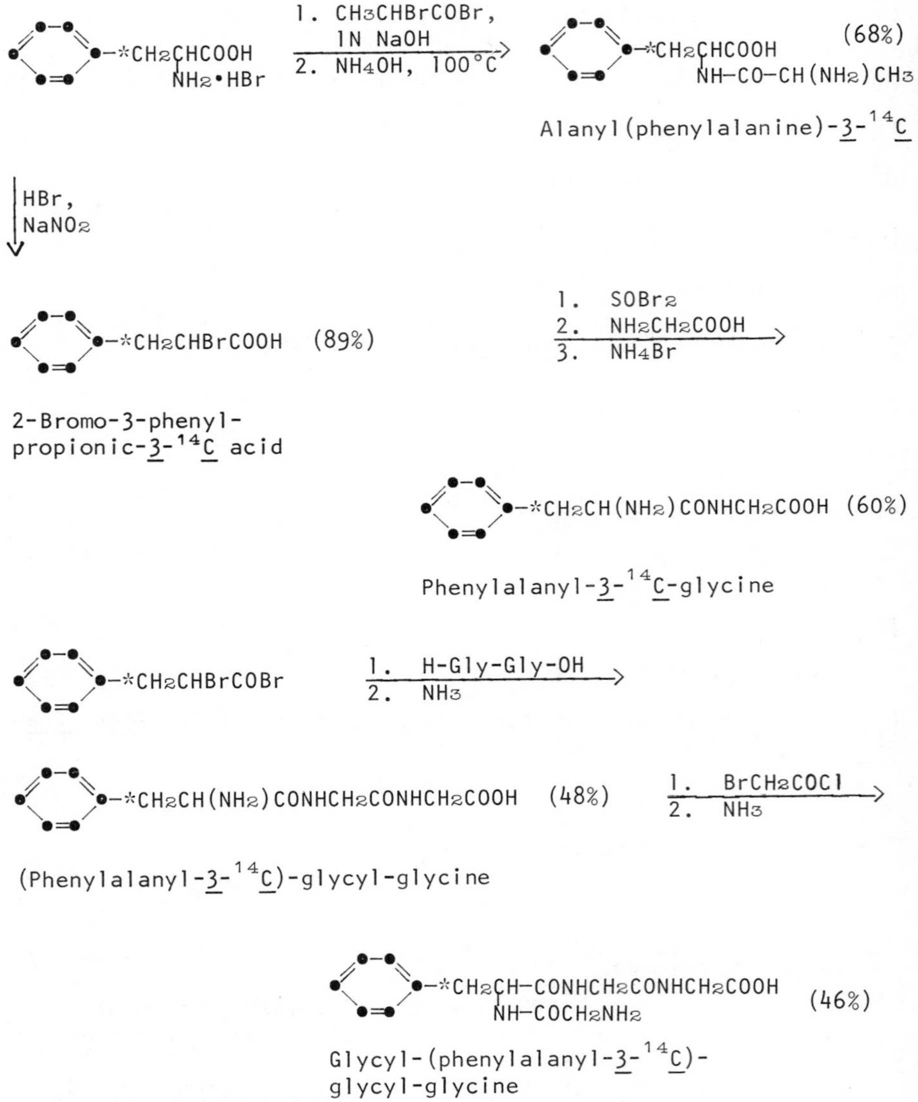
*CH2CHCOOH
NH2·HBr
1. CH3CHBrCOBr,
1N NaOH
2. NH4OH, 100°C
*CH2CHCOOH
NH-CO-CH(NH2)CH3
(68%)
Alanyl(phenylalanine)-3-14C
HBr,
NaNO2
*CH2CHBrCOOH
(89%)
2-Bromo-3-phenyl-
propionic-3-14C acid
1. SOBr2
2. NH2CH2COOH
3. NH4Br
*CH2CH(NH2)CONHCH2COOH
(60%)
Phenylalanyl-3-14C-glycine
*CH2CHBrCOBr
1. H-Gly-Gly-OH
2. NH3
*CH2CH(NH2)CONHCH2CONHCH2COOH
(48%)
1. BrCH2COCl
2. NH3
(Phenylalanyl-3-14C)-glycyl-glycine
*CH2CH-CONHCH2CONHCH2COOH
NH-COCH2NH2
(46%)
Glycyl-(phenylalanyl-3-14C)-
glycyl-glycine

M. Viscontini and G. Mattern, *Helv. Chim. Acta*, **53**, 377 (1970).

Glycine-2-^{14}C ethyl ester•HCl + Z-Val-Leu-Pro ---------> L-Valyl-L-leucyl-l-prolyl-glycine-2-^{14}C

L-Proline-U-^{14}C benzyl ester•HCl + Z-L-Alanyl-L-phenylalanine --> Ala-Phe-Pro-U-^{14}C

L-Phenylalanine-U-^{14}C methyl ester•HCl + Z-L-Phenylalanine ----> cyclo-Phe-(Phe-U-^{14}C)

S. Hartling, S. Johne, and D. Gröger, Z. Chem., 16, 272 (1976).

L-Z-Arg-OH-U-^{14}C + Gly-Phe-Phe-Tyr-NH_2 --(p-TsOH, DMF / DCC, HONB)-->

(54% from L-arginine-U-^{14}C)

Z-Arg-U-^{14}C-Gly-Phe-Phe-Tyr-NH_2•p-TSOH --(1. H_2, Pd/C, AcOH; 2. Z-β-Ala-ONB; DMF (22% from L-arginine); 3. H_2, Pd/C, AcOH; 4. IRA-410 (acetate))-->

(44% from L-arginine)

β-Ala-Arg-U-^{14}C-Gly-Phe-Phe-Tyr-NH_2•AcOH

(17% from L-arginine)

N. Hayashi, T. Kawakami, K. Shinozaki, M. Wakimasu, and M. Fujino, J. Label. Compound. Radiopharm., 14, 527 (1978).

Edeine A sulfate --(NH_2-*C(OCH_3)=NH•HCl / H_2O/EtOH, $N(C_2H_5)_3$, NaOH)-->

Edeine B-(guanyl-^{14}C) (10%)

J. Zupańska, J. Wasowicz, and K. Dziegielewski, J. Label. Compound. Radiopharm., 15, 79 (1978).

Ile-Gln-Asn-Cys(Bzl)-Pro-Arg(Tos)-Gly-resin $\xrightarrow[\text{2. elongation}]{\text{1. BOC-Tyr-}\underline{U}\text{-}^{14}\underline{C}\text{, DMF}}$

(prepared by Merrifield approach)

(Bzl)Cys-Tyr-U-^{14}C-Ile-Gln-Asn-Cys(Bzl)-Pro-Arg(TOS)-Gly-NH_2

$\xrightarrow[\text{2. oxidation (diiodoethane)}]{\text{1. deprotection (Na, }NH_3\text{)}}$ [Tyrosine-U-^{14}C]arginine vasotocin

(40% average yield)

G. L. Stahl and R. Walter, J. Label. Compound.Radiopharm., 14, 881 (1978).

$NH_2CH_2{*}COOH$ $\xrightarrow[\text{2. 2,4,5-trichlorophenol, DCC, AcOH (67\%)}]{\text{1. BOC-}N_3\text{, }H_2O\text{/dioxane, Zn,NaOH (58\%)}}$

Glycine-1-^{14}C

BOC-Gly-1-^{14}C-2,4,5-trichlorophenyl ester

$\xrightarrow[\text{DMF, }(C_2H_5)_3N\text{ (68\%)}]{\text{Asn-Ala-Phe-Ile-Gly-Leu-Met}NH_2}$

Glycyl-1-^{14}C-Asn-Ala-Phe-Ile-Gly-Leu-MetNH_2

R. Grupe and H. Niedrich, Z. Chem., 12, 22 (1972).

Glycine-1-^{14}C $\xrightarrow[\text{2. chloromethylated copoly-styrene-2\% divinylbenzene resin}]{\text{1. protecting group (77\%)}}$ BOC-Gly-1-^{14}C-resin

$\xrightarrow{\text{solid phase synthesis}}$ N-Tos-Cys(Bzl)-Tyr-Phe-Gln-Asn-Cys(Bzl)-Pro-Arg(Tos)-Gly-NH_2-1-^{14}C (27%)

$\xrightarrow{\text{deprotect}}$ Arginine-vasopressin-[9-glycinamide-1-^{14}C] [AVP-^{14}C]

Similarly prepared:

N-Z-Cys(Bzl)-Tyr-Phe-Gln-Asn-Cys(Bzl)-Pro-Lys(Z)-Gly-NH_2-1-^{14}C

$\xrightarrow{\text{deprotect}}$ Lysine-vasopressin-(9-glycinamide-1-^{14}C) (20%)
[LVP-^{14}C]

N-Z-Cys(Bzl)-Tyr-Ile-Gln-Asn-Cys(Bzl)-Pro-Leu-Gly-NH_2-1-^{14}C

$\xrightarrow{\text{deprotect}}$ Oxytocin-[9-glycinamide-1-^{14}C] (10%)
[OT-^{14}C]

R. Walter and R. T. Havran, Experientia, 27, 645 (1971).

$[(CH_3)_2C{=}C(COOH)\text{-}NHCOCH(NH_2)CH_2S]_2 \xrightarrow[\text{pH 9.8}]{C_6H_5{*}COCl} [(CH_3)_2C{=}C(COOH)\text{-}NHCOCH(NH{*}COC_6H_5)CH_2S]_2$

N,N'-[Bisphenylacetyl-1-^{14}C]-L-cystylbisdidehydrovaline

J. Cheney, C. J. Moores, J. A. Raleigh, A. I. Scott, and D. W. Young, J. Chem. Soc., Perkin Trans. I, 986 (1974).

$(CH_3)_2CHCH(NH_2)COO$-t-Bu

L-Valine-U-^{14}C-t-butyl ester
(83% from L-valine-U-^{14}C)

$\xrightarrow[\text{2. HBr/HOAc (90\%)}]{\text{1. Di-N-Z-L-cystine, DCC, ether, } CH_2Cl_2 \text{ (92\%)}}$

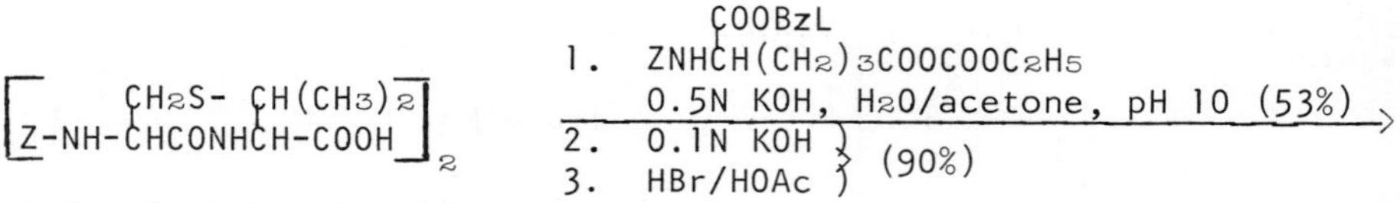
COOBzL
1. ZNHCH(CH2)3COOCOOC2H5
0.5N KOH, H2O/acetone, pH 10 (53%)
2. 0.1N KOH
3. HBr/HOAc
(90%)
CH2S- CH(CH3)2
Z-NH-CHCONHCH-COOH
2

L-Cystinyl-bis-L-valine-U-^{14}C

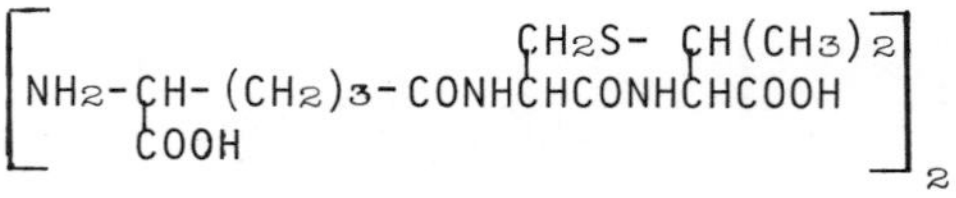
CH2S- CH(CH3)2
NH2-CH-(CH2)3-CONHCHCONHCHCOOH
COOH
2

Bis-6-(L-2-aminoadipyl)-L-cystinyl-bis-L-valine-U-^{14}C

H. Vanderhaeghe and P. Adriaens, J. Label. Compound.Radiopharm., 12, 381 (1976).

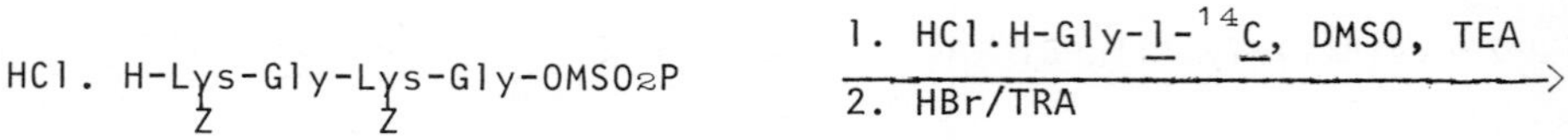
1. HCl.H-Gly-1-14C, DMSO, TEA
HCl. H-Lys-Gly-Lys-Gly-OMSO2P
Z Z
2. HBr/TRA

ε-N-Z-L-Lysylglycyl-ε-N-Z-L-lysylglycine-4-methylsulfonlyphenyl ester hydrochloride

2HBr.H-[Lys-Gly]n-Gly-1-^{14}C (64% incorporation of glycine)

Poly-(L-lysylglycyl)-glycine-1-^{14}C ethyl ester hydrobromide

Starting material was prepared from N-t-butyloxycarbonyl-ε-N-Z-L-lysine pentachlorophenyl ester in 7 steps in ∿6% yield.

B. J. Johnson and D. S. Rea, Can. J. Chem., 48, 2509 (1970).

1. HCl.NH2CH2*COOC2H5,
N(C2H5)3, DMSO (61%)
HCl.H2NCHCONHCHCONHCH(i-Pr)CONHCH2CO2PCP
t-BuOC6H4CH2 CH2CH2CO2-t-Bu
2. TFA (82%)

O-t-Butyl-L-tyrosyl-γ-t-butyl-L-glutamyl-L-valylglycine pentachlorophenyl ester hydrochloride

[NHCHCONHCHCONHCH(i-Pr-)CONHCH$_2$CO-
p-HOC$_6$H$_4$CH$_2$ CH$_2$CH$_2$COOH]$_n$ -NHCH$_2$*COOC$_2$H$_5$

Poly(L-tyrosyl-L-glutamyl-L-valylglycyl)glycine-1-^{14}C ethyl ester

B. J. Johnson and E. G. Trask, J. Chem. Soc. (C), 2247 (1970).

HCl.NH$_2$CHCONHCHCONHCH(CH$_3$)CONHCH$_2$COOC$_6$Cl$_5$
p-t-Bu-O-C$_6$H$_4$-CH$_2$ CH$_2$CH$_2$COO-t-Bu

1. HCl.NH$_2$CH$_2$*COOC$_2$H$_5$, N(C$_2$H$_5$)$_3$, DMSO (53%) →
2. 90% TFA (79%)

[-NHCHCONHCHCONHCH(CH$_3$)CONHCH$_2$CO-]$_n$NHCH$_2$*COOC$_2$H$_5$ (80% ^{14}C incorporation; MW ~1x10^5)
HO-C$_6$H$_4$CH$_2$ CH$_2$CH$_2$COOH

Poly(L-tyrosyl-L-glutamyl-L-alanylglycyl)glycine-1-^{14}C ethyl ester

B. J. Johnson and E. G. Trask, J. Chem. Soc. (C), 2644 (1969).

Z-(Pro-U-^{14}C)-ONSu →
1. Pro (73%)
2. H-Gly-ONP, HBr (50-77%)
3. HBr, HOAc (65%)
4. DMSO, TEA (78%)

[(Pro-U-^{14}C)-Pro-Gly]$_n$

Similarly:

Z-Pro-Gly-ONSu →
1. L-proline-U-^{14}C, DME/H$_2$O (quant.)
2. HBr/HOAc (65%)
3. TEPP (~78%)

[Pro-Gly-(Pro-U-^{14}C)]$_n$

Z-(Pro-U-^{14}C)-ONSu →
1. H-Gly-Pro-OH, HBr
2. HBr/HOAc
3. TEPP

→ [(Pro-U-^{14}C)-Gly-Pro]$_n$

Z-Pro-ONSu $\xrightarrow[\text{3. HBr, HOAc; 4. DMSO, TEA}]{\text{1. L-proline-}\underline{U}\text{-}^{14}\underline{C}\text{; 2. H-Gly-ONP, HBr, DCC}}$ [Pro-(Pro-U-^{14}C)-Gly]$_n$

Z-Gly-ONSu $\xrightarrow[\text{3. NaOH; 4. HBr, HOAc; 5. TEPP}]{\text{1. L-proline-}\underline{U}\text{-}^{14}\underline{C}\text{; 2. H-Pro-OCH}_3\text{, HCl, DCC}}$ [Gly-(Pro-U-^{14}C)-Pro]$_n$

H-(Pro-U-^{14}C)-OCH_3 $\xrightarrow[\text{3. HBr, HOAc; 4. TEPP}]{\text{1. Z-Gly-Pro-OH, DCC; 2. NaOH}}$ [Gly-Pro-(Pro-U-^{14}C)]$_n$

E. Adams, N. V. Rao, and S. Ramaswamy, J. Label. Compound. Radiopharm., 15, 425 (1978).

HBr.H-Tyr-Glu-Ala-Gly-OPCP $\xrightarrow[\text{TEA, DMSO}]{\text{HCl.H-GlyOC}_2\text{H}_5\text{-}\underline{1}\text{-}^{14}\underline{C}}$

H-[Tyr-Glu-Ala-Gly]$_n$-Gly-OC_2H_5-1-^{14}C

Poly(L-tyrosyl-L-glutamyl-L-alanylglycyl) glycine ethyl ester-1-^{14}C

(85% incorporation of monomer)

B. J. Johnson, J. Pharm. Sci., 59, 1849 (1970); see also, B. J. Johnson and E. G. Trask, J. Chem. Soc. (C), 2644 (1969).

HCl.Ala-Glu(OtBu)-Ala-Gly-OPCP $\xrightarrow[\text{N(C}_2\text{H}_5)_3]{\text{1. NH}_2\text{CH}_2\text{*COOC}_2\text{H}_5\text{.HCl}}$ 2. TFA

Poly(Ala-Glu-Ala-Gly)Gly-1-^{14}C ethyl ester (14%)

B. J. Johnson, C. Cheng, and N. Tsang, J. Med. Chem., 15, 95 (1972).

HCl•Phe-Glu(O*t*Bu)-Ala-Gly-OPCP + $NH_2CH_2{*}COOC_2H_5 \cdot HCl$

$\xrightarrow[\text{2. TFA}]{\text{1. DMSO, } N(C_2H_5)_3}$ Poly(Phe-Glu-Ala-Gly)$_n$Gly-1-^{14}C ethyl ester

B. R. Johnson and C. Cheng, J. Med. Chem., 14, 1238 (1971).

HCl•Tyr(OCH_3)-Glu(o*t*Bu)-Ala-Gly-OPCP + glycine-1-^{14}C

$\xrightarrow[\text{2. TFA}]{\text{1. } N(C_2H_5)_3\text{, DMSO}}$ Poly(Tyr(OCH_3)-Glu-Ala-Gly)$_n$Gly-1-^{14}C-ethyl ester

(24% yield; 47% incorporation of radioactive label; estimated MW 1×10^5)

B. J. Johnson and F. Chen, J. Med. Chem., 14, 640 (1971).

14

Organic Phosphorus Compounds

14-1 Phosphoric Acid And Phosphoric Acid Esters

Glycerol-1,3-^{14}C $\xrightarrow[\text{MgCl}_2\text{, KF, KHCO}_3\text{, glycerokinase}]{\text{ATP}}$ $HO{*}CH_2CHOH{*}CH_2O\text{-}\overset{O}{\overset{\|}{P}}(OH)_2$ (48%)

L-α-Glycerophosphate
[1,2,4-Propanetriol-1-(dihydrogen phosphate)-1,3-^{14}C]

E. W. Haeffner, Anal. Biochem., 34, 338 (1970).

CH_2OH
$C(OCH_3)_2$
$CH_2OCH_2C_6H_5$

→ 1. Br-*$CH_2(CH_2)_{16}CH_3$, KOH, C_6H_6 (89%); 2. H_2, Pd, hexane (66%) →

$CH_2O\text{-}{*}CH_2(CH_2)_{16}CH_3$
$C(OCH_3)_2$
CH_2OH

→ 1. $(C_6H_5O)_2POCl$, pyr (80%); 2. H_2, PtO_2, EtOH; 3. cyclohexylamine; 4. HCl →

$CH_2O\text{-}{*}CH_2(CH_2)_{16}CH_3$
$C{=}O$
$CH_2O\text{-}\underset{O}{\underset{\|}{P}}(OH)_2$

1-(Octadecyl-1-^{14}C-oxy)-3-(phosphonoxy)-2-propanone

C. Piantadosi, K. Chae, K. S. Ishaq, and F. Snyder, J. Pharm. Sci., 62, 320 (1973).

$*CH_3OH$ + $(CH_3O)_3P$ $\xrightarrow[95°C]{2\ hr}$ $(*CH_3O)_3P$ $\xrightarrow[AcOH,\ \Delta]{CH_3COCHClCOR}$

$\quad$ O $\quad$ CH_3
$*CH_3O$-P-OC=CHCOR + $(*CH_3Cl\uparrow)$
$\quad$ $O*CH_3$

$R=N(CH_3)_2$, Dictrotophos [(E)-Phosphoric acid 3-(dimethylamino)-1-methyl-3-oxo-1-propenyl (dimethyl-^{14}C) ester] (90% yield of a mixture of isomers)

$R=NHCH_3$, Monocrotophos [(E)-Phosphoric acid dimethyl-^{14}C [1-methyl-3-(methylamino)-3-oxo-1-propenyl] ester] (95% yield of a mixture of isomers)

$CH_3COCH_2CON(*CH_3)_2$ $\xrightarrow[2.\ P(OCH_3)_3\ (57\%)]{1.\ SOCl_2\ (75-91\%)}$

$\quad$ O $\quad$ CH_3
CH_3O-P-OC=CHCON$(*CH_3)_2$ (mixture of isomers)
$\quad$ OCH_3

Dictrotophos
[(E)-Phosphoric acid 3-(dimethyl-^{14}C-amino)-1-methyl-3-oxo-1-propenyl dimethyl ester]

$\quad$ O CH_3
$(CH_3O)_2$POC=CHCOCl $\xrightarrow[NaOH]{*CH_3NH_2.HCl}$

$\quad$ O $\quad$ CH_3
CH_3O-P-OC=CHCONH$*CH_3$ (99% yield of a mixture of isomers)
$\quad$ OCH_3

Monocrotophos
[(E)-Phosphoric acid dimethyl [1-methyl-3-(methyl-^{14}C amino)-3-oxo-1-propenyl] ester]

W. B. Burton, J. Label. Compounds, 7, 111 (1971).

$P(OCH_3)_3$ $\xrightarrow[\Delta]{*CH_3OH}$ $P(O{*}CH_3)_3$ (86% yield; 83% exchange) $\xrightarrow{CCl_3CHO}$

Phosphorous acid trimethyl-^{14}C ester

$*CH_3O{-}P(=O)(O{*}CH_3){-}O{-}CH{=}CCl_2$ (48% from $*CH_3OH$)

Dichlorvos [Phosphoric acid 2,2-dichloroethenyl-(dimethyl-^{14}C) ester]

$CCl_3{*}CHO$ $\xrightarrow{P(OCH_3)_3}$ $CH_3O{-}P(=O)(OCH_3){-}O{-}{*}CH{=}CCl_2$ (44% from $CH_3{*}CH_2OH$)

Chloral [Trichloroacetaldehyde-^{14}C]

Dichlorvos [Phosphoric acid 2,2-dichloroethenyl-1-^{14}C dimethyl ester]

W. B. Burton, J. Agr. Food. Chem., 19, 869 (1971).

$Cl_2{*}CH{*}COCl$

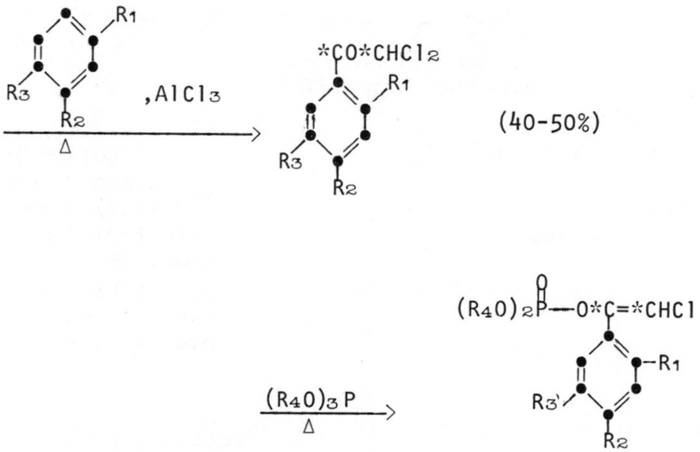
R1
R3
R2
,AlCl3
Δ
*CO*CHCl2
R1
R3
R2
(40-50%)
(R4O)2P—O*C=*CHCl
O
R1
R3
R2
(R4O)3P
Δ

Dichloroacetyl chloride-^{14}C

R_1=R_2=Cl, R_3=H, R_4=C_2H_5; Chlorfenvinphos [Phosphoric acid 2-chloro-1-(2,4-dichlorophenyl) ethenyl-1,2-^{14}C diethyl ester] (99%)

R_1=R_2=R_3=Cl, R_4=CH_3; Tetrachlorvinphos [Phosphoric acid 2-chloro-1-(2,4,5-trichlorophenyl) ethenyl-1,2-^{14}C dimethyl ester] (79%)

R_1=R_3=Cl, R_2=H, R_4=CH_3; Phosphoric acid 2-chloro-1-(2,5 dichlorophenyl)ethenyl-1,2-^{14}C dimethyl ester (92%)

The above compounds were also prepared methoxy and ethoxy labeled.

W. B. Burton and T. F. Sullivan, J. Agr. Food Chem., 20, 1180 (1972).

$$H_2N{*}CH_2{*}CH_2OH \xrightarrow[60°C]{(HO)_2\ P(O)\ Cl} H_2N{*}CH_2{*}CH_2O\text{-}P(=O)(OH)_2 \quad (75\%)$$

2-Aminoethanoldihydrogen-phosphate-1,2-^{14}C

G. Porcellati and F. diJeso, J. Label. Compounds, 3, 206 (1967).

14-2 Phosphoryl Choline Derivatives

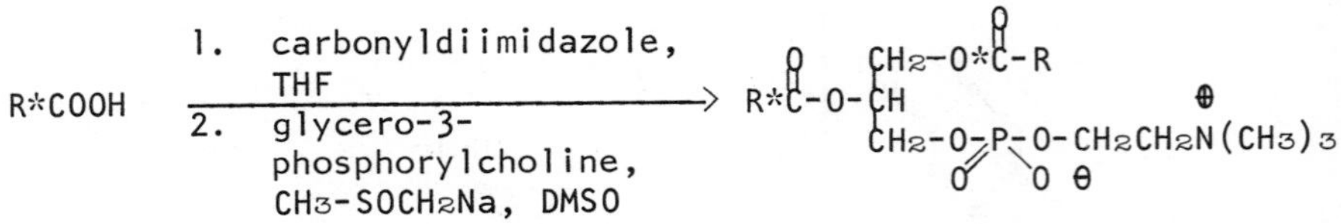
R*COOH
1. carbonyldiimidazole, THF
2. glycero-3-phosphorylcholine, CH3-SOCH2Na, DMSO

R=$CH_3(CH_2)_7CH$=$CH(CH_2)_7$-

Oleic acid [(Z)-9-Octadecenoic-1-^{14}C acid]

1,2-Di-(oleoyl)-sn-glycero-3-phosphoryl-choline [[R-(Z,Z)]-4-Hydroxy-N,N,N-trimethyl-9-oxo-7-[[(1-oxo-9-octade-cenyl-1-^{14}C)oxy]-3,5,9-trioxa-4-phosphaheptacos-18-en-1-aminium-10-^{14}C hydroxide inner salt oxide]]

T. G. Warner and A. A. Benson, J. Lipid Res., 18, 548 (1977).

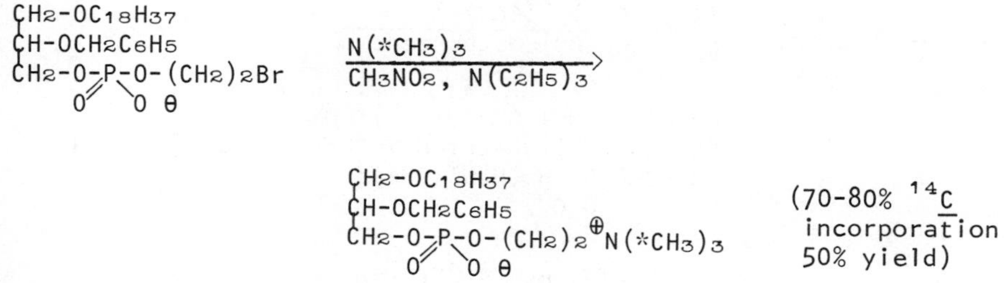

rac-4-Hydroxy-N,N,N-trimethyl-^{14}C-7-(phenylmethoxy)-3,5,9-trioxa-4-phosphaheptacosan-1-aminium hydroxide inner salt 4-oxide trihydrate

H. U. Weltzien, B. Arnold, and O. Westphal, Liebigs Ann. Chem., 1439 (1973).

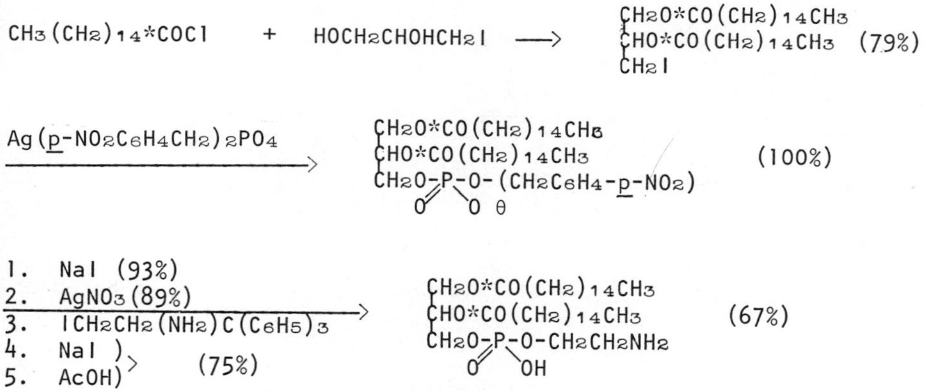

Hexadecanoic-1,1'-^{14}C acid 1-[[[(2-aminoethoxy)phosphinyl]oxy]methyl]-1,2-ethanediyl ester

J. S. Owen, G. H. Scott, M. S. Harvey, and J. D. Billimoria, Chem. Ind. (London), 727 (1971).

Oleic acid-1-^{14}C $\xrightarrow[\text{pyr, } (CF_3CO)_2O\text{, benzene}]{(3\text{-sn-GPC})_2\ (CdCl_3)_3}$

$CH_2O^*CO(CH_2)_7CH{=}CH(CH_2)_7CH_3$
$CHO^*CO(CH_2)_7CH{=}CH(CH_2)_7CH_3$ (12% from GPC)
$CH_2{-}O{-}P(=O)(O^{\ominus}){-}O{-}CH_2CH_2N^{\oplus}(CH_3)_3$

1,2-Di-[oleoyl-1-^{14}C]-sn-glycero-3-phosphorylcholine
(GPC=glycerophosphorylcholine)

Starting with linoleic acid-1-^{14}C, 1,2-di-[linoleoyl-1-^{14}C]-sn-glycero-3-phosphorylcholine was prepared in 24% yield; starting with homo-γ-[linolenic-1-^{14}C] acid, 1,2-di-[eicosatrienoyl-1-^{14}C]-sn-glycero-3-phosphorylcholine was prepared in 12% yield.

E. L. Pugh and M. Kates, J. Lipid Res., 16, 392 (1975).

14-3 Phosphoric Acid Thioesters

$PSCl_3$ + $CH_3{}^*CH_2OH$ $\xrightarrow[\text{2. NaOEt}]{\text{1. 60°C}}$

$Cl{-}P(=S){-}(O^*CH_2CH_3)_2$ (78% yield based on $PSCl_3$)

O,O-Diethyl phosphorochloridothionate-(ethoxy-1^{14}C)

Similarly, $PSCl(O^*Me)_2$ was prepared in 65% yield (based on $PSCl_3$). Ag_2CO_3-catalyzed coupling of labeled O-alkoxy phosphorochloridothionate with substituted phenols in benzene/water or ethyl acetate gave the following pesticides: EPN (93%), parathion (89%), methyl parathion (79%), O,O-dimethyl-O-(4-cyanophenyl)phosphorothionate (68%), sumithion (69%), O,O, diethyl-O-(4-methylthiophenyl)phosphorothionate (94%), diazinon (64%).

B. R. Smith, W. C. Dauterman, and E. Hodgson, J. Label. Compounds, 11, 155 (1975).

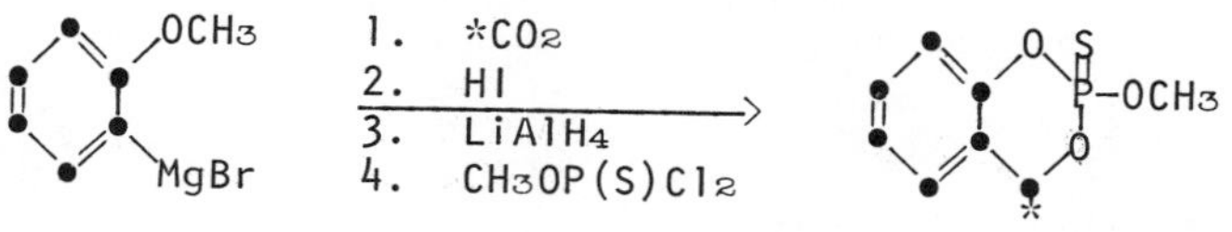
OCH3
MgBr
1. *CO2
2. HI
3. LiAlH4
4. CH3OP(S)Cl2
O
S
P-OCH3
O
*

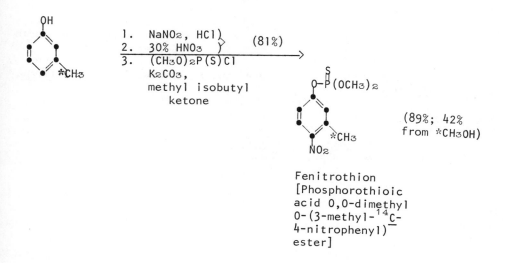

Salithion
[2-Methoxy-4H-1,3,2-benzodioxaphosphorin-2-sulfide-4-^{14}C]

K. Mihara and J. Miyamoto, Agr. Biol. Chem., 38, 1913 (1974).

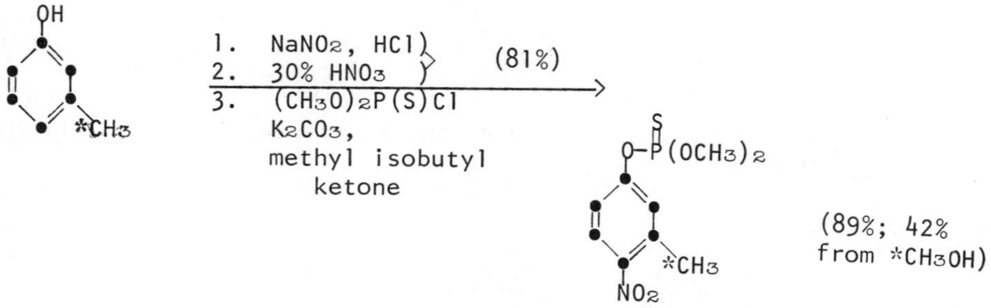
OH
*CH3
1. NaNO2, HCl
2. 30% HNO3
(81%)
3. (CH3O)2P(S)Cl
K2CO3,
methyl isobutyl
ketone
S
O-P(OCH3)2
*CH3
NO2
(89%; 42%
from *CH3OH)

Fenitrothion
[Phosphorothioic acid O,O-dimethyl O-(3-methyl-^{14}C-4-nitrophenyl) ester]

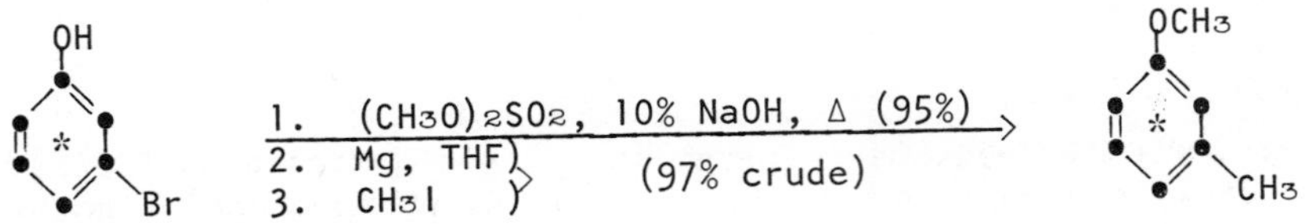
OH
1. $(CH_3O)_2SO_2$, 10% NaOH, Δ (95%)
2. Mg, THF
3. CH_3I
(97% crude)
Br
OCH_3
CH_3

3-Bromophenol-U-^{14}C

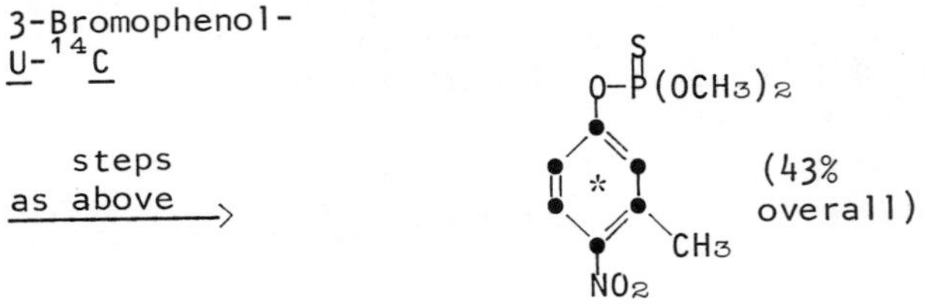
steps
as above
$O-P(S)(OCH_3)_2$
CH_3
NO_2
(43% overall)

Fenitrothion [Phosphorothioic acid O,O-dimethyl-O-(3-methyl-4-(phenyl-U-^{14}C)) ester]

A. Yoshitake, K. Kawahara, T. Kamada, and M. Endo, J. Label. Compound. Radiopharm., 13, 323 (1977).

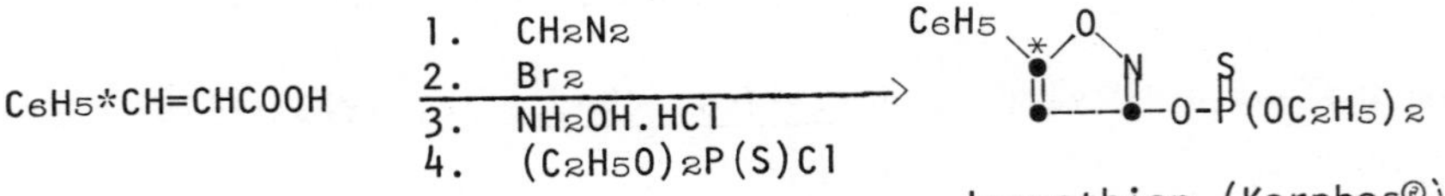
C_6H_5*CH=CHCOOH
1. CH_2N_2
2. Br_2
3. $NH_2OH.HCl$
4. $(C_2H_5O)_2P(S)Cl$
C_6H_5
O
N
$O-P(S)(OC_2H_5)_2$

Isoxathion (Karphos®) [O-(5-phenyl-3-isoxazolyl-5-^{14}C)phosphorothioic acid O,O-diethyl ester]

M. Ando, M. Nakagawa, T. Nakamura, and K. Tomita, Agr. Biol. Chem., 39, 803 (1975).

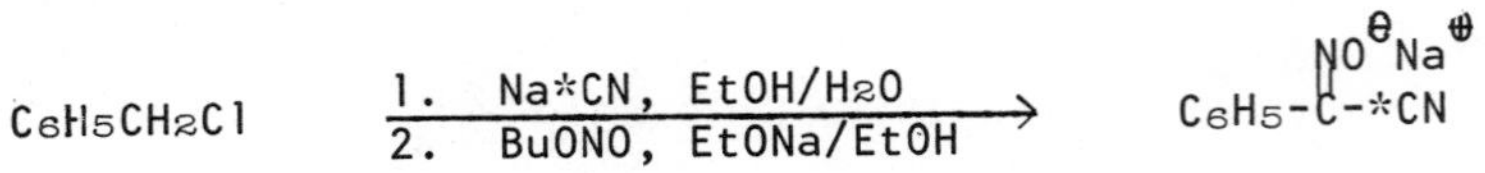
$C_6H_5CH_2Cl$
1. Na*CN, EtOH/H_2O
2. BuONO, EtONa/EtOH
$NO^{\ominus}Na^{\oplus}$
C_6H_5-C-*CN

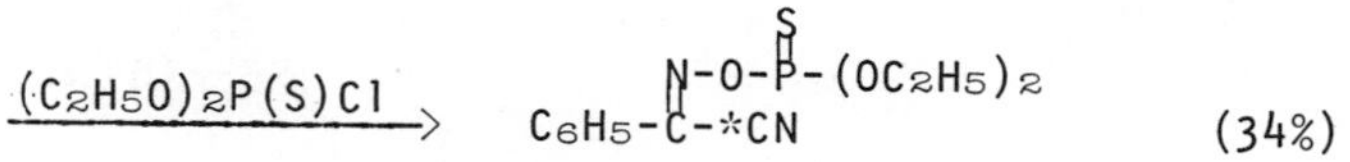
$(C_2H_5O)_2P(S)Cl$
$N-O-P(S)-(OC_2H_5)_2$
$C_6H_5-C-*CN$
(34%)

Phoxim
[α-[[(Diethoxyphosphinothioyl)-oxy]imino]benzeneaceotnitrile-(cyano-^{14}C)]

W. A. Mason and C. E. Meloan, J. Agr. Food. Chem., 21, 762 (1973).

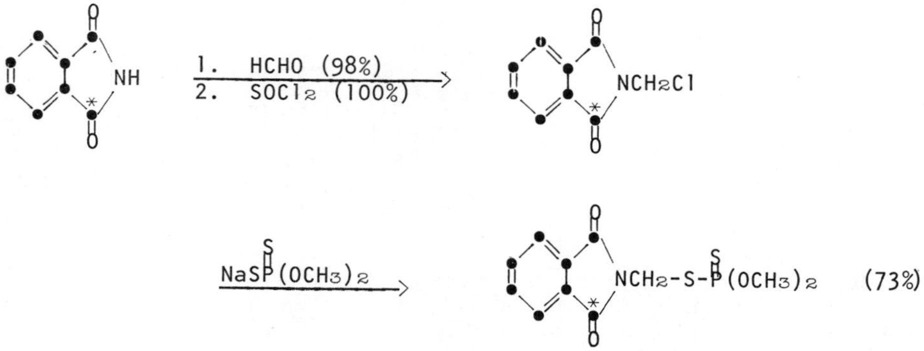
NH
1. HCHO (98%)
2. $SOCl_2$ (100%)
NCH_2Cl
$NaSP(S)(OCH_3)_2$
$NCH_2-S-P(S)(OCH_3)_2$
(73%)

S-[(1,3-Dihydro-1,3-dioxo-2H-isoindol-2-yl)methyl-1-^{14}C]phosphorodithioic acid O,O-dimethyl ester

M. A. Leaffer, W. A. Skinner, J. Menn, J. B. McBain, and L. W. Fancher, J. Label. Compounds, 3, 334 (1967).

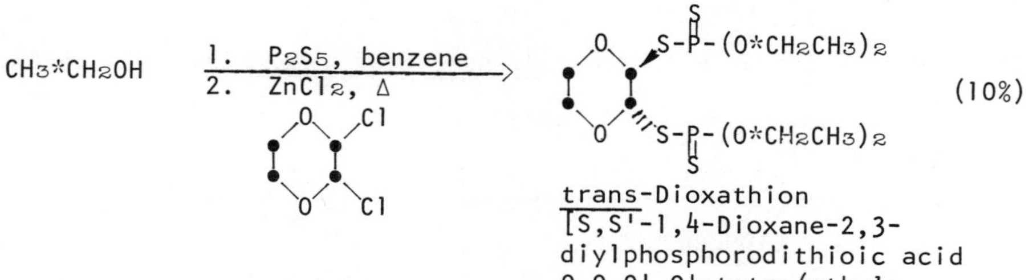
CH_3*CH_2OH
1. P_2S_5, benzene
2. $ZnCl_2$, Δ
O
Cl
O
Cl
$S-P(S)-(O*CH_2CH_3)_2$
$S-P(S)-(O*CH_2CH_3)_2$
(10%)

trans-Dioxathion
[S,S'-1,4-Dioxane-2,3-diylphosphorodithioic acid O,O,O',O'-tetra(ethyl-1-^{14}C)ester]

plus

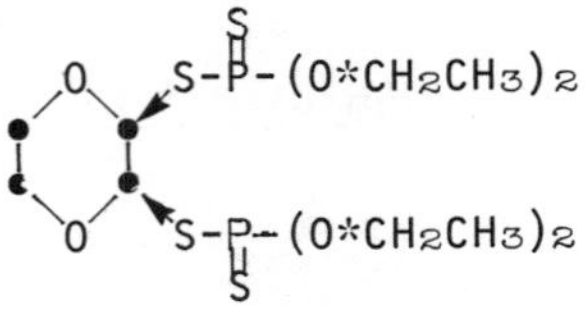
S-P-(O*CH2CH3)2
S-P-(O*CH2CH3)2

(8%)

cis-Dioxathion-(ethoxy-1-^{14}C)

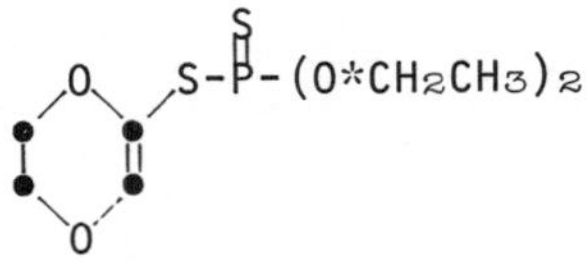
S-P-(O*CH2CH3)2

(7%)

Dioxenethion
[Phosphorodithioic acid S-(5,6-dihydro-1,4-dioxin-2-yl) O,O-di(ethyl-1-^{14}C)ester]

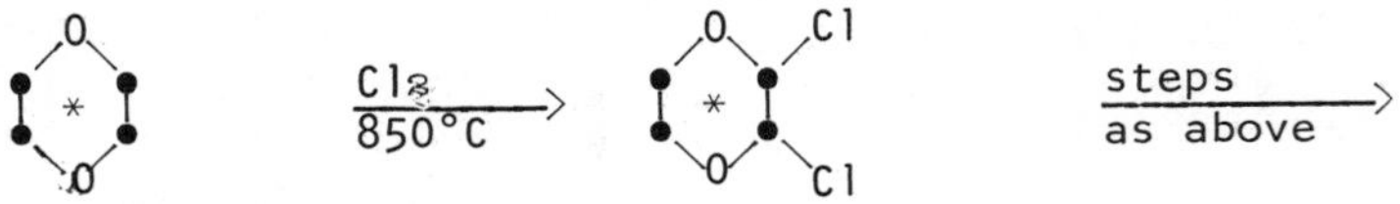
Cl2
850°C
Cl
Cl
steps
as above

1,4-Dioxane-U-^{14}C

trans-Dioxathion-(ring-U-^{14}C) (1.8%) + cis-Dioxathion-(ring-U-^{14}C) (0.6%) + Dioxenethion-(ring-U-^{14}C) (0.5%)

The products are components of the insecticide Delanov [(2,3-p-dioxanedithiol)-S,S-bis(O,O-diethyl phosphorodithioate)]; yields are for purified products.

W. H. Harned and J. E. Casida, J. Agr. Food Chem., 24, 689 (1976).

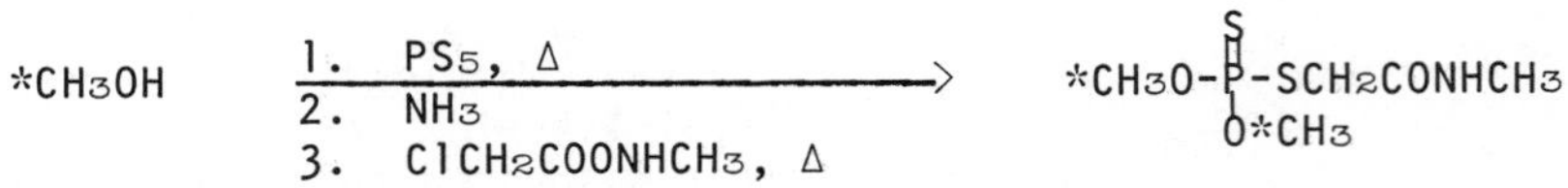
*CH3OH
1. PS5, Δ
2. NH3
3. ClCH2COONHCH3, Δ
*CH3O-P-SCH2CONHCH3
O*CH3

Dimethoate
[Phosphorodithioic acid O,O-di(methyl-^{14}C) S-[2-(methyl-amino)-2-oxoethyl]ester]

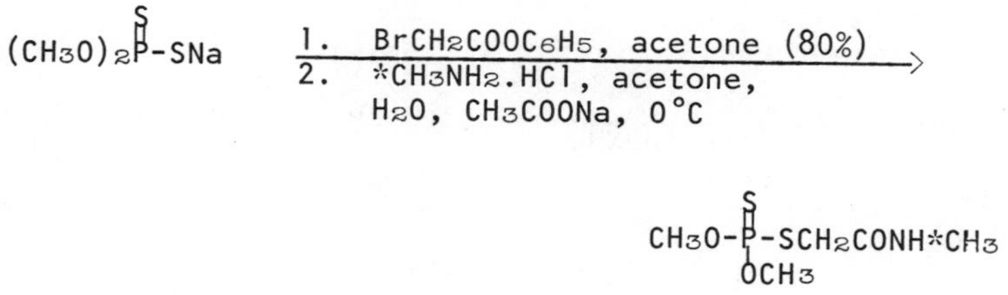
(CH3O)2P(S)-SNa
1. BrCH2COOC6H5, acetone (80%)
2. *CH3NH2.HCl, acetone, H2O, CH3COONa, 0°C
CH3O-P(S)-SCH2CONH*CH3
OCH3

Dimethoate
[Phosphorodithioc acid O,O-dimethyl S-[2-(methylamino-^{14}C)-2-oxoethyl]ester]

S. M. A. D. Zayed, A. Hussan, I. M. I. Fakhr, and M. R. E. Bahig, Biochem. Pharmacol., 19, 17 (1970).

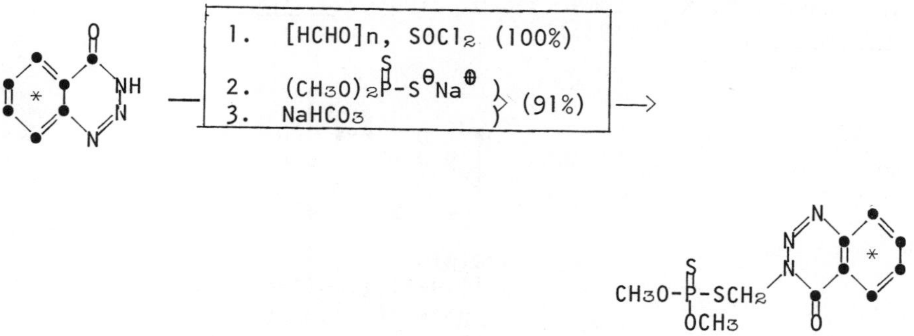
1. [HCHO]n, SOCl2 (100%)
2. (CH3O)2P(S)-S⊖Na⊕
3. NaHCO3
(91%)
CH3O-P(S)-SCH2
OCH3

Azinphos-methyl
[Phosphorodithioic acid O,O-dimethyl S-[(4-oxo-1,2,3-benzotriazin-3 (4H)-yl-ring-^{14}C)methy] ester]

E. R. White, K. M. Al-Adil, W. L. Winterlin, and W. W. Kilgore, J. Agr. Food Chem., 20, 1184 (1972).

14-4 Phosphoramides

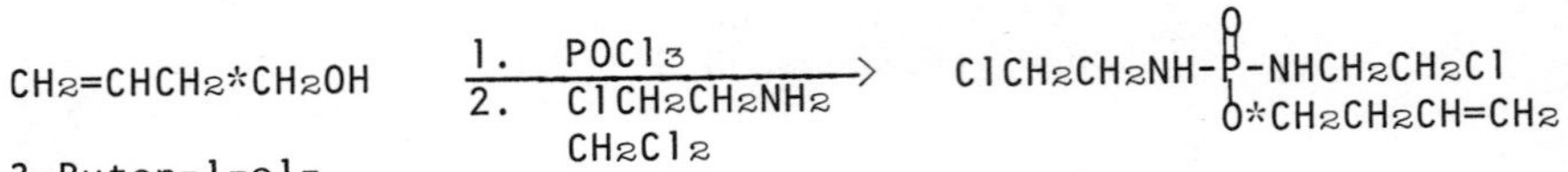

3-Buten-1-ol-1-^{14}C

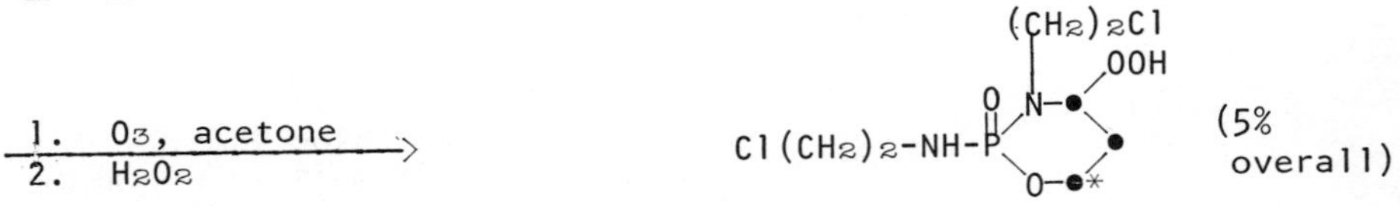

3-(2-Chloroethyl)-2-[(2-chloroethyl)amino]tetrahydro-2H-1,3,2-oxaphosphorin-4-yl-6-^{14}C hydroperoxide P-oxide

N. Nagasai, Y. Katsuyama, and H. Minato, J. Label. Compound Radiopharm., 12, 7 (1976).

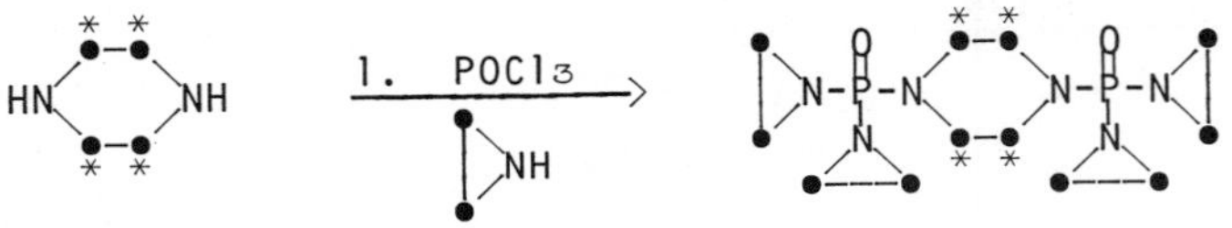

Dipin
[1,4-Bis[bis(1-aziridinyl)phosphinyl][piperazine-U-^{14}C]]

Y. I. Savin, A. S. Singin, G. K. Korolev, T. S. Safonova, V. G. Kurasova, and V. V. Kurchatova, Khim.-Farm. Zh., 10, 49 (1976).

14-5 Thiophosphoramides

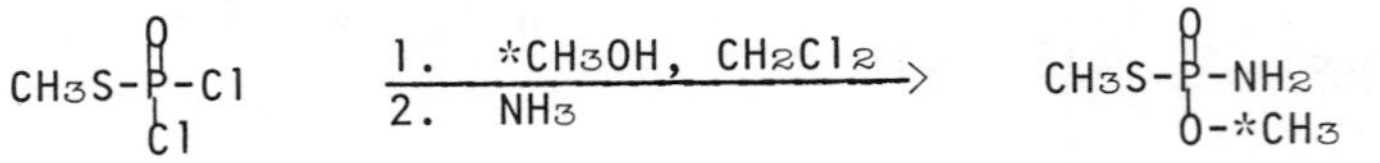

(from phosphorus thiochloride in 2 steps; 64% overall)

Tamaron (Monitor)
[Phosphoramidothioic acid S-methyl O-(methyl-^{14}C) ester]

J. A. Lubkowitz, A. P. Revilla, and J. Baruel, J. Agr. Food Chem., 22, 151 (1974).

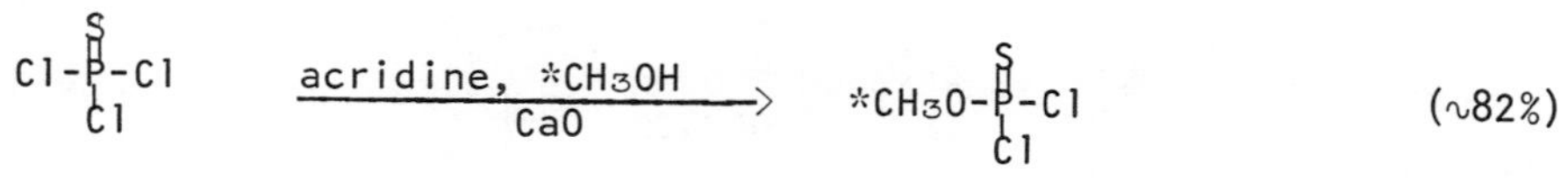

$$Cl-\overset{\overset{\displaystyle S}{\|}}{\underset{\underset{\displaystyle Cl}{|}}{P}}-Cl \xrightarrow[\text{CaO}]{\text{acridine, *CH}_3\text{OH}} \text{*CH}_3\text{O}-\overset{\overset{\displaystyle S}{\|}}{\underset{\underset{\displaystyle Cl}{|}}{P}}-Cl \qquad (\sim82\%)$$

Phosphorodichloridothioic acid O-(methyl-^{14}C) ester

$$\xrightarrow{100°C} \quad Cl-\overset{\overset{\displaystyle O}{\|}}{\underset{\underset{\displaystyle S\text{*CH}_3}{|}}{P}}-Cl \quad (\sim78\%) \quad \frac{1. \quad CH_3OH, \quad CH_2Cl_2}{2. \quad NH_3}$$

$$CH_3-\overset{\overset{\displaystyle O}{\|}}{\underset{\underset{\displaystyle NH_2}{|}}{P}}-S\text{*CH}_3 \qquad (77\%)$$

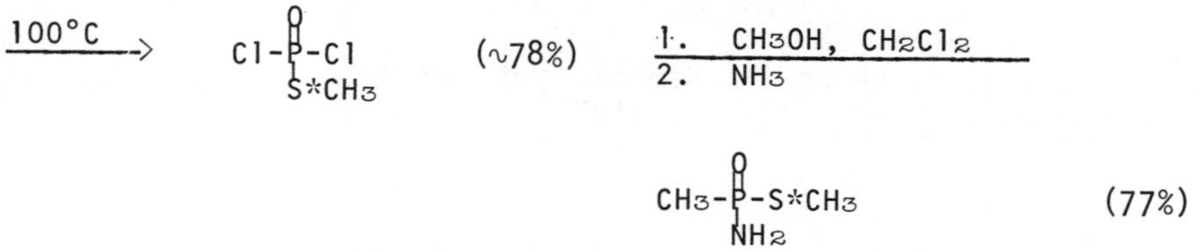

Phosphoramidothioic acid S-(methyl-^{14}C) O-methyl ester

Similarly:

$$Cl-\overset{\overset{\displaystyle O}{\|}}{\underset{\underset{\displaystyle SCH_3}{|}}{P}}-Cl \xrightarrow[2. \quad NH_3]{1. \quad \text{*CH}_3OH, \quad CH_2Cl_2} \text{*CH}_3O-\overset{\overset{\displaystyle O}{\|}}{\underset{\underset{\displaystyle NH_2}{|}}{P}}-SCH_3 \qquad (57\%)$$

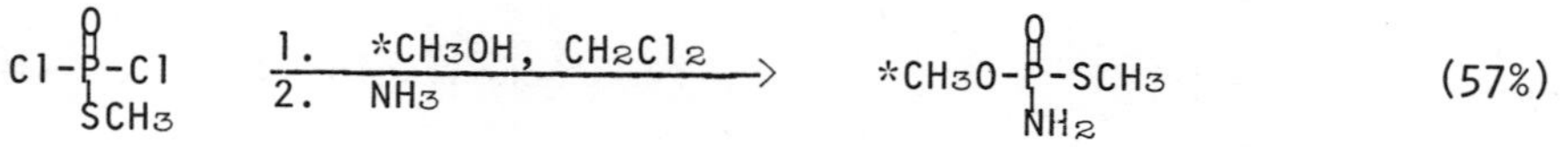

Phosphoramidothioic acid S-methyl O-(methyl-^{14}C) ester

The position of the ^{14}C label was confirmed by selective hydrolyses.

J. A. Lubkowitz, D. F. Horler, and J. Baruel, J. Label. Compounds, 10, 599 (1974).

$$\xrightarrow[K_2CO_3, \text{ MEK}]{\underline{sec}-C_4H_9NH-P(OCH_2CH_3)(S)Cl}$$

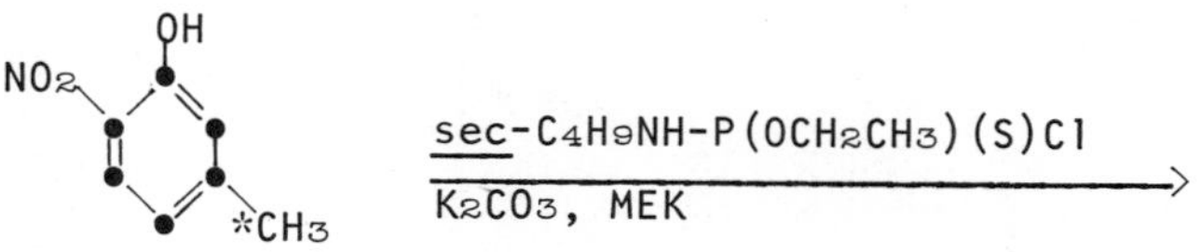

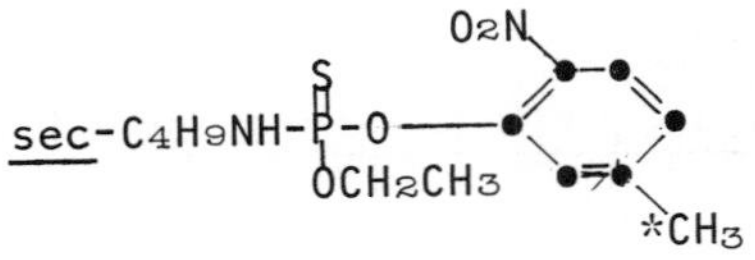
O2N
S
sec-C4H9NH-P-O
OCH2CH3
*CH3

(49%; 9% from MeOH)

Cremart
[(1-Methylpropyl)phosphoramidothioic acid O-ethyl O-(5-(methyl-^{14}C)-2-nitrophenyl) ester]

A. Yoshitake, F. Shono, T. Kamada, and I. Nakatsuka, J. Label. Compound. Radiopharm., 13, 333 (1977).

14-6 Phosphoranes

$CH_3{*}COCOOH$ —— 1. CH_3CONH_2, C_6H_6, Δ; 2. $P(OCH_3)_3$, $HOP(OCH_3)_2$, Δ; 3. HCl, Δ ——>

Pyruvic acid-2-^{14}C

β-Phosphonoalanine-2-^{14}C (10%)

${*}CH_2OH{*}CH_2NH_2 \cdot HCl$ —— 1. phthalic anhydride, Δ; 2. PBr_3, Δ; 3. $P(OCH_3)_3$, Δ; 4. HBr, Δ ——>

Ethanolamine-1,2-^{14}C hydrochloride

Aminoethylphosphonic-1,2-^{14}C acid (5%)

J. D. Smith and J. H. Law, Biochemistry, 9, 2152 (1970).

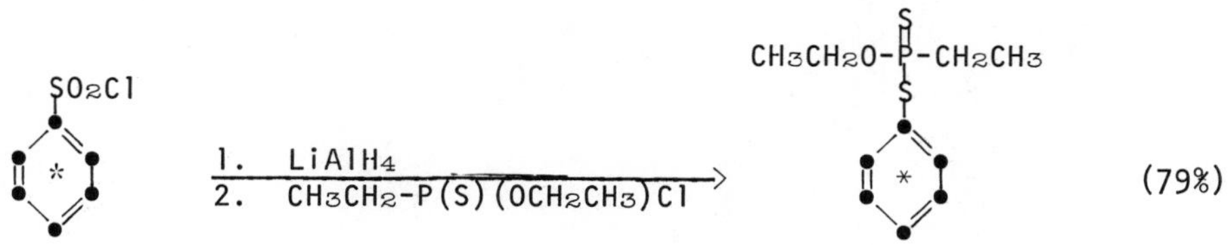
SO2Cl
1. LiAlH4
2. CH3CH2-P(S)(OCH2CH3)Cl
CH3CH2O-P-CH2CH3
S
S
(79%)

Dyfonate
[Ethyl phosphonodithioic acid O-ethyl S-(phenyl-U-^{14}C) ester]

J. Kalbfeld, H. M. Pitt, and D. A. Hermann, J. Label. Compounds, 5, 351 (1969).

15

Organic Sulfur Compounds

15-1 Sulfides

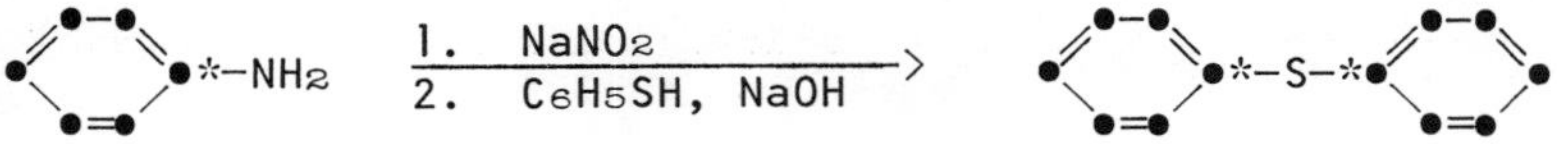
NH2
1. NaNO2
2. C6H5SH, NaOH
S

(76%)

Aniline-1-^{14}C

Diphenyl sulfide
[1,1'-Thiobisbenzene-1,1'-^{14}C]

The above compound was used to prepare N-p-tosylsulilimine, which was used for subsequent rearrangement studies with phenyl Grignard reagent.

S. Oae, T. Yoshimura, and N. Furukawa, Bull. Chem. Soc. Jap., 45, 2019 (1972); Bull. Chem. Soc. Jap., 39, 2260 (1966).

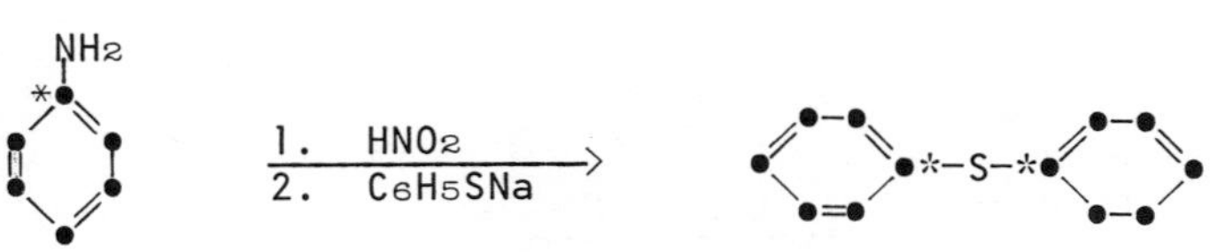
NH2
1. HNO2
2. C6H5SNa
S

1,1'-Thiobisbenzene-1,1'-^{14}C

S. Oae, M. Nakai, Y. Tsuchida, and N. Furukawa, Bull. Chem. Soc. Jap., 44, 445 (1971).

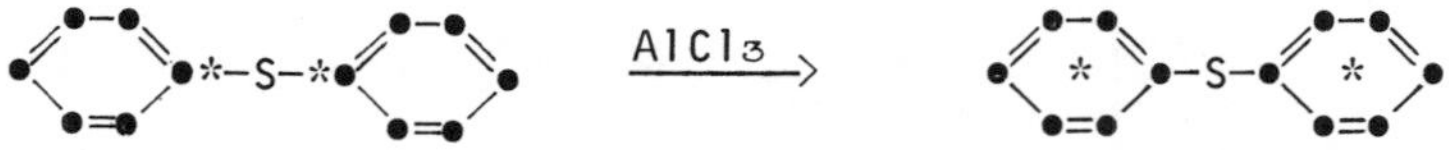
AlCl3

1,1'-Thiobisbenzene-U-^{14}C

Degradation studies showed that 14.5% of the ^{14}C label was at position 1, 31% at position 2, and 58.5% at positions 3 and 4; a mechanism involving a triphenylsulfonium ion was proposed.

S. Oae, M. Nakai, and N. Furukawa, Chem. Ind. (London), 1438 (1970).

15-2 Sulfoxides

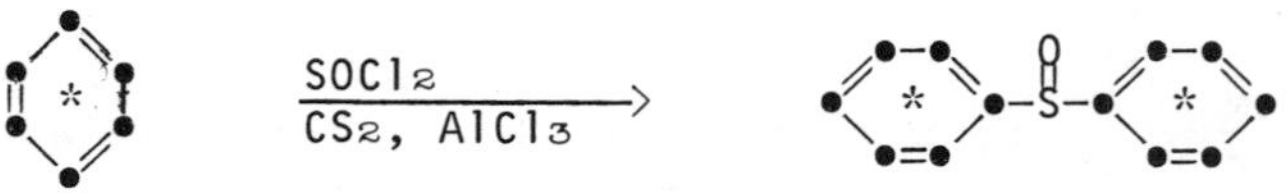
SOCl2
CS2, AlCl3

(93%)

1,1'-Sulfinylbisbenzene-U-^{14}C

B. Liedtke and K.-O. Vollmer, J. Label. Compound. Radiopharm., 14, 825 (1978).

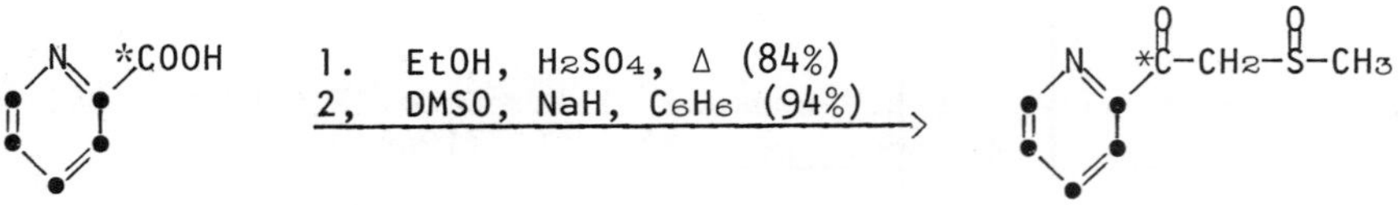
*COOH
1. EtOH, H2SO4, Δ (84%)
2, DMSO, NaH, C6H6 (94%)
*C-CH2-S-CH3

2-(Methylsulfinyl)-1-(2-pyridinyl) ethanone-1-^{14}C

E. J. Merril and G. G. Vernice, J. Label. Compounds, 8, 589 (1972).

15-3 Sulfones

C_6H_5-*C(=O)-C_6H_5 1. DMSO, NaH (73%) 2. H_2O_2, AcOH (75%) 3. H_3PO_4 (62%) →

(30% from Ba*CO_3)

$(C_6H_5)_2$*C=CH-S(O_2)-CH_3 (10% overall)

1,1'-[(Methylsulfonyl)ethenyl-idene]bisbenzene-1-^{14}C

H. Fillion, C.L. Duc, and C. Agnius-Delord, Bull. Soc. Chim. Fr., Part 2, 2923 (1974).

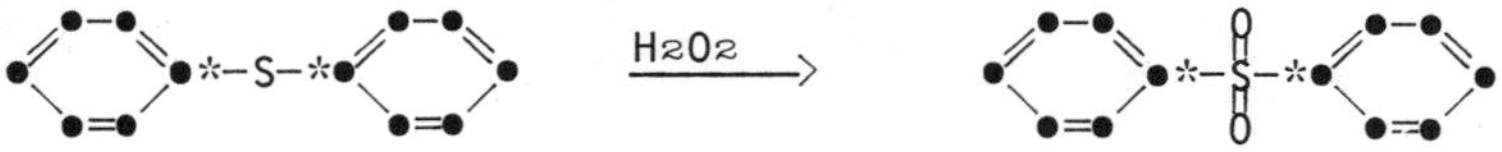

H_2O_2

Diphenyl sulfone
[1,1'-Sulfonylbisbenzene-1,1'-^{14}C]

The diphenyl sulfone-1-^{14}C was reconverted to diphenyl sulfide-1-^{14}C (S, 310-320°C) with only 5% rearrangement of the C-1 label as determined by degradation studies. A simple sulfur displacement mechanism at C-1 is proposed.

S. Oae, M. Nakai, Y. Tsuchida, and N. Furukawa, Bull. Chem. Soc. Jap., 44, 445 (1971).

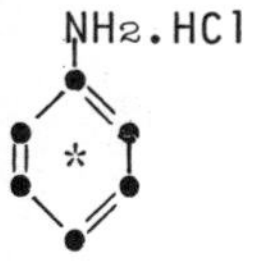

NH_2.HCl

1. Ac_2O, CCl_4 (95%)
2. $SOCl_2$, $AlCl_3$ (82%), CS_2 →

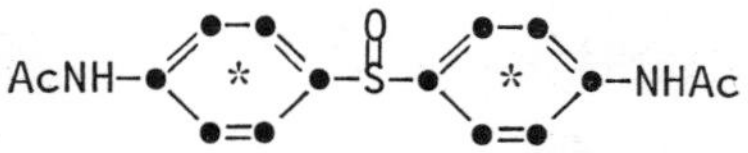

AcNH-
-NHAc

1. H_2O_2, Ac_2O, HOAc (63%)
2. HCl (78%) →

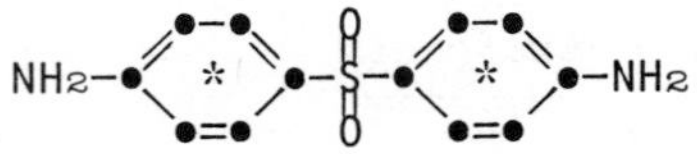
NH2
NH2

4,4'-Sulfonylbisbenzene-amine-U-^{14}C

C. E. Blackburn and A. J. Glazko, J. Label. Compounds, 8, 63 (1972).

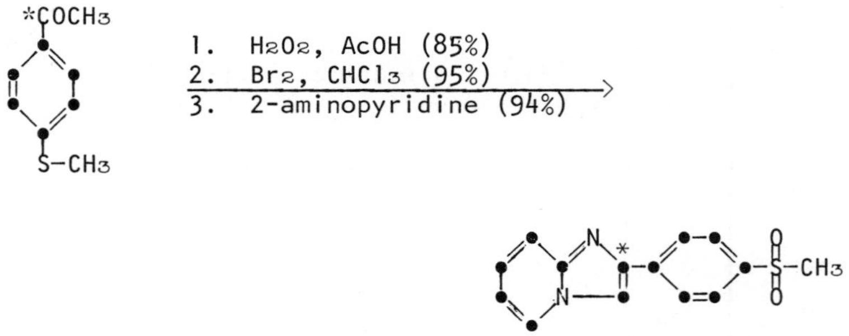
*COCH3
S-CH3
1. H2O2, AcOH (85%)
2. Br2, CHCl3 (95%)
3. 2-aminopyridine (94%)
N
N
S-CH3

Zolimidine
[2-(4-methylsulfonyl)phenyl]-imidazo-(1,2a)pyridine-2-^{14}C]

E. Schraven and D. Trottnow, Arzneim.-Forsch.-(Drug Res.), 26, 213 (1976).

15-4 Sulfonic Acid

RMgBr → (1. $^{*}CO_2$ (80-85%); 2. CH_2N_2 (quant.); 3. $LiAlH_4$ (75%); 4. HBr (58%)) → $R^{*}CH_2Br$ → (1. NH_2CSNH_2, EtOH, Δ; 2. 70% HNO_3, Δ) →

$R^{*}CH_2SO_3H$ (18-24% overall)

Compounds prepared:

Undecyl sulfonate-1-^{14}C
Dodecyl sulfonate-1-^{14}C
Hexadecyl sulfonate-1-^{14}C

A. J. Taylor and A. H. Olavesen, J. Label. Compound. Radiopharm., 14, 249 (1978).

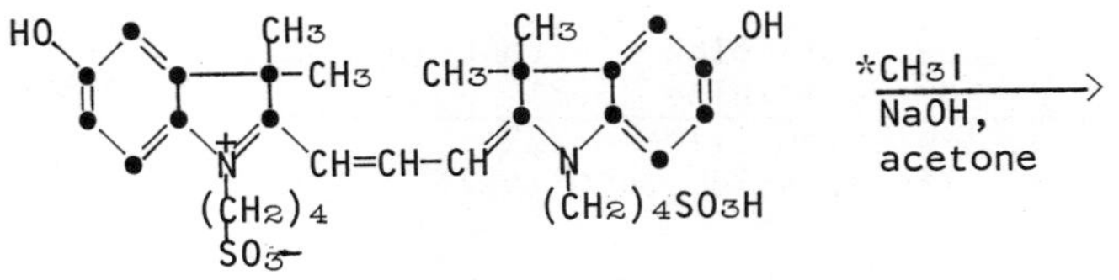
*CH3I
NaOH,
acetone

5,5'-Dihydroxy-indomonocarbo-
cyanine=DIMC

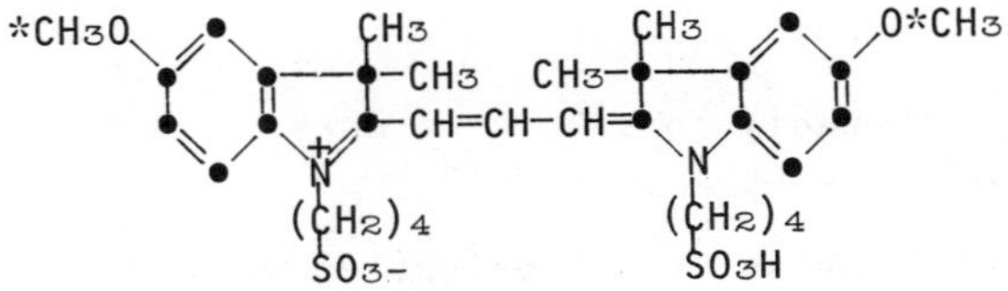

(45%)

2-[3-[1,3-Dihydro-5-(methoxy-^{14}C)-3,3-dimethyl-1-sulfobutyl-2H-indol-2-ylidene] 1-propenyl]-3,3-dimethyl-1-(4-sulfobutyl)-3H-indolium hydroxide inner salt

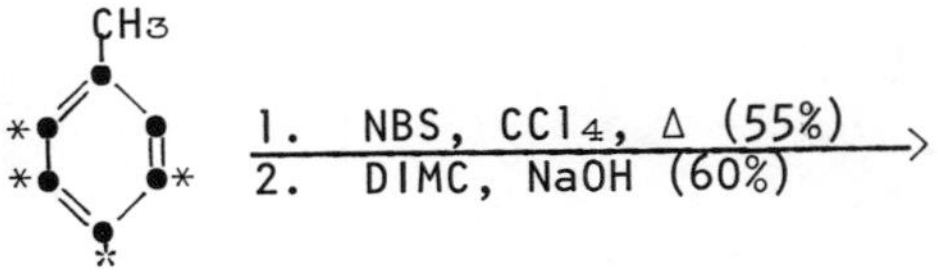
1. NBS, CCl4, Δ (55%)
2. DIMC, NaOH (60%)

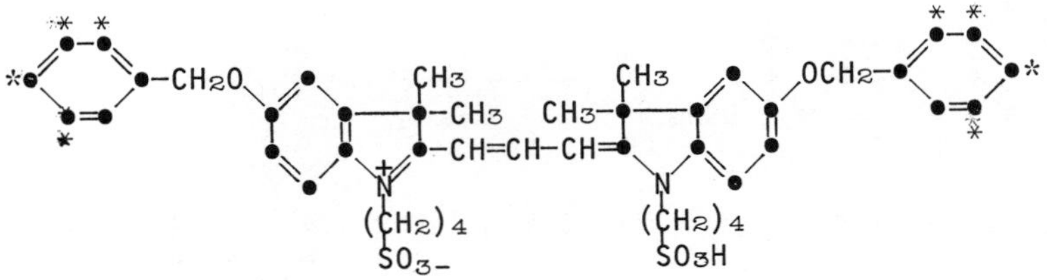

2-[3-[1,3-Dihydro-5-((phenyl-^{14}C)methoxy)-3,3-dimethyl-1-sulfobutyl-2H-indol-2-ylidene]-1-propenyl]-3,3-dimethyl-1-(4-sulfobutyl)-3H-indolium hydroxide inner salt

M.-F. Moreau and F. Lapalus, J. Label. Compounds, 11, 265 (1975).

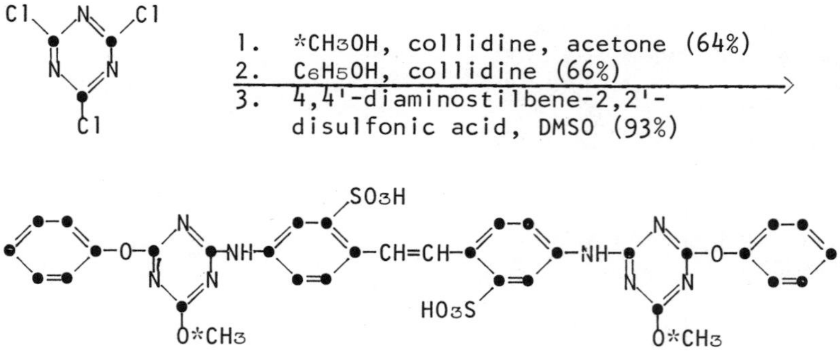
Cl
N
Cl
N
N
Cl
1. *CH3OH, collidine, acetone (64%)
2. C6H5OH, collidine (66%)
3. 4,4'-diaminostilbene-2,2'-disulfonic acid, DMSO (93%)
SO3H
O
N
NH
CH=CH
NH
N
O
N
N
N
N
HO3S
O*CH3
O*CH3

2,2'-(1,2-Ethenediyl)bis[5-(4-methoxy-$^{14}\underline{C}$-6-phenoxy-1,3,5-triazin-2-yl)amino]benzenesulfonic acid

Oxidation of the stilbene derivative with $KMnO_4$ at room temperature gave 2-formyl-[5-(4'-methoxy-$^{14}\underline{C}$-6'-phenoxy-s-triazin-2'-yl)amino] benzenesulfonic acid collidine salt while oxidation at 70-80°C for 2 hr gave [4-(4'-methoxy-$^{14}\underline{C}$-6'-phenoxy-s-triazin-2'-yl)amino]-2-sulfobenzoic acid. Reaction of the above intermediate, 2-chloro-4-methoxy-$^{14}\underline{C}$-6-phenoxy-s-triazine, with 2,2'-ethylenebis-(5-aminobenzene sulfonic acid in DMSO/collidine gave 2,2'-ethylenebis [5-(4-methoxy-$^{14}\underline{C}$-6-phenoxy-s-triazin-2-yl)amino]benzenesulfonic acid in 77% yield.

B. Milligan and L. A. Holt, Aust. J. Chem., 27, 195 (1974).

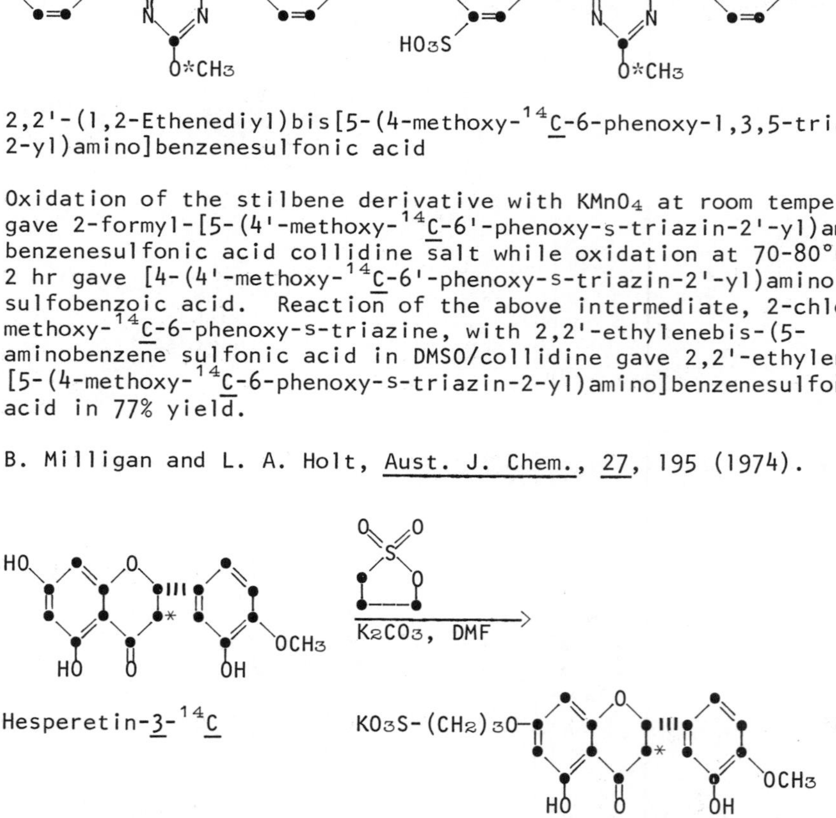
HO
O
*
OCH3
HO
O
OH
O
S
O
O
K2CO3, DMF
KO3S-(CH2)3O
O
*
OCH3
HO
O
OH

Hesperetin-3-^{14}C (6%)

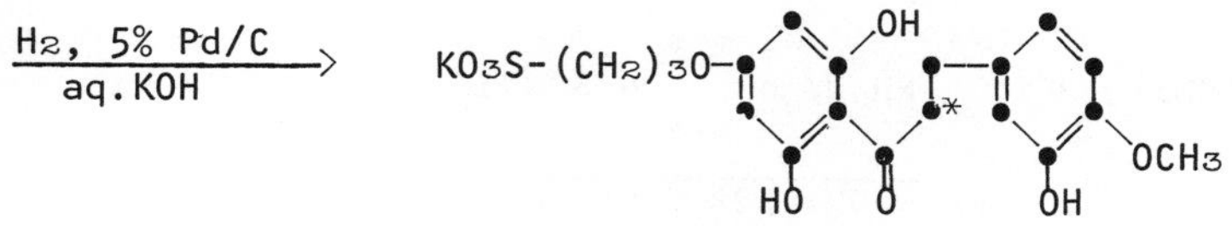
H2, 5% Pd/C
aq.KOH
KO3S-(CH2)3O
OH
HO
O
OH
OCH3

(13%)

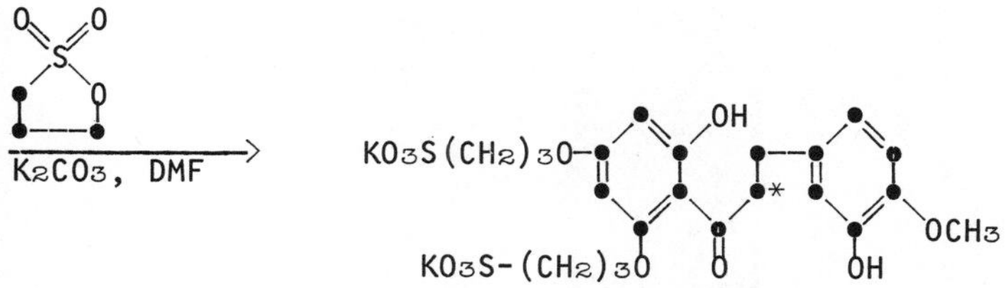
K2CO3, DMF
KO3S(CH2)3O
OH
KO3S-(CH2)3O
O
OH
OCH3

3,3-[[5-Hydroxy-4-[3-(3-hydroxy-4-methoxyphenyl)-1-oxopropyl-2-^{14}C]-1,3-phenylene]bis(oxy)bis-1-propanesulfonic acid dipotassium salt

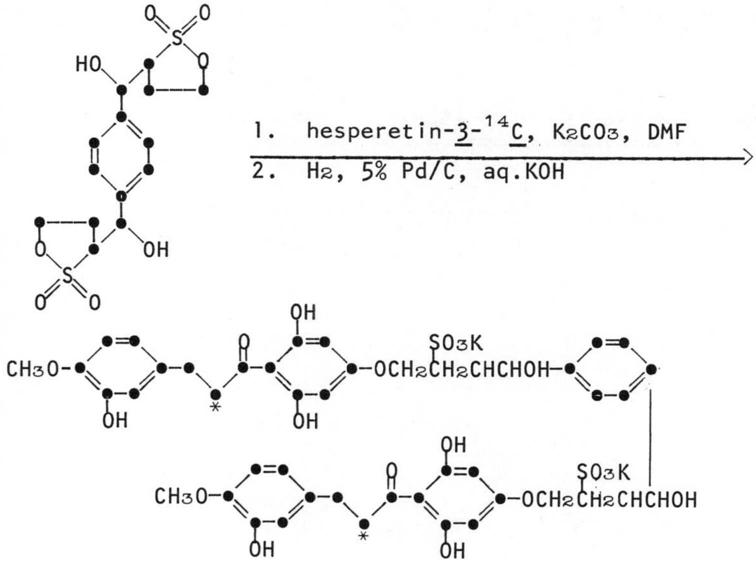
HO
OH
1. hesperetin-3-14C, K2CO3, DMF
2. H2, 5% Pd/C, aq.KOH
CH3O
SO3K
OCH2CH2CHCHOH
OCH2CH2CHCHOH
OH

Hesperetin dihydrochalcone-β-^{14}C dimer
[α,α'-Bis[2-[3,5-dihydroxy-4-[3-(3-hydroxy-4-methoxyphenyl)-1-oxopropyl-2-^{14}C]phenoxy]ethyl]-β,β'-dihydroxy-1,4-benzenediethanesulfonic acid dipotassium salt]

J. P. Brown, G. A. Crosby, G. E. DuBois, F. E. Enderlin, R. L. Hale, and R. E. Wingard, Jr., J. Agric. Food Chem., 26, 1418 (1978).

$C_6H_5COCH_2{*}CH_2N(CH_3)_2 \cdot HCl$

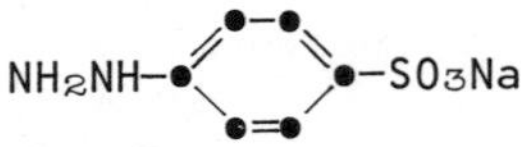
NH2NH-
-SO3Na

NaOH, 50% EtOH, Δ →

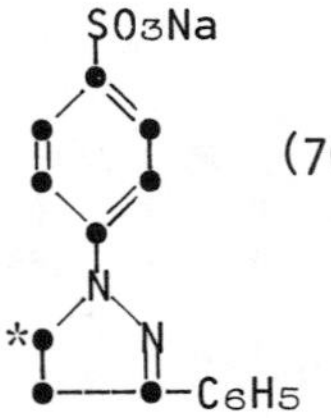
SO3Na
N
N
*
-C6H5

(70%)

4-(4,5-Dihydro-3-phenyl-1H-pyrazol-1-yl-5-^{14}C)benzenesulfonic acid sodium salt

L. A. Holt and B. Milligan, Aust. J. Biol. Sci., 27, 23 (1974); Aust. J. Chem., 30, 2277 (1977).

15-5 Sulfonic Acid Esters and Sulfonic Acid Halides

$C_6H_5CH_2{*}COC_6H_5$ (97%)

1,2-Diphenyl-1-ethanone-1-[14]C

1. Br_2, CCl_4, (95%)
2. R-C_6H_4SH, NaOEt, EtOH, Δ (60-90%) →

R-C_6H_4S-CHC_6H_5-${*}COC_6H_5$

p-Br-C_6H_4-SO_2Cl, NaH, acetone →

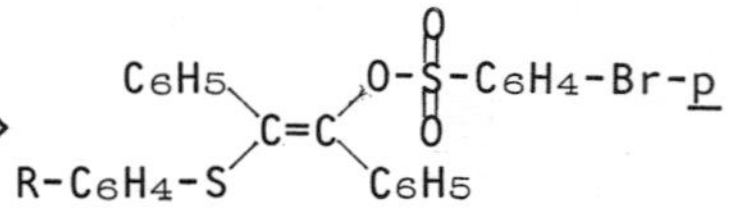
C6H5
O-S-C6H4-Br-p
O
O
C=C
R-C6H4-S
C6H5

2-Arylthio-1,2-diphenyl vinyl-1-[14]C p-bromobenzene sulfonates

R=H, p-OCH_3, m-Cl, or m-OCH_3

(40-50% yield; position of label is determined by degradation reactions)

Cyclization of the above compounds (BF_3, CH_2Cl_2) gave 2,3-diphenyl-benzo[b]thiophens (mechanisms are proposed).

G. Capozzi, G. Melloni, and G. Modena, J. Chem. Soc., (C), 3018 (1971).

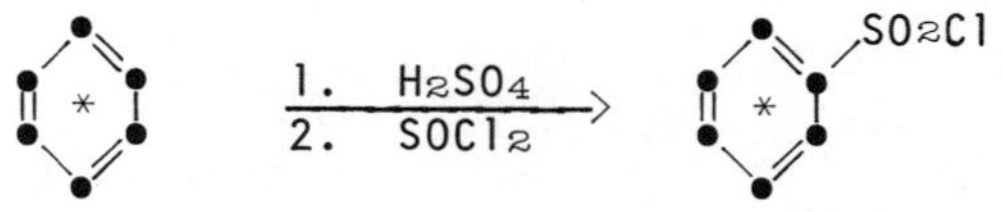

(97%)

Benzenesulfonyl chloride-U-^{14}C

J. Kalbfeld, H. M. Pitt, and D. A. Hermann, J. Label. Compounds, 5, 351 (1969).

$CN\text{-}N{=}C(NH_2)_2$ +

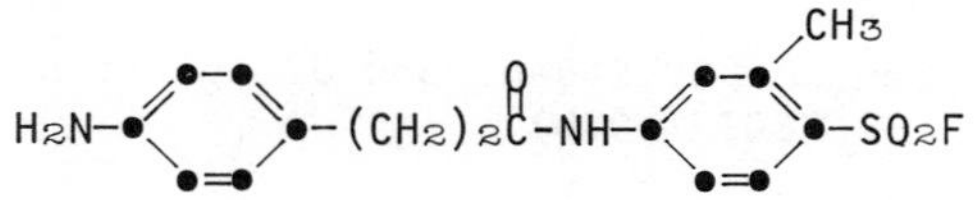

Dicyanodiamide-^{14}C [cyanoguanidine-^{14}C] (position of label is not specified)

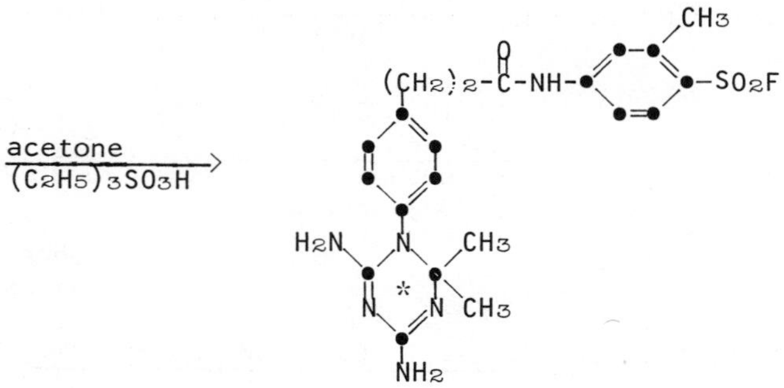

4-(4,6-Diamino-2,2-dimethyl-1,3,5-triazin-1-yl-U-^{14}C)-N-[3-methyl-4-(fluorosulfonyl)-phenyl]benzenepropanamide

A. J. Ryan, N. M. J. Vermeulen, and B. R. Baker, J. Med. Chem., 13, 1140 (1970).

15-6 Sulfonamides

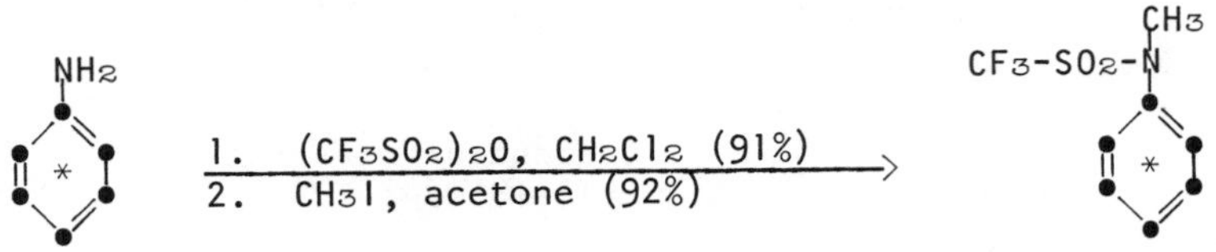

1,1,1-Trifluoro-N-methyl-N-phenylmethanesulfonamide-(ring-^{14}C)

C. J. Grandjean, M. C. Eagen, and J. Goldston, J. Label. Compound. Radiopharm., 12, 207 (1976).

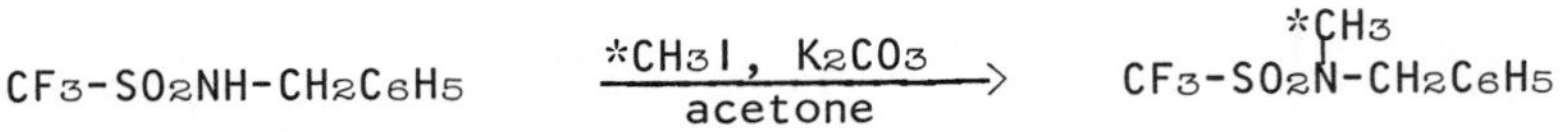

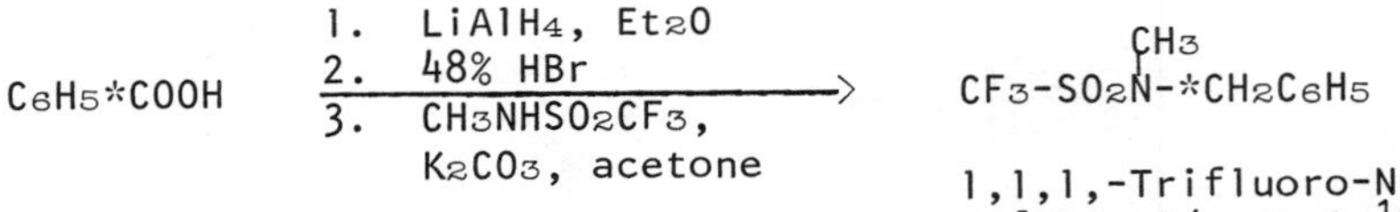

1,1,1,-Trifluoro-N-methyl-N-[phenyl(methyl-^{14}C)] methanesulfonamide

P. L. Skipper, J. Label. Compound.Radiopharm., 15, 575 (1978).

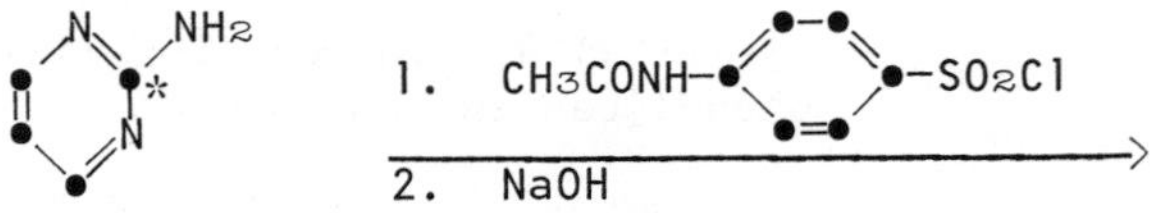

2-Pyrimidinamine-2-^{14}C

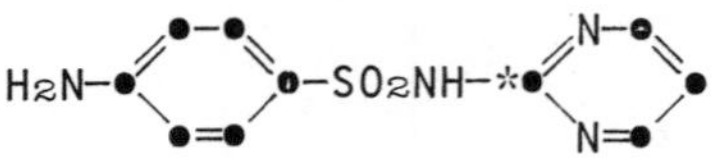

(55%)

Sulfadiazine
[4-Amino-N-(2-pyrimidinyl-2-^{14}C)benzene sulfonamide]

Similarly:

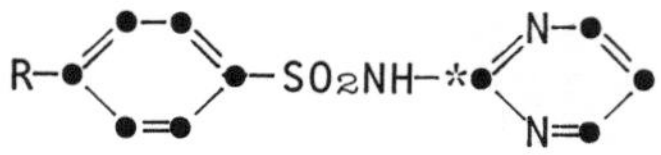
R
SO2NH
N
N

R=H; N-(2-Pyrimidinyl-2-^{14}C) benzenesulfonamide
R=CH_3; 4-Methyl-N-(2-pyrimidinyl-2-^{14}C) benzenesulfonamide
R=$N(CH_2CHClCH_3)_2$; 4-[di(2-chloro-n-propyl)amino]-N-(2-pyrimidinyl-2-^{14}C)-benzenesulfonamide

Nguyen-Hoang-Nam, M. Herbert, Nguyen-Dat-Xuong, and L. Pichat, J. Label. Compounds, 7, 299 (1971); see also M. Hoellinger, Nguyen-Hoang-Nam, and L. Pichat, J. Label. Compounds, 9, 161 (1973).

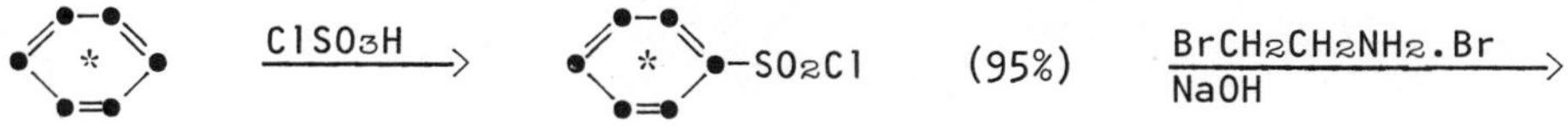
ClSO3H
SO2Cl
(95%)
BrCH2CH2NH2.Br
NaOH

Benzenesulfonyl chloride-U-^{14}C

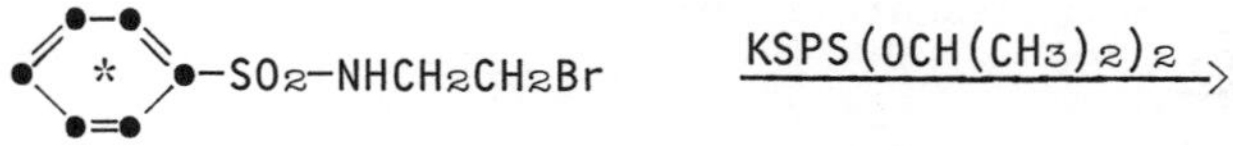
SO2–NHCH2CH2Br
KSPS(OCH(CH3)2)2

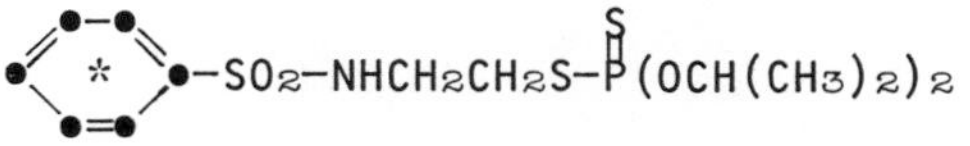
SO2–NHCH2CH2S–P(OCH(CH3)2)2
S

(60% from benzene*)

S-(O,O-Diisopropylphosphorodithioate)-N-(2-mercaptoethyl)benzene sulfonamide-(benzene-U-^{14}C)

A. D. Gutman and M. E. Brokke, J. Label. Compounds, 2, 317 (1966).

15-7 Other Sulfur Compounds

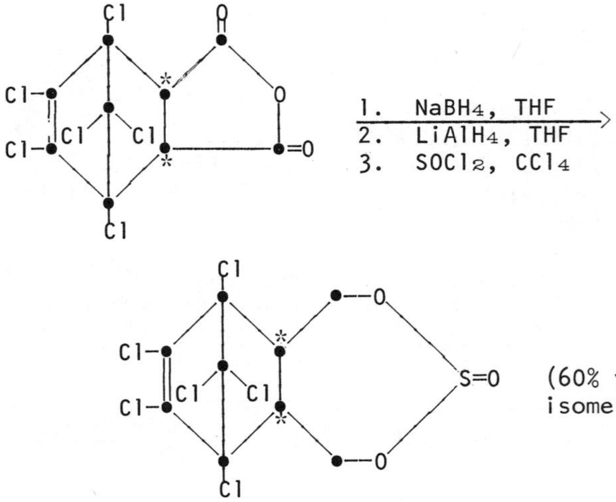
1. $NaBH_4$, THF
2. $LiAlH_4$, THF
3. $SOCl_2$, CCl_4

(60% yield included 15% beta isomer and 45% alpha isomer)

Endosulfan
[6,7,8,9,10,10-Hexachloro-1,5,5a,6,9,9a-hexahydro-6,9-methano-2,4,3-benzodioxathiepin-3-oxide-5a,9a-^{14}C]

K. L. Huhtanen and H. W. Dorough, J. Label. Compound. Radiopharm., 14, 321 (1978).

$(C_2H_5)_2NCH_2{*}CH_2OH$ —— 1. $SOCl_2$, Δ (83%); 2. $(C_6H_5)_2S(O)=NH$, NaH, toluene ——>

N,N-Diethylaminoethanol-1-^{14}C

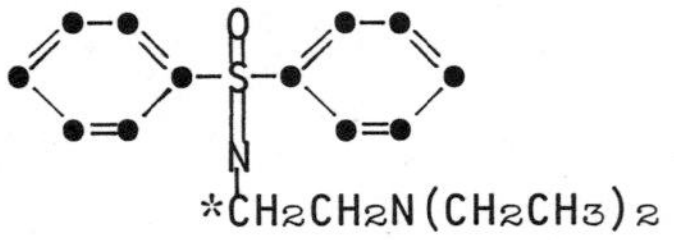

(63%; 45% from $Ba{*}CO_3$)

Suloxifen
[N-(2-Diethylaminoethyl-1-^{14}C)-S,S-diphenylsulfoximine]

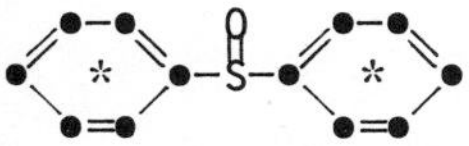

1. NaN_3, PPA (52%)
2. $(C_2H_5)_2N(CH_2)_2Cl$ toluene, NaH (64%)

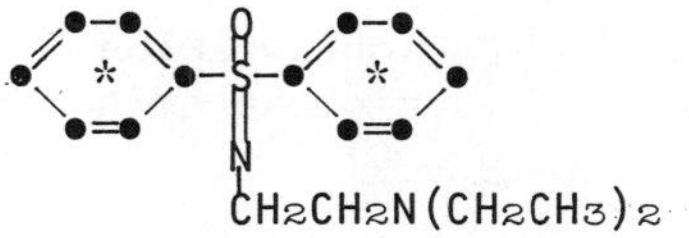
CH2CH2N(CH2CH3)2

(30% from benzene)

Suloxifen
[N-(2-Diethylaminoethyl)-S,S-diphenyl-U-^{14}C-sulfoximine]

B. Liedtke and K.-O. Vollmer, J. Label. Compound. Radiopharm., 14, 825 (1978).

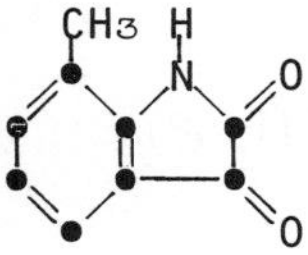
CH3 H
N
O
O

1. C_6H_5OH, H_2SO_4 (54%)
2. $ClSO_3H$, NaOH (67%)

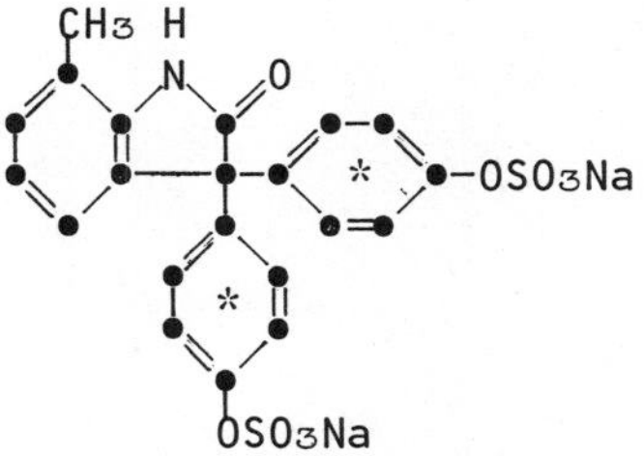
CH3 H
N
O
OSO3Na
OSO3Na

(37% overall)

1,3-Dihydro-7-methyl-3,3-bis-[4-(sulfoxy)phenyl-U-^{14}C]-2H-indol-2-one

J. Ibañez-Catalan, M. P. Forn, and F. J. DeOsso, An. Quim., 72, 571 (1976).

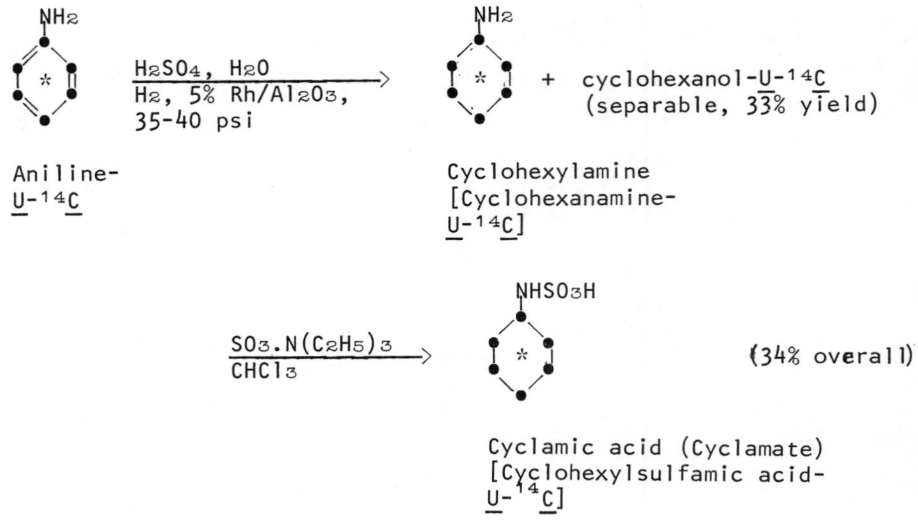
NH2
H2SO4, H2O
H2, 5% Rh/Al2O3,
35-40 psi
NH2
+ cyclohexanol-U-14C
(separable, 33% yield)
Aniline-U-14C
Cyclohexylamine
[Cyclohexanamine-U-14C]
NHSO3H
SO3.N(C2H5)3
CHCl3
(34% overall)
Cyclamic acid (Cyclamate)
[Cyclohexylsulfamic acid-U-14C]

A. Alter and J. C. Forman, J. Label. Compounds, 4, 320 (1968).

Formula Index

Subject Index